APPLIED MATHEMATICS

11

SECOND EDITION

THE McGRAW-HILL RYERSON MATHEMATICS PROGRAM

MATH 1 SOURCE BOOK
MATH 2 SOURCE BOOK
MATH 3
MATH 4
MATH 5
MATH 6

TEACHER'S EDITION FOR:
MATH 3
MATH 4
MATH 5
MATH 6

BLACKLINE MASTERS FOR:
MATH 3
MATH 4
MATH 5
MATH 6

LIFE MATH 1
LIFE MATH 2
LIFE MATH 3

INTERMEDIATE MATHEMATICS 1
INTERMEDIATE MATHEMATICS 2
INTERMEDIATE MATHEMATICS 3

TEACHER'S EDITION FOR:
INTERMEDIATE MATHEMATICS 1
INTERMEDIATE MATHEMATICS 2
INTERMEDIATE MATHEMATICS 3

BLACKLINE MASTERS FOR:
INTERMEDIATE MATHEMATICS 1
INTERMEDIATE MATHEMATICS 2

APPLIED MATHEMATICS 9
APPLIED MATHEMATICS 10
APPLIED MATHEMATICS 11
APPLIED MATHEMATICS 12

TEACHER'S EDITION FOR:
APPLIED MATHEMATICS 9

TEACHER'S GUIDE FOR:
AM 10
AM11
AM12

FOUNDATIONS OF MATHEMATICS 9
FOUNDATIONS OF MATHEMATICS 10
FOUNDATIONS OF MATHEMATICS 11
FOUNDATIONS OF MATHEMATICS 12

TEACHER'S EDITION FOR:
FOUNDATIONS OF MATHEMATICS 9

TEACHER'S GUIDE FOR:
FM 10
FM 11
FM 12

APPLIED MATHEMATICS

11

SECOND EDITION

Dino Dottori, B.Sc., M.S.Ed.
George Knill, B.Sc., M.S.Ed.
John Seymour, B.A., M.Ed.
Ann Jones, B.A., M.Ed.
Robert Alderson, B.A., M.Ed.
Darrell McPhail, B.Sc., M.Sc.

McGRAW-HILL RYERSON LIMITED

TORONTO MONTREAL NEW YORK AUCKLAND BOGOTÁ CAIRO CARACAS HAMBURG
LISBON LONDON MADRID MEXICO MILAN NEW DELHI PANAMA PARIS SAN JUAN
SÃO PAULO SINGAPORE SYDNEY TOKYO

APPLIED MATHEMATICS 11
SECOND EDITION

ISBN 0-07-548738-1

234567890 JD 7654321098

Technical illustrations by Frank Zsigo

A complete list of notes and photograph credits appears on page 570.

Printed and bound in Canada

Canadian Cataloguing in Publication Data

Main entry under title:

Applied mathematics 11

(The McGraw-Hill Ryerson mathematics program)
2nd ed.
ISBN 0-07-548738-1

1. Mathematics — 1961– . I. Dottori, Dino, date – . II. Series.

QA39.2.A68 1988 510 C88-093593-6

Communications Branch, Consumer and Corporate Affairs Canada, has granted permission for the use of the National Symbol for Metric Conversion.

Care has been taken to trace ownership of copyright material contained in this text. The publishers will gladly take any information that will enable them to rectify any reference or credit in subsequent editions.

CONTENTS

NUMERICAL METHODS

REVIEW AND PREVIEW TO CHAPTER 1

MENTAL MATH

EXERCISE 1

1. Perform the following calculations mentally.
(a) $6 + 7 - 6 + 12 - 4 - 3 + 6$
(b) $5 - 3 + 15 + 2 - 9 - 2 + 11$
(c) $(5 \times 2) + (12 \div 4) - (3 \times 6)$
(d) $8 - (5 - 3) + (18 \div 6) + (7 \times 3)$
(e) $9 + 8 - (5 \times 2) + 3 + (32 \div 4)$
(f) $39 - (5 + 7 + 3) + (16 - 5)$
(g) $14 + 12 + 5 - 30 + 5 - 15 - 9$
(h) $(8 \times 6 \div 12) + (18 \div 6 \times 2)$
(i) $8\frac{1}{2} - 5\frac{1}{2} + 3\frac{1}{2} + 2\frac{1}{2} + 4 - 8$
(j) $42 \div 7 + 5 - 3 + 2(\frac{2}{3} \text{ of } 24)$

2. Multiply mentally.
(a) (2)(0.3)
(b) 12×0.05
(c) 0.03×0.21
(d) (41)(0.03)
(e) (2.4)(0.5)
(f) 32×100
(g) (0.3)(1.07)
(h) (200)(0.1)
(i) 350×0.01
(j) 0.56×100
(k) 1.23×1000
(l) 0.02×10

3. Divide mentally.

(a) $360 \div 9$	(b) $63 \div 9$
(c) $350 \div 100$	(d) $72 \div 6$
(e) $276 \div 4$	(f) $154 \div 2$
(g) $930 \div 0.1$	(h) $56 \div 8$
(i) $40 \div 5$	(j) $972 \div 9$
(k) $144 \div 12$	(l) $760 \div 10$
(m) $25 \div 5$	(n) $912 \div 6$
(o) $45 \div 1000$	(p) $70 \div 0.01$

PERCENT

EXERCISE 2

1. Evaluate the following.

(a) 10% of 50	(b) 25% of 300
(c) 5% of 20	(d) 21% of 400
(e) 2% of 65	(f) 5.5% of 30
(g) 12.5% of 70	(h) 2.5% of 35
(i) 2.25% of 60	(j) 3.75% of 44
(k) 100% of 71	(l) 200% of 120

2. (a) What percent of 30 is 15?
(b) What percent of 20 is 5?
(c) What percent of 60 is 15?
(d) What percent of 70 is 7?
(e) What percent of 2.5 is 0.5?
(f) What percent of 3.6 is 0.06?

3. Express as percents.

(a) $\frac{5}{8}$	(b) $\frac{3}{4}$
(c) $2\frac{1}{2}$	(d) $1\frac{1}{4}$
(e) 0.2	(f) 0.35
(g) 1.1	(h) 0.05

4. A small radio sells regularly for \$49.95. It is on sale at 25% off.
(a) How much is the discount?
(b) What is the sale price of the radio?

5. A meal in a restaurant costs \$18.50. The actual food cost is 43% in this restaurant.
What is the actual food cost of the \$18.50 meal?

6. There are 375 girls and 318 boys in the school.
What percent of the students in the school are boys?

7. A real estate salesman receives 1.5% commission on sales.
What is the commission on a house that sold for \$260 000?

ROUNDING RULES

The key digit is the first digit to the right of the required place value.

Rules	Number	Required Place	Key Digit	Rounded Number
If the key digit is less than 5, we round down.	4812 5.63	nearest 100 nearest tenth	4812 5.63	4800 5.6
If the key digit is greater than 5, or if it is 5 followed by non-zero digits, we round up.	18 276 17.29 3157 1.1852	nearest 10 nearest tenth nearest 100 nearest hundredth	18 276 17.29 3157 1.1852	18 280 17.3 3200 1.19
If the key digit is 5 followed by zeros, we round to the nearest even digit.	6500 5500 17.965	nearest 1000 nearest 1000 nearest hundredth	6500 5500 17.965	6000 6000 17.96

EXERCISE 3

1. Round to the nearest ten.
(a) 64.35 (b) 538.3
(c) 9386.15 (d) 126.81

2. Round to the nearest tenth.
(a) 13.26 (b) 853.35
(c) 928.515 (d) 0.816

3. Round to the nearest hundredth.
(a) 37.426 (b) 6.125
(c) 7.2851 (d) 256.199

4. Calculate and round to the nearest tenth.
(a) $5.375 + 16.48 + 0.71 + 2.2231$
(b) $16.45 + 7.932 + 70.2 + 0.968$
(c) $51.125 + 30.5$
(d) $342.6 - 245.92$
(e) 0.8923×7.45
(f) $175.56 \div 33.44$
(g) $3.1 \div 0.42$

5. Using rounding and estimation, locate the decimal in each of the following answers.
(a) 4.35×16.86 ■ 73 341
(b) 27.25×16.23 ■ 4 422 675
(c) $8.1 \times 4.86 \times 6.16$ ■ 24 249 456
(d) $\frac{48.3138}{2.16}$ ■ 223 675
(e) $\frac{243.375}{11.8}$ ■ 20 625
(f) $\frac{7.42 \times 19.76}{12.5}$ ■ 11 729 536
(g) $\frac{2.65 + 3.82}{1.15 + 4.75}$ ■ 109 661 017
(h) $6.05(5.28 + 7.25)$ ■ 758 065
(i) $\frac{46.7 \times 10.216}{5.35 \times 4.25}$ ■ 209 823 947
(j) $\frac{0.062 \times 0.58}{1.24 + 2.68}$ ■ 9 173 469

PRECISION AND ACCURACY IN MEASUREMENT

Precision is determined by the instrument used to make the measurement. It can be indicated by the number of significant digits to the right of the decimal point. Accuracy, on the other hand, depends on the number of significant digits.

The measurement 7.261 cm is a more precise measurement than 472.21 cm, even though the latter contains more significant digits.

Significant digits are those digits in the numerical value of a measurement that are consequential to its precision and/or accuracy. The following rules help us determine which digits in a measurement are significant.

Rules	Examples	Significant Digits
The digits 1, 2, 3, ..., 9 are significant.	762.5 m	4
Zeros to the left of the first non-zero digit are not significant.	0.1762 km 0.043 km	4 2
Zeros between non-zero digits are significant.	1003.04 m	6
Zeros to the right of a non-zero digit may be significant because of the precision of measurement.	450.0 m 0.60 m	4 2
The zeros are placeholders. If the zeros were not just placeholders but significant, we would write 7000 as 7.000×10^3.	7000 km 4.5 km or 4.5×10^3 m	1 2 2

In most problems, unless otherwise stated, the accuracy of the answers should reflect the precision of the numbers given.

When numbers are added or subtracted, the result after the answer is rounded should be as precise as the least precise of the numbers used in the calculation.

For example, $0.5392 + 6.11 + 0.284 \doteq 6.93$

When numbers are multiplied or divided, the result after the answer is rounded, should contain as many significant digits as are contained in the number with the fewest significant digits that is used in the calculation.

For example, $542.294 \times 0.629 \doteq 341$ or 3.41×10^2

When the original data are assumed to be exact, we round the answer to what is reasonable and qualify the accuracy of the answer. For example, if a 7 m cable is to be divided into 4 equal parts, the length of each part is $7 \div 4 \doteq 1.8$ m, to the nearest tenth of a metre.

EXERCISE 4

1. State the number of significant digits in each of the following.

(a) 896 (b) 22.7
(c) 64.03 (d) 0.0076
(e) 8 500 000 (f) 8.127
(g) 18 600 (h) 17 402
(i) 0.072 08 (j) 17.0

2. Round the following values to three significant digits.

(a) 66.78 (b) 5468
(c) 564.73 (d) 3.089
(e) 5.815 (f) 899.7

3. Round each number and estimate the answer.

(a) 7.1×6.3 (b) 4.91×21
(c) 61.2×9.8 (d) 1.958×30.41
(e) 193.5×5.31 (f) $4.8 \times 3.9 \times 5.1$
(g) $\frac{55.1}{7.02}$ (h) $\frac{149.1}{29.3}$
(i) $\frac{352}{71}$ (j) $\frac{47.9}{6.12}$

4. Calculate each of the following. Round your answer to the appropriate number of significant digits.

(a) $56.789\,24 - 43.435$
(b) $4.632\,59 + 564.23$
(c) $43.764 + 46.235\,9$
(d) $976.1 - 65.989$
(e) $(6.3)(8.13)$
(f) $(203)(0.17)$
(g) $(691.1)(0.032)$
(h) $8.65 \div 0.17637$
(i) $(0.35) \div (2.003)$
(j) $(470)(1.07)$
(k) $(1.62 \times 10^2)(4.70 \times 10^3)$
(l) $0.0107 \div 0.125\,06$

5. Use the rules for accuracy and precision to find the perimeter, given the following measurements.

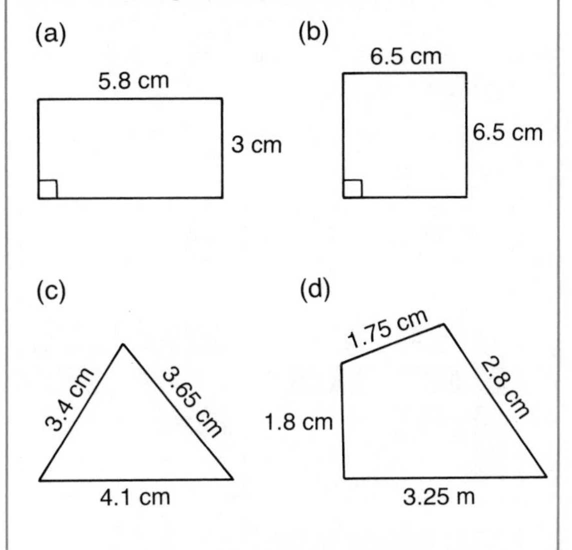

6. Use the rules for accuracy and precision to find the area, given the following measurements.

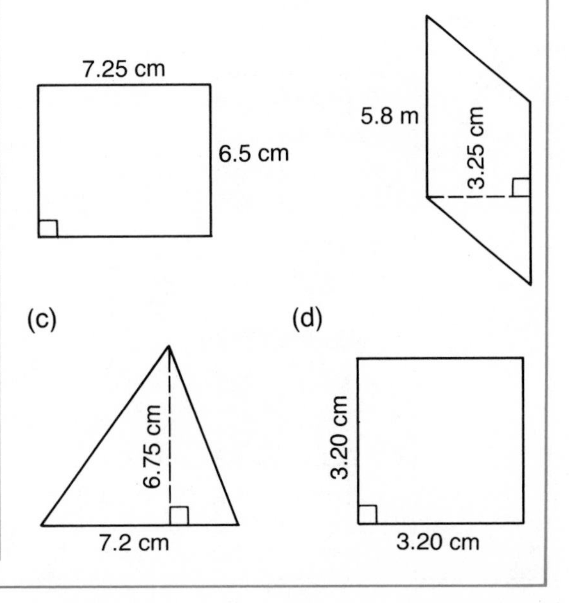

CALCULATOR MATH

USING YOUR CALCULATOR

Some features are found on most calculators. For special features found on more advanced calculators, check the user's manual.

We can divide the calculator keys into three groups.

Number Keys	Operation Keys	Special Function Keys
7 8 9 4 5 6 1 2 3 0	× ÷ + −	M+ M− MR MC % C/CE + − ·

BASIC OPERATIONS

Use a calculator to help you do these questions.

1. In a magic square all columns, rows, and diagonals add to the same number. Copy and complete these magic squares.

(a)

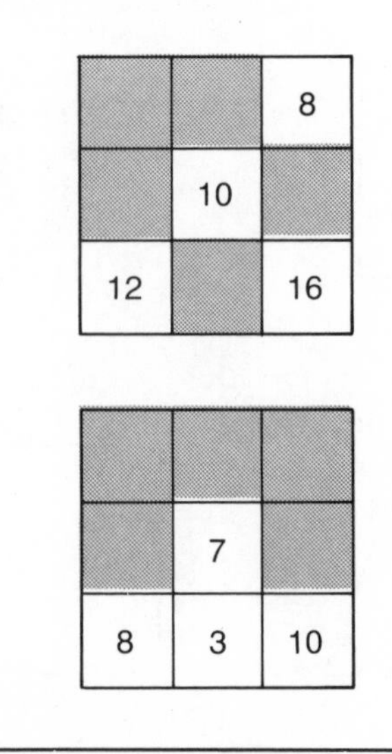

(b)

(c)

	1404	624
1092		
936		

(d)

1974		3948
5922		7896

2. Here are three magic squares, one inside another.
(a) Find the magic numbers.
(b) Complete the magic squares.

12				10		2
	20		35		14	
8		24		22		
9			25		33	
44				26	32	
47		13			30	
	1	4	5			38

ROUNDING OR TRUNCATING

Some calculators round off numbers, while others truncate, or "chop off" the extra digits without rounding. The following exercise demonstrates how your calculator handles the extra digits.

The displays from two different kinds of calculators are shown.

Press	Calculator #1 Display	Calculator #2 Display
C	0.	0.
5	5.	5.
÷	5.	5.
6	6.	6.
=	0.8333333	0.8333333
×	0.8333333	0.8333333
6	6.	6.
=	4.9999998	5.

The two calculators give slightly different answers to the problem

$5 \div 6 \times 6$

The difference arises because calculator #1 truncates and drops the digits after dividing. Calculator #2 does two things: (i) only the display is rounded off; (ii) digits are saved in the memory and not dropped off.

The solution is

$5 \div 6 \times 6 = 5$

as we multiply and divide in order from left to right.

EXERCISE

Use the following questions to determine whether your calculator truncates or rounds.

1. $4 \div 3 \times 3$
2. $5 \div 7 \times 7$
3. $1 \div 9 \times 9$
4. $3 \div 11 \times 11$

CONSTANT FEATURE: = KEY

1. Does your calculator have a constant for addition?
Press

C 3 + 5 = = = =

If your display reads:

8. — you do not have the repeating function.

23. — you have the repeating function.

What will your calculator display after you press the following?

(a) C 7 + 3 = = = =
(b) C 1 + 8 = = =
(c) C 4 + = = = =
(d) C 2 + 3 = = 6 = =
(e) Start with 2 and make your calculator count by 9.
(f) Start with 5 and make your calculator count by 5.

2. Does your calculator have a constant function for multiplication?
Press

C 2 × 5 = = = =

If your display reads:

80. — the 2 is the constant multiplier.

1250. — the 5 is the constant multiplier.

What will your calculator display after you press the following?

(a) C 2 × 3 = =
(b) C 8 × 1 = = =
(c) C 1 × 8 = = =
(d) C 2 × 3 = 5 =
(e) Multiply 9 by 2 four times.
(f) Start with 5 and multiply by 5 four times.

1.1 EVALUATING NUMERICAL EXPRESSIONS

Putting a compact disc into a CD player and playing.

Removing a compact disc from a CD player after playing.

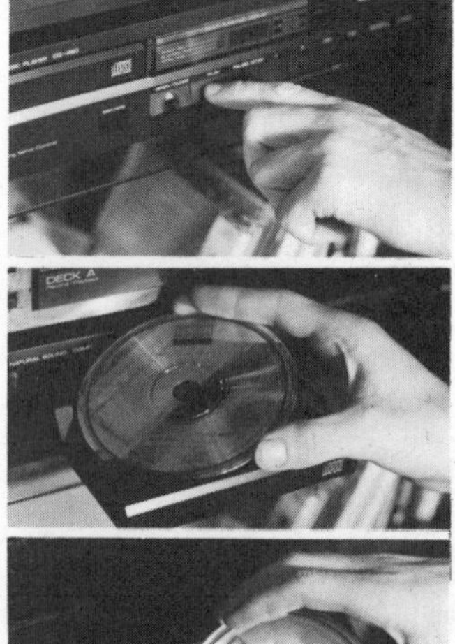

The two arrangements of photographs in the margin tell different stories, depending on the order in which they are seen.

In the same way, we can get different values for the numerical expression $60 \div 4 + 2 \times 5$ by performing the operations in different orders.

$$60 \div 4 + 2 \times 5 \quad\quad 60 \div 4 + 2 \times 5 \quad\quad 60 \div 4 + 2 \times 5$$
$$15 + 2 \times 5 \quad\quad 60 \div 6 \times 5 \quad\quad 60 \div 6 \times 5$$
$$17 \times 5 \quad\quad 10 \times 5 \quad\quad 60 \div 30$$
$$85 \quad\quad 50 \quad\quad 2$$

We eliminate this confusion by agreeing to the order of operations as summarized in the following chart.

B	E	DM	AS
Do the computations in brackets first.	Simplify numbers with exponents and "of".	Divide or multiply in the order in which ÷ and × appear from left to right.	Add or subtract in the order in which + and − appear from left to right.

The acronym BEDMAS helps us to remember the order.

According to this order of operations, the correct way to simplify $60 \div 4 + 2 \times 5$ is

$$60 \div 4 + 2 \times 5$$
$$= 15 + 10$$
$$= 25$$

DM division and multiplication

A addition

To change the order of operations so that the addition $4 + 2$ is performed first, brackets are used as grouping symbols.

$$60 \div (4 + 2) \times 5$$
$$= 60 \div 6 \times 5$$
$$= 50$$

B brackets

DM division and multiplication from left to right.

The following examples illustrate how the order of operations is applied to simplify numerical expressions.

Example 1. Simplify. $25 - 36 \div 2^2 \times (10 - 8)$

Solution:

$25 - 36 \div 2^2 \times (10 - 8)$		
$= 25 - 36 \div 2^2 \times 2$	B	brackets
$= 25 - 36 \div 4 \times 2$	E	exponents
$= 25 - 9 \times 2$	D	division
$= 25 - 18$	M	multiplication
$= 7$	AS	addition, subtraction

Example 2. Evaluate. $3.25 + 2.5(1.3 + 2.6) - 1.5^2$

Solution:

$3.25 + 2.5(1.3 + 2.6) - 1.5^2$	
$= 3.25 + 2.5 \times 3.9 - 1.5^2$	B
$= 3.25 + 2.5 \times 3.9 - 2.25$	E
$= 3.25 + 9.75 - 2.25$	M
$= 10.75$	AS

In some applications, numerical expressions result from substituting into algebraic expressions. Expressions such as $x^2 - 5$ and $3x + 2y - 5$ are called algebraic expressions because they involve the variables x and y. We can evaluate algebraic expressions when given the values of the variables. To do so, we substitute the number values for the variables, as in the following examples.

Substitutions are shown in red.

Example 3. Evaluate. $3(x + y) - 2(x - y)$ for $x = 5, y = 3$

Solution:

$$\begin{aligned} 3(x + y) - 2(x - y) &= 3(5 + 3) - 2(5 - 3) \\ &= 3(8) - 2(2) \\ &= 24 - 4 \\ &= 20 \end{aligned}$$

Example 4. Evaluate. $0.5(a + b)h$ for $a = 2.5$, $b = 3.8$, $h = 4.2$

Solution:

$$\begin{aligned} 0.5(a + b)h &= 0.5 \times (2.5 + 3.8) \times 4.2 \\ &= 0.5 \times 6.3 \times 4.2 \\ &= 13.23 \end{aligned}$$

Later we will see examples where the work is made easier if we simplify the expression first.

EXERCISE 1.1

A

1. Evaluate each of the following.
(a) $31 - 24 + 16$ (b) 5×4^2
(c) 4×5^2 (d) $(4 \times 5)^2$
(e) $4^2 \times 5^2$ (f) $3(5 - 2)^2$
(g) $3(5 - 2^2)$ (h) $3^2(7 - 4)$

B

2. Evaluate.
(a) $7 + 2 \times 5$
(b) $(3 + 2) \times 4$
(c) $76 - 11 \times 3$
(d) $35 - (2)(7)$
(e) $(2 + 6) - 2^2$
(f) $(18) \div (6) \times 3$
(g) $19 + 2 - 7 \times 3$
(h) $(72 + 35) \times (49 - 26)$
(i) $147 - (37 \times 3)$
(j) $343 \div (98 \div 14)$
(k) $132 \div (47 + 16 - 39)$
(l) $(14 + 96) \div 22$
(m) $\dfrac{43 + 78}{86 - 75}$
(n) $\dfrac{17 \times 4 + 30}{32 \times 3 - 82}$

3. Evaluate.
(a) $6(5 - 2) + 3(8 - 4)$
(b) $2(8 - 3) - 3(7 - 5)$
(c) $(4 + 2)(5 + 3) \div (8 - 4)$
(d) $(5 + 3)(6 - 2) \div (7 - 3)(4 + 4)$
(e) $(5 - 4)(8 - 2) \div (5 - 2)(8 - 2)$
(f) $4^2(7 - 5) \div (6 + 2)(3 + 2)$
(g) $(5 + 3)3^2 - (4 \times 3) + 7$
(h) $7 + (2 + 3) \div (10 \div 2) - 2$

4. Insert brackets in the following to make true statements.
(a) $3 \times 2 + 5 - 8 = 13$
(b) $5 + 3 \times 2 \div 4 = 12$
(c) $3 + 2 \times 5 + 3 - 7 = 12$
(d) $4 \times 5 - 2 + 7 = 19$
(e) $5 \times 4 + 3 \times 2 - 10 = 60$
(f) $7 + 5 \times 3 + 4 + 11 = 95$
(g) $16 - 5 + 4 + 7 = 14$

5. Evaluate.
(a) $32.6 + 25.8 - 47.6$
(b) $2.6 \times 5.8 + 3.7 \times 4.2$
(c) $3.5(2.6 + 5.3) - 15.65$
(d) $3.2(1.5 - 0.8) + 2.6(1.4 + 2.1)$
(e) $8.2(3.2 + 4.8 - 5.5) + 6.25$
(f) $(4.28 - 2.65)(5.8 - 2.8)$

6. Evaluate. Round your answers to the nearest tenth.
(a) $3.5 \times 4.8 + 6.3 \times 7.9$
(b) $12.6 - 4.3$
(c) $14.6 - 3.2(4.2 - 3.9)$
(d) $(24.6 + 42.8) - (4.1 + 3.7)$
(e) $3.5(6.4 + 4.6) + 2.4 \times 5.8$
(f) $54.65 - 3.2(4.8 - 2.6)$

7. Evaluate the following. Round your answers according to the rules.
(a) $3.234\,61 + 5.23 - 6.8154 + 2.472$
(b) $34.25 - 21.675\,4$
(c) 4.25×5.65
(d) $67.374 \div 7.24$
(e) 5.28×25.6
(f) $6.275 + 5.3 \times 8.2$

8. Evaluate and round your answer.

(a) $\dfrac{4.3 + 7.9}{6.8 - 5.2}$

(b) $\dfrac{4.255 - 3.125}{4.65 + 1.23}$

(c) $\dfrac{1.75 \times 4.5 + 32.1}{3.25 \times 4 - 8.2}$

(d) $\dfrac{63.5 + 5.148 - 6.3}{5.7 \times 2.6 - 3.3}$

(e) $\dfrac{5.35(2.4 + 5.3)}{6.34(5.35 - 1.68)}$

(f) $\dfrac{5.356 + 2.64}{2.35 \times 6.32}$

(g) $\dfrac{53.6 - 2.6}{4.8 \times 2.7}$

9. Evaluate. $x = 7$

(a) $3x^2 + 5x - 8$
(b) $(4x - 2)(2x - 4)$
(c) $2x(x - 5)$
(d) $3x(x - 3) - x(2x - 10)$

10. Evaluate. $x = 3.5$

(a) $5x^2 + 3 - 2x$
(b) $2.4x + 17x(x - 1.7)$
(c) $5.25x + 3.75(2x - 4.45)$
(d) $3.2x^2 - 4.7x + 6.25$

11. Evaluate 0.5bh for the following values.

(a) $b = 6.5$, $h = 2.6$
(b) $b = 8.75$, $h = 12.5$
(c) $b = 5.8$, $h = 10.4$
(d) $b = 0.265$, $h = 1.15$

12. Evaluate $A = \pi r^2$, where $\pi = 3.14$ and

(a) $r = 8$ (b) $r = 4.5$
(c) $r = 6.3$ (d) $r = 2.35$
(e) $r = 5.235$ (f) $r = 6.025$

13. Evaluate $A = \dfrac{(a + b)}{2}h$ for the following values.

(a) $a = 5$, $b = 7$, $h = 11$
(b) $a = 1.8$, $b = 2.7$, $h = 4.6$
(c) $a = 3.5$, $b = 4.0$, $h = 2.8$
(d) $a = b = h = 4.25$
(e) $a = 6.8$, $b = 5.3$, $h = 4.5$
(f) $a = 6.4$, $b = 5.6$, $h = 4.7$

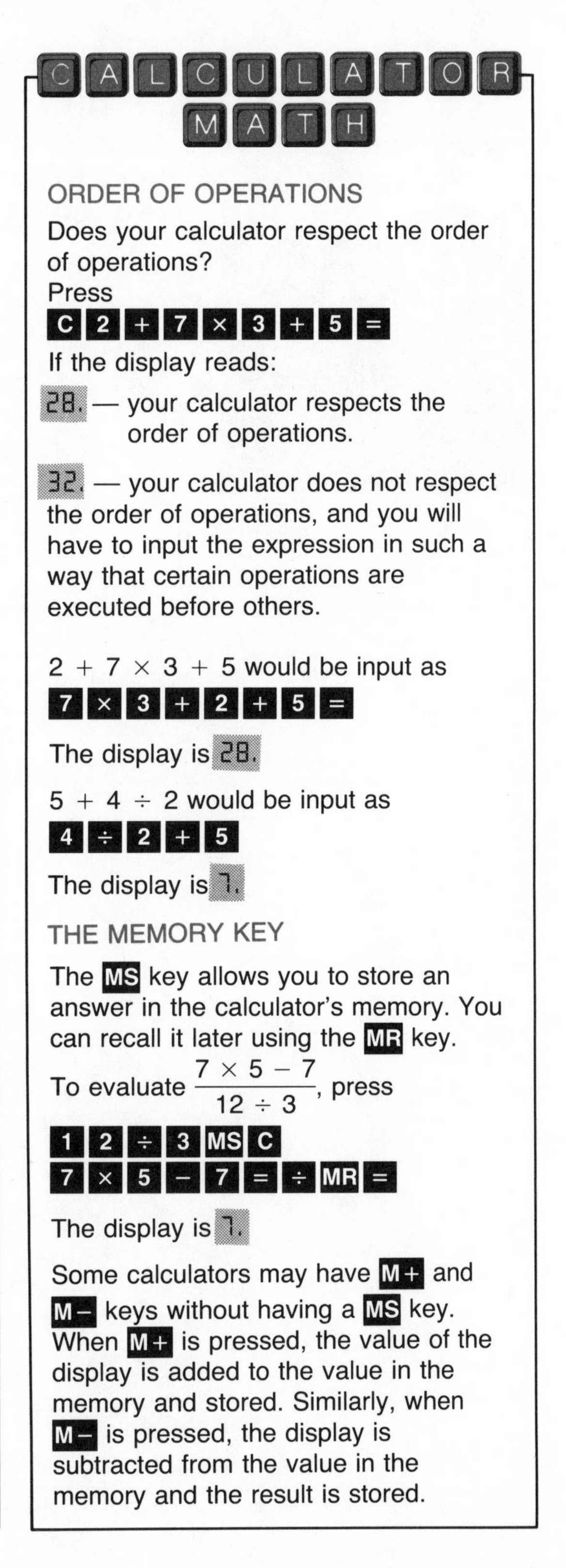

CALCULATOR MATH

ORDER OF OPERATIONS

Does your calculator respect the order of operations?

Press

[C] [2] [+] [7] [×] [3] [+] [5] [=]

If the display reads:

28. — your calculator respects the order of operations.

32. — your calculator does not respect the order of operations, and you will have to input the expression in such a way that certain operations are executed before others.

$2 + 7 \times 3 + 5$ would be input as

[7] [×] [3] [+] [2] [+] [5] [=]

The display is 28.

$5 + 4 \div 2$ would be input as

[4] [÷] [2] [+] [5]

The display is 7.

THE MEMORY KEY

The [MS] key allows you to store an answer in the calculator's memory. You can recall it later using the [MR] key.

To evaluate $\dfrac{7 \times 5 - 7}{12 \div 3}$, press

[1] [2] [÷] [3] [MS] [C]
[7] [×] [5] [−] [7] [=] [÷] [MR] [=]

The display is 7.

Some calculators may have [M+] and [M−] keys without having a [MS] key. When [M+] is pressed, the value of the display is added to the value in the memory and stored. Similarly, when [M−] is pressed, the display is subtracted from the value in the memory and the result is stored.

$$\frac{5}{2} = \frac{5 \times 24}{2 \times 24} = \frac{120}{48}$$

1.2 APPLICATIONS OF WHOLE NUMBERS AND DECIMALS

There are very few areas of our lives that do not involve the use of numbers in one way or another.

Example 1. In an orchard there are 5 apple trees for every 2 pear trees. There are 48 pear trees in the orchard. How many trees are in the orchard?

Solution: The number of pairs of pear trees $= 48 \div 2$
$= 24$
For a pair of pear trees there are 5 apple trees.
Number of apple trees $= 5 \times 24$
$= 120$
Total number of trees $= 48 + 120$
$= 168$
There are 168 trees in the orchard.

Example 2. A power company charges the following rates for electricity:
7.9¢/kW·h for the first 100 kW·h
4.4¢/kW·h for the next 400 kW·h
3.1¢/kW·h for the remaining kilowatt hours.

Peter's consumption for two months was 930 kW·h. What will he be charged?

Solution: Since Peter's consumption exceeds 500 kW·h all three rates will apply.

The charge is 7.9¢ for each of the first 100 kW·h consumed.
7.9¢ × 100 = 790¢
Peter must pay $7.90 for the first 100 kW·h.

For the next 400 kW·h the charge is 4.4¢/kW·h.
4.4¢ × 400 = 1760¢
Peter must pay $17.60 for the next 400 kW·h.

There are 930 − 500 = 430 kW·h remaining and the charge is 3.1¢ for each.
3.1¢ × 430 = 1333¢
Peter must pay $13.33 for the remaining 430 kW·h.

The total bill = 7.90 + 17.60 + 13.33
= 38.83
Peter will be charged $38.83.

EXERCISE 1.2

B

1. It takes 40 L of maple sap to make 1 L of syrup.
How much sap is required to make 150 L of syrup?

2. James had a balance of $743.54 in his chequing account. He deposited $301.23. Could he write a cheque for a camera selling for $1068.00?

3. Amanda received a $75 gift certificate for AM's Record Store. She made the following purchases: 2 compact disks at $13.62 each, a tape for $7.95, and a cassette case for $12.65.
How much money will she still be able to spend at AM's?

4. A pond is stocked with 725 rainbow trout. For each 5 rainbow trout released into the pond, 3 speckled trout are also released into the pond.
How many speckled trout is the pond stocked with?

5. Saul earns $8.55/h at his part-time job. What did he earn last week if he worked 16.25 h?

6. A Canadian family consumes, on the average, 0.389 kg of poultry per day.
How much poultry would a family consume in one week?

7. A power company charges the following rates: 6.8¢/kW·h for the first 200 kW·h
3.2¢/kW·h for the next 350 kW·h
2.3¢/kW·h for the remaining kilowatt hours
Melina's consumption for two months was 786 kW·h.
What did the power company charge her?

8. Calculate the missing values on each of the gasoline pumps shown.

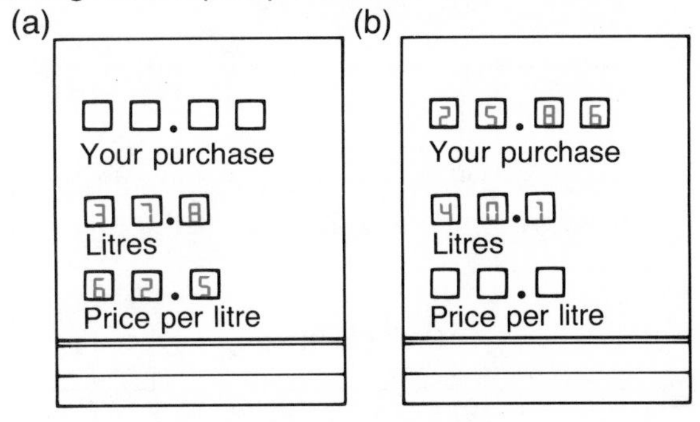

9. Ham slices sell for $1.29/100 g.
What is the cost of 0.7 kg of ham slices?

10. The dimensions of a room are 3.5 m by 4.5 m. Calculate the cost of installing wall-to-wall carpeting if the carpet costs $21.95/m², underpadding is $4.50/m², and installation is $2.50/m².

11. An ambulance operator has 4 ambulances in operation 24 h/d. Each ambulance has a crew of 2 and each crew works a 6 h shift. If each crew member earns $23.50/h, calculate the cost of the ambulance crews for one day.

12. Which of the following is the best rate of pay for 40 h per week for 52 weeks including holidays?
$64 000 annual salary
$5380 per month
$2660 twice a month
$2520 every two weeks
$1240 per week
$25.50/h

1.3 INTEGERS

We can make a calculator count backwards.

Press	C 3 − 1 = = = = = = = = =
The display is	0. 3. 3. 1. 2. 1. 0. −1. −2. −3. −4. −5. −6.

°C 40 30 20 10 0 -10 -20 -30 -40

The positive and negative integers, including zero (0), which is neither positive nor negative, form the set of integers. This set of integers can be represented graphically as a line.

$$I = \{\ldots -3, -2, -1, 0, 1, 2, 3, \ldots\}$$

−4 −3 −2 −1 0 1 2 3 4 5

Working with integers is an important part of mathematics. The following charts summarize the rules for multiplying and dividing integers.

Multiplication

$(+3) \times (+2) = +6$	$(+) \times (+) = (+)$
$(-3) \times (-2) = +6$	$(-) \times (-) = (+)$
$(-3) \times (+2) = -6$	$(-) \times (+) = (-)$
$(+3) \times (-2) = -6$	$(+) \times (-) = (-)$

Division

$(+6) \div (+3) = +2$	$(+) \div (+) = (+)$
$(-6) \div (-3) = +2$	$(-) \div (-) = (+)$
$(-6) \div (+3) = -2$	$(-) \div (+) = (-)$
$(+6) \div (-3) = -2$	$(+) \div (-) = (-)$

Example. Simplify each of the following.

(a) $6 - 9 + 2$ (b) $-5 - (-3)$ (c) $(-7)(+11)$ (d) $(-20) \div (-5)$

Solution:

(a) $6 - 9 + 2$
$= -3 + 2$
$= -1$

(b) $-5 - (-3)$
$= -5 + 3$
$= -2$

(c) $(-7)(+11)$
$= -77$

(d) $(-20) \div (-5)$
$= 4$

EXERCISE 1.3

A

1. Simplify.

(a) $(+4) + (+9)$ (b) $(-5) + (-6)$
(c) $(-7) + (+3)$ (d) $(+12) + (-13)$
(e) $(+6)(-4)$ (f) $(-3)(-9)$
(g) $(-15)(+3)$ (h) $(+8)(-6)$
(i) $(-30) \div (-5)$ (j) $(-21) \div (+7)$
(k) $(+24) \div (-3)$ (l) $(+40) \div (+8)$

2. Simplify.

(a) $-3 + 5 + 6$ (b) $-3 - 4 - 5$
(c) $4 - 11 + 1$ (d) $-6 + 5 - 13$
(e) $5 - (-6) + 3$ (f) $-9 - (+3) - 2$
(g) $0 - (-5) + 4$ (h) $13 - (-1) - 7$
(i) $-5 - (+3) - 4$ (j) $15 - 17 - 16$
(k) $2 - 7 - 8 - 1$ (l) $18 + 7 - 4 - 15$

3. Calculate.

(a) $(-7)(-5)$
(b) $(-2)(+12)$
(c) $(+8)(-6)$
(d) $(+12)(+3)$
(e) $(-4)(-9)$
(f) $(-6)(+8)$
(g) $(-2)(+11)$
(h) $(+12)(-1)$
(i) $(-1)(-2)(+3)$
(j) $(+2)(-3)(+2)$

4. Calculate.

(a) $(-50) \div (+10)$
(b) $(+18) \div (-6)$
(c) $(-22) \div (+2)$
(d) $(+16) \div (+4)$
(e) $(+14) \div (-7)$
(f) $(-26) \div (+2)$
(g) $(-32) \div (-8)$
(h) $(-25) \div (+5)$
(i) $(+28) \div (-7)$
(j) $(-11) \div (-1)$

B

5. Simplify.

(a) $-7 + 8 - 13 + 2$
(b) $(-6)(-5)(+2)$
(c) $(-40) \div (+5) \div (-4)$
(d) $(-3)(-4) \div (+2)$
(e) $(-7)(-2) + 3$
(f) $(+10) \div (-5) \times (-2)$
(g) $(-24) \div (+3) - 6$
(h) $-3 - 4 - 5 - 6$

6. Evaluate.

$(-2)^3$ means $(-2)(-2)(-2)$
-2^3 means $-(2)(2)(2)$

(a) $(-2)^3$
(b) -2^3
(c) $(-4)^2$
(d) -4^2
(e) $(-3)^3$
(f) -3^3
(g) $(-5)^2$
(h) -5^2
(i) $(-1)^3$

7. Simplify each of the following.

(a) $\dfrac{-12 + 50}{-2}$
(b) $\dfrac{-21 - 9}{-15 + 5}$
(c) $\dfrac{-14}{4 - 6}$
(d) $\dfrac{-9 + 17}{6 - 10}$
(e) $\dfrac{-7 - 23}{(-2)(-3)}$
(f) $\dfrac{40 - 52}{-2 - 4}$

8. Find the value of $3x - 2y + z$ for each of the following.

(a) $x = 2, y = -1, z = 3$
(b) $x = 0, y = 4, z = -2$
(c) $x = -1, y = -2, z = -1$

9. Use $x = -1$, $y = -2$ and $z = -3$, and evaluate each of the following.

(a) $2x + 3y + 4z$
(b) $x - 3y - 2z$
(c) $3x - y + 4z$
(d) $-2x + 3y - z$
(e) $-x - y - z$
(f) $x^2 + y^2 + z^2$
(g) $3xy - 2z$
(h) $2x^2 - 3yz$

CALCULATOR MATH

THE +/− KEY

Most calculators have a change-sign key labelled +/−. When the key is pressed, the sign of the number in the display is changed. To enter −4 you press 4, then +/−.

1. To compute $-7 + 2$, press

C 7 +/− + 2 =

2. To compute $(-3)(-5)$, press

C 3 +/− × 5 +/− =

3. To compute $(-9) \div (+3)$, press

C 9 +/− ÷ 3 =

EXERCISE

Simplify each of the following.

(a) $-34 + 56$
(b) $-157 - 473$
(c) $(-713)(-45)$
(d) $(-2024) \div (23)$
(e) $3746 - 5984 - 7925$
(f) $(-118\,464) \div (-96)$
(g) $-47\,602 - 593\,843 + 64\,738$
(h) $(-7934)(-503)$
(i) $-66\,401 + 893 - 5213 + 474$
(j) $351\,480 \div (-4040)$

1.4 APPLYING FRACTIONS

Tuesday, September 21					
Stock	**High**	**Low**	**Close**	**Chge**	**Volume**
Amca	$22\frac{1}{2}$	22	$21\frac{1}{8}$	$+\frac{7}{8}$	3100
Astra	$5\frac{1}{4}$	$4\frac{1}{2}$	5	$-\frac{1}{4}$	500
Atyl	$13\frac{7}{8}$	$13\frac{3}{8}$	$13\frac{3}{4}$	$+\frac{3}{8}$	6000
Ayrco	$64\frac{1}{4}$	$62\frac{5}{8}$	$62\frac{5}{8}$	$-\frac{1}{2}$	13 000

The prices of stocks are recorded as fractions of dollars on the Stock Exchange.

- "High" means the highest price bid for one share of stock that day.
- "Low" means the lowest price bid.
- "Close" means the price of one share of stock when the market closed.
- "Chge" gives the difference between yesterday's closing price and today's.
- "Volume" gives the number of shares traded (bought and sold) during the day.

Example 1. Jerry owns 400 shares of Amca. By how much did the value of his shares increase on Tuesday?

Solution: The stock increased in value by $\$\frac{7}{8}$ per share.

$$\text{Profit} = 400 \times \frac{7}{8}$$
$$= 350$$

Jerry's stock increased $350 in value.

Example 2. What was the difference between the high and the close of Ayrco?

Solution: High $= 64\frac{1}{4}$ and Close $= 62\frac{5}{8}$

$$\text{Difference} = 64\frac{1}{4} - 62\frac{5}{8}$$
$$= 64\frac{2}{8} - 62\frac{5}{8}$$
$$= 63\frac{10}{8} - 62\frac{5}{8}$$
$$= 1\frac{5}{8}$$

The Lowest Common Denominator of 4 and 8 is 8.

The difference was $\$1\frac{5}{8}$.

Example 3. What was Monday's closing price of Atyl?

Solution: Tuesday's close $= 13\frac{3}{4}$

$$\text{Change} = +\frac{3}{8}$$
$$\text{Monday's close} = 13\frac{3}{4} - (+\frac{3}{8})$$
$$= 13\frac{6}{8} - \frac{3}{8}$$
$$= 13\frac{3}{8}$$

The closing price on Monday was $\$13\frac{3}{8}$.

EXERCISE 1.4

A

1. Evaluate.

(a) $\frac{2}{3} - \frac{1}{3}$

(b) $\frac{3}{4} - \frac{1}{4}$

(c) $\frac{1}{10} + \frac{2}{5}$

(d) $\frac{5}{8} - \frac{1}{4}$

(e) $\frac{5}{6} + \frac{2}{3}$

(f) $\frac{3}{8} - \frac{1}{3}$

(g) $\frac{4}{5} - \frac{2}{3}$

(h) $\frac{2}{3} + \frac{1}{2}$

B

2. Calculate. Express answers in lowest terms.

(a) $6\frac{3}{8} + 4\frac{1}{8}$

(b) $4\frac{2}{3} + 7\frac{5}{6}$

(c) $9\frac{4}{9} + 5\frac{2}{3}$

(d) $13\frac{5}{8} + 4$

(e) $2\frac{4}{5} - 1\frac{3}{5}$

(f) $14\frac{1}{9} - 6\frac{2}{9}$

(g) $9\frac{2}{3} - 2\frac{1}{2}$

(h) $1\frac{1}{5} - \frac{3}{4}$

3. Multiply.

(a) $\frac{1}{6} \times \frac{4}{5}$

(b) $\frac{4}{9} \times \frac{3}{4}$

(c) $(\frac{8}{12})(\frac{9}{16})$

(d) $\frac{3}{10} \times 3$

(e) $(6\frac{1}{3})(-7)$

(f) $(9)(2\frac{1}{2})$

(g) $7\frac{1}{3} \times \frac{4}{11}$

(h) $(4\frac{1}{3})(6\frac{1}{2})$

4. Divide.

(a) $\frac{1}{3} \div \frac{1}{2}$

(b) $\frac{9}{10} \div \frac{1}{2}$

(c) $(-2) \div \frac{4}{5}$

(d) $\frac{4}{5} \div 6$

(e) $1\frac{1}{2} \div 2\frac{2}{3}$

(f) $1\frac{3}{4} \div 7\frac{1}{5}$

(g) $12\frac{1}{8} \div 4$

(h) $8\frac{1}{2} \div 1\frac{1}{3}$

5. State which fraction in each pair is greater.

(a) $\frac{3}{4}$ or $\frac{27}{16}$

(b) $2\frac{7}{8}$ or $2\frac{15}{16}$

(c) $\frac{3}{4}$ or $\frac{17}{24}$

(d) $\frac{13}{15}$ or $\frac{19}{20}$

6. Simplify.

(a) $\frac{1}{2} - \frac{1}{3} + \frac{1}{4}$

(b) $\frac{1}{2} \times \frac{1}{2} \div \frac{1}{4}$

(c) $\frac{1}{2} \times (\frac{2}{3} + \frac{1}{6})$

(d) $(1\frac{1}{2} + \frac{1}{3}) \div \frac{3}{4}$

(e) $1\frac{1}{8} \times (\frac{4}{5} \div \frac{5}{6})$

(f) $\frac{1}{8} \div \frac{1}{2} \times \frac{1}{3}$

7. Charlene types reports on a word processor for other students. She worked $3\frac{3}{4}$ h on Monday, $2\frac{1}{3}$ h on Wednesday, and $3\frac{1}{3}$ h on Thursday.

(a) How much time did she spend typing?
(b) If she charges \$9.50/h, how much money did she earn?

8. A stock that opened at $\$17\frac{1}{8}$ fell $\$2\frac{3}{4}$ during morning trading.

(a) What was the noon price of the stock?
(b) What was the closing price of the stock if it fell another $\$1\frac{5}{8}$ in the afternoon?
(c) How much did the stock fall during the day?
(d) If Jaime has 480 shares of this stock, what will be the change in value of her shares at the end of the day?

MIND BENDER

The word RAISING ends in the letters ING. If you drop the letter G, the result is RAISIN.

Find a five-letter word ending in ING that becomes a new word when the final G is dropped.

1.5 TWO-TERM RATIOS

A ratio is a comparison of two or more quantities with the same units. For a ratio of three golf balls to four baseballs we can write

$$\frac{3}{4} \text{ or } 3:4$$

Example 1. In a true or false quiz, 12 answers were "True" and 8 answers were "False."
What is the ratio of "True" to "False" answers?

Solution: The ratio of "True" to "False" is 12 : 8
In lowest terms, 12 : 8 = 3 : 2

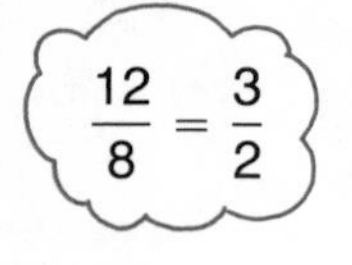

> The statement of the equality of two ratios is called a proportion.
>
> $$\frac{a}{b} = \frac{c}{d} \qquad \text{or} \qquad a:b = c:d$$

Example 2. In a survey, 4 out of 25 students eat salad for lunch. There are 800 students in the school who eat lunch. How many students eat salad?

Solution: Let x be the number of students who eat salad.

$$\frac{x}{800} = \frac{4}{25} \quad \leftarrow \text{The LCD of 800 and 25 is 800.}$$

$$800 \times \left(\frac{x}{800}\right) = \left(\frac{4}{25}\right) \times 800 \quad \leftarrow \text{Clear fractions.}$$

$$x = 128$$

∴ 128 students eat salad for lunch.

Example 3. At Bruce's Brake and Muffler Centre, the ratio of muffler to brake jobs was 4 : 11.
About how many of 100 jobs are muffler jobs?

Solution: The ratio of muffler to brake jobs is 4 : 11.
The ratio of muffler jobs to total jobs is 4 : 15.
Let x represent the number of muffler jobs.

$$\frac{x}{100} = \frac{4}{15}$$

$$300\left(\frac{x}{100}\right) = \left(\frac{4}{15}\right)300$$

$$\frac{3x}{3} = \frac{80}{3}$$

$$3x = 80$$

$$x = 26\tfrac{2}{3}$$

∴ about 27 of 100 jobs are for mufflers.

EXERCISE 1.5

A

1. Express the following ratios in lowest terms.

(a) 12 : 15 (b) 8 : 24

(c) $\frac{12}{16}$ (d) $\frac{20}{25}$

(e) $\frac{15}{20}$ (f) $\frac{24}{32}$

(g) 32 : 40 (h) 16 : 80

B

2. Solve the following proportions for x.

(a) $\frac{x}{20} = \frac{15}{40}$ (b) $\frac{x}{12} = \frac{12}{48}$

(c) $\frac{x}{7} = \frac{21}{49}$ (d) $\frac{x}{9} = \frac{4}{36}$

(e) $\frac{2}{5} = \frac{x}{45}$ (f) $\frac{4}{3} = \frac{x}{24}$

(g) $\frac{12}{x} = \frac{3}{7}$ (h) $\frac{3}{4} = \frac{18}{x}$

3. Solve for x to the nearest tenth.

(a) $\frac{x}{5} = \frac{7}{11}$ (b) $\frac{x}{18} = \frac{5}{8}$

(c) $\frac{x}{24} = \frac{3}{11}$ (d) $\frac{x}{18} = \frac{7}{5}$

(e) $\frac{5}{7} = \frac{x}{12}$ (f) $\frac{11}{15} = \frac{x}{7}$

(g) $\frac{24}{17} = \frac{10}{x}$ (h) $\frac{12}{x} = \frac{15}{11}$

(i) $\frac{x}{23} = \frac{77}{12}$ (j) $\frac{x}{77} = \frac{12}{23}$

(k) $\frac{3x}{14} = \frac{11}{3}$ (l) $\frac{5}{42} = \frac{13}{11x}$

4. The ratio of men to women shopping in a store is 4 : 5.
How many shoppers are there if there are 500 men in the store?

5. Georgette and Royale invest \$5000 and \$3000 respectively in a small business. They agree to share the profit in the same ratio.
How much should each receive of a profit of \$4800?

6. In a radio survey it was found that 2 out of 5 households listened to the station CHAM.
In an area of 30 000 households, how many would you expect to listen to CHAM?

7. In a mixture of nuts the ratio of peanuts to cashews is 5 : 2.
If the mixture contains 760 g of peanuts, how many grams of cashews would you expect to find?

8. Sodium and chlorine combine in an approximate ratio of 23 : 36 by mass to make table salt.
About how many grams of sodium would combine with 45 g of chlorine to make salt?

9. Two gears are in the ratio of 4 to 5.
If the larger of the two gears has 70 teeth, how many teeth are there in the other gear?

10. The total number of teeth in two gears is 105. The ratio of teeth on the larger gear to teeth on the smaller gear is 4 : 3.
How many teeth does the smaller gear have?

11. Two bicycle wheels have diameters of 70 cm and 60 cm.
What is the ratio of the larger wheel to the smaller wheel in terms of
(a) area?
(b) circumference?

$A = \pi r^2$
$C = 2\pi r$

1.6 THREE-TERM RATIOS

In the previous section we worked with two-term ratios. It is also possible to have ratios with more than two terms. For example, if there are 3 parents, 3 students, and 2 teachers on a committee, the ratio of parents to students to teachers is 3 : 3 : 2.

Example 1. A hockey team finished the season with a record of 50 wins, 25 losses, and 5 ties. What is the ratio of wins to losses to ties?

$$\frac{50}{10} = \frac{25}{5} = \frac{5}{1}$$

Solution: The ratio of wins to losses to ties is 50 : 25 : 5
In lowest terms, 50 : 25 : 5 = 10 : 5 : 1

If, on the other hand, we were given the win-to-loss-to-tie ratio and the number of games played, we could determine the record of the hockey team. Example 2 will illustrate the method.

Example 2. Three entrepreneurs, Will, Lorne, and Tamara, invest in a business in the ratio 2 : 3 : 7. Profits are divided in the same ratio as the investment. The business made a profit of $240 000. What is each investor's share?

Solution:
Consider the sum $2 + 3 + 7 = 12$ to be the number of shares in the business. To determine what each share is worth we divide.
$240 000 ÷ 12 = $20 000.
Will's 2 shares are worth 2 × $20 000 = $40 000.
Lorne's 3 shares are worth 3 × $20 000 = $60 000.
Tamara's 7 shares are worth 7 × $20 000 = $140 000.
The profit is divided into the sums $40 000, $60 000, and $140 000.

We can solve three-term ratio problems using proportions in the same way as with two-term ratios. The results of example 2 can be shown as the proportion

$$\frac{2}{40\,000} = \frac{3}{60\,000} = \frac{7}{140\,000}$$

because 2 : 3 : 7 = 40 000 : 60 000 : 140 000.

Example 3. Find the missing terms.
3 : k : 9 = 5 : 8 : n

Solution: Rewrite 3 : k : 9 = 5 : 8 : n in the form $\frac{3}{5} = \frac{k}{8} = \frac{9}{n}$

From this statement we may use the $\frac{3}{5}$ to write the equations.

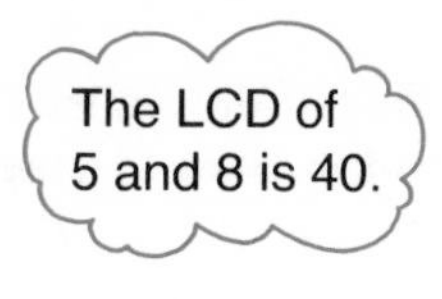

$$\frac{3}{5} = \frac{k}{8} \qquad \text{and} \qquad \frac{3}{5} = \frac{9}{n}$$

$$40 \times \left(\frac{3}{5}\right) = \left(\frac{k}{8}\right) \times 40 \qquad 5n \times \left(\frac{3}{5}\right) = \left(\frac{9}{n}\right) \times 5n$$

$$24 = 5k \qquad 3n = 45$$

$$\tfrac{24}{5} = k \qquad n = 15$$

$\therefore k = 4\frac{4}{5}$ or 4.8

$\therefore 3 : 4.8 : 9 = 5 : 8 : 15$

EXERCISE 1.6

A

1. Determine whether the following ratios are equivalent.
(a) 2 : 3 : 4 and 6 : 9 : 12
(b) 1 : 2 : 3 and 3 : 2 : 1
(c) 1 : 2 : 5 and 5 : 10 : 20
(d) 5 : 10 : 15 and 1 : 2 : 3
(e) 45 : 50 : 60 and 9 : 10 : 11
(f) 12 : 4 : 15 and 3 : 1 : 5

2. Find the factor that multiplies the first ratio to give the second.
(a) 3 : 6 : 9 = 1 : 2 : 3
(b) 2 : 4 : 7 = 8 : 16 : 28
(c) 8 : 12 : 16 = 2 : 3 : 4
(d) 3 : 12 : 9 = 1 : 4 : 3
(e) 2 : 6 : 5 = 10 : 30 : 25
(f) a : b : c = ak : bk : ck
(g) am : bm : cm = a : b : c
(h) x : y : z = 2ax : 2ay : 2az

B

3. Find the missing terms.
(a) 4 : k : 8 = n : 3 : 4
(b) m : 4 : 7 = 15 : 12 : n
(c) 2 : 11 : 17 = k : m : 51
(d) k : 1 : n = 40 : 8 : 104
(e) 2.3 : 4.7 : 5.1 = n : 28.2 : m
(f) 3.1 : 11.4 : m = n : 148.2 : 100.1

4. Find the missing terms to the nearest tenth.
(a) 7 : 3 : 4 = 6 : m : n
(b) 11 : m : 3 = 13 : 4 : k
(c) 2 : m : 5 = 3 : 4 : p
(d) m : 5 : n = 11 : 9 : 5
(e) 13 : m : n = 7 : 6 : 5
(f) 3 : 2 : 1 = k : p : 7.71

5. The ratio of red cars to blue cars to grey cars that are sold at a car dealership is 2 : 5 : 8.
(a) How many red and grey cars were sold if 25 blue cars were sold?
(b) What is the total number of red, blue and grey cars sold if 16 red cars were sold?

6. Sam, Carol, and Pat sold snowmobiles in the ratio 3 : 5 : 7. Together they sold a total of 315 snowmobiles.
How many snowmobiles did each sell?

7. Three people invest in a business, with Sue investing $30 000, Elaine $40 000, and Jennifer $25 000. They agree to share the profit in the same ratio.
How much will each receive if the profit is $42 500?

1.7 RATES: THE RULE OF THREE

A rate is a comparison of two quantities in different units. In order to work with rates, we establish the Rule of Three, so called because it involves three steps.

Example 1. If Crystal earns \$120.75 for teaching sailing for 7 h, how much can she earn in 44 h?

Solution: ① Statement: In 7 h she earns \$120.75

② Reduce to 1: In 1 h she earns $\frac{\$120.75}{7}$

③ Multiply: In 44 h she earns $44 \times \frac{\$120.75}{7}$

In 44 h Crystal can earn \$759.00.

Unit pricing is used to help shoppers compare the prices of food that is packaged in different sizes. Unit pricing is a rate of cost, and is found by using the first two steps of the Rule of Three.

Example 2. Feather Food bird seed costs \$8.75 for a 5 kg bag. Northern bird seed costs \$14.50 for an 8 kg bag.
If the quality is the same, which is the better buy?

Solution: Calculate the cost per kilogram for each seed using the first two steps of the Rule of Three.

Feather Food: ① 5 kg cost \$8.75

② 1 kg costs $\frac{\$8.75}{5} = \$1.75$

Northern: ① 8 kg cost \$14.50

② 1 kg costs $\frac{\$14.50}{8} = \$1.8125$

$\doteq \$1.81$

Feather Food bird seed is the better buy.

Example 3. Pipeline A will fill a storage tank in 6 h.
Pipeline B can fill the tank in half the time it takes pipeline A.
How long will it take to fill the tank using both pipelines?

Solution: ① Pipeline A takes 6 h to fill the tank.

Pipeline B takes $\frac{1}{2}$ of 6 = 3 h to fill the tank.

② In 1 h, Pipeline A fills $\frac{1}{6}$ of the tank,

Pipeline B fills $\frac{1}{3}$ of the tank.

Together, both pipelines fill $\frac{1}{6} + \frac{1}{3}$ of the tank.

$$\begin{aligned}\frac{1}{6} + \frac{1}{3} &= \frac{1}{6} + \frac{2}{6} \\ &= \frac{3}{6} \\ &= \frac{1}{2}\end{aligned}$$

$\therefore$ in 1 h pipelines together fill $\frac{1}{2}$ of the tank.

③ Using both pipelines together, it would take 2 h to fill the tank.

EXERCISE 1.7

B

1. If 1.5 L of spring water costs 75¢, what is the cost of 20 L?

2. Twenty-two placemats can be cut from 2.75 m of material.
How much material is required to cut 100 placemats?

3. If Frank can earn $217.25 for 11 h of guiding tours in caves, how much can he earn in 23 h?

4. A truck can travel 370 km in 5 h.
How far can it travel in 8 h?

5. An engine will run for 3.25 h on 20 L of fuel.
What volume of fuel is required to run the engine for 24 h?

6. Theo bought a 4.8 kg roast for $29.52. The next day he saw roasts advertised in another store at $6.37/kg.
Which store had the better buy on roasts?

7. The rate of fuel consumption by a car is measured in litres per hundred kilometres (L/100 km). A car that travels 100 km on 8.4 L of gasoline consumes fuel at the rate of 8.4 L/100 km.
Find the rate of fuel consumption for each of the following cars.

(a) A Buick that travelled 500 km on 46 L of gasoline.
(b) A Ford that travelled 750 km on 60 L of gasoline.
(c) A Lincoln that travelled 800 km on 75 L of gasoline.

8. Katy's car burns gasoline at the rate of 8.2 L/100 km.
How much gasoline will be used to travel
(a) 700 km? (b) 950 km? (c) 1200 km?

9. It takes Sandra 3 h to clean the Central Pool. It takes Paul 4 h to do the same job. How long will it take them to clean the pool working together?

1.8 BASIC COMPUTER LANGUAGE

BASIC is one of several languages that is understood by a computer. The word BASIC is an abbreviation for Beginner's All-purpose Symbolic Instruction Code. Some of the operations symbols in BASIC are the same as in algebra.

Algebra	BASIC
$+$	$+$
$-$	$-$
$\times$	$*$
$\div$	$/$
a^x	$a \wedge x$ or $a \uparrow x$

Algebra	BASIC
$=$	$=$
$<$	$<$
$>$	$>$
$\leqslant$	$<=$
$\geqslant$	$>=$
$\neq$	$<>$

The order of operations on a computer follows the BEDMAS rule of algebra.

B Operations in inner brackets are performed first.
E Powers are evaluated from left to right.
DM Divisions and multiplications are performed in order from left to right.
AS Additions and subtractions are performed in order from left to right.

These rules are illustrated in the following:

42/7 − 3^2 + (10 − 4)*4	= 42/7 − 3^2 + 6*4	B
	= 42/7 − 9 + 6*4	E
	= 6 − 9 + 24	DM
	= 21	AS

Mathematical statements are combined with system commands that have a special meaning to the computer. Following are some of the more useful system commands.

RUN: RUN instructs the computer to run the program.
LIST: LIST tells the computer to print in order, all statements in the program on the screen.
PRINT: PRINT causes the computer to print what follows on the screen.
END: END tells the computer that the program is finished.
INPUT: INPUT is used to enter data from the keyboard.
GO TO: GO TO (also GOTO) tells the computer to go to another statement and continue from there.

`IF . . . THEN`: If the given condition is true, the computer continues to the given statement. If the statement is false, the next statement is executed.

$: the dollar sign, $, indicates to the computer that the incoming data are alphabetic.

EXERCISE 1.8

A

1. Evaluate the following examples which are written in BASIC.
(a) 2^3+3^2
(b) 5*(2+3)
(c) 30/4*5
(d) 5*((7+25)/4+4)/3
(e) 6*3^2
(f) (6*3)^2
(g) 5^3−3^4

B

2. Write the following expressions in BASIC.
(a) $7 + 8(5 + 6)$
(b) $42 - 4 \times 2(7 - 5)$
(c) $6 \times 5 - 8$
(d) $2(\ell + w)$
(e) $3.14r$
(f) $\frac{x + y}{2}$

3. Evaluate each of the following for $A = 6$, $B = -4$, and $C = 2$.
(a) A*B+C
(b) A*(B+C)
(c) (A+B)/2*10
(d) A/B^C

4. Write the output for each program.
(a)
```
NEW
10 PRINT"HELLO PROFESSOR"
20 END
RUN
```
(b)
```
NEW
10 A=5.3
20 B=7.2
30 PRINT B+C,B*C
40 END
RUN
```

5. This program prints the first 25 multiples of 4. Enter and RUN the program on a computer.
```
NEW
10 PRINT"MULTIPLES OF 4"
20 PRINT"NUMBER","MULTIPLE"
30 FOR N = 1 TO 25
40 PRINT N,4*N
50 NEXT N
60 END
RUN
```

6. The following program will evaluate the polynomial $5x^2 + 7x - 6$ for any value of the variable.
```
NEW
10 PRINT"EVALUATING"
20 INPUT"X = ";X
30 LET P=5*X*X+7*X-6
40 PRINT"THE VALUE IS"
50 PRINT P
60 END
RUN
```
Run the program and input $x = 7.2$.
To make such a program reiterative, we add these statements.
```
NEW
53 PRINT"ANOTHER VALUE?"
54 INPUT"Y OR N";Z$
55 IF Z$ = "Y" THEN 10
RUN
```

OUTPUT TO A PRINTER

In BASIC, the command PRINT means to display the data on the screen. In order to get hard copy (words on paper) when running a BASIC program,insert the LPRINT command into the program.

1.9 PRINCIPLES OF PROBLEM SOLVING

A problem is a situation that requires a solution. The word itself implies that the solution is not obvious and requires a conscientious effort.

The question "What is 2 + 3?" can hardly be called a problem because in fact it poses no problem. However, the question "How many AM 11 textbooks placed end-to-end would span the distance from Halifax to Vancouver?" would at first be considered a problem, since its solution requires a conscientious approach. If you were to solve many problems similar to this one, their solutions would eventually become so methodical and routine that they would be considered drill exercises rather than problems.

Though there are no hard and fast rules for solving problems, most mathematical problems can be solved using the following four-step approach: READ — PLAN — SOLVE — ANSWER.

Whether it be in everyday situations or in a mathematics class, common sense and confidence are the key ingredients to problem solving. The READ — PLAN — SOLVE — ANSWER model presented in this section and used throughout the book will help you to develop both.

READ

Read the problem carefully and devote sufficient time to understanding the problem before trying to solve it. Note key words. Put the problem in your own words. Know what you are asked to find. Be aware of what is given.

PLAN

Think of a plan. Find a connection between the given information and the unknown which will enable you to calculate the unknown.

1. Classify information. Study the information carefully to determine what is needed to solve the problem. Identify the relevant and irrelevant information. Some information may be extraneous or redundant.

You may find it helpful to summarize the information or make lists.

2. Search for a pattern. Try to recognize patterns. Some problems are solved by recognizing that some kind of pattern is occurring. The pattern could be geometric, numerical, or algebraic. If you can see there is some sort of regularity or repetition in a problem, then you might be able to guess what the continuing pattern is, and then prove it.

3. Draw a diagram or flow chart. For many problems it is useful to draw a diagram and identify the given and required quantities on the diagram. A flow chart can be used to organize a series of steps that must be performed in a definite order.

4. Estimate, guess, and check. This is a valid method to solve a problem where a direct method is not apparent. You may find it necessary to improve your guess and "zero in" on the correct answer.

5. Sequence operations. To solve some problems, several operations performed in a definite order are needed.

6. Work backwards. Sometimes it is useful to imagine that your problem is solved and work backwards step by step until you arrive at the given data. Then, you may be able to reverse your steps to solve the original problem.

7. Use a formula or an equation. In some problems, after analyzing the data, the problem can be written as an equation, or the data can be substituted into a formula.

8. Solve a simpler problem. A problem can sometimes be broken into smaller problems that can be solved more easily.

9. Account for all possibilities. List all of the cases. Your solution must account for all of these cases. You may sometimes be able to solve your problem using a process of elimination.

10. Make a table. In some problems, it is helpful to organize the data in a table, chart, or grid.

11. Check for hidden assumptions. In some problems, the information concerning what is given is presented in a subtle manner that may not attract your attention. Re-read the problem carefully and look for the implied information.

12. Conclude from assumptions. In some problems, it will be necessary to make assumptions. The conclusions that you draw from these assumptions should be those that you have made in the past, from the same types of information.

13. Introduce something extra. Sometimes it may be necessary to introduce something new, an auxiliary aid, to help make the connection between the given and the unknown. For instance in geometry, the auxiliary could be a new line drawn in the diagram. In algebra, it could be a new unknown which is related to the original unknown.

SOLVE

Before solving the problem, look at the reasons for selecting your strategy. If you have more than one strategy available, you should consider familiarity, efficiency, and ease, in making your choice. In carrying out your strategy, work with care and check each step as you proceed. Remember to present your ideas clearly.

ANSWER

State the answer in a clear and concise manner. Check your answer in the original problem and use estimation to decide if your answer is reasonable. In checking your answer, you may discover an easier way to solve the problem. You may wish to generalize your method of solution so that it can be applied to similar problems.

READ

Example 1. An excavation is 25 m long, 8 m wide, and 5 m deep.
How many truck loads of earth were carried away, if each truck has a capacity of $3.8\ m^3$?

PLAN

Solution:
The excavation is rectangular: 25 m $\times$ 8 m $\times$ 5 m
The volume of one truck load is $3.8\ m^3$.
Find the number of truck loads.

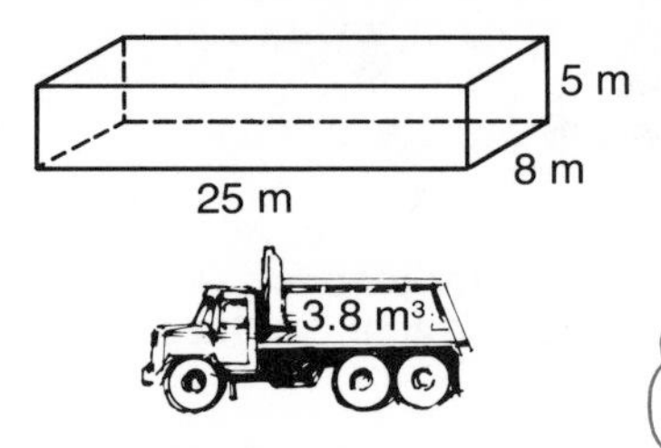

Find the volume using $V = \ell wh$.
Divide the volume by the amount of one load, which is $3.8\ m^3$.

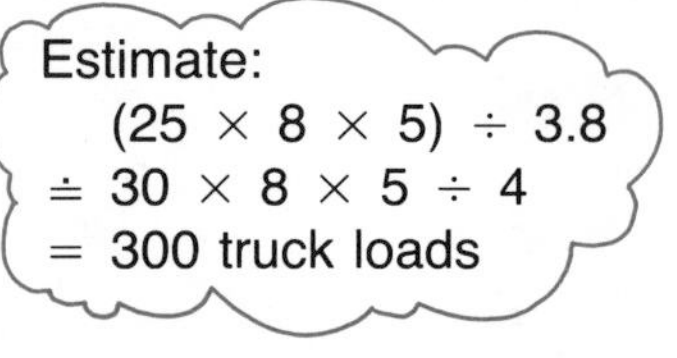

SOLVE

$\ell = 25,\ w = 8,\ h = 5$
$V = \ell wh$
$V = 25 \times 8 \times 5$
$\quad = 1000$
The volume of the excavation is $1000\ m^3$.

Number of loads:
$1000 \div 3.8 = 263.2$ (to the nearest tenth)

ANSWER

$\therefore$ the number of truck loads is 264.

READ

Example 2. Francine attended an outdoor concert in Halifax. She sat about 50 m from a speaker. Carl listened to the concert on his radio while jogging in Vancouver.
If sound travels at about 350 m/s and light travels at 300 000 000 m/s, who heard the concert first?

PLAN

Solution:
Radio waves travel at the speed of light.
Vancouver is about 6000 km from Halifax.
Time = Distance $\div$ Speed

SOLVE

Francine: She is 50 m from the sound source. At a speed of 350 m/s it will take $\frac{50}{350}$ s or 0.14 s for the sound to reach Francine.

Carl: He is 6000 km or 6 000 000 m from Halifax.
At a speed of 300 000 000 m/s it will take $\frac{6\ 000\ 000}{300\ 000\ 000}$ s or 0.02 s for the sound to reach Carl.

ANSWER

Carl will hear the concert before Francine does.

EXERCISE 1.9

B

1. How many times between nine-thirty in the morning and three-thirty in the afternoon will the hands of a clock cross?

2. The Best-Ride car rental company charges \$31.75/d plus \$0.12/km to rent a van. Carol rented a van for fourteen days. When she left the Best-Ride lot the odometer on the van read 9008.7 km. When she returned the odometer read 13234.7 km.
How much did she owe for the van?

3. When the commuter train arrived at Gallery station, 9 people got on and 8 people got off.
At Delta station, 14 people got on and 7 people got off.
At Westdale station, 15 people got on and 5 got off.
When the train left Westdale station, there were 56 passengers on it.
How many passengers were on the train when it arrived at Gallery station?

4. Sandra bought 3 sweaters at \$63.75 each, and two pairs of jeans at \$36.40 each.
If the sales tax is 7%, how much change did she receive from three hundred dollars?

5. For each of the following, make an assumption and find the next two terms.
(a) 13, 19, 25, 31, ■, ■
(b) 5, 10, 16, 23, 31, 40, ■, ■
(c) 88, 44, 22, ■, ■

6. If you take a number, multiply it by 5, then subtract 9, and finally add 7, you get 38.
What is the number?

7. The Parks Department wants to put a fence around the 30 m by 20 m rectangular community pool. There is to be a 4 m wide grass area between the pool and the fence.

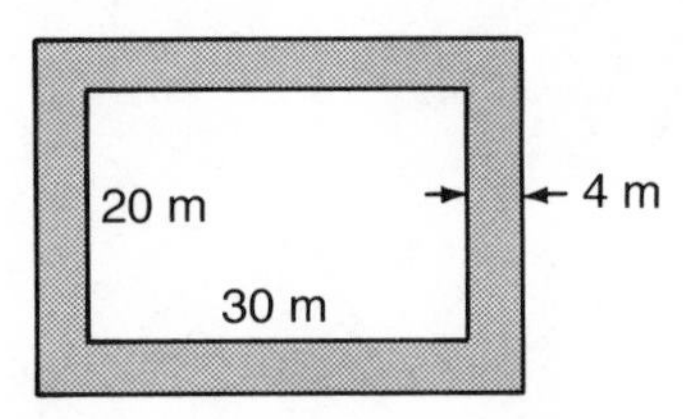

(a) How much fence will be needed?
(b) If fencing costs \$19.90/m, how much will the fencing cost, including sales tax of 7%?
(c) How many posts are required if there is to be a post every 2 m?
(d) Posts cost \$11.50 each.
How much will the posts cost, including sales tax of 7%?
(e) The cost of labour for the job is \$1230.00.
What is the total cost of installing the fence?

8. On your next birthday, how old will you be in minutes?

9. Place 4 dots in the following figure so that there will be no more than one dot in each row, column, or diagonal.

10. Four students belong to the golf team. They decide to form a committee of three to organize a county tournament.
How many different committees can be formed?

11. Caroline has three part-time jobs. Last week she worked 4 h at a shoe store where she earns $11.60/h. She worked 5 h at a record store where she earns $9.95/h. She also worked 7 h at a gas station where she earns $12.50/h.
How much did she earn last week?

12. Michael and Sue leave from the same place at the same time on bicycles. Michael rides at a speed of 300 m/min and Sue rides at 400 m/min.
(a) How far apart are they after 12 min if they ride in the same direction?
(b) How far apart are they after 12 min if they ride in opposite directions?

13. Jennifer had twenty-seven rare seashells. She put them into three bags so that there was an odd number of shells in each bag.
How many different ways could she do this?

14. A radio station is heard at 1150 AM on the radio dial.
What does the 1150 mean?

15.

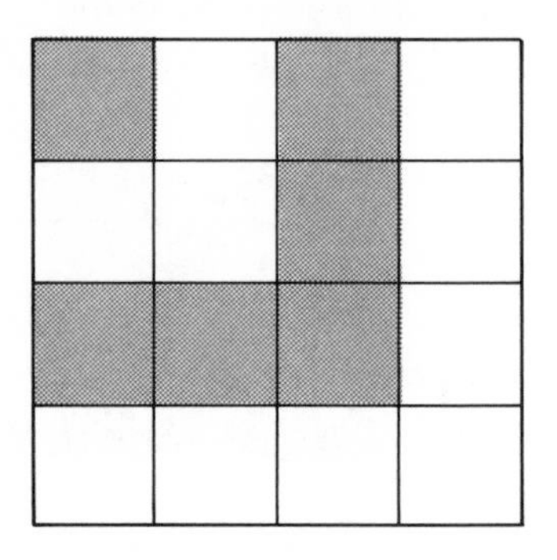

The figure above contains a pattern of red and white squares illustrating the sequence 1, 3, 5, 7.
(a) What kind of numbers are these?
(b) How are the sum of the first four terms and the area of this figure related?
(c) Draw a diagram in your notebook to show the sum of the first
(i) five,
(ii) six,
(iii) seven
odd numbers.
(d) How would you find the sum of the first 125 odd numbers? (Do not add.)

16. Place the numbers from 11 to 19 in the circles so that the sum along each side of the triangle is 60.

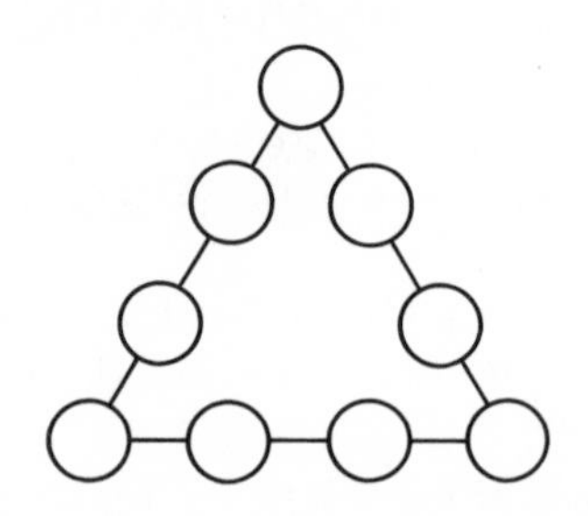

CALCULATOR MATH

1.10 FRACTION KEY [a b/c]

Some calculators have a fraction key. To enter fractions in fractional form, press the correct number(s) for the integer (if any), press [a b/c], press the correct number(s) for the numerator, press [a b/c] and press the correct number(s) for the denominator.

Example 1. Enter $35\frac{2}{13}$ in fractional form.

Press	Display
[3] [5] [a b/c]	
[2] [a b/c] [1] [3]	35⌋2⌋13.

Example 2. $3\frac{3}{4} + \frac{4}{5} - 2\frac{1}{3} = 2\frac{13}{60}$

Press	Display
[3] [a b/c] [3] [a b/c] [4]	3⌋3⌋4.
[+] [4] [a b/c] [5]	4⌋5.
[−]	4⌋11⌋20.

(Intermediary calculation: $3\frac{3}{4} + \frac{4}{5} = 4\frac{11}{20}$)

Press	Display
[2] [a b/c] [1] [a b/c] [3]	2⌋1⌋3.
[=]	2⌋13⌋60.

To obtain the result as a decimal, continuing from above:

Press	Display
[a b/c]	2.216666667

To return to fractional form, continuing from above:

Press	Display
[a b/c]	2⌋13⌋60.

To obtain the result as an improper fraction, continuing from above:

Press	Display
[INV] [a b/c]	133⌋60.

To return to fractional form, continuing from above:

Press	Display
[a b/c] or [=]	2⌋13⌋60.

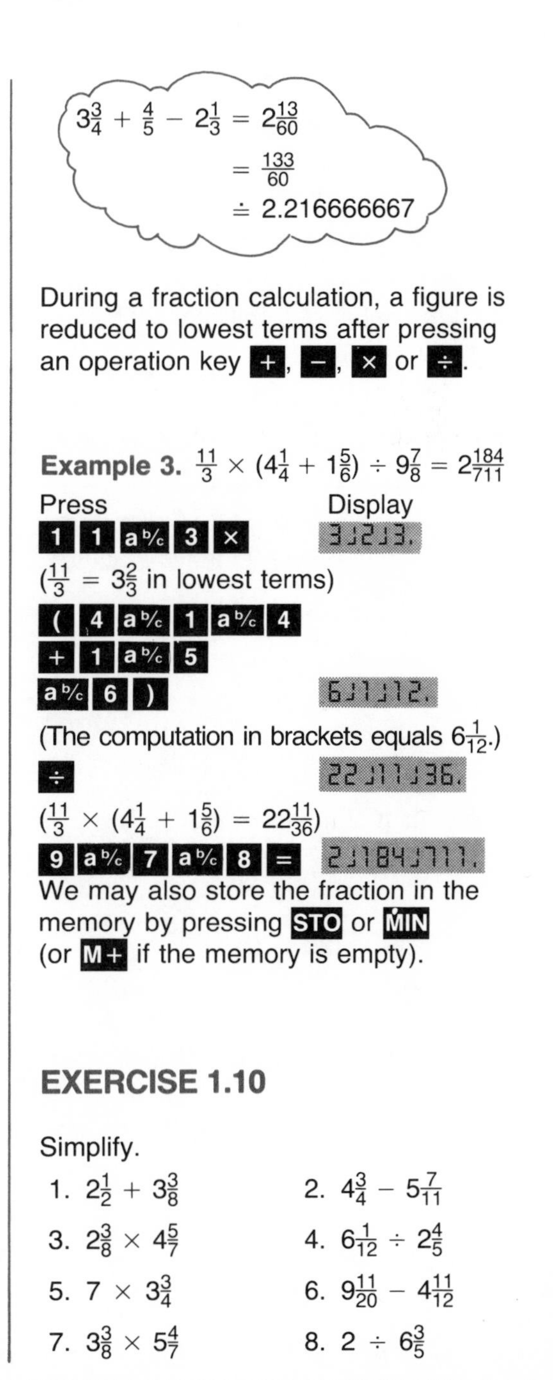

$$3\frac{3}{4} + \frac{4}{5} - 2\frac{1}{3} = 2\frac{13}{60} = \frac{133}{60} \doteq 2.216666667$$

During a fraction calculation, a figure is reduced to lowest terms after pressing an operation key [+], [−], [×] or [÷].

Example 3. $\frac{11}{3} \times (4\frac{1}{4} + 1\frac{5}{6}) \div 9\frac{7}{8} = 2\frac{184}{711}$

Press	Display
[1] [1] [a b/c] [3] [×]	3⌋2⌋3.

($\frac{11}{3} = 3\frac{2}{3}$ in lowest terms)

Press	Display
[(] [4] [a b/c] [1] [a b/c] [4]	
[+] [1] [a b/c] [5]	
[a b/c] [6] [)]	6⌋1⌋12.

(The computation in brackets equals $6\frac{1}{12}$.)

Press	Display
[÷]	22⌋11⌋36.

($\frac{11}{3} \times (4\frac{1}{4} + 1\frac{5}{6}) = 22\frac{11}{36}$)

Press	Display
[9] [a b/c] [7] [a b/c] [8] [=]	2⌋184⌋711.

We may also store the fraction in the memory by pressing [STO] or [MIN] (or [M+] if the memory is empty).

EXERCISE 1.10

Simplify.

1. $2\frac{1}{2} + 3\frac{3}{8}$
2. $4\frac{3}{4} - 5\frac{7}{11}$
3. $2\frac{3}{8} \times 4\frac{5}{7}$
4. $6\frac{1}{12} \div 2\frac{4}{5}$
5. $7 \times 3\frac{3}{4}$
6. $9\frac{11}{20} - 4\frac{11}{12}$
7. $3\frac{3}{8} \times 5\frac{4}{7}$
8. $2 \div 6\frac{3}{5}$

1.11 REVIEW EXERCISE

1. Round each of the following to the required place.

(a) 4.125 (hundredth)
(b) 36 732 (hundred)
(c) 15.18 (tenth)
(d) 6500 (thousand)
(e) 7500 (thousand)
(f) 0.0506 (thousandth)

2. Find the area of a square with sides 4.12 cm.

3. State the number of significant digits in each of the following.

(a) 1705
(b) 4.70×10^4
(c) 3200
(d) 0.076

4. A blueprint has a scale of 2 : 5. If a part appears as 5.36 mm long on the blueprint, how large is it actually?

5. Estimate.

(a) $\frac{35 \times 26}{81}$ (b) $\frac{197 - 43}{57}$
(c) $\frac{19.4 \times 17.8}{9.4}$ (d) $\frac{368 \times 217}{189 - 93}$

6. Simplify each of the following.

(a) $17 - 64 \div 8 \times 2$
(b) $49 \div 7 \times (13 - 6) + 3^2$
(c) $18 \div 3^2 \times 4 - (6 - 4) \times 3$
(d) $24 + 6 \div 5 \times (20 \div 2)$

7. Simplify.

(a) $(-7)(-4)$ (b) $(-12) \div (+3)$
(c) $-9 + 3 - 4$ (d) $11 - 13 - 3$
(e) $(-10)(-2) \div (-5)$ (f) $-3 - 6 - 2$
(g) $15 \div (-3) - 6$ (h) $-21 + (-3)(-8)$
(i) $16 \div (-4) - 1$ (j) $(-3)^3$
(k) -3^3 (l) $-21 \div 7 + 8$

8. Use $x = -2$, $y = -1$ and $z = 3$ and evaluate each of the following.

(a) $3x + y + z$ (b) $x^2 + y^2 - z^2$
(c) $x^3 - y^3 - z^3$ (d) $2x - y - z$
(e) $4z - 3y - 2x$ (f) $-x - y - z$
(g) $3x^2 - 14$ (h) $2y^2 - 2x^2 + z^2$

9. Evaluate.

(a) $\frac{1}{2} + \frac{3}{4}$ (b) $\frac{7}{8} - \frac{1}{6}$
(c) $\frac{5}{6} \div \frac{1}{3}$ (d) $\frac{4}{5} \times \frac{3}{4}$
(e) $\frac{1}{5} + \frac{1}{2} + \frac{1}{4}$ (f) $\frac{7}{10} - \frac{1}{4}$
(g) $3\frac{1}{2} + 2\frac{1}{3}$ (h) $4\frac{1}{5} - 1\frac{9}{10}$
(i) $4\frac{3}{4} \times 1\frac{1}{3}$ (j) $3\frac{2}{3} \div 1\frac{1}{4}$
(k) $13\frac{5}{8} + 5\frac{3}{4}$ (l) $8\frac{2}{3} - 7\frac{1}{2}$
(m) $\frac{1}{12} \times \frac{1}{3}$ (n) $\frac{3}{4} \times (-\frac{2}{3})$
(o) $\frac{3}{10} \div (-\frac{2}{5})$ (p) $\frac{2}{9} \div \frac{3}{4}$

10. Evaluate $A = \frac{h}{2}(a + b)$ for the following values.

(a) $h = 5$, $a = 2$, $b = 4$
(b) $h = 3.2$, $a = 1.5$, $b = 2.1$
(c) $h = 16$, $a = 3.125$, $b = 4.375$
(d) $h = 6.0$, $a = 0.315$, $b = 2.4$

11. Calculate the lengths of A, B, C, D.

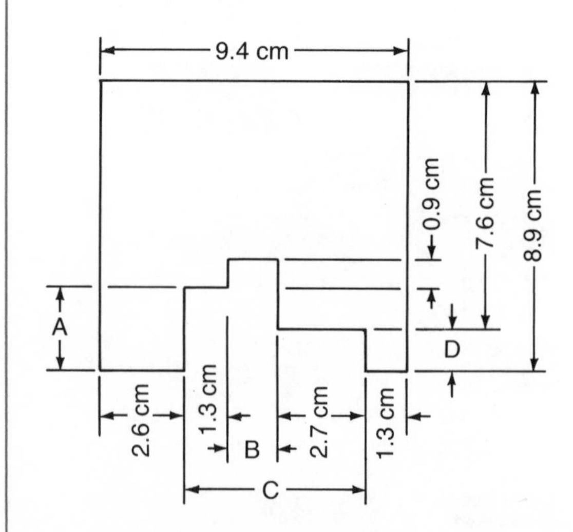

12. Order the following fractions from largest to smallest.

$\frac{-5}{6}, \frac{5}{9}, \frac{11}{18}, \frac{13}{11}, \frac{-2}{3}, \frac{-17}{20}, \frac{13}{10}$

13. Solve the following proportions for x.

(a) $\frac{x}{32} = \frac{1}{4}$ (b) $\frac{x}{24} = \frac{4}{3}$

(c) $\frac{2}{x} = \frac{0.5}{1.5}$ (d) $\frac{5}{3} = \frac{25}{x}$

14. Determine the fractions into which a pie will be cut if it is to be divided in the ratio

(a) 3 : 2 : 1 (b) 7 : 4 : 3

15. In a city, the newspaper market is shared by three papers, Good News, Bad News, and All The News in the ratio of 4 : 1 : 3.

What percent of the market does each paper have?

16.

Monday, September 30				
Stock	**High**	**Low**	**Close**	**Chge**
Barton	$15\frac{1}{4}$	$14\frac{7}{8}$	$15\frac{1}{8}$	$+\frac{3}{4}$
Bestway	$9\frac{1}{2}$	9	$9\frac{1}{2}$	$-\frac{1}{2}$

(a) Frank owns 800 shares of Barton stock. By how much did the total value of his shares increase on Monday?

(b) What was the difference between the High and Low of Barton?

(c) If you bought 1500 shares of Bestway at today's lowest price and sold it at its highest price, what was your profit?

(d) What was Friday's closing price of Barton?

(e) What was Friday's closing price of Bestway?

17. The following seat prices were set for a July 1 concert.

Orchestra \$23.50
1st Balcony \$14.75
2nd Balcony \$11.50

(a) How much do 5 Orchestra seats cost?

(b) What is the difference in cost between eight 1st Balcony seats and eight 2nd Balcony seats?

(c) If you have \$200.00,
 (i) what is the maximum number of seats you can buy?
 (ii) what is the maximum number of seats you can buy if you want at least two of each type?
 (iii) and if you bought as many Orchestra seats as you could, how much change from your \$200.00 would you receive?

18. A car wheel revolves 530 times per minute when the car is travelling 60 km/h. How many revolutions per minute will the wheel make when the car is travelling 90 km/h?

19. Pipeline A will drain a storage tank in 5 h. Pipelines A and B will together drain the tank in 3 h.

How long will it take to drain the tank using only Pipeline B?

20. Evaluate each of the following for A = 2, B = 5, C = 3.

(a) (A+C)/B*C

(b) B^A*C/B

(c) A^A^C

(d) A^(A^C)

21. Write the following expressions in BASIC.

(a) $\frac{5^2 \times 3}{4}$ (b) $\frac{h}{2}(a + b)$

(c) $x^y \div y^x$ (d) $a^{b \times c}$

(e) $\frac{x + y}{x - 2y}$ (f) $\left(\frac{a}{b}\right)^c$

1.12 CHAPTER 1 TEST

1. Round to the required place.

(a) 36 547	(hundred)
(b) 0.0725	(hundredth)
(c) 13.27	(tenth)
(d) 37.150	(tenth)

2. State the number of significant digits.
(a) 6215
(b) 4300
(c) 1.7×10^2
(d) 8.60×10^3

3. Find the area of a rectangle 5.76 cm by 2.8 cm.

4. Calculate each answer and round it to the appropriate number of significant digits.
(a) (1.76)(243.1)
(b) $\dfrac{12.25}{6.1}$
(c) $\dfrac{(1.62 \times 10^3)(1.40 \times 10^2)}{3.51 \times 10}$

5. Evaluate each of the following using $x = -1$, $y = 2$, and $z = -3$.
(a) $2x - 2y - 3z$
(b) $y - x + z$
(c) xyz
(d) $\dfrac{x + z}{y}$

6. Solve the following for the indicated variables.
(a) $3.5 : x = 5 : 2$
(b) $4 : y : 10 = 6 : 9 : z$

7. How much pure alcohol is required to make 100 mL of a 2 : 5 alcohol/water solution?

8. A 1.2 m beam has a mass of 45 kg.
What is the mass of the same type of beam 7.6 m long?

9. Write the following expressions in BASIC.
(a) $3.14r^2$
(b) $2 \times 3.14r(r + h)$

10. Change 7.13 h into hours, minutes, and seconds.

EXPONENTS AND RADICALS

REVIEW AND PREVIEW TO CHAPTER 2

EXERCISE 1

1. Simplify.

(a) $\frac{3}{4} \times \frac{1}{2}$ (b) $\frac{7}{8} \times \frac{5}{6}$

(c) $6\frac{1}{2} \times 3\frac{3}{5}$ (d) $2\frac{3}{4} \times 1\frac{1}{8}$

(e) $2 \times 3\frac{1}{8}$ (f) $4\frac{2}{3} \times 4$

(g) $\frac{4}{7} \times \frac{3}{8}$ (h) $1\frac{1}{2} \times \frac{3}{4}$

(i) $5\frac{7}{5} \times 2\frac{1}{3}$ (j) $\frac{11}{4} \times 2\frac{3}{5}$

2. Simplify.

(a) $2\frac{1}{4} \div \frac{1}{2}$ (b) $3\frac{1}{3} \div 2\frac{5}{6}$

(c) $\frac{11}{3} \div \frac{11}{5}$ (d) $2\frac{3}{4} \div 1\frac{5}{8}$

(e) $6 \div 2\frac{1}{9}$ (f) $4\frac{1}{5} \div 3\frac{5}{6}$

(g) $4 \div 2\frac{1}{4}$ (h) $3\frac{1}{8} \div 2$

(i) $4 \div 3\frac{1}{6}$ (j) $2\frac{7}{8} \div 3\frac{3}{4}$

3. Simplify.

(a) $\frac{2}{3} + \frac{3}{4}$

(b) $1\frac{1}{2} + 2\frac{3}{5}$

(c) $4\frac{1}{6} + 3\frac{1}{2} + \frac{1}{4}$

(d) $2\frac{1}{8} + 3\frac{1}{6} + \frac{3}{4}$

(e) $4\frac{3}{8} + 7\frac{5}{6} + \frac{1}{3}$

(f) $\frac{12}{5} + 3\frac{7}{8} + 7\frac{17}{20}$

(g) $5\frac{3}{5} + 2\frac{1}{10} + 3\frac{1}{20}$

(h) $\frac{22}{3} + 5 + 6\frac{1}{4}$

(i) $22 + 3\frac{5}{6} + \frac{23}{3}$

4. Simplify.

(a) $2\frac{3}{4} - 1\frac{1}{8}$ (b) $7 - 3\frac{3}{8}$

(c) $\frac{33}{4} - 2\frac{1}{2}$ (d) $5\frac{1}{2} - 4\frac{5}{8}$

(e) $16\frac{1}{8} - 3\frac{4}{5}$

(f) $3\frac{4}{5} - 2\frac{1}{4}$

(g) $\frac{25}{4} - 1\frac{1}{2}$

(h) $11 - 3\frac{7}{8}$

(i) $6\frac{1}{5} - 2\frac{3}{4}$

(j) $9 - 1\frac{3}{7}$

5. Perform the operations indicated.

(a) $2\frac{1}{2} \times \frac{3}{5} \times \frac{7}{3}$

(b) $(1\frac{1}{7} - \frac{5}{6}) \times \frac{7}{8}$

(c) $(\frac{11}{8} + 1\frac{1}{2}) \div 3$

(d) $1\frac{1}{4} \div (\frac{3}{5} \times \frac{1}{2})$

(e) $5 \times \frac{2}{9} \div 1\frac{1}{3}$

(f) $4 \div (1\frac{1}{4} - \frac{3}{7})$

(g) $\frac{3}{4} \times (\frac{1}{5} + 1\frac{1}{3})$

(h) $(\frac{1}{2} + \frac{1}{3}) \times (\frac{3}{4} - \frac{5}{8})$

(i) $\frac{2}{3} \div 1\frac{1}{6} \times 2\frac{1}{4}$

EXERCISE 2

Calculate each of the following. Round off your answer to the appropriate number of significant digits.

1. (a) 26.5×3.7
(b) 60.5×14.2
(c) 0.3×0.52
(d) 763×2.1
(e) 4.8×11.6
(f) 0.7×25.5
(g) 136×9.8
(h) 0.062×0.59

2. (a) $12.3 \times 7.4 \times 16.2$
(b) $23.6 \times 13.3 \times 0.72$
(c) $7.7 \times 0.005 \times 60$
(d) $5.9 \times 2.3 \times 942$
(e) $66.5 \times 0.42 \times 1.1$
(f) $798 \times 0.43 \times 1.07$
(g) $605 \times 7.9 \times 0.35$
(h) $6.30 \times 2.19 \times 0.142$

3. (a) $66.5 \div 32$
(b) $33.5 \div 8.6$
(c) $0.073 \div 0.56$
(d) $9.01 \div 27.3$
(e) $127 \div 2.7$
(f) $0.81 \div 3.2$
(g) $176 \div 133$
(h) $4.6 \div 83.5$

4. (a) $\frac{77.2 \times 11.3}{12.1}$
(b) $\frac{2.8 \times 9.65}{3.7 \times 12.2}$
(c) $\frac{83.5 \times 124}{6.3}$
(d) $\frac{6.8 \times 7.25}{4.6}$
(e) $\frac{0.76 \times 4.2}{0.083 \times 161}$
(f) $\frac{22.2 \times 871}{4.3}$
(g) $\frac{42.7 \times 0.631}{0.427 \times 724}$
(h) $\frac{56.4 \times 33.2}{64.3 \times 0.158}$

EXERCISE 3

Evaluate each of the following powers.

1. (a) 2^2 (b) 3^2 (c) 5^2 (d) 8^2
(e) 1^2 (f) 4^2 (g) 7^2 (h) 9^2
(i) 11^2 (j) 12^2 (k) 6^2 (l) 10^2

2. (a) $(-5)^2$ (b) $(-2)^2$ (c) 2^3
(d) $(-2)^3$ (e) 4^3 (f) 2^4
(g) $(-6)^2$ (h) $(-11)^2$ (i) 3^3
(j) $(-3)^3$ (k) 3^4 (l) 5^3

EXERCISE 4

Evaluate the following. Round off your answer to the appropriate number of significant digits.

1. $(6.374)^2$
2. $(0.8163)^3$
3. $(81.44)^4$
4. $(0.0816)^3$
5. $(6.813)^2 + (4.761)^3$
6. $(0.4167)^3 + (0.5843)^4$
7. $(1.683)^2 + (2.418)^3 - (8.713)^2$
8. $(2.481)^2(0.973)^3$
9. $(56.81)^4(2.78)^2$
10. $\frac{(1.813)^4}{(1.721)^3}$

EXERCISE 5

Find the positive square root of each of the following.

1. 25
2. 49
3. 64
4. 100
5. 1
6. 4
7. 169
8. 225
9. 16
10. 81
11. 121
12. 144
13. 36
14. 9
15. 196
16. 10 000
17. 1.21
18. 1.44
19. 2.25
20. 0.25
21. 0.36
22. 0.81

2.1 INTEGRAL EXPONENTS

With a calculator, the internal constant feature can be used for repeated multiplication by the same factor.

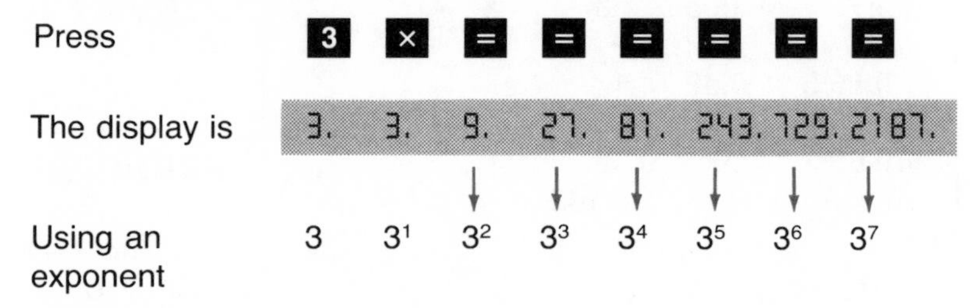

BASIC LAWS OF EXPONENTS

a^n means $a \times a \times a$ ... to n factors
a is the base, n is the exponent ($n \in N$)

This definition helps us to state the following three basic laws of exponents.

MULTIPLICATION

$$3^3 \times 3^2 = 3 \times 3 \times 3 \times 3 \times 3 = 3^5$$

$$3^3 \times 3^2 = 3^{3+2} = 3^5$$

$$a^3 \times a^2 = a \times a \times a \times a \times a = a^5$$

$$a^3 \times a^2 = a^{3+2} = a^5$$

$$a^m \times a^n = a^{m+n}$$

DIVISION

$$2^5 \div 2^3 = \frac{2 \times 2 \times 2 \times 2 \times 2}{2 \times 2 \times 2} = 2^2$$

$$2^5 \div 2^3 = 2^{5-3} = 2^2$$

$$a^5 \div a^3 = \frac{a \times a \times a \times a \times a}{a \times a \times a} = a^2$$

$$a^5 \div a^3 = a^{5-3} = a^2$$

If $a \neq 0$, $a^m \div a^n = a^{m-n}$

POWERS

$$(5^2)^3 = 5^2 \times 5^2 \times 5^2 = 5^{2+2+2} = 5^6$$

$$(5^2)^3 = 5^{2 \times 3} = 5^6$$

$$(a^2)^3 = a^2 \times a^2 \times a^2 = a^{2+2+2} = a^6$$

$$(a^2)^3 = a^{2 \times 3} = a^6$$

$$(a^n)^m = a^{mn}$$

The three basic laws can be used to develop two further properties.

POWER OF A PRODUCT

$$(5^3 \times 7^4)^2 = (5^3 \times 7^4) \times (5^3 \times 7^4)$$
$$= 5^3 \times 5^3 \times 7^4 \times 7^4$$
$$= 5^6 \times 7^8$$

$$(5^3 \times 7^4)^2 = 5^{3 \times 2} \times 7^{4 \times 2}$$
$$= 5^6 \times 7^8$$

$$(a^3b^4)^2 = (a^3b^4)(a^3b^4)$$
$$= a^3 \times a^3 \times b^4 \times b^4$$
$$= a^6b^8$$

$$(a^3b^4)^2 = a^{3 \times 2}b^{4 \times 2}$$
$$= a^6b^8$$

$$(a^mb^n)^p = a^{mp}b^{np}$$

POWER OF A QUOTIENT

$$\left(\frac{7^5}{5^3}\right)^2 = \left(\frac{7^5}{5^3}\right)\left(\frac{7^5}{5^3}\right)$$
$$= \frac{7^5 \times 7^5}{5^3 \times 5^3}$$
$$= \frac{7^{10}}{5^6}$$

$$\left(\frac{7^5}{5^3}\right)^2 = \frac{7^{5 \times 2}}{5^{3 \times 2}}$$
$$= \frac{7^{10}}{5^6}$$

$$\left(\frac{a^5}{b^3}\right)^2 = \left(\frac{a^5}{b^3}\right)\left(\frac{a^5}{b^3}\right)$$
$$= \frac{a^5 \times a^5}{b^3 \times b^3}$$
$$= \frac{a^{10}}{b^6}$$

$$\left(\frac{a^5}{b^3}\right)^2 = \frac{a^{5 \times 2}}{b^{3 \times 2}}$$
$$= \frac{a^{10}}{b^6}$$

$$\text{If } b \neq 0, \left(\frac{a^m}{b^n}\right)^p = \frac{a^{mp}}{b^{np}}$$

Example 1. Simplify. (a) $5a^4 \times 6a^3$
(b) $15b^{12} \div 5b^7$
(c) $(5c^2)^3$

Solution: (a) $5a^4 \times 6a^3 = 5 \times 6 \times a^4 \times a^3$
$= 30a^7$

(b) $$15b^{12} \div 5b^7 = \frac{15b^{12}}{5b^7}$$
$$= \frac{15}{5} \times b^{12-7}$$
$$= 3b^5$$

(c) $(5c^2)^3 = 5^3(c^2)^3$
$= 125c^6$

Example 2. Simplify. (a) $(2x^2)^3(2x^5)$ (b) $\dfrac{(3x^2)^3}{-3x}$

Solution:

(a) $(2x^2)^3(2x^5) = 2^3(x^2)^3(2x^5)$
$= 8x^6 \times 2x^5$
$= 16x^{11}$

(b) $\dfrac{(3x^2)^3}{-3x} = \dfrac{3^3(x^2)^3}{-3x}$
$= \dfrac{27x^6}{-3x}$
$= -9x^5$

ZERO AND NEGATIVE EXPONENTS

We now use the basic laws to give meaning to powers with zero and negative exponents.

Question | Conclusion

$$a^5 \div a^5 = \frac{a^5}{a^5} = \frac{a \times a \times a \times a \times a}{a \times a \times a \times a \times a} = 1$$

$$a^5 \div a^5 = a^{5-5} = a^0$$

$$a^0 = 1$$

The above example (worked two ways) suggests the general rule:

$$\boxed{a^0 = 1,\ a \neq 0}$$

Question | Conclusion

$$a^5 \div a^8 = \frac{a \times a \times a \times a \times a}{a \times a \times a \times a \times a \times a \times a \times a} = \frac{1}{a \times a \times a} = \frac{1}{a^3}$$

$$a^5 \div a^8 = a^{5-8} = a^{-3}$$

$$a^{-3} = \frac{1}{a^3}$$

This example (worked two ways) suggests the general rule:

$$\boxed{a^{-n} = \frac{1}{a^n} \text{ or } a^n = \frac{1}{a^{-n}}\ (a \neq 0)}$$

Example 3. Simplify. (a) 4^{-2} (b) $\dfrac{1}{3^{-4}}$

Solution:

(a) $4^{-2} = \dfrac{1}{4^2} = \dfrac{1}{16}$

(b) $\dfrac{1}{3^{-4}} = 3^4 = 81$

Example 4. Simplify. (a) $\frac{2 \times 5^{-3}}{10^{-2}}$ (b) $(-2)^{-4}$

Solution:

(a) $\frac{2 \times 5^{-3}}{10^{-2}} = \frac{2 \times 10^2}{5^3}$
$= \frac{2 \times 100}{125}$
$= \frac{2 \times 4}{5}$
$= \frac{8}{5}$

(b) $(-2)^{-4} = \frac{1}{(-2)^4}$
$= \frac{1}{16}$

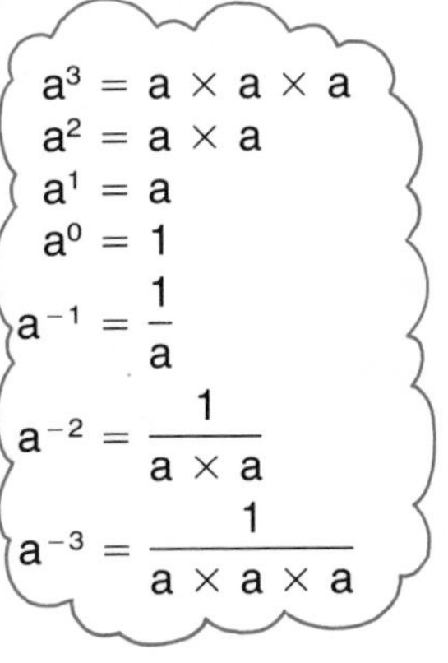

Example 5. Simplify. (a) $9a^5 \div 3a^{-3}$ (b) $3^{-1} + 2^{-2}$

Solution:

(a) $9a^5 \div 3a^{-3} = \frac{9}{3} \times a^{5-(-3)}$
$= 3a^{5+3}$
$= 3a^8$

(b) $3^{-1} + 2^{-2} = \frac{1}{3} + \frac{1}{2^2}$
$= \frac{1}{3} + \frac{1}{4}$
$= \frac{4 + 3}{12}$
$= \frac{7}{12}$

EXERCISE 2.1

A

1. Evaluate.
(a) 2^4 (b) 3^2 (c) 2^5 (d) 3^4
(e) 5^3 (f) 9^2 (g) 7^2 (h) 10^3

2. Simplify.
(a) $a^4 \times a^3$ (b) $a^2 \times a^3 \times a^4$
(c) $a^5 \times a^3$ (d) $b^5 \times b^6$
(e) $(3x)(x^3)$ (f) $(2x^2)(3x^3)$
(g) $(7x^4)(5x^3)$ (h) $(4a^3)(2a^2)$

3. Simplify.
(a) $6a^4 \div 3a$ (b) $9a^5 \div 3a^2$
(c) $9x^3 \div 3x$ (d) $12m^3 \div 4m^2$
(e) $32a^5 \div 8a^4$ (f) $9t^6 \div 9t^4$

4. Evaluate.
(a) 5^{-2} (b) 3^0 (c) $(-3)^0$
(d) 3^{-2} (e) $5^0 \times 2^0$ (f) 10^{-3}

5. Simplify.
(a) $a^3 \times a^{-5}$ (b) $a^{-1} \times a^7$
(c) $a^{10} \times a^4 \times a^{-5}$ (d) $x \times x^0 \times x^3$
(e) $a^0 \times a^4$ (f) $a^{-1} \times a^{-3}$

B

6. Simplify.
(a) $(2^3)^2$ (b) $(3^2)^2$ (c) $(m^5)^3$
(d) $(2p^3)^4$ (e) $(5a)^4$ (f) $(3x^3)^3$
(g) $(-1)^5$ (h) $(-1)^{27}$ (i) $(-1)^{125}$
(j) $5(n^2)^7$ (k) $(2x^2)^3$ (l) $(-1)^{121}$

7. Simplify.
(a) $\frac{(3a^2b^2)(7a^4b^3)}{21a^3b^3}$ (b) $\frac{(6a^2b^2)(4a^2b)}{12ab^2}$
(c) $\frac{(7a^2b^2)(3a^4b^3)}{7a^4b^4}$ (d) $\frac{(3ab)(5ab^2)}{15a^2b^2}$
(e) $\frac{(5a^4b^3)(4ab^2)}{10ab}$ (f) $\frac{24m^3n^4}{(3m^2)(4n^2)}$

C

8. Simplify.
(a) $2^a \times 2^b \times 2^c$ (b) $2^{a+b} \times 2^{a+2b}$
(c) $\frac{3^a \times 3^b \times 3^c}{3^{a+b}}$ (d) $\frac{3^{abc}}{(3^a)^b}$
(e) $2^{a+b} \div 2^a$ (f) $\frac{a^b \times a^{a+b}}{a^{a+1}}$

2.2 THE yˣ KEY

We can evaluate 4.1^3 in several ways using a calculator.

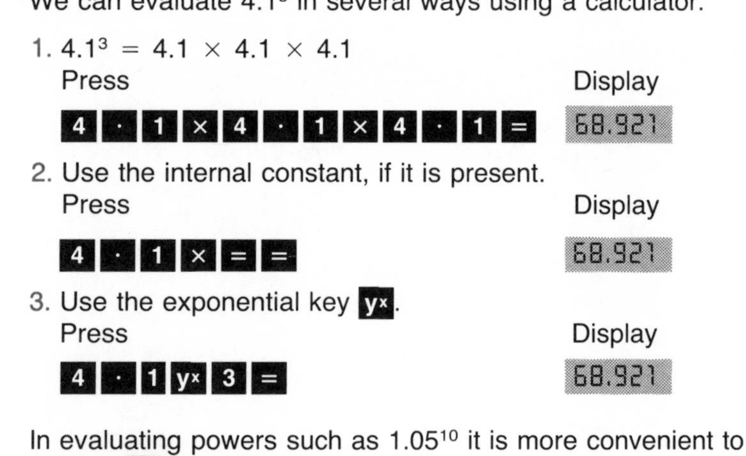

1. $4.1^3 = 4.1 \times 4.1 \times 4.1$

   Press | Display
   4 · 1 × 4 · 1 × 4 · 1 = | 68.921

2. Use the internal constant, if it is present.

   Press | Display
   4 · 1 × = = | 68.921

3. Use the exponential key yˣ.

   Press | Display
   4 · 1 yˣ 3 = | 68.921

In evaluating powers such as 1.05^{10} it is more convenient to use the yˣ key.
Press
1 · 0 5 yˣ 1 0 =

and the display is 1.628894627

$\therefore 1.05^{10} = 1.63$ to the nearest hundredth.

To evaluate 5^{-4} where the exponent -4 is a negative quantity, on a calculator, press
5 yˣ 4 +/− =

The display is 0.0016

$\therefore 5^{-4} = 0.0016$

Example 1. The formula $A = P(1 + i)^n$ gives the amount, A, of a principal sum of money, P, invested at an interest rate, i, for n interest periods.
Find the amount for \$1500, invested at 6% for 12 interest periods.

Solution: $P = 1500 \quad i = 6\% \quad n = 12$
$\qquad = 0.06$

$A = P(1 + i)^n$
$A = 1500(1 + 0.06)^{12}$
$\quad = 1500(1.06)^{12}$

Using a calculator, press
1 5 0 0 × 1 · 0 6 yˣ 1 2 =

and the display is 3018.294708

The amount is \$3018.29 (to the nearest cent).

Example 2. Simplify and find the value of $\frac{3^2x^{12}y^7}{3x^4y^{-1}}$ to the nearest hundredth when $x = 1.23$ and $y = -1.42$.

Solution:
Simplify the expression using exponent laws.

$$\begin{aligned}\frac{3^2x^{12}y^7}{3x^4y^{-1}} &= 3^{2-1}x^{12-4}y^{7-(-1)} \\ &= 3x^8y^8\end{aligned}$$

Using a calculator,
$3x^8y^8 = 3(1.23)^8(-1.42)^8$
Press

3 × 1 · 2 3 y^x 8 × 1 · 4 2 +/− y^x 8 =

and the display is 259.8178001
$\therefore 3x^8y^8 = 259.82$ (to the nearest hundredth).

EXERCISE 2.2

A

1. Use the y^x key to evaluate each of the following to the nearest tenth.
(a) 3.7^4 (b) 4.2^5 (c) 1.3^{11}

2. Evaluate to the nearest hundredth.
(a) $(\frac{1}{2})^7$ (b) $(1.23)^{23}$ (c) $(4.96)^{12}$

B

3. Calculate to the nearest hundredth.
(a) $453(1.03)^{13}$
(b) $(3.57)^7 - (2.56)^9$
(c) $(16.2 - 13.4)^6 - 81.7$
(d) $\frac{(1.03)^7 - 1}{0.03}$

4. Calculate the area of a circle with radius 2.12 cm.

5. The formula $A = P(1 + i)^n$ gives the amount, A, of a principal sum of money, P, invested at an interest rate, i, for n interest periods.
Find the amount in each of the following.
(a) a principal of $2500 in 6 interest periods at 8%
(b) a principal of $5000 in 9 interest periods at 6%
(c) a principal of $2000 in 10 interest periods at 7.17734%

6. Interest on $1000 at 10%/a, compounded semi-annually for 10 a is given by the expression

$$1000[(1.05)^{20} - 1]$$

Find the interest to the nearest dollar.

7. Simplify and evaluate to the nearest hundredth when $x = 3.42$ and $y = 0.72$.
(a) $\frac{36x^7y^8}{9x^3y^{-2}}$ (b) $\frac{3^{10}x^{14}y^2}{3^6x^8y^{-6}}$

8. The formula

$$PV = \frac{A}{(1 + i)^n}$$

gives the present value, PV, of an amount, A, at an interest rate, i, for n interest periods.
Find the present value of each of the following.
(a) an amount of $3000 in 4 interest periods at 8%
(b) an amount of $4500 in 7 interest periods at 9%
(c) an amount of $5265 in 11 interest periods at 12%

2.3 FRACTIONAL EXPONENTS

From our earlier work, $x^3 = x \times x \times x$

$$x^0 = 1$$

$$x^{-1} = \frac{1}{x}$$

What meaning can be given to $x^{\frac{1}{2}}$?

The following example shows how the basic laws are used to find a meaning for fractional exponents.

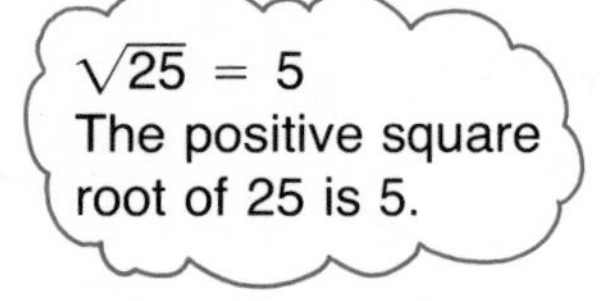

$$25^{\frac{1}{2}} \times 25^{\frac{1}{2}} = 25^{\frac{1}{2}+\frac{1}{2}} = 25^1 = 25$$
$$\sqrt{25} \times \sqrt{25} = 5 \times 5 = 25$$
$$\therefore 25^{\frac{1}{2}} = \sqrt{25}$$

This result is generalized in the following statement.

$$x^{\frac{1}{2}} = \sqrt{x}, \quad \text{where } x \geqslant 0$$

Similarly,

$$x^{\frac{1}{5}} \times x^{\frac{1}{5}} \times x^{\frac{1}{5}} \times x^{\frac{1}{5}} \times x^{\frac{1}{5}} = x$$
$$(x^{\frac{1}{5}})^5 = x$$

Taking the fifth root of both sides,

$$\sqrt[5]{\left(x^{\frac{1}{5}}\right)^5} = \sqrt[5]{x}, \text{ or}$$

$$x^{\frac{1}{5}} = \sqrt[5]{x}$$

This result is generalized in the following statement.

$$x^{\frac{1}{r}} = \sqrt[r]{x},\ x \geqslant 0,\ r \neq 0$$

Further,

$$x^{\frac{p}{r}} = \begin{cases} (x^p)^{\frac{1}{r}} = \sqrt[r]{x^p} \\ (x^{\frac{1}{r}})^p = (\sqrt[r]{x})^p \end{cases}$$

Example 1. Simplify. (a) $64^{\frac{1}{3}}$ (b) $81^{-\frac{1}{4}}$ (c) $125^{\frac{2}{3}}$

Solution:

(a) $64^{\frac{1}{3}} = \sqrt[3]{64}$
$= 4$

(b) $81^{-\frac{1}{4}} = \dfrac{1}{81^{\frac{1}{4}}}$
$= \dfrac{1}{\sqrt[4]{81}}$
$= \dfrac{1}{3}$

(c) $125^{\frac{2}{3}} = (\sqrt[3]{125})^2$
$= 5^2$
$= 25$

Example 2. Simplify. (a) $16^{-\frac{3}{2}}$ (b) $27^{0.\bar{3}}$ (c) $10^{-0.5} \times 10^{1.5}$

Solution:

(a) $16^{-\frac{3}{2}} = \dfrac{1}{16^{\frac{3}{2}}}$
$= \dfrac{1}{\sqrt{16^3}}$
$= \dfrac{1}{4^3} = \dfrac{1}{64}$

(b) $27^{0.\bar{3}} = 27^{\frac{1}{3}}$
$= \sqrt[3]{27}$
$= 3$

(c) $10^{-0.5} \times 10^{1.5} = 10^{-0.5+1.5}$
$= 10^{1.0}$
$= 10$

Example 3. Evaluate $\sqrt{4096}$ using a calculator.

Solution:
We can evaluate $\sqrt{4096}$ using the √ key or the y^x key.

Use the y^x key.
Press
4 0 9 6 y^x · 5 =
Display
64.

Example 3 shows two ways to find the square root using a calculator and our exponent laws. Since most calculators do not have keys for higher order roots such as $\sqrt[3]{8}$ or $\sqrt[5]{243}$, we use the y^x key.

Example 4. Evaluate. (a) $\sqrt[3]{8}$
(b) $\sqrt[5]{243}$

Solution:
(a) $\sqrt[3]{8} = 8^{\frac{1}{3}}$
$= (2^3)^{\frac{1}{3}}$
$= 2^{3 \times \frac{1}{3}}$
$= 2$

Using a calculator,
$\sqrt[3]{8} = 8^{\frac{1}{3}}$
Press
8 y^x (1 ÷ 3) =
Display
2.

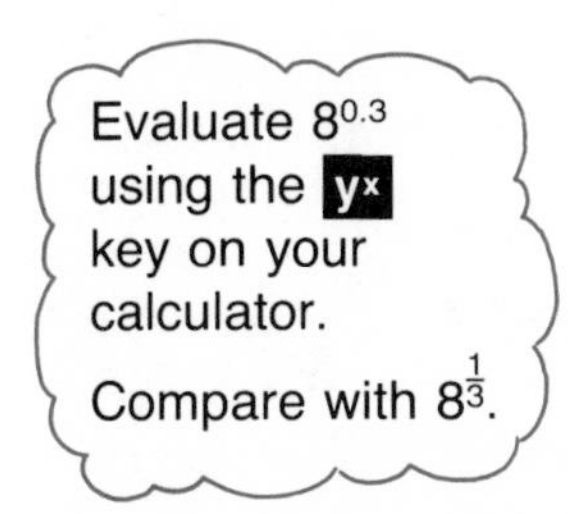

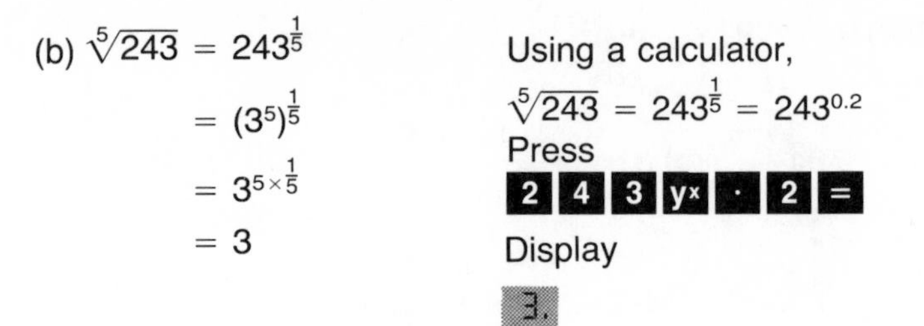

(b) $\sqrt[5]{243} = 243^{\frac{1}{5}}$

$= (3^5)^{\frac{1}{5}}$

$= 3^{5 \times \frac{1}{5}}$

$= 3$

Using a calculator,

$\sqrt[5]{243} = 243^{\frac{1}{5}} = 243^{0.2}$

Press

2 4 3 y^x · 2 =

Display

3.

Example 5. Simplify and find the value of

$$\frac{3^{\frac{5}{2}}x^{\frac{1}{4}}y^{\frac{3}{8}}}{3^{\frac{1}{2}}x^{\frac{1}{12}}y^{\frac{1}{4}}} \text{ when } x = 729 \text{ and } y = 256.$$

Solution: Simplify the expression using exponent laws.

$$\frac{3^{\frac{5}{2}}x^{\frac{1}{4}}y^{\frac{3}{8}}}{3^{\frac{1}{2}}x^{\frac{1}{12}}y^{\frac{1}{4}}} = 3^{\frac{5}{2}-\frac{1}{2}}x^{\frac{1}{4}-\frac{1}{12}}y^{\frac{3}{8}-\frac{1}{4}}$$

$$= 3^{\frac{4}{2}}x^{\frac{3}{12}-\frac{1}{12}}y^{\frac{3}{8}-\frac{2}{8}}$$

$$= 3^2x^{\frac{2}{12}}y^{\frac{1}{8}}$$

$$= 9x^{\frac{1}{6}}y^{\frac{1}{8}}$$

$$9x^{\frac{1}{6}}y^{\frac{1}{8}} = 9(729)^{\frac{1}{6}}(256)^{\frac{1}{8}}$$

$$= 9 \times 3 \times 2$$

$$= 54$$

$2^8 = 256$
$3^6 = 729$

Using a calculator, press

9 × 7 2 9 y^x (1 ÷ 6) × 2 5 6 y^x (1 ÷ 8) =

and the display is 54.

EXERCISE 2.3

1. Evaluate.

(a) $9^{\frac{1}{2}}$ (b) $25^{\frac{1}{2}}$ (c) $8^{\frac{1}{3}}$
(d) $64^{\frac{1}{3}}$ (e) $125^{\frac{1}{3}}$ (f) $81^{\frac{1}{2}}$
(g) $81^{\frac{1}{4}}$ (h) $625^{\frac{1}{2}}$ (i) $625^{\frac{1}{4}}$

2. Evaluate.

(a) $81^{-\frac{1}{4}}$ (b) 5^{-2} (c) $16^{-\frac{1}{2}}$
(d) $16^{-\frac{1}{4}}$ (e) $4^{-\frac{1}{2}}$ (f) $36^{-\frac{1}{2}}$
(g) $27^{\frac{2}{3}}$ (h) $8^{\frac{2}{3}}$ (i) $9^{\frac{3}{2}}$
(j) $16^{\frac{3}{4}}$ (k) $25^{\frac{3}{2}}$ (l) $8^{-\frac{2}{3}}$

3. Evaluate.

(a) $27^{\frac{1}{3}}$ (b) $64^{-\frac{5}{6}}$ (c) $4^{\frac{3}{2}}$
(d) $32^{-\frac{3}{5}}$ (e) $\sqrt[3]{64^2}$ (f) $125^{\frac{4}{3}}$
(g) $\sqrt[4]{16^3}$ (h) $(\frac{1}{4})^{-\frac{1}{2}}$ (i) $32^{-\frac{4}{5}}$
(j) $32^{\frac{2}{5}}$ (k) $27^{-\frac{4}{3}}$ (l) $(\frac{1}{81})^{-\frac{1}{4}}$

4. Simplify.

(a) $2^{\frac{1}{5}} \times 2^{\frac{4}{5}}$ (b) $10^{0.5} \times 10^{0.25}$
(c) $10^{0.5} \div 10^{0.25}$ (d) $10 \times 10^{0.\overline{3}} \div 10^{\frac{2}{3}}$
(e) $5^{\frac{4}{3}} \div 5^{\frac{1}{3}}$ (f) $2^{0.3} \times 2^{0.25} \times 2^{0.45}$

5. Simplify.

(a) $(a^{16})^{\frac{1}{4}}$ (b) $(27a^3b^6)^{\frac{1}{3}}$ (c) $(125a^3)^{\frac{2}{3}}$
(d) $(32a^5)^{\frac{2}{5}}$ (e) $(81a^4)^{\frac{3}{4}}$ (f) $(8a^3b^6)^{\frac{1}{3}}$

6. Evaluate using a calculator.

(a) $\sqrt{2.36}$ (b) $\sqrt{\frac{1}{2}}$
(c) $\sqrt[3]{0.27}$ (d) $\sqrt{0.0054}$
(e) $2073.2^{-\frac{1}{6}}$ (f) $57.23^{-\frac{1}{4}}$
(g) $6.2(7.1)^{\frac{1}{3}} \div 5.6^{\frac{1}{5}}$

7. Simplify the following expressions by using the exponent laws, and then evaluate.

(a) $\frac{x^8}{x^5}$ when $x = 3$
(b) $\left(\frac{x^6}{x^3}\right)^2$ when $x = 2$
(c) $\frac{x^4y^{\frac{3}{2}}}{xy}$ when $x = 2$, $y = 36$
(d) $(2x^2y^3)(5x^{-1}y)$ when $x = -1$, $y = 3$
(e) $\frac{25^0x^7y^{\frac{10}{3}}}{x^{\frac{7}{2}}y^{\frac{1}{3}}}$ when $x = 4$, $y = 3$
(f) $(5^{\frac{2}{3}}x^2y^{\frac{1}{4}})^3$ when $x = 2$, $y = 16$
(g) $\frac{64^{\frac{2}{3}}x^{\frac{1}{3}}y^{\frac{2}{5}}z^{\frac{3}{4}}}{x^{-\frac{2}{3}}y^{-\frac{1}{5}}z^{\frac{1}{2}}}$ when $x = 7$, $y = 32$, $z = 81$
(h) $\frac{32^{\frac{7}{10}}x^{-\frac{3}{4}}y^{-\frac{3}{8}}z^3}{32^{\frac{1}{10}}x^{-\frac{3}{2}}y^{-\frac{3}{4}}z^{\frac{1}{2}}}$ when $x = 16$, $y = 256$, $z = 9$

8. A ship left port and sailed 28 km due east and then 17 km due north.
To the nearest kilometre, how far was the ship from port?

9. The voltage, V, required for a circuit is given by $V = \sqrt{PR}$, where P is the power in watts and R is the resistance in ohms.

(a) What voltage is required to light a 24 W bulb with a resistance of 6 ohms?
(b) What voltage is required to light a 100 W bulb with a resistance of 144 ohms?
(c) The current, I, in amperes, is given by

$$I = \sqrt{\frac{P}{R}}$$

Find the current in parts (a) and (b).

10. The radius of a sphere is given by the following formula.

$$r = \left(\frac{3V}{4\pi}\right)^{\frac{1}{3}}$$

r = radius
V = volume

Calculate to the nearest hundredth the radius of a sphere, if the volume is
(a) 1 m^3 (b) 8 m^3 (c) 4.19 cm^3

11. The time for an object to fall a distance h is given by the formula

$$t = \sqrt{\frac{h}{4.9}}$$

t = time in seconds,
h = height in metres.

Calculate to the nearest tenth of a second the time for an object to fall
(a) 95 m (b) 115.3 m (c) 150 m

12. The time, T, in seconds, for one swing of a pendulum is given by

$$T = 2\pi\sqrt{\frac{\ell}{g}}$$

where ℓ is the length of the pendulum in centimetres, and $g = 980$ cm/s^2 is the gravitational constant.

(a) A clockmaker is making a grandfather clock. If the pendulum has a length of 100 cm, how long will it take for one complete swing?
(b) What is the period of a wall clock with a pendulum 25.0 cm long?

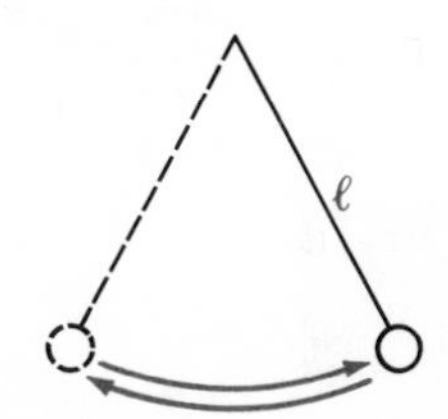

One period is a complete swing.

2.4 APPROXIMATING RADICALS

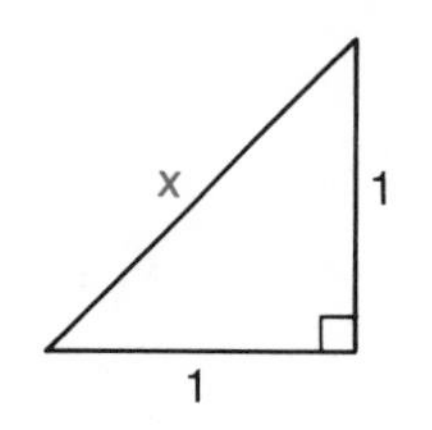

$$\begin{aligned} x^2 &= 1^2 + 1^2 \\ &= 1 + 1 \\ &= 2 \\ x &= \sqrt{2} \\ &\doteq 1.414 \end{aligned}$$

Squaring a number means multiplying the number by itself.

$$\begin{aligned} 2^2 &= 2 \times 2 \\ &= 4 \end{aligned} \qquad \begin{aligned} 1.5^2 &= 1.5 \times 1.5 \\ &= 2.25 \end{aligned}$$

Finding the square root is the inverse operation to squaring a number. It is represented by the symbol $\sqrt{}$. Although 9 has two square roots, $+3$ and -3, when we write $\sqrt{9}$ we mean the principal (positive) square root, $+3$.

Numbers such as $\sqrt{2}$, $\sqrt{3}$, and $\sqrt{8}$ are called radicals. When radicals appear in practical problems it is often necessary to convert them to decimals, or to decimal approximations, so that they can be used.

We can use a calculator with a $\sqrt{}$ key to approximate radicals.

Radical	Press	Display	Decimal Equivalent (nearest 100th)
$\sqrt{2}$	2 √	1.414213562	1.41
$\frac{\sqrt{3}}{2}$	3 √ ÷ 2 =	0.866025403	0.87
$\frac{\sqrt{88}}{\sqrt{44}}$	8 8 √ ÷ 4 4 √ =	1.414213562	1.41
$\frac{3\sqrt{60}}{\sqrt{27}}$	6 0 √ × 3 ÷ 2 7 √ =	4.472135955	4.47

The area of a triangle whose three sides are known can be found using Heron's formula.

$$\text{Area} = \sqrt{s(s-a)(s-b)(s-c)}$$
$$\text{where } s = \frac{a+b+c}{2}$$

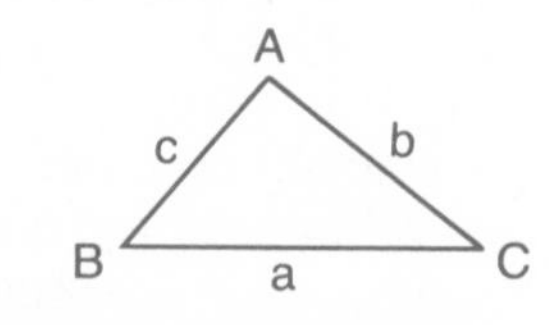

Example 1. Find the area of a triangle with sides of 7.0 cm, 8.0 cm and 9.0 cm.

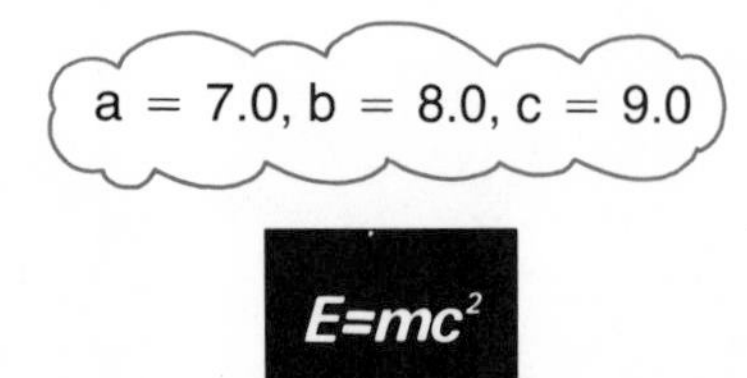

Solution:

$$s = \frac{a+b+c}{2}$$
$$s = \frac{7.0 + 8.0 + 9.0}{2}$$
$$= 12.0$$

$$\text{Area} = \sqrt{s(s-a)(s-b)(s-c)}$$
$$\text{Area} = \sqrt{12(12-7)(12-8)(12-9)}$$
$$= \sqrt{720}$$
$$\doteq 26.8$$

The area is 26.8 cm^2.

Example 2. Use the Pythagorean relationship to solve for c.

c
7.0 cm
4.0 cm

Solution: $c^2 = a^2 + b^2$ where $a = 4.0$, $b = 7.0$

$c^2 = (7.0)^2 + (4.0)^2$

Using a calculator, press

7 x2 + 4 x2 =

Display is 65.

$c^2 = 65$

$c = \sqrt{65}$

Using a calculator, press

6 5 √

Display is 8.062257748

c = 8.1 cm (to the nearest tenth)

EXERCISE 2.4

B

Unless otherwise stated, give all answers to the nearest tenth.

1. Evaluate.

(a) $\sqrt{42}$ (b) $\sqrt{128}$ (c) $\sqrt{29}$

(d) $\sqrt{140}$ (e) $\sqrt{345}$ (f) $\sqrt{61.25}$

(g) $\sqrt{0.0345}$ (h) $\sqrt{0.02745}$ (i) $\sqrt{0.5789}$

2. Evaluate.

(a) $\frac{\sqrt{42}}{\sqrt{6}}$ (b) $\frac{\sqrt{12}}{\sqrt{6}}$ (c) $\frac{\sqrt{42}}{\sqrt{7}}$

(d) $\frac{15\sqrt{20}}{\sqrt{2}}$ (e) $\frac{20\sqrt{15}}{\sqrt{3}}$ (f) $\frac{\sqrt{36}}{3}$

(g) $\frac{\sqrt{26}}{\sqrt{2}}$ (h) $\frac{3\sqrt{50}}{\sqrt{10}}$ (i) $\frac{2\sqrt{75}}{\sqrt{15}}$

(j) $\frac{\sqrt{18} + \sqrt{12}}{\sqrt{3}}$ (k) $\frac{15 - \sqrt{75}}{5}$

3. Determine the value of x in each of the following using the Pythagorean relationship.

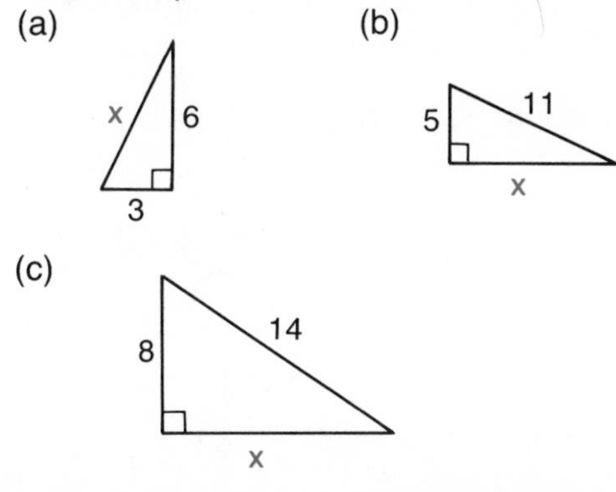

4. A 6 m ladder leans against a wall and the foot of the ladder is 2 m from the wall. Find the distance the ladder reaches up the wall.

5. A ladder 3.2 m from the foot of a wall reaches 8.4 m up the wall.
How long is the ladder?

6. Find the length of the sides of a square having the same area as a rectangle with dimensions 4 cm by 7 cm.

7. The perimeter of a square can be found using the formula $P = 4\sqrt{A}$, where A is the area.
Find the perimeter of a square having an area of 136 cm^2.

8. A square has sides 7 cm long.
Use the Pythagorean relation to find the length of a diagonal.

9. A rectangle is 5 cm by 7 cm.
Find the length of a diagonal.

10. Find the diameter of a circle that will circumscribe a square with sides 3 cm.

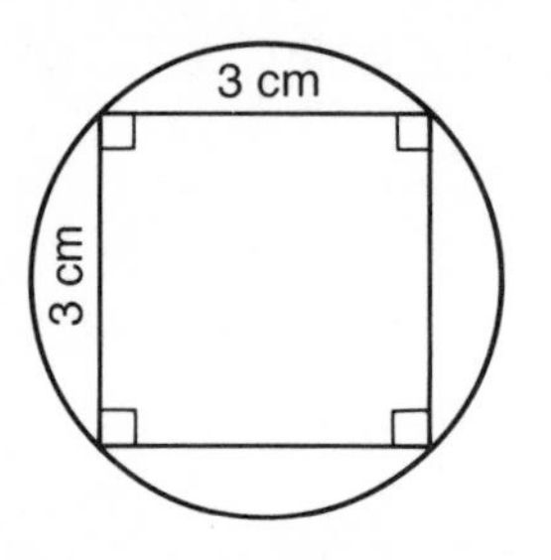

11. In order to cut paper into square pieces, each with an area of 39 cm^2, how long should the sides be?

12. Find the centre-to-centre distance between the two holes.

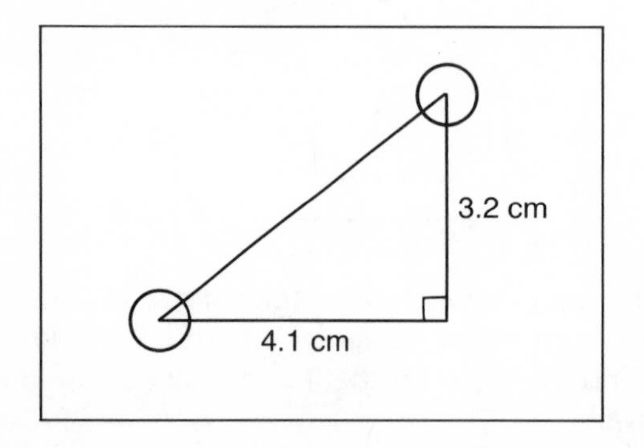

13. Find the length of a guy wire required to secure a 20 m tower 14 m from the base if you must add 4 m for fastenings.

cable

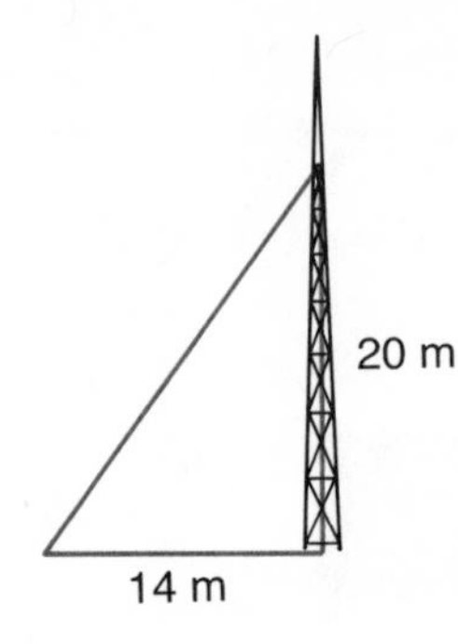

14. Three towns A, B, and C are situated so that A is 10 km east of B and C is 7 km north of B.
Find the distance from A to C.

15. Jan and Maria drive away from an intersection at the same time. One travels 3.2 km east and the other 4.8 km south.
How far apart are they?

16. Two speed boats leave a dock at the same time. One travels north at 32 km/h; the other travels west at 28 km/h.
How far apart are they after 45 min?

17. Find the altitude of an equilateral triangle with sides 8 cm.

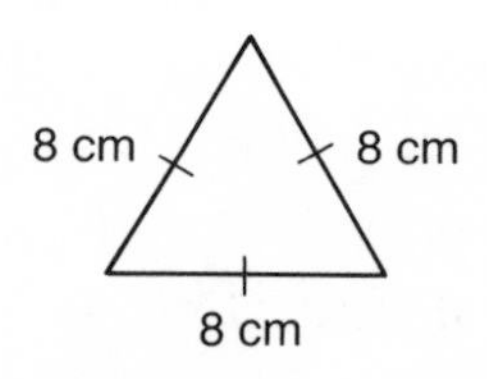

18. Find the altitude to the shortest side of an isosceles triangle with sides 10 cm, 10 cm, and 6 cm.

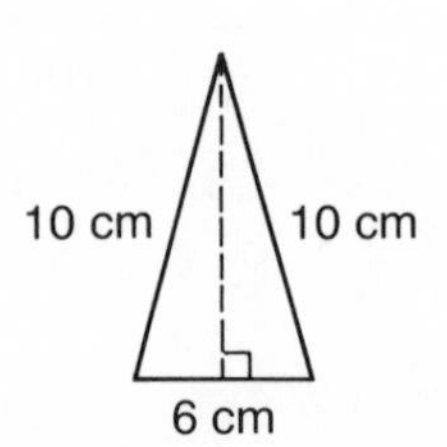

19. Police can use the length of a skid mark to approximate the speed of a car. The formula is $s = 13\sqrt{\ell}$ where s is the speed in kilometres per hour, and ℓ is the length of the skid mark in metres. Determine the speed of the car if the length of the skid mark was
(a) 30 m (b) 25.5 m (c) 15.2 m

20. The greatest distance from which an object of height h can be seen from the same level is given by the formula

$$d = \sqrt{0.8h}$$

where d is in kilometres and h is in metres. From what distance can you see the light at the 300 m mark of the CN tower in Toronto?

21. The area of the top of a piston is 10 cm^2.
What is the diameter?

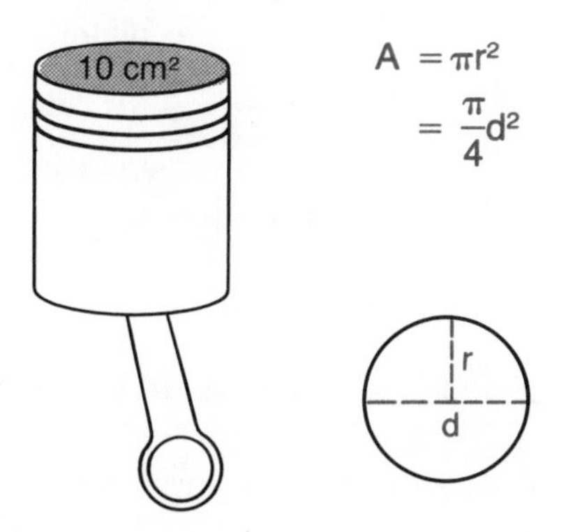

22. The period of a pendulum is given by the formula

$$T = 2\pi\sqrt{\frac{L}{9.8}}$$

where T is the period in seconds and L is the length of the pendulum in metres. Calculate the period to the nearest second when the length is
(a) 19.6 m (b) 2 m

23. The time t (in seconds) it takes an object to reach the ground when dropped from a height h (in metres), is determined by

$$t = \sqrt{\frac{h}{4.9}}$$

Determine to the nearest second the time it takes an object to hit the ground when dropped from each of the following heights.
(a) 20 m (b) 100 m (c) 42.7 m

C

24. The area of a triangle can be found using Heron's formula

$$A = \sqrt{s(s - a)(s - b)(s - c)}$$

where a, b, c are the lengths of the sides of the triangle and

$$S = \tfrac{1}{2}(a + b + c)$$

Calculate the area of the following triangles.
(a)

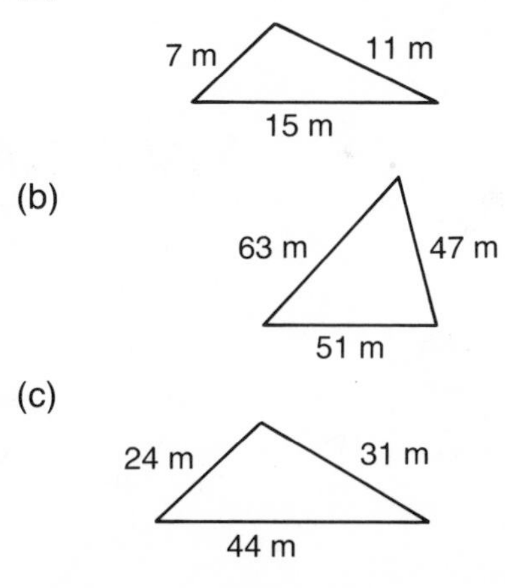

25. In a building under renovation two square heating ducts with sides of 10 cm and 12 cm are to be replaced by one square duct the same area.
Find the length of the sides of this single duct.

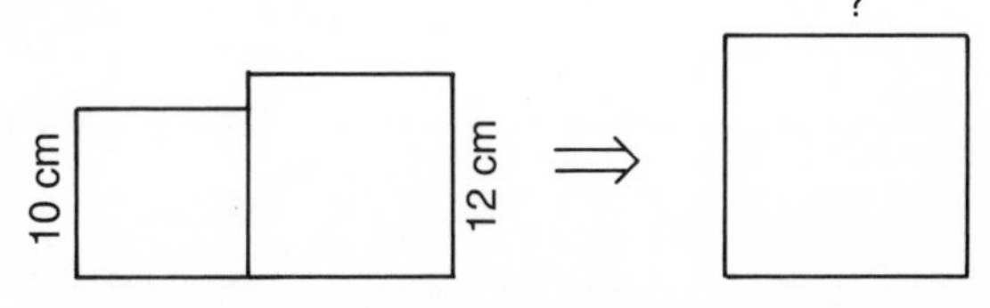

2.5 MIXED AND ENTIRE RADICALS

In our previous work, when radicals appeared we found an approximation using tables, a formal method, or a calculator. In this section we will simplify expressions involving radicals before finding an approximation.

n	$\sqrt{n}$
1	1.000
2	1.414
3	1.732
4	2.000
5	2.236
6	2.450
7	2.646
8	2.828
9	3.000
10	3.162
11	3.317
12	3.464
13	3.606
14	3.742
15	3.873
16	4.000
17	4.123
18	4.243
19	4.359
20	4.472
21	4.583
22	4.690
23	4.796
24	4.899
25	5.000

For convenience, the entire table of Square Roots may be found in the Appendix.

Since $\sqrt{25} = 5$ and $\sqrt{4} = 2$

then $\sqrt{25} \times \sqrt{4} = 5 \times 2$

$\sqrt{25 \times 4} = 10$

$\sqrt{100} = 10$

This result can be generalized to the law

$$\sqrt{a} \times \sqrt{b} = \sqrt{ab}, \text{ where } a, b \geqslant 0$$

Example 1. Determine $\sqrt{5} \times \sqrt{3}$ to the nearest hundredth.

Solution:

METHOD I

$\sqrt{5} \times \sqrt{3} \doteq 2.236 \times 1.732$

$\doteq 3.873$

Use a calculator.
Press
5 √ × 3 √ =
and the display is
3.872983346

METHOD II

$\sqrt{5} \times \sqrt{3} = \sqrt{15}$

$\doteq 3.873$

Use a calculator.
Press
1 5 √
and the display is
3.872983346

$\therefore \sqrt{5} \times \sqrt{3} \doteq 3.87$ to the nearest hundredth.

Radicals such as $\sqrt{18}$, $\sqrt{12}$ and $\sqrt{75}$ are called entire radicals.
Radicals such as $3\sqrt{2}$, $2\sqrt{3}$, and $5\sqrt{3}$ are called mixed radicals.

Example 2. Express as entire radicals.
(a) $5\sqrt{2}$ (b) $4\sqrt{5}$

Solution:

(a) $5\sqrt{2} = \sqrt{25} \times \sqrt{2}$

$= \sqrt{25 \times 2}$

$= \sqrt{50}$

(b) $4\sqrt{5} = \sqrt{16} \times \sqrt{5}$

$= \sqrt{16 \times 5}$

$= \sqrt{80}$

Example 3. Express as mixed radicals in simplest form.
(a) $\sqrt{27}$ (b) $\sqrt{48}$

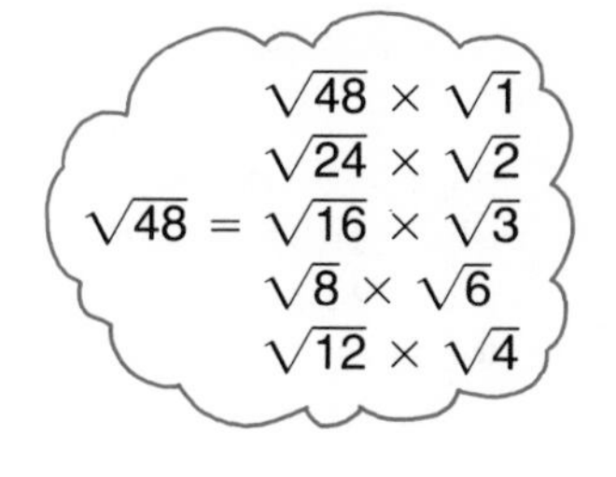

Solution:
A radical is in simplest form when it has the smallest possible number under the radical sign.

(a) $\sqrt{27} = \sqrt{9} \times \sqrt{3}$
$= 3\sqrt{3}$

(b) $\sqrt{48} = \sqrt{16} \times \sqrt{3}$
$= 4\sqrt{3}$

entire to mixed →

$$\sqrt{8} = \sqrt{4} \times \sqrt{2} = 2\sqrt{2}$$

← mixed to entire

Example 4. Simplify. (a) $3\sqrt{2} \times 2\sqrt{7}$ (b) $2\sqrt{5} \times 3\sqrt{15}$

Solution:
(a) $3\sqrt{2} \times 2\sqrt{7} = 3 \times 2 \times \sqrt{2} \times \sqrt{7}$
$= 6\sqrt{14}$

(b) *METHOD I*
$2\sqrt{5} \times 3\sqrt{15} = 6\sqrt{75}$
$= 6 \times \sqrt{25} \times \sqrt{3}$
$= 6 \times 5\sqrt{3}$
$= 30\sqrt{3}$

METHOD II
$2\sqrt{5} \times 3\sqrt{15} = 2 \times 3 \times \sqrt{5} \times \sqrt{15}$
$= 6 \times \sqrt{5} \times \sqrt{5} \times \sqrt{3}$
$= 6 \times 5 \times \sqrt{3}$
$= 30\sqrt{3}$

EXERCISE 2.5

A

1. Evaluate.

(a) $\sqrt{16}$ (b) $\sqrt{49}$ (c) $\sqrt{81}$
(d) $\sqrt{100}$ (e) $\sqrt{121}$ (f) $\sqrt{\frac{9}{16}}$
(g) $\sqrt{\frac{25}{36}}$ (h) $\sqrt{\frac{81}{100}}$ (i) $\sqrt{\frac{64}{81}}$
(j) $\sqrt{\frac{1}{25}}$ (k) $\sqrt{225}$ (l) $\sqrt{289}$
(m) $\sqrt{441}$ (n) $\sqrt{0.01}$ (o) $\sqrt{0.0025}$

2. Simplify.

(a) $\sqrt{3} \times \sqrt{2}$ (b) $\sqrt{5} \times \sqrt{11}$
(c) $\sqrt{2} \times \sqrt{7}$ (d) $\sqrt{7} \times \sqrt{10}$
(e) $\sqrt{7} \times \sqrt{5}$ (f) $\sqrt{3} \times \sqrt{11}$
(g) $\sqrt{6} \times \sqrt{5}$ (h) $\sqrt{2} \times \sqrt{5}$
(i) $\sqrt{6} \times \sqrt{7}$ (j) $\sqrt{5} \times \sqrt{13}$
(k) $\sqrt{11} \times \sqrt{13}$ (l) $\sqrt{7} \times \sqrt{7}$

3. Simplify.

(a) $2\sqrt{3} \times 3\sqrt{5}$
(b) $3\sqrt{7} \times \sqrt{2}$
(c) $4\sqrt{5} \times 2\sqrt{3}$
(d) $\sqrt{3} \times 2\sqrt{7}$
(e) $3\sqrt{2} \times \sqrt{11}$
(f) $2\sqrt{5} \times 3\sqrt{3}$
(g) $2\sqrt{2} \times 3\sqrt{3}$
(h) $4\sqrt{7} \times 2\sqrt{5}$
(i) $4\sqrt{6} \times 3\sqrt{11}$
(j) $7\sqrt{2} \times 5\sqrt{3}$
(k) $6\sqrt{5} \times 2\sqrt{6}$
(l) $3\sqrt{2} \times 5\sqrt{2}$

B

4. Change the following to mixed radicals in simplest form.

(a) $\sqrt{12}$
(b) $\sqrt{18}$
(c) $\sqrt{75}$
(d) $\sqrt{45}$
(e) $\sqrt{98}$
(f) $\sqrt{32}$
(g) $\sqrt{68}$
(h) $\sqrt{20}$
(i) $\sqrt{200}$
(j) $\sqrt{28}$
(k) $\sqrt{441}$
(l) $\sqrt{1024}$
(m) $\sqrt{72}$
(n) $\sqrt{50}$
(o) $\sqrt{8}$

5. Change the following to entire radicals.

(a) $2\sqrt{5}$
(b) $3\sqrt{7}$
(c) $3\sqrt{2}$
(d) $5\sqrt{2}$
(e) $3\sqrt{11}$
(f) $10\sqrt{5}$
(g) $10\sqrt{3}$
(h) $7\sqrt{2}$
(i) $5\sqrt{8}$
(j) $2\sqrt{14}$
(k) $7\sqrt{6}$
(l) $6\sqrt{11}$
(m) $20\sqrt{3}$
(n) $25\sqrt{2}$
(o) $4\sqrt{10}$

6. Simplify.

(a) $\sqrt{7} \times \sqrt{14}$
(b) $\sqrt{10} \times \sqrt{6}$
(c) $\sqrt{21} \times \sqrt{35}$
(d) $\sqrt{7} \times \sqrt{7}$
(e) $\sqrt{3} \times \sqrt{6}$
(f) $\sqrt{5} \times \sqrt{15}$
(g) $\sqrt{50} \times \sqrt{75}$
(h) $\sqrt{5} \times \sqrt{50}$
(i) $\sqrt{6} \times 3\sqrt{2}$
(j) $5\sqrt{7} \times 2\sqrt{14}$
(k) $3\sqrt{10} \times 2\sqrt{5}$
(l) $5\sqrt{3} \times 2\sqrt{15}$
(m) $\sqrt{6} \times \sqrt{3} \times \sqrt{2}$
(n) $\sqrt{10} \times \sqrt{15} \times \sqrt{6}$
(o) $3\sqrt{5} \times 2\sqrt{3} \times 3\sqrt{5}$
(p) $\sqrt{5} \times \sqrt{2} \times \sqrt{15}$
(q) $3\sqrt{2} \times 2\sqrt{6} \times \sqrt{3}$
(r) $2\sqrt{6} \times 3\sqrt{3} \times 4\sqrt{2}$

EXTRA

IS $\sqrt{x^2} = x$ ALWAYS TRUE?
Suppose $x = -3$. Then $x^2 = 9$ and $\sqrt{x^2} = \sqrt{9} = 3$, since we take the positive square root. Therefore, when x is negative, $\sqrt{x^2} \neq x$. We can avoid this difficulty by specifying the variable to be non-negative.

Example. Simplify. $\sqrt{75x^3}$, $x \geqslant 0$

Solution: $\sqrt{75x^3} = \sqrt{25x^2} \times \sqrt{3x}$
$= 5x\sqrt{3x}$

EXERCISE

1. Simplify. $(x \geqslant 0)$

(a) $\sqrt{25x^2}$
(b) $\sqrt{49x^4}$
(c) $\sqrt{x^4 \times x^2}$
(d) $3\sqrt{x^2}$
(e) $5x\sqrt{4x^2}$
(f) $\sqrt{3x} \times \sqrt{6x^3}$
(g) $\sqrt{5x^2} \times \sqrt{15x^3}$
(h) $\sqrt{6x} \times \sqrt{6x^3}$
(i) $\sqrt{45x^3}$
(j) $\sqrt{18x^4}$
(k) $\sqrt{20x}$
(l) $3x\sqrt{3x^2}$
(m) $5x\sqrt{5x^3}$
(n) $\sqrt{5x} \times \sqrt{3x}$
(o) $\sqrt{27x^3}$
(p) $\sqrt{8x^6}$
(q) $\sqrt{125x^4}$
(r) $5x\sqrt{5x^2}$
(s) $\sqrt{64x^3}$
(t) $\sqrt{99x^3}$

2.6 SCIENTIFIC NOTATION AND THE EE KEY

Many technicians have to work with extremely large or small numbers. For example, the half-life of uranium 235 is 750 000 000 a. Very large or small numbers may be written using scientific notation.

> A number written in scientific notation is written as the product of a number between 1 and 10 and a power of 10.

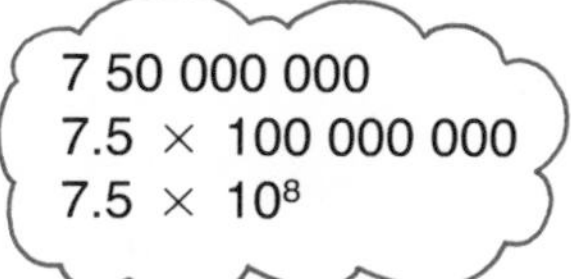

In scientific notation $750\ 000\ 000 = 7.5 \times 10^8$. Note the exponent 8 comes from the number of places the decimal point was moved in changing to scientific notation.

Example 1. Write 0.000 052 in scientific notation.

Solution:

$$0.000\ 052 = \frac{5.2}{100\ 000} = \frac{5.2}{10^5} = 5.2 \times 10^{-5}$$

$$\frac{1}{100\ 000} = 0.000\ 01$$

Example 2. Write each number in scientific notation and perform the indicated operation.
(83 000 000)(1700)

Solution:

$$(83\ 000\ 000)(1700) = (8.3 \times 10^7)(1.7 \times 10^3)$$
$$= 14.11 \times 10^{10} \quad \text{(exponent law)}$$
$$\doteq 1.4 \times 10^{11} \quad \text{(accurate to two digits)}$$

We can use a scientific calculator to work with numbers in scientific notation. Different calculators have different symbols on the keys used to enter a number in scientific notation but the most common are EE and EXP.

To enter 4×10^5 into your calculator,
press 4 EE 5

Display 4. 4.00 4.05

If we follow the above with the = key,
4 EE 5 =
the display is
400000.

Example 3. Using your calculator, evaluate to 2 significant digits.

$$\frac{(4.7 \times 10^4)(8.35 \times 10^3)}{2.61 \times 10^{-5}}$$

Solution: Press

4 · 7 EE 4 × 8 · 3 5 EE 3 ÷ 2 · 6 1 EE 5 +/− =

The display is 1.503639847

$$\frac{(4.7 \times 10^4)(8.35 \times 10^3)}{2.61 \times 10^{-5}} \doteq 1.5 \times 10^{13}$$

One of the benefits of being able to write numbers in scientific notation is in estimating. For example, to estimate the answer to Example 3, we write

$$\begin{aligned}\frac{(4.7 \times 10^4)(8.35 \times 10^3)}{2.61 \times 10^{-5}} &\doteq \left(\frac{5 \times 8}{3}\right)\left(\frac{10^4 \times 10^3}{10^{-5}}\right)\\ &= \frac{40}{3} \times 10^{(4+3)-(-5)}\\ &\doteq 13 \times 10^{12}\\ &= 1.3 \times 10^{13}\end{aligned}$$

EXERCISE 2.6

A

1. Express in scientific notation.

(a) 11.2
(b) 3.75
(c) 0.2575
(d) 0.0325
(e) 0.001 25
(f) 0.000 578
(g) 0.005 63
(h) 0.425
(i) 93 000 000
(j) 186 000
(k) 35 127
(l) 425 000
(m) 32.5
(n) 3.125

B

2. Write in standard notation.

(a) 3.5×10^4
(b) 2.65×10^2
(c) 7.84×10^7
(d) 4.6×10^{-2}
(e) 5.7×10^{-3}
(f) 3.56×10^{-11}

3. Write in scientific notation.

(a) The size of a virus is 0.000 000 45 mm.
(b) The distance from the earth to the sun is approximately 149 000 000 km.
(c) The area of the United States is approximately 9 363 000 km^2.
(d) The area of Canada is 9 976 000 km^2.
(e) The population of the U.S.S.R. is 272 500 000.
(f) One millimetre is equal to 0.000 001 km.

4. First estimate. Then use your calculator.

(a) $\dfrac{(3 \times 10^{7})(8 \times 10^{-2})}{2 \times 10^{6}}$

(b) $\dfrac{(6.37 \times 10^{4})(3.17 \times 10^{8})}{1.92 \times 10^{4}}$

(c) $\dfrac{(1.32 \times 10^{-4})(5.61 \times 10^{5})}{2.02 \times 10^{3}}$

(d) $\dfrac{(7.9 \times 10^{8})(3.4 \times 10^{4})}{8.9 \times 10^{-2}}$

5. State the exponent in the following.

(a) $\dfrac{(3.7 \times 10^{4})(8.6 \times 10^{-7})}{6.2 \times 10^{-2}} \doteq 5.1 \times 10^{■}$

(b) $\dfrac{(5.8 \times 10^{13})(1.9 \times 10^{-22})}{5.2 \times 10^{-15}} \doteq 2.1 \times 10^{■}$

(c) $\dfrac{(7.3 \times 10^{9})(4.4 \times 10^{8})}{(5.4 \times 10^{-3})(3.6 \times 10^{25})} \doteq 1.7 \times 10^{■}$

(d) $\dfrac{(9.8 \times 10^{14})(7.4 \times 10^{-3})}{(2.4 \times 10^{17})(1.6 \times 10^{-5})} \doteq 1.9 \times 10^{■}$

6. Perform the indicated operations and express the answer in scientific notation.

(a) (85 760)(5 716)

(b) (0.007 562)(3 815)

(c) $\dfrac{(350)(0.002\,5)}{13.6}$

(d) $\dfrac{(492)(0.032\,5)}{62.7}$

(e) $\dfrac{1}{(315)(0.000\,000\,56)}$

(f) $\dfrac{1}{(43 \times 10^{-2})(350 \times 10^{-3})}$

(g) $\dfrac{(220 \times 10^{4})(0.000\,27)}{(120 \times 10^{5})(3.002\,5)}$

(h) $\dfrac{(3.25 \times 10^{3})^{2}}{(5 \times 10^{2})^{3}}$

(i) $\sqrt{1.44 \times 10^{4}}$

(j) $\sqrt{(0.60)(2.56 \times 10^{2})}$

(k) $\sqrt{0.50 \times 3.7}$

(l) $\dfrac{4.5 \times 10^{4}}{1.8 \times 10^{2}}$

(m) $\dfrac{\sqrt{5.75 \times 10^{3}}}{\sqrt{2.6 \times 10^{2}}}$

7. A sheet of paper was measured with a micrometer and found to be 0.007 62 cm thick.
Imagine, if the paper were folded 50 times, how thick would the stack of paper be?

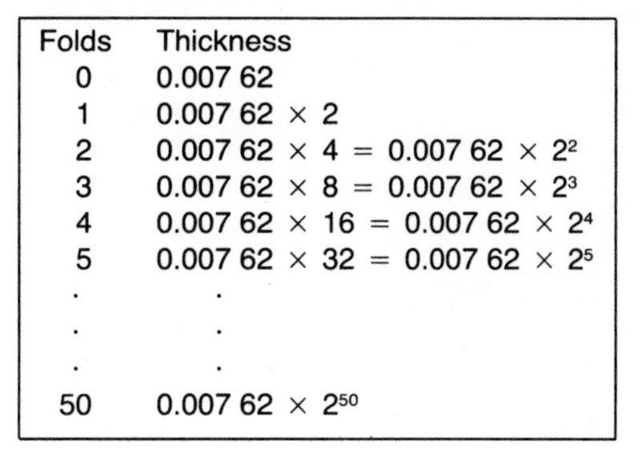

Folds	Thickness
0	0.007 62
1	$0.007\,62 \times 2$
2	$0.007\,62 \times 4 = 0.007\,62 \times 2^{2}$
3	$0.007\,62 \times 8 = 0.007\,62 \times 2^{3}$
4	$0.007\,62 \times 16 = 0.007\,62 \times 2^{4}$
5	$0.007\,62 \times 32 = 0.007\,62 \times 2^{5}$
.	.
.	.
.	.
50	$0.007\,62 \times 2^{50}$

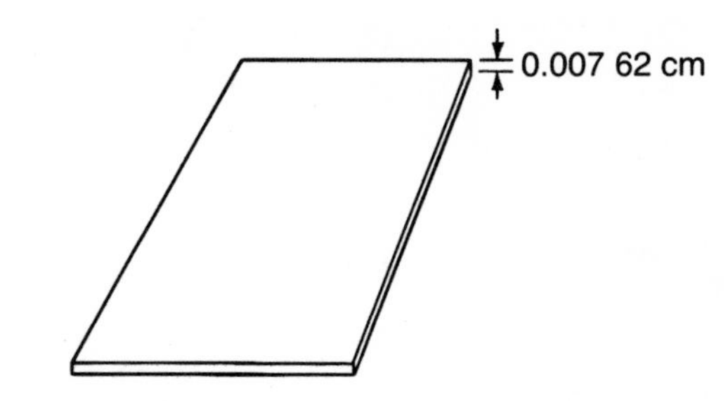

There are 100×1000 cm $= 10^{5}$ cm in one kilometre. The thickness of the stack of paper is

$$\frac{0.007\,62 \times 2^{50}}{10^{5}} \text{ km}$$

Evaluate this number to find the thickness.

Determine the pattern.
Find the missing number.

21	62	74	55
29	45	61	
33	18	25	21
25	35	38	58

2.7 NUMBER SYSTEMS

We have used the following sets of numbers.

Natural numbers	$N = \{1, 2, 3, ...\}$
Whole numbers	$W = \{0, 1, 2, 3, ...\}$
Integers	$I = \{..., -3, -2, -1, 0, 1, 2, 3, ...\}$

Any number that can be expressed as the quotient of two integers (the divisor not being zero) is a rational number.

$$Q = \left\{ \frac{a}{b} \;\middle|\; a, b \in I, b \neq 0 \right\}$$

Q is called the set of rational numbers. The following are examples of rational numbers.

$\frac{2}{3}, \frac{1}{4}, \frac{13}{-2}, \frac{1}{1}, \frac{4}{2}, \frac{7}{9}$

Rational numbers can be expressed in decimal form by dividing the numerator by the denominator. Decimal equivalents such as

$\frac{1}{2} = 0.5, \quad \frac{1}{4} = 0.25, \quad \frac{3}{8} = 0.375$

and also $\frac{2}{1} = 2, \quad \frac{0}{3} = 0, \quad \frac{-6}{3} = -2$

are called terminating decimals because the division process stops, or terminates.
Decimal equivalents such as

$\frac{1}{3} = 0.333...$, or $0.\overline{3}$, $\quad \frac{1}{6} = 0.166\,6...$ or $0.1\overline{6}$

are called repeating decimals because the division process does not terminate and a portion of the decimal repeats.
A number is rational if, and only if, it can be expressed as a terminating or repeating decimal.
Not all numbers are repeating decimals. The following are some examples of non-repeating decimals.

$0.215\,793\,286... \quad \sqrt{2} = 1.414\,213\,56... \quad \pi = 3.141592654...$

These non-repeating decimals are called irrational numbers
An irrational number is a number that is not a rational number; it cannot be expressed as a ratio of integers.

$\overline{Q}$ is the set of non-repeating decimals.

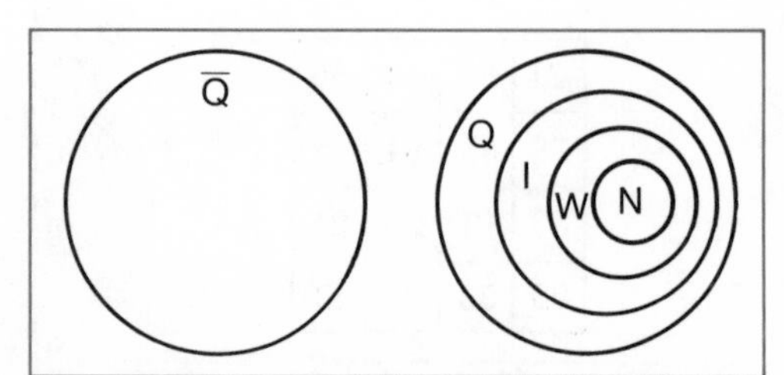

The relationship between sets of numbers is shown.
N is the set of natural numbers;
W is the set of whole numbers;
I is the set of integers;
Q is the set of rational numbers; and
$N \subset W \subset I \subset Q$.
$Q \cup \overline{Q}$ is the set of real numbers R.

Example. Find a decimal equivalent for each.

(a) $\frac{6}{5}$ (b) $\frac{-3}{11}$

Solution:

(a) $\frac{6}{5}$ means $6 \div 5$.

Using a calculator, press

6 ÷ 5 =

and the display is 1.2

$\frac{6}{5} = 1.2$

(b) $\frac{-3}{11}$ means $-3 \div 11$

Using a calculator, press

3 +/− ÷ 1 1 =

and the display is −0.272727272

Since a calculator shows only a finite number of decimal places we understand that −0.2727272 means −0.2727...

$\frac{-3}{11} = -0.2727 \ldots$ or $-0.\overline{27}$

EXERCISE 2.7

A

1. Identify each of the following numbers as rational or irrational.

(a) 0.225 225 225 ... (b) 0.252 255 222 ...
(c) 3.125 125 ... (d) 4.317 327 337 ...
(e) 2.141 516 ... (f) 0.230 530 530 5 ...

B

2. Express each rational number in decimal form.

(a) $\frac{3}{4}$ (b) $\frac{5}{8}$ (c) $\frac{9}{16}$ (d) $\frac{7}{4}$
(e) $\frac{5}{32}$ (f) $\frac{41}{50}$ (g) $\frac{3}{11}$ (h) $\frac{15}{11}$

3. Express each of the following rational numbers as a repeating or terminating decimal.

(a) $\frac{7}{8}$ (b) $\frac{1}{3}$ (c) $\frac{1}{2}$ (d) $\frac{-3}{7}$
(e) $\frac{2}{11}$ (f) $\frac{5}{6}$ (g) $\frac{5}{4}$ (h) $1\frac{1}{2}$
(i) $-\frac{1}{6}$ (j) $\frac{13}{3}$ (k) $\frac{143}{2}$ (l) $\frac{-136}{6}$

4. Identify each of the following numbers as rational or irrational.

(a) $\frac{22}{7}$ (b) $\sqrt{16}$ (c) $\frac{2}{3}$
(d) $5.\overline{23}$ (e) $\sqrt{18}$ (f) $\sqrt{27}$
(g) $1 + \sqrt{3}$ (h) $-\sqrt{3}$ (i) $14\sqrt{2}$

A calculator can display only a certain number of digits.

To divide 1 by 7, we press

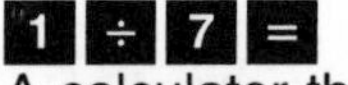

A calculator that displays up to 8 digits will display the result 0.1428571

In this case, by realizing that the length of the period is 6 and that the period is 142857, we can continue the decimal equivalent to read
0.142 857 142 857 ...

Most calculators will not display enough digits for us to establish the period of a decimal.

To convert $\frac{9}{53}$, we press

9 ÷ 5 3 =

The display 0.1698113

does not provide any hint for determining the period, which happens to be 1698113207547 and whose length is 13.

Determine a method for finding the period of a common fraction such as $\frac{12}{19}$ using a calculator.

2.8 PROBLEM SOLVING

The following example uses the strategies Guess and Check, and also Make a Table.

READ

Example. Find the largest whole number x, such that
$x(x + 1)(x + 2) < 1\ 000\ 000$

PLAN

Solution:
We need to find the three largest consecutive numbers whose product is less than 1 000 000.

SOLVE

Organize the work in a table, and use Guess and Check.

x	x(x + 1)(x + 2)	Result
90	$90 \times 91 \times 92 = 753\ 480$	too small
105	$105 \times 106 \times 107 = 1\ 190\ 910$	too large
95	$95 \times 96 \times 97 = 884\ 640$	too small
100	$100 \times 101 \times 102 = 1\ 030\ 200$	too large
99	$99 \times 100 \times 101 = 999\ 900$	correct

ANSWER

$\therefore$ when $x = 99$, $x(x + 1)(x + 2) < 1\ 000\ 000$
and when $x = 100$, $x(x + 1)(x + 2) = 1\ 030\ 200$
then 99 is the largest whole number such that the product is less than 1 000 000.

EXERCISE 2.8

1. Find the smallest whole number such that
$x(2x + 1) > 10\ 000$

2. Find the set of all whole numbers that will give the expression
$x(x + 1)(x + 2)$
a value between 1700 and 160 000.

3. Find the largest whole number x such that
$x(x - 1)(x - 2) < 1\ 000\ 000$

4. Find the smallest whole number x such that
$(x - 1) \times (x + 1) < 1\ 000\ 000$

5. The school band members sell tickets for the annual concert. If they charge $4.00 per ticket, 600 people will attend. For every $1.00 increase in the price of a ticket, the attendance will drop by 100 people.
What should the ticket price be in order to have the greatest gross receipts?

6. Fence posts are to be placed 4 m apart around a small square field.
How many fence posts are required to enclose a square field having an area of 1600 m^2?

7. The following are the first four triangular numbers.

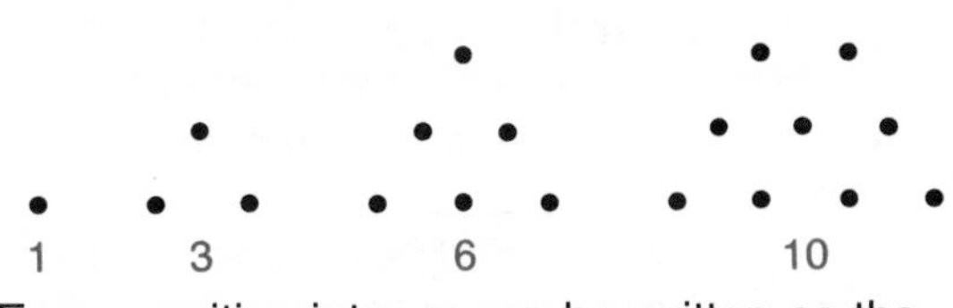

Every positive integer can be written as the sum of, at most, three triangular numbers. Write the following numbers as the sum of, at most, three triangular numbers.

(a) 21 (b) 60 (c) 75

8. A cottage lot along a river is to be fenced on three sides using 400 m of fence. Find the dimensions that will give the greatest possible area.

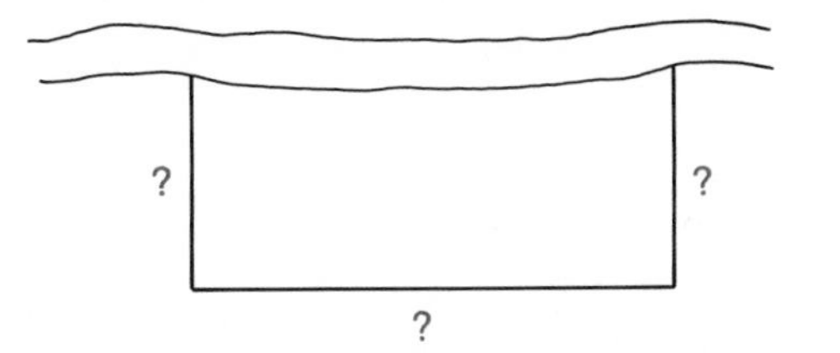

9. How many triangles are there in the following diagram?

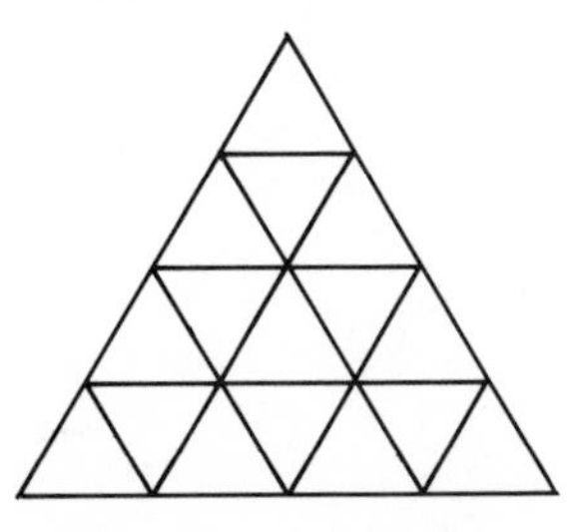

10. A store buys basketballs for $48.00 from a supplier and sells them to make a profit of $\frac{1}{5}$ of the cost price. Those not sold after a certain time are reduced by $\frac{1}{4}$ of the selling price.

What was the profit or loss on the balls which were sold at the reduced price?

11. If you add 17 to a number, multiply by 2, and finally subtract 19, you get 31. What is the number?

12. Find the missing number.

(a)

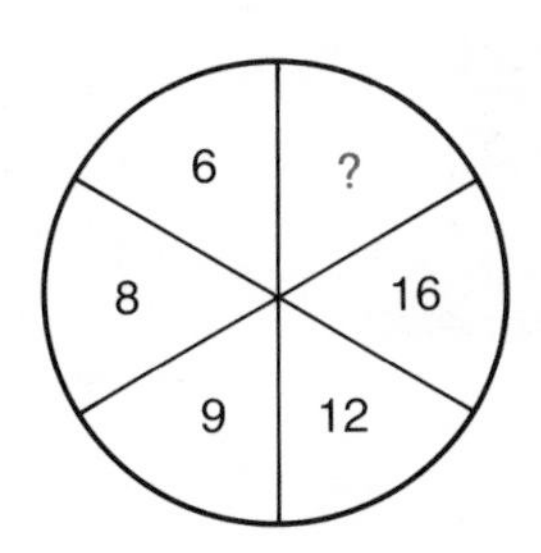

(b)

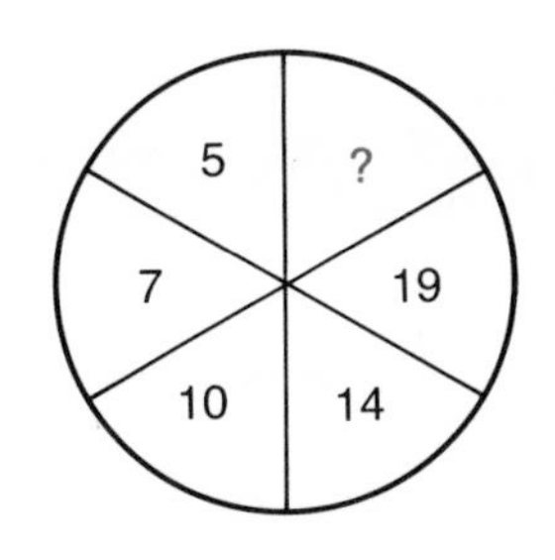

(c)

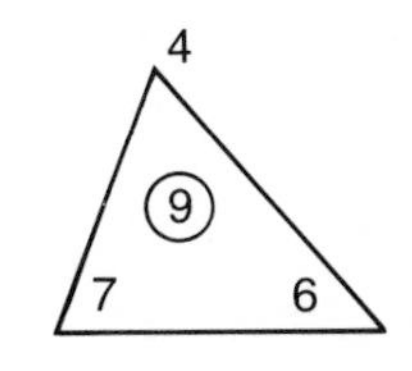

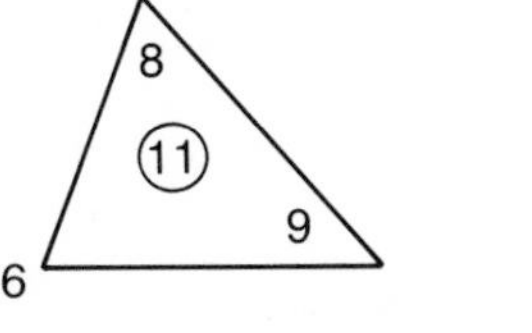

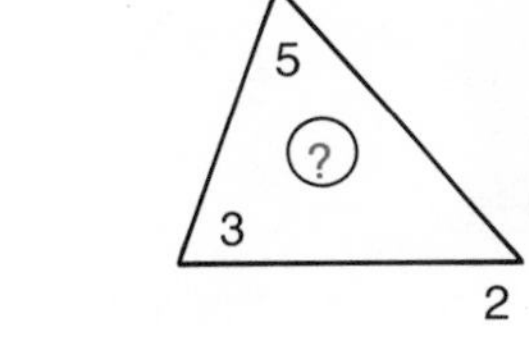

(d)

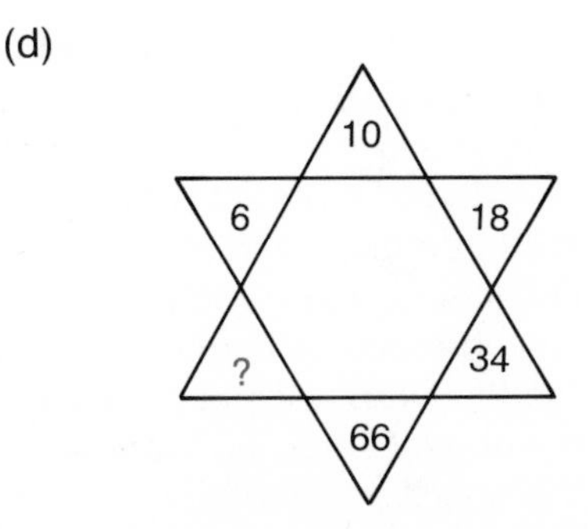

2.9 SPREADSHEETS IN MATHEMATICS

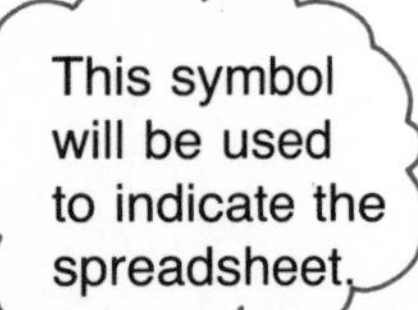

The electronic spreadsheet is a computer application that allows you to store information and to perform a variety of calculations using formulas. Some of the more common applications occur in accounting, statistics, budgeting, income tax, and estimating. Using a spreadsheet, it is possible to quickly and easily change format, project, calculate, and print almost anything that can be set up in a table.

An electronic spreadsheet is a collection of cells which are set up in vertical columns and horizontal rows on a computer screen. The following figure shows how the upper left portion of a spreadsheet appears on the screen.

The columns are designated by letters, while the rows are identified by numbers. Each cell is identified by a column and row. The highlighted cell above is cell C7 because it lies in column C and row 7. To reach a location in a spreadsheet, you enter first the column coordinate (a letter A, B, C, ..., AA, BB, CC, ...) followed by the row coordinate (a number 1, 2, 3, ...). For example, the first entry point in the spreadsheet is located in the upper left corner and is referred to as A1. The spreadsheet can be several times larger than the amount that can be displayed on the screen at one time. This means that for larger spreadsheets, it is necessary to move around in the spreadsheet, working on smaller segments until the spreadsheet is complete. The column–letter, row–number coordinate system is used to keep track of the cells. The cursor, , can be moved by keystroke, trackball, or mouse. Check the manual for the spreadsheet software you are using to determine the specific methods.

Example 1. From the following partial display of the computer screen, state the information in each of the following cells.
(a) E5 (b) B6 (c) F8 (d) A1 (e) C3

	A	B	C	D	E	F	G
1	Example 1	Locate the information in the cell.			0.00	3.25	
2	43.45	43550.00	546.00	635.00	4.65	6.35	
3	43.84	636367.00	640.00	534.00	4.86	1.44	
4	25.50	63750.00	629.00	650.00	0.00	4.65	
5	19.95	54500.00	5355.00	887.00	4.50	1.25	
6	39.95	25675.00	645.00	225.00	6.95	3.25	
7							
8	January	February	March	April	May	June	

Solution:
(a) 887.00 (b) 25675.00 (c) June (d) Example 1 (e) 640.00

In each cell it is possible to enter
(i) letters or words (ii) a numerical expression

Numerical expressions can be simple numbers, a combination of numbers and coordinates, a math function, and a range of coordinates. Each numerical expression must contain one or more of the following:
(i) a number or coordinate reference (ii) a math function understood by the program

Where a cell, for example E12, contains only a coordinate reference such as D8, the value which appears in E12 would be taken from D8.

Some of the more commonly used math functions are

SUM(......) sums the values within (......)
INT(X) gives the integer portion of X
MEAN(....) gives the average of the values within (....)
SQRT(...) gives the square root of the value in (...)

Math functions are preceded by @

Example 2. Ten students sold yearbooks as shown in the following spreadsheet. Calculate the average sales using a math function.

Solution:
To find the average, add the values in the cells B4, B5, B6, .. B13 and divide by 10.
Enter the information:
A15 Total B15 @SUM(B4 .. B13)
A16 Average B16 B15/10
The screen display is

	A	B	C
1	Yearbook Sales For 10 Students		
2			
3	Student	Sales	
4	Arne	78.00	
5	Basil	45.00	
6	Corrine	67.00	
7	Des	48.00	
8	Luba	89.00	
9	Mei	65.00	
10	Rene	53.00	
11	Sue	78.00	
12	Teresa	82.00	
13	Walter	57.00	
14			
15			

This information can be combined in one step as follows:
A15 Average B15 @SUM(B4 .. B13)/10
The screen display is reduced to

EXERCISE 2.9

B

1. Using spreadsheet software, check the manual for the method required to do the following.
(a) Move the cursor left, right, up, down.
(b) Enter numeric data in a cell.
(c) Enter alpha data in a cell.
In some spreadsheet software, the numeric data are called values, and alpha data are called labels.
(d) Enter numeric data as if it were alpha data.
(e) Copy the contents in one cell into another cell.
(f) Enter a formula that takes the values in two cells and performs the operation of
   (i) addition   (ii) subtraction
   (iii) multiplication   (iv) division
(g) Enter the built-in function, SUM, to add the values in a series of cells.
(h) Change the width of a cell.
(i) Set numeric data to format
   (i) dollars
   (ii) percents
   (iii) decimal place value

2. Move the cursor to the following cells.
(a) A10   (b) Z23
(c) AA102   (d) D150

3. Enter the numbers in cells B5 and B6 respectively. Enter the formula which performs the indicated operation so that the answer appears in cell B8.
(a) $478 + 987$
(b) $9123 - 7892$
(c) 0.893×0.9
(d) $475 \div 5$

4. Using the same cells as in question 3, change the values in cells B5 and B6. Observe and record the results in cell B8.

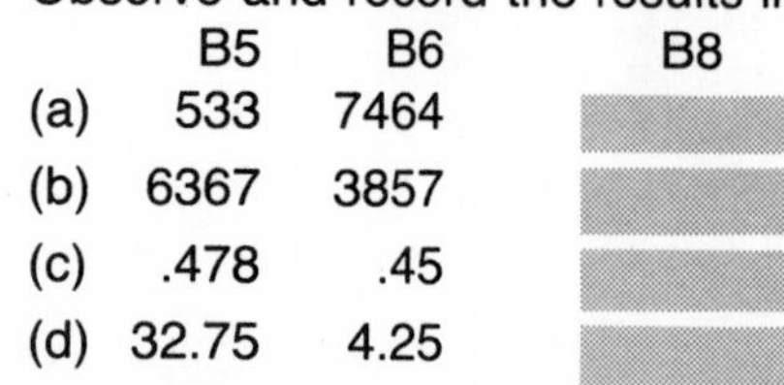

	B5	B6	B8
(a)	533	7464	
(b)	6367	3857	
(c)	.478	.45	
(d)	32.75	4.25	

5. Enter a formula which averages the following sets of numbers. Set the format to give answers to two decimal places (nearest hundredth).
(a) 93, 82, 45, 73, 87, 23, 91, 47
(b) 0.89, 0.91, 0.8, 0.73, 0.68
(c) 2348, 4789, 9432, 8712, 9333
(d) 9.8, 7.6, 4.8, 9.3, 1.2, 4.3

6. Perform the following functions using a spreadsheet. Choose the appropriate cells for the numeric values and for the answer. Set the format to give the answer to one decimal place (nearest tenth).
(a) $\frac{(45.1 \times 8.7) - 34.2}{4.8}$
(b) $[(47 + 82) - (106 - 82)]91$
(c) $\frac{45}{7} + \frac{78}{12} - \frac{92}{23}$
(d) $(45.6 - 87)78 + 78 - 80 \times 4.3$

7. The average wage at a computer company is $48 500. The management and union negotiate salary increases of 5.5% in the first year and 4.2% in the second year. Using spreadsheet software, write and enter formulas to find the new average salary after two years.

8. A person has a gross income of \$46 000/a. Using a spreadsheet, write and enter formulas to find the amount of net income after the following deductions are subtracted.
(a) 12% of gross income
(b) 21% of gross income
(c) 25% of gross income
(d) 31% of gross income

9. (a) Design a spreadsheet from the following table. Include a title and a spreadsheet file label for each column. Enter the data.

MONTHLY AUTO SALES FOR FOUR PEOPLE				
Month	Bella	Kasmir	Hoa	Andre
Jan	78	81	89	76
Feb	89	71	63	55
Mar	45	57	61	72
Apr	56	57	58	67
May	76	67	71	61
June	63	55	60	71
July	65	68	70	68
Aug	72	93	87	83
Sept	32	45	50	32
Oct	45	57	68	39
Nov	98	96	89	79
Dec	27	32	39	31

(b) Write and enter formulas to calculate
(i) the total yearly auto sales for each person.
(ii) the average monthly sales for each person.
(c) Write and enter formulas to find the yearly totals for each person in sales.
(d) Write and enter formulas to find the monthly average auto sales per person for the whole year.
(e) Write a formula to increase each person's total yearly sales by 5%. Have these results shown in another row.

10. The formula for the area of a circle is $A = \pi r^2$ and the formula for the volume of a sphere is $V = \frac{4}{3}\pi r^3$.
Using spreadsheet software, find
(i) the area of a circle
(ii) the volume of a sphere
to two decimal places, given the following radii.
(a) 7.8 cm (b) 2.3 cm
(c) 8.9 cm (d) 121.8 cm

11. Design a spreadsheet with the following information to prepare an income statement for the Students' Summer Painting Company.
Find the total revenue, total expenses, and net income.

(i) Revenues:

Labour	120 436
Paint	32 600
Repairs	14 700

Find the total revenues using the spreadsheet.

(ii) Expenses:

Wages	91 240
Insurance	400
Advertising	350
Telephone	85
Building rental	11 500
Equipment rental	24 750
Paint	18 250
Utilities	300
Miscellaneous	125

Find the total expenses on the same spreadsheet.

(iii) Net income is calculated by
Revenues − Expenses

Find the net income for the Students' Summer Painting Company.

2.10 REVIEW EXERCISE

1. Evaluate.

(a) 4^2 (b) $(-4)^2$
(c) 4^{-2} (d) $(-4)^{-2}$
(e) $(0.5)^{-2}$ (f) $(\frac{3}{4})^{-1}$
(g) $(\frac{5}{6})^0$ (h) $(-3)^3$
(i) $4^{-\frac{1}{2}}$ (j) $(\frac{1}{4})^{-\frac{1}{2}}$
(k) $27^{-\frac{1}{3}}$ (l) $(-27)^{-\frac{1}{3}}$

2. Simplify.

(a) $a^4 \times a^7$
(b) $a^7 \div a^4$
(c) $a^0 \times a^{11}$
(d) $a^{11} \div a^0$
(e) $(3a^4)(2a^5)$
(f) $(4x^3y)(3xy^{-1})$
(g) $(2t^2s)(5t^{-3}s^{-2})$
(h) $(5x^5y^{-3})(4x^{-1}y^{-1})$

3. Simplify.

(a) $2^a \times 2^b$
(b) $3^{a+b} \times 3^{b-a}$
(c) $16m^3 \div (2m)^2$
(d) $4t^2 \div 8t \times 12t^4$
(e) $\dfrac{(6a^2b^3)(2a^3b)}{3ab^2}$
(f) $\dfrac{(4a^{-3}b)(7ab^{-4})}{14a^{-5}b^{-6}}$
(g) $\dfrac{a^{\frac{3}{2}}b^{\frac{10}{3}}}{a^{\frac{1}{2}}b^{\frac{4}{3}}}$
(h) $\dfrac{x^{-\frac{1}{3}}y^{-\frac{2}{3}}}{x^{-\frac{4}{3}}y^{-\frac{8}{3}}}$

4. Evaluate.

(a) $4^{\frac{5}{2}}$ (b) $81^{-\frac{1}{2}}$
(c) $(-343)^{\frac{2}{3}}$ (d) $(16^2)^{\frac{1}{4}}$
(e) $(32^{-\frac{1}{5}})^{-3}$ (f) $(256^{\frac{1}{16}})^2$

5. Evaluate each of the following and round to 3 decimal places.

(a) $(0.85)^{10}$ (b) $(1.19)^{20}$ (c) $(1.1)^{101}$

6. Evaluate each of the following to the nearest tenth.

(a) $\sqrt{43}$ (b) $\sqrt{149}$
(c) $\sqrt{9.9}$ (d) $\sqrt{30}$

7. Express each of the following as entire radicals.

(a) $3\sqrt{10}$ (b) $10\sqrt{3}$
(c) $9\sqrt{3}$ (d) $4\sqrt{15}$
(e) $7\sqrt{2}$ (f) $6\sqrt{5}$

8. Express each of the following as mixed radicals in simplest form.

(a) $\sqrt{63}$
(b) $\sqrt{125}$
(c) $\sqrt{27}$
(d) $\sqrt{54}$
(e) $\sqrt{375}$
(f) $\sqrt{500}$

9. Simplify.

(a) $\sqrt{3} \times \sqrt{27}$
(b) $3\sqrt{2} \times 4\sqrt{6}$
(c) $3\sqrt{10} \times \sqrt{20}$
(d) $2\sqrt{5} \times 7\sqrt{35}$

10. Write in scientific notation.

(a) 172 000
(b) 0.000 3
(c) 87 000 000
(d) 173 200
(e) 0.000 000 072
(f) 6 430 000
(g) 0.000 041
(h) 0.010 20

11. Write in standard notation.

(a) 3.01×10^6
(b) 2.150×10^{-4}
(c) 4.8×10^5
(d) 9.8×10^{-9}
(e) 2.00×10^{-1}
(f) 5.0×10^2

12. Express each of the following in decimal form.

(a) $\frac{23}{100}$ (b) $\frac{15}{8}$ (c) $\frac{13}{9}$ (d) $\frac{9}{13}$

(e) $\frac{6}{6}$ (f) $\frac{2}{5}$ (g) $\frac{2}{9}$ (h) $\frac{4}{7}$

13. Identify each of the following numbers as rational or irrational.

(a) $\sqrt{2}$ (b) $\sqrt{9}$ (c) $\sqrt{121}$ (d) $\sqrt{63}$

(e) $\frac{0}{\sqrt{5}}$ (f) $\frac{2}{3}$ (g) $\frac{2}{\sqrt{9}}$ (h) $\frac{\sqrt{2}}{\sqrt{18}}$

14. If we know the radius, r, of a sphere we can calculate its volume, V, and surface area, SA, using the following formulas.

$$V = \frac{4}{3}\pi r^3 \qquad SA = 4\pi r^2$$

(a) Find the volume to the nearest tenth if the radius is

(i) 0.62 m (ii) 0.984 m (iii) 2.9 m

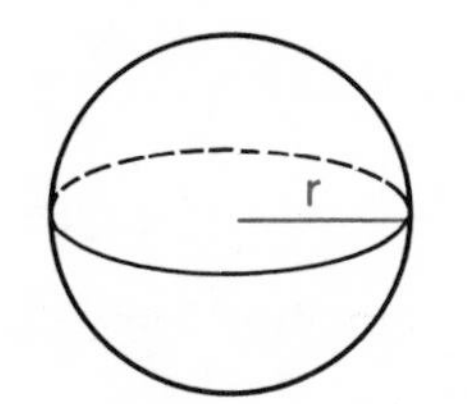

(b) Find the surface area to the nearest tenth if the radius is

(i) 0.5 m (ii) 0.282 m (iii) 0.564 m

15. If we know the surface area, SA, of a sphere we can calculate its volume using the formula

$$V = \sqrt{\left(\frac{SA^3}{36\pi}\right)}$$

Calculate the volume to the nearest hundredth if the surface area is

(a) 4.84 m^2 (b) 1 m^2 (c) 8 m^2

16. If we know the volume, V, of a sphere we can calculate its surface area using the formula

$$SA = (36\pi V^2)^{\frac{1}{3}}$$

Calculate the surface area to the nearest hundredth if the volume is

(a) 0.094 m^3 (b) 2.97 m^3 (c) 33.25 m^3

17. Find, to the nearest hundredth, the surface area of a ball bearing if

(a) the radius is 1 cm

(b) the volume is 1 cm^3

18. A conical pile of sand has a diameter of 20 m and a height of 15 m. The sand is to be moved by a wheelbarrow whose capacity is 0.5 m^3.

How many trips must be made?

$$V = \frac{\pi}{3}r^2h$$

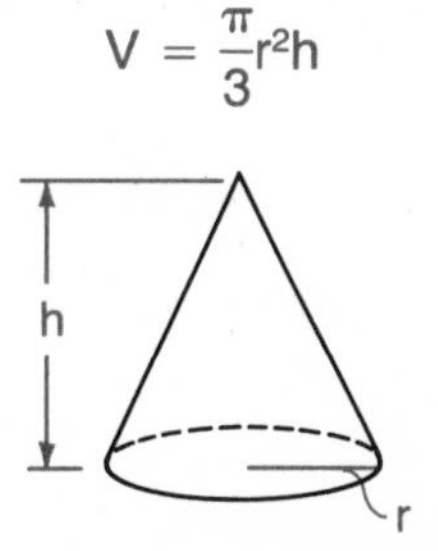

19. Find, to the nearest hundredth, the length of a side of a cubical warehouse that will hold 65 000 m^3 of storage.

20. The period of a pendulum is given by the formula

$$T = 2\pi\sqrt{\frac{L}{9.8}}$$

where T is the period in seconds, and L is the length of the pendulum in metres.

By what factor must the length L be increased if you wish to

(a) double the period?

(b) triple the period?

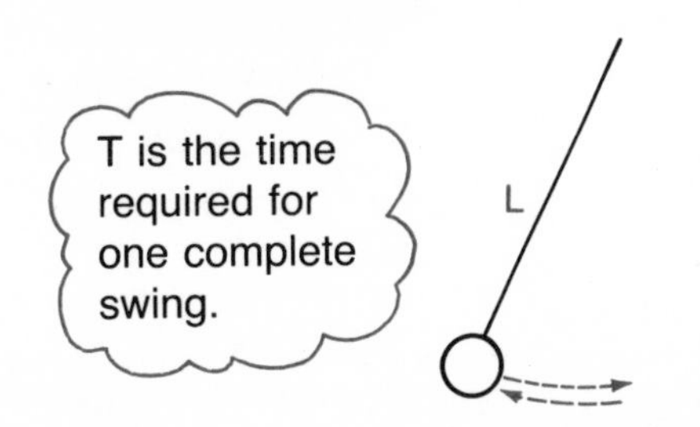

2.11 CHAPTER 2 TEST

1. Use the exponent laws and simplify the following.

(a) $\frac{9^{\frac{1}{2}}x^2}{-3x}$ (b) $3(z^{\frac{1}{3}}y^0)^3$ (c) $\frac{(2a^3b)(3a^{-1}b^{-2})}{12a^{-2}b^{-5}}$

2. Evaluate.

(a) $9^{\frac{3}{2}}$ (b) $64^{\frac{2}{3}}$ (c) $(2^3)^2$

3. (a) Express $5\sqrt{7}$ as an entire radical.
(b) Express $\sqrt{250}$ as a mixed radical.
(c) Simplify $4\sqrt{6} \times 2\sqrt{15}$

4. Write in scientific notation and estimate the final answer.

(a) $\frac{(432)(1700)}{(29\ 000)}$ (b) $\frac{(39\ 000)^{\frac{1}{2}}(635)}{0.021}$

5. Write in standard notation.

(a) 5.92×10^4 (b) 3.0×10^{-5}

6. Express in decimal form.

(a) $\frac{5}{9}$ (b) $-\frac{7}{5}$ (c) $\frac{5}{11}$

7. Identify as rational or irrational numbers.

(a) $\frac{\sqrt{3}}{2}$ (b) $\frac{\sqrt{16}}{4}$ (c) $\frac{\sqrt{8}}{\sqrt{2}}$

8. Find, to the nearest tenth, the length of the sides of a square having
(a) the same perimeter as a rectangle with dimensions 6.2 cm by 8 cm
(b) the same area as a rectangle with dimensions 5 cm by 8 cm

ALGEBRA

REVIEW AND PREVIEW TO CHAPTER 3

THE DISTRIBUTIVE PROPERTY

EXERCISE 1

$a(b + c) = ab + ac$
$3(x + 2) = 3x + 6$

1. Expand the following.
(a) $2(a + 4)$
(b) $3(a - 2)$
(c) $4(x - 3)$
(d) $2(a - b)$
(e) $7(x + y)$
(f) $8(2x + 1)$
(g) $2(a + 2b + c)$
(h) $6(x - 2y + 7)$
(i) $-2(x - 4)$
(j) $-3(2a - 4b)$
(k) $-5(3a - 2b + c)$
(l) $-(x + 5)$
(m) $10(1 - 3x + 2y)$
(n) $-7(-2 - 3x + 4y)$

2. Simplify the following.

$ax + bx = (a + b)x$
$2x + 3x = (2 + 3)x$
$= 5x$

(a) $3x + 4x - 2x$
(b) $6m + 4a - 3a + 6m$
(c) $6a - 3b + 2a - 4b$
(d) $7ab - 3m + 4m + 6ab$
(e) $12t - 3s + 16s - 14t$
(f) $21ab - 3bc + 16bc - 11ab$
(g) $-3e + 4 - 6e + 3ef + 7$
(h) $3a + 7a - 5a$
(i) $12x - 3x + 2y + x$
(j) $11x - 4y - 12x + 3y$
(k) $6 - 3a + 7b - a + 11$
(l) $6xy - 4a - 3a - 7xy$
(m) $3d - 5 - 7d + 6d - 8$
(n) $2x^2 + 3x - 5 - 7x^2 + 2x - 1$
(o) $4a^2 - 3ab + 6ab - 2a^2 + 3ab$

EXPONENTS

EXERCISE 2

Simplify.

1. $(a^4)(a^7)$
2. $(b^3)(b^5)(b^7)$
3. $(2m^4)(4m^6)$
4. $(-3xy)(-2x^2y)$
5. $(4mn)(3m^2)(-2n)$
6. $(6x^3y)(-3xy^4)$
7. $(-2ab^2)(-4ab)(2b^2)$
8. $a^4 \div a^2$
9. $x^7 \div x^5$
10. $(8m^2) \div (4m)$
11. $(-12a^2b^2)(-3ab^2)$
12. $(20a^4b^6) \div (-5a^3b^4)$
13. $(-60a^3x^6) \div (-12a^3x^6)$
14. $(-3a^2b)(-4b^2) \div (6ab)$

EVALUATING POLYNOMIALS

EXERCISE 3

If $a = 2$, $b = -3$, $c = 4$, and $d = -1$, evaluate the following.

1. $3ac + a^2$
2. $2d - 3bc + a$
3. $2ab - 3bc$
4. $a^2 + b^2$
5. $4a^2 - 3d$
6. $2b^2d - 3d^2$

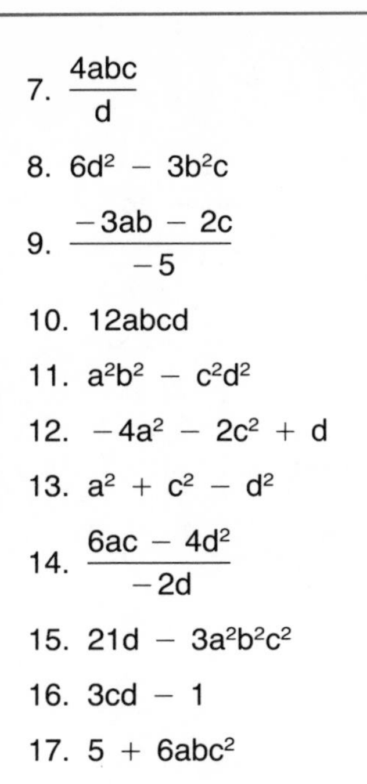

7. $\dfrac{4abc}{d}$

8. $6d^2 - 3b^2c$

9. $\dfrac{-3ab - 2c}{-5}$

10. $12abcd$

11. $a^2b^2 - c^2d^2$

12. $-4a^2 - 2c^2 + d$

13. $a^2 + c^2 - d^2$

14. $\dfrac{6ac - 4d^2}{-2d}$

15. $21d - 3a^2b^2c^2$

16. $3cd - 1$

17. $5 + 6abc^2$

PERIMETER AND AREA

EXERCISE 4

1. Find the area of each of the following.

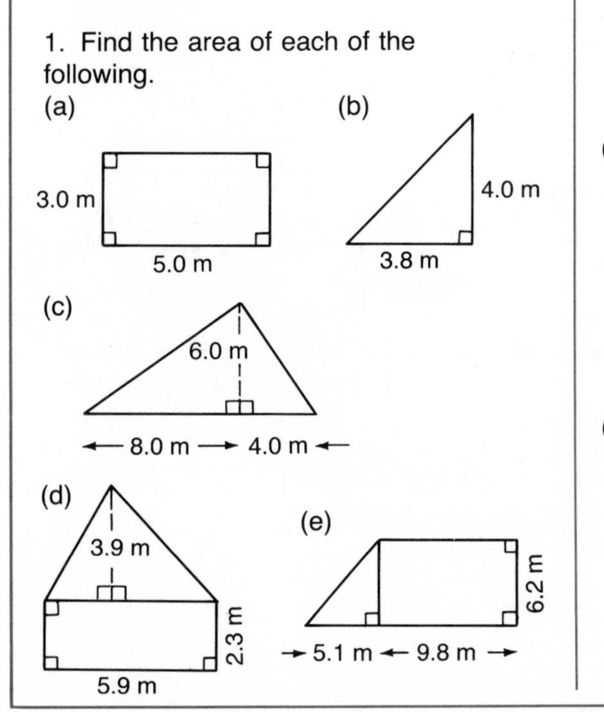

2. Calculate the perimeter and area of each figure to the nearest tenth of a metre.

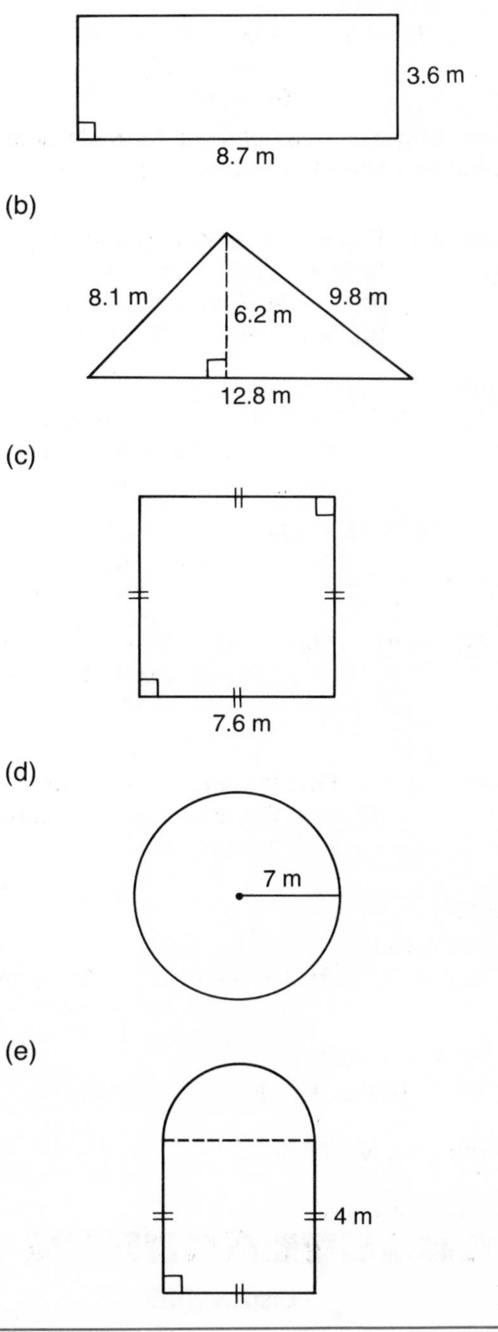

3.1 MULTIPLYING A POLYNOMIAL BY A MONOMIAL

$a(b + c) = ab + ac$

The distributive property is used when multiplying a polynomial by a monomial. For example:

$$\begin{aligned} 2(3x + 5) &= 2(3x + 5) \\ &= 2(3x) + 2(5) \\ &= 6x + 10 \end{aligned}$$

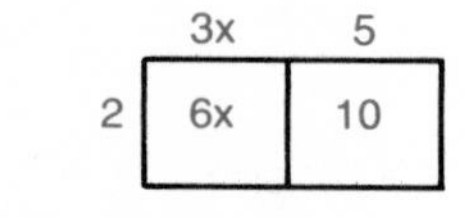

By recalling the "rules of signs for multiplication" we can expand and simplify algebraic expressions.

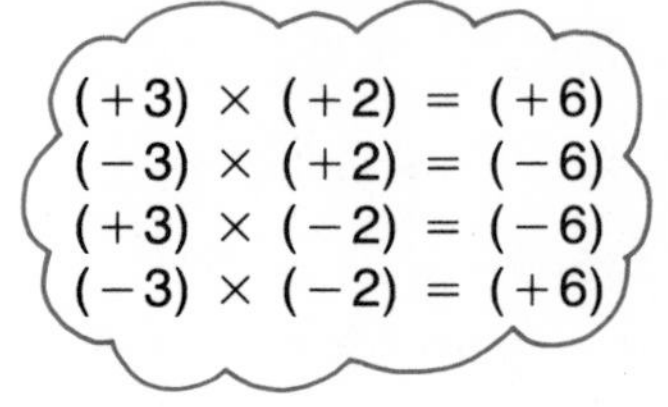

Example 1. Expand the following and simplify.
(a) $2(x + 3) + 3(x - 4)$
(b) $-3(2a - 4) - (3a - 2)$
(c) $2x(x - 4) - x(2x + 3)$

Solution:

(a) $$\begin{aligned} 2(x + 3) + 3(x - 4) &= 2(x + 3) + 3(x - 4) \\ &= 2x + 6 + 3x - 12 \\ &= 5x - 6 \end{aligned}$$

(b) $$\begin{aligned} -3(2a - 4) - (3a - 2) &= -3(2a - 4) - 1(3a - 2) \\ &= -6a + 12 - 3a + 2 \\ &= -9a + 14 \end{aligned}$$

The unwritten factor in front of a bracket is always 1 or −1.

(c) $$\begin{aligned} 2x(x - 4) - x(2x + 3) &= 2x(x - 4) - x(2x + 3) \\ &= 2x^2 - 8x - 2x^2 - 3x \\ &= -11x \end{aligned}$$

Example 2. (a) Find the area in terms of x.
(b) Find the area in square centimetres if $x = 0.3$ cm.

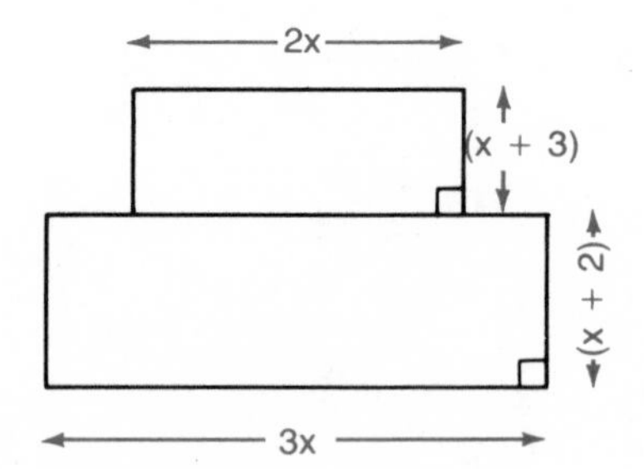

Solution:

(a) The area is
$$\begin{aligned} 2x(x + 3) + 3x(x + 2) &= 2x^2 + 6x + 3x^2 + 6x \\ &= 5x^2 + 12x \end{aligned}$$

(b) For $x = 0.3$ cm
$$\begin{aligned} 5x^2 + 12x &= 5(0.3)(0.3) + 12(0.3) \\ &= 4.05 \end{aligned}$$
The area is 4.05 cm².

On a calculator, press
5 × · 3 x² + 1 2 × · 3 =
Display 4.05

EXERCISE 3.1

A

1. Expand each of the following.

(a) $2(3x + 1)$ (b) $4(2a - 3)$
(c) $-2(x - 7)$ (d) $-3(x - y)$
(e) $7(-3y - 2)$ (f) $2x(x + 2)$
(g) $-(2x - 4)$ (h) $-2x(x - y)$

2. (a) $3(x - y - t)$
(b) $-(2p - 3q - 6)$
(c) $2x(x^2 - 3x - 3)$
(d) $-4(2a - 3b - c)$
(e) $2a(x - y - t)$
(f) $ab(a^2 - b - 1)$

B

3. Expand and simplify.

(a) $2(a + 3) + 3(a - 2)$
(b) $3(x + 3) - (x - 7)$
(c) $4(y - 3) - 2(y - 7)$
(d) $2(4b + 1) - 3(1 - 2b)$
(e) $4(a - 1) - (a - 3) - 2(a + 7)$
(f) $-3(1 - 2x) + (2x - 1) - (3x - 2)$
(g) $4(x^2 - x - 2) - 3(2x^2 - x + 1)$
(h) $2(a - 3b + c) - (a - 4b - 4c)$
(i) $-3(a^2 - 2a - 1) + 7(1 - 2a)$
(j) $3x - 2(x - 7) - 3(1 - 2x^2)$

4. Expand and simplify.

(a) $x(2x - 1) - 2x(x + 3)$
(b) $2b(1 - 3b) + 4(2b - 1)$
(c) $-4(x - 3xy) + x(x - y)$
(d) $2(x^2 - 3x + 1) - x(x - 4)$
(e) $7 - 2(a - 3b + 4) - 4(a + b)$
(f) $4a(a - b) - 3a(b - a)$
(g) $-3m(m - n) - 2n(m - n)$
(h) $2a(3a - 1) + 2a^2 - (a - 7)$

5. (a) Find the area in terms of x.
(b) Find the area in square metres if $x = 3.0$ m.

(i)

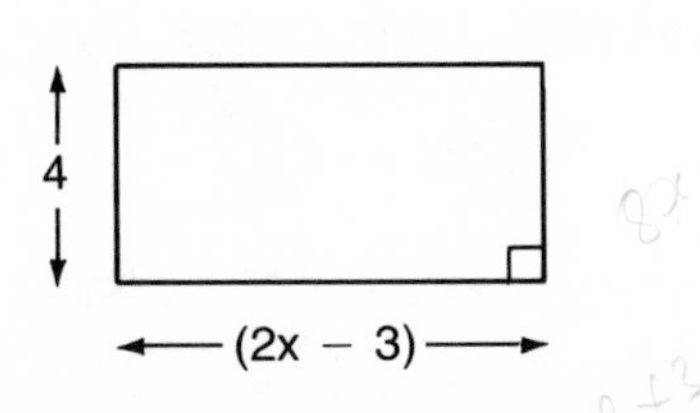

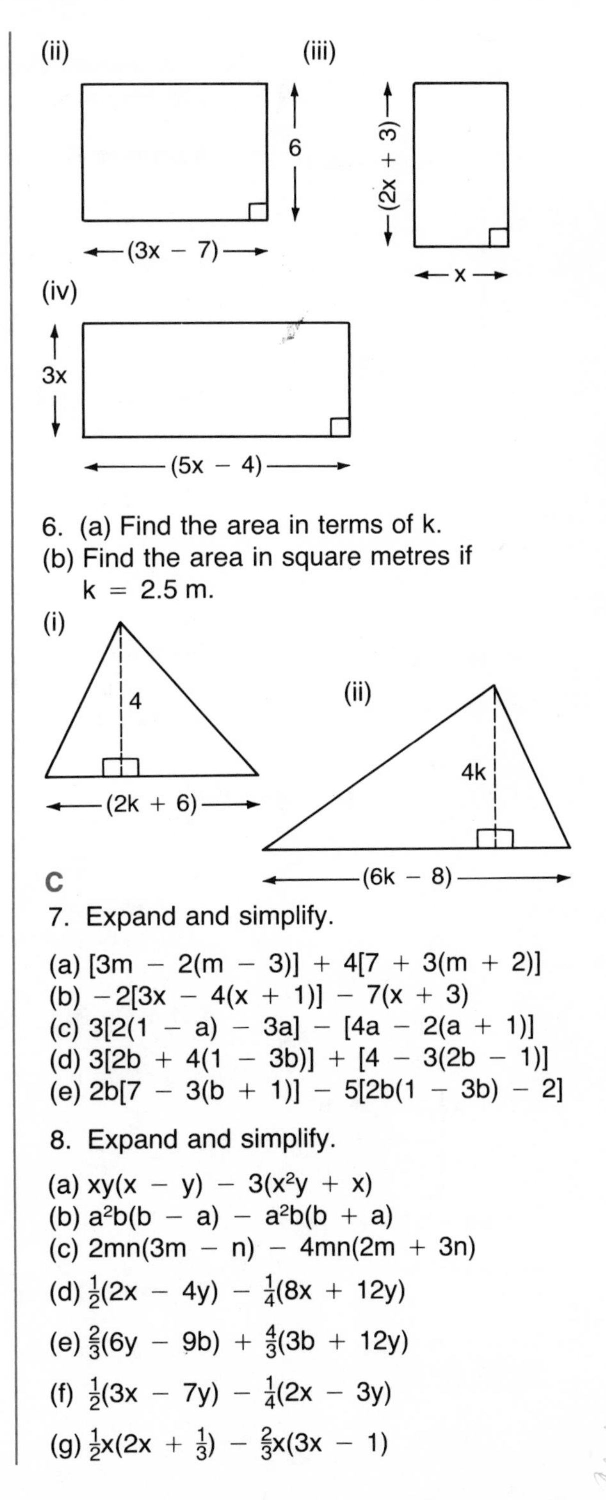

6. (a) Find the area in terms of k.
(b) Find the area in square metres if $k = 2.5$ m.

C

7. Expand and simplify.

(a) $[3m - 2(m - 3)] + 4[7 + 3(m + 2)]$
(b) $-2[3x - 4(x + 1)] - 7(x + 3)$
(c) $3[2(1 - a) - 3a] - [4a - 2(a + 1)]$
(d) $3[2b + 4(1 - 3b)] + [4 - 3(2b - 1)]$
(e) $2b[7 - 3(b + 1)] - 5[2b(1 - 3b) - 2]$

8. Expand and simplify.

(a) $xy(x - y) - 3(x^2y + x)$
(b) $a^2b(b - a) - a^2b(b + a)$
(c) $2mn(3m - n) - 4mn(2m + 3n)$
(d) $\frac{1}{2}(2x - 4y) - \frac{1}{4}(8x + 12y)$
(e) $\frac{2}{3}(6y - 9b) + \frac{4}{3}(3b + 12y)$
(f) $\frac{1}{2}(3x - 7y) - \frac{1}{4}(2x - 3y)$
(g) $\frac{1}{2}x(2x + \frac{1}{3}) - \frac{2}{3}x(3x - 1)$

3.2 MULTIPLYING A BINOMIAL BY A BINOMIAL

The distributive property is used to expand the product of two binomials.

	x	2
x	x^2	$2x$
3	$3x$	6

(Rows: $x + 3$; columns: $x + 2$)

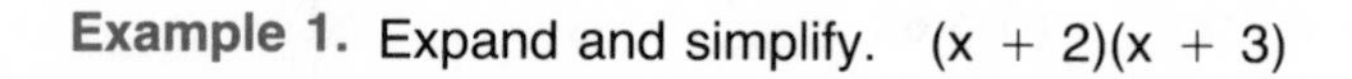

Example 1. Expand and simplify. $(x + 2)(x + 3)$

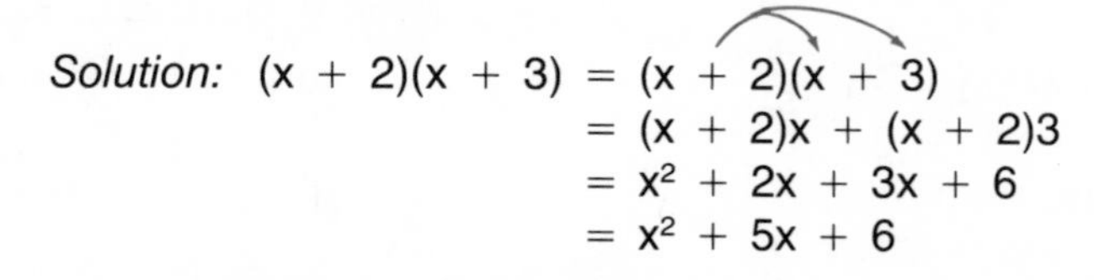

Solution:

$$\begin{aligned}(x + 2)(x + 3) &= (x + 2)(x + 3)\\ &= (x + 2)x + (x + 2)3\\ &= x^2 + 2x + 3x + 6\\ &= x^2 + 5x + 6\end{aligned}$$

The same result is obtained using the following procedure.

$$\begin{aligned}(x + 2)(x + 3) &= (x + 2)(x + 3)\\ &= x^2 + 3x + 2x + 6\\ &= x^2 + 5x + 6\end{aligned}$$

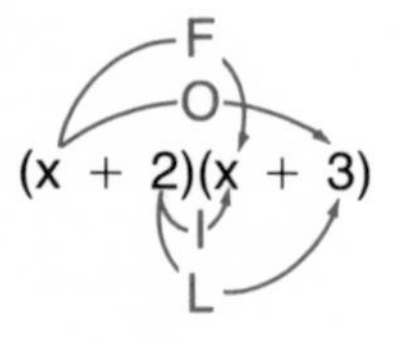

Each term in the first binomial multiplies each term in the second binomial. The word FOIL will help you remember the procedure.

$(x + 2)(x + 3) =$	x^2	+	$3x$	+	$2x$	+	6
	F		**O**		**I**		**L**
	Product of First Terms		Product of Outside Terms		Product of Inside Terms		Product of Last Terms

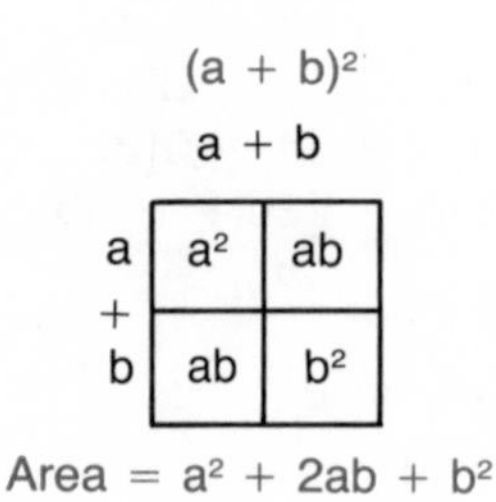

Example 2. Expand and simplify. $(2x - 3)^2$

Solution:

$$\begin{aligned}(2x - 3)^2 &= (2x - 3)(2x - 3)\\ &= (2x - 3)(2x - 3)\\ &= 4x^2 - 6x - 6x + 9\\ &= 4x^2 - 12x + 9\end{aligned}$$

Example 3. Expand and simplify. $(2x - y)(2x + y)$

Solution:

$$\begin{aligned}(2x - y)(2x + y) &= (2x - y)(2x + y)\\ &= 4x^2 + 2xy - 2xy - y^2\\ &= 4x^2 - y^2\end{aligned}$$

Example 4. Find an expression for the area of the picture.

Solution:

$$A = \ell \times w$$
$$A = (x + 4)(x - 2)$$
$$= x^2 - 2x + 4x - 8$$
$$= x^2 + 2x - 8$$

Example 5. Expand and simplify. $(x + 3)(x^2 + 2x - 1)$

Each term in the binomial multiplies each term in the trinomial.

Solution:

$$(x + 3)(x^2 + 2x - 1) = (x + 3)(x^2 + 2x - 1)$$
$$= x^3 + 2x^2 - x + 3x^2 + 6x - 3$$
$$= x^3 + 5x^2 + 5x - 3$$

EXERCISE 3.2

B Expand the following and simplify.

1. (a) $(x + 2)(x + 3)$ (b) $(a - 3)(a + 7)$
(c) $(y - 2)(y - 3)$ (d) $(m - 1)(m + 1)$
(e) $(c - 2)(c - 6)$ (f) $(x - 5)(x - 4)$
(g) $(2x - 1)(x + 3)$ (h) $(3b + 2)(2b - 1)$
(i) $(b - 7)(b - 2)$ (j) $(m + 7)(m + 6)$
(k) $(t + 2)(t + 3)$ (l) $(5a - 1)(5a + 1)$

2. (a) $(x + 7)^2$ (b) $(m - 2)^2$
(c) $(2x + 1)^2$ (d) $(4y - 3)^2$
(e) $(2m + 5)^2$ (f) $(1 - 5x)^2$
(g) $(a + 3)^2$ (h) $(1 + 3x)^2$

3. (a) $(4a - 3x)(2a + x)$
(b) $(2a - b)(a + b)$
(c) $(x - 2y)^2$
(d) $(2d - 3g)(7d + 3g)$
(e) $(6a - 7b)^2$
(f) $(1 - 3x)(2x + 5)$
(g) $(x - 2y)(x + 3y)$
(h) $(3m - 2b)(3m + 2b)$
(i) $(2a + b)^2$
(j) $(2x - y)(2x + y)$
(k) $(2m - 1)(m + 4)$
(l) $(4 - 3x)(5 - 7x)$

4. (a) Find the area of each figure in terms of x.
(b) Find the area in square centimetres if x = 4.5 cm.

(i)

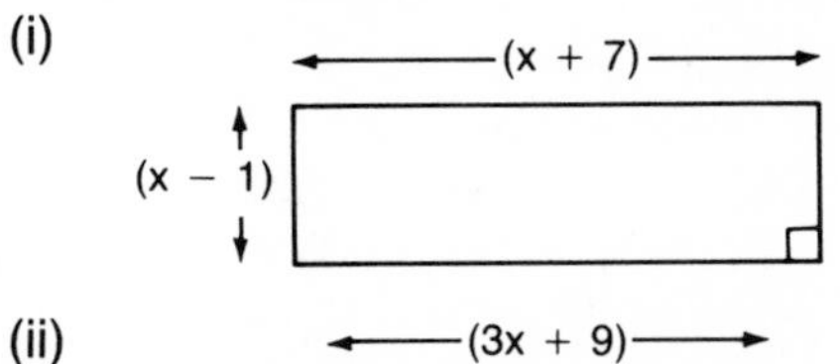

(ii)

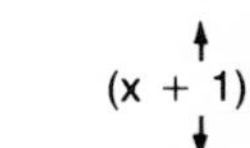

(iii)

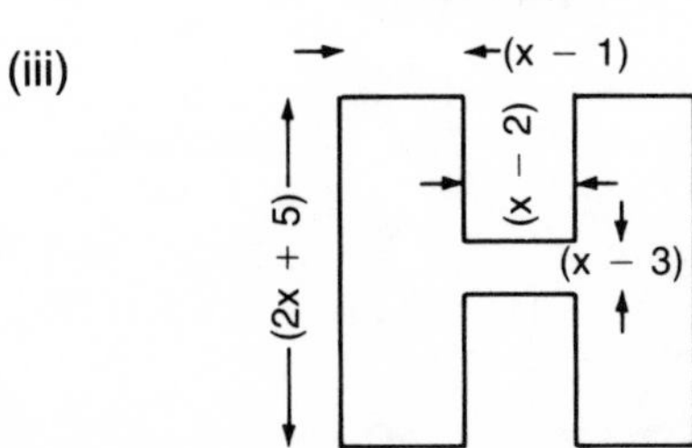

3.3 EXPRESSIONS INVOLVING POLYNOMIALS

In this section the rules for multiplication of polynomials are applied to the simplification of expressions.

Example 1. Simplify. $(2x - 1)(3x + 2) - 4(x - 7)$

Solution:

$$\begin{aligned}(2x - 1)(3x + 2) - 4(x - 7) &= (2x - 1)(3x + 2) - 4(x - 7)\\ &= (6x^2 + 4x - 3x - 2) - 4x + 28\\ &= 6x^2 + x - 2 - 4x + 28\\ &= 6x^2 - 3x + 26\end{aligned}$$

Example 2. Simplify. $3(a - 2)(2a - 1) - 2(a + 3)(3a + 2)$

Solution:

$$\begin{aligned}3(a - 2)(2a - 1) - 2(a + 3)(3a + 2) &= 3(2a^2 - a - 4a + 2) - 2(3a^2 + 2a + 9a + 6)\\ &= 3(2a^2 - 5a + 2) - 2(3a^2 + 11a + 6)\\ &= 6a^2 - 15a + 6 - 6a^2 - 22a - 12\\ &= -37a - 6\end{aligned}$$

EXERCISE 3.3

B 1. Simplify the following.

(a) $2(x - 3) + (x + 1)(x + 4)$
(b) $2(m - 3) + (m + 2)(m - 3)$
(c) $(4x - 1)(x + 3) + (2x - 3)(x - 1)$
(d) $(4a + 1)(4a - 1) + (a + 3)(a + 2)$

2. Simplify.

(a) $2(2x - 1) + 3(x + 2)(x - 4)$
(b) $3(a - 2)(a - 3) + 2(a + 6)$
(c) $2(m - 1)(m + 3) + 4(m - 2) + 6$
(d) $3(2x + 1)(x + 2) + 2(x - 1)(2x + 3)$
(e) $(x + 3)^2 + (x - 2)^2$
(f) $2(a - 3)^2 - (a + 1)^2$

3. Simplify.

(a) $2(a - 2)(a + 2) - 3(a + 4)(a + 6)$
(b) $2(t - 3)(t + 4) - (3t + 1)(t - 6)$
(c) $5(m + 3)(2m - 1) - (m + 2)$
(d) $3(a + 6)(2a + 1) - 4(2a - 1)(a + 3)$
(e) $2(x + 1)^2 - (x + 2)(x + 3)$
(f) $(m - 1)^2 - 3(2m - 1)^2$

C 4. Simplify and evaluate.

(a) $-3(2m - 1)(m + 2) - 4 + 3m$ for $m = 2.4$
(b) $3(1 - 2x)(1 + x) - 2(3x + 7)(x - 4)$ for $x = 6.7$
(c) $3(x - 3)(7 - x) - 5(2x - 1)(2x + 1)$ for $x = 4.3$
(d) $-4(t + 3)(2t - 1) - 6(1 - 3t)$ for $t = 2.5$
(e) $3(m + 1)(m + 2) - (2m - 1)^2$ for $m = 3.1$

MIND BENDER

Use each of the ten digits once to make two five-digit numbers with the largest possible product.

■■■■■
× ■■■■■

3.4 DIVISION OF A POLYNOMIAL BY A MONOMIAL

The division of two monomials is illustrated in the examples.

Example 1. Simplify. $\frac{12ab}{3b}$, $b \neq 0$

Solution: $\frac{12ab}{3b} = \frac{(4a)(3b)}{3b}$
$= 4a$

$\frac{12ab}{3b}$
$= \frac{12}{3} \times a \times \frac{b}{b}$
$= 4a$

How does your calculator respond to division by zero?

We state the restriction $b \neq 0$ because division by zero is not defined.

Multiplication distributes over addition and subtraction.

$2(x + 3) = 2x + 6 \qquad a(b + c) = ab + ac$

Division also distributes over addition and subtraction.

$\frac{x + 3}{2} = \frac{x}{2} + \frac{3}{2}$ and $\frac{b + c}{a} = \frac{b}{a} + \frac{c}{a}$

Example 2. Simplify. $\frac{15ax + 3ab}{3a}$, $a \neq 0$

Solution: $\frac{15ax + 3ab}{3a} = \frac{15ax}{3a} + \frac{3ab}{3a}$
$= 5x + b$

EXERCISE 3.4

A

1. Simplify. What are the restrictions on the variables?

(a) $\frac{10ab}{2a}$ (b) $\frac{24bc}{6c}$ (c) $\frac{-15xy}{3x}$

(d) $\frac{-21abc}{-7ab}$ (e) $\frac{30dc}{-6dc}$ (f) $\frac{24a^2}{12a}$

B

2. Simplify.

(a) $\frac{3x + 3m}{3}$ (b) $\frac{12a - 4b}{4}$

(c) $\frac{3a^2 - 3}{3}$ (d) $\frac{24ab - 6b}{-6}$

(e) $\frac{21mt - 7m}{7}$ (f) $\frac{2ab - 4a + 6}{2}$

3. Divide and state the restrictions on the variables.

(a) $\frac{12ab - 6ac}{3a}$ (b) $\frac{10ac - 2a}{2a}$

(c) $\frac{2x^2 - x}{x}$ (d) $\frac{-6mn - 3m - 9mt}{-3m}$

4. Divide and state the restrictions on the variables.

(a) $\frac{100a^2b - 50ab^2}{-10ab}$

(b) $\frac{-12x^4 - 8x^3 + 2x^2}{2x^2}$

(c) $\frac{10a - 20a^2 + 30a^3}{-10a}$

3.5 COMMON FACTORING

The distributive property has been used to multiply a polynomial by a monomial. In this section we shall do the reverse. This reverse operation is known as factoring.

$ab + ac = a(b + c)$ $\quad$ $5x + 5y = 5(x + y)$

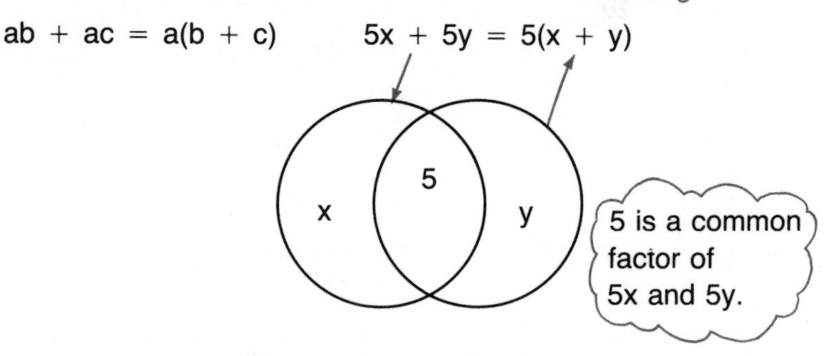

Compare: $6a = 2 \times 3 \times a = 2 \times 3a$

$3a^2 = 3 \times a \times a = 3a \times a$

3 and a are common factors of 6a and $3a^2$.
$3 \times a = 3a$ is the greatest common factor.

When factoring an expression, we look for the greatest common factor of its terms.

Example 1. Factor. $2x^2 + 6y$

Solution: By inspection, 2 is the greatest common factor. The other factor may be found by division.

$$2x^2 + 6y = 2\left(\frac{2x^2 + 6y}{2}\right)$$
$$= 2(x^2 + 3y)$$

Check: $2(x^2 + 3y) = 2(x^2 + 3y)$
$= 2x^2 + 6y$

> Common Factoring
> 1. Find the greatest common factor by inspection.
> 2. Find the other factor by division.

Example 2. Factor. $3a^2 - 6a$

Solution: The greatest common factor is 3a.

$$3a^2 - 6a = 3a\left(\frac{3a^2 - 6a}{3a}\right)$$
$$= 3a(a - 2)$$

Check: $3a(a - 2) = 3a(a - 2)$
$= 3a^2 - 6a$

Example 3. Factor. $12mn^2 + 8n$

Solution:

$$12mn^2 = 2 \times 2 \times 3 \times m \times n \times n$$
$$8n = 2 \times 2 \times 2 \times n$$
$$4 \quad n$$

Both 4 and n are common to each term.

$$12mn^2 + 8n = 4n\left(\frac{12mn^2 + 8n}{4n}\right)$$
$$= 4n(3mn + 2)$$

Check: $4n(3mn + 2) = 4n(3mn + 2)$
$= 12mn^2 + 8n$

EXERCISE 3.5

A

1. Find the greatest common factor of each pair.
(a) $2x$ and $4y$
(b) $14a$ and $7b$
(c) $12x$ and $18y$
(d) $3x$ and $5x$
(e) $4ab$ and $3ac$
(f) $5x^2$ and $10x$
(g) $8abc$ and $12ab$
(h) $4xy$ and $5xy$

B

2. Complete.
(a) $2x + 4 = 2(x + \blacksquare)$
(b) $3a + 9 = 3(a + \blacksquare)$
(c) $x^2 - 4x = x(x - \blacksquare)$
(d) $a^2 + 6a = a(a + \blacksquare)$
(e) $3a - 6b = 3(a - \blacksquare)$
(f) $2x^2 - 8x = 2x(x - \blacksquare)$

3. Complete.
(a) $5a + 5b = 5(\blacksquare)$
(b) $7x - 7y = 7(\blacksquare)$
(c) $3x + 6 = 3(\blacksquare)$
(d) $4a - 12 = 4(\blacksquare)$
(e) $2a + 4b + 6c = 2(\blacksquare)$
(f) $3x^2 - 6x = 3x(\blacksquare)$
(g) $6x^3 + 4x^2 + 2x = 2x(\blacksquare)$

4. Complete.
(a) $\blacksquare(x + y) = 3x + 3y$
(b) $\blacksquare(a - b) = 2a - 2b$
(c) $\blacksquare(x + 2) = x^2 + 2x$
(d) $\blacksquare(a - 4) = a^2 - 4a$
(e) $\blacksquare(2x + 1) = 2x^2 + x$
(f) $\blacksquare(x - 1) = x^3 - x^2$
(g) $\blacksquare(3a + 4) = 3a^2 + 4a$

5. Factor.
(a) $4a + 4b$
(b) $2x - 2y$
(c) $3x + 6$
(d) $5b - 10$
(e) $8y - 4$
(f) $2a + 6b - 8c$
(g) $4x^2 + 2y$
(h) $7x^2 - 14x + 21$
(i) $20a + 5b - 15$
(j) $6t^2 - 6t + 12$

6. Factor.
(a) $x^2 + 3x$
(b) $a^2 - 2a$
(c) $5ax + 6ay$
(d) $4xy - 7ax$
(e) $2ax + 2ay$
(f) $3mx - 6my$
(g) $10tx - 5ty$
(h) $3x^2 + 12x$
(i) $5a^2 - 15a$
(j) $8x^3 - 4x^2$

C

7. Factor.
(a) $6x^2y - 3xy^2$
(b) $4a^2b + 6ab - 8ab^2$
(c) $14x^2y^2 - 7xy^2 + 7xy$
(d) $6abc - 2abx + 10aby$
(e) $7a^3 + 14a^2 - 7a$

3.6 USING YOUR COMPUTER: EVALUATING ALGEBRAIC EXPRESSIONS

Expressions such as $3x^2 - 5x + 3$ can be evaluated by substituting values for x, as in Example 1.

Example 1. Evaluate $3x^2 - 5x + 3$ for $x = 1, 2, 3, 4, 5, 6$.

Solution: Evaluating expressions for several values of the variable can be organized in a table.

x	$3x^2 - 5x + 3$	Value
1	$3(1)^2 - 5(1) + 3 = 3 - 5 + 3$	1
2	$3(2)^2 - 5(2) + 3 = 12 - 10 + 3$	5
3	$3(3)^2 - 5(3) + 3 = 27 - 15 + 3$	15
4	$3(4)^2 - 5(4) + 3 = 48 - 20 + 3$	31
5	$3(5)^2 - 5(5) + 3 = 75 - 25 + 3$	53
6	$3(6)^2 - 5(6) + 3 = 108 - 30 + 3$	81

Tables as in Example 1, can be produced quickly using the FOR ... NEXT statements in a BASIC computer program. In BASIC, $3x^2 - 5x + 3$ is written 3*x*x−5*x+3

Line 20:
tells the computer we want the values 1, 2, 3, 4, 5, 6
Line 50:
tells the computer to return to line 20 FOR the NEXT value of x.

```
NEW
10 PRINT"PRINTING A TABLE OF VALUES"
20 FOR X = 1 TO 6
30 Y=3*X*X-5*X+3
40 PRINT X,Y
50 NEXT X
60 END
RUN

PRINTING A TABLE OF VALUES
1          1
2          5
3          15
4          31
5          53
6          81
```

Example 2. The following program prints a table of squares and cubes.

Line 30:
tells the computer we want values from 1 to 2 in "steps" of 0.1

```
NEW
10 PRINT"SQUARES AND CUBES"
20 PRINT"NUMBER","SQUARE","CUBE"
30 FOR X = 1 TO 2 STEP 0.1
40 PRINT X, X*X, X^3
50 NEXT X
60 END
RUN
```

Solution:

SQUARES AND CUBES		
NUMBER	SQUARE	CUBE
1	1	1
1.1	1.21	1.331
1.2	1.44	1.728
1.3	1.69	2.197
1.4	1.96	2.744
1.5	2.25	3.375
1.6	2.56	4.096
1.7	2.89	4.913
1.8	3.24	5.832
1.9	3.61	6.859
2	4	8

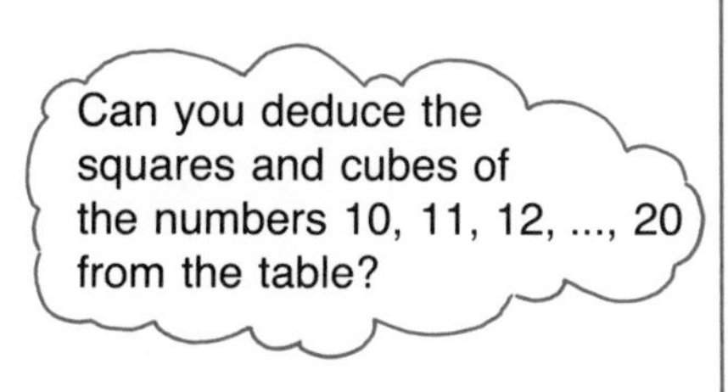

EXERCISE 3.6

B

1. Write the following expressions in BASIC.
(a) $3x + 4$
(b) $3.14r^2$
(c) $x^2 + 3x + 2$
(d) $2x^3 + 3x^2 - x + 17$
(e) $4x^2 - 2x^4$

2. Prepare computer programs to produce tables of values for the following expressions using FOR ... NEXT statements.
(a) $x^2 + 5$ for $x = 1, 2, 3, 4, 5$
(b) $x^3 - 27$ for $x = 1, 2, 3, 4, 5, 6$
(c) $2x^3 - 5x^2 - 6x + 10$ for $x = 1, 2, 3, ..., 10$
(d) $x^2 - 2$ for $x = 1, 1.1, 1.2, ..., 2$
(e) $3.14r^2$ for $r = 1, 1.5, 2, 2.5, ..., 5$
(f) $x^3 - 4096$ for $x = 0, 2, 4, ..., 16$

3. Prepare a computer program to produce a table giving the amount of interest on a principal of $5000 at an interest rate of 5.95% in n interest periods for n = 1, 2, 3, ..., 10.

4. Prepare a computer program to produce a table giving the amount of interest on a principal of $10 000 for 5 interest periods at interest rates of 5%, 5.5%, 6%, ..., 10%.

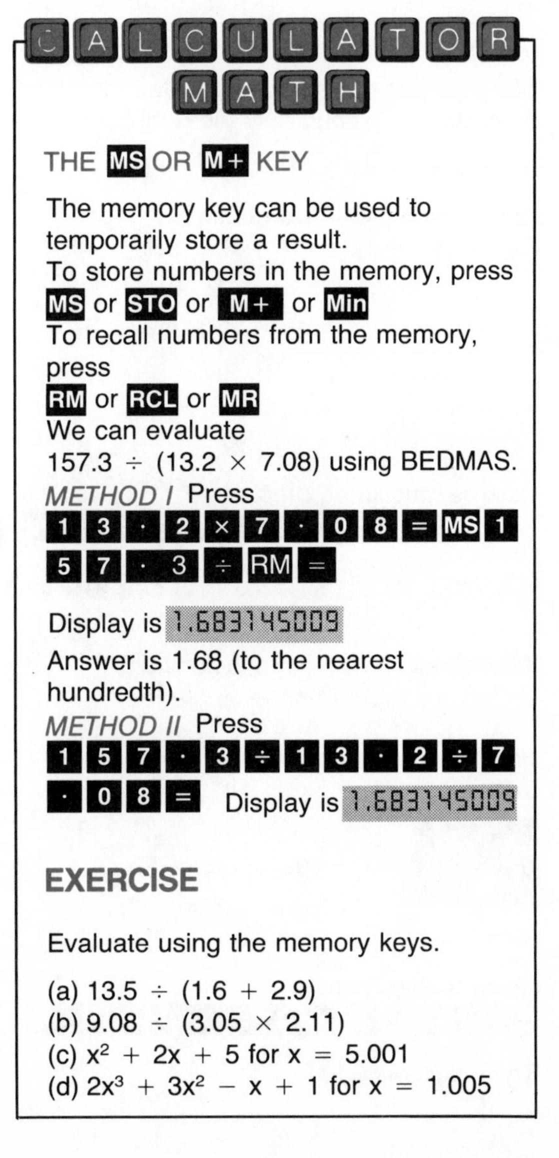

3.7 POLYNOMIALS IN NESTED FORM

When evaluating a polynomial such as $3x^3 - 5x^2 + 4x - 3$ with a calculator, it is simpler and quicker to factor the polynomial first. This is illustrated in the following examples.

Example 1. Write the polynomial $3x^3 - 5x^2 + 4x - 3$ in nested form and evaluate for $x = 2$.

Solution:

Factor the polynomial from right to left.

$3x^3 - 5x^2 + 4x - 3 = [3x^2 - 5x + 4]x - 3$ ← factor x from the first 3 terms

$= [(3x - 5)x + 4]x - 3$ ← factor x from the first 2 terms

$= [(\langle 3\rangle x - 5)x + 4]x - 3$ ← factor x from the first term

We write this polynomial in nested form by dropping the left brackets and writing only the right brackets, as follows.

$3x^3 - 5x^2 + 4x - 3 = 3]x - 5]x + 4]x - 3$

Replacing x with 2 we obtain

$3]2 - 5]2 + 4]2 - 3 = 6 - 5]2 + 4]2 - 3$ ($3 \times 2 = 6$)

$= 1]2 + 4]2 - 3$ ($6 - 5 = 1$)

$= 2 + 4]2 - 3$ ($1 \times 2 = 2$)

$= 6]2 - 3$ ($2 + 4 = 6$)

$= 12 - 3$ ($6 \times 2 = 12$)

$= 9$

Using a calculator, press

3 × 2 − 5 = × 2 + 4 = × 2 − 3 =

Display 3. 3. 2. 6. 5. 1. 1. 2. 2. 4. 6. 6. 2. 12. 3. 9.

Example 2. Write the polynomial $5x^3 - 2x + 1$ in nested form and evaluate for $x = 4$.

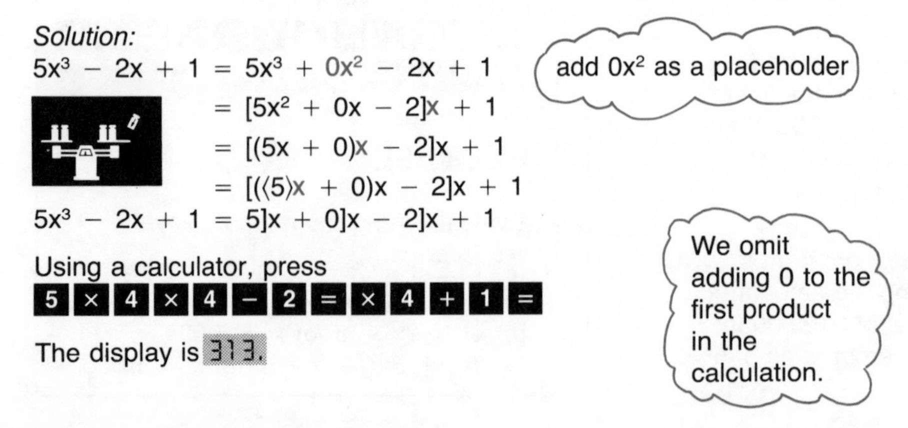

Solution:

$5x^3 - 2x + 1 = 5x^3 + 0x^2 - 2x + 1$ (add $0x^2$ as a placeholder)

$= [5x^2 + 0x - 2]x + 1$

$= [(5x + 0)x - 2]x + 1$

$= [(\langle 5\rangle x + 0)x - 2]x + 1$

$5x^3 - 2x + 1 = 5]x + 0]x - 2]x + 1$

Using a calculator, press

5 × 4 × 4 − 2 = × 4 + 1 =

The display is 313.

We omit adding 0 to the first product in the calculation.

The memory key on your calculator is useful when the number we substitute for x has many digits.

Example 3. Evaluate $3]x - 2]x + 4]x - 1$ for $x = 1.024$

Solution:
Press **1** **·** **0** **2** **4** **STO**
3 **×** **RM** **−** **2** **=** **×** **RM** **+** **4** **=** **×** **RM** **−** **1** **=**

Display 4.220073472 $\doteq$ 4.220 (to the nearest thousandth).

In general, an expression such as
$Ax^4 + Bx^3 + Cx^2 + Dx + E$ in nested form is
$A]x + B]x + C]x + D]x + E$

EXERCISE 3.7

A

1. Evaluate for $x = 3$.
(a) $3]x + 5]x + 2$
(b) $4]x + 3]x - 5$
(c) $2]x - 3]x - 4$
(d) $-5]x + 3]x - 2$
(e) $7]x - 6]x - 5]x$
(f) $-5]x + 6]x + 0]x + 4$

2. Evaluate for $x = -2$.
(a) $2]x + 3]x - 1]x + 3$
(b) $3]x - 5]x + 2]x + 4$
(c) $-2]x + 1]x - 3]x + 0$
(d) $5]x + 0]x + 3]x - 5$
(e) $-3]x - 2]x + 4$
(f) $5]x + 0]x + 0]x + 4$

B

3. Express in nested form.
(a) $5x^2 - 7x + 3$
(b) $3x^3 + 4x^2 - 5x + 2$
(c) $3x^3 - 2x + 5$
(d) $4x^3 + 3x^2 - 7$
(e) $3x^3 - 7x^2 + 5x - 3$
(f) $-2x^3 + 7x - 11$

4. Express in nested form, and evaluate for the given value.
(a) $2x^3 - 5x + 7$, for $x = 2$
(b) $3x^3 + 7x^2 - 5x + 3$, for $x = -2$
(c) $2x^3 - 5x^2 + 6$, for $x = -1$
(d) $6x^3 - 3x^2 + 5$, for $x = -2$
(e) $-2x^3 + 5x^2 - 2x + 3$, for $x = 3$
(f) $3x^4 - 2x^2 + 3x - 1$, for $x = 3$

5. A ball is thrown vertically upward with an initial velocity of 24.4 m/s. The formula for the height, d, of the ball from the point of release in time, t, seconds is

$$d = -4.9t^2 + 24.4t + 1.4$$

(a) Express the polynomial in nested form.
(b) Find d for $t = 1$, $t = 2$, $t = 3$, $t = 4$, and $t = 5$.
(c) What is the greatest height the ball reaches?

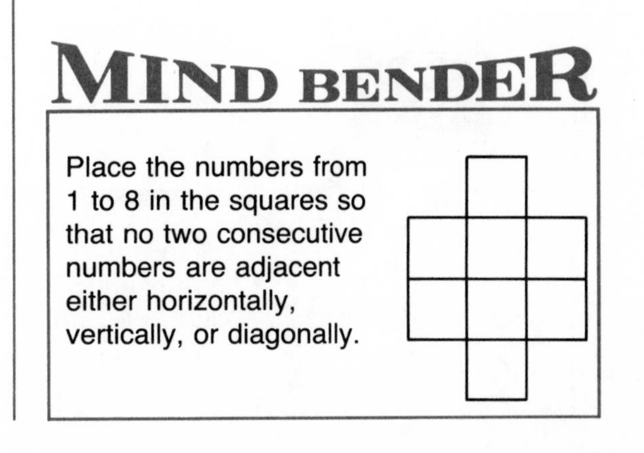

3.8 FACTORING $x^2 + bx + c$

Some trinomials can be factored as the product of two binomials. We can see how this is done by studying the expansion of two binomials.

Consider the expansion

$$\begin{aligned}(x + 2)(x + 4) &= x^2 + 4x + 2x + 8\\ &= x^2 + 6x + 8\end{aligned}$$

The expression $x^2 + 4x + 2x + 8$ is the key to factoring $x^2 + 6x + 8$. You can see that $6x$ is the sum of the two terms $4x$ and $2x$ and that 8 is the product of 4 and 2.

Consider the expansion

$$\begin{aligned}(x + r)(x + s) &= x^2 + sx + rx + rs\\ &= x^2 + (s + r)x + rs\end{aligned}$$

Example 1. Factor. $x^2 + 7x + 12$

Solution:
To factor $x^2 + 7x + 12$ compare the trinomial with $x^2 + (s + r)x + rs$.

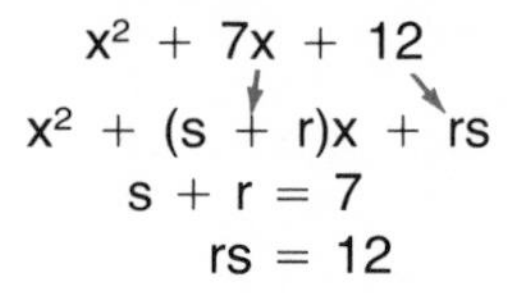

$$s + r = 7$$
$$rs = 12$$

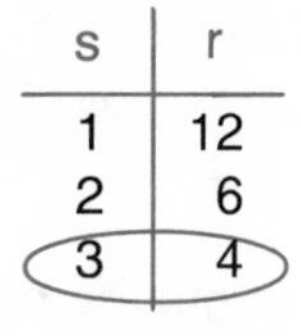

s	r
1	12
2	6
3	4

Two numbers whose sum is 7 and product is 12 are 3 and 4.

$$\begin{aligned}x^2 + 7x + 12 &= x^2 + (3 + 4)x + 12\\ &= x^2 + 3x + 4x + 12\\ &= x(x + 3) + 4(x + 3)\\ &= (x + 4)(x + 3)\end{aligned}$$

Example 2. Factor. $x^2 - 2x - 15$

Solution:
Again, by comparison, we must find two numbers that have a product of -15 and at the same time a sum of -2. The numbers are -5 and 3.

$x^2 - 2x - 15 = (x - 5)(x + 3)$

Factors of -20		Sum
-20	1	-19
-10	2	-8
-5	4	-1
-4	5	1
-2	10	8
-1	20	19

Example 3. Factor. $x^2 + x - 20$

Solution:
We need to find two numbers that multiply to -20 and add to 1. We can set up a table to find the correct factors.

The numbers are -4 and 5.

$x^2 + x - 20 = (x - 4)(x + 5)$

EXERCISE 3.8

A 1. State the values of r and s.

	r + s	rs	r	s
(a)	5	6		
(b)	6	8		
(c)	3	2		
(d)	−4	3		
(e)	−2	1		
(f)	−7	12		
(g)	−7	10		
(h)	−1	−12		
(i)	2	−8		

B 2. Find the missing factor.

(a) $x^2 + 5x + 6 = (x + 3)(\blacksquare)$
(b) $m^2 + 9m + 8 = (\blacksquare)(m + 8)$
(c) $t^2 + 7t + 12 = (t + 4)(\blacksquare)$
(d) $y^2 - 4y + 3 = (y - 1)(\blacksquare)$
(e) $a^2 - 6a + 9 = (\blacksquare)(a - 3)$
(f) $z^2 - 10z + 16 = (z - 2)(\blacksquare)$
(g) $x^2 + 4x - 5 = (x - 1)(\blacksquare)$
(h) $t^2 - 2t - 24 = (\blacksquare)(t + 4)$
(i) $r^2 + 5r - 14 = (r + 7)(\blacksquare)$
(j) $n^2 - n - 20 = (\blacksquare)(n + 4)$
(k) $2x^2 - 12x - 14 = 2(x - 7)(\blacksquare)$
(l) $5y^2 + 10y - 120 = 5(\blacksquare)(y - 4)$

3. Factor.

(a) $x^2 + 6x + 5$
(b) $t^2 + 9t + 14$
(c) $m^2 + 9m + 20$
(d) $n^2 + 4n + 4$
(e) $y^2 - 3y + 2$
(f) $k^2 - 5k + 6$
(g) $a^2 - 7a + 12$
(h) $b^2 - 8b + 12$
(i) $x^2 - 2x - 24$
(j) $m^2 + m - 12$
(k) $x^2 - 2x - 35$
(l) $n^2 + 5n - 24$
(m) $y^2 - 4y - 21$
(n) $a^2 - 6a + 9$
(o) $x^2 - 2x + 1$
(p) $9x^2 + 27x + 18$
(q) $5x^2 + 15x - 90$
(r) $7x^2 + 14x - 21$
(s) $30y^2 + 60y + 30$

Common factor first

EXTRA

FACTORING $ax^2 + bx + c, a \neq 1$

If it is possible to factor
$ax^2 + bx + c = (\blacksquare)(\blacksquare)$
we can decompose the term bx into a sum mx + nx where $m \times n = ac$.

Example. Factor. $6x^2 - 7x - 3$

Solution: To replace −7x by mx + nx we must determine m and n.
$m + n = b = -7$ and
$mn = ac = -18$
Therefore $m = -9$ and $n = 2$.

$$\begin{aligned} &6x^2 - 7x - 3 \\ &= 6x^2 - 9x + 2x - 3 \\ &= (6x^2 - 9x) + (2x - 3) \\ &= 3x(2x - 3) + 1(2x - 3) \\ &= (3x + 1)(2x - 3) \end{aligned}$$

EXERCISE

1. Determine integer values for m and n.

(a) $m + n = 7, mn = 10$
(b) $m + n = 5, mn = 6$
(c) $m + n = -7, mn = 12$
(d) $m + n = -2, mn = -15$
(e) $m + n = -6, mn = 5$

2. Factor.

(a) $6x^2 + 13x + 5$
(b) $2w^2 + 5w + 3$
(c) $6x^2 - 7x + 2$
(d) $4m^2 + 27m + 18$
(e) $3w^2 - 10w + 8$
(f) $15t^2 - t - 2$
(g) $2m^2 - m - 10$
(h) $4x^2 + 25x + 6$
(i) $6n^2 - 13n + 6$
(j) $3x^2 - 23x + 14$

3.9 FACTORING SPECIAL QUADRATICS

We can use the following identities to factor special quadratics.

$$a^2 + 2ab + b^2 = (a + b)(a + b) = (a + b)^2$$
$$a^2 - 2ab + b^2 = (a - b)(a - b) = (a - b)^2$$
} Perfect Squares

$$a^2 - b^2 = (a - b)(a + b)$$
} Difference of Squares

Example 1. Factor. $9x^2 + 30x + 25$

Solution:

$a = 3x$
$b = 5$

$$\begin{aligned} 9x^2 + 30x + 25 &= (3x)^2 + 2(3x)(5) - (5)^2 \leftarrow a^2 + 2ab + b^2 \\ &= (3x + 5)(3x + 5) \\ &= (3x + 5)^2 \qquad \leftarrow (a + b)^2 \end{aligned}$$

Example 2. Factor. $4x^2 - 12x + 9$

Solution:

$a = 2x$
$b = 3$

$$\begin{aligned} 4x^2 - 12x + 9 &= (2x)^2 - 2(2x)(3) + (3)^2 \leftarrow a^2 - 2ab + b^2 \\ &= (2x - 3)(2x - 3) \\ &= (2x - 3)^2 \qquad \leftarrow (a - b)^2 \end{aligned}$$

Example 3. Factor. $x^2 - 16$

Solution:

$a = x$
$b = 4$

$$\begin{aligned} x^2 - 16 &= (x)^2 - (4)^2 \qquad \leftarrow a^2 - b^2 \\ &= (x - 4)(x + 4) \leftarrow (a - b)(a + b) \end{aligned}$$

Factoring is also useful in simplifying numerical expressions.

Example 4. Use factoring to simplify the following.
(a) 103×97 (b) 102^2

Solution: (a)
$$\begin{aligned} 103 \times 97 &= (100 + 3)(100 - 3) \\ &= 100^2 - 3^2 \\ &= 10\,000 - 9 \\ &= 9991 \end{aligned}$$

(b)
$$\begin{aligned} 102^2 &= (100 + 2)^2 \\ &= 100^2 + 2(2)(100) + 2^2 \\ &= 10\,000 + 400 + 4 \\ &= 10\,404 \end{aligned}$$

EXERCISE 3.9

A

1. State whether each of the following binomials can be factored as a difference of squares.

(a) $x^2 - 25$
(b) $x^2 + 25$
(c) $x^2 - 64$
(d) $36 - x^2$
(e) $49x^2 - 25$
(f) $9x^2 + 16$
(g) $16x^2 - 5$
(h) $x - 9$

2. Complete the following.

(a) $x^2 - 16 = (x - 4)(x + \blacksquare)$
(b) $m^2 - 4 = (m - \blacksquare)(m + 2)$
(c) $t^2 - 9 = (t - \blacksquare)(t + \blacksquare)$
(d) $x^2 - 1 = (x - 1)(\blacksquare + 1)$
(e) $a^2 - 49 = (\blacksquare - 7)(\blacksquare + 7)$

3. State the missing factor.

(a) $x^2 - 9 = (x - 3)(\blacksquare)$
(b) $a^2 - 100 = (\blacksquare)(a + 10)$
(c) $m^2 - 25 = (m - 5)(\blacksquare)$
(d) $r^2 - 36 = (\blacksquare)(r + 6)$
(e) $9x^2 - 4 = (3x - 2)(\blacksquare)$
(f) $25m^2 - 1 = (\blacksquare)(5m + 1)$

B

4. Factor.

(a) $x^2 - 16$
(b) $n^2 - 9$
(c) $t^2 - 1$
(d) $r^2 - 121$
(e) $y^2 - 49$
(f) $s^2 - 81$
(g) $x^2 - 64$
(h) $b^2 - 144$

5. Factor.

(a) $4x^2 - 25$
(b) $9m^2 - 1$
(c) $16t^2 - 49$
(d) $25n^2 - 121$
(e) $64x^2 - 9$
(f) $100a^2 - 1$
(g) $4s^2 - 81$

C

6. Factor.

(a) $16 - x^2$
(b) $36 - y^2$
(c) $81 - m^2$
(d) $100 - t^2$
(e) $9 - 4x^2$
(f) $121 - 16m^2$
(g) $81 - 25t^2$
(h) $64 - 9x^2$
(i) $\frac{1}{4}x^2 - 16$

7. Factor.

(a) $x^2 + 4x + 4$
(b) $x^2 - 6x + 9$
(c) $t^2 - 2t + 1$
(d) $r^2 + 10r + 25$
(e) $m^2 - 14m + 49$
(f) $w^2 + 16w + 64$

8. Factor.

(a) $9x^2 - 30x + 25$
(b) $4x^2 + 4x + 1$
(c) $4t^2 + 12t + 9$
(d) $9s^2 - 24s + 16$
(e) $16t^2 + 40t + 25$
(f) $9x^2 - 6x + 1$
(g) $25y^2 - 40y + 16$
(h) $4y^2 + 20y + 25$
(i) $36x^2 + 12x + 1$
(j) $4s^2 - 28s + 49$

9. Use factoring to simplify these expressions.

(a) 105×95
(b) 93×107
(c) 104^2
(d) 95^2
(e) 999×1001
(f) 999^2
(g) 85×115
(h) 995×1005

Place the numbers from 0 to 8 in the circles to give the indicated sum.

(a)
●●●
●●●
+●●●
666

(b)
●●●
●●●
+●●●
999

3.10 PROBLEM SOLVING: A MODEL FOR MAKING DECISIONS

Mathematics is very useful when you have to make decisions involving numbers such as time, temperature, and money. When making decisions it is best to have an organized plan. The following example illustrates the PACED model for decision making.

PROBLEM

Identify the problem.

The Saltfleet High School Wilderness Club has a total of thirty staff and students — sixteen males and fourteen females. They decide to go white water rafting on the Race River for two days. The train trip to the river costs $125 per person. The bus trip costs $70 per person. If they go by bus they will have to spend two nights at a hotel. If they take the train they will spend one night at a hotel and one night sleeping on the train.

Sandra, who is organizing the trip, has to decide which hotel and which method of travel will provide the lowest cost per club member.

ALTERNATIVES

List the alternatives or choices.

Hotel	Single Room	Double Room	Each Extra Person	Maximum to a room
Canoe	$155	$200	$10	5
River	$180	$220	$15	6
Oar	$200	$230	$15	5
Raft	$220	$250	$ 5	6

CRITERIA

State the restrictions on the alternatives.

Sandra listed the following criteria.

1. Room maximums cannot be exceeded.
2. Males and females cannot share the same room.
3. All club members must stay at the same hotel.
4. The hotels are of equal quality.
5. The club members do not have a choice of travel method.

OWL IMAGES

EVALUATE Evaluate criteria based on the alternatives.

1. Chart for 16 males for one night

Hotel	Maximum to a Room	Number of Rooms	Full-room Cost	Cost for Additionals	Total Cost
Canoe	5	4	3 × 230 = 690	155	$ 845
River	6	3	2 × 280 = 560	250	$ 810
Oar	5	4	3 × 275 = 825	200	$1025
Raft	6	3	2 × 270 = 540	260	$ 800

2. Chart for 14 females for one night

Hotel	Maximum to a Room	Number of Rooms	Full-room Cost	Cost for Additionals	Total Cost
Canoe	5	3	2 × 230 = 460	220	$680
River	6	3	2 × 280 = 560	220	$780
Oar	5	3	2 × 275 = 550	260	$810
Raft	6	3	2 × 270 = 540	250	$790

3. Chart of cost for each hotel for one night

Hotel	Males	Females	Total
Canoe	845	680	1525
River	810	780	1590
Oar	1025	810	1835
Raft	800	790	1590

DECIDE Decide on the best alternative.

Cost for trip including transportation:

Bus: 30 × \$70 + 2 × \$1525
= \$2100 + \$3050
= \$5150

Train: 30 × \$125 + 1 × \$1525
= \$3750 + \$1525
= \$5275

The club members should travel by bus and stay at the Canoe Hotel.

Each club member will pay $\frac{\$5150}{30} \doteq \$171.67$

EXERCISE 3.10

1. The organizers of the class picnic decided to purchase the following items:
   - 5 dozen hamburger patties
   - 5 dozen hamburger rolls
   - 1 large jar of relish
   - 1 large jar of mustard
   - 6 large tomatoes
   - 6 large onions
   - 2 cases of lemonade

The prices at four stores are shown.

	Alf's	Seven Seven	Quick Stop	A-1
Hamburgers	45.70	44.30	46.10	47.00
Rolls	11.50	11.25	10.80	13.00
Relish	3.70	4.10	3.65	3.60
Mustard	3.30	3.75	3.50	3.50
Tomatoes	3.80	4.50	3.30	4.00
Onions	2.10	2.30	2.00	2.45
Lemonade	21.30	22.00	23.00	19.50

(a) What is the total cost if they buy each item at the lowest price?
(b) If the students are willing to buy at a maximum of two stores, where should they buy the items to keep the cost to a minimum?
(c) What other things besides price might be considered before buying?

2. There are 61 males and 73 females in the school marching band. While at the provincial championships the band had to spend one night in a hotel. The championship organizers provided the band leaders with the following hotel information.

Hotel	Single Room	Double Room	Extra Person	Maximum in a Room
Ace	\$160	\$192	\$25	5
Blue	\$140	\$172	\$24	4
Delta	\$152	\$184	\$21	4
Fox	\$164	\$188	\$30	5

The band leaders had to choose one of the hotels, keeping in mind that
(i) hotel quality is assumed to be equal;
(ii) males and females cannot share rooms;
(iii) costs must be kept to a minimum.

(a) What hotel should they choose?
(b) What is the cost per band member if costs are to be shared equally?

3. Kerry Adams is the promotion manager of a baseball team. She has been directed to purchase T-shirts, caps, pennants, and wrist bands to sell at home games. The following table gives a list of cost prices from four suppliers.

	Arco	Dent	Star	Pro
Shirts	20.50	21.20	22.00	20.00
Caps	18.00	17.00	20.50	19.50
Pennants	10.00	9.00	9.50	7.00
Bands	11.00	10.50	9.75	12.00

Kerry is going to buy 10 000 of each item. After visiting each supplier, she determined that the quality is the same.

(a) How much would she pay if she bought each item at the lowest price?

(b) The Dent Supply Company offered her a five percent discount if she bought all four items from Dent.
What are the advantages and disadvantages of such an offer?

(c) What discount would Arco have to give if they were going to beat the price Kerry could get by buying each item at the lowest price?

(d) What is the lowest price Terry could get if she limited the purchases to just two suppliers?

(e) Pro Suppliers buy a lot of season tickets, and Kerry is instructed by the team's Board of Directors to purchase at least two of the items from Pro.
What is her lowest cost under these conditions?

4. You have a van full of camping equipment. You are driving on a six-lane expressway during the day when the van suddenly loses power and rolls to a stop, blocking two lanes of the expressway. There is not much traffic, but the van has stopped at the end of a curve in the expressway.

On the edge of the expressway is a group of trees that blocks the view of your van from oncoming traffic. You are not in danger because you can get out of the van and walk to the side of the road. However, drivers approaching your van in the two right lanes are sure to hit your van.
The van is too heavy for you to push out of the way and there are no flares in the van.
How do you prevent other vehicles from hitting your van?

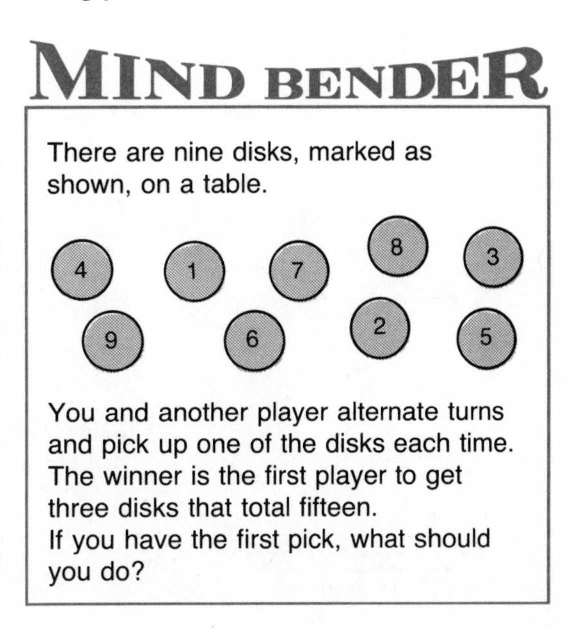

3.11 REVIEW EXERCISE

1. Expand and simplify.

(a) $3(x + 7) - 4(x + 2) + 6$

(b) $(x + 2)(x - 3) + (x + 5)(x - 1)$

(c) $(3 - 2x)(x + 1) + (5x - 2)(x - 1)$

(d) $(x + 3)^2 + (2x - 1)^2$

(e) $(x + 2)(2x - 1) - (3x - 1)(4x + 5)$

(f) $(x - 3)(2x + 5) - (x - 1)^2$

(g) $-(x + 3)5 - 6x(x - 5)$

2. (a) Find an expression for the area of the given figures.

(b) Evaluate for the indicated value of the variable.

(i)

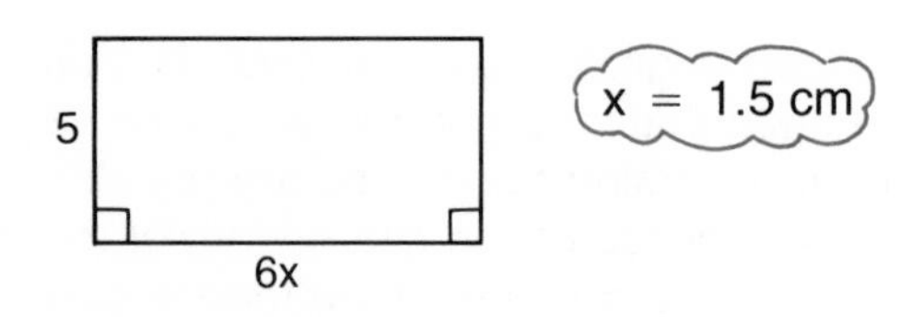

(ii)

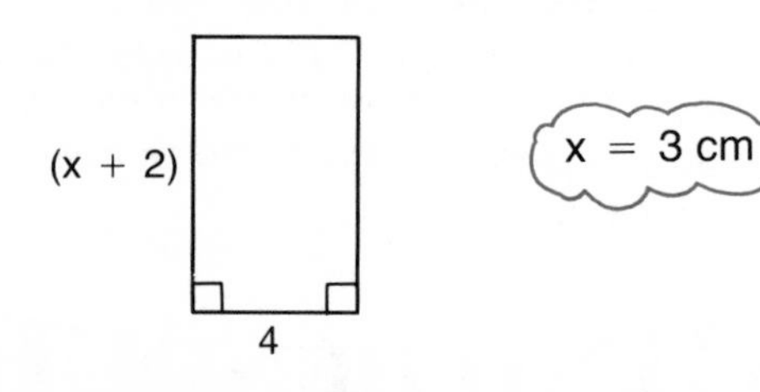

(iii)

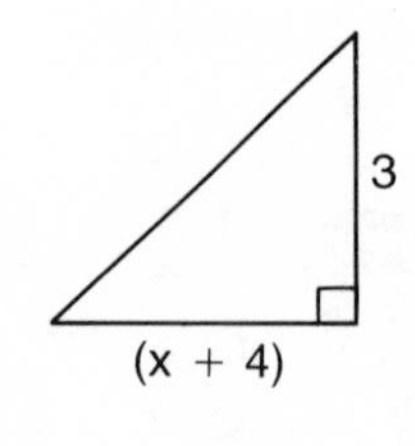

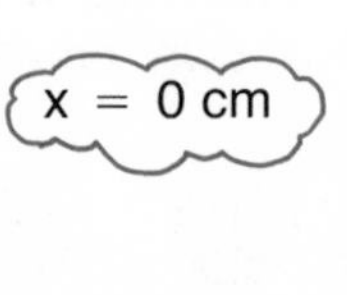

(iv)

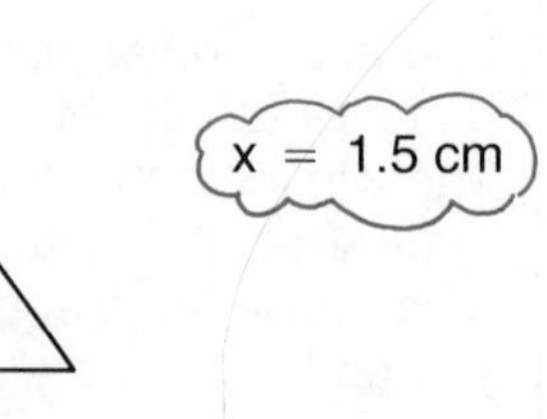

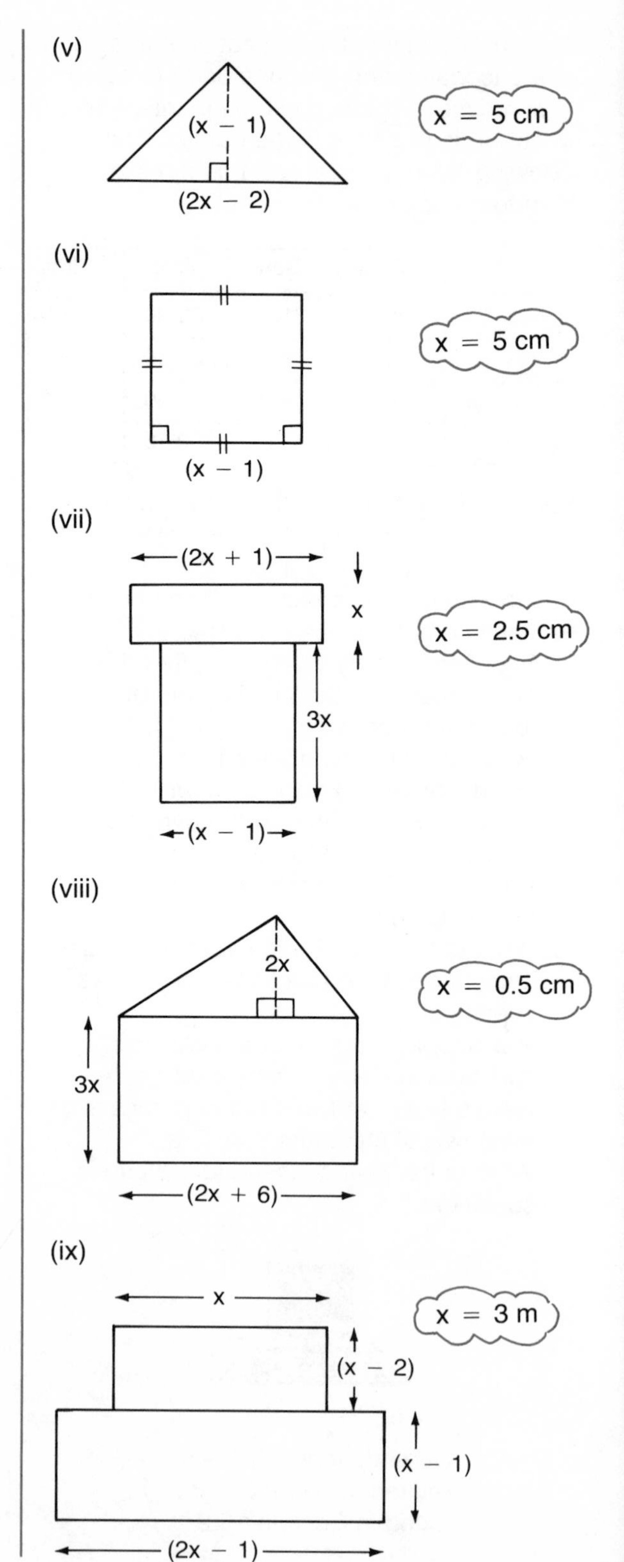

(x)

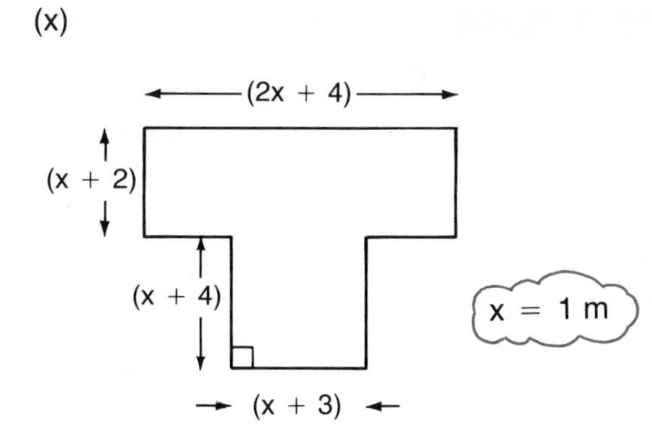

(xi)

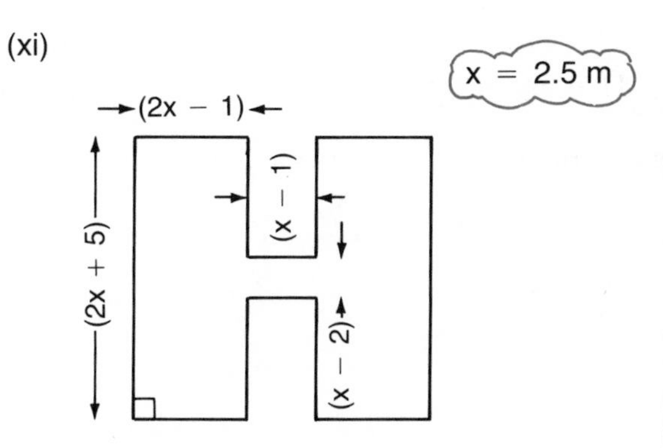

(xii)

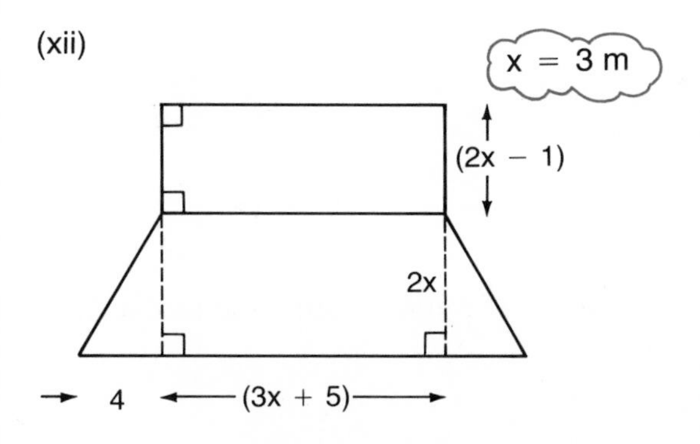

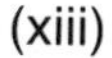

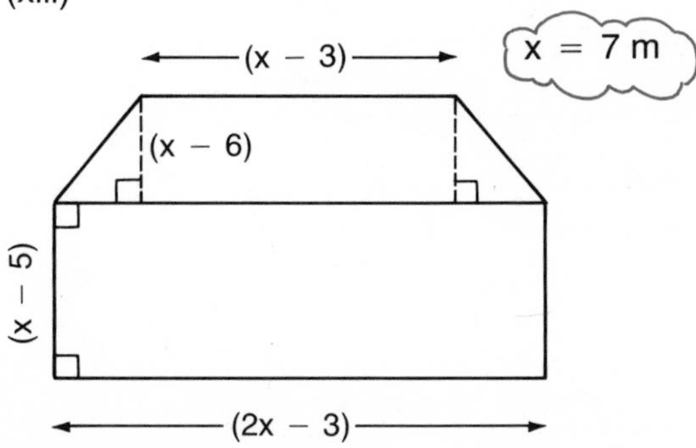

(xiv)

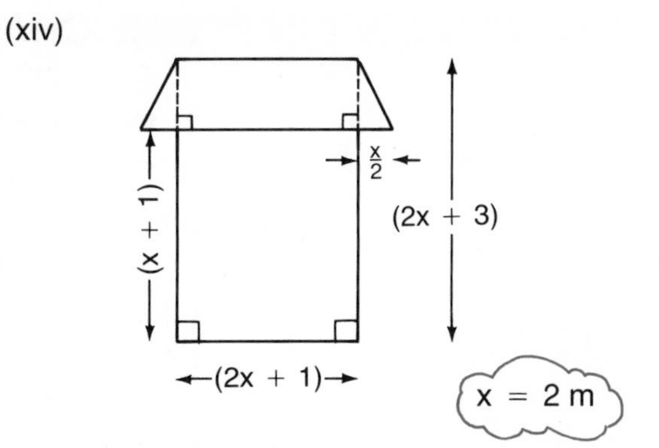

3. Simplify. State any restrictions on the variables.

(a) $\dfrac{16x^2y}{4x}$

(b) $\dfrac{-25x^3y^2}{5xy^2}$

(c) $\dfrac{-36a^2b^5y}{-6ab^4y}$

(d) $\dfrac{6xy - 8x}{2x}$

(e) $\dfrac{4x^2 - 7x}{x}$

(f) $\dfrac{6x^2 - 9x - 12}{3}$

4. Factor each of the following.

(a) $2x + 14$
(b) $x^2 - 7x + 12$
(c) $x^2 + 5x - 36$
(d) $x^2 - 64$
(e) $x^2 - 2x + x - 2$
(f) $6x^2y + 9xy$
(g) $14ab - 21ab$
(h) $y^2 + 7y + 10$
(i) $25x^2 - 1$
(j) $9x^2 - 30x + 25$
(k) $x^2 + 8x + 16$
(l) $5x^2y - 10xy^2$

5. Express each of the following in nested form and evaluate for the indicated value of the variable.

(a) $3x^3 - 2x^2 - 6x + 5;\ x = 4$
(b) $2x^3 - 3x^2 + 10;\ x = 3$
(c) $x^3 + 5x^2 - 4x - 6;\ x = 2$
(d) $x^4 + x^3 - x^2 + 1;\ x = 4$

3.12 CHAPTER 3 TEST

1. Expand and simplify.

(a) $3(x - 2) + 4(5 - x)$

(b) $(x - 2)^2$

(c) $-2(3 - x) + 6(2x - 1)$

(d) $2(x + 3)^2 - 2(x + 5)$

(e) $(3x - 1)4$

(f) $-3(-2x - 1)^2$

(g) $6x(x - 5) - 3(x + 4)$

(h) $(x - 1)(2x + 5) - 4x(x - 6)$

(i) $(3 - 2x)(2x + 1) - (x - 2)(x + 3)$

2. Simplify. State any restrictions on the variables.

(a) $\frac{6x^2 - 9x}{3x}$

(b) $\frac{-40x^2y^5z}{-10x^2y^3}$

3. Factor.

(a) $3x + 12$

(b) $x^2 - 81$

(c) $25x^2 - 16$

(d) $x^2 - 8x + 15$

(e) $10xy - 5xy^2$

(f) $x^2 - 8x + 16$

(g) $x^2 + 11x + 30$

(h) $3x^2 - 6x$

4. Express $4x^3 - x^2 + 2x - 5$ in nested form and evaluate for $x = 3$.

EQUATIONS

4

REVIEW AND PREVIEW TO CHAPTER 4

EXERCISE 1

Complete to make true statements.

1. $\frac{\blacksquare}{4} = \frac{2}{8}$
2. $\frac{4}{\blacksquare} = \frac{2}{8}$
3. $\frac{5}{2} = \frac{15}{\blacksquare}$
4. $\frac{7}{3} = \frac{\blacksquare}{15}$
5. $\frac{\blacksquare}{7} = \frac{12}{14}$
6. $\frac{\blacksquare}{12} = \frac{3}{4}$
7. $\frac{5}{\blacksquare} = \frac{15}{36}$
8. $\frac{5}{\blacksquare} = \frac{15}{12}$
9. $\frac{7}{28} = \frac{\blacksquare}{16}$
10. $\frac{5}{8} = \frac{\blacksquare}{16} = \frac{40}{\blacksquare}$
11. $\frac{3}{7} = \frac{9}{\blacksquare} = \frac{24}{\blacksquare}$
12. $\frac{\blacksquare}{2} = 2 = \frac{14}{\blacksquare}$
13. $2\frac{2}{3} = \frac{8}{\blacksquare} = \frac{\blacksquare}{9}$
14. $\frac{2}{5} = \frac{\blacksquare}{20} = \frac{10}{\blacksquare}$
15. $\frac{\blacksquare}{8} = \frac{21}{24} = \frac{\blacksquare}{40}$
16. $\frac{\blacksquare}{6} = \frac{4}{24} = \frac{\blacksquare}{30}$
17. $3\frac{1}{2} = \frac{\blacksquare}{2} = \frac{\blacksquare}{8}$
18. $\frac{\blacksquare}{20} = \frac{9}{5} = \frac{45}{\blacksquare}$

EXERCISE 2

Expand.

1. $3(x - 2)$
2. $-3(x + 5)$
3. $-2(x - 5)$
4. $-(-3 - x)$
5. $7x(x + 1)$
6. $-2x(1 - x)$
7. $-x(-x + 1)$
8. $5x(x - 2)$
9. $(x - 1)(2x + 4)$
10. $-(x + 4)(x - 5)$
11. $(x + 2)^2$
12. $(x + 2)(x + 3)$
13. $(x - 2)(4x - 3)$
14. $(3x + 1)(4 - 5x)$
15. $-(2x - 3)^2$
16. $-(x - 1)^2$
17. $-(1 - x)^2$
18. $2(x + 1)(x - 3) - 4(x + 5)$
19. $2(x - 4)(x + 3) + 5(2x - 1)$
20. $3(x - 3y)(x - 4y) - (x - 2y)^2$
21. $2(x - 3)(x - 4) - 3(x + 5)^2$
22. $(x - y)(x + y)(x^2 + y^2)$
23. $(x - 2)(x + 2)(x^2 + 4)$
24. $3(x - 1)(x - 2) + (x - 3)^2$

EXERCISE 3

Calculate the area of the following triangles.

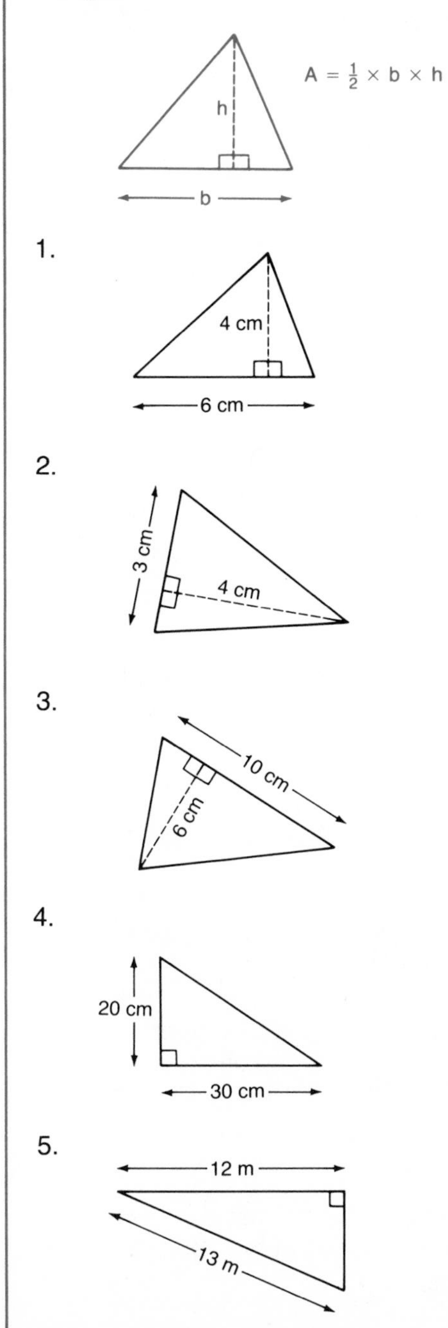

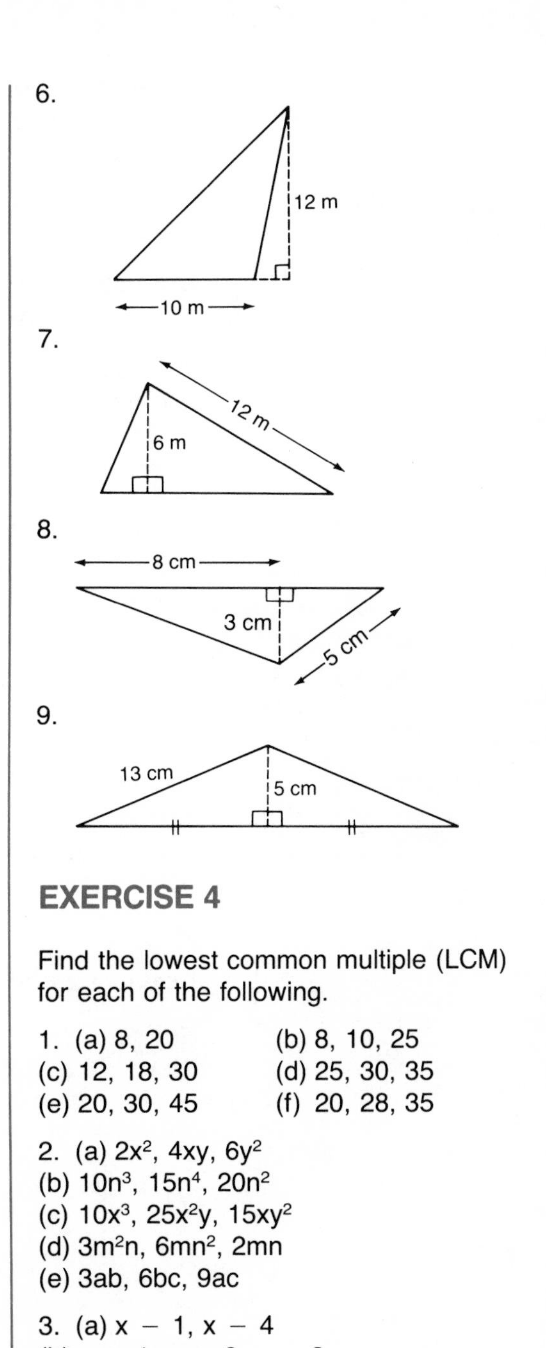

EXERCISE 4

Find the lowest common multiple (LCM) for each of the following.

1. (a) 8, 20 (b) 8, 10, 25
(c) 12, 18, 30 (d) 25, 30, 35
(e) 20, 30, 45 (f) 20, 28, 35

2. (a) $2x^2$, $4xy$, $6y^2$
(b) $10n^3$, $15n^4$, $20n^2$
(c) $10x^3$, $25x^2y$, $15xy^2$
(d) $3m^2n$, $6mn^2$, $2mn$
(e) $3ab$, $6bc$, $9ac$

3. (a) $x - 1$, $x - 4$
(b) $x + 1$, $x + 2$, $x - 3$
(c) $x^2 + 7x + 12$, $x^2 + 9x + 20$
(d) $x^2 + 1$, $x^2 - 1$
(e) $2x - 6$, $6x - 18$

4.1 SOLVING LINEAR EQUATIONS

The skills developed in solving equations are essential to working with formulas, which appear often in business, science, and technology. To solve an equation means to find a value of the variable that makes the statement true. This value is called a root.

Example 1. Solve and check the equation
$2(x - 4) - 3(x + 1) = 5 - 3x$

Solution:

$$\begin{aligned} 2(x - 4) - 3(x + 1) &= 5 - 3x \\ 2x - 8 - 3x - 3 &= 5 - 3x \\ -x - 11 &= 5 - 3x \\ 2x &= 16 \\ x &= 8 \end{aligned}$$

Remove brackets.
Collect like terms.

Check:

$$\begin{aligned} \text{L.S.} &= 2(x - 4) - 3(x + 1) \\ &= 2(8 - 4) - 3(8 + 1) \\ &= 2(4) - 3(9) \\ &= 8 - 27 \\ &= -19 \end{aligned}$$

$$\begin{aligned} \text{R.S.} &= 5 - 3x \\ &= 5 - 3(8) \\ &= 5 - 24 \\ &= -19 \end{aligned}$$

L.S. means "Left Side."
R.S. means "Right Side."

The collection of all solutions to an equation is called the solution set. The equation in Example 1 has {8} as its solution set.

Example 2. Solve. $2(2x - 1) - 3(x - 2) = 3x + 3$

Solution:

$$\begin{aligned} 2(2x - 1) - 3(x - 2) &= 3x + 3 \\ 4x - 2 - 3x + 6 &= 3x + 3 \\ x + 4 &= 3x + 3 \\ -2x &= -1 \\ x &= \tfrac{1}{2} \end{aligned}$$

Isolate all terms containing the variable on one side, all numbers on the other.

$\therefore$ The root is $\frac{1}{2}$.

In solving equations with fractional coefficients we first clear the fractions by multiplying both sides of the equation by the lowest common denominator (LCD).

Example 3. Solve. $\frac{2}{5}x + \frac{x}{2} = 9$

Solution:

$$\frac{2}{5}x + \frac{x}{2} = 9$$
$$10 \times \left[\frac{2}{5}x + \frac{x}{2}\right] = 10 \times [9]$$
$$4x + 5x = 90$$
$$9x = 90$$
$$x = 10$$

The LCD of 5 and 2 is 10.

$\therefore$ 10 is a root of the equation.

Example 4. Solve and check. $\frac{x + 3}{5} - \frac{x - 1}{4} = 1$

Solution:

$$\frac{x + 3}{5} - \frac{x - 1}{4} = 1$$
$$20\left(\frac{x + 3}{5} - \frac{x - 1}{4}\right) = 20 \times 1$$
$$4(x + 3) - 5(x - 1) = 20$$
$$4x + 12 - 5x + 5 = 20$$
$$-x + 17 = 20$$
$$-x = 3$$
$$x = -3$$

The LCD of 5 and 4 is 20.

Check:

$$\text{L.S.} = \frac{-3 + 3}{5} - \frac{-3 - 1}{4} = \frac{0}{5} - \frac{-4}{4} = 1$$

R.S. = 1

$\therefore$The root is -3.

EXERCISE 4.1

A

1. Solve the following equations.

(a) $x - 7 = 10$ (b) $a + 3 = 13$
(c) $m - 4 = 12$ (d) $a - 2 = -8$
(e) $b + 1 = -11$ (f) $2 + x = -6$
(g) $3x = 15$ (h) $2x = 40$
(i) $5a = -20$ (j) $-3a = -9$
(k) $-4m = 16$ (l) $3b = 0$

2. (a) $2x + 1 = 7$ (b) $4b - 2 = 10$
(c) $3a - 3 = 0$ (d) $2 + 5m = 22$
(e) $7 = 1 + 2x$ (f) $2x = x + 3$
(g) $7r + 5 = 6r + 6$ (h) $2m + 3 = 3$

3. Determine if the given value is a root of the equation.

(a) $2x + 1 = 7$; 3
(b) $3x - 2 = 10$; 5
(c) $1 + 3x = 10$; 3
(d) $4m - 1 = 15$; 4
(e) $3y + 2 = 4y$; 1
(f) $-2a = -4$; -1
(g) $3b + 2 = b$; -1
(h) $3x + 2 = 2x + 5$; 4
(i) $2x - 7 = x + 1$; 4

B

4. Solve and check.

(a) $4x - 7 = 2x + 3$
(b) $10y - 6 = 4y + 6$
(c) $3x + 2 - 5x = -x + 3$
(d) $4a - 3 = 6a - 11$
(e) $2 + 3y - 4 = -5y + 6$
(f) $3a + 6 - 7a = 12 - 8a + 2$
(g) $x + 5 = 20 - 4x$
(h) $11x + 2 = 26 + 7x$
(i) $-4c + 4 + 2c = 3c - 16$
(j) $3 - 6b + 6 = 2b - 7$

5. (a) $5a + 3(8 - a) = 36$
(b) $2k - 5 - (k - 3) = 7$
(c) $6x + 1 - 3 = 12x - (8x - 4)$
(d) $y - 5 = 8 - (2y + 4)$
(e) $5(3x - 4) = -14 - 3(x - 10)$
(f) $6(x + 1) - 3 = 12x - 4(2x - 1)$
(g) $6x - 4(5x + 9) = 4(2x - 9)$
(h) $5m - (3m - 7) + (2m - 3) = 12$
(i) $2(x - 3) + 3(x + 2) = 10$
(j) $4(2x - 1) - 3(2x + 2) = 0$

6. (a) $5(3x - 1) + 12 = 4(2x + 3) + 9$
(b) $3(2a - 5) - 7(a + 1) = 2(a + 1)$
(c) $3(2x - 4) - (x - 3) = 7(x + 2) - 1$
(d) $3(m - 7) - 5(m + 2) = -41$
(e) $-2(2m - 3) + 5(m + 7) = 40$
(f) $2(x^2 - 3x + 1) = 2(x^2 + x - 4) - 6$
(g) $2(a^2 + 3a + 2) - (2a^2 + 3a) = -2$
(h) $12 = 2(x - 1) + 4(x + 2)$

7. Solve for x, correct to three significant figures.

(a) $1.2x + 0.3 = 1.74$
(b) $6.3a + 7.4 = 2.1a$
(c) $12x + 0.3 = 5x + 8.1$
(d) $3b + 0.7 + 0.2b = 14.1$
(e) $11.3 + 0.7a = 9.1$
(f) $9.8m + 6 = 7.2m - 6.3$

8. Solve for x.

(a) $x + b = 7$
(b) $x - m = t$
(c) $ax = m$
(d) $-2x = a$
(e) $bx + t = m$
(f) $ax - m = t$
(g) $x - d = -t$
(h) $2bx - 3 = a$

Solve the following equations.

9. (a) $\frac{x}{3} = 10$
(b) $\frac{1}{2}m = 4$
(c) $\frac{x}{5} = -6$
(d) $\frac{x}{2} = \frac{4}{3}$
(e) $\frac{2b}{3} = 6$
(f) $\frac{m + 1}{3} = 5$

10. (a) $\frac{x}{2} + \frac{x}{3} = 10$
(b) $\frac{x}{3} - \frac{1}{2} = \frac{1}{4}$
(c) $\frac{x}{4} - \frac{1}{5} = \frac{x}{2}$
(d) $\frac{3x}{5} + 1 = \frac{x}{4}$
(e) $\frac{b}{4} - \frac{b}{6} = 3$
(f) $\frac{2a}{3} - \frac{3a}{5} = \frac{1}{2}$
(g) $\frac{5y}{4} - 2y = 1\frac{1}{3}$
(h) $2m - \frac{1}{2} = \frac{m}{7} + \frac{m}{2}$

11. (a) $\frac{x + 5}{2} + \frac{3x - 3}{8} = -4$
(b) $\frac{x + 2}{2} - \frac{x}{3} = 2$
(c) $\frac{2x + 1}{3} = 6$
(d) $\frac{a - 1}{3} = \frac{a}{6}$
(e) $\frac{m - 1}{4} = \frac{3m - 1}{6}$

12. (a) $\frac{x}{2} - \frac{x + 1}{3} = 6$
(b) $\frac{m - 2}{3} - \frac{m + 1}{2} = 4$
(c) $\frac{1}{2}(x + 3) - \frac{3x + 1}{4} = 2$
(d) $\frac{1}{3}(2x - 1) - \frac{1}{5}(4x - 6) = \frac{7}{15}$
(e) $\frac{x + 1}{2} - \frac{x - 2}{3} + \frac{x + 4}{4} = 3$

4.2 SOLVING EQUATIONS INVOLVING POLYNOMIALS

In this section the rules for simplifying polynomials, and the rules for solving equations, are used to solve equations containing polynomials.

Example. Solve and check.

$2(a - 3)(a + 2) - 15 = (2a - 1)(a + 2)$

Solution:

$$\begin{aligned}
2(a - 3)(a + 2) - 15 &= (2a - 1)(a + 2) \\
2(a^2 + 2a - 3a - 6) - 15 &= (2a^2 + 4a - a - 2) \\
2(a^2 - a - 6) - 15 &= (2a^2 + 3a - 2) \\
2a^2 - 2a - 12 - 15 &= 2a^2 + 3a - 2 \\
2a^2 - 2a - 27 &= 2a^2 + 3a - 2 \\
-2a - 3a &= -2 + 27 \\
-5a &= 25 \\
a &= -5
\end{aligned}$$

Check:

$$\begin{aligned}
\text{L.S.} &= 2(a - 3)(a + 2) - 15 \\
&= 2(-5 - 3)(-5 + 2) - 15 \\
&= 2(-8)(-3) - 15 \\
&= 48 - 15 \\
&= 33 \\
\text{R.S.} &= (2a - 1)(a + 2) \\
&= (-10 - 1)(-5 + 2) \\
&= (-11)(-3) \\
&= 33
\end{aligned}$$

$\therefore$ -5 is a root of the equation.

EXERCISE 4.2

B

Solve and check the following.

1. (a) $(k + 1)(k + 2) = k^2 - 9k + 26$
(b) $(x - 1)(x + 2) = x^2 - 5x + 6$
(c) $(m + 4)^2 = m(m + 6)$
(d) $(a - 3)(a + 4) - (a + 2)(a + 1) = -16$
(e) $(2y - 3)(y - 1) - 2(y + 2)(y + 3) = 6$
(f) $(2x - 3)(x - 2) - 2(x + 1)(x + 4) = 16$
(g) $(x + 3)(x - 2) + x^2 = 2x^2$
(h) $(x + 4)^2 - (x - 2)^2 = 0$
(i) $(x + 7)(x - 1) - (x + 3)^2 = x$

2. (a) $2(2x - 3) + (x - 4)(2x + 1) = 2x^2 - 1$
(b) $4x^2 - (2x - 1)(2x + 1) = x$
(c) $(a + 1)(a + 2) = (a - 1)(a - 3) + 6$
(d) $(x - 5)(x - 2) = (x + 1)(x - 4)$
(e) $(x + 3)^2 = 2x(x + 1) - (x - 1)^2$
(f) $(m - 5)^2 + 3(m + 2)^2 = 4(m^2 - 1) - 7$

3. (a) $3(c - 1)^2 - 3(c^2 - 1) = c - 15$
(b) $5(x + 1)^2 + 7(x + 3)^2 = 12(x + 2)^2$
(c) $3(s - 1)(s + 2) - 2(s - 4)^2 = s^2 + 19$

4.3 FORMULA SOLVING AND SUBSTITUTION

Formulas have many important uses in technology, science, and business. Formulas are equations with symbols that may be replaced by specific values for a particular problem.

Since formulas are equations, we may make use of the techniques previously learned.

Example 1. The formula for the perimeter of a rectangle is given by

$P = 2(\ell + w)$

where ℓ is the length and w is the width.

Find the width of a rectangle with a perimeter of 50 cm and a length of 18 cm.

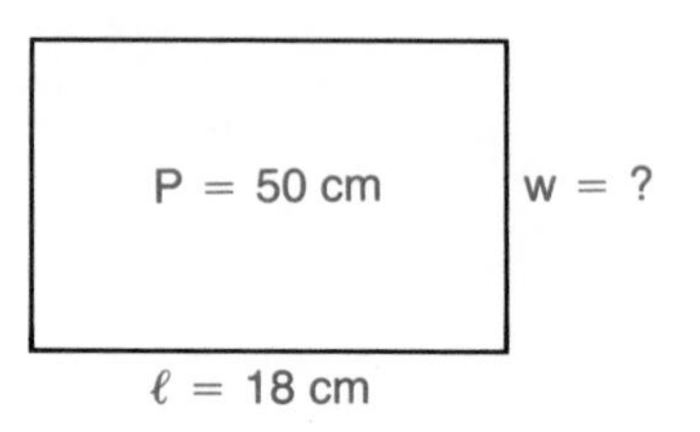

Solution:

METHOD I

Substitute the known values of P and ℓ into the formula. Then find w.

$$P = 2(\ell + w)$$
$$50 = 2(18 + w)$$
$$50 = 36 + 2w$$
$$50 - 36 = 2w$$
$$\frac{14}{2} = w$$
$$7 = w$$

METHOD II

Solve the formula for w. Then substitute the values of P and ℓ.

$$P = 2(\ell + w)$$
$$\frac{P}{2} = \ell + w$$
$$w = \frac{P}{2} - \ell$$

Substitute $P = 50$, $\ell = 18$

$$w = \frac{P}{2} - \ell$$
$$w = \frac{50}{2} - 18$$
$$= 25 - 18$$
$$= 7$$

The width of the rectangle is 7 cm.

Example 2. The cost of renting a hot air balloon is given by the formula

$$C = 85 + 36h$$

where C is the cost in dollars and h is the number of hours. If the cost was \$409, for how long was the balloon rented?

Solution:

METHOD I

Substitute first.

$$C = 85 + 36h$$
$$409 = 85 + 36h$$
$$409 - 85 = 36h$$
$$324 = 36h$$
$$9 = h$$

METHOD II

Solve for h first.

$$C = 85 + 36h$$
$$C - 85 = 36h$$
$$\frac{C - 85}{36} = h$$
$$\text{or } h = \frac{C - 85}{36}$$

Substitute C = 409

$$h = \frac{409 - 85}{36}$$
$$= \frac{324}{36}$$
$$= 9$$

The balloon was rented for 9 h.

Example 3. Ohm's law states $E = IR$

where E is the voltage (measured in volts)
I is the current (measured in amperes)
R is the resistance (measured in ohms)
Find I if E = 320 V and R = 5.0 Ω.

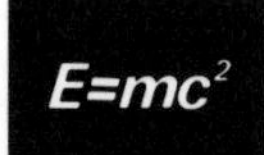

Solution:

METHOD I

Substitute first.

$$E = IR$$
$$320 = I(5)$$
$$5.0I = 320$$
$$I = \frac{320}{5}$$
$$I = 64$$

METHOD II

Solve the formula for I first.

$$E = IR$$
$$\frac{E}{R} = I \quad \text{or} \quad I = \frac{E}{R}$$

Substitute E = 320, R = 5.0.

$$I = \frac{E}{R}$$
$$I = \frac{320}{5.0}$$
$$= 64$$

The current is 64 A.

Example 4. The town of Addison has a spherical water tower that has a volume of 900 m^3. Calculate to the nearest tenth of a metre the radius of the sphere. (The formula for the volume of a sphere is $V = \frac{4}{3}\pi r^3$.)

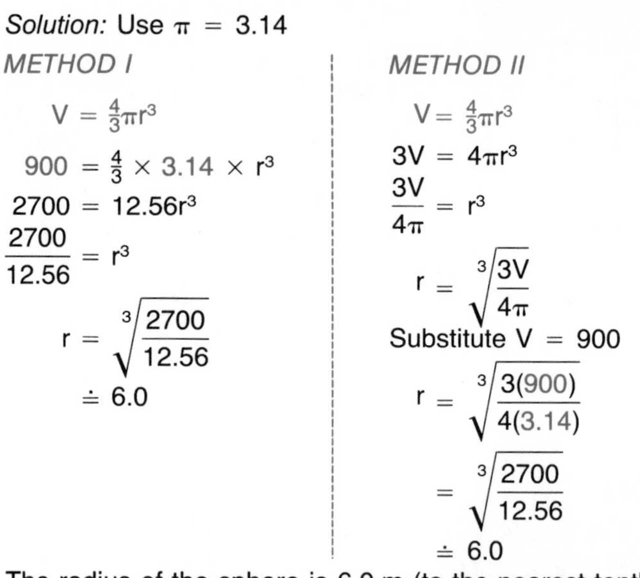

Solution: Use $\pi = 3.14$

METHOD I

$$V = \frac{4}{3}\pi r^3$$
$$900 = \frac{4}{3} \times 3.14 \times r^3$$
$$2700 = 12.56r^3$$
$$\frac{2700}{12.56} = r^3$$
$$r = \sqrt[3]{\frac{2700}{12.56}}$$
$$\doteq 6.0$$

METHOD II

$$V = \frac{4}{3}\pi r^3$$
$$3V = 4\pi r^3$$
$$\frac{3V}{4\pi} = r^3$$
$$r = \sqrt[3]{\frac{3V}{4\pi}}$$

Substitute $V = 900$

$$r = \sqrt[3]{\frac{3(900)}{4(3.14)}}$$
$$= \sqrt[3]{\frac{2700}{12.56}}$$
$$\doteq 6.0$$

The radius of the sphere is 6.0 m (to the nearest tenth).

Using a calculator, press

C 2 7 0 0 ÷ 1 2 · 5 6 = y^x · 3 3 3 =

The display is 5.97972

EXERCISE 4.3

B

1. The formula for the volume of a rectangular solid is given by $V = \ell wh$ where

V is the volume,
ℓ is the length,
w is the width,
and h is the height.

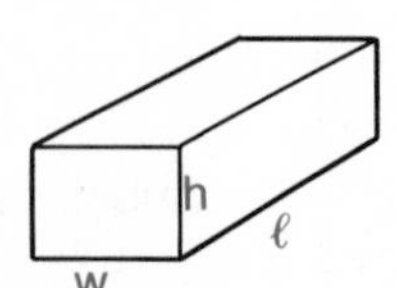

(a) Find the volume of a tractor trailer with $\ell = 8.0$ m, $w = 2.5$ m, and $h = 3.0$ m.
(b) Find the length when $w = 2.6$ m, $h = 3.5$ m, and $V = 91$ m^3.

2. The formula for the area of a triangle is given by $A = \frac{1}{2}bh$

where b is the length of the base and h is the height.

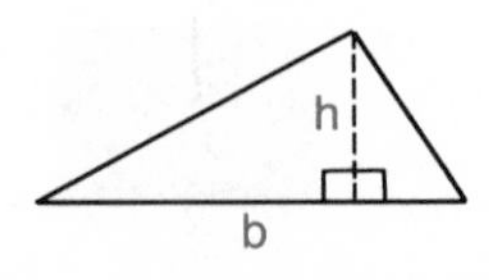

(a) Find the area of a sail with $b = 7.0$ m and $h = 8.5$ m.
(b) Find the height when $b = 10$ m and $A = 67.5$ m^2.

3. The formula for the perimeter of a rectangle is given by $P = 2(\ell + w)$ where
P is the perimeter,
ℓ is the length,
and w is the width.

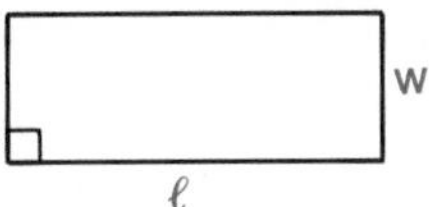

(a) To determine how much fencing is required, find the perimeter of a rectangular field with $\ell = 40.0$ m and $w = 25.0$ m
(b) Find the length of a rectangular field when $w = 35$ m and $P = 205$ m.

4. The formula for the area of a trapezoid is given by $A = \frac{h}{2}(a + b)$ where

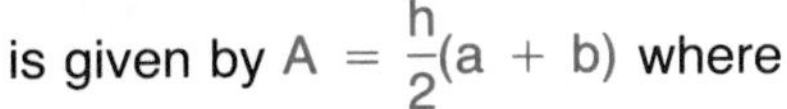

A is the area,
h is the height, and
a and b are the lengths of the parallel sides.

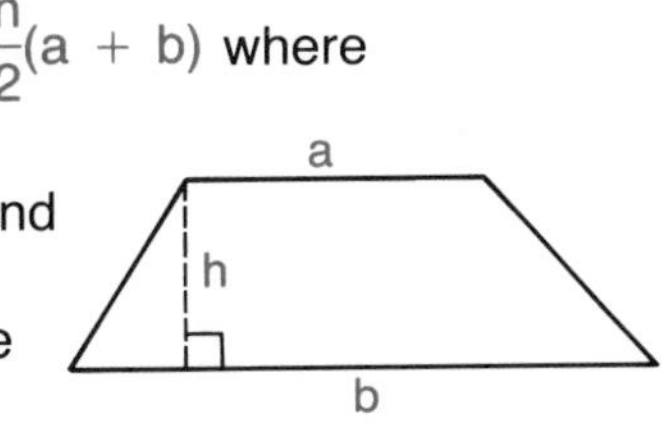

(a) Find the area of a trapezoid with $a = 3.5$ cm, $b = 5.5$ cm, and $h = 4.0$ cm.
(b) Find the length of the base when $a = 45$ cm, $h = 15$ cm, and $A = 750\ \text{cm}^2$.

5. The formula for the area of a circle is given by $A = \pi r^2$ where A is the area and r is the radius.

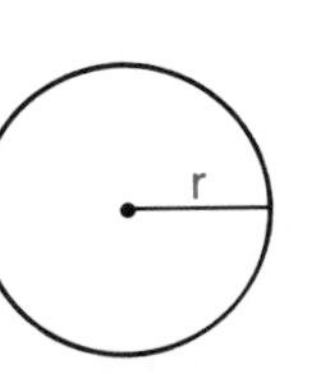

(a) Oil is spreading on the surface of the ocean from an oil tanker leak. The pattern formed by this leak is circular. Find the area of the spill if the radius is 150 m.
(b) Find the radius of a spill with an area four times as large as the area of the spill in part (a).

6. The formula for the circumference of a circle is given by $C = \pi d$ where C is the circumference and d is the diameter.
(a) Find the circumference of a bicycle wheel with a diameter of 60.0 cm.
(b) Find the radius of a wheel when the circumference is 220 cm.

7. The formula for the volume of a cylinder is given by $V = \pi r^2 h$ where
V is the volume,
r is the radius,
and h is the height.

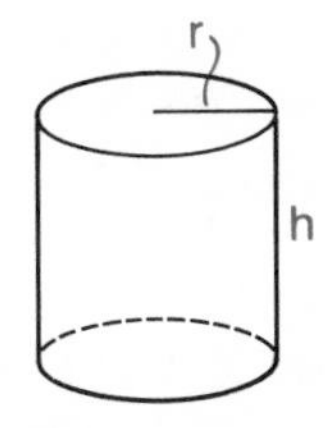

(a) Find the volume of a cylindrical waste can with radius 45 cm and height 66 cm.
(b) Find the radius when $h = 90$ cm and $V = 0.50\ \text{m}^3$.

$1\ \text{m}^3 = 10^6\ \text{cm}^3$

8. The formula for the volume of a cone is given by $V = \frac{\pi}{3}r^2 h$ where
V is the volume,
r is the radius,
and h is the height.

(a) What volume of ice cream will fill a cone with $r = 2.5$ cm and $h = 10$ cm?
(b) Find the height when $r = 10$ cm and $V = 1256\ \text{cm}^3$.

9. The area of the shaded figure is given by the formula $A = \frac{11(h - 40)}{2}$ where A is the area in square metres and h is the height in metres.
(a) Find the area when $h = 70.0$ m.
(b) Find the height when the area is $160\ \text{m}^2$.

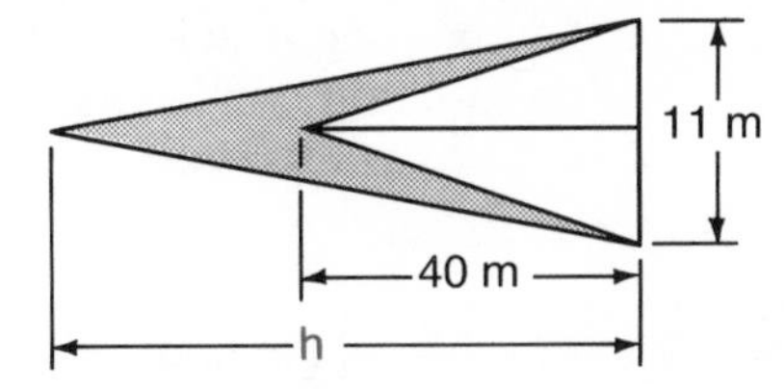

10. The formula for simple interest is given by $I = Prt$ where I is the interest, P is the principal, r is the interest rate, and t is the length of time.
(a) Find the simple interest that will be charged on a loan of \$4000 at 12% for 2 a.
(b) A deposit of \$230 earned \$39.10 interest in 2 a. Find the rate of interest.

11. The cost of removing a pollutant from waste water is given by the formula $C = \frac{15x}{100 - x}$ where C is the cost in thousands of dollars, and x is the percentage of the pollutant removed.

(a) Determine the cost of removing the following amounts of pollutant: 25%, 50%, 75%, 95%.

(b) What percentage of pollutant can be removed for $100 000?

(c) According to this formula, is it possible to remove all of the pollutant?

12. Solve each of the following formulas for the variable indicated.

(a) $p = 4t$, for t

(b) $d = vt$, for v

(c) $pv = Rt$, for R

(d) $S = \frac{n}{2}(a + \ell)$, for a

(e) $A = p + prt$, for r

(f) $V = \ell wh$, for w

(g) $V = IR$, for I

(h) $P = 2(\ell + w)$, for ℓ

(i) $s = ut + \frac{1}{2}at^2$, for a

EXTRA

The formula for the volume of a segment of a sphere is

$$V = \pi h^2\left(r - \frac{h}{3}\right)$$

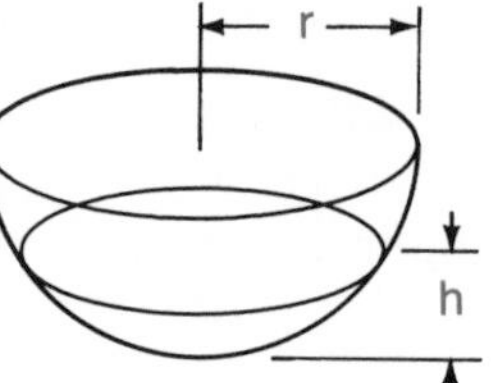

where
V is the volume,
r is the radius of the sphere, and
h is the height of the segment.

Example. Find the volume of milk in a hemispherical bowl of radius 21 cm if the milk is 5 cm deep at the centre. Express the answer in litres.

Solution:
The volume of the milk in cubic centimetres is given by the formula, with $r = 21$ and $h = 5$.

Use $\pi = 3.14$

$$V = \pi h^2\left(r - \frac{h}{3}\right)$$

$$V = (3.14)5^2(21 - \tfrac{5}{3})$$

$$= (3.14)25(\tfrac{58}{3})$$

$= 1518$ to the nearest one.
The volume is 1518 cm^3.

To express this answer in litres we may use the Rule of Three.

$1000\ cm^3 = 1\ L$
$1\ cm^3 = 0.001\ L$
$1518\ cm^3 = 1.518\ L$

There are 1.5 L of milk in the bowl (to the nearest tenth).

EXERCISE

1. Find the volume of water in a hemispherical tank of radius 7.4 m if the water is 1.8 m deep at the centre. Express your answer in litres.

$1\ m^3 = 1000\ L$

2. If water begins leaking out of the bottom of the tank at a rate of 5 L/min, how long will it be before the tank is empty?
Express your answer in days, hours, and minutes.

3. Rework questions 1 and 2 if the water is 2 m deep at the centre.

4.4 SOLVING EQUATIONS BY FACTORING

Equations such as $x^2 + 5x + 6$ are called quadratic equations. Many quadratic equations can be solved by factoring. A solution depends on the following fact.

> If $a \times b = 0$, then either $a = 0$, or $b = 0$, or both a and b equal zero.

Example 1. Solve. $x(x - 2) = 0$

Solution: Since the product of the two factors is zero, one or both factors must be zero.

$x(x - 2) = 0$

$x = 0$ or $x - 2 = 0$

$x = 2$

Check:

$x = 0$	$x = 2$
L.S. $= x(x - 2)$	L.S. $= x(x - 2)$
$= 0(0 - 2)$	$= 2(2 - 2)$
$= 0$	$= 0$
R.S. $= 0$	R.S. $= 0$

The roots are 0 and 2.

Example 2. Solve. $(x - 3)(x + 5) = 0$

Solution: $(x - 3)(x + 5) = 0$

Then either

$x - 3 = 0$ or $x + 5 = 0$

$x = 3$ $\quad$ $x = -5$

The roots of the equation are 3 and -5.

Example 3. Solve. $x^2 - x - 6 = 0$

Solution: First factor the left side of the equation.

$s + r = -1$
$rs = -6$
$s = -3, r = 2$

$x^2 - x - 6 = 0$

$(x - 3)(x + 2) = 0$

Then either

$x - 3 = 0$ or $x + 2 = 0$

$x = 3$ $\quad$ $x = -2$

Check:

$x = 3$	$x = -2$
L.S. $= x^2 - x - 6$	L.S. $= x^2 - x - 6$
$= 3^2 - 3 - 6$	$= (-2)^2 - (-2) - 6$
$= 9 - 3 - 6$	$= 4 + 2 - 6$
$= 0$	$= 0$
R.S. $= 0$	R.S. $= 0$

The roots are 3 and -2.

READ

Example 4. A painting is 90 cm by 120 cm. The painting is to be surrounded by a border with an area equal to 7200 cm², and then framed. Find the width of the border.

PLAN

Solution:
Make a diagram.

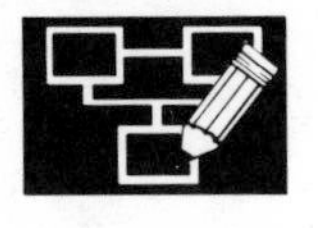

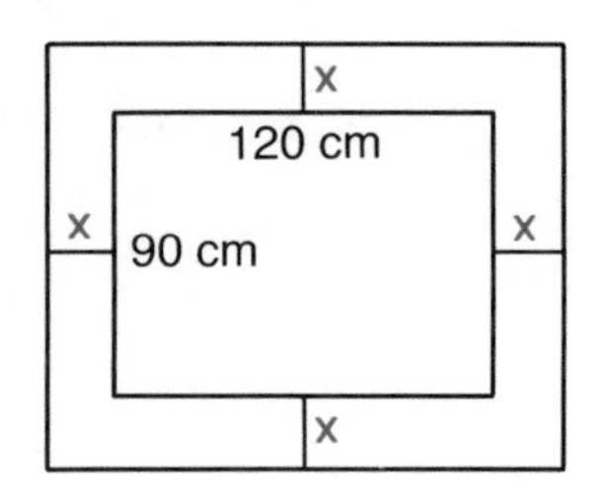

Let the width of the border be x cm.
Then the dimensions of the painting and border are
$90 + 2x$ cm by $120 + 2x$ cm.
The area of the painting and border is
$(120 + 2x)(90 + 2x)$ in terms of x
$(120 \times 90) + 7200$ in numbers

SOLVE

E=mc²

Since these quantities are equal, the equation is

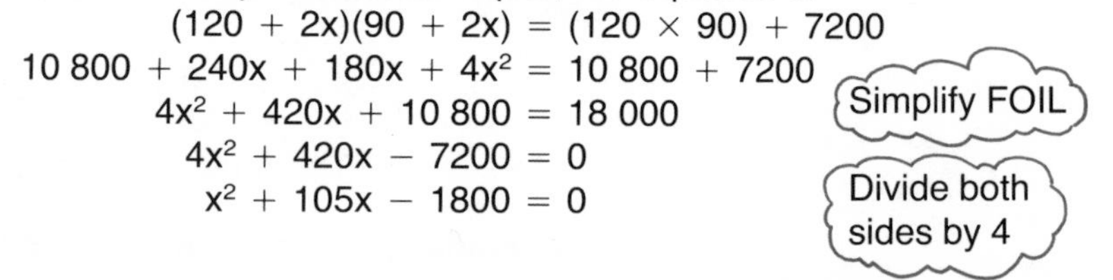

$$(120 + 2x)(90 + 2x) = (120 \times 90) + 7200$$
$$10\,800 + 240x + 180x + 4x^2 = 10\,800 + 7200$$
$$4x^2 + 420x + 10\,800 = 18\,000$$
$$4x^2 + 420x - 7200 = 0$$
$$x^2 + 105x - 1800 = 0$$

Simplify FOIL

Divide both sides by 4

In order to factor the left side of the equation, we need two numbers, m and n, such that $s + r = 105$ and $rs = -1800$.
The numbers are 120 and -15.

$$(x + 120)(x - 15) = 0$$
$$x + 120 = 0 \quad \text{or} \quad x - 15 = 0$$
$$x = -120 \qquad x = 15$$

We reject the value -120

ANSWER

The width of the border is 15 cm.

Check:
Area of painting and border:
$(120 + 30)(90 + 30) = 18\,000$ cm²
Area of painting: $120 \times 90 = 10\,800$ cm²
Area of border (by subtraction): 7200 cm²

EXERCISE 4.4

A

1. What are the roots of each equation?
(a) $x(x - 5) = 0$
(b) $x(x + 7) = 0$
(c) $x(x + 4) = 0$
(d) $5x(x - 6) = 0$

2. State the roots of the following quadratic equations.
(a) $(x + 6)(x - 1) = 0$
(b) $(x - 2)(x - 7) = 0$
(c) $(x + 5)(x - 4) = 0$
(d) $(y - 7)(y + 9) = 0$
(e) $(w - 11)(w - 8) = 0$
(f) $(t + 3)(t - 6) = 0$
(g) $(3x - 1)(3x + 5) = 0$
(h) $(4w - 3)(w - 5) = 0$
(i) $(2t + 5)(3t + 1) = 0$
(j) $(9w + 11)(3w + 14) = 0$

B

3. Solve by factoring.
(a) $x^2 - 7x = 0$
(b) $x^2 + 3x = 0$
(c) $x^2 - 4 = 0$
(d) $x^2 - 25 = 0$
(e) $x^2 - x - 12 = 0$
(f) $x^2 + 9x + 18 = 0$
(g) $x^2 - x - 20 = 0$
(h) $x^2 + 8x + 16 = 0$
(i) $x^2 - 4x - 77 = 0$
(j) $x^2 + 2x + 1 = 0$
(k) $x^2 + 3x - 40 = 0$
(l) $x^2 - 8x + 16 = 0$
(m) $x^2 + 8x - 65 = 0$

4. Transform each equation so that one side is zero. Solve by factoring.
(a) $3x^2 - 12x = 36$
(b) $4w^2 + 28w = 72$
(c) $x^2 + 12 = 8x$
(d) $t^2 + 16 = 8t$
(e) $y^2 + y = 56$
(f) $x^2 - 4 = 2 - 5x$
(g) $2x^2 + 21 = 20x - 21$

5. Solve.
(a) $2x(x - 2) = x(x + 3) - 6$
(b) $(t + 5)(t - 1) = 19 - t$
(c) $(x - 4)(x + 2) = 3(x + 2) - 2(x - 7)$
(d) $(x - 5)^2 = x - 5$

6. A rectangular garden plot is to be increased by x metres in each direction. Find the new dimensions of the garden if the area is to be 88 m^2.

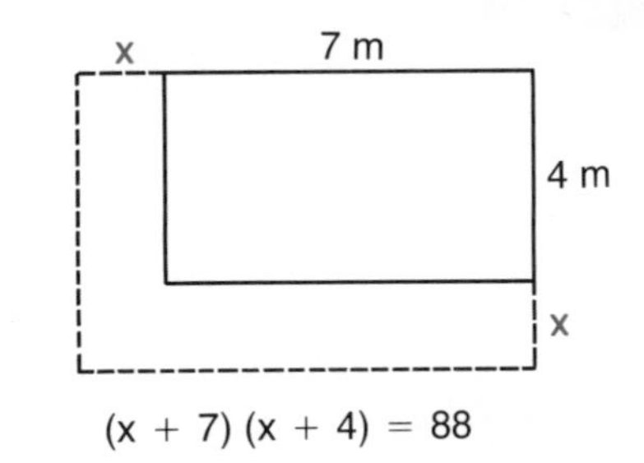

$(x + 7)(x + 4) = 88$

C

7. The sum of the squares of two consecutive integers is 113. What are these integers?

8. Find the dimensions of a rectangle if the diagonal is 2 more than the longer side, which in turn is 2 more than the shorter side.

A fire fighter can climb a ladder by going up 1 rung, or up 2 rungs, at a time. There is only one way to reach the first rung. There are two ways to reach the second rung.

$1 + 1$ or 2 at once

There are three ways to reach the third rung.

$1 + 1 + 1$ or $2 + 1$ or $1 + 2$

(a) In how many different ways can the fire fighter reach the fifth rung?
(b) Look for a pattern and determine how many ways the fire fighter can reach the fifteenth rung.

4.5 PROBLEM SOLVING

READ

PLAN

Example. A rectangular room has a tiled floor. There are 126 tiles around the outer edge of the room. It took 900 tiles to cover the entire floor.
Find the dimensions of the room in terms of tiles.

Solution:
Make a diagram.

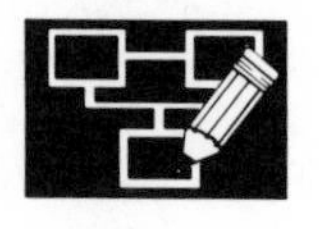

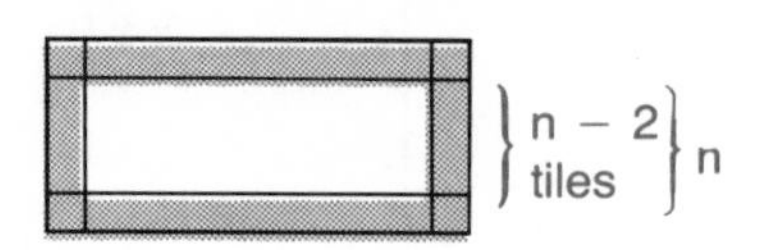

There are 126 tiles around the outer edge.
The perimeter is
$126 + 4 = 130$
The semi-perimeter is 65.
We need two numbers whose sum is 65 and whose product is 900.

SOLVE

Semi-perimeter = 65

Length and Width	Area
10×55	550
15×50	750
20×45	900
25×40	1000
30×35	1050

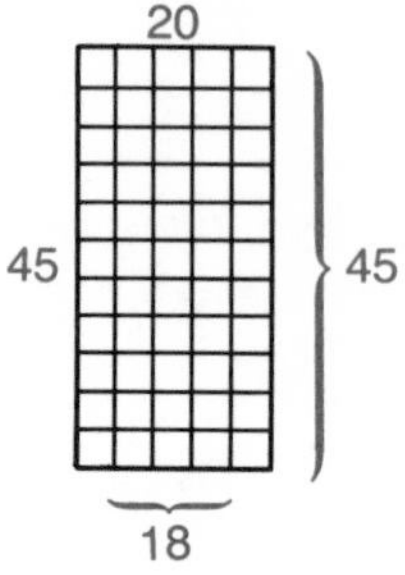

ANSWER

The dimensions are 20 tiles by 45 tiles.

Check:
Total number of tiles: $45 \times 20 = 900$
Tiles on outer edge: $45 + 45 + 18 + 18 = 126$

EXERCISE

1. A sheet of paper is folded in half, and then folded in half again until 5 folds have been made.
How many thicknesses are there in the folded paper?

2. The gasoline tank on a car is one-third full. After 10 L of gasoline are added, the tank is one-half full.
What is the capacity of the tank?

3. Paul, Simon, Margaret, Lotus, Lidwin, and Peter try out for the three parts in a play. Boys and girls have equal opportunities to win one of the parts.
How many different ways can the cast for these parts be chosen?

4. At 12:00, the minute hand on a clock crosses over the hour hand.
How many times will the hands on a clock cross between 1:00 and 11:00?

5. Each digit on a calculator is made up of a combination of up to seven lines.

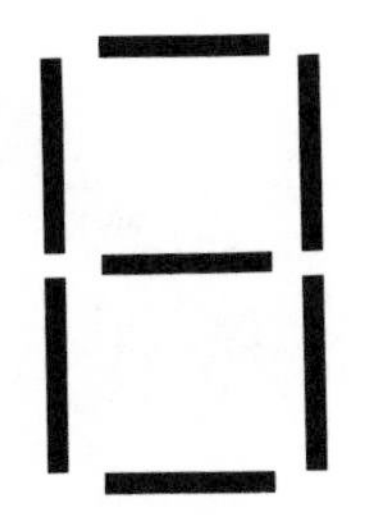

What is the total number of lines used to form the following digits?
1, 2, 3, 4, 5, 6, 7, 8, 9

6. A bar of soap is 2.8 cm thick. After 8 showers, the bar of soap is only 1.6 cm thick.
How many millimetres in thickness of soap are used in one shower?

7. Five identical squares are placed side by side to form a rectangle.

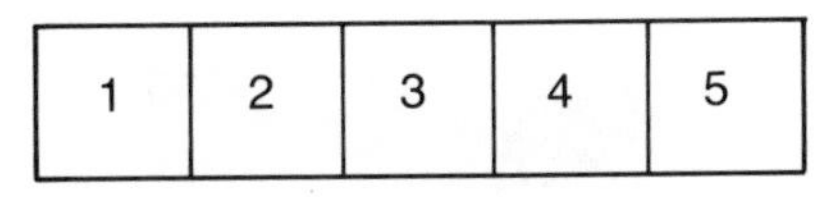

The perimeter of the rectangle is 60 cm.
What is the area of each square?

8. The area of square A is 25 cm^2 and the perimeter of square B is 12 cm.

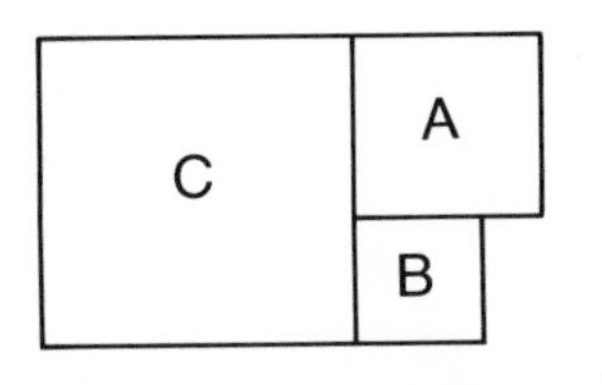

What is the perimeter of square C?

9. In a group of elephants and ostriches, there were 160 legs and 56 heads.
How many elephants and how many ostriches were there?

10. The ages of three people are consecutive even numbers. The sum of the youngest and the oldest is 56.
How old is each person?

11. What is the longest pencil that can be placed in a box 3 cm by 4 cm by 5 cm?

12. The outer diameter of a tire when new was 65 cm. After driving 60 000 km, it was found that the tread had worn down by 11.2 mm.
Find the amount of tread that is worn with each full turn of the tire.

13. The drivers of two cars are 900 km apart and they start to drive towards each other. They meet in 5 h.
What are the speeds of the cars?

14. (a) What is the smallest possible number of pitches required to play a regulation baseball game?
(b) Who won the game, and by what score?

EXTRA

4.6 OCEAN YACHT RACING

One of the most prestigious sailboat races in the world is called the America's Cup. The race takes place at a site decided by the current holder of the Cup.

Today the yachts used are called twelve-metre boats. At the right is a drawing of a typical twelve-metre yacht. There are no standard dimensions for a twelve-metre yacht.

The drawing shows the dimensions of a boat. Notice that there are no dimensions that are equal to 12 m.

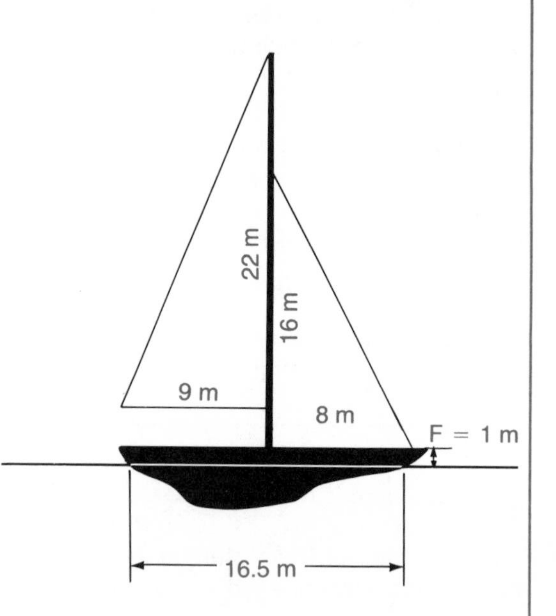

To determine whether or not a boat can be classified as a twelve-metre, the following rating formula can be used.

$$\frac{\sqrt{S} + L - F}{2.37}$$

S is the sum of the areas of the two sail triangles. (The overlap of the foresail behind the mainsail is not counted.)

L is the length of the boat at the waterline.

F is the distance from the deck of the boat to the waterline.

2.37 is a mathematical constant.

After substitution, if the result is 12 or less, the boat is classed as a twelve-metre.

To determine if the boat at right is a twelve-metre, we proceed as follows.

$$\begin{aligned} S &= \tfrac{1}{2} \times 9 \times 22 + \tfrac{1}{2} \times 16 \times 8 \\ &= 99 + 64 \\ &= 163 \end{aligned}$$

$$\frac{\sqrt{S} + L - F}{2.37} = \frac{\sqrt{163} + 16.5 - 1}{2.37} \doteq 11.93 \text{ m}$$

The boat is a twelve-metre.

EXERCISE 4.6

1. Is the following yacht a twelve-metre yacht?

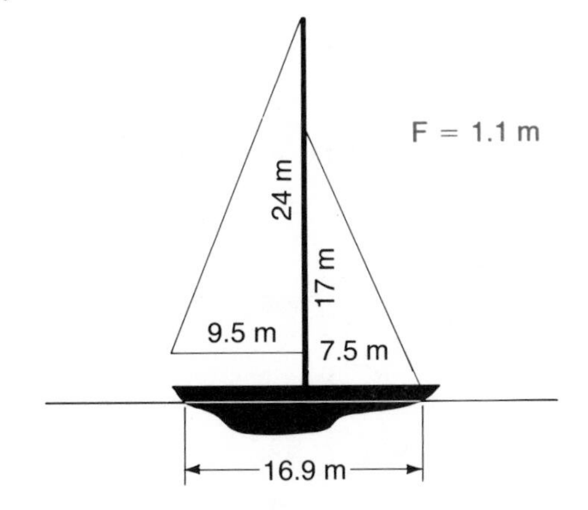

2. (a) Calculate the rating of the following yacht.

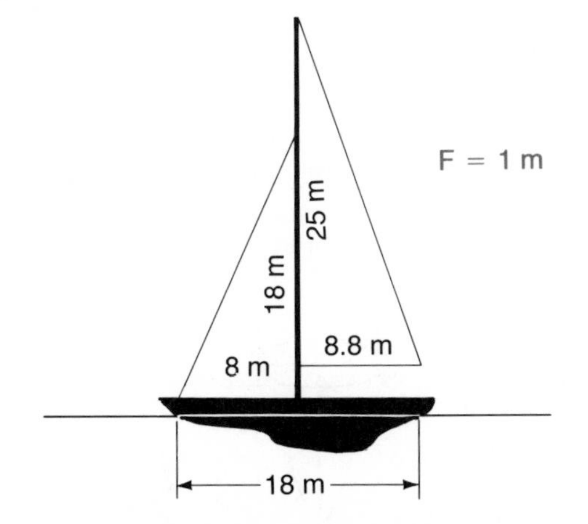

(b) Change the dimensions of the yacht to make it a twelve-metre. Adjust the dimensions to get the rating to work out as close to 12 m as possible.

3. The biggest race for twelve-metre yachts is the America's Cup. The first race was held in 1851. The course was once around the Isle of Wight.
(a) Where is the Isle of Wight?
(b) Use a map to approximate the distance around the Isle of Wight.

4. The following diagram illustrates a typical America's Cup course. Distances are measured between buoys.

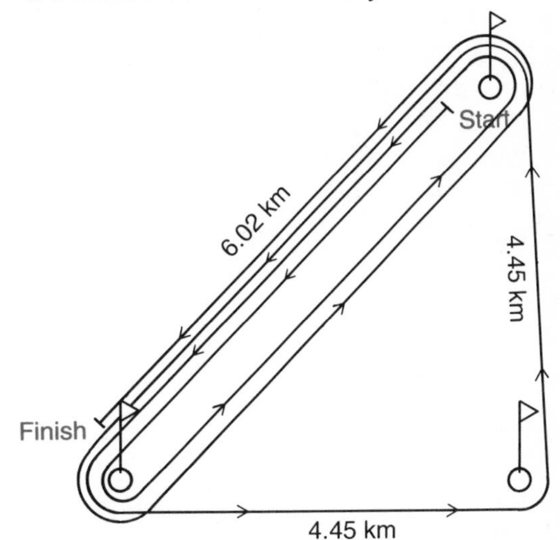

(a) What is the minimum distance a yacht would sail in completing the course?
(b) Explain why the minimum distance would never be covered by a yacht in an actual race.

5. What was the last year that Canada challenged for the America's Cup? (The challenger is the boat that survives all the elimination races and races the Cup holder one-on-one.)

6. Draw a bar graph to show the challengers to the America's Cup by country versus the number of times the country has challenged.

4.7 REVIEW EXERCISE

1. Solve and check.
(a) $3x + 7 = 2x - 4$
(b) $2(x - 1) = x + 6$
(c) $5b = 7b - 4$
(d) $3(m + 1) + 4 = 2(m - 1)$
(e) $2(x + 3) + 3(x - 1) = 3(x - 2) + 1$
(f) $5 + 2(b - 3) - (b - 7) + 6 = 11$
(g) $3 + 2(2x - 1) + 6 = 5(x - 3)$
(h) $3a - 2(a - 3) + 7 = 4a - (a - 1)$
(i) $4x - (3x - 1) - 3 + 6(x - 2) = 0$

2. Solve.
(a) $\frac{2x}{3} = \frac{3}{2}$
(b) $\frac{a}{2} + 1 = \frac{a}{3}$
(c) $\frac{b - 1}{2} = 4$
(d) $\frac{a + 3}{2} - 1 = 0$
(e) $\frac{b + 7}{4} = \frac{2b - 1}{3}$
(f) $\frac{2m - 1}{3} = 5$
(g) $\frac{x + 2}{2} = \frac{x - 1}{3}$
(h) $\frac{1}{2}(x + 1) + \frac{1}{3}(x + 1) = 5$
(i) $\frac{1}{3}(2m + 1) - \frac{1}{4}(m + 1) = 3$
(j) $\frac{1 - 3a}{4} - \frac{a - 1}{3} = -a$
(k) $\frac{m + 7}{6} + \frac{1}{2} = \frac{m - 2}{4} + \frac{1}{2}$
(l) $\frac{3x + 7}{4} - \frac{x}{3} = -\frac{1}{3}$
(m) $\frac{2}{5}(3a - 1) + \frac{1}{2}(a + 2) = 4$

3. Solve and check.
(a) $(a + 1)(a + 4) = (a + 2)(a + 1)$
(b) $(x - 3)(x + 2) - (x + 3)(x + 1) = 1$
(c) $(b - 3)(2b + 1) = 2(b - 1)(b + 1) + 9$
(d) $2(x + 3)(x + 2) - 2(x - 6) = 2x^2$
(e) $(2a - 3)(a - 2) - 2(a^2 - 1) = -6$
(f) $2(b + 1)(b + 2) - (2b - 1)(b + 3) = 6$
(g) $3(2x - 3)(x + 2) = (3x - 1)(2x - 1) + 5$
(h) $2\frac{1}{3} - \frac{3 - x}{6} + 4 = \frac{2x - 1}{2}$

4. (a) If $A = \ell w$, find A when $\ell = 5$ and $w = 3$.
(b) If $A = \ell w$, find ℓ when $A = 40$ and $w = 4$.
(c) If $P = 2(\ell + w)$, find ℓ when $P = 30$ and $w = 5$.
(d) If $A = \frac{h}{2}(a + b)$, find b when $A = 40$, $h = 10$, and $a = 3$.
(e) If $A = \frac{1}{2}bh$, find h when $A = 50$ and $b = 10$.
(f) If $I = prt$, find p when $I = 400$, $r = \frac{1}{10}$, and $t = 20$.

5. Find the volume of ice cream if the cone has a hemispherical scoop of ice cream on top and the cone is filled. The radius of the cone is 3.0 cm and the height is 10 cm.

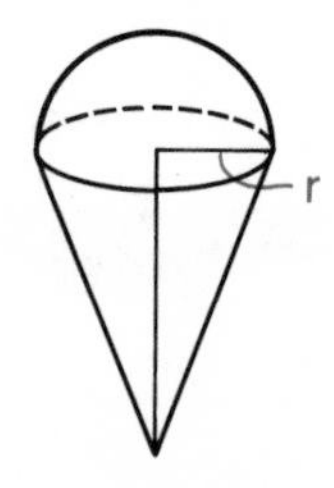

6. One formula for wages paid for work beyond forty hours a week is

$$W = r\left(40 + h + \frac{h}{2}\right)$$

where W is the wages, r is the hourly wage, and h is the number of hours worked over forty.
Find the wages when r = \$16.50 and h is 13.

7. The formula for the volume of a rectangular solid is

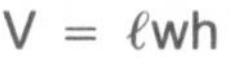
$V = \ell wh$

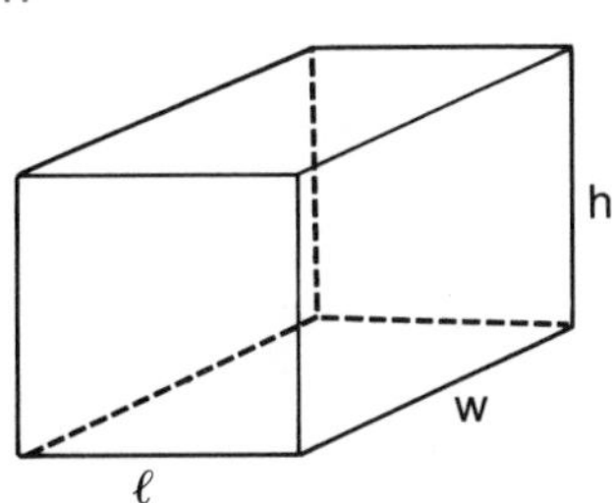

Find the volume of the following solid to the nearest tenth.

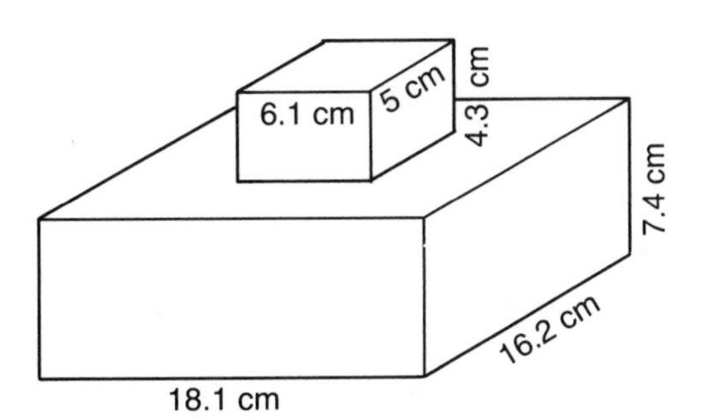

8. Solve by factoring.
(a) $x^2 - 8x = 0$
(b) $3x^2 - 7x = 0$
(c) $5x^2 - 25x = 0$
(d) $x^2 + 3x + 2 = 0$
(e) $x^2 + 5x + 4 = 0$
(f) $x^2 + 5x + 6 = 0$
(g) $x^2 + 6x - 91 = 0$
(h) $x^2 - 64 = 0$

9. Solve.
(a) $(x + 5)^2 + 3 = -4(x + 5)$
(b) $(x + 6)(x - 4) - 3(x + 6) = -3(x - 7)$
(c) $(x + 2)(x + 1) + 3 = 2(x + 2) + 3x$
(d) $(x + 5)(x + 6) = 10x + 42$
(e) $30 + 15(1 - t) = (t - 3)(t + 15)$

10. Find two consecutive positive integers whose cubes differ by 1261.

11. The edges of two cubes differ by 2 m and their volumes differ by 728 m^3. Find the dimensions of each.

CAREER

MEDICAL LABORATORY TECHNOLOGIST

Pat Chow is a medical laboratory technologist who carries out tests to assist in diagnosing illness. Pat prepares slides of tissues and blood for microscopic work. Taking blood from patients, typing blood for future transfusions, and reporting any abnormalities in colour, size, or shape of cells, and the number of cells are tasks carried out by the technologist.

Medical laboratory technologists need a background in mathematics and science. Knowing what to look for is the key in being able to execute the job effectively.

EXERCISE

1. A mole is the number of chemical units of a substance in a given volume. Avogadro found this number to be

$$6.023 \times 10^{23}$$

Find the number of moles if each sample contains the following number of chemical units.
(a) 5.246×10^{25} (b) 9.463×10^{28}
(c) 1.145×10^{24} (d) 4.256×10^{27}
(e) 1.205×10^{26} (f) 1.807×10^{25}

2. When a smaller unit is required, the technologist works with the millimole.

1000 millimoles (mmol) = 1 mol

Diabetes is diagnosed through a glucose tolerance test. Normal sugar level for adults is between 3.4 mmol/L and 6.4 mmol/L.
Identify which of the following readings are within the normal range.
(a) 0.0076 mol/L (b) 0.0134 mol/L
(c) 0.0048 mol/L (d) 0.0018 mol/L

4.8 CHAPTER 4 TEST

1. Solve the following equations.

(a) $10x - 6 = 4x + 6$

(b) $y - 7 = 8 - (3y + 4)$

(c) $\frac{3}{5}(x - 2) + \frac{1}{2} = \frac{4}{7}(2x - 1)$

(d) $\dfrac{x - 2}{3} - \dfrac{x + 1}{4} = 5$

(e) $-3(2 - x) + 7x = -4 + 2x$

(f) $(y + 3)^2 = 2y(y + 1) - (y - 1)^2$

2. If $P = 2(\ell + w)$, find ℓ when $P = 72$ cm and $w = 6.0$ cm.

3. If $A = \dfrac{\pi}{4}d^2$, find d when $A = 340.8\ \text{cm}^2$.

4. If $V = \ell wh$, solve for ℓ.

5. If $S = ut + \frac{1}{2}at^2$, solve for u.

6. Solve by factoring. Check your solutions.

(a) $x^2 + 19x = 0$

(b) $x^2 + 2x - 15 = 0$

(c) $x^2 + 14x - 15 = 0$

(d) $(x + 5)(x - 1) = 19 - x$

(e) $(x - 2)(x - 13) = 4x - 8$

7. The edges of two squares differ by 5.0 cm, and their areas differ by 115 cm^2.
Find the side length of each square.

THE STRAIGHT LINE

REVIEW AND PREVIEW TO CHAPTER 5

PYTHAGOREAN RELATIONSHIP

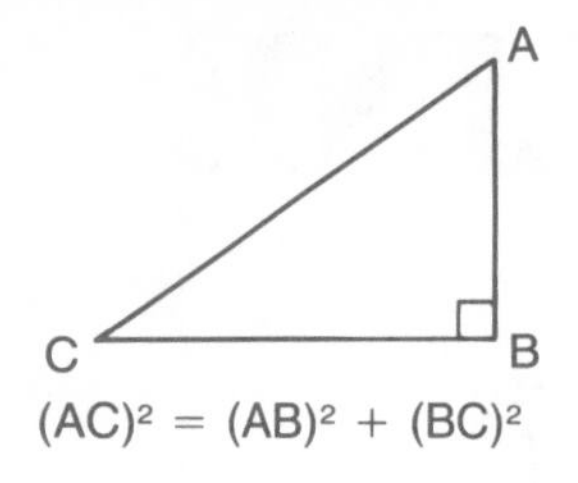

$(AC)^2 = (AB)^2 + (BC)^2$

EXERCISE 1

Find the missing lengths.

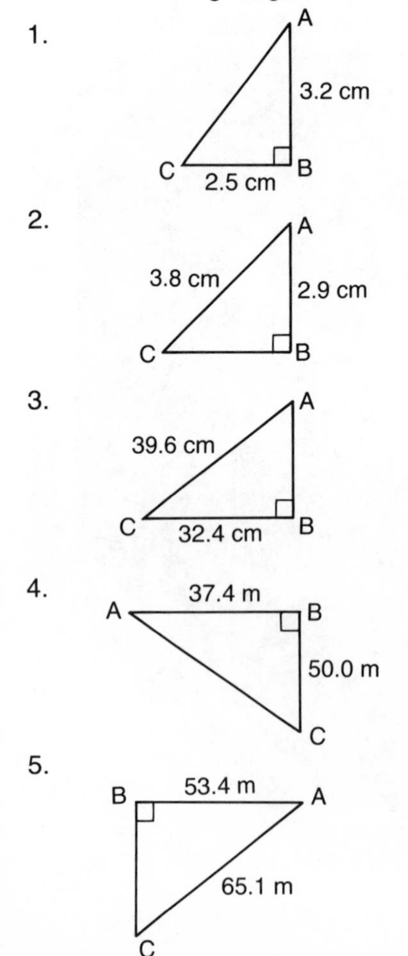

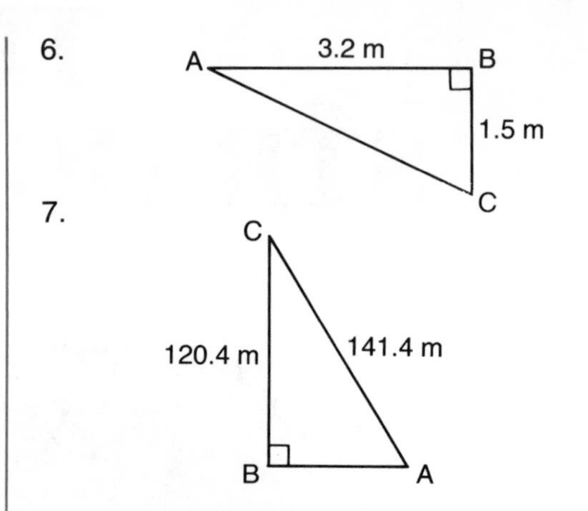

EXERCISE 2

Use the Pythagorean relationship to calculate the missing lengths in $\triangle ABC$.

1. $\angle B = 90°$, AB = 4 cm, BC = 3 cm
2. $\angle B = 90°$, AB = 12 cm, BC = 5 cm
3. $\angle A = 90°$, AB = 6 cm, AC = 4 cm
4. $\angle C = 90°$, AB = 10 cm, BC = 3 cm
5. $\angle A = 90°$, BC = 12 cm, AC = 7 cm
6. $\angle C = 90°$, AB = 20 cm, BC = 16 cm

EXERCISE 3

Graph lines from the given tables of values.

1.

x	y
1	−1
2	5
3	11
4	17
5	23
6	29

2.

x	y
1	3
2	5
3	7
4	9
5	11
6	13

3.

x	y
1	13
2	20
3	27
4	34

4.

x	y
−3	−3
−2	−1
−1	1
0	3

5.

x	y
−1	9
1	−1

6.

x	y
−3	−4
4	3

EXERCISE 4

1. Determine each of the following.
(a) Plot the given data and draw a line of best fit.
(b) Using your line from (a), estimate y for the indicated values of x.
(c) Compare these estimates with the values obtained from the given equation.

(i)

x	1	2	3	4	5	6
y	3.4	6.1	8.8	12.3	14.9	17.4

Values of x: 2.5, 3.5, 4.5
Equation: $y = 3x$

(ii)

x	y
1.1	5.0
1.7	6.2
2.3	7.8
3.1	9.3
3.3	9.3
4.1	11.0
4.5	11.8
5.5	14.3
6.1	15.4
6.6	16.1

Values of x: 2, 4, 6, 8
Equation: $y = 2x + 3$

(iii)

x	y
1.1	10.2
1.7	8.5
2.2	6.3
2.9	3.1
3.4	1.6
4.1	−1.2
4.7	−3.9
5.2	−5.6
5.5	−7.0
5.9	−8.7
6.4	−10.9
6.9	−12.2
7.1	−13.7
7.6	−15.1

Values of x: 2, 4, 6, 8, 10
Equation: $y = 15 - 4x$

2. (a) Plot the given data and draw a smooth curve of best fit.

x	y
4	16.0
6	10.6
8	8.0
10	6.4
12	5.3
14	4.6
16	4.0

(b) From this curve, estimate the value of y when x = 7, 9, 11. Predict the value of y when x = 1, 2.
(c) Compare your results with the values obtained from the equation $y = \frac{64}{x}$.

5.1 DIRECT VARIATION

Suppose a car is travelling at a constant speed of 60 km/h. This means that the car will travel 60 km in 1 h and 120 km in 2 h. The table of values shows this relationship.

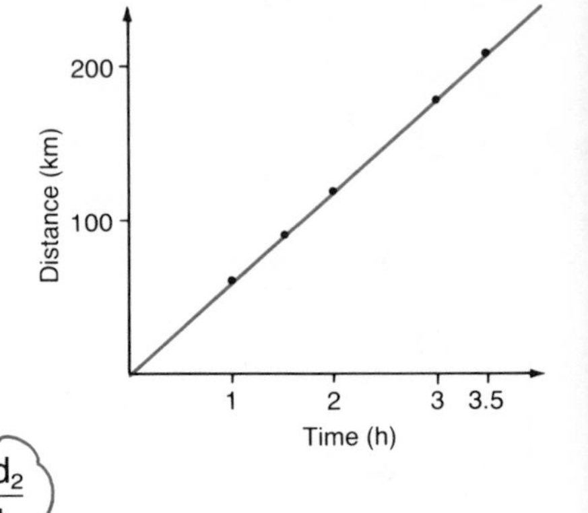

Distance, d	60	90	120	150	180	210
Time, t	1	1.5	2	2.5	3	3.5

The distance travelled is directly related to the time. The distance divided by the time is a constant value.

$$\frac{60}{1} = 60 \qquad \frac{90}{1.5} = 60 \qquad \frac{120}{2} = 60$$

$$\frac{d_1}{t_1} = \frac{d_2}{t_2}$$

This relationship can be written as follows.

$$\frac{d}{t} = k \quad \text{or} \quad d = kt, \text{ where k is a constant.}$$

When two variables x and y are related such that $\frac{y}{x} = k$, a constant, we say that y is directly proportional to x, or that y varies directly as x. We can use a variation symbol, ∝, to write this statement.

When x increases, y increases. When x decreases, y decreases.

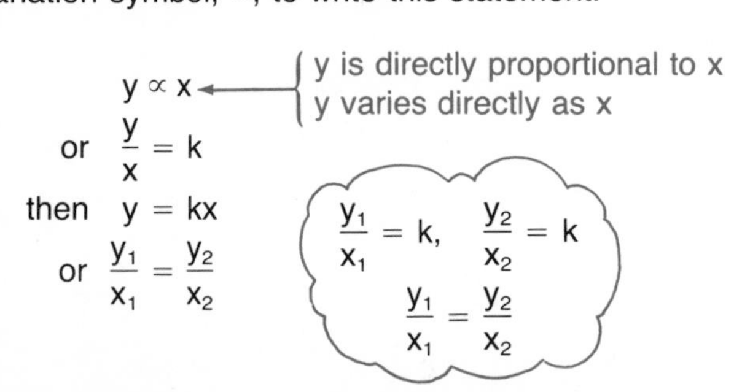

Here are three other examples of direct variation.

If a 50 g mass on a spring produces a stretch of 10 cm, and if the mass is then increased to 100 g, the stretch will be 20 cm. Stretch varies directly with the mass.

If a ball is dropped 12 cm, and the resulting height of bounce is 8 cm, and if the ball is then dropped 36 cm, the height of bounce will be 24 cm. The height of bounce varies directly with the initial height.

The Greeks discovered long ago that when the circumference of a circle was divided by the diameter, the quotient was always equal to approximately 3.14. The circumference of the circle varies directly with the diameter, π being the constant.

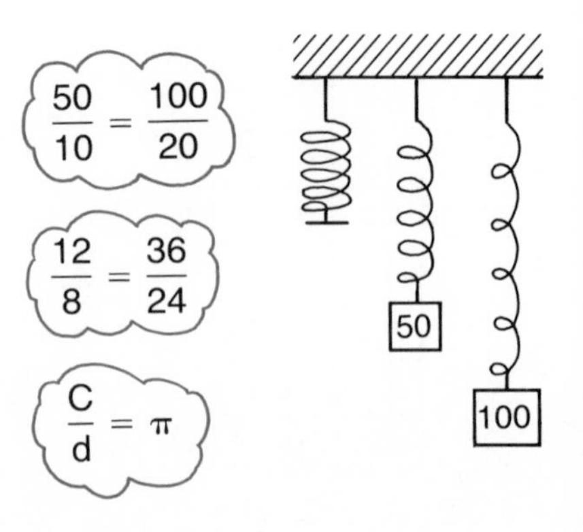

READ

Example. Grapes are sold at a fruit stand in a market. The total cost of the grapes varies directly with the amount purchased. If the total cost is \$3.20 when the amount purchased is 0.8 kg,
(a) find an equation representing the relation between total cost and amount purchased.
(b) How much will 1.7 kg of grapes cost?

PLAN

Solution:
(a) Since the total cost varies directly with the amount purchased we know that the total cost T, divided by the mass w, is always a constant value.

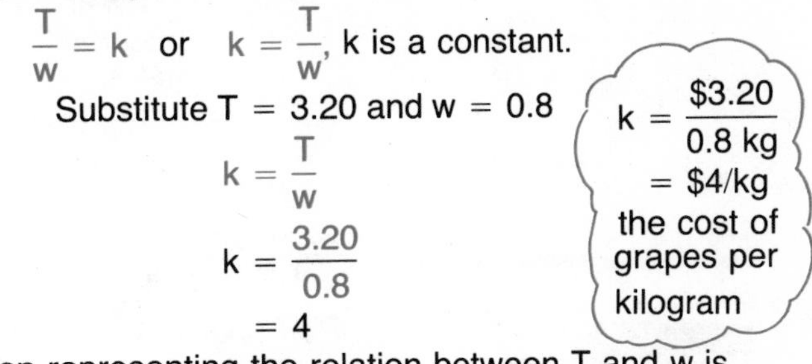

$\frac{T}{w} = k$ or $k = \frac{T}{w}$, k is a constant.

Substitute $T = 3.20$ and $w = 0.8$

$$k = \frac{T}{w}$$

$$k = \frac{3.20}{0.8} = 4$$

The equation representing the relation between T and w is

$$\frac{T}{w} = 4 \quad \text{or} \quad T = 4w$$

(b) To find the cost of 1.7 kg of grapes, substitute 1.7 for w.

$$T = 4w$$
$$T = 4(1.7) = 6.8$$

$$\frac{3.20}{0.8} = \frac{6.80}{1.7}$$

1.7 kg of grapes will cost \$6.80.

Note: The equation $T = 4w$ is of the form $y = kx$, where y corresponds to T and x corresponds to w.

EXERCISE 5.1

A

1. I varies directly as t.
(a) Find an equation representing the relation between I and t, using the constant k.
(b) If $I = 100$ when $t = 2$, find k, the constant of variation.
(c) Find I when $t = 3.5$.

2. If $\frac{d_1}{t_1} = \frac{d_2}{t_2}$ find the missing variables in each of the following.
(a) $d_1 = 160$, $t_1 = 2$, $d_2 = ?$, $t_2 = 1$
(b) $d_1 = 100$, $t_1 = 2$, $d_2 = 25$, $t_2 = ?$
(c) $d_1 = 45$, $t_1 = 0.5$, $d_2 = ?$, $t_2 = 1.25$

B

3. In an electrical circuit the voltage varies directly with the current.
If the power is 9 V when the current is 6 A,
(a) find an equation representing the relation between voltage and current.
(b) find the voltage when the current is 8 A.

4. The expense of building a sidewalk varies directly as its length.
If the cost of 2000 m is \$60 000, how much will a sidewalk 3200 m long cost?

5.2 PARTIAL VARIATION

In some applications, part of the variation is constant. For example, the cost of school T-shirts is $100 for the crest design and $5 per shirt thereafter. A variation which is partly constant and partly variable is called a partial variation.

Example. The Piston Car Club wants to buy bumper stickers for a fund-raising project. Publisher A will sell them the stickers at 20¢ per sticker. Publisher B makes an initial charge of $50 plus 10¢ per sticker. Which plan is better if the club expects to sell (a) 1000 stickers, (b) 300 stickers? How many stickers would have the same cost from both publishers? Draw a graph to illustrate the two plans.

PLAN

Solution:
Let N be the number of stickers.

E=mc²

Publisher A

Cost = (Cost per sticker) × (Number of stickers)

C = $0.20N

Publisher B

Cost = Initial cost + (Cost per sticker × Number of stickers)

C = $50 + $0.10N

SOLVE

Publisher A

(a) C = $0.20 × 1000
= $200

(b) C = $0.20 × 300
= $60

Publisher B

(a) C = $50 + $0.10(1000)
= $50 + $100 = $150

(b) C = $50 + $0.10(300)
= $50 + $30 = $80

ANSWER

It is better to buy from Publisher B for 1000 stickers and from Publisher A for 300 stickers.

Plan A C = 0.20N

No.	100	200	300
Cost ($)	20	40	60

Plan B C = 50 + 0.10N

No.	100	200	300
Cost ($)	60	70	80

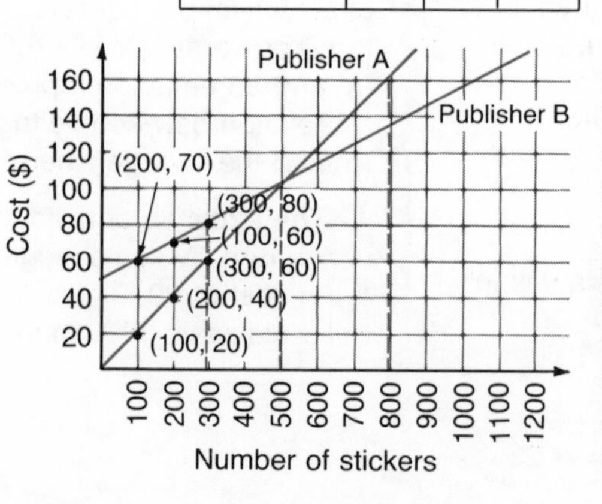

From the graph we see that the point common to both plans corresponds to the purchase of 500 stickers. At 500, both plans will cost the same. If more than 500 stickers are bought, Publisher B will be more economical. If fewer than 500 stickers are bought, Publisher A will charge less. The graph shows the saving in each case.

EXERCISE 5.2

B

1. TV Care charges $18.00 for a service call plus an hourly rate of $12.00 for labour.
(a) Write a statement for the partial variation expressing the total charge as a formula. Use T for the total charge and h for the number of hours of labour.
(b) Calculate the total charge for a service call if the technician worked for
(i) 1 h (ii) 1 h 20 min
(iii) 1 h 45 min (iv) 2 h 10 min

2. E-Z-Rent-a-Car Agency charges $25/d plus 15¢/km for one of their cars. When a car is picked up at 18:00 on Friday night the odometer reads 21 837 km. When the car is returned on Sunday at 17:00 the odometer reads 22 161.
How much does the weekend's drive cost?

3. It costs $106/h to rent a bulldozer. Moving the bulldozer to a job site and taking it away after the job is finished costs a flat rate of $135.
If you have a job requiring 12 h work, how much will the bulldozer cost?

4. Many people work on a certain basic salary plus commission. Mr. Cell receives a basic salary of $200 a week plus 5% of sales. Last week he made the following sales:

Monday	$1210.35
Tuesday	$1226.65
Wednesday	$1120.00
Thursday	$1230.50
Friday	$1350.00
Saturday	$1246.00

What was his salary for last week?

5. Publisher A will print posters for an initial charge of $150 plus $1.00 a poster. Publisher B has an initial charge of $100 plus $1.50 a poster.
(a) Which publisher gives the better price for 50 posters and what is it?
(b) For what number of posters is the price the same?

MICRO MATH

CAR RENTAL

This program computes the cost of renting a car.

```
NEW
 10 PRINT "COST OF CAR RENTAL"
 20 PRINT "ENTER THE DAILY RATE"
 30 INPUT R
 40 PRINT "ENTER THE NUMBER OF DAYS"
 50 INPUT D
 60 PRINT "ENTER THE KILOMETRE CHARGE"
 70 INPUT K
 80 PRINT "ENTER THE NUMBER OF
    KILOMETRES"
 90 INPUT N
100 C = R*D + K*N
110 PRINT "THE COST IS $" ;C
120 END
RUN
```

EXERCISE

Rent-a-Car rents automobiles for $39.95/d plus 15¢/km. Lend-a-Car charges $49.95/d with 100 km/d included and 18¢/km after that.

1. Graph the cost of renting a car from each company for 0 to 300 km for one day.

2. What will each company charge for renting a car for one day and driving 100 km?

3. What is the cheaper price for renting a car for one day and driving 200 km?

4. What is the cheaper price for two days and a total distance of 200 km?

5.3 SLOPE OF A LINE SEGMENT

The slope of a straight line is a measure of the steepness of the line.

Line AB has a greater slope (steepness) than line CD.

The slope is defined as the vertical change (called the rise) divided by the horizontal change (called the run).

$$\text{slope} = \frac{\text{rise}}{\text{run}} = \frac{\text{vertical change}}{\text{horizontal change}}$$

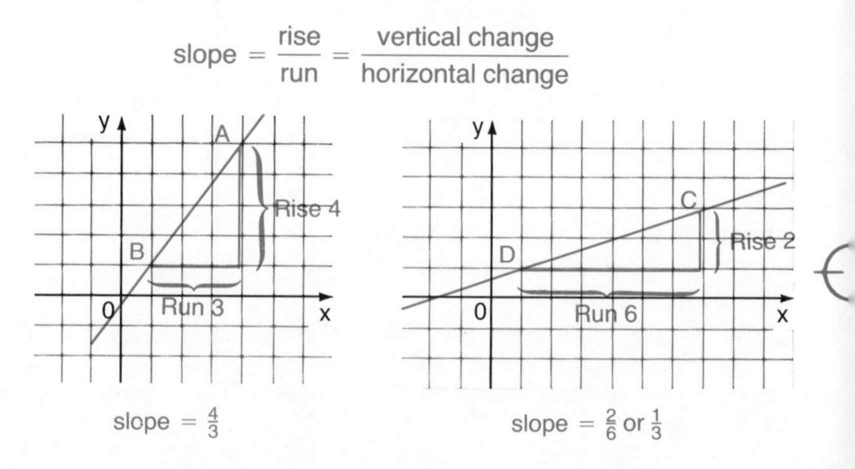

slope $= \frac{4}{3}$

slope $= \frac{2}{6}$ or $\frac{1}{3}$

Example 1. Find the slope of the line segment from the point A(2, 1) to the point B(5, 3).

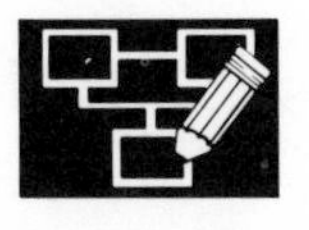

Solution:

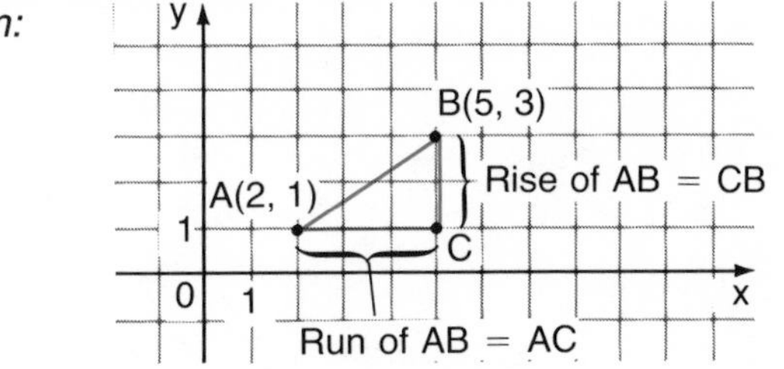

The vertical change or rise of AB is 2,(3 − 1), while the horizontal change or run of AB is 3,(5 − 2). Therefore:

$$\text{slope AB} = \frac{\text{rise AB}}{\text{run AB}} = \frac{3-1}{5-2} = \frac{2}{3}$$

△ is the fourth letter of the Greek alphabet and corresponds to "d" — the first letter of the word difference.

We use Δy (read "delta y") to denote the change in y and Δx to denote the change in x. We use the letter m to denote slope.

$$\text{slope} = \frac{\text{rise}}{\text{run}} = \frac{\Delta y}{\Delta x} = m$$

Example 2. Find the slope of the line segment joining $P_1(x_1, y_1)$ and $P_2(x_2, y_2)$.

Solution:

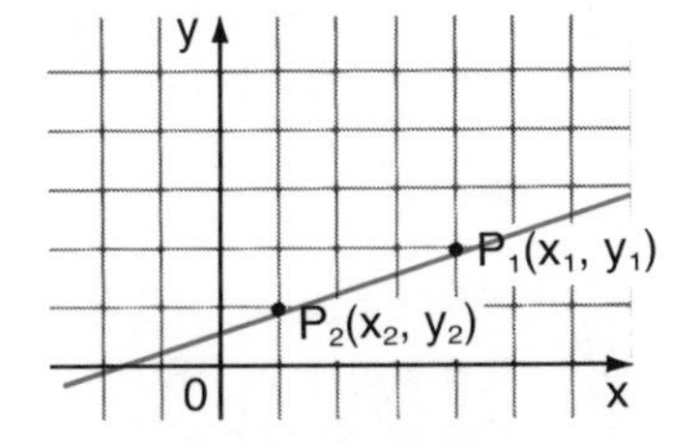

Δy = (the y-coordinate of P_2) − (the y-coordinate of P_1)
$= y_2 - y_1$
Δx = (the x-coordinate of P_2) − (the x-coordinate of P_1)
$= x_2 - x_1$

Representing the slope of P_1P_2 by m,

$$m = \frac{\Delta y}{\Delta x}$$
$$= \frac{y_2 - y_1}{x_2 - x_1}$$

The slope of the line segment from any point $P_1(x_1, y_1)$ to any point $P_2(x_2, y_2)$ is $\dfrac{y_2 - y_1}{x_2 - x_1}$

Example 3. Find (a) slope AB; and (b) slope BA.

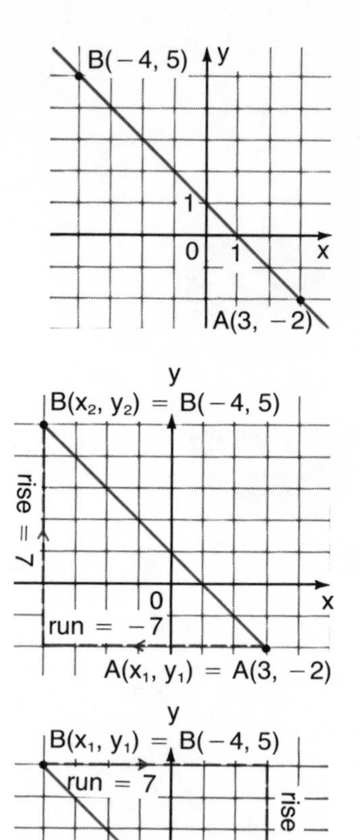

Solution:

(a) The slope of AB.

$$m = \frac{y_2 - y_1}{x_2 - x_1} = \frac{5 - (-2)}{-4 - 3} = \frac{7}{-7} = -1$$

(b) The slope of BA.

$$m = \frac{y_2 - y_1}{x_2 - x_1} = \frac{-2 - 5}{3 - (-4)} = \frac{-7}{7} = -1$$

The slope of AB is the same as the slope of BA. Remember, the slope of the hill to be climbed is the same as the slope of the hill to be walked down.

The run from A to B is −7 while the run from B to A is 7. This indicates different directions. The rise from A to B is 7 (going up) while the rise from B to A is −7 (going down). Slope AB = slope BA.

Example 4. Determine the slope of the line passing through (2.01, 1.26) and (3.44, 7.11).

Solution: $m = \frac{\triangle y}{\triangle x}$

$$m = \frac{y_2 - y_1}{x_2 - x_1} = \frac{7.11 - 1.26}{3.44 - 2.01}$$

Press

(7 · 1 1 − 1 · 2 6) ÷ (3 · 4 4 − 2 · 0 1) =

The display is 4.090909091

The slope is 4.09.

The final answer is given to the nearest hundredth (two decimal places) since this corresponds with the accuracy of the given data.

EXERCISE 5.3

B

1. A, B, C, D are four points lying on a straight line.

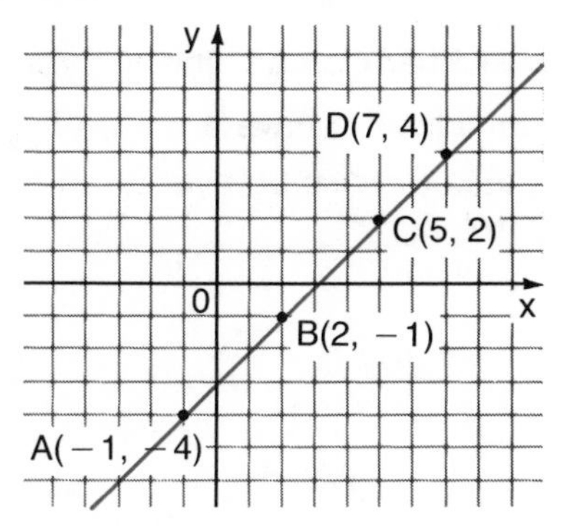

(a) Complete the table below.

Segment	Δy	Δx	$\frac{\Delta y}{\Delta x}$
AB			
AC			
BC			
BD			
CD			

(b) What do you notice about $\frac{\Delta y}{\Delta x}$ for different pairs of points on the straight line?

(c) What can be said about the slope of a straight line with respect to the slope of any segment of the line?

2. (a) Find the slope of the line segment from:
   (i) R(−4, −5) to S(0, 1)
   (ii) R(−4, −5) to T(4, 7)
   (iii) S(0, 1) to T(4, 7)

(b) What can you say about the three points R, S, and T?

3. (a) Find the slope of the line segment joining A(−2, −1) to B(3, 2).

(b) What sign has the slope of a line segment which rises towards the right?

4. (a) Find the slope of the line segment joining C(5, −2) to D(−1, 3).

(b) What sign has the slope of a line segment which rises toward the left?

5. (a) Find the slope of a line through E(3, −2) and F(−3, −2).

(b) What is the slope of a line parallel to the x-axis?

(c) Does this answer seem reasonable in connection with our everyday use of the word slope?

6. (a) Find the slope of a line through E(3, −2) and G(3, 5).

(b) What is the slope of a line parallel to the y-axis?

(c) Does this answer seem reasonable in connection with our everyday use of the word slope?

7. Determine the slope of the line that passes through each of the following pairs of points.
(a) (6, 8) and (10, 5)
(b) (0, 0) and (3, 5)
(c) $(-2, 0)$ and (1, 0)
(d) $(-2, -4)$ and $(3, -5)$
(e) (10, 2) and $(16, -1)$
(f) (0, 2) and $(0, -3)$
(g) (3, 5) and $(-2, -1)$
(h) $(-5, 1)$ and $(3, -6)$
(i) $(7, -6)$ and $(0, -3)$
(j) $(-8, -1)$ and $(-6, -3)$
(k) $(-5, 1)$ and $(4, -3)$
(l) $(-1, -1)$ and $(-5, 6)$

8. (a) Calculate the slope of $J(-4, 2)$, $K(5, -2)$.
(b) Calculate the slope of $K(5, -2)$, $J(-4, 2)$.
(c) Compare the slopes.

9. (a) When calculating the slope of a line, does the order in which the points are named make any difference?
(b) When calculating $\triangle x$ and $\triangle y$, does the order in which the points are named make any difference?

10. Determine the slope of the lines passing through:
(a) (0.255, 3.215) and (1.271, 5.327)
(b) (3.217, 4.615) and (8.575, 2.125)
(c) (4.385, 6.124) and $(-3.255, -4.173)$
(d) $(0.0255, -0.3125)$ and $(-0.2557, 0.4255)$
(e) $(-12.37, -4.21)$ and $(5.72, -8.63)$
(f) $(27.38, -33.81)$ and $(16.81, -35.46)$
(g) $(-0.713, 0.848)$ and $(-0.991, -0.322)$
(h) (123.6, 47.8) and $(-156.9, -66.8)$
(i) $(-4.317, -5.481)$ and $(-7.922, -10.473)$
(j) $(-728.4, 561.2)$ and $(555.5, -685.7)$

11. By finding the values of the run and the rise of each of the following, state where the second point is located relative to the first.
(a) (4, 7) to $(2, -3)$
(b) (3, 4) to $(-2, 4)$
(c) $(-1, 7)$ to (3, 2)
(d) $(-3, 4)$ to (4, 1)
(e) $(-2, -3)$ to $(2, -1)$
(f) $(-6, 2)$ to $(-6, -7)$

C

12. A line through $(-4, 3)$ and $(x_2, 6)$ has a slope of $\frac{3}{4}$.
Find x_2.

13. Find p if the slope of the line through (p, 2) and (1, 0) is the same as the slope of the line through $(-2, 1)$ and (2, 3).

14. Find the point on the y-axis such that the line segment from this point to (4, 7) has slope $\frac{5}{2}$.

15. (a) Use the slope formula to show that the points $X(-2, -2)$, $Y(2, 1)$, $Z(6, 4)$ lie on a straight line.
(b) Determine the value of k such that $P(k, 5)$, $Q(1, 3)$, $R(-2, 1)$ lie on a straight line.

16. A switchback on a highway through the mountains is to have a slope of $\frac{1}{20}$. What should the rise be over a run of 1000 m?

MIND BENDER

Place six coins in a row as shown.

(H) (T) (H) (T) (H) (T)

The object is to move the coins so that all the "Tails" end up on the left, followed by all the "Heads."

The coins must be moved in pairs, moving two adjacent coins at a time (without disturbing their order) and sliding them to a vacant place.

The problem must be solved in three moves.

5.4 THE INTERCEPTS

There are many ordered pairs that satisfy the equation $x + y = 7$.

Some of them are
$(0, 7), (1, 6), (2, 5), (3, 4), (7, 0), (9, -2)$

The graph of $x + y = 7$ is shown at the right.

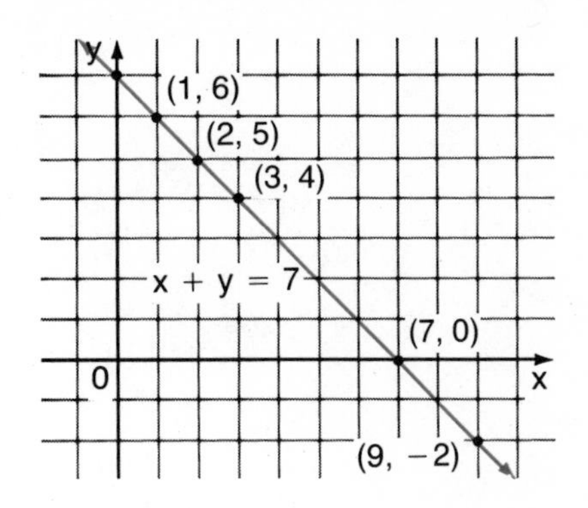

The equation $x + y = 7$ is called a linear equation because the graph is a straight line.

The rules of algebra permit us to write the linear equation $x + y = 7$ in many forms.

The following are some examples:

(i) $x + y - 7 = 0$ (ii) $x = 7 - y$
(iii) $y = 7 - x$ (iv) $y = -x + 7$

Since each of these equations is equivalent to $x + y = 7$, the graph of each is the graph of $x + y = 7$.

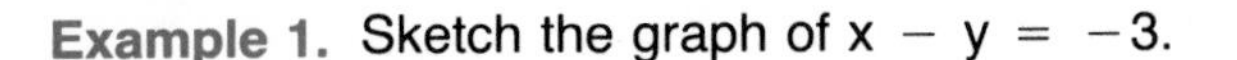

Example 1. Sketch the graph of $x - y = -3$.

Solution:
Make a table of values.

$$x - y = -3$$

When $x = 2$, $2 - y = -3$
$5 = y$

When $x = 1$, $1 - y = -3$
$4 = y$

When $x = 0$, $0 - y = -3$
$3 = y$

When $x = -1$, $-1 - y = -3$
$2 = y$

x	y
2	5
1	4
0	3
−1	2

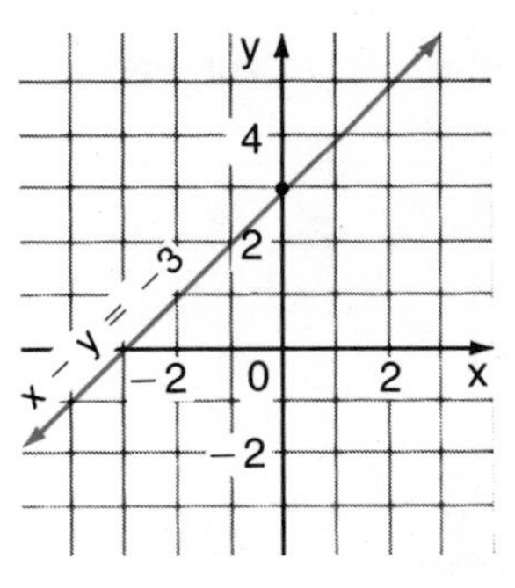

Lines may be graphed using the intercepts.

The x-intercept is the x-coordinate of the point where the line crosses the x-axis. When the graph crosses the x-axis, its y-coordinate is zero.

The y-intercept is the y-coordinate of the point where the line crosses the y-axis. When the graph crosses the y-axis, its x-coordinate is zero.

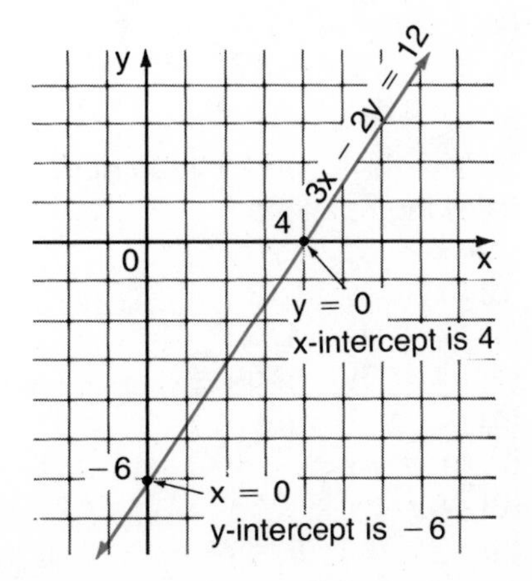

Example 2. Graph the relation $3x - 2y = 6$.

Solution:

To find the x-intercept, let $y = 0$.

$$3x - 2y = 6$$
$$3x - 2(0) = 6$$
$$3x = 6$$
$$x = 2$$

To find the y-intercept, let $x = 0$.

$$3x - 2y = 6$$
$$3(0) - 2y = 6$$
$$-2y = 6$$
$$y = -3$$

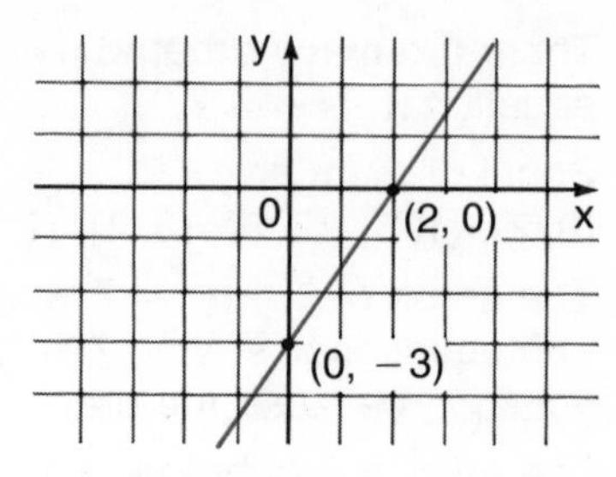

EXERCISE 5.4

A

1. State the x- and y-intercepts of each of the following.

(a) $2x + 3y = 6$
(b) $4x + 3y = 12$
(c) $3x + y = 9$
(d) $x + 4y = 8$
(e) $5x - 2y = 10$
(f) $7x - 3y = 21$
(g) $4x - 5y = -20$
(h) $3x - 5y = -15$
(i) $7x + 2y - 14 = 0$
(j) $8x - 3y + 24 = 0$
(k) $y = 4x - 8$
(l) $y = -3x + 12$

B

2. Use the x- and y-intercepts to graph the following relations.

(a) $4x + 5y = 20$
(b) $3x - 4y = 12$
(c) $2x + y = 4$
(d) $5x + 3y = 15$
(e) $x - y = -7$
(f) $5x + 2y = -10$
(g) $2x + 7y - 14 = 0$
(h) $x - 3y + 6 = 0$

C

3. (a) Draw the graph of each of the following lines.
(b) Calculate the slope of each line.
(c) What is the y-intercept of each line?

(i) $y = 3x - 6$
(ii) $y = -2x + 4$
(iii) $y = -x - 3$
(iv) $y = \frac{1}{2}x + 2$
(v) $y = \frac{1}{3}x + 1$

MICRO MATH

SLOPE OF A LINE SEGMENT

```
NEW
10 PRINT "SLOPE IS"
20 PRINT "(Y2-Y1)/(X2-X1)"
30 INPUT X1, Y1, X2, Y2
40 M = (Y2 - Y1)/(X2 - X1)
50 PRINT "THE SLOPE IS ";M
60 END
RUN
```

5.5 INVESTIGATING THE ROLES OF m AND b IN $y = mx + b$

The following investigations show the relationship between the slope of a line, the y-intercept of the line, and the equation for the line.

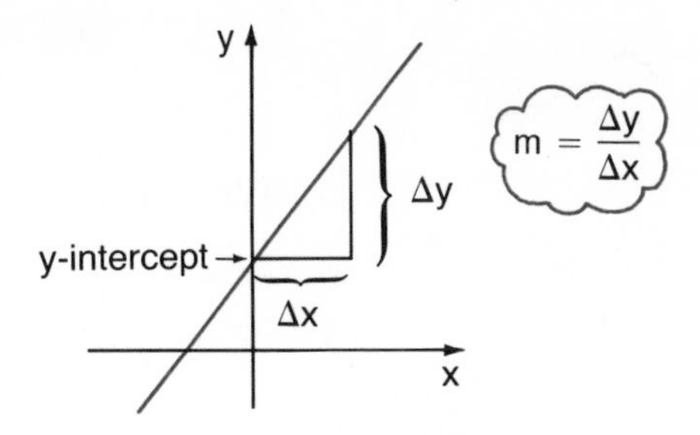

EXERCISE 5.5

B 1. (a) Using the same set of axes draw graphs representing relations having the following defining equations:

(i) $y = 2x + 3$ (ii) $y = 2x$
(iii) $y = 2x - 3$ (iv) $y = 2x + 5$

(b) In each of these equations, written in the form $y = mx + b$, what are the values of m and b?

(c) How are the graphs of these four lines related to each other?

(d) By choosing two points on each line, find the slope of each line.

(e) What can you conclude about the slopes of lines which are related such as those you have found in (c)?

(f) How is the slope of a line related to the equation of the line?

(g) What is the slope of the line represented by $y = mx + b$?

2. (a) State the slope of each line whose defining equation is given as:

(i) $y = 3x + 1$ (ii) $y = 4x - 5$
(iii) $y = -2x + 7$ (iv) $y = \frac{1}{2}x + 1$
(v) $y = 4$ (vi) $y = -\frac{1}{5}x - 2$

(b) Describe each line in (a) as "rising upward to the right", "rising upward to the left", or "parallel to the x-axis".

(c) How is the slope of a line related to its steepness?

3. (a) Each of the four equations in question 1 could have been written in the form $y = 2x + b$. What substitution would have had to be made for b in order to get the original equations? Such a set of lines is called a family of lines because each member of the family has a common characteristic, in this case a slope of 2. $y = 2x + b$ represents a family of parallel lines with slope 2.

(b) Describe each of these families of lines.

(i) $y = 3x + b$ (ii) $y = -\frac{1}{2}x + b$

4. (a) Using the same set of axes, draw graphs representing relations having the following defining equations:

(i) $y = x + 5$ (ii) $y = \frac{2}{3}x + 5$
(iii) $y = -3x + 5$ (iv) $y = 5$

(b) In each of these equations, written in the form $y = mx + b$, what are the values of m and b?

(c) How are the graphs of these four lines related to each other?

(d) What is the y-intercept of each line in (a)?

(e) What is the y-intercept of $y = mx + b$?

5. (a) Each of the four equations in question 4 could have been written in the form $y = mx + 5$. What substitution would have had to be made for m in order to get the original equations?

(b) What is the common characteristic of the family of lines $y = mx + 5$?

(c) Describe each of these families of lines.

(i) $y = mx + 4$ (ii) $y = mx - \frac{1}{3}$

6. Write the defining equation of the family of lines:

(a) with slope $\frac{1}{5}$

(b) with y-intercept 17

(c) parallel to the x-axis

(d) passing through the origin

5.6 LINEAR EQUATIONS: SLOPE y-INTERCEPT FORM

In the previous section we investigated the equation of a straight line in the form $y = mx + b$. From the equation in this form, the slope and the y-intercept can be found. The graph of the equation of a line expressed in the form

$$y = mx + b$$

has a slope m and a y-intercept b.

This is called the slope y-intercept form of a straight line equation.

Example 1. State the slope and y-intercept of the line $2x - 3y - 7 = 0$.

Solution: Express the equation in the form $y = mx + b$.

$$2x - 3y - 7 = 0$$

$$-3y = -2x + 7$$

$$\frac{-3y}{-3} = \frac{-2x}{-3} + \frac{7}{-3}$$

$$y = \frac{2}{3}x - \frac{7}{3}$$

$$y = mx + b$$

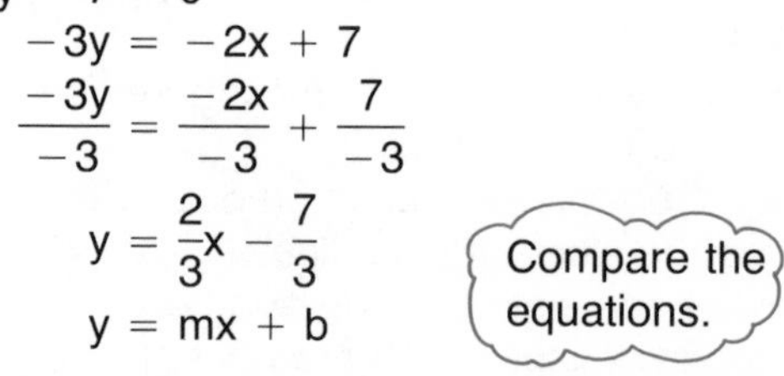

The slope is $m = \frac{2}{3}$ and y-intercept $b = -\frac{7}{3}$.

Example 2. Find the equation of the line with slope -8 passing through the point $(0, \frac{5}{7})$.

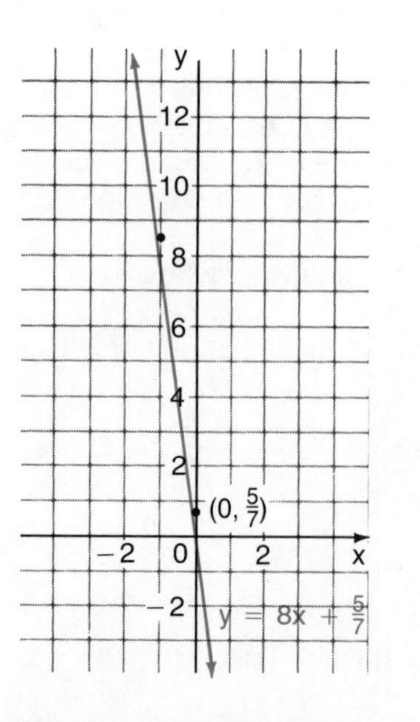

Solution: The slope $m = -8$. Since $(0, \frac{5}{7})$ is on the line, the y-intercept $b = \frac{5}{7}$. (Recall that when the graph of the line crosses the y-axis, its x-coordinate is zero.)

Compare with $y = mx + b$

$$y = -8x + \frac{5}{7}$$

The equation of the line is $y = -8x + \frac{5}{7}$.

EXERCISE 5.6

B

1. (a) By changing the following equations to the form $y = mx + b$, determine the slope and the y-intercept.
   (i) $2x + y = 5$
   (ii) $2x + 3y = 4$
   (iii) $3x + 2y + 6 = 0$
   (iv) $2x - 5y = 10$
(b) Graph each of these lines.

2. Find the coordinates of the point of intersection of the x-axis, the y-axis and the line defined by each of the following.
(a) $2x + 5y = 10$
(b) $3x + 4y - 12 = 0$
(c) $2x + 4y = 9$
(d) $3x - 2y = 6$
(e) $x + y = 1$
(f) $3x + 5y + 15 = 0$

3. State the slope, x-intercept and y-intercept of the lines represented by each of the following.
(a) $3x - 2y + 6 = 0$
(b) $2x - 3y + 2 = 0$
(c) $9y - 27 = 0$
(d) $5x + 3y - 10 = 0$
(e) $5x - 20 = 0$
(f) $2x + 3y + 7 = 0$

4. What is the equation of a line passing through the origin with slope
(a) 1 (b) -5 (c) m

5. Write the equation of each of the following lines.
(a) with slope 3 and y-intercept 8
(b) with slope $\frac{3}{4}$ and y-intercept $-\frac{2}{3}$
(c) with slope $-\frac{4}{5}$ and y-intercept $-\frac{7}{3}$
(d) with slope 0 and y-intercept 5

6. Write the equation of each of the following lines.
(a) through (0, 2) with slope 3
(b) through (0, 2) with slope 4
(c) through (0, 0) with slope 1
(d) through (0, 4) with slope -7

EXTRA

SLOPE x-INTERCEPT FORM

From the slope y-intercept form of a straight line equation we may determine the slope x-intercept form of a straight line equation.

Example. Find the equation of a line with slope m and x-intercept a.

Solution:
Since the slope is m we may begin with the slope y-intercept form $y = mx + b$ where the y-intercept b is to be determined from the given data. Since the x-intercept is a, the point (a, 0) is on the line. This means that $y = 0$ when $x = a$.

$$y = mx + b$$
$$0 = ma + b$$
$$ma + b = 0$$
$$b = -ma$$
$$\text{Thus } y = mx - ma$$
$$= m(x - a)$$

The slope x-intercept form of a straight line equation is

$$\boxed{y = m(x - a)}$$

EXERCISE

Write the equation of each of the following lines.

1. With slope 4 and x-intercept 2
2. With slope $\frac{3}{7}$ and x-intercept $-\frac{7}{3}$
3. With slope 1 and x-intercept $\frac{1}{10}$
4. Through (5, 0) with slope 5
5. Through $(\frac{1}{2}, 0)$ and $(0, \frac{3}{2})$

5.7 LINEAR EQUATIONS: POINT-SLOPE FORM

In the previous section we determined the equation of a line given the slope and the y-intercept. We shall now determine the equation of a line given the slope and any point on the line.

Example 1. Find the equation of the line passing through the point A(1, 3) with slope 2.

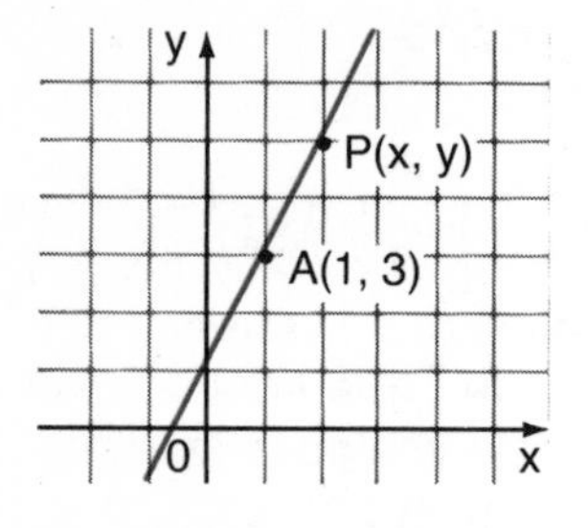

Solution: Let P(x, y) be any other point on the line. By the basic slope property of a straight line, slope AP = 2.

$$\frac{\triangle y}{\triangle x} = m$$

$$\frac{y - 3}{x - 1} = 2 \text{ and } y - 3 = 2(x - 1)$$

Sometimes it is more convenient to simplify the equation and put it in the standard form — the x term, then the y term, then the constant term, equals zero.

$Ax + By + C = 0$ where $A, B, C \in R$, is called the standard form for the equation of a straight line.

Example 2. Write the equation $y - 3 = 2(x - 1)$ in the form, $Ax + By + C = 0$.

Solution:

$$y - 3 = 2(x - 1)$$
$$\therefore y - 3 = 2x - 2$$
$$\therefore 2x - 2 - y + 3 = 0$$
$$\therefore 2x - y + 1 = 0$$

Example 3. Find the equation of the line through $P_1(x_1, y_1)$ with slope m.

Solution: Let P(x, y) be any other point on this line. Therefore the slope of

$$P_1P = m,$$

$$\frac{y - y_1}{x - x_1} = m, \text{ and}$$

$$\boxed{y - y_1 = m(x - x_1)}$$

This form of a line equation is called the point-slope form of the line equation.

EXERCISE 5.7

A 1. State the following equations in standard form ($Ax + By + C = 0$) and state the values of A, B, and C.
(a) $4x + 2y = 6$ (b) $2x = y - 4$
(c) $3x = 2 - 4y$ (d) $4x - 5y = 0$
(e) $4y = 1 - 2x$ (f) $4 - 5y = 0$

B 2. Determine an equation of the line through the given point having the given slope. Express the equation in standard form.
(a) $(4, 3)$; $m = 5$
(b) $(6, 8)$; $m = 3$
(c) $(-6, 3)$; $m = -4$
(d) $(-5, -2)$; $m = -2$
(e) $(-7, -5)$; $m = 2$
(f) $(-5, -3)$; $m = -7$
(g) $(5, 7)$; $m = \frac{1}{2}$
(h) $(-2, 4)$; $m = -\frac{1}{3}$
(i) $(\frac{1}{2}, -3)$; $m = -\frac{1}{2}$
(j) $(\frac{1}{4}, -\frac{1}{5})$; $m = \frac{5}{3}$
(k) $(0.3, 0.5)$; $m = 0.1$
(l) $(2.7, -3.7)$; $m = -1.3$
(m) $(3, -5.4)$; $m = 6.1$

3. Find an equation of the line through the given point having the given slope. Use the equation to find two other points on the line. Graph your solutions.
(a) $(1, 2)$; $m = 3$
(b) $(-1, -2)$; $m = -3$
(c) $(-1, -3)$; $m = 5$
(d) $(2, -3)$; $m = -2$
(e) $(-6, 3)$; $m = -4$
(f) $(0, 1)$; $m = 2$
(g) $(5, 0)$; $m = \frac{1}{5}$
(h) $(-2, -1)$; $m = -\frac{1}{2}$
(i) $(4, -4)$; $m = -\frac{1}{2}$
(j) $(0.6, 0.2)$; $m = -0.1$
(k) $(0.4, -1.2)$; $m = -1.4$
(l) $(0.3, 0.6)$; $m = 2$

EXTRA

USING THE y-INTERCEPT

Using the slope y-intercept form of a straight line equation, we may determine the equation of a line given the slope and any point on the line by algebraically solving for the y-intercept.

Example. Find the equation of the line passing through $(\frac{7}{3}, 9)$ with slope 3.

Solution: Since the slope is 3 we may begin with

$$y = 3x + b.$$

We may determine b from the given data. Since $(\frac{7}{3}, 9)$ is on the line, we know that $y = 9$ when $x = \frac{7}{3}$.

$$y = 3x + b$$
$$9 = 3(\tfrac{7}{3}) + b$$
$$9 = 7 + b$$

Thus $b = 9 - 7 = 2$
Thus $y = 3x + b$
$= 3x + 2$
The equation of the line is $y = 3x + 2$.

EXERCISE

Find an equation of the line through the given point having the given slope using the method of the previous example. Verify your results using the point-slope form of a straight line equation.

1. $(5, 7)$; $m = 2$
2. $(-3, -2)$; $m = 3$
3. $(-2, 3)$; $m = 5$
4. $(\frac{1}{2}, 6)$; $m = \frac{2}{3}$

5.8 LINEAR EQUATIONS: TWO-POINT FORM

We can determine the equation of a line if we are given two points on the line.

Example. Find the equation of the line passing through the points A(−3, 1) and B(3, −4). Express the equation in standard form.

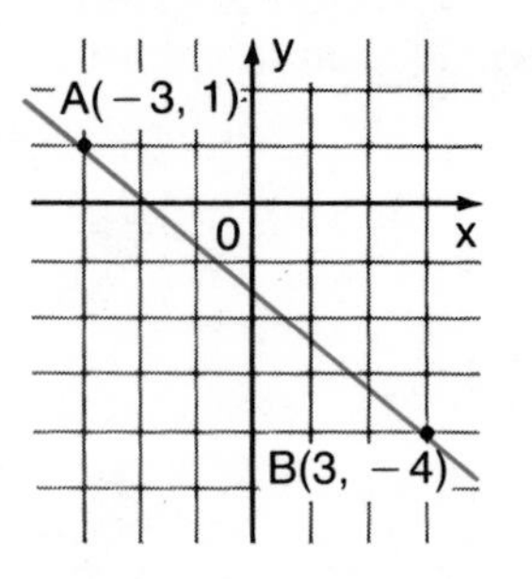

Solution: Since we know two points on the line, we can determine the slope of the line.
The slope of the line through AB is

$$m = \frac{\triangle y}{\triangle x} = \frac{-4 - 1}{3 - (-3)} = \frac{-5}{6}$$

Use the point (3, −4) and the slope $m = \frac{-5}{6}$,

$$\begin{aligned} y - y_1 &= m(x - x_1) \\ y - (-4) &= \frac{-5}{6}(x - 3) \\ 6(y + 4) &= -5(x - 3) \\ 6y + 24 &= -5x + 15 \\ 5x - 15 + 6y + 24 &= 0 \\ 5x + 6y + 9 &= 0 \end{aligned}$$

Using the point (−3, 1) and the slope $m = \frac{-5}{6}$ will give the same result.

$$\begin{aligned} y - y_1 &= m(x - x_1) \\ y - 1 &= -\frac{5}{6}(x + 3) \\ 6(y - 1) &= -5(x + 3) \\ 6y - 6 &= -5x - 15 \\ 5x + 15 + 6y - 6 &= 0 \\ 5x + 6y + 9 &= 0 \end{aligned}$$

EXERCISE 5.8

A

1. State the slope of the line determined by the following pairs of points.
(a) (5, 4), (3, −1)
(b) (1, 3), (7, 2)
(c) (0, −3), (4, 0)
(d) (2, −2), (−2, 2)
(e) (−4, 3), (3, −1)
(f) (2, −6), (−5, −1)

2. State in unsimplified form the equation of each line represented in question 1.

B

3. Find the equation of the line determined by the following pairs of points, and express the equation in standard form.
(a) (2, 1), (1, 2)
(b) (2, 1), (1, −3)
(c) (1, −1), (4, 7)
(d) (4, 2), (5, −7)
(e) (3, 10), (−1, −3)
(f) $(\frac{1}{2}, \frac{1}{3}), (1, \frac{1}{2})$
(g) $(0, \frac{1}{2}), (\frac{1}{3}, 0)$

4. (a) Find the equation of the line passing through $P(x_1, y_1)$ and parallel to the x-axis.
(b) What is the equation of the x-axis?

5. (a) Find the equation of the line passing through $P(x_1, y_1)$ and parallel to the y-axis.
(b) What is the equation of the y-axis?

6. Find the equation of the line through the point (3, 4) and
(a) with slope $\frac{1}{2}$
(b) through (−5, −2)
(c) through (0, 0)
(d) parallel to the x-axis
(e) parallel to the y-axis

C

7. Find the equation of the line passing through (a, b) and (−b, a).

EXTRA

TWO-INTERCEPT FORM

We may derive a formula to determine the equation of a line when both the x- and y-intercepts are given.

Example. Show that the equation of a line with x-intercept a and y-intercept b is $\frac{x}{a} + \frac{y}{b} = 1$

Solution:
Since the y-intercept is b, we may begin with the slope y-intercept form $y = mx + b$, where the slope m is to be determined from the given data. Since the x-intercept is a and the y-intercept is b, the points (a, 0) and (0, b) are on the line.

Thus $\quad m = \frac{b - 0}{0 - a} = \frac{-b}{a}$

And so $\quad y = mx + b$

$$= \frac{-b}{a}x + b$$

$$\frac{b}{a}x + y = b \quad \text{(Divide by b.)}$$

$$\frac{x}{a} + \frac{y}{b} = 1$$

EXERCISE

1. Find the two-intercept form of the equation of the lines with the following intercepts.
(a) x-intercept 1, y-intercept 2
(b) x-intercept 3, y-intercept 5
(c) x-intercept $\frac{1}{3}$, y-intercept $\frac{1}{2}$

2. Find the x- and y-intercepts of the lines determined by the following equations by expressing the equations in two-intercept form.
(a) $3x + 4y = 12$
(b) $2x + 7y - 14 = 0$
(c) $6x + y - 3 = 0$

3. Identify the three families of lines that cannot be expressed in two-intercept form.

5.9 PARALLEL AND PERPENDICULAR LINES

The slope of lines can be used to determine if the lines are parallel or perpendicular.

Two parallel lines are drawn on the graph.

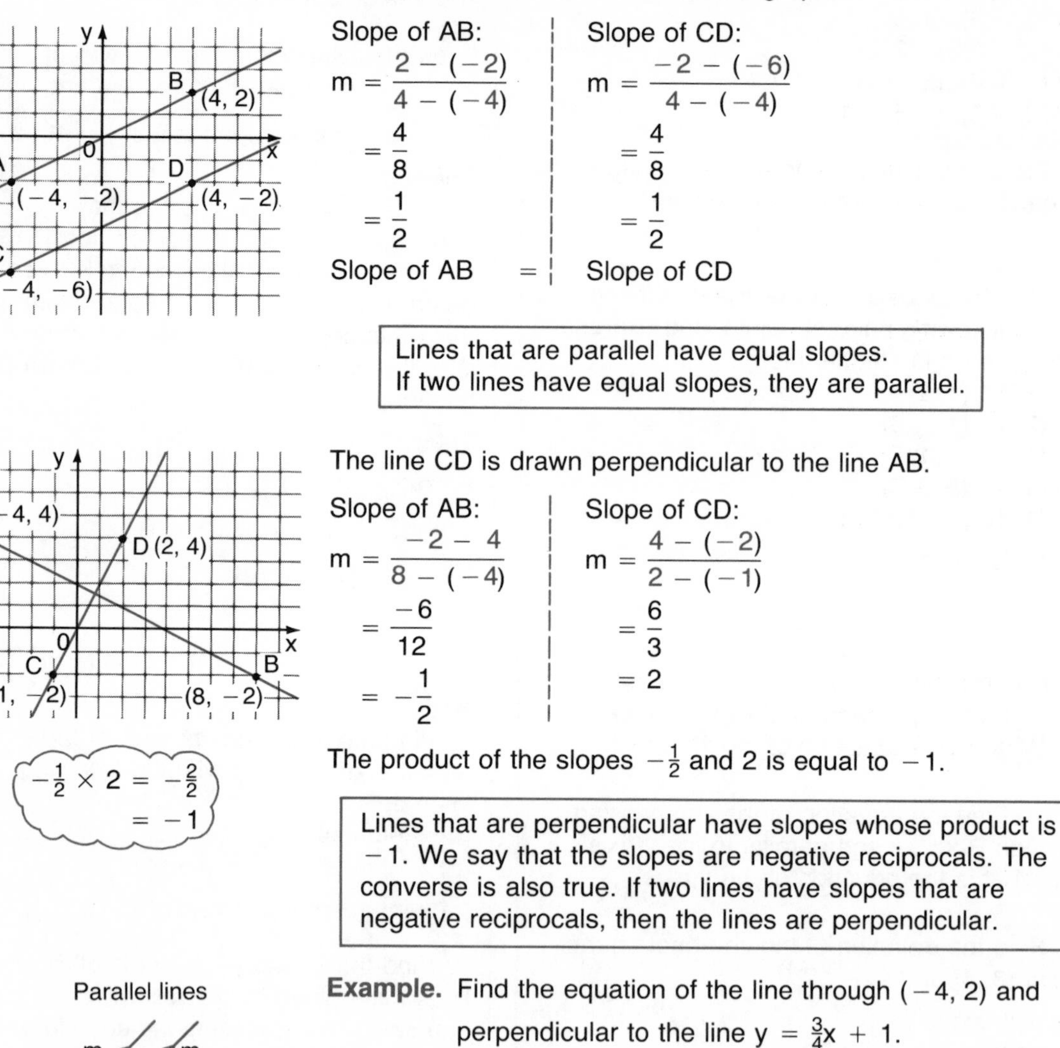

Slope of AB:

$$m = \frac{2-(-2)}{4-(-4)} = \frac{4}{8} = \frac{1}{2}$$

Slope of CD:

$$m = \frac{-2-(-6)}{4-(-4)} = \frac{4}{8} = \frac{1}{2}$$

Slope of AB = Slope of CD

> Lines that are parallel have equal slopes.
> If two lines have equal slopes, they are parallel.

The line CD is drawn perpendicular to the line AB.

Slope of AB:

$$m = \frac{-2-4}{8-(-4)} = \frac{-6}{12} = -\frac{1}{2}$$

Slope of CD:

$$m = \frac{4-(-2)}{2-(-1)} = \frac{6}{3} = 2$$

$-\frac{1}{2} \times 2 = -\frac{2}{2}$
$= -1$

The product of the slopes $-\frac{1}{2}$ and 2 is equal to -1.

> Lines that are perpendicular have slopes whose product is -1. We say that the slopes are negative reciprocals. The converse is also true. If two lines have slopes that are negative reciprocals, then the lines are perpendicular.

Parallel lines

$m_1 \quad m_2$

$m_1 = m_2$

Perpendicular lines

$m_1 \quad m_2$

$m_1 \times m_2 = -1$

Example. Find the equation of the line through $(-4, 2)$ and perpendicular to the line $y = \frac{3}{4}x + 1$.

Solution: The slope of $y = \frac{3}{4}x + 1$ is $\frac{3}{4}$.
Since the lines are perpendicular

$$m_1 \times m_2 = -1$$
$$\frac{3}{4} \times m_2 = -1$$
$$m_2 = \frac{-4}{3}$$

$\therefore$ the slope of a line perpendicular to the given line is $\frac{-4}{3}$.

$$y - y_1 = m(x - x_1)$$
$$y - 2 = \frac{-4}{3}(x + 4)$$
$$y - 2 = \frac{-4}{3}x - \frac{16}{3}$$
$$y = -\frac{4}{3}x - \frac{10}{3}$$

or $4x + 3y + 10 = 0$ in standard form.

EXERCISE 5.9

B 1. Find the slope of (i) a line parallel to and (ii) a line perpendicular to the following lines.

(a) $y = 2x + 3$ (b) $y = 4x - 1$
(c) $y = -3x + 1$ (d) $y = -x - 4$
(e) $y = \frac{1}{3}x + 4$ (f) $y = \frac{4}{3}x + 2$
(g) $y + 6x = 1$ (h) $y - 5x + 3 = 0$
(i) $2y + 3x = 4$ (j) $2x + 4y - 7 = 0$
(k) $3x - 2y = 7$ (l) $x - 3y + 1 = 0$

2. Find the equation of the line parallel to $y = 4x - 1$ and containing the point $(3, -2)$.

3. Find the equation of the line through $(7, 11)$ and perpendicular to the line $y = \frac{4}{3}x + 7$.

4. Find the equation of the line parallel to $2x + 3y = 1$ and containing the point $(3, 2)$.

5. Find the equation of the line through $(-2, -3)$ and perpendicular to the line $5x - 3y + 2 = 0$.

6. Find an equation of a line through $(2, -7)$ and
(a) parallel to the x-axis
(b) parallel to the y-axis

7. Find the equation of a line passing through the origin perpendicular to $3x + 4y + 5 = 0$.

8. A line has y-intercept 3 and is perpendicular to the line $y = \frac{1}{5}x - 7$. Find an equation for the line.

9. Find an equation of the line with slope $\frac{5}{4}$ having the same x-intercept as the line $3x + 4y = 12$.

10. (a) Graph $A(2, -3)$, $B(5, 1)$, $C(0, -4)$, $D(5, 2)$.
(b) Find an equation of the line through A perpendicular to AB.
(c) Find an equation of the line through A parallel to BC.

11. Find the equation of each side of the quadrilateral ABCD.

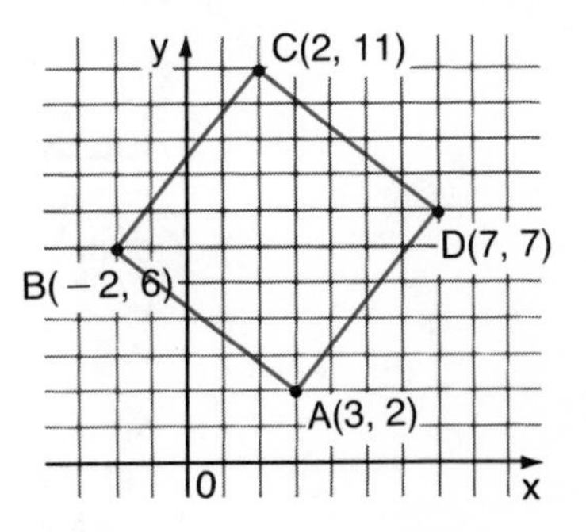

12. Prove that the following points are the vertices of a right-angled triangle.
(a) $(-3, 2)$, $(7, 2)$, $(5, 6)$
(b) $(-6, 1)$, $(-2, -7)$, $(-4, -8)$

13. (a) Prove that the following points are the vertices of a parallelogram.
(i) $(2, 1)$, $(14, 11)$, $(6, 5)$, $(-6, -5)$
(ii) $(6, 5)$, $(2, 7)$, $(-2, -1)$, $(2, -3)$
(b) What kind of parallelogram is (a) (ii)?

5.10 APPLICATIONS OF STRAIGHT LINES

The following problems involve applications of linear equations.

Example 1. Distilled water costs 15¢/L.
(a) Construct a table of values for the cost of 0 L to 10 L.
(b) Draw a graph of the relationship.
(c) What is the cost of 3 L?
(d) How many litres can you buy for $1.35?

Solution:

(a)

No. litres	n	0	1	2	3	4	5	6	7	8	9	10
Total cost ¢	C	0	15	30	45	60	75	90	105	120	135	150

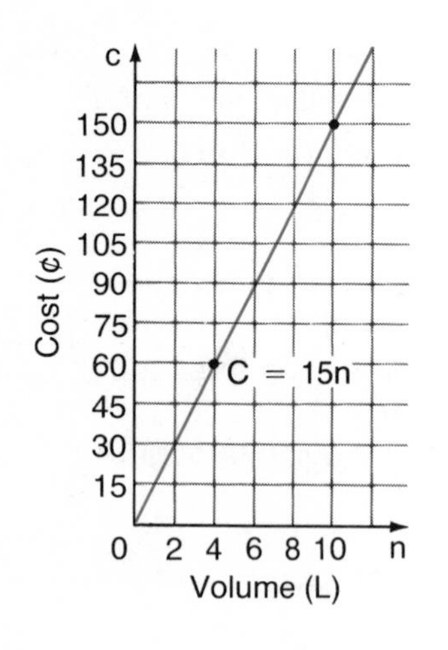

(b) The graph is a straight line. The equation of this line (the relationship between n and C) is C = 15n. Comparing this line with the equation y = mx, the slope of the line is 15.

The quotient $\frac{C}{n}$ is always 15. We say the cost, C, depends directly on the number of litres, n. We say C varies directly as n, or C is in direct proportion to n. The constant of variation is also the slope of the line.

(c) From the graph or table of values, the cost of 3 L is 45¢.

(d) You can buy 9 L of distilled water for $1.35.

Example 2. The circumference of a circle is directly proportional to its diameter. A circle of diameter 10 cm has a circumference of 31 cm.
(a) Calculate the circumference of a circle of diameter 14 cm.
(b) Calculate the radius of a circle of circumference 47.2 cm.

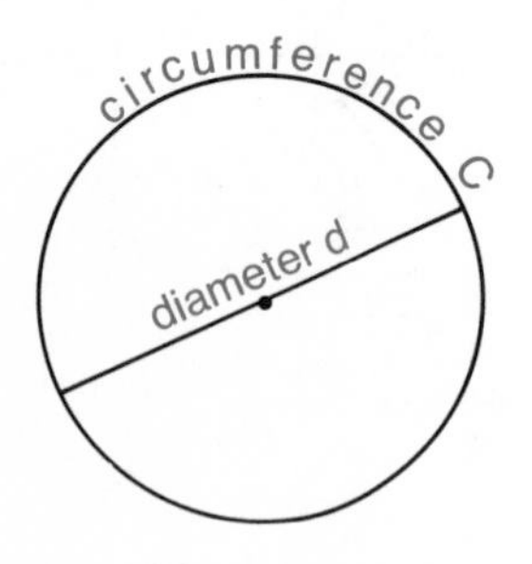

Solution:
Let the circumference in centimetres be C and the diameter in centimetres be d. Because C is directly proportional to d we say $\frac{C}{d}$ = a constant. To find the value of the constant we know that if d = 10, then C = 31. Thus $\frac{C}{d} = \frac{31}{10} = 3.1$. The relationship between C and d is C = 3.1d.

(a) If d = 14, C = 3.1 × 14 = 43.4. Therefore the circumference is 43.4 cm.

(b) If C = 47.2, 47.2 = 3.1d. Therefore $d = \frac{47.2}{3.1} = 15.2$ and the radius is 7.6 cm (correct to two digits).

The previous examples have been examples of direct variation in which one variable, y, is directly proportional to another, x; that is, $y = mx$ for some constant, m. The following is an example of partial variation.

The cost, C, of printing election posters is partly a constant sum (the cost of setting the type, etc.) and partly variable (directly proportional to the number of copies). Thus the total cost is the sum of a constant, b, and a direct proportion. In this example $C = b + mx$, where b is the constant fixed cost, m the proportionality constant, x the number of copies, and C the total cost.

Example 3. The cost of election posters will be \$300 plus 50¢ per copy.
(a) Write an equation to represent the relationship between C and n.
(b) Draw a graph.
(c) With respect to the graph, what does 0.50 represent? What does 300 represent?
(d) From the graph, how much will 450 election posters cost?

Solution:
Let C represent the cost of the posters and n represent the number of copies.

(a) $C = 300 + 0.50n$, or
$C = 0.50n + 300$

(b)

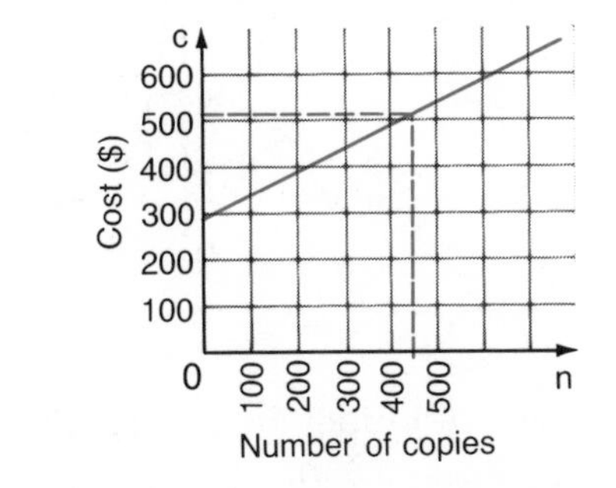

(c) By comparing $C = 0.50n + 300$ to $y = mx + b$, it can be seen that 0.50 represents m, the slope of the line, and 300 represents b, the y-intercept of the line.

(d) From the graph, 450 election posters will cost \$525.

To check, press

Display 525.

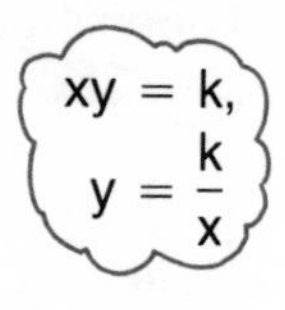

We now consider an application that does not lead to a straight line graph. If $\frac{y}{x}$ is a constant, y is directly proportional to x. If xy is a constant, we say y is inversely proportional to x. Example 4 is an example of inverse variation.

Example 4. If a rectangle has a constant area its length, ℓ, is inversely proportional to its width, w.
(a) If the area of a certain rectangle is 64 m^2, construct a table of values.
(b) Use the values in the table to draw a graph.
(c) Find ℓ when w = 12 m.

Solution:

$\ell w = 64$
$w = \frac{64}{\ell}$

(a)

ℓ(m)	1	2	4	8	16	32	64
w(m)	64	32	16	8	4	2	1

The results show that when the area is kept constant,
(i) the length must increase as the width decreases.
(ii) the width must increase as the length decreases.

(b)

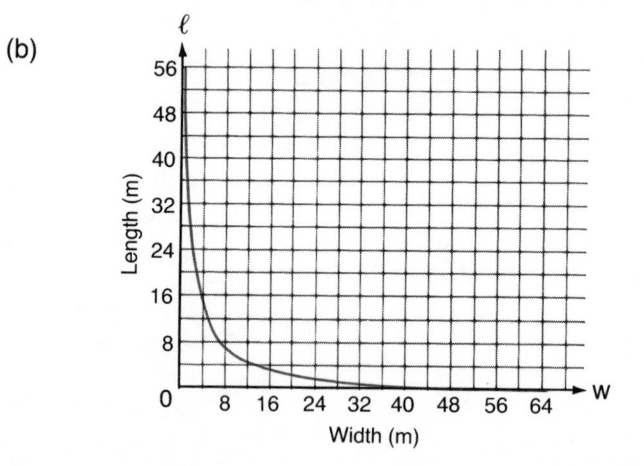

(c) From the graph, when w = 12 m, ℓ appears to be about 5.5 m.
Using the equation $\ell w = 64$, when w = 12:

$$\ell = \frac{64}{w} = \frac{64}{12} = 5\tfrac{1}{3}$$

When w = 12 m, the length $\ell = 5\frac{1}{3}$ m.

EXERCISE 5.10

B 1. (a) The distance d, in kilometres, which a car travels at a uniform speed is directly proportional to the time taken, t, in hours. If the car travels 300 km in 6 h, find an equation representing the relationship between distance and time.
(b) Draw the graph of this relation.
(c) From the graph find:
 (i) the distance travelled in 2.5 h.
 (ii) the time required to travel 500 km.

2. The cost of having a party will be \$15 plus \$1 for each guest who attends.
(a) Express the relationship between the cost, C, and the number of guests, n.
(b) Draw the graph of this linear relation using the slope and the coordinates of one point on the graph.
(c) Find from the graph the cost of having a class party of 15 girls and 13 boys.

3. The cost of a certain entertainment can be determined two ways:
(i) \$11.50 per guest;
(ii) \$10.00 per guest plus the fixed cost of \$120.00 to rent a hall.
(a) By plotting the number of guests along the x-axis and the total cost along the y-axis, draw a graph to represent methods (i) and (ii) on the same set of axes.
(b) For how many guests is the total cost the same whether you use methods (i) or (ii)?
(c) What is this cost?
(d) For how many guests is it preferable to calculate the cost by method (i)?
(e) For how many guests is it preferable to calculate the cost by method (ii)?

4. (a) Simple interest, i, in dollars, is earned in direct proportion to the time, t, in years. If \$35 interest is earned in 5 a, how much interest is earned in 2 a?
(b) How long would it take to earn \$3.50?

a comes from the Latin word for year.

5. The length of the diagonal of a square is directly proportional to the length of the side of the square.
If a square has a side of 10 m and a diagonal of approximately 14 m, find the length of a diagonal of a 50 m square.

6. The volume of a certain gas, which is kept at a constant pressure, is directly proportional to the temperature in kelvin. If 625 cm³ at 500 K are raised 50 K, what will be the resulting volume?

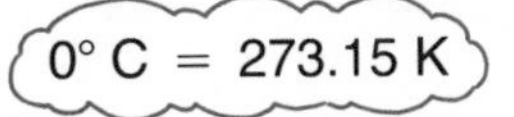

7. The length of a shadow is proportional to the height of an object. A Boy Scout found that a 6 m pole casts a 2.4 m shadow.
How high would a telephone pole be if its shadow was 9.7 m long?

8. The yearly expenses for operating an automobile are partly constant (the depreciation) and partly dependent upon the number of kilometres travelled. A certain car costs \$0.05/km to operate and depreciates \$800 during its first year. How much will it cost to drive this car 10 000 km in the first year?

9. The time taken to travel a fixed distance is inversely proportional to the speed. Suppose you are planning a 300 km trip.
(a) Draw up a table of values showing the relationship between time and speed to make this trip.
(b) Draw a graph.
(c) From the graph, how long will it take if an average speed of 45 km/h can be maintained?

10. In a given electrical circuit the voltage is directly proportional to the current. If the voltage is 9 V, then the current is 12 A.
(a) Find an equation representing the relation between the voltage (V) and the current (I).

(b) By comparing this equation to $y = mx$, where y corresponds to V and x corresponds to I, find the slope of the line.

(c) Draw the graph of the relation in (a) using the slope and the coordinates of one point on the line.

(d) From the graph complete the following table.

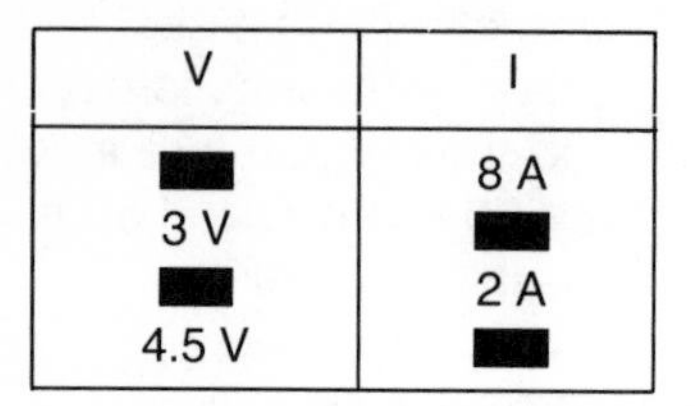

V	I
■	8 A
3 V	■
■	2 A
4.5 V	■

11. When the temperature is kept constant, the volume of a gas is inversely proportional to the pressure. If 300 cm^3 of gas are under 315 kPa of pressure, what would the pressure become if the volume were increased to 360 cm^3?

1 kPa = one kilopascal

12. The current, I in amperes, in an electrical circuit is inversely proportional to the resistance, R. If the current is 5 A, then the resistance is 2 Ω.

(a) Find an equation representing the relation between the current, I, and the resistance, R.

(b) Complete the following table.

R Ω	1	2	4	5	6	8	10
I A							

(c) Draw a graph.

(d) From the graph, complete the following.

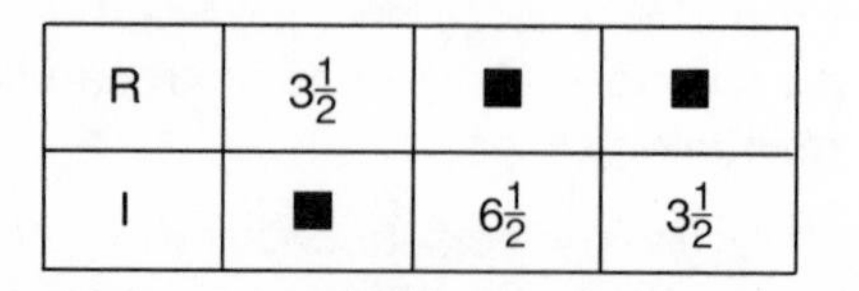

R	$3\frac{1}{2}$	■	■
I	■	$6\frac{1}{2}$	$3\frac{1}{2}$

(e) Draw a second graph by plotting R and $\frac{1}{I}$.

(f) What kind of graph is this?

MICRO MATH

SLOPE AND y-INTERCEPT

The following program computes the slope and y-intercept for an equation in standard form

$$Ax + By + C = 0$$

when you enter A, B, C.

```
NEW
10 PRINT "EQUATION OF A LINE"
20 PRINT "AX + BY + C = 0"
30 PRINT "ENTER A,B,C IN ORDER"
40 INPUT A,B,C
45 PRINT A"X";"+";B;"Y";"+";C;"=0"
50 IF B = 0 THEN PRINT "VERTICAL
   LINE; IT HAS NO SLOPE AND NO
   Y-INTERCEPT": GO TO 90
55 M = -A/B
60 I = -C/B
70 PRINT "SLOPE IS";M
80 PRINT "Y-INTERCEPT IS";I
90 END
RUN
```

EXERCISE

Run the program to find the slope and y-intercept for each of the following.

1. $x + 2y + 3 = 0$ is done for you.

```
EQUATION OF A LINE
AX + BY + C = 0
ENTER A,B,C IN ORDER
? 1,2,3
1 X + 2 Y + 3 =0
SLOPE IS -.5
Y-INTERCEPT IS -1.5
```

2. $3x - 5y + 15 = 0$

3. $4.7x - 2.8y + 6.4 = 0$

4. $5.3x + 6.7y - 4.3 = 0$

5. $4.75x + 6.85y + 7.25 = 0$

6. $43.8x + 24.7y = 0$

7. $65.1x - 10 = 0$

8. $4y - 72.4 = 0$

5.11 DISTANCE BETWEEN TWO POINTS

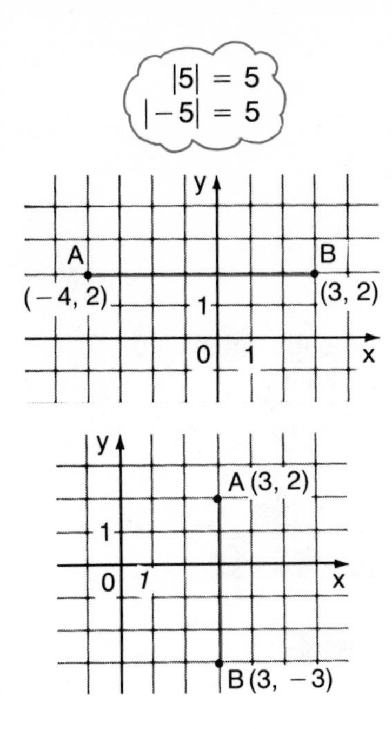

The length of a horizontal line segment may be determined by calculating $|\triangle x|$ for the line.

The symbol $|\triangle x|$ means "the magnitude of $\triangle x$."

The length of AB, $\ell_{AB} = |\triangle x|$
$= |(3) - (-4)|$
$= 7$

The length of a vertical line segment may be determined by calculating $|\triangle y|$ for the line.

The length of AB, $\ell_{AB} = |\triangle y|$
$= |(2) - (-3)|$
$= 5$

The length of any other line segment may be found by using the Pythagorean theorem.

Example 1. Find the length of the line segment from A(−2, 3) to B(3, −4).

Solution:
Construct right triangle ABC.

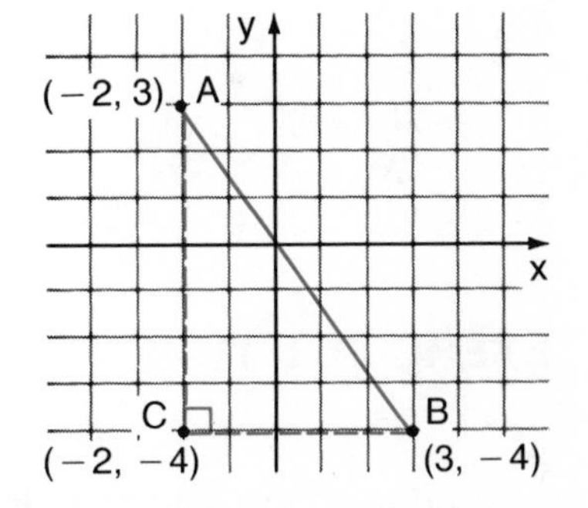

For the line segment AB,
length of BC $= |\triangle x|$
$= |(3) - (-2)|$
$= 5$
length of AC $= |\triangle y|$
$= |(3) - (-4)|$
$= 7$

By Pythagoras, $(AB)^2 = (BC)^2 + (AC)^2$

$$\therefore AB = \sqrt{(BC)^2 + (AC)^2}$$
$$= \sqrt{5^2 + 7^2}$$
$$= \sqrt{25 + 49}$$
$$= \sqrt{74}$$

Since $(BC)^2 = (\triangle x)^2$ and $(AC)^2 = (\triangle y)^2$ the length formula may be generalized as follows

$$\ell = \sqrt{(\triangle x)^2 + (\triangle y)^2}$$
$$= \sqrt{(x_2 - x_1)^2 + (y_2 - y_1)^2}$$

Example 2. Find to the nearest tenth the length of the line segment joining C(1, −3) to D(4, 7).

Solution:
$$\begin{aligned}\ell_{CD} &= \sqrt{(x_2 - x_1)^2 + (y_2 - y_1)^2}\\ &= \sqrt{(4 - 1)^2 + (7 - (-3))^2}\\ &= \sqrt{3^2 + 10^2}\\ &= \sqrt{9 + 100}\\ &= \sqrt{109}\\ &\doteq 10.4\end{aligned}$$

Example 3. Find the length of the line segment joining E(3.25, −6.48) to F(1.35, 2.78).

Solution: $\ell_{EF} = \sqrt{(1.35 - 3.25)^2 + (2.78 + 6.48)^2}$

Press

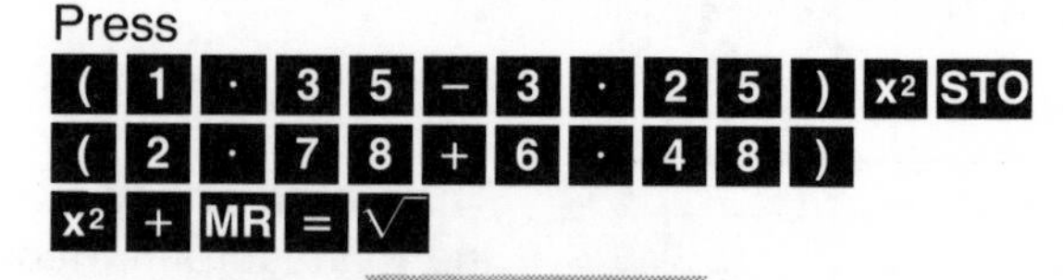

The display is 9.452914894

∴ the length of EF is 9.45.
Note that the final answer given to the nearest hundredth (two decimal places) corresponds with the given data.

EXERCISE 5.11

A

1. Determine the lengths of the following line segments.
(a) A(2, 4), B(2, 2)
(b) M(8, 6), N(2, 6)
(c) D(−3, 4), E(−3, 8)
(d) F(2, −1), G(−3, −1)
(e) M(0, 7), N(−4, 7)
(f) T(4, 0), S(−6, 0)
(g) R(6, −5), P(2, −5)
(h) Q(−6, −7), T(−6, −13)
(i) L(2, −3), S(2, 5)
(j) K(3, −11), T(−5, −11)
(k) A(0, 0), B(−3, −4)
(l) M(5, −9), N(0, 0)

B

2. Calculate the lengths of the following line segments.
(a) A(2, 3), B(1, 1)
(b) C(4, 11), B(2, 6)
(c) X(3, −7), P(2, −6)
(d) Q(−4, −2), S(3, −4)
(e) M(4, 8), N(4, 2)
(f) S(3, 6), T(−4, 6)
(g) O(0, 0), M(−4, 6)
(h) F(−2, −4), G(−3, −8)
(i) J(−2, −6), T(2, −9)
(j) A(0, −3), B(−2, −6)
(k) D(0, 5), F(4, 0)
(l) S(5, −5), M(−5, 5)

3. Find the lengths of the sides of a triangle with vertices A(10, 0), B(9, 7), C(1, 5).

4. Find the perimeter of a triangle whose vertices are D(5, 7), E(1, 10), F(−3, −8).

5. In a circle, the diameter has endpoints (4, 2) and (−2, 4).
Find its length.

6. Determine the type of the following triangles by finding the lengths of the sides in each case.
(a) (3, 2), (6, −5), (10, 5)
(b) (3, −2), (0, 2), (4, 1)
(c) (10, 0), (9, 7), (1, 5)
(d) (−1, 0), (1, 0), (0, $\sqrt{3}$)

7. A quadrilateral has vertices P(−3, 4), Q(10, 7), R(2, −8) and S(−5, −1).
What are the lengths of the diagonals?

8. Find the distance between the following pairs of points.

(a) (44.23, 66.89) and (21.26, 43.57)
(b) (163.4, 287.6) and (142.6, 283.7)
(c) (−5.713, 4.216) and (1.434, −2.745)
(d) (16.3, −15.4) and (17.4, −11.8)
(e) (0.713, 0.253) and (0.517, 0.173)
(f) (−48.21, −66.81) and (−22.43, −81.77)
(g) (0.0813, −0.0153) and (0.0716, −0.0216)
(h) (444.2, 683.7) and (581.6, 763.2)
(i) (−8.1, −9.3) and (−6.6, 7.8)
(j) (78.73, −66.66) and (−84.32, −11.75)

C

9. Show that (2, 3) is the midpoint of the line segment joining (7, 8) and (−3, −2).

10. Find the coordinates of a point on the x-axis which is equidistant from the points A(4, 8) and B(6, 6).

11. Find the coordinates of a point on the y-axis which is equidistant from C(7, −1) and D(1, 3).

MICRO MATH

DISTANCE BETWEEN TWO POINTS

The following program computes the distance from (x_1, y_1) to (x_2, y_2). In BASIC, a subscripted variable such as x_1 is entered as X1.

```
NEW
10 PRINT "DISTANCE FORMULA"
20 PRINT"(X1,Y1) TO (X2,Y2)"
30 PRINT"ENTER X1,Y1,X2,Y2 IN ORDER"
31 PRINT"SEPARATED BY COMMAS"
40 INPUT X1,Y1,X2,Y2
50 D=((X2-X1)^2+(Y2-Y1)^2)^.5
60 PRINT"THE DISTANCE IS ";D
70 END
RUN
```

The printout shows the results when you RUN the program to find the distance from (3, 4) to (7, 7).

```
DISTANCE FORMULA
(X1,Y1) TO (X2,Y2)
ENTER X1,Y1,X2,Y2 IN ORDER
SEPARATED BY COMMAS
? 3,4,7,7
THE DISTANCE IS 5
```

EXERCISE

Run the program to find the distance between the following pairs of points.

1. (1, 3) and (6, 15)
2. (7, 5) and (15, −1)
3. (5, 6) and (13, −9)
4. (2.5, 3.2) and (3.7, 3.7)
5. (14.8, 1.7) and (−6.4, 1.7)
6. (13.07, 0.01) and (12.99, −0.05)
7. (1.78, 8.48) and (−1.32, 0.56)
8. (105 −236) and (−714, 606)

5.12 SOLVING LINEAR SYSTEMS GRAPHICALLY

A pair of linear equations in two variables is called a system of equations

A solution of a system of equations is an ordered pair which satisfies both equations in the system. You can solve a system of equations by graphing each equation. The point of intersection of the two graphs, if any, is a solution of the system. Unless otherwise stated all variables represent real numbers.

Example. Solve the following system graphically.

$$x - 2y = 2 \quad ①$$
$$3x + 4y = 16 \quad ②$$

Solution:
Write each equation in the form $y = mx + b$.

① $x - 2y = 2$
$2y = x - 2$
$y = \frac{x}{2} - 1$

② $3x + 4y = 16$
$4y = -3x + 16$
$y = -\frac{3x}{4} + 4$

Draw the graph of each equation.

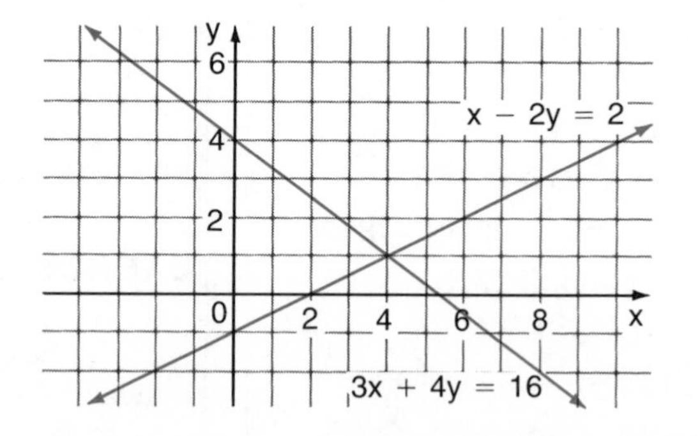

From the graph, the solution is the ordered pair (4, 1). We can check the solution by substitution.

Check in ①.
L.S. $= x - 2y$
$= 4 - 2(1)$
$= 4 - 2$
$= 2$
R.S. $= 2$

Check in ②.
L.S. $= 3x + 4y$
$= 3(4) + 4(1)$
$= 12 + 4$
$= 16$
R.S. $= 16$

When you graph two linear equations in two variables, the resulting lines may
(a) intersect at one point, (b) be parallel, (c) coincide.

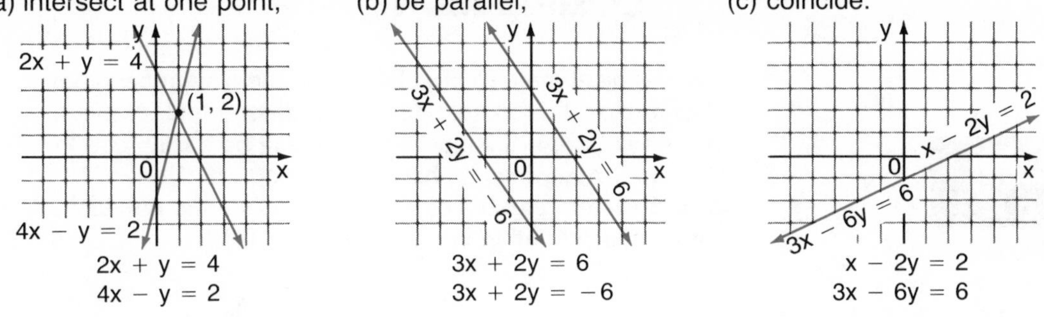

$2x + y = 4$
$4x - y = 2$

$3x + 2y = 6$
$3x + 2y = -6$

$x - 2y = 2$
$3x - 6y = 6$

Linear Systems

1. A linear system may have exactly one solution. This is true when the lines determining the system intersect at a point. Such a system is said to be consistent.
2. A linear system may have no solutions. This is true when the lines determining the system are parallel. Such a system is said to be inconsistent.
3. A linear system may have an unlimited number of solutions. This is true when the two equations defining the system determine the same straight line. Such a system is said to be dependent.

EXERCISE 5.12

B 1. Solve the following linear systems by graphing.
Check your solution in each equation. (Why check both?)

(a) $y = 2x - 6$
$y = -\frac{1}{2}x + 4$

(b) $y = 2x + 1$
$y = -x - 5$

(c) $y = \frac{1}{3}x + 2$
$y = \frac{1}{3}x - 1$

(d) $x + 4y = 2$
$x + 4y = 4$

2. If a linear system has no solution:
(a) What conclusions can be made about the lines from which the system was derived?
(b) How are the slopes related?

3. (a) By inspection, determine which of the following have no solution.

(i) $y = \frac{2}{3}x - 1$
$y = \frac{2}{3}x - \frac{1}{2}$

(ii) $y = 3x - 5$
$y = 2x - 5$

(iii) $2x + y = 5$
$6x + 3y = 7$

(iv) $x - 3y = 3$
$\frac{1}{2}x - y = \frac{3}{2}$

(b) Check your results in (a) by graphing.

4. Solve the following linear systems graphically. Check each solution by substitution.

(a) $y = \frac{1}{3}x + 3$
$y = -\frac{4}{3}x - 2$

(b) $y = \frac{3}{4}x - 1$
$y = x - 2$

(c) $y = -x + 4$
$y = -3x + 7$

(d) $y = -\frac{2}{3}x + 2$
$y = \frac{1}{2}x + 4$

5. The FB Manufacturing Co. and the Toyto Novelty Co. both produce googles, the former according to the cost relation $C = 500 + 150n$ and the latter according to the cost relation $C = 800 + 100n$, where C is in cents and n is the number of googles produced. By plotting C along the vertical axis and n along the horizontal axis, $n \geqslant 0$, determine the following.
(a) On what size order would the FB Co. have the edge in competition?
(b) On what size order would the companies be even in competition? What is the cost for this size order?
(c) On what size order would the Toyto Co. have the edge in competition?

5.13 SOLVING LINEAR SYSTEMS BY COMPARISON

The graphical method of solving a linear system becomes difficult when the coordinates of the ordered pair of the solution set are not integers and cannot be easily read from the graph. Algebraic methods of solution are needed. To solve a system algebraically we manipulate the equations so that a linear equation in one variable results.

If $a = b$
and $a = c$
then $b = c$

Example 1. Solve. $y = 2x + 3$ ①
$y = x + 7$ ②

Solution: Since $y = y$ for the point of intersection of the lines,

then $2x + 3 = x + 7$
and $2x - x = 7 - 3$
$x = 4$

$2x + 3 = y = x + 7$

Substitute in ① $y = 2x + 3$
$= 2(4) + 3$
$= 8 + 3$
$= 11$

Check in ② L.S. $= y$
$= 11$

R.S. $= x + 7$
$= 4 + 7$
$= 11$

$x = 4$ and $y = 11$

Example 2. Solve. $3x - 2y = 1$ ①
$2x - 3y = -1$ ②

Solution: Express each equation in the form $y = mx + b$.

①

$3x - 2y = 1$
$-2y = -3x + 1$
$y = \frac{3x}{2} - \frac{1}{2}$
or $y = \frac{3x - 1}{2}$

②

$2x - 3y = -1$
$-3y = -2x - 1$
$y = \frac{2}{3}x + \frac{1}{3}$
or $y = \frac{2x + 1}{3}$

$$\text{Since } y = y$$
$$\text{then } \frac{3x - 1}{2} = \frac{2x + 1}{3}$$

LCD for 2 and 3 is 6

$$6 \times \left[\frac{3x - 1}{2}\right] = 6 \times \left[\frac{2x + 1}{3}\right]$$
$$3(3x - 1) = 2(2x + 1)$$
$$9x - 3 = 4x + 2$$
$$5x = 5$$
$$x = 1$$

Substitute in ①

$$3x - 2y = 1$$
$$3(1) - 2y = 1$$
$$-2y = -2$$
$$y = 1$$

Check in ①.

L.S. $= 3x - 2y$ R.S. $= 1$
$= 3(1) - 2(1)$
$= 3 - 2$
$= 1$

Check in ②.

L.S. $= 2x - 3y$ R.S. $= -1$
$= 2(1) - 3(1)$
$= 2 - 3$
$= -1$

$$(x, y) = (1, 1)$$

EXERCISE 5.13

A 1. Express the following in the form $y = mx + b$.
(a) $2x + y = 7$
(b) $-2x + y = 4$
(c) $2x + 3y = 6$
(d) $4x - 2y = 7$
(e) $3y - 5x + 4 = 0$
(f) $3y + 2x = -4$
(g) $3x + y + 7 = 0$
(h) $-2y - 3x = 7$
(i) $x + 3y - 7 = 0$
(j) $-x - 6y - 2 = 0$

B Solve and check the following.

2. (a) $y = 3x - 1$, $y = x + 5$
(b) $y = 4x - 5$, $y = x + 7$
(c) $y = 2x + 1$, $y = x + 3$
(d) $y = -2x + 3$, $y = x + 6$

3. (a) $y = -4x + 3$, $y = -2x - 7$
(b) $y = 4x + 3$, $y = -x - 7$
(c) $y = 2x + 3$, $y = 6 - 2x$
(d) $y = x + 3$, $y = 8 - 9x$
(e) $y = 2x + 5$, $y = 3$
(f) $y = -2x + 6$, $y = 0$

4. (a) $y = x + 2$, $y = \frac{1}{2}x + 3$
(b) $y = \frac{1}{2}x - 2$, $y = \frac{1}{4}x + 1$
(c) $y = \frac{x - 1}{2}$, $y = \frac{x + 2}{3}$
(d) $y = \frac{5x + 2}{3}$, $y = 2x + 1$
(e) $y = \frac{1 - 3x}{4}$, $y = \frac{2x - 3}{2}$
(f) $y = \frac{1}{2}x + 3$, $y = \frac{2x + 1}{3}$

C 5. $x - 2y = -5$, $3x - y = 5$, and $2x + y = 0$ are the equations of three sides of a triangle. Find the coordinates of the vertices by solving the equations in pairs. Draw the figure.

5.14 SOLVING LINEAR SYSTEMS BY SUBSTITUTION

Substitution is another algebraic method of solving a system of linear equations.

Example 1. Solve. $y = 3x - 1$ ①
$5x + 3y = 11$ ②

Solution:

From ①, $y = 3x - 1$

Substituting in ② we have

$5x + 3(3x - 1) = 11$

$5x + 9x - 3 = 11$ Removing brackets

$14x = 14$ Simplifying

$x = 1$

Substitute in ① to find y.

$y = 3x - 1$

$= 3(1) - 1$

$= 2$

$(x, y) = (1, 2)$

Example 2. Solve. $2x - 3y = -13$ ①
$4x + 5y = 7$ ②

Solution:

From ① $2x - 3y = -13$

$2x = 3y - 13$

$$x = \frac{3y - 13}{2}$$

Substituting in ②.

$$4\left(\frac{3y - 13}{2}\right) + 5y = 7$$

$2(3y - 13) + 5y = 7$

$6y - 26 + 5y = 7$

$11y = 33$

$y = 3$

Substituting to find x.

$$x = \frac{3y - 13}{2}$$

$$= \frac{3(3) - 13}{2}$$

$= -2$

$(x, y) = (-2, 3)$

EXERCISE 5.14

A 1. For each of the following equations,
(a) state an expression for x
(b) an expression for y.

(i) $x + y = 13$
(ii) $2x + y = 6$
(iii) $3x - y = 4$
(iv) $2y - x = 9$
(v) $3y - 2x = -2$
(vi) $2x + 3y - 6 = 0$
(vii) $2x + 3y = 7$
(viii) $x + 3y = 0$
(ix) $5x - 4y = 8$
(x) $2x = 4y + 5$
(xi) $\frac{1}{2}x - y = \frac{1}{3}$
(xii) $\frac{1}{3}x - \frac{1}{4}y = \frac{1}{12}$

B 2. Solve the following linear systems by substitution.

(a) $y = 3x + 1$
$5x - 3y = -11$

(b) $y = 2x - 3$
$3x + y = 5$

(c) $3x + y = 4$
$2x - 3y = 43$

(d) $4x - y = 8$
$3x - 2y = 6$

3. Solve by substitution.

(a) $4x - 7y = 18$
$x - 3y = 2$

(b) $6x + 2y = 34$
$5x - 2y = -1$

(c) $5x + 4y = 0$
$4x + 5y = 9$

(d) $4x + 3y = 5$
$12x + 6y = 13$

4. Solve by substitution.

(a) $4x + 6y = 11$
$3x + 7y = 12$

(b) $3x + 4y = 4$
$12x + 12y = 13$

(c) $7x + 2y = 7$
$35x - 15y = 20$

(d) $3x + 2y = 1$
$6x + 8y = 3$

(e) $2x - 5y = 1$
$x + y = 4$

MICRO MATH

SOLVING LINEAR SYSTEMS

We can write the general case for a linear system of equations in two variables as

$ax + by = c$ ①
$dx + ey = f$ ②

Solving for x.

① × e	$aex + bey = ce$
② × b	$bdx + bey = bf$
Subtracting.	$aex - bdx = ce - bf$
Factoring.	$x(ae - bd) = ce - bf$
	$x = \dfrac{ce - bf}{ae - bd}$

Solving for y.

① × d	$adx + bdy = cd$
② × a	$adx + aey = af$
Subtracting.	$bdy - aey = cd - af$
Factoring.	$y(bd - ae) = cd - af$
	$y = \dfrac{cd - af}{bd - ae}$

The following BASIC program can be used to solve a linear system in two variables in the form

$$Ax + By = C$$
$$Dx + Ey = F$$

where the solution is consistent and independent.

```
NEW
 10 INPUT "A=";A
 20 INPUT "B=";B
 30 INPUT "C=";C
 40 INPUT "D=";D
 50 INPUT "E=";E
 60 INPUT "F=";F
 61 IF A*E < > B*D THEN 70
 62 IF A*F = C*D THEN PRINT
    "DEPENDENT SYSTEM": GOTO 110
 63 PRINT "INCONSISTENT SYSTEM":
    GOTO 110
 70 X=(C*E-B*F)/(A*E-B*D)
 80 Y=(C*D-A*F)/(B*D-A*E)
 90 PRINT "X =";X;"Y =";Y
100 PRINT "CONSISTENT AND
    INDEPENDENT SYSTEM"
110 END
RUN
```

Statements 62, 63, and 100 in this program should be entered on one line.

EXERCISE

1. Use the program to solve the following linear systems.

(a) $x + y = 9$
$x - y = 1$

(b) $2x + 3y = 35$
$5x - 2y = 2$

(c) $7x - 8y = -10$
$11x + 5y = -86$

(d) $-13x + 24y = 285$
$21x - 17y = 308$

(e) $34x - 25y = -3$
$-66x + 45y = 3$

5.15 SOLVING LINEAR SYSTEMS BY ELIMINATION

Another algebraic method of solving two simultaneous equations is based on the elimination of one of the variables by addition or subtraction.

Example 1. Solve. $x + y = 5$ ①
$x - y = 1$ ②

Solution: Add the equations vertically to eliminate one of the variables.

$$\begin{array}{rl} x + y = 5 & ① \\ \underline{x - y = 1} & ② \end{array}$$

Adding. $2x = 6$
$x = 3$

Substitute $x = 3$ in ①.

$x + y = 5$
$3 + y = 5$
$y = 2$

Check in ①.
$\text{L.S.} = x + y \quad \text{R.S.} = 5$
$= 3 + 2$
$= 5$

Check in ②.
$\text{L.S.} = x - y \quad \text{R.S.} = 3$
$= 5 - 2$
$= 3$

$\therefore x = 3, y = 2$

Example 2. Solve. $2x + y = 7$ ①
$x + y = 5$ ②

Solution: In this case, vertical addition will not eliminate one of the variables. However, vertical subtraction will.

$$\begin{array}{rl} 2x + y = 7 & ① \\ \underline{x + y = 5} & ② \\ x \quad\; = 2 & \end{array}$$

Subtracting.
(Add the opposite.)

Substitute $x = 2$ in ①.

$2x + y = 7$
$2(2) + y = 7$
$4 + y = 7$
$y = 3$

Check in ①.
$\text{L.S.} = 2x + y \quad \text{R.S.} = 7$
$= 2(2) + 3$
$= 4 + 3$
$= 7$

Check in ②.
$\text{L.S.} = x + y \quad \text{R.S.} = 5$
$= 2 + 3$
$= 5$

$\therefore x = 2, y = 3$

Example 3. Solve. $4x - 3y = 2$ ①
$3x + 5y = 16$ ②

Neither addition nor subtraction eliminates one of the variables. Elimination will not occur unless either the "x" terms or "y" terms are identical or opposites. This can be achieved by multiplication.

Solution I:
(eliminating x)

$4x - 3y = 2$ ①
$3x + 5y = 16$ ②

3 × ① $12x - 9y = 6$
4 × ② $12x + 20y = 64$

Subtracting. $-29y = -58$
$y = 2$

Substitute in ①.

$$4x - 3y = 2$$
$$4x - 3(2) = 2$$
$$4x - 6 = 2$$
$$4x = 8$$
$$x = 2$$

Check in ①.

L.S. $= 4x - 3y$
$= 4(2) - 3(2)$
$= 8 - 6$
$= 2$
R.S. $= 2$

Solution II:
(eliminating y)

$4x - 3y = 2$
$3x + 5y = 16$

5 × ① $20x - 15y = 10$
3 × ② $9x + 15y = 48$

Adding. $29x = 58$
$x = 2$

Substitute in ①.

$$4x - 3y = 2$$
$$4(2) - 3y = 2$$
$$8 - 3y = 2$$
$$-3y = -6$$
$$y = 2$$

Check in ②.

L.S. $= 3x + 5y$
$= 3(2) + 5(2)$
$= 6 + 10$
$= 16$
R.S. $= 16$

∴ The solution is (2, 2).

EXERCISE 5.15

B Solve and check.

1. (a) $3x + 2y = 13$, $3x - 2y = 5$ (b) $2x + y = 8$, $x + y = 5$
(c) $5x - y = 8$, $3x + 2y = 10$ (d) $x + 2y = 14$, $5x + 4y = 40$

2. (a) $5x + y = 15$, $2x - 3y = 6$ (b) $2x + 3y = 7$, $x + 2y = 4$
(c) $5x - 6y = 31$, $6x - 3y = 33$ (d) $2x + y = 8$, $3x + 2y = 13$

3. (a) $7x + 3y = 27$, $2x + 5y = 16$ (b) $4x + 3y = 15$, $6x - 5y = -6$
(c) $3y + 9x = 42$, $2y - 4x = -2$ (d) $2x + 7y = 30$, $7x + 2y = 15$

Solve.

4. (a) $3x = 6 - 2y$, $6y = 5x + 30$ (b) $3y + 4x = 5$, $12x + 6y = 13$
(c) $3(y + 7) - 4(x + 6) = 0$, $7(y + 5) = 2(x + 10)$

5. (a) $x + y = 11$, $\frac{1}{2}x + \frac{1}{3}y = 5$ (b) $3x - y = 23$, $\frac{x}{3} + \frac{y}{4} = 4$
(c) $0.2x + 0.5y = 10$, $3x + 4y = 108$

6. $\frac{x}{3} - \frac{y+1}{4} = \frac{3x+5y}{4} = x - 2$

5.16 PROBLEM SOLVING

PREPARATION

E=mc²

Many practical problems can be solved by first representing the information as algebraic equations and then solving these equations using the methods of the previous sections. However, before attempting these problems, you must become familiar with the technique of representing words as algebraic expressions.

READ

Example. Represent the statement "Two times a number increased by seven" as an algebraic expression.

PLAN

Solution: Begin by representing the "a number" portion of the statement by a suitable variable. In this case we choose n (the first letter of the word number).

We transform the statement into symbols as follows:

$$\underbrace{\text{Two}}_{2}\ \underbrace{\text{times}}_{\times}\ \underbrace{\text{a number}}_{n}\ \underbrace{\text{increased}}_{+}\ \underbrace{\text{by seven}}_{7}$$

The algebraic expression is $2 \times n + 7$, or $2n + 7$.

Note that this translation corresponds with our BEDMAS rules. The statement should not be translated into the expression $2(n + 7)$. This latter expression could be described by the statement, "The product of 2 and a number which has been increased by seven."

EXERCISE

B 1. Represent each of the following as an algebraic expression.

(a) x plus five
(b) four more than x
(c) y minus three
(d) six times y
(e) 3 multiplied by b
(f) the sum of four and m
(g) two added to x
(h) five less than q
(i) the difference between r and seven
(j) b divided by 4
(k) the product of x and eight
(l) twice d
(m) x plus three times x
(n) 2x divided by y
(o) four times b increased by six
(p) five times the length increased by three
(q) four times the width decreased by ten
(r) Nicole's age two years from now
(s) Melissa's age three years ago
(t) double the speed less forty
(u) six times the price less four
(v) half the radius plus two
(w) Sam's age plus twice his age
(x) twice Susan's age two years from now
(y) 5% of the cost of your text book
(z) The product of nine and the speed which has been decreased by 10

2. Represent the following as algebraic equations in one unknown.
(a) Twice the length is thirty-six.
(b) Three times John's age is twenty-seven.
(c) A number decreased by two is eight.
(d) A number increased by three is twelve.
(e) The width divided by five is twenty.
(f) Twice the width increased by two is twelve.
(g) Five times the height decreased by four is sixteen.
(h) Mary's age three years ago was seven.
(i) Double John's weight and add four and the result is eighty-four.

3. Represent the following as algebraic equations in two unknowns. Let x and y represent the unknown quantities.
(a) The sum of two numbers is twenty-one.
(b) The length and width total forty.
(c) The difference between two numbers is one.
(d) Twice the width plus three times the length is seventy.
(e) One half the base increased by three equals four times the height.
(f) When twice one number is decreased by two-thirds of another number, the result is five.
(g) A given number differs from half a smaller number by twelve.
(h) John has 15 tickets, some red and the rest yellow.

4. Write algebraic equations from each of the diagrams.

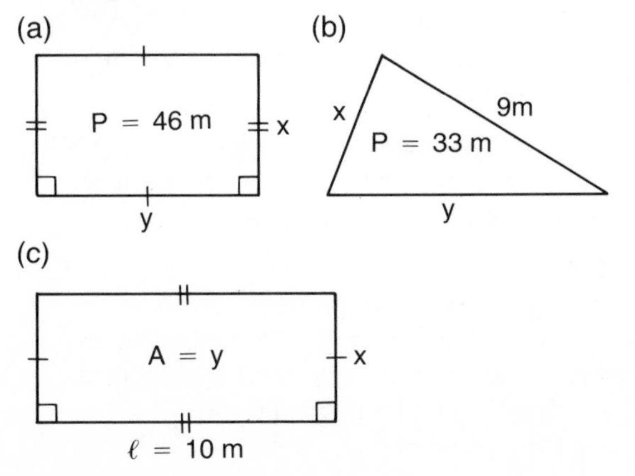

EXTRA

PERFECT SQUARES

1. When you add the odd numbers from 1 on, you get a perfect square as the sum.
$1 + 3 + 5 = 9 = 3^2$
$1 + 3 + 5 + 7 + 9 = 25 = 5^2$

2. When you add the whole numbers from 1 to a number and back to 1 again the sum is a perfect square.
$1 + 2 + 3 + 2 + 1 = 9 = 3^2$
$1 + 2 + 3 + 4 + 3 + 2 + 1 = 16 = 4^2$

3. If you add the cubes of numbers from 1 up you get a perfect square.
$1^3 + 2^3 = 9 = 3^2$
$1^3 + 2^3 + 3^3 = 36 = 6^2$

4. When you draw straight lines so that all the lines intersect and no three lines meet at the same point, the number of line segments formed is a perfect square.

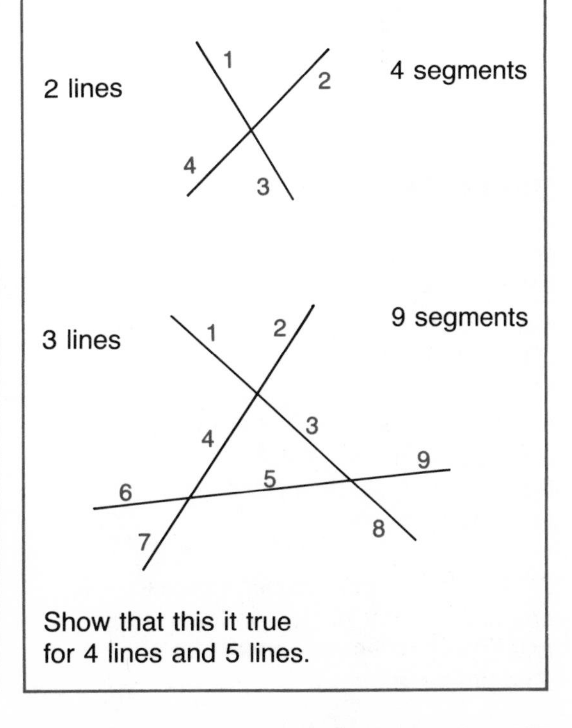

Show that this it true for 4 lines and 5 lines.

PROBLEMS INVOLVING TWO UNKNOWNS

We now combine the skills of the previous sections to solve word problems.

(i) NUMBER PROBLEMS

READ

Example 1. The sum of 2 numbers is 25. Twice the first plus 3 times the second is 70. Find the numbers.

PLAN

Solution: Let x represent the first number and y the second.

SOLVE

$$x + y = 25 \quad ①$$
$$2x + 3y = 70 \quad ②$$

① × 2 $\quad 2x + 2y = 50$

② × 1 $\quad 2x + 3y = 70$

Subtracting. $\quad -y = -20$

$$y = 20$$

Substitute y = 20 in ①. $\quad x + y = 25$

$$x + 20 = 25$$
$$x = 5$$

ANSWER

∴ the two numbers are 5 and 20.

Check in ①. $5 + 20 = 25$ (The sum is 25.)

Check in ②. $(2 \times 5) + (3 \times 20) = 70$

EXERCISE

B

5. The sum of two numbers is eight. Three times the first plus 4 times the second is 29. Find the numbers.

6. Three times one number plus twice a second number is 29. Four times the first less 3 times the second is 16. Find the numbers.

7. Four times one number increased by one half another number is 24. Three times the first less the second is 7. Find the numbers.

8. The sum of two numbers is 9. Ten times the first plus eight times the second is 76. Find the numbers.

9. The difference between two numbers is five. Twice the larger plus six times the smaller is 26. Find the numbers.

C

10. Two times one number less 3 times a second number is 6. The product of three and the first less twice the second is 7 after being increased by 4. Find the numbers.

(ii) MONEY PROBLEMS

READ

Example 2. Tony had \$1.85 in dimes and quarters. If there were 11 coins in all, how many dimes did he have?

PLAN

Solution:

Let x represent the number of quarters.
Let y represent the number of dimes.

E=mc²

x quarters = 25x ¢
y dimes = 10y ¢
\$1.85 = 185 ¢

$$25x + 10y = 185 \quad ①$$
$$x + y = 11 \quad ②$$

SOLVE

$$① \quad 25x + 10y = 185$$
$$10 \times ② \quad 10x + 10y = 110$$

Subtracting.
$$15x = 75$$
$$x = 5$$

Substitute x = 5 in ②.
$$x + y = 11$$
$$5 + y = 11$$
$$y = 6$$

ANSWER

∴ He had six dimes.

Check in ①. \$0.25 × 5 + \$0.10 × 6 = \$1.85
Check in ②. 5 quarters + 6 dimes = 11 coins

EXERCISE

B

11. Kim paid \$3.95 for a notebook. If he used dimes and quarters and there were 20 coins in all, how many dimes did he have?

12. A grade one class collected \$3.55 in nickels and dimes for the Red Cross. There were 56 coins. How many of each coin were there?

13. Tony bought a new suit for \$185. He paid the bill using \$5 bills and \$10 bills. If there were 26 bills in all, how many \$5 bills did he use?

14. Curt paid \$1760 for a used sports car. He used \$100 bills and \$20 bills to pay for it. If there were 28 bills in all, how many of each did he have?

15. A storekeeper wishes to mix tea worth \$15.00/kg with tea worth \$19.00/kg to make 100 kg of mixture valued at \$17.20/kg. How many kilograms of each kind should she use?

16. A sum of \$7.40 is made up of quarters and dimes. If there are 10 more quarters than dimes, how many coins of each kind are there?

C

17. Mr. Cane mixes jelly beans at \$4.00/kg with saltwater taffy at \$8.00/kg resulting in a 100 kg candy mixture worth \$4.80/kg. How many kilograms of each candy are in the mixture?

(iii) PERCENT PROBLEMS

READ

Example 3. Mark invested \$1500, part at 5% interest and part at 6%. If the interest on his investments totalled \$85, how much did he invest at each rate?

PLAN

Solution:
Let \$x be the amount invested at 5%.
Let \$y be the amount invested at 6%.

E=mc²

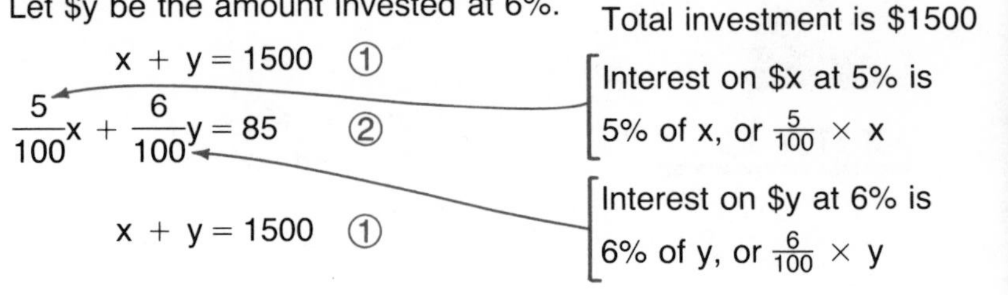

$$x + y = 1500 \quad ①$$
$$\frac{5}{100}x + \frac{6}{100}y = 85 \quad ②$$

SOLVE

$$x + y = 1500 \quad ①$$

100 × ② to clear fractions $5x + 6y = 8500$ ②

5 × ① $5x + 5y = 7500$ ①

$5x + 6y = 8500$ ②

Subtracting. $-y = -1000$

$y = 1000$

Substitute $y = 1000$ in ①

$x + y = 1500$

$x + 1000 = 1500$

$x = 500$

ANSWER

∴ He invested \$500 at 5% and \$1000 at 6%.

Check in ①. 500 + 1000 = 1500 Total investment was \$1500

Check in ②. 5% of \$500 is \$25 Total interest on investments is \$85
6% of \$1000 is \$60
\$25 + \$60 = \$85

EXERCISE

B 18. Mary invested \$2000, part at 4% interest and part at 7%.
If the interest on her investments totalled \$92, how much did she invest at each rate?

19. The interest on Ruby's two investments totalled \$367. She had invested a total of \$3500, part at 11% and part at 10%.
How much did she invest at each rate?

20. By investing \$5000, part at 8% and part at 9%, Terry received \$420 in interest.
How much did he invest at each rate?

21. Keino invested \$200 and received \$13.50 in interest. Part of the \$200 was invested at 7%, the remainder at 6%.
How much did he invest at each rate?

C 22. Brian invested \$3500, part at 6% interest and part at 9% interest. The interest received at the higher rate was double the interest received at the lower rate.
How much was invested at each rate?

(iv) DISTANCE – RATE – TIME PROBLEMS

It is usual to represent distance by d, rate by r, and time by t.

$$\text{Rate} = \frac{\text{Distance}}{\text{Time}} \qquad \text{Time} = \frac{\text{Distance}}{\text{Rate}} \qquad \text{Distance} = \text{Rate} \times \text{Time}$$

$$r = \frac{d}{t} \qquad t = \frac{d}{r} \qquad d = rt$$

READ

Example 4. On a motor trip of 470 km, Sam drove part of the way at 100 km/h and the remainder at 90 km/h. If the total trip took 5 h, how far did he drive at each rate?

PLAN

Solution:
Let the distance travelled at 100 km/h be x.
Let the distance travelled at 90 km/h be y.
Set up a distance/rate/time table.

The following triangle helps us to remember the relationship between distance, rate, and time.

D
R | T

D = RT

$R = \frac{D}{T}$

$T = \frac{D}{R}$

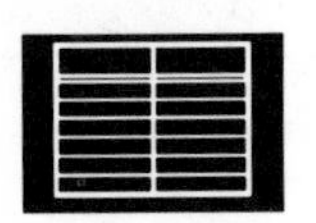

d	r	t
x	100 km/h	$\frac{x}{100}$
y	90 km/h	$\frac{y}{90}$

SOLVE

$x + y = 470$ ① Total distance is 470 km

$\frac{x}{100} + \frac{y}{90} = 5$ ② Total time is 5 h

$x + y = 470$ ①

900 × ② to clear fractions $9x + 10y = 4500$ ②

9 × ① $9x + 9y = 4230$ ①

$9x + 10y = 4500$ ②

Subtracting. $-y = -270$

$y = 270$

Substitute $y = 270$ in ①.

$x + y = 470$

$x + 270 = 470$

$x = 200$

ANSWER

∴ He drove 200 km at 100 km/h and 270 km at 90 km/h.

Check in ①. $200 + 270 = 470$ Total distance is 470 km.

Check in ②. $\frac{200}{100} + \frac{270}{90} = 5$ Total time is 5 h.

EXERCISE

23. The distance from Vancouver to Halifax is 6251 km.
(a) How many days would it take to drive from Halifax to Vancouver if you average 800 km/d?
(b) How many hours of driving time are required to drive this distance at an average speed of 63 km/h?
(c) What average speed is required to drive this distance in 300 h of driving time?
(d) What average distance must be travelled each day in order to drive this distance in 9 d?
(e) A commercial passenger jet flies from Vancouver to Halifax at an average speed of 575 km/h.
What is the flying time required, including a 1 h stopover for refuelling in Toronto?

24. From the following DRT chart, state
(a) the total distance,
(b) the total time,
(c) the difference in time.

D(km)	R(km/h)	T(h)
x	85	
y	75	

25. From the following DRT chart, state
(a) the rate for each distance,
(b) the difference in time,
(c) the total distance.

D(km)	R(km/h)	T(h)
x		
y		

26. From the following DRT chart, state
(a) an equation, if the total time is 6 h.
(b) an equation, if the total distance is 300 km.

D(km)	R(km/h)	T(h)
x	100	
y	90	

B 27. On a trip of 600 km, Zoe drove part of the way at 80 km/h and the remainder at 90 km/h.
If the total trip took 7 h, how far did she drive at each rate?

28. Bill drove for 5.5 h, part of the time at 90 km/h and part at 70 km/h. He covered a distance of 445 km.
How far did he drive at each rate?

29. A car covered a total distance of 205 km averaging a speed of 90 km/h on highways and 35 km/h on country roads. The trip took 3.5 h.
How many hours and how many kilometres did the car travel on country roads?

30. Two persons, 18 km apart, setting out at the same time meet in 4.5 h if they walk in the same direction, but in 2 h if they walk towards each other.
Find their rates of walking.

C 31. A commercial airliner travelled 4725 km with the wind in $4\frac{1}{2}$ h and returned the same distance against the wind in $5\frac{1}{4}$ h.
Find
(a) its airspeed in still air,
(b) the wind velocity.

MIND BENDER

A car travels from New York to Edmonton at an average speed of 80 km/h and returns at an average speed of 60 km/h.
What was the average speed for the round trip?

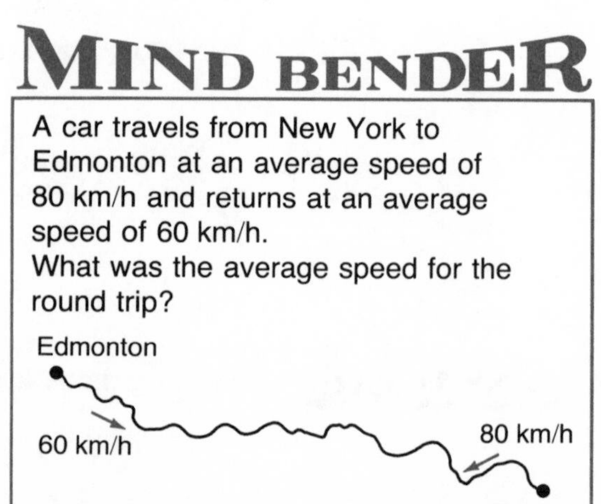

EXTRA

5.17 MIDPOINT

The coordinates of the midpoint of the segment joining $P_1(x_1, y_1)$ to $P_2(x_2, y_2)$ are
$$\left(\frac{x_1 + x_2}{2}, \frac{y_1 + y_2}{2}\right)$$

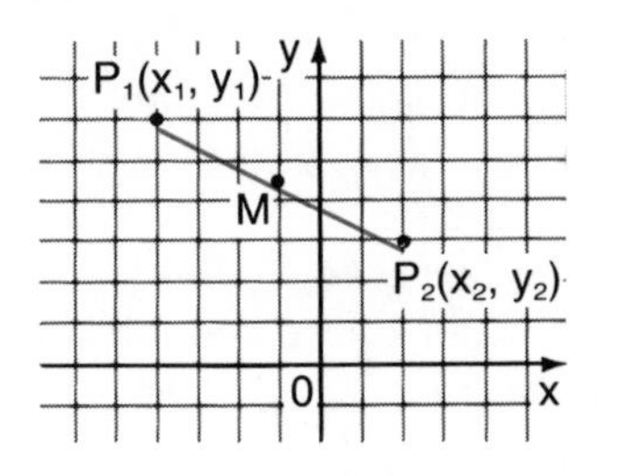

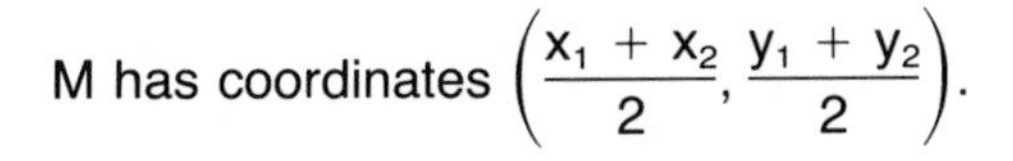

M has coordinates $\left(\frac{x_1 + x_2}{2}, \frac{y_1 + y_2}{2}\right)$.

Example. Find the midpoint of the segment joining $P_1(-3, 4)$ to $P_2(5, 6)$.

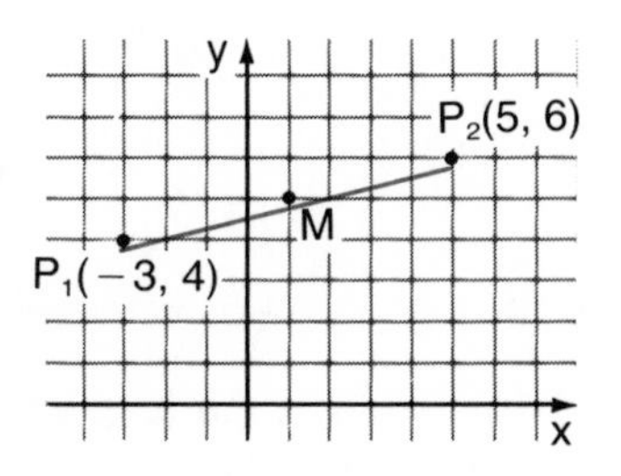

Solution:
Let the coordinates of M be (x, y). Then:

$$x = \frac{x_1 + x_2}{2} = \frac{-3 + 5}{2} = 1 \qquad y = \frac{y_1 + y_2}{2} = \frac{4 + 6}{2} = 5$$

The midpoint is M(1, 5).

EXERCISE 5.17

1. Find the equation of the median PS.

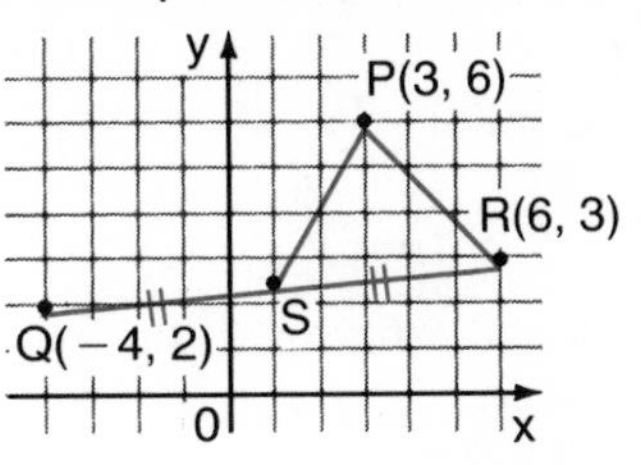

2. Find the equation of the right bisector of AB.

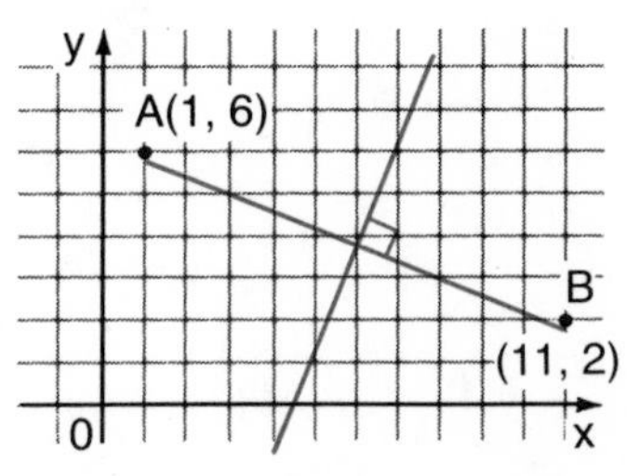

3. Find the equation of the right bisector of CD.

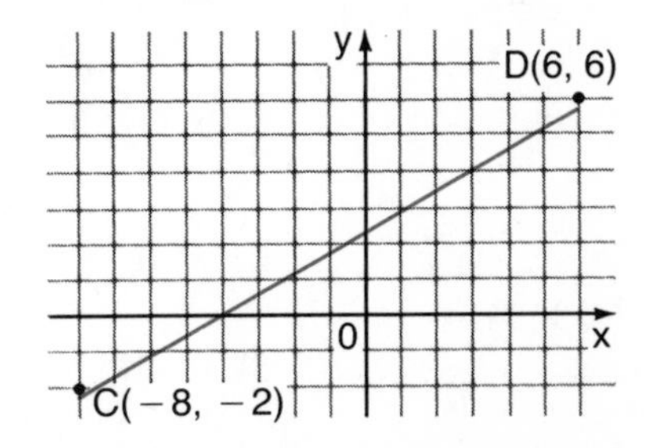

4. Find the equation of the radius of the circle.

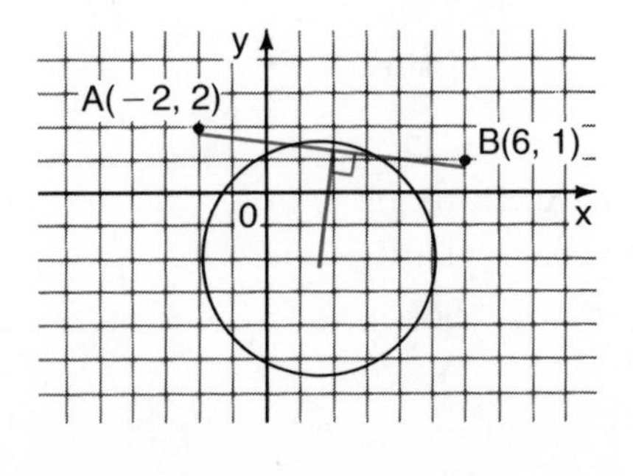

5.18 REVIEW EXERCISE

1. Determine the slope of the line passing through:
(a) (5, 10) and (8, 6)
(b) (16, 1) and (10, −2)
(c) (2, 1) and (5, −6)
(d) (−4, −2) and (−1, 7)
(e) (−1, 4) and (−3, −5)
(f) (6, −5) and (2, −7)

2. Determine the lengths of the following line segments.
(a) D(0, 3), E(4, 2)
(b) A(−1, −1), B(6, −3)
(c) G(9, 8), H(3, 4)
(d) D(−1, −2), E(3, −2)
(e) R(4, −3), T(−2, 4)
(f) M(6, 6), N(2, 2)
(g) Q(−3, 0), R(0, −3)
(h) A(3, 0), B(9, 0)

3. Draw the graph of each of the following lines.
(a) $y = 2x - 7$
(b) $y = -3x + 2$
(c) $2x - 5y = 10$
(d) $3y - 2x - 6 = 0$
(e) $3x = y - 10$
(f) $y = \frac{2x - 1}{3}$

4. Find the equation of the lines given the following conditions.
(a) point (3, −2), slope $\frac{1}{2}$
(b) point (−1, 7), slope $-\frac{3}{5}$
(c) y-intercept −4, slope −6
(d) y-intercept $\frac{2}{3}$, slope 4
(e) points (−1, 5), (9, 0)
(f) points (7, 12), (5, −2)
(g) point $(\frac{2}{3}, -\frac{1}{3})$, slope 2
(h) point (0, 6), slope $\frac{2}{3}$
(i) points (0, 6), (3, 0)
(j) point (2, 4), slope 0

5. Find the solution for each of the following linear systems.
(a) $2x + y = 3$
$5x - 2y = 3$
(b) $x + 2y = -3$
$3x - y = 5$
(c) $2x - y = -2$
$x - 2y = 2$
(d) $3x + 2y = 4$
$5x - 3y = 13$
(e) $3m - n = 3$
$3m - 5n = 3$
(f) $y = 2x - 7$
$y = 3 - 3x$
(g) $\frac{1}{5}x + \frac{1}{2}y = 5$
$x - y = 4$
(h) $\frac{a}{2} - \frac{b}{5} = 4$
$\frac{a}{7} + \frac{b}{15} = 3$
(i) $3(x - 1) + 2(y + 3) = 4$
$4(x + 1) - (y - 2) = 0$

6. (a) The line joining (x, 2) and (1, 0) is parallel to the line joining (−2, 1) and (2, 3). Find x.
(b) The line joining (x, 2) and (1, 0) is perpendicular to the line joining (−2, 1) and (2, 3). Find x.

7. Plot the points G(4, 1), H(2, 3), J(6, 4), K(8, 2).
(a) Show that GHJK is a parallelogram.
(b) Is GHJK a rectangle?

8. Determine the equation of each line in the form $Ax + By + C = 0$
(a) passing through (−4, 3) with slope $\frac{1}{2}$
(b) passing through (0, 5) with slope −2
(c) passing through (2, 0) with slope $\frac{3}{4}$
(d) passing through (−1, −3) with slope $-\frac{2}{3}$
(e) passing through (2, −5) with slope $\frac{2}{5}$

9. Write the equation of the line with the same y-intercept as $y = 3x + 4$ and having slope −1.

10. Write the equation of the line perpendicular to $y = 3x - 2$ and passing through (3, 2).

11. Determine the equation of a line through (1, 2) with slope $-\frac{1}{4}$.

12. Determine the equation of a line through (−2, −3) parallel to $5x + 3y = 2$.

13. Determine the equation of the line passing (3, 5) and perpendicular to $3x - 2y + 13 = 0$.

14. Write the equation of the line whose x- and y-intercepts are 5 and -3 respectively.

15. Find the slope and y-intercept of $3x + 2y = 7$.

16. Determine the value of k so that:
(a) $4x - ky = 7$ has slope 3.
(b) $kx - y = -15$ has x-intercept 5.

17. What must be the value of m if the line $y = mx + 7$ passes through $(-2, 5)$?

18. Find the equation of the straight line parallel to $6x - 7y = 13$ and passing through $(-2, -5)$.

19. Find the equation of the straight line through (2, 6) and perpendicular to the line through $(-3, 5)$ and $(7, -1)$.

20. Calculate the length of A(7, 2), B(-3, 4) correct to two decimal places.

21. Find the area of a quadrilateral whose vertices are P(4, -3), Q(2, 3), R(3, 3), and S(-6, -1).

22. The sum of two numbers is 18. Four times the first plus twice the second is 50. Find the numbers.

23. Three times a number plus twice a second number is 41. Four times the first plus five times the second is 71. Find the numbers.

24. Sean had $1.90 in dimes and nickels. If there were 25 coins in all, how many dimes did he have?

25. Denise invested $4000, part at 7% and part at 8%. The interest rate on her investment totalled $310. How much did she invest at each rate?

26. The total interest on an investment was $109. The investment was $1100, part invested at 9% and the remainder at 11%. How much was invested at each rate?

27. On a trip of 625 km, Yoko drove part of the way at 95 km/h and the remainder at 85 km/h. If the total trip took 7 h, how far did she drive at each rate?

28. Find the point on the y-axis which is on the line through $(6, -3)$ and $(-12, 12)$.

29. A perpendicular from the point $(4, -2)$ to a line meets the line at the point $(-3, 1)$. Find the equation of the line.

30. Find the equation of a line with slope $\frac{2}{3}$ and having the same y-intercept as the line $2x - 5y + 20 = 0$.

31. Find the coordinates of the point on the x-axis so that the slope of the line joining it to $(5, -2)$ is $-\frac{3}{4}$.

32. The y-intercept of a line is -4 and it passes through $(-2, 5)$. Find the equation of the line.

33. Find the value of k if $3x - 2y + 5 = 0$ and $6x + ky + 9 = 0$ are parallel.

34. Find the equation of each side of the triangle PQR.

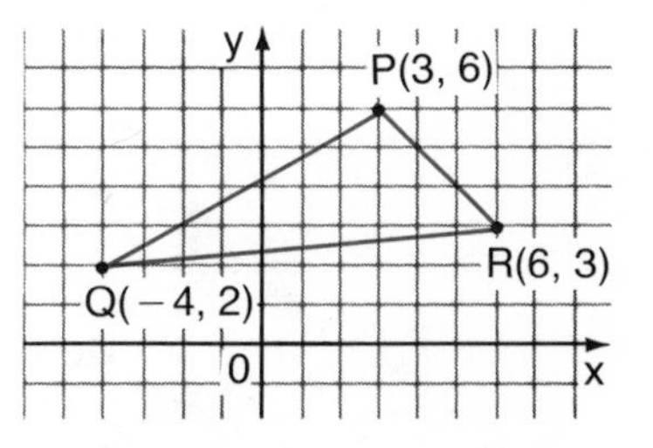

35. Find the equation of the median AD.

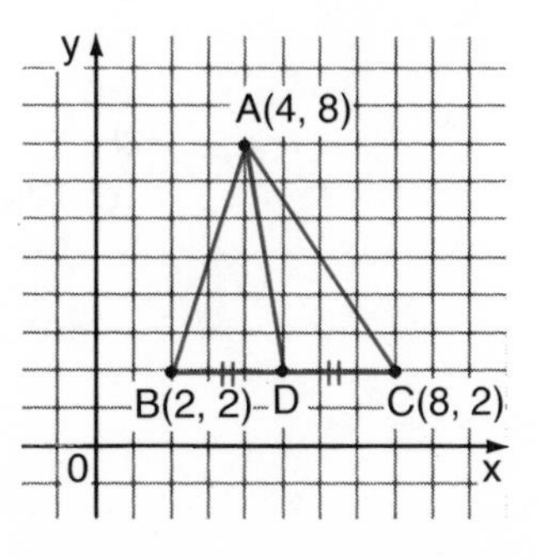

5.19 CHAPTER 5 TEST

1. Determine the slope of the line between
(a) $(-2, 4)$ and $(7, 8)$ (b) $(-3, -4)$ and $(-6, -8)$

2. Find the distance between
(a) $(-1, 5)$ and $(7, 8)$ (b) $(-8, 3)$ and $(4, 3)$

3. Find the equation of the line given the following conditions.
(a) point $(2, -4)$, slope 2
(b) point $(-3, -2)$ and point $(7, -8)$
(c) x-intercept 2 and point $(5, -2)$
(d) y-intercept 3 and point $(1, 3)$

4. Determine the slope of the lines represented by each of the following.
(a) $y = -2x + 6$ (b) $3x - 4y = 7$

5. State the x- and y- intercept of the lines represented by each of the following.
(a) $y = -4x + 5$ (b) $-3x + 4y - 5 = 0$

6. Determine an equation for the following lines.
(a) (b)

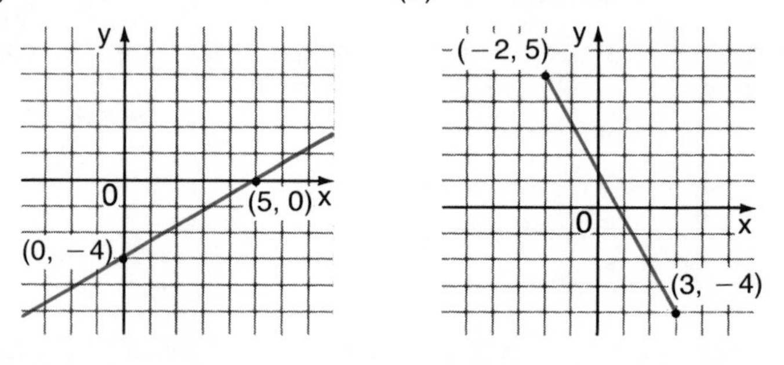

7. Solve the following system of equations.
(a) $3x - 4y = 4$
$5x + 4y = 12$
(b) $y = -2x + 4$
$x = -2y + 4$

8. The cost of skiing is \$25 for club membership plus \$8 a day for the tow ticket.
(a) Prepare a table of values for 0 to 10 days.
(b) Draw a graph to show the cost for 0 to 10 days of skiing.
(c) Write an equation where C is the cost in dollars and n is the number of days.

APPLICATIONS OF MEASUREMENT

REVIEW AND PREVIEW TO CHAPTER 6

EXERCISE 1

Multiply each of the following by 10.

(a) 23 (b) 2.3 (c) 0.23
(d) 3.1 (e) 0.51 (f) 0.02
(g) 0.07 (h) 1.40 (i) 9.08

EXERCISE 2

Multiply each of the following by 100.

(a) 23 (b) 2.3 (c) 0.23
(d) 5.2 (e) 6.1 (f) 0.61
(g) 6.061 (h) 0.001 (i) 0.0004

EXERCISE 3

Multiply each of the following by 1000.

(a) 23 (b) 2.3 (c) 0.23
(d) 7.4 (e) 9.01 (f) 10.01
(g) 0.02 (h) 0.102 (i) 0.0006

EXERCISE 4

Divide each of the following by 10.

(a) 23 (b) 2.3 (c) 0.23
(d) 52 (e) 67 (f) 7.4
(g) 0.01 (h) 0.61 (i) 14.02

EXERCISE 5

Divide each of the following by 100.

(a) 23 (b) 2.3 (c) 0.23
(d) 62 (e) 785 (f) 9001
(g) 0.01 (h) 85 604 (i) 0.002 01

EXERCISE 6

Divide each of the following by 1000.

(a) 23 (b) 2.3 (c) 0.23
(d) 5.1 (e) 104 (f) 11 709
(g) 110 (h) 10 170 (i) 0.0023

EXERCISE 7

1 cm = 10 mm

Convert each of the following to millimetres.

(a) 5.1 cm (b) 6.2 cm (c) 0.1 cm
(d) 0.01 cm (e) 10.2 cm (f) 64.20 cm
(g) 901 cm (h) 100.2 cm (i) 10.61 cm

EXERCISE 8

1 m = 100 cm

Convert each of the following to centimetres.

(a) 5 m (b) 5.1 m (c) 0.9 m
(d) 0.02 m (e) 6.4 m (f) 0.005 m
(g) 19.02 m (h) 0.105 m (i) 650 m

EXERCISE 9

1 m^3 = 1000 L

Convert each of the following to litres.

(a) 1 m^3 (b) 1.1 m^3
(c) 0.5 m^3 (d) 1.04 m^3
(e) 15.05 m^3 (f) 19.404 m^3
(g) 0.002 01 m^3 (h) 0.02 m^3
(i) 1.019 m^3 (j) 6 m^3
(k) 17.201 m^3 (l) 0.505 m^3

EXERCISE 10

Convert each of the following to centimetres.

(a) 5 mm (b) 15 mm
(c) 3.10 mm (d) 50 mm
(e) 500 mm (f) 26 mm
(g) 17.1 mm (h) 0.01 mm

EXERCISE 11

Convert each of the following to metres.

(a) 50 cm (b) 10 cm (c) 15 cm
(d) 1.5 cm (e) 105 cm (f) 1215 cm
(g) 0.01 cm (h) 194.5 cm (i) 32.64 cm

THREE-DIMENSIONAL FIGURES

We use the following rules to draw figures in three dimensions. Graph paper is used to indicate the positions of lines in order to show how the rules are used.

1. Parallel edges in space are represented by parallel lines on the page.

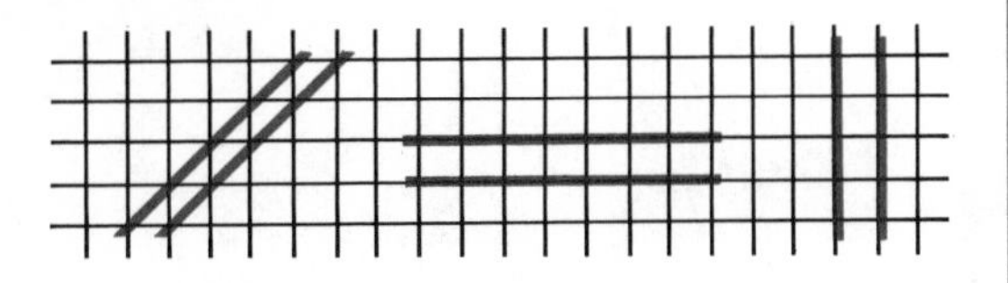

2. Edges that are invisible to us are drawn with broken lines.

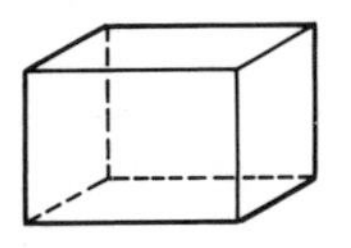

3. When drawing scale figures on squared graph paper, edges which are perpendicular to the page are drawn diagonally through the squares. Each square's diagonal represents two units.

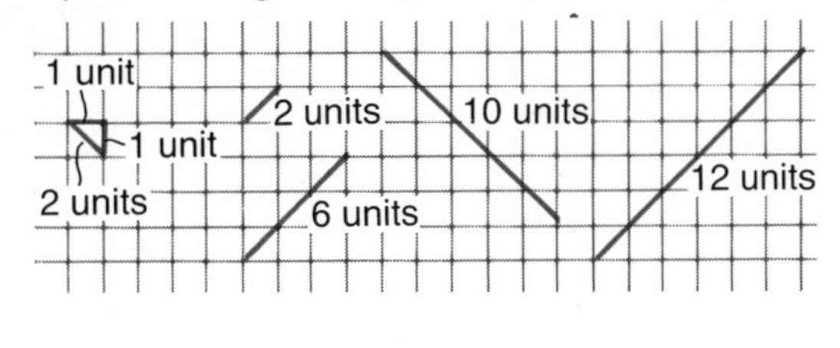

4. Circular faces in space can be represented by circles or ellipses, depending on the view.

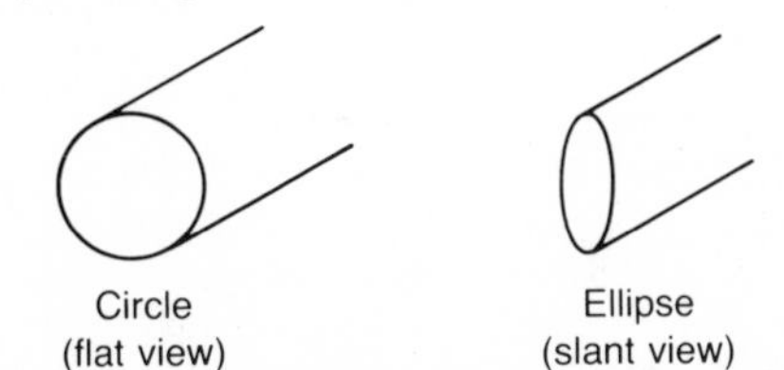
Circle (flat view)   Ellipse (slant view)

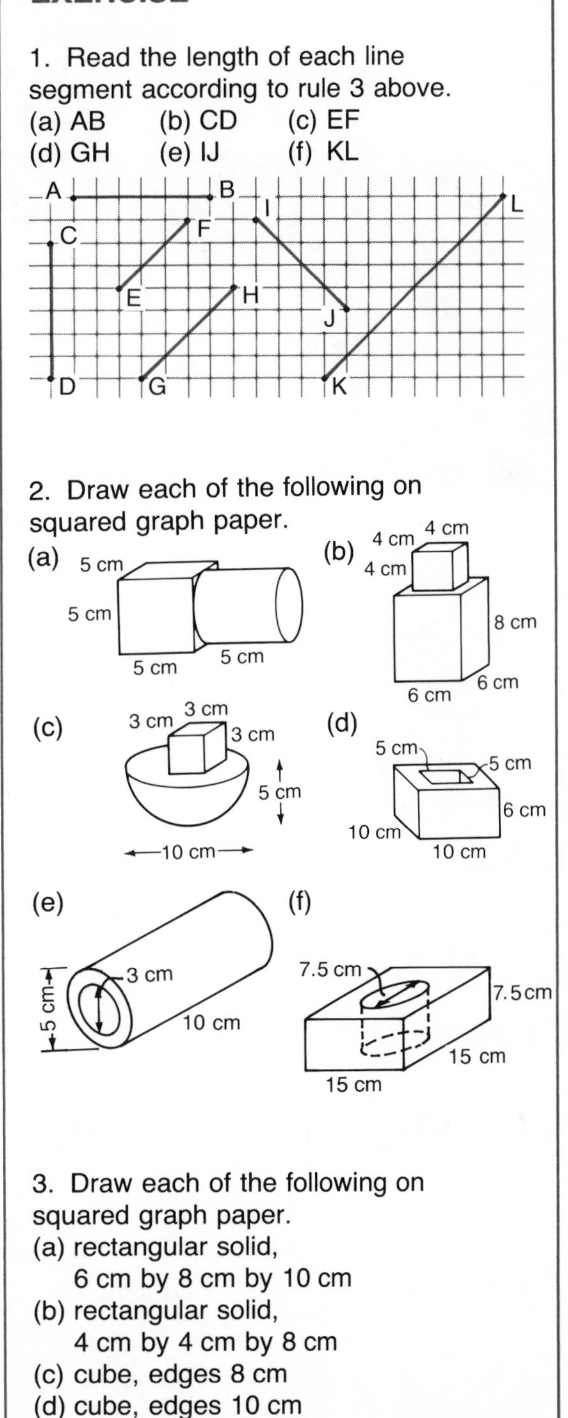

EXERCISE

1. Read the length of each line segment according to rule 3 above.
(a) AB (b) CD (c) EF
(d) GH (e) IJ (f) KL

2. Draw each of the following on squared graph paper.
(a) (b) (c) (d) (e) (f)

3. Draw each of the following on squared graph paper.
(a) rectangular solid, 6 cm by 8 cm by 10 cm
(b) rectangular solid, 4 cm by 4 cm by 8 cm
(c) cube, edges 8 cm
(d) cube, edges 10 cm
(e) cylinder, radius 10 cm, height 8 cm

6.1 PERIMETER

The distance around a figure is called the perimeter. Problems involving perimeter occur in many situations. Picture framing, fencing fields, and sports car driving are three examples.

The tennis court in the picture has dimensions of 33.5 m by 13.6 m. It would require 94.2 m of fence to go around the perimeter of the court.

The table gives the formulas for the perimeters of some figures. The perimeter of a circle is called the circumference.

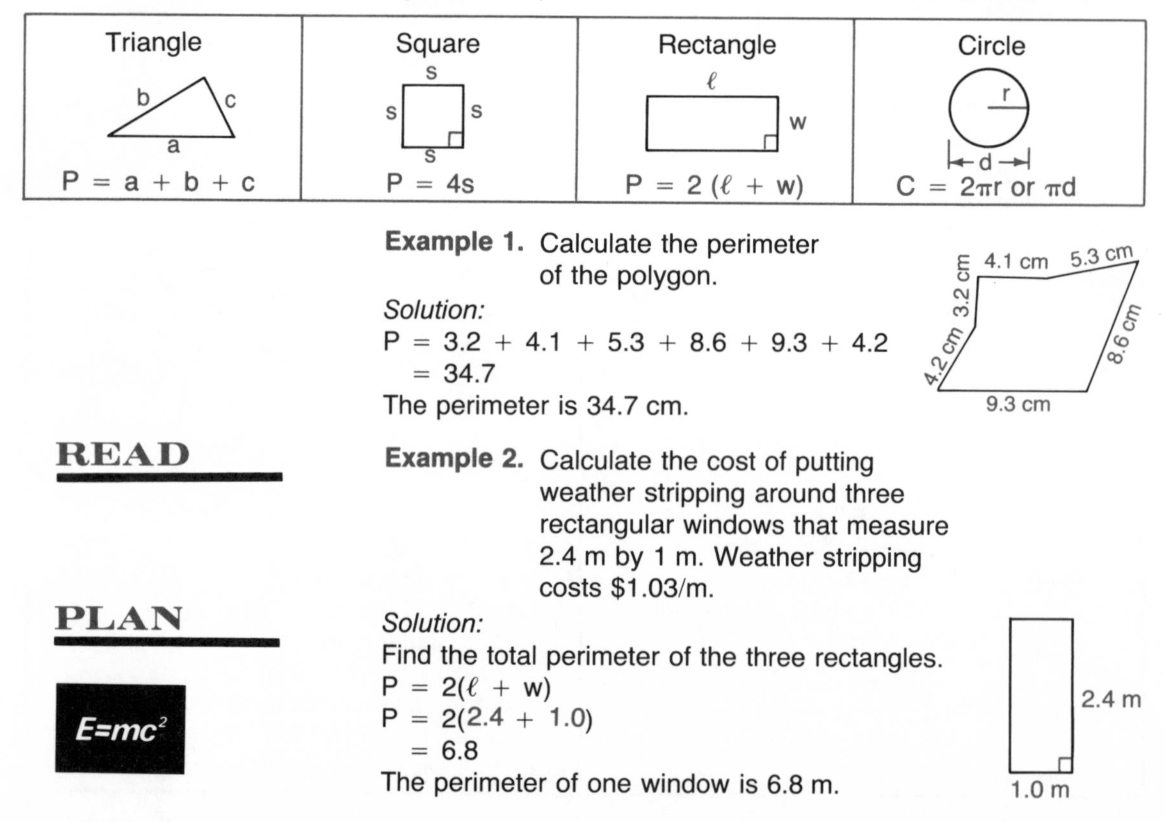

Triangle	Square	Rectangle	Circle
$P = a + b + c$	$P = 4s$	$P = 2(\ell + w)$	$C = 2\pi r$ or πd

Example 1. Calculate the perimeter of the polygon.

Solution:

$P = 3.2 + 4.1 + 5.3 + 8.6 + 9.3 + 4.2$
$= 34.7$

The perimeter is 34.7 cm.

READ

Example 2. Calculate the cost of putting weather stripping around three rectangular windows that measure 2.4 m by 1 m. Weather stripping costs \$1.03/m.

PLAN

E=mc²

Solution:

Find the total perimeter of the three rectangles.

$P = 2(\ell + w)$
$P = 2(2.4 + 1.0)$
$= 6.8$

The perimeter of one window is 6.8 m.

SOLVE

For three windows you need 6.8 m × 3 = 20.4 m of weather stripping. The cost of weather stripping is calculated 20.4 × 1.03 = 21.012

ANSWER

The weather stripping costs $21.02 (to the next cent).

Using a calculator, press
2 · 4 + 1 = × 2 × 3
× 1 · 0 3 =

The display is 21.012

READ

Example 3. A window is in the shape of a 1.8 m by 0.9 m rectangle surmounted by a semi-circle. Determine to the next metre the required length of a string of Christmas lights to surround the window. Use $\pi = 3.14$

0.9 m
1.8 m

PLAN

Solution:
The perimeter of the window may be found by calculating the perimeter of the semi-circular portion, and adding to this the lengths of the three sides of the rectangular portion.

When using a calculator, press π and the display is 3.14159
Without a calculator, use $\pi = 3.14$

SOLVE

Perimeter of the semi-circular portion:

$P_1 = \frac{1}{2} \times \pi \times d$

$P_1 = \frac{1}{2} \times 3.14 \times 0.9$
$= 1.4$ (to the nearest tenth)

The perimeter of the semi-circle is 1.4 m.

Perimeter of the remaining three sides:

$P_2 = 1.8 \times 2 + 0.9$
$= 4.5$

The additional perimeter is 4.5 m.
The total perimeter is 1.4 m + 4.5 m = 5.9 m.

ANSWER

The required length of the string of lights is 6 m to the next metre).

Using a calculator, press

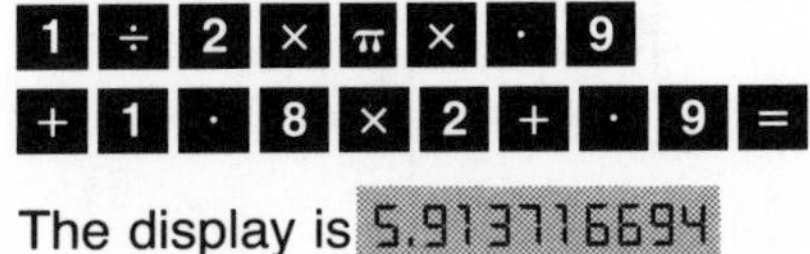

The perimeter is 6 m (to the next metre).

EXERCISE 6.1

B

1. Calculate the perimeter of each polygon.

2. Find any missing dimensions. Then calculate the perimeter of each figure.

3. Find the perimeter of each figure.

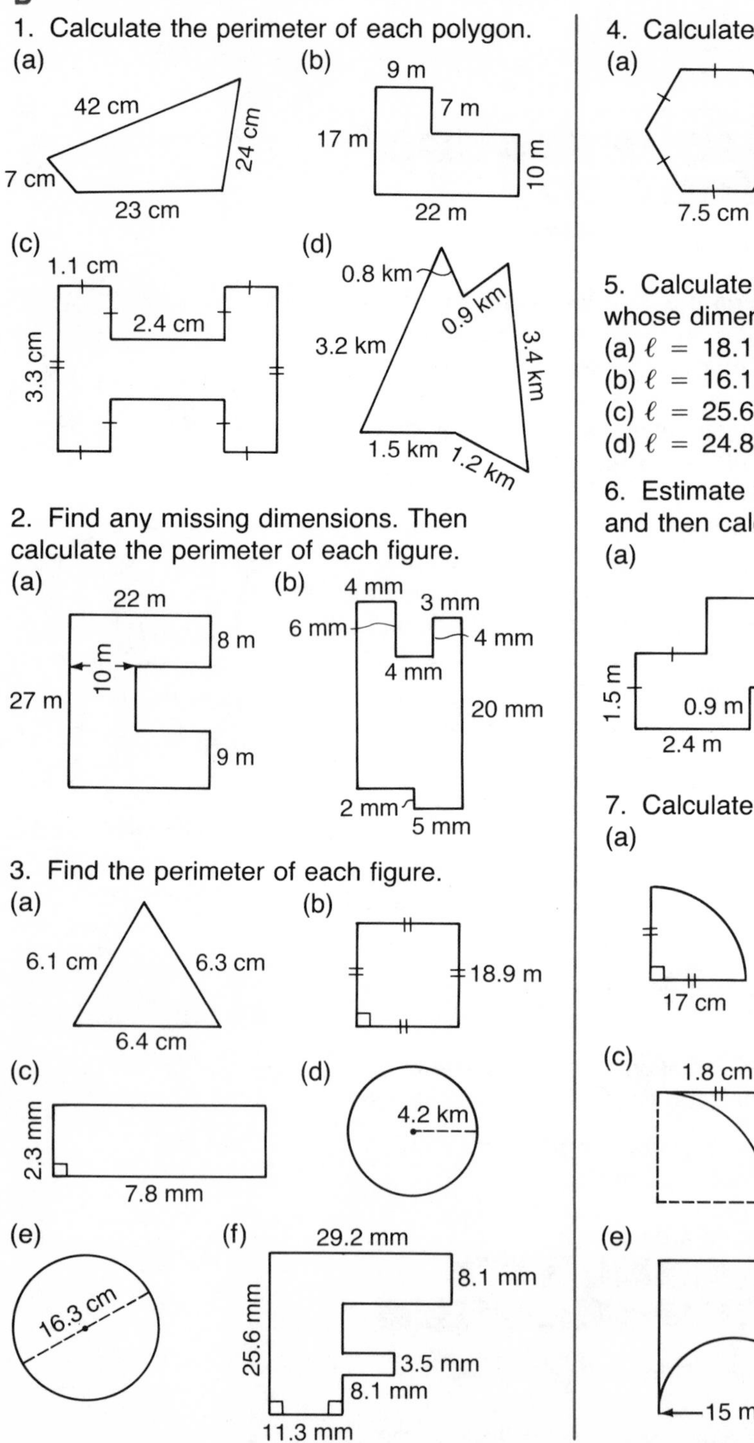

4. Calculate the perimeter of each figure.

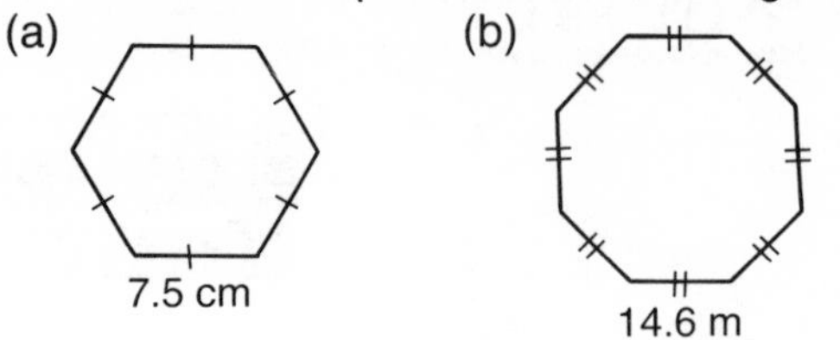

5. Calculate the perimeter of the rectangles whose dimensions are as follows.
(a) $\ell = 18.1$ m, w = 16.4 m
(b) $\ell = 16.1$ cm, w = 5.9 cm
(c) $\ell = 25.6$ m, w = 8.9 m
(d) $\ell = 24.8$ cm, w = 21.9 cm

6. Estimate the perimeter of each figure, and then calculate the perimeter.

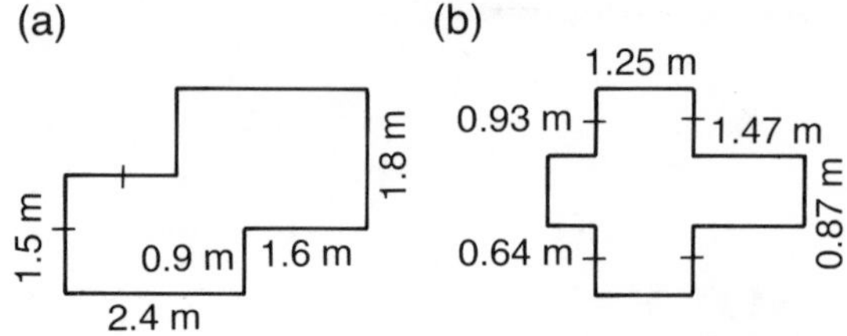

7. Calculate the perimeter of each figure.

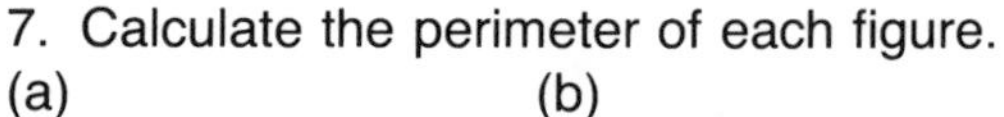

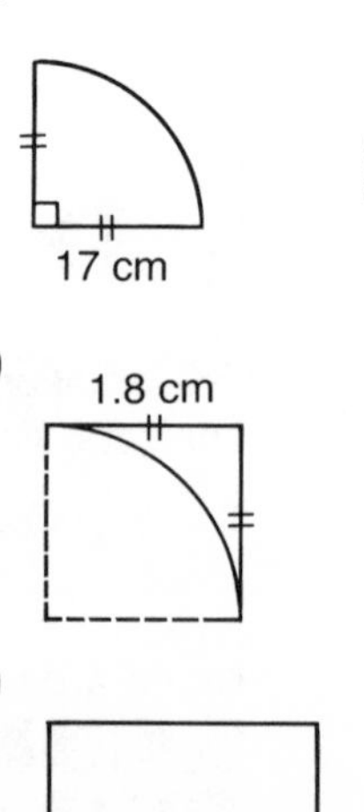

(b) 6.6 mm, 5.3 mm

(d) 40 m

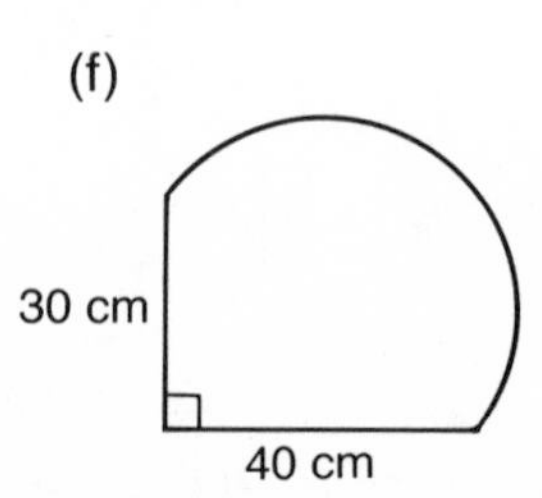

8. The perimeter of each figure is given. Find the missing dimensions.

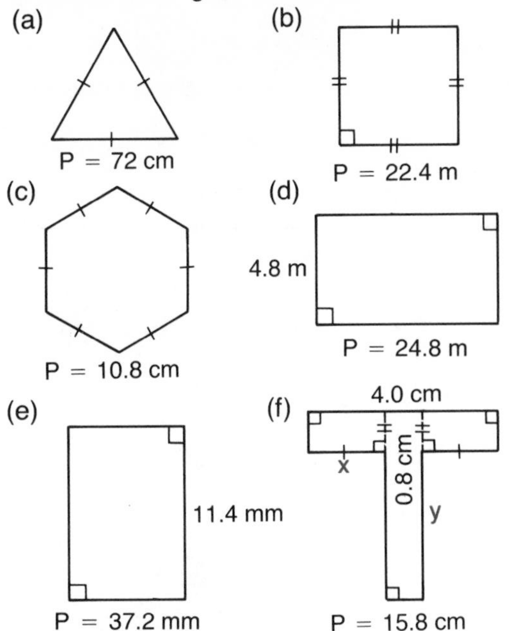

9. Two pulleys are connected by a belt as shown.
Calculate the length of the pulley belt.

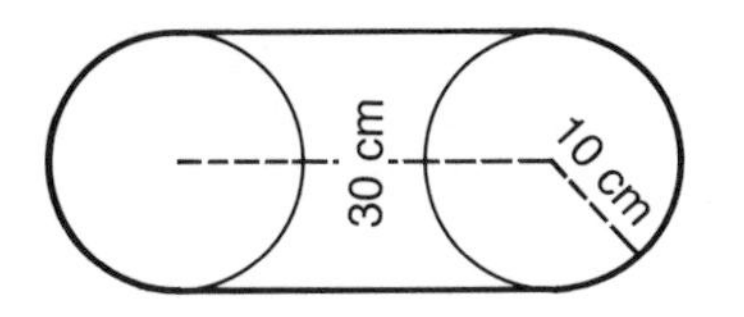

10. A rectangular field with dimensions 48.7 m by 19.8 m is to be fenced. Calculate the cost of enclosing the field if fencing costs $7.70/m.

11. A diagram of a room is shown.

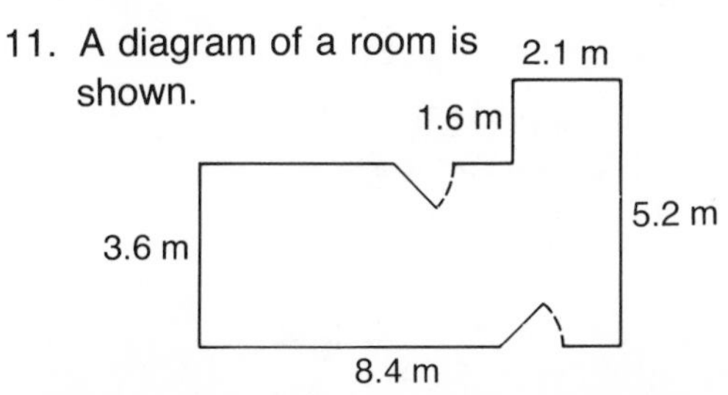

Calculate the cost of installing baseboard moulding around the perimeter of the room if the moulding costs $1.75/m. The width of each door is 1 m.

12. A bicycle wheel has a diameter of 70 cm.

(a) How far will the bicycle wheel travel in 200 revolutions?

(b) How many turns would the wheel make if the bicycle was driven 100 m?

13. Ken's property borders on the river. How much will it cost him to fence in a field 88.6 m by 93.7 m, if the cost of fencing is $9.60/m and he plans to install a gate 1 m wide costing $86.50.

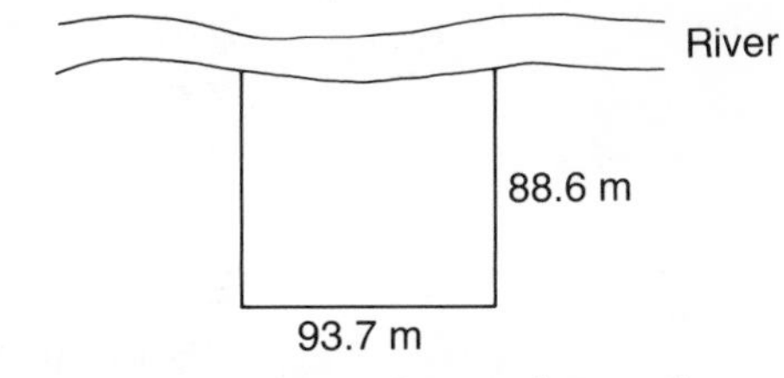

14. The dimensions of a track are shown.

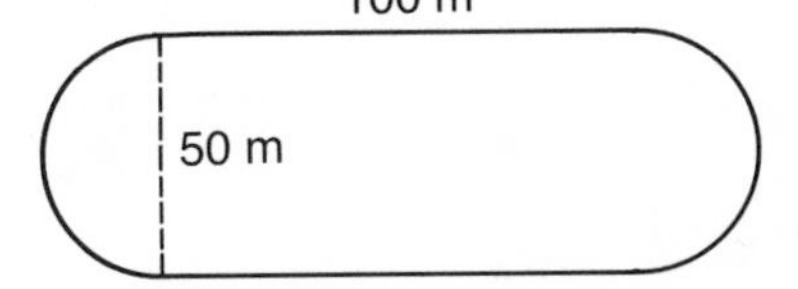

How many kilometres (to the nearest tenth) does Kara run if she goes around the track 8 times?

15. Calculate the distance around the earth at the equator, if the diameter of the earth is about 12 700 km.

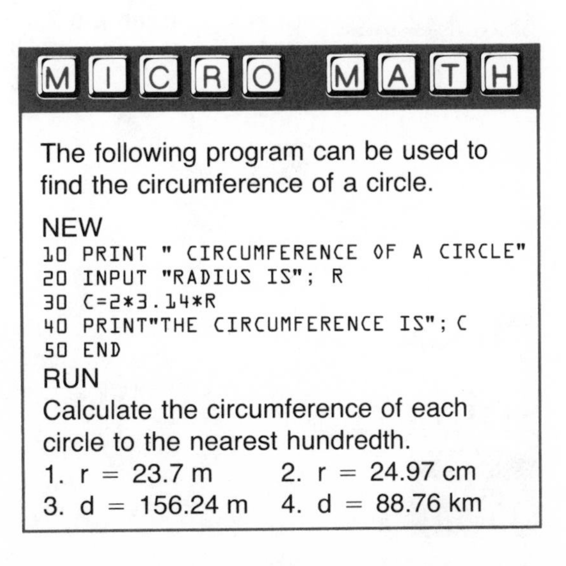

MICRO MATH

The following program can be used to find the circumference of a circle.

NEW
```
10 PRINT " CIRCUMFERENCE OF A CIRCLE"
20 INPUT "RADIUS IS"; R
30 C=2*3.14*R
40 PRINT"THE CIRCUMFERENCE IS"; C
50 END
```
RUN

Calculate the circumference of each circle to the nearest hundredth.

1. r = 23.7 m
2. r = 24.97 cm
3. d = 156.24 m
4. d = 88.76 km

6.2 AREA

The area of a figure is the amount of surface that it covers. The area of the driveway is 6 m^2.

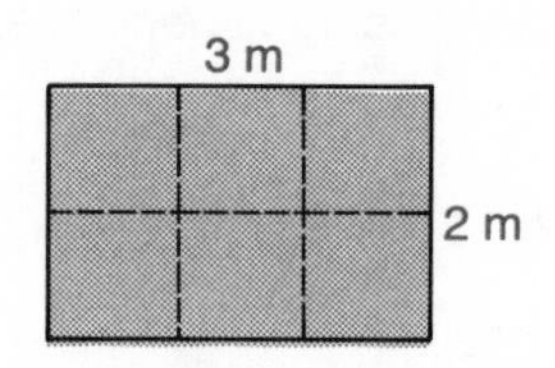

The table gives the formulas for the areas of some figures.

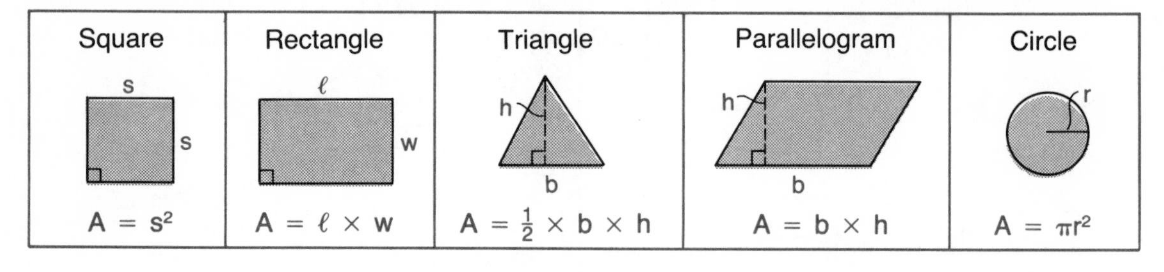

Square	Rectangle	Triangle	Parallelogram	Circle
$A = s^2$	$A = \ell \times w$	$A = \frac{1}{2} \times b \times h$	$A = b \times h$	$A = \pi r^2$

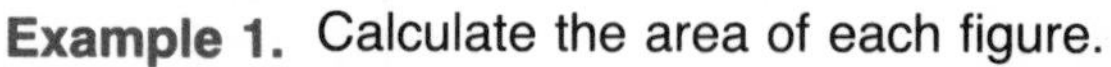

Example 1. Calculate the area of each figure.

(a)

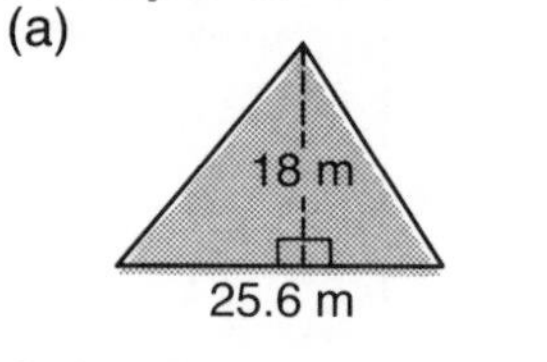

(b)

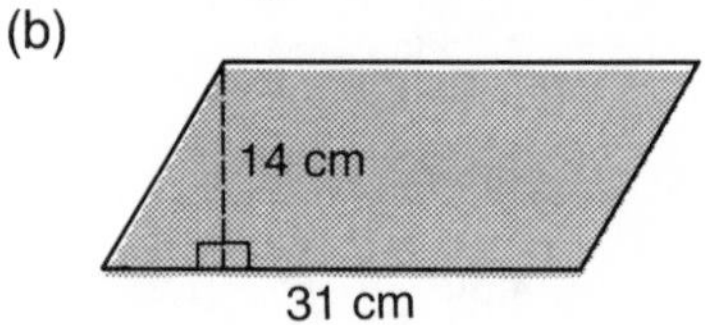

Solution:

(a) $A = \frac{1}{2} \times b \times h$

$A = \frac{1}{2} \times 25.6 \times 18$

$= 230.4$

The area is 230.4 m^2.

(b) $A = b \times h$

$A = 31 \times 14$

$= 434$

The area is 434 cm^2.

READ

Example 2. Calculate the cost of putting artificial grass in the infield of the track. The artificial grass costs \$48.00/m^2 installed.

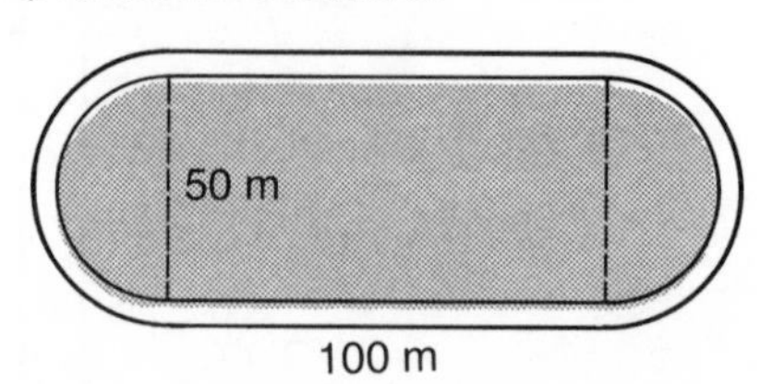

PLAN

Solution:

The area consists of a circle with radius 25 m and a rectangle with $\ell = 100$ m and $w = 50$ m.

SOLVE

$A_c = \pi r^2$

$A_c = 3.14(25)^2$

$= 1962.5$

$A_r = \ell \times w$

$A_r = 100 \times 50$

$= 5000$

Total area $= 1962.5\text{ m}^2 + 5000\text{ m}^2$
$= 6962.5\text{ m}^2$
Total cost $= 6962.5\text{ m}^2 \times \$48.00/\text{m}^2$
$= \$334\,200.00$

ANSWER

The cost is \$334 200.00.

Using a calculator, press

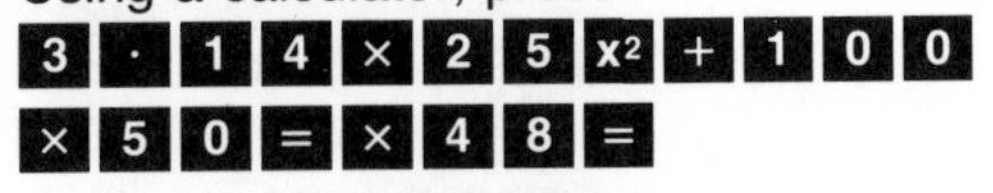

The display is 334200.

READ

Example 3. Calculate the area of the given quadrilateral.

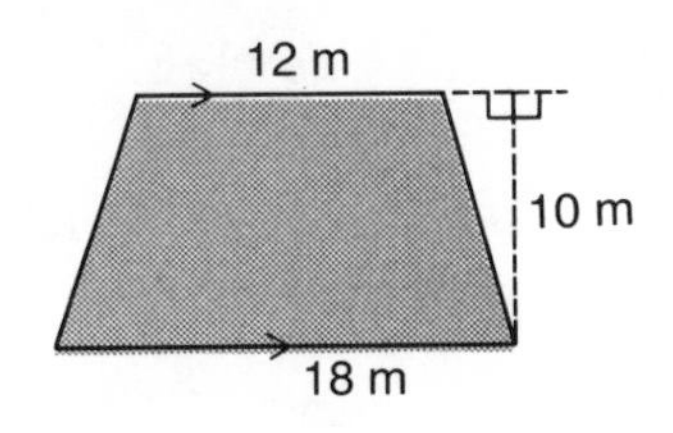

PLAN

Solution:
Draw and label a diagram. The figure may be divided into two triangles by drawing the diagonal AC. Add the areas of the two triangles to find the area of the figure.

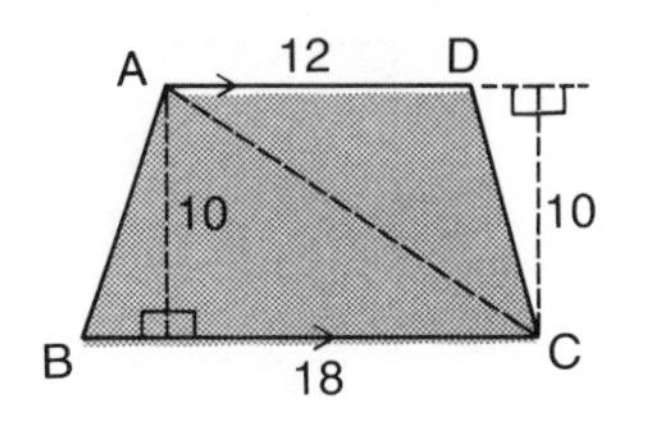

SOLVE

Area of $\triangle ABC = \frac{1}{2} \times b \times h$
$= \frac{1}{2} \times 18 \times 10$
$= 90$
The area of $\triangle ABC$ is 90 m^2.

Area of $\triangle ACD = \frac{1}{2} \times b \times h$
$= \frac{1}{2} \times 12 \times 10$
$= 60$
The area of $\triangle ACD$ is 60 m^2.

Total area = area of $\triangle ABC$ + area of $\triangle ACD$
Total area $= 90 + 60$
$= 150$

ANSWER

The area of the quadrilateral is 150 m^2.

A quadrilateral with only one pair of parallel sides is called a trapezoid.

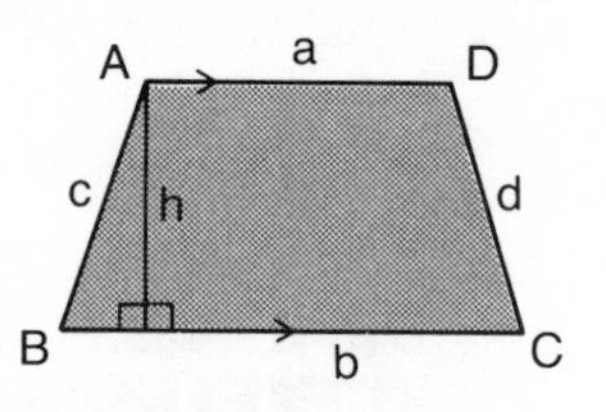

We may find a formula for the area of a trapezoid using the method of Example 3. Divide the trapezoid into two triangles by drawing the diagonal AC.

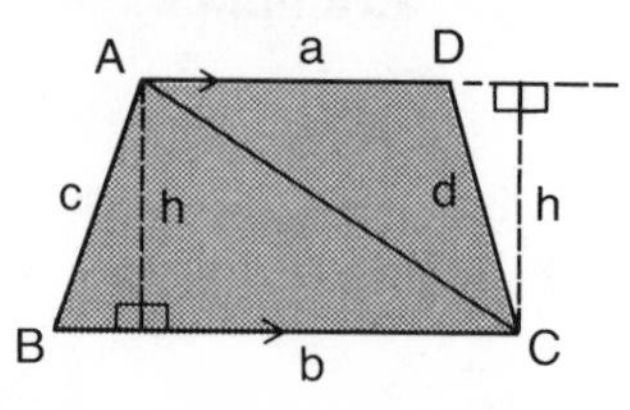

The height of △ABC is the same as the height of △ACD, since they both are between the same parallel lines.

The area of trapezoid ABCD = Area △ABC + Area △ACD

$= \frac{1}{2}bh + \frac{1}{2}ah$

$= \frac{1}{2}h(b + a)$ or $\frac{1}{2}(a + b)h$

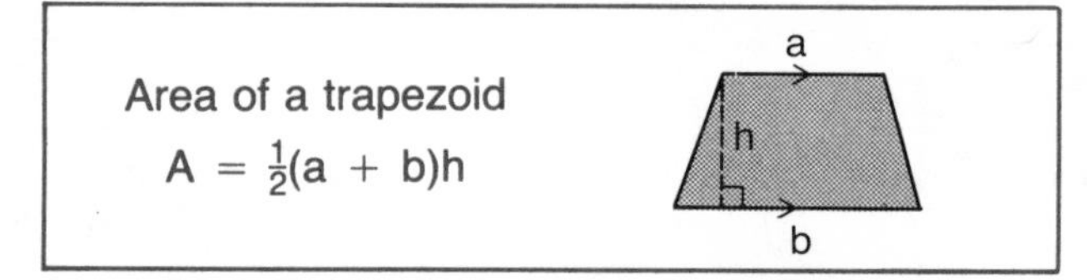

Example 4. Find the area of a cross section of a trough that is 7.5 cm deep and measures 10.5 cm across the top and 7.5 cm across the bottom.

Solution: The cross section has the shape of a trapezoid.

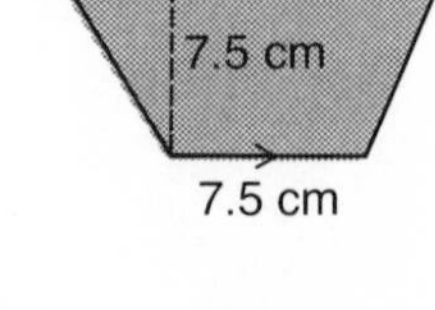

$A = \frac{1}{2}(a + b)h$

$A = \frac{1}{2}(10.5 + 7.5)7.5$

$= 67.5 \text{ cm}^2$

Using a calculator, press

The display is 67.5

EXERCISE 6.2

B

1. Calculate the area of each figure.

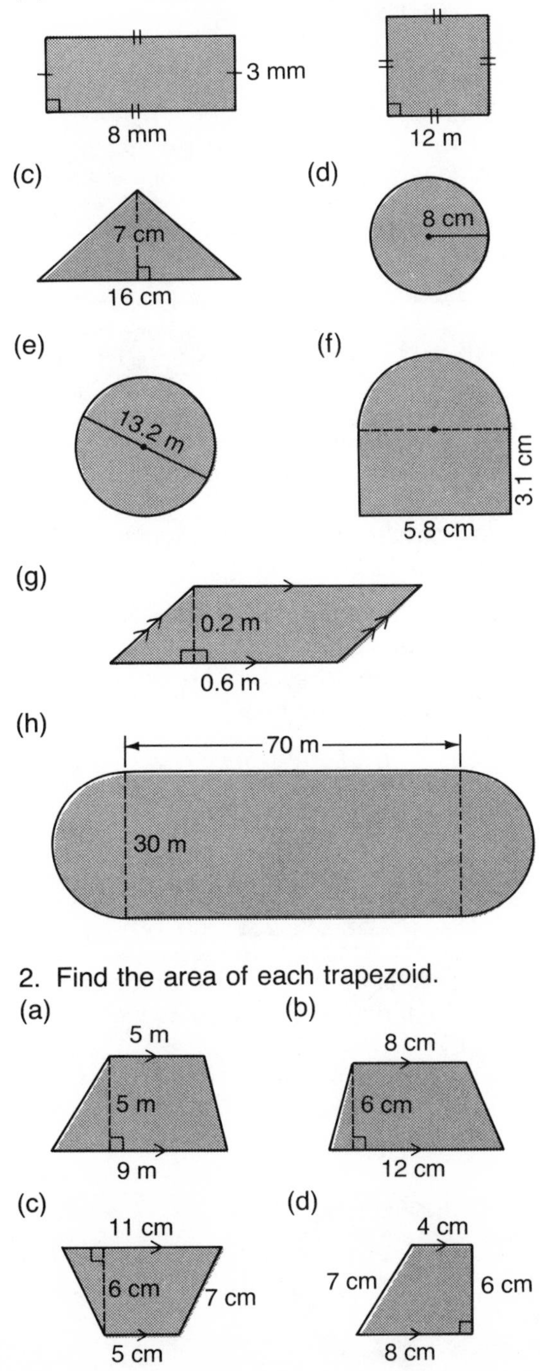

3. Find the area of each of the following.
(a) A square with sides 3.5 cm each.
(b) A rectangle with length 5.7 m and width 4.5 m.
(c) A triangle with base 9.4 cm and height 6.8 cm.
(d) A parallelogram with base 28.8 m and height 19.7 m.
(e) A circle with diameter 44.6 cm.
(f) A trapezoid with parallel sides 8.0 cm and 12.6 cm, and the perpendicular distance beween them 10.0 cm.

4. (a) The area of a triangle is 68.45 cm^2. If the base of the triangle is 7.40 cm, what is the height?
(b) The area of a trapezoid is 60 m^2. The length of one parallel side is 12 cm, and the height is 6 cm.
Find the length of the other parallel side.

5. Find the area of the shaded region in each of the following. All measurements are in centimetres.

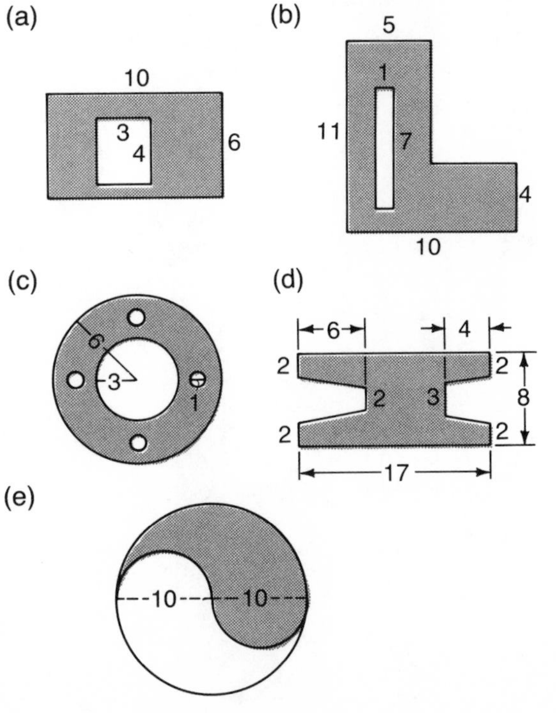

6. (a) Calculate the area of the parking lot.

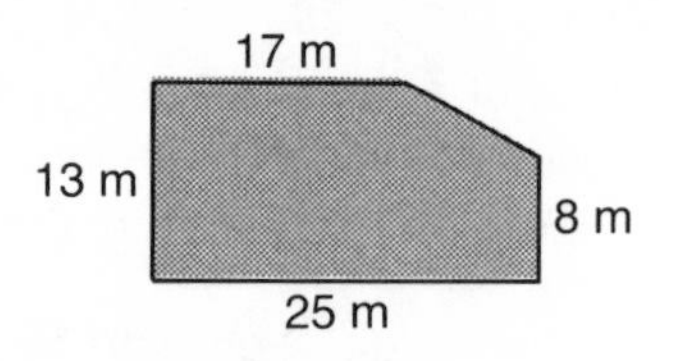

(b) How much would it cost to pave the lot at $8.75/m²?

7. The dimensions of a room are shown in the diagram.

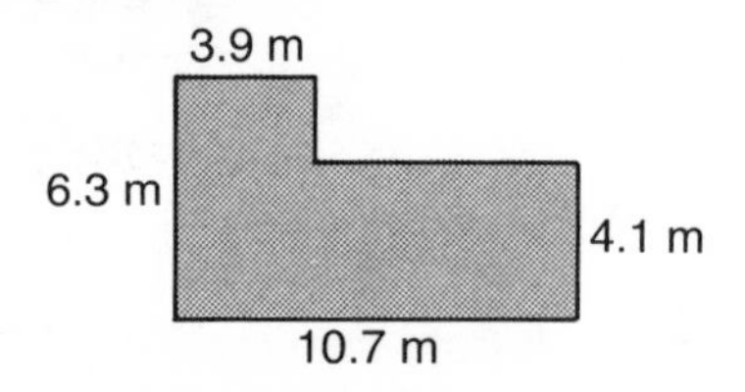

Find the cost of carpeting the room at $27.50/m² including installation.

8. The dimensions of a room are 3.7 m by 4.5 m. The height of the walls is 2.5 m. There is a doorway 2.3 m by 1.0 m and a window 2.3 m by 2.0 m. How many rolls of wallpaper would be needed to paper the room, if one roll covers 3 m²?

9. The face of a clock has dimensions as shown.
What area of plexiglass would be required to construct the face?

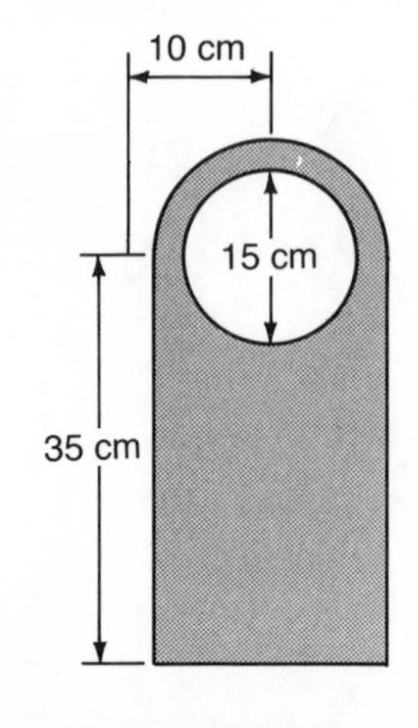

10. (a) Calculate the area of the field shown in the diagram.

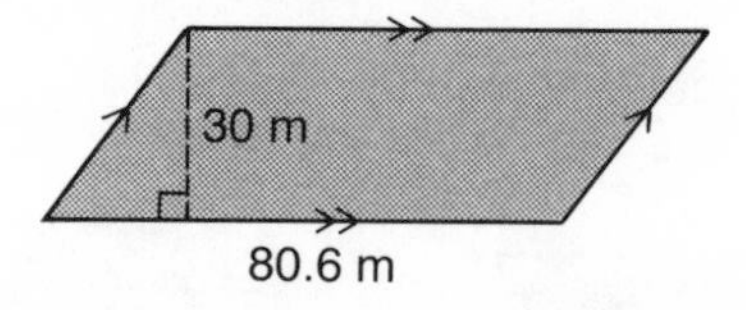

(b) How much would it cost to fertilize the field if 1 kg of fertilizer is needed for 10 m² of field and fertilizer costs $3.50/kg?

11. (a) Calculate the area of the flower bed.

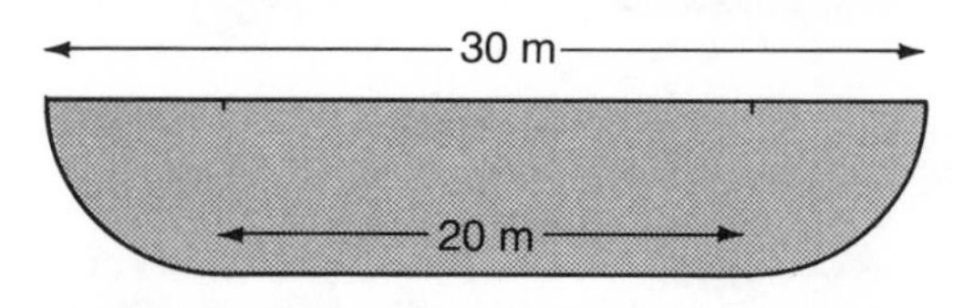

(b) Calculate the perimeter of the flower bed.
(c) How much would it cost to fence the bed at $1.43/m²?

12. A barn has an end section as shown in the diagram.
Find the number of square metres of sheeting to cover the end.

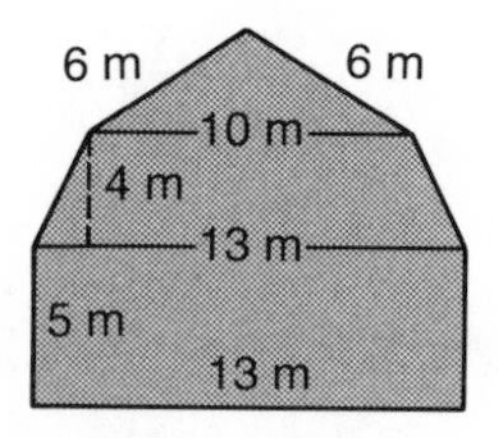

13. A castle is surrounded by a moat.
(a) What is the inner perimeter of the moat?
(b) What is the outer perimeter of the moat?
(c) What is the area of the moat?

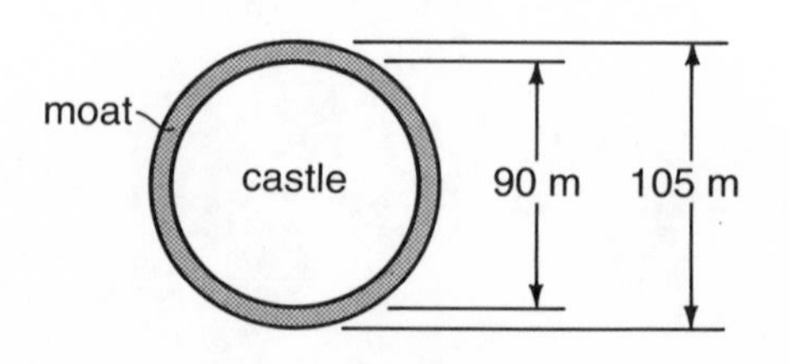

EXTRA

6.3 THE ISOPERIMETRIC PROBLEM

What configuration encloses the largest area for a given perimeter?

iso -perimetric
↓ ↓
equal perimeter

EXERCISE 6.3

Although Europe is the second smallest continent in terms of area (9 907 000 km^2), it has the second longest coastline (60 972 km).

1. Verify that the perimeter of each of the following figures is 100 m, to the nearest metre.

2. Calculate the area of each figure to the nearest square metre.

3. Order the figures in terms of area, from smallest to largest.

4. Which of these figures encloses the largest area?

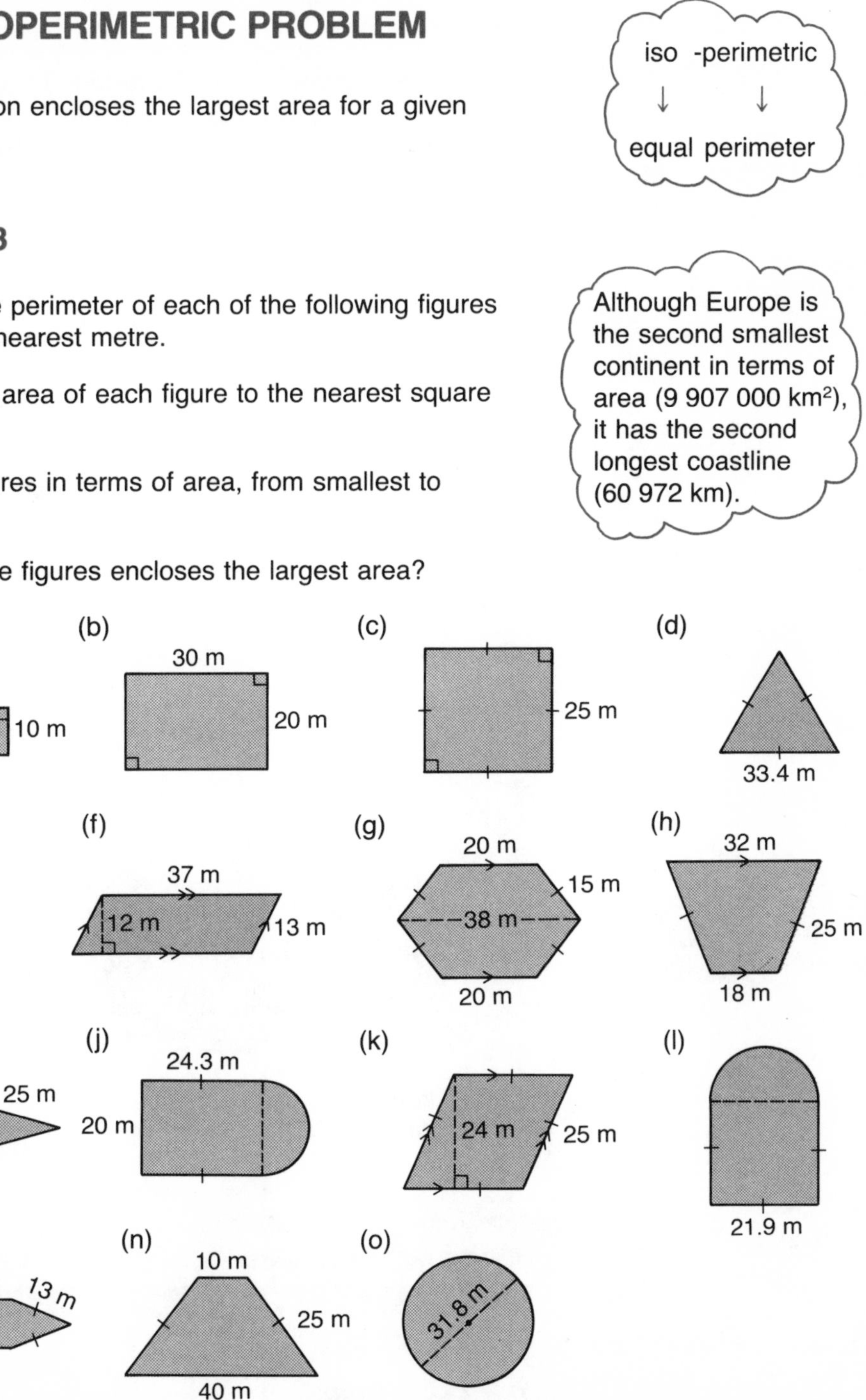

6.4 SURFACE AREA OF PRISMS AND PYRAMIDS

A prism is a solid figure whose ends are congruent and parallel, and whose sides are parallelograms. A right prism has sides which are perpendicular to the ends of the prism, so the sides are rectangles. Any side of a prism is a lateral face and either end of a prism can be the base.

The three most common prisms are shown.

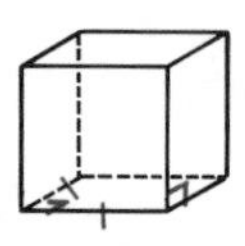
cube

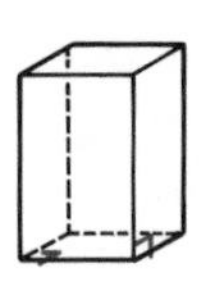
rectangular prism

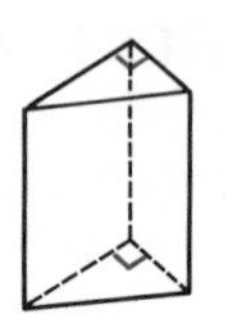
triangular prism

Example 1. Calculate the surface area of the computer diskette box.

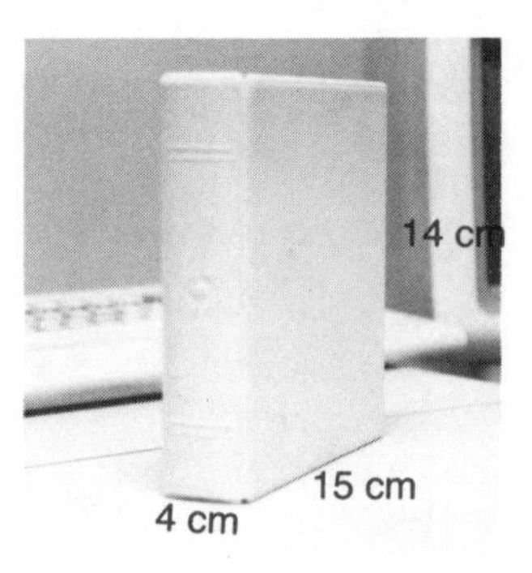

Solution: Draw a net of the box.

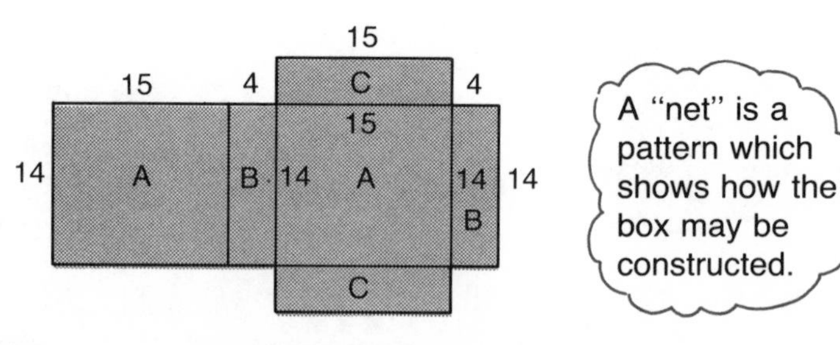

A "net" is a pattern which shows how the box may be constructed.

Surface Area $= 2(\text{area A} + \text{area B} + \text{area C})$
Surface Area $= 2(15 \times 14 + 14 \times 4 + 15 \times 4)$
$= 2(326)$
$= 652$

The surface area is 652 cm².
Using a calculator, press

1 5 × 1 4 = M+ C 1 4 × 4 = M+ C
1 5 × 4 = M+ RM × 2 =

The display is 652.

Example 2. Calculate the surface area of the triangular prism.

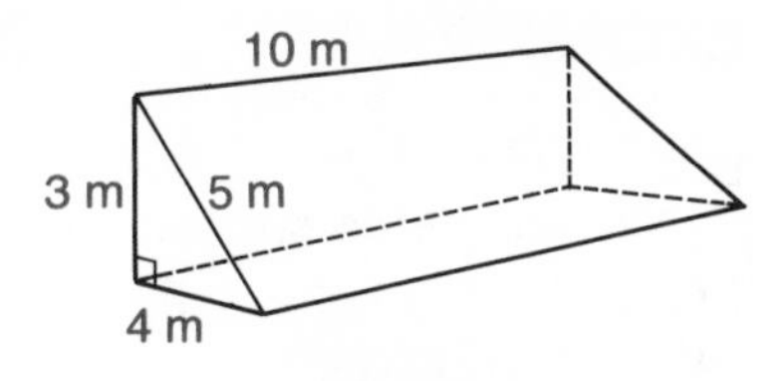

Solution: Draw the net.

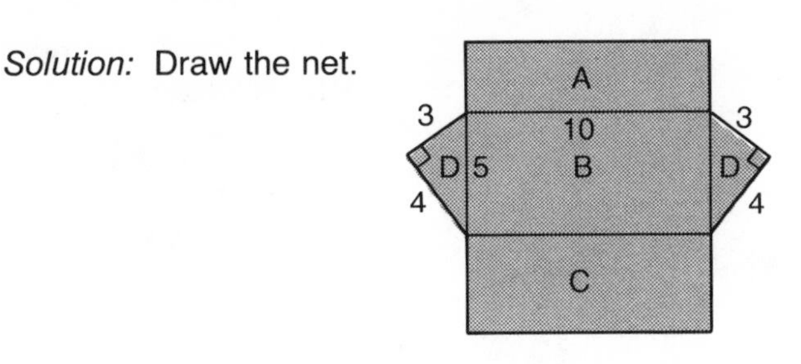

Surface Area = area A + area B + area C + 2 × area D

Surface Area = $10 \times 3 + 10 \times 5 + 10 \times 4 + 2\left(\frac{1}{2} \times 4 \times 3\right)$
$= 30 + 50 + 40 + 12$
$= 132$

The surface area is 132 m^2.

Using a calculator, press

1 0 × 3 = M+ 1 0 × 5 = M+ 1 0 × 4
= M+ 2 × · 5 × 4 × 3 = M+ RM

The display is 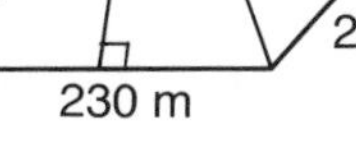

Example 3. Calculate the surface area of the Great Pyramid of Cheops (including the area of the base).

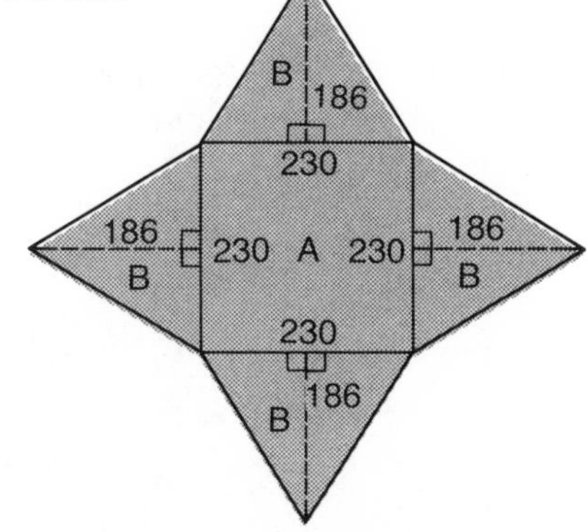

Solution: Draw the net.

Surface Area = area A + 4 × area B

Surface Area = $230^2 + 4\left(\frac{1}{2} \times 230 \times 186\right)$
$= 138\ 460$

The surface area is 138 460 m^2.

Using a calculator, press

2 3 0 x^2 + 4 × · 5
× 2 3 0 × 1 8 6 =

The display is 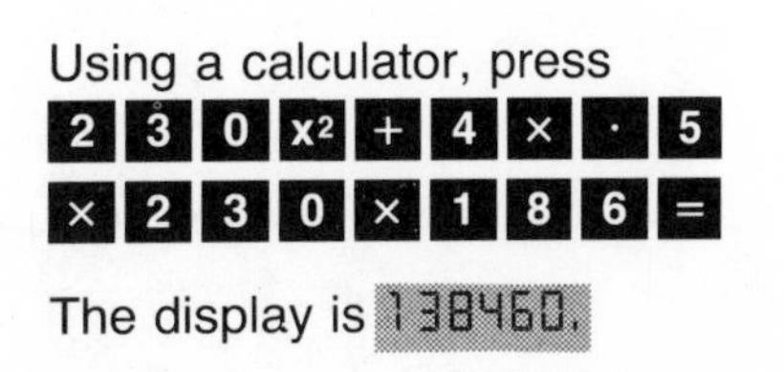

EXERCISE 6.4

B

1. Use the net to calculate the surface area of the pyramid and the prism.

(a)

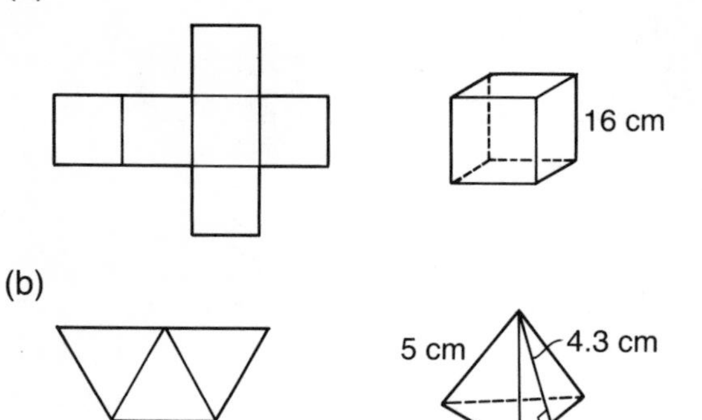

2. Calculate the surface area of each prism.

(a) (b)

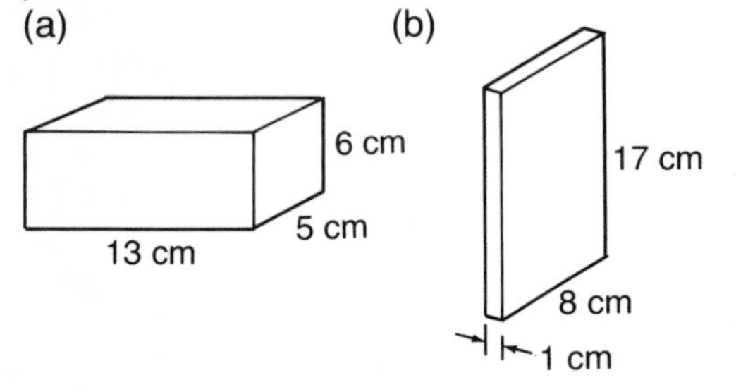

3. For each of the following, sketch a net and then calculate the surface area.

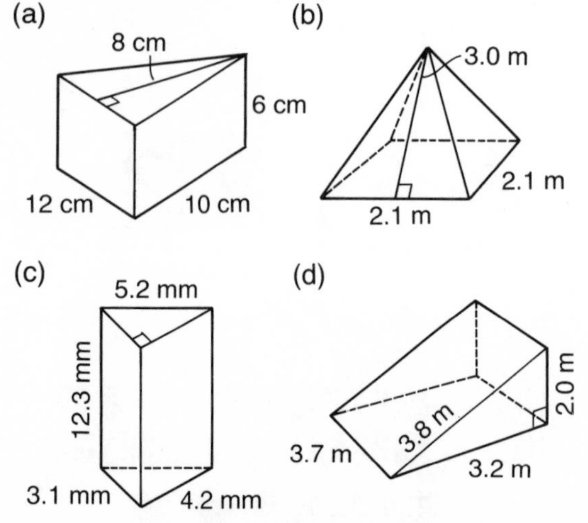

4. Each cadet is provided with a wooden trunk with dimensions as shown.

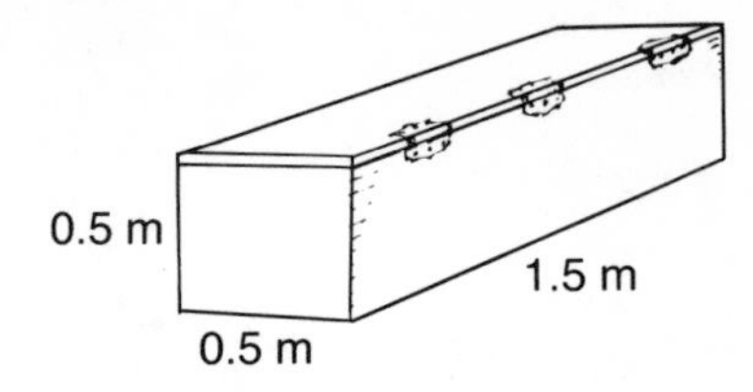

(a) If there are 80 cadets, what is the total amount of wood required to construct the trunks?

(b) If the wood costs $3.60/m^2$, what is the cost of the wood necessary for the 80 trunks?

5. A swimming pool cabana is made out of cloth. It consists of a rectangular prism with a square-based pyramid on top.
What is the total area of material needed for the cabana?

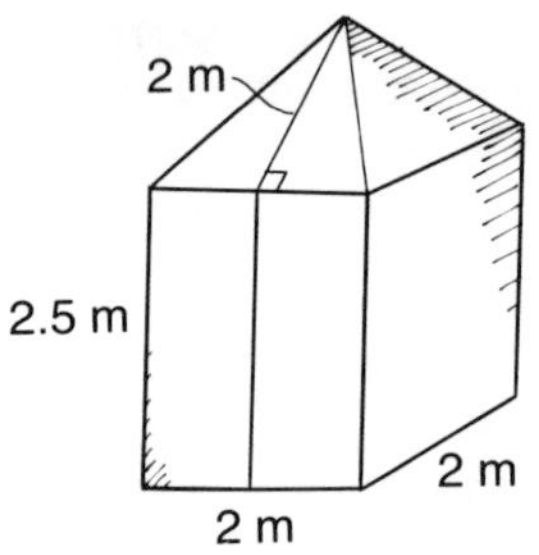

6. A saltwater aquarium has dimensions as shown in the diagram.

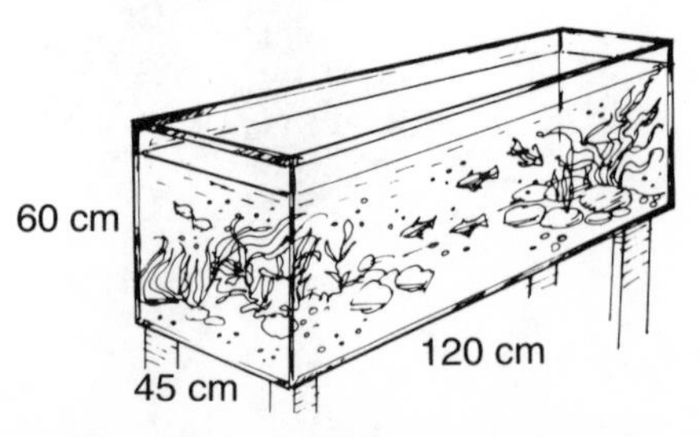

(a) How much glass is required to construct the aquarium if the top is open?

(b) If glass costs 2¢/cm^2, what is the cost of the glass needed to make the aquarium?

6.5 SURFACE AREA OF CIRCULAR OBJECTS

The surface of a cylinder is made up of three parts — two circles called bases, and a curved surface or side. If we open out and flatten a cylinder, we have two circles and a rectangle.

We can find the surface area of the cylinder as follows.

The length of the rectangle is equal to the circumference of the cylinder.

The area of the bases is the area of the two circles.

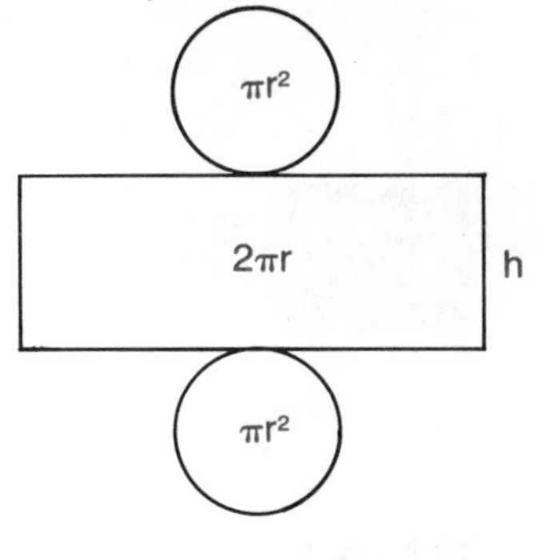

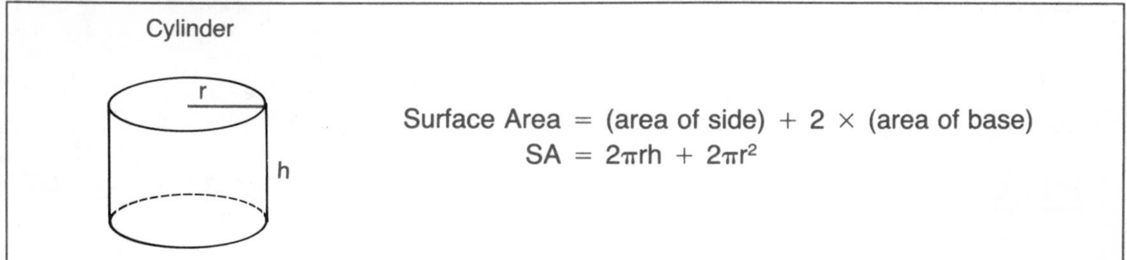

Surface Area = (area of side) + 2 × (area of base)

$$SA = 2\pi rh + 2\pi r^2$$

The formulas for the surface area of some common figures are given below.

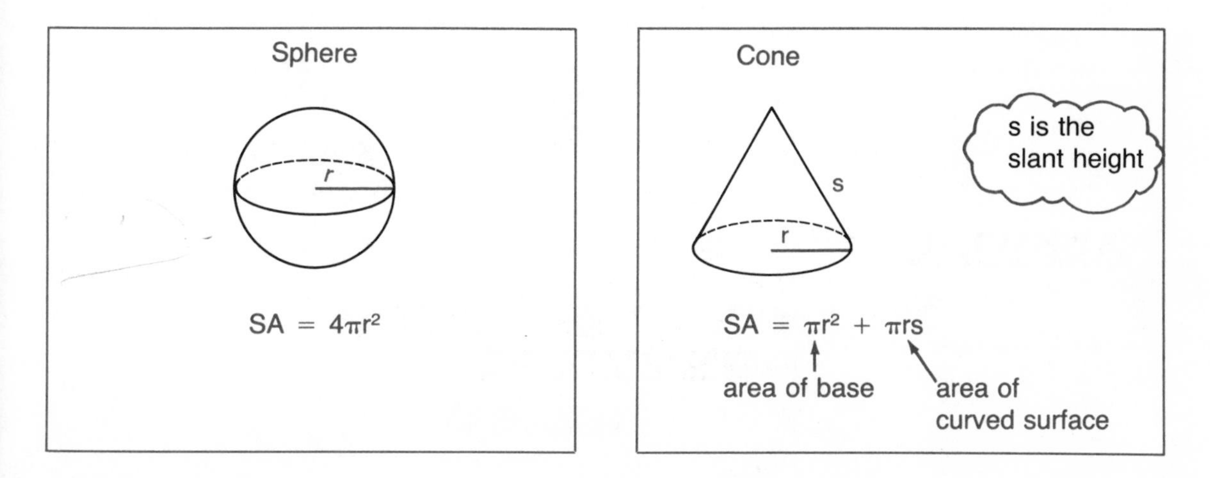

Example 1. Calculate the surface area of each figure to the nearest tenth.

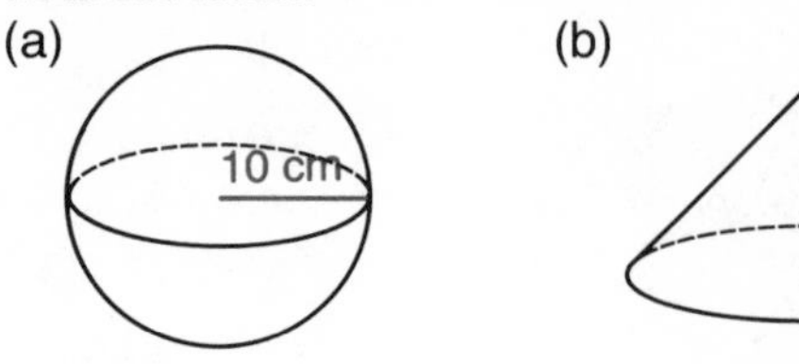

Solution: (a) $SA = 4\pi r^2$

$SA = 4 \times 3.14 \times 10 \times 10$

$= 1256$

The surface area is 1256 cm^2.

E=mc²

(b) $SA = \pi r^2 + \pi rs$

$SA = 3.14 \times 5^2 + 3.14 \times 5 \times 7$

$= 188.4$

The surface area is 188.4 cm^2.

READ

Example 2. Calculate the cost to paint the exposed area of the storage tank. Paint costs $18.60 a can, and one can of paint covers 16 m^2.

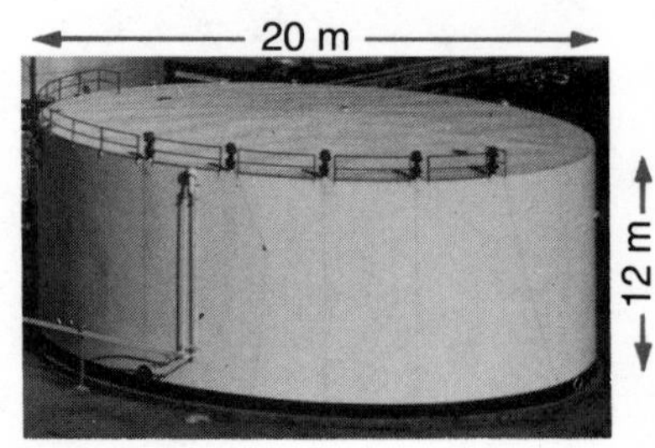

PLAN

Solution:

Calculate the area of the top and the side.

SOLVE

$SA = \pi r^2 + 2\pi rh$

$SA = 3.14 \times 10^2 + 2 \times 3.14 \times 10 \times 12$

$= 1067.6$

The surface area of the tank is 1067.6 m^2 to the nearest tenth.

Find the number of cans of paint required.

Cans of paint needed $= \frac{1067.6}{16} \doteq 66.7$ or 67 cans

Cost of the paint = 67 × $18.60 = $1246.20

It will cost $1246.20 to paint the storage tank.

Using a calculator, press

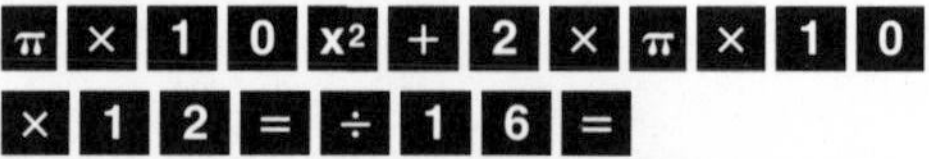

The display is 66.75884389

Press

The display is 1246.2

EXERCISE 6.5

B

1. Find the surface area of each cylinder.

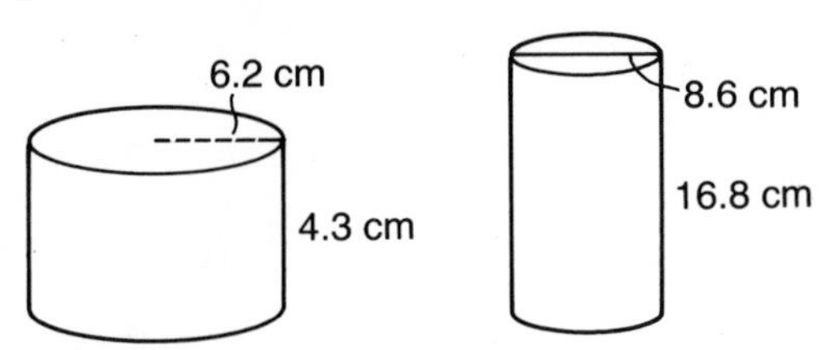

2. Calculate the surface area of each cone.

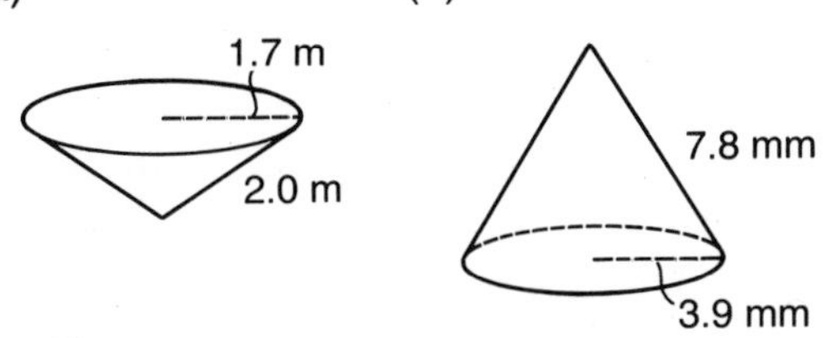

3. What is the surface area of each sphere?

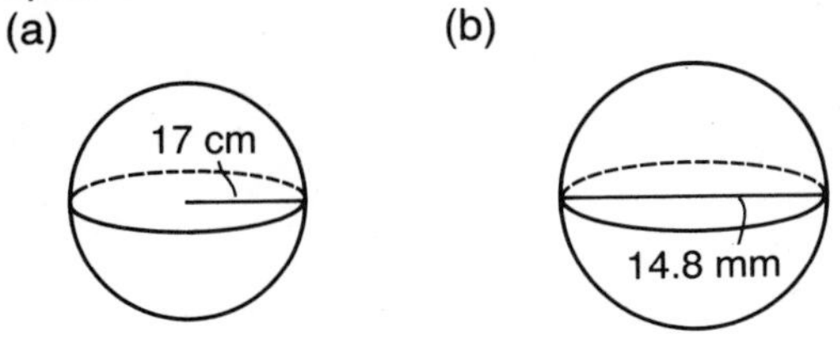

4. (a) Calculate the surface area of the water tank.
(b) Find the cost of painting the exterior of the tank. A can of paint costs \$12, and one can covers 10 m^2.

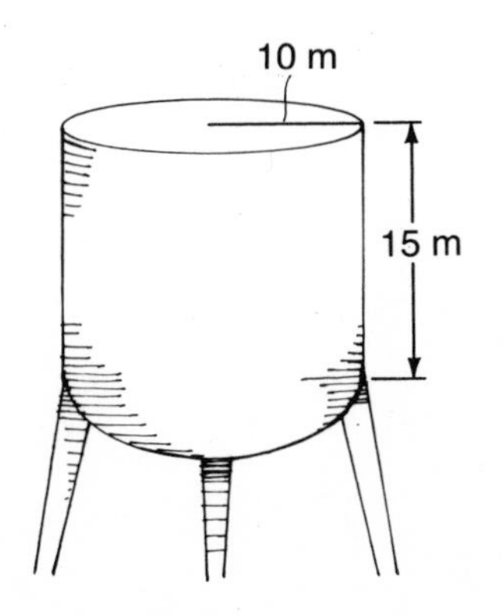

5. Calculate the surface area of the propane storage tank.

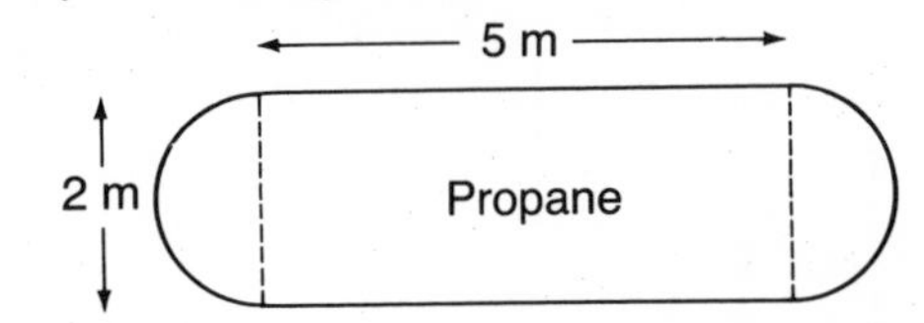

6. Calculate the area of the paper required to cover the STARFLIGHT rocket.

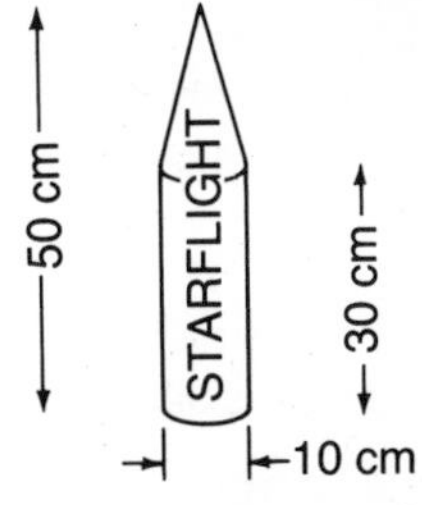

7. There are 24 cans of soup in a carton. Each can has a diameter of 7 cm and a height of 10 cm.
How much paper is needed to make the labels for the 24 cans?

8. The diameter of the earth is 12 700 km. The diameter of the sun is 1 400 000 km.
(a) Calculate the surface area of the earth.
(b) Calculate the surface area of the sun.
(c) How many times larger in area is the sun than the earth?

MICRO MATH

The following program can be used to find the surface area of a sphere.

```
NEW
10 PRINT "SURFACE AREA OF A SPHERE"
20 INPUT "THE RADIUS IS"; R
30 S = 4*3.14*R^2
40 PRINT "THE SURFACE AREA IS "; S
50 END
RUN
```

Find the surface area of each sphere.

1. r = 15 cm
2. r = 9.7 cm
3. d = 45.4 cm
4. d = 18.8 m

6.6 VOLUME

The volume of a solid is the number of cubic units required to fill the solid.

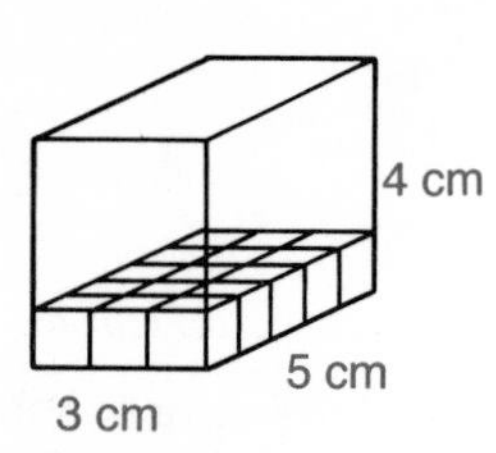

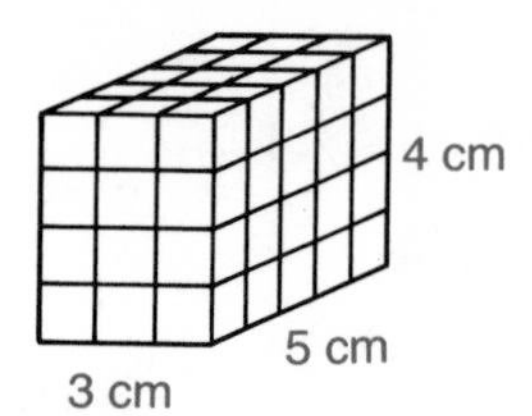

The area of the base of the solid is $5 \times 3 = 15$ cm². It takes 15 cm³ to make the bottom layer.

The solid is 4 cm high so 4 layers of 15 cm³ each will be needed to fill the solid.

The volume of the solid is 60 cm³.
The volume can be calculated using the formula

$$V = \ell \times w \times h$$

(15×4) cm³ $= 60$ cm³

However, if the area of the cross section remains constant, we can use another formula to calculate volume.

Volume = Area of Base × height or $\quad V = B \times h$

B is the area of the base of a solid.

Example. Calculate the volume of each solid.
(a) (b)

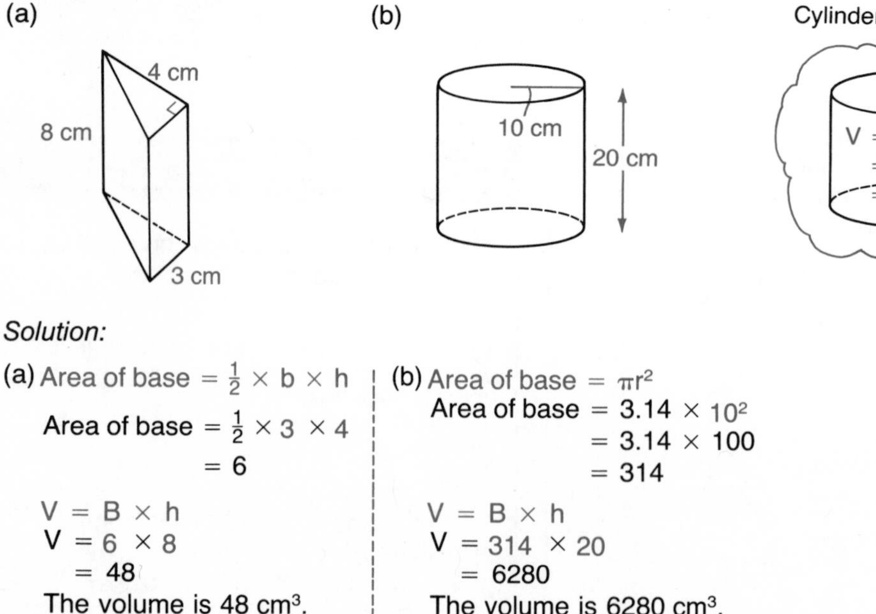

Cylinder

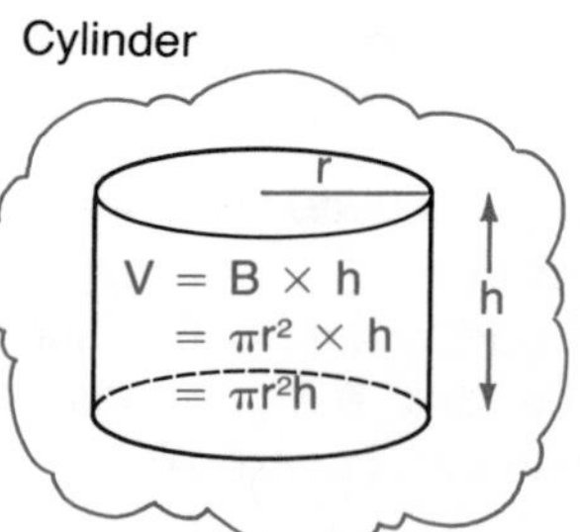

Solution:

(a) Area of base $= \frac{1}{2} \times b \times h$

Area of base $= \frac{1}{2} \times 3 \times 4$
$= 6$

$V = B \times h$
$V = 6 \times 8$
$= 48$
The volume is 48 cm³.

(b) Area of base $= \pi r^2$
Area of base $= 3.14 \times 10^2$
$= 3.14 \times 100$
$= 314$

$V = B \times h$
$V = 314 \times 20$
$= 6280$
The volume is 6280 cm³.

EXERCISE 6.6

B

1. Find the volume of each solid.

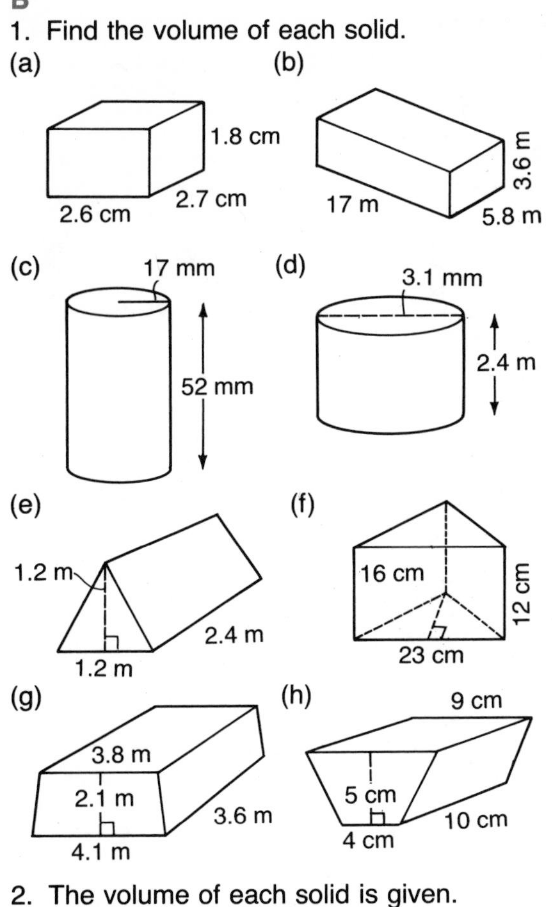

2. The volume of each solid is given.
Find the missing dimensions.
(a) $V = 45\ \text{cm}^3$ (b) $V = 5024\ \text{mm}^3$

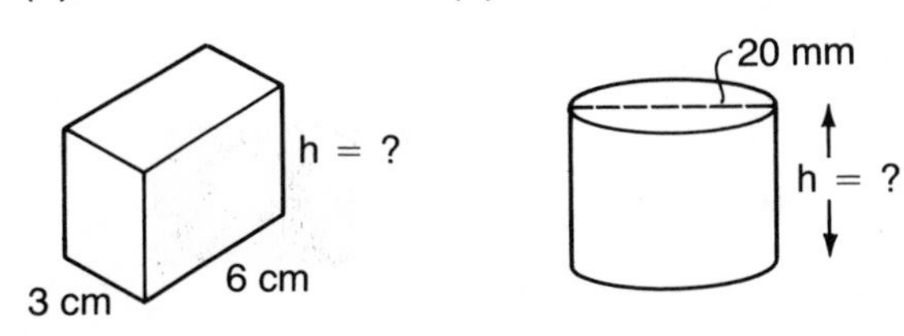

3. Find the volume of each of the following.
(a) (b)

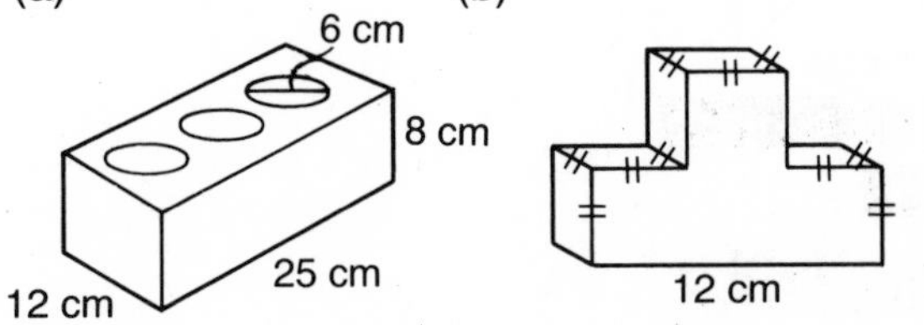

4. Calculate the volume of the water tank to the nearest litre.

$1\ \text{L} = 1000\ \text{cm}^3$

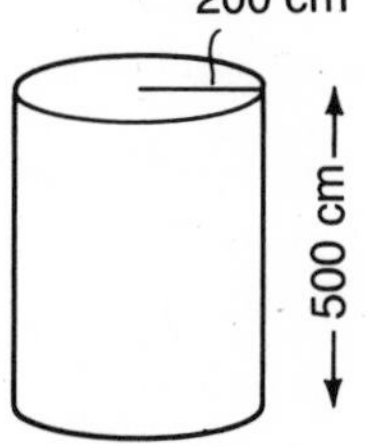

5. Find the volume of the garage shown in the diagram.

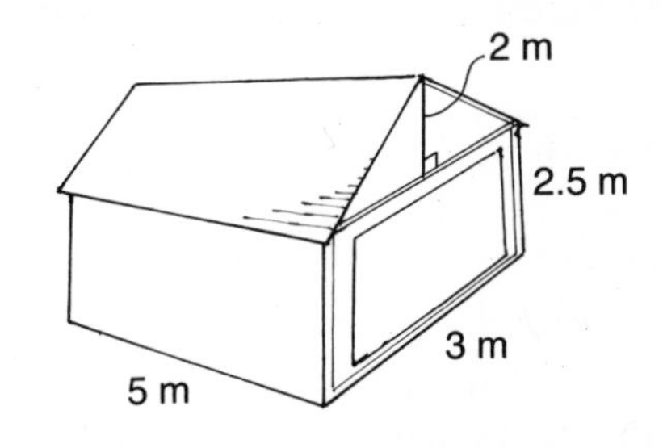

6. A sketch of the tank at Undersea World is shown. The water level in the tank is kept 0.5 m from the top.
How many litres of water are in the tank?

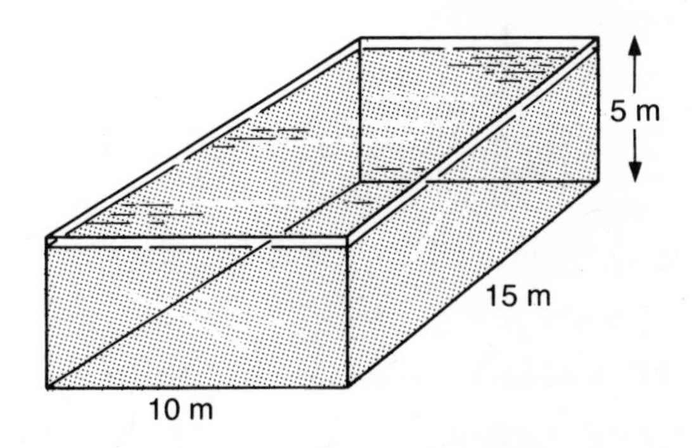

C

7. Calculate the volume of your classroom.

8. Cement pillars used in construction are sometimes cylindrical.
(a) Calculate the volume of a pillar 0.5 m in radius and 15 m tall.
(b) Find the mass of a pillar if $100\ \text{cm}^3$ of concrete has a mass of 0.9 kg.

6.7 VOLUME FORMULAS

The volume of a cone is $\frac{1}{3}$ the volume of a cylinder with the same radius and height.

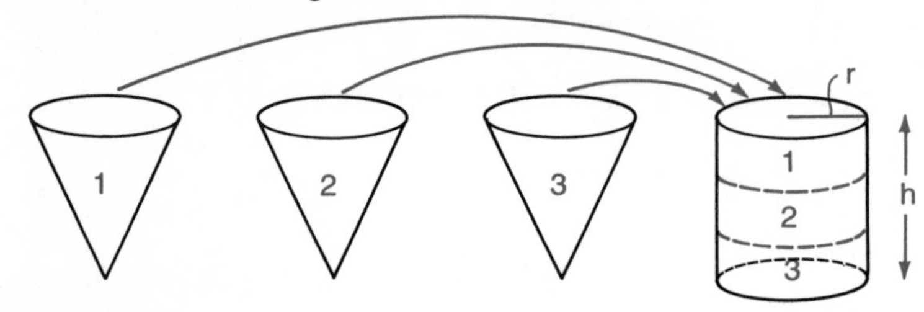

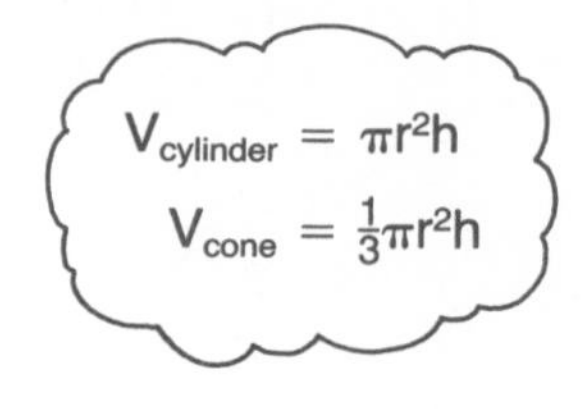

The formulas for the volume of several solids are given below.

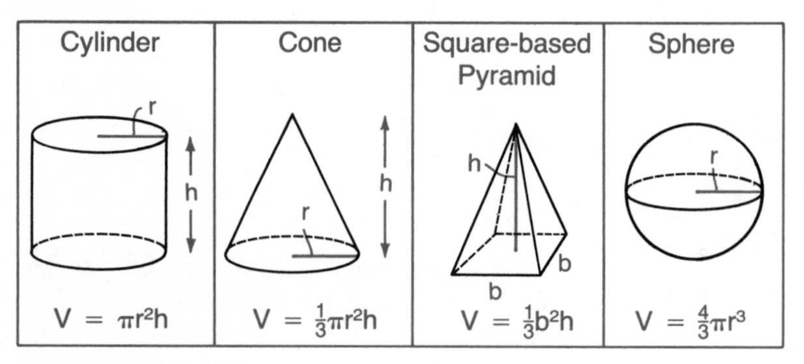

Cylinder	Cone	Square-based Pyramid	Sphere
$V = \pi r^2 h$	$V = \frac{1}{3}\pi r^2 h$	$V = \frac{1}{3}b^2 h$	$V = \frac{4}{3}\pi r^3$

Example. Calculate the volume of the following.

(a)

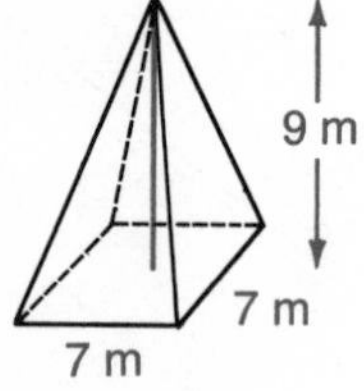

(b)

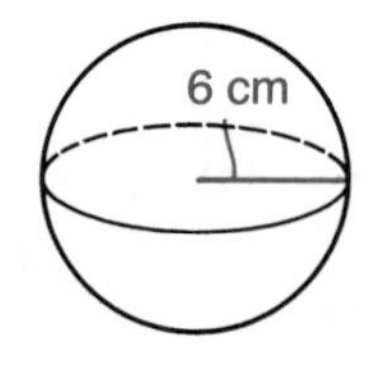

Solution:

(a) $V = \frac{1}{3}b^2 h$

$V = \frac{1}{3}(7)^2 9$

$= 147$

The volume is 147 m^3.

On a calculator, press

7 | x^2 | × | 9 | ÷ | 3 | =

The display is 147.

(b) $V = \frac{4}{3}\pi r^3$

$V = \frac{4}{3} \times \pi \times 6^3$

$\doteq 904.7$

The volume is 904.7 cm^3 to the nearest tenth.

On a calculator, press

4 | ÷ | 3 | × | 3 | · | 1 | 4 | ×

(| 6 | y^x | 3 |) | =

The display is 904.7786842

$E=mc^2$

EXERCISE 6.7

B

1. Find the volume of each solid.

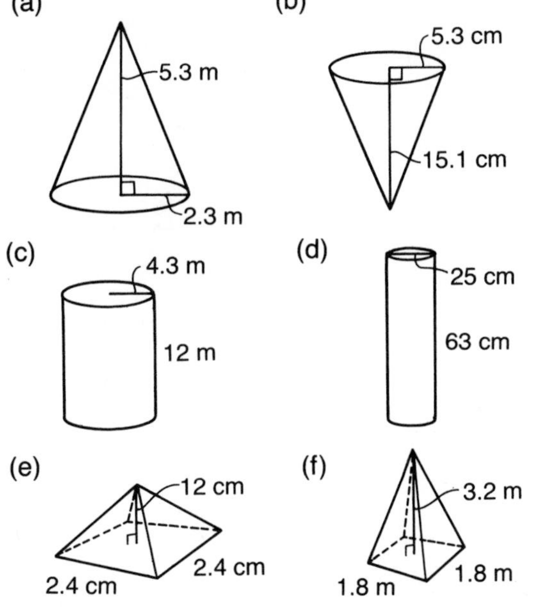

2. (a) The volume of a cone is 154 cm³. If the base has a diameter of 7 cm, find the height of the cone.
(b) A square-based pyramid has a volume of 686 cm³. If the height of the pyramid is 16 cm, find the dimensions of the base.

3. Calculate the volume of each solid.

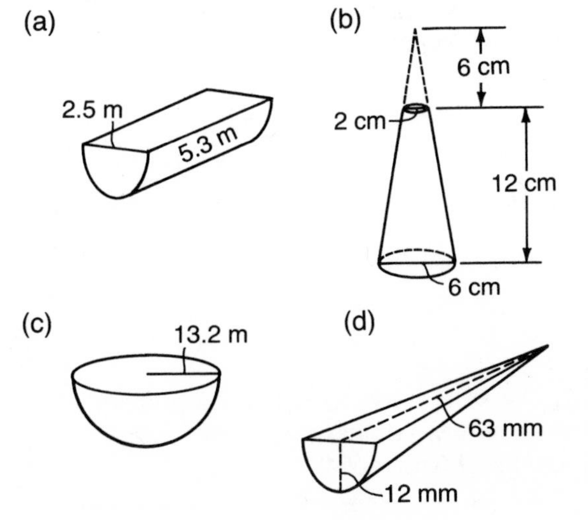

4. Calculate the volume of the silo in the picture.

5. The dimensions of a grain hopper are shown in the diagram.
Find the volume of the hopper.

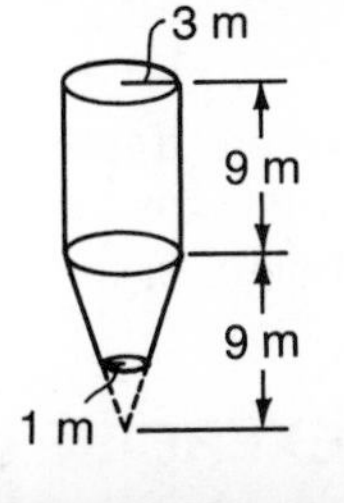

6. Approximate the volume of the hot air balloon.

35 m

7. The dimensions of the Great Pyramid of Cheops are shown.
Find the volume.

EXTRA

6.8 VOLUME OF A FRUSTUM OF A CONE

A frustum of a cone is the part of a cone-shaped solid that is left when the top is cut off by a plane parallel to the base.

If we are given the height of the frustum and the radius of both the top and bottom of the frustum, we can determine the height of the original cone and thereby obtain a formula for the volume of the frustum.

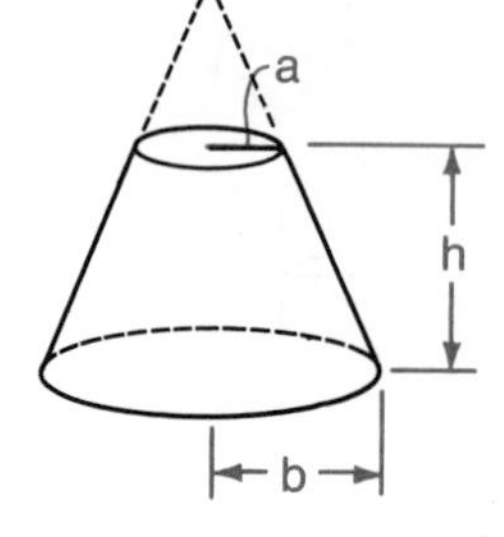

The formula for the volume of the frustum is

$$V = \frac{\pi}{3}h(a^2 + ab + b^2)$$

where a is the radius of the top of the frustum, b is the radius of the base, and h is the height of the frustum (not the height of the cone).

EXERCISE 6.8

1. Calculate the volume of the following frustums.

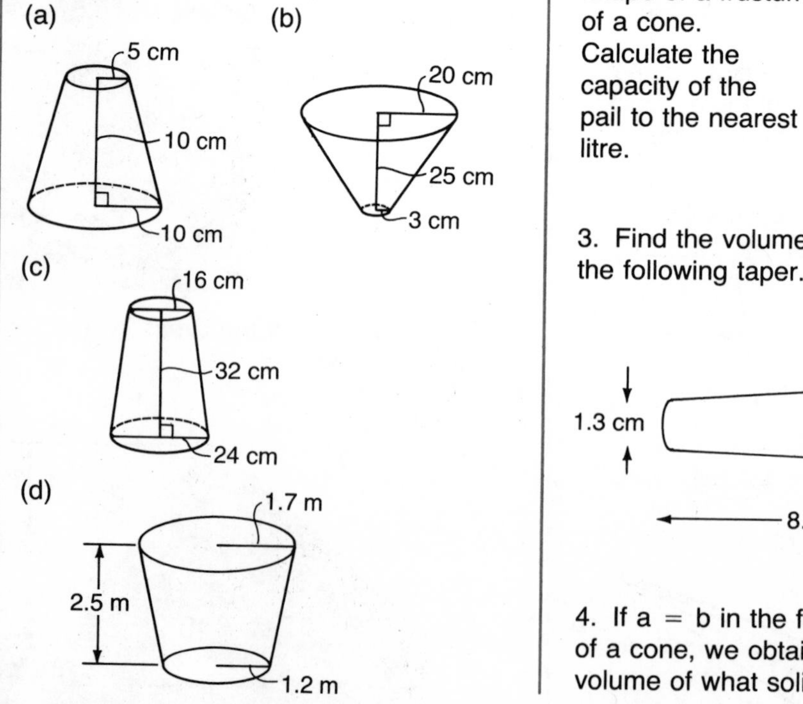

2. A pail is in the shape of a frustum of a cone. Calculate the capacity of the pail to the nearest litre.

30 cm
20 cm
20 cm

3. Find the volume of material in the following taper.

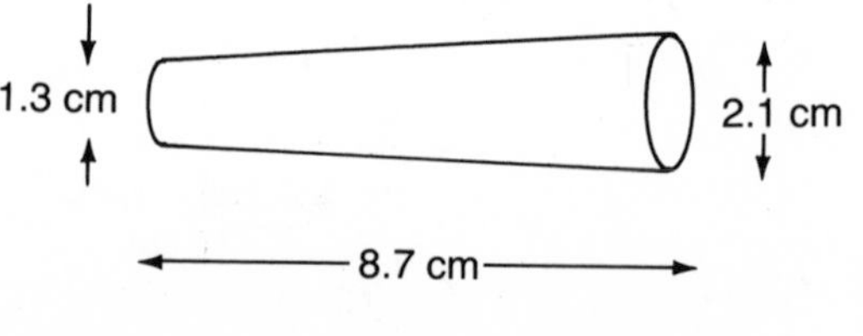

4. If a = b in the formula for a frustum of a cone, we obtain a formula for the volume of what solid?

EXTRA

6.9 SURFACE AREAS OF THE EARTH

On the earth, a parallel of latitude is a line around the planet running parallel to the equator. A zone is any region between two parallels.

If we assume that the earth is spherical, then the surface area of any zone is given by the formula

$$SA = \pi hd$$

where d is the diameter of the earth (approximately 12 700 km) and h is the vertical distance between parallels, measured in kilometres. Observe that the formula shows that zones with the same vertical distance between parallels have the same surface area — no matter where they are positioned on the sphere!

The diagram shows the five great latitudinal divisions of the earth's surface, named according to the prevailing climate.

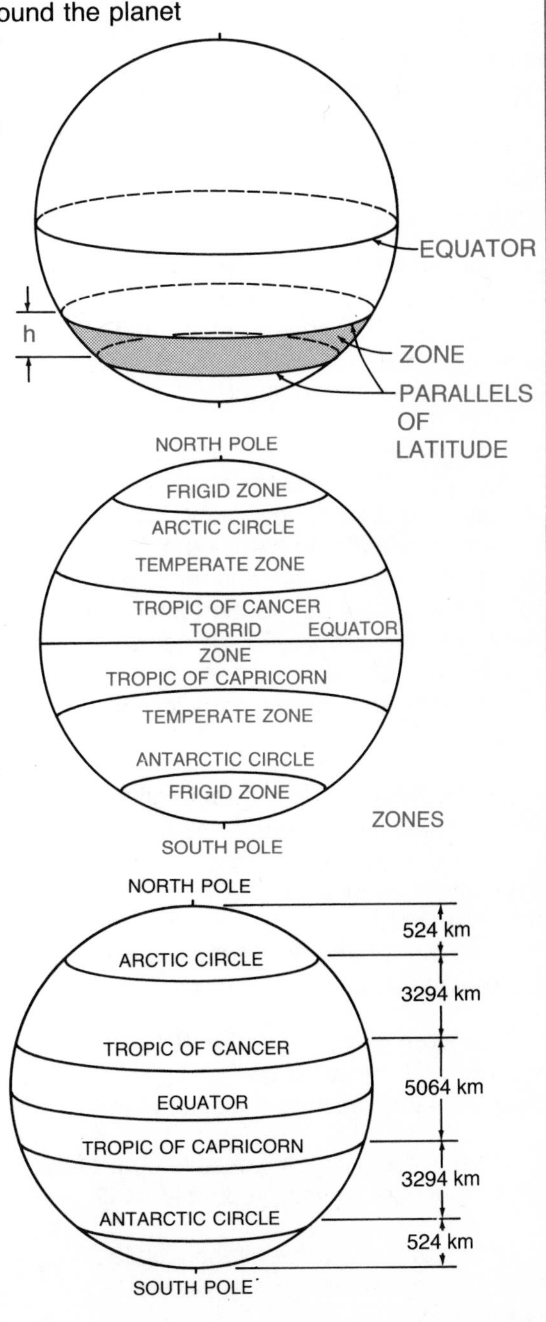

EXERCISE 6.9

1. Calculate the area of
(a) the Torrid Zone
(b) both Temperate Zones combined
(c) both Frigid Zones combined

2. What percentage of the earth's total surface area is
(a) the Torrid Zone?
(b) both Temperate Zones combined?
(c) both Frigid Zones combined?

Give your answers to the nearest whole number.

3. Express your percentages in a ratio, in lowest terms, of Frigid Zone to Temperate Zone to Torrid Zone.

6.10 PROBLEM SOLVING

1. An eight-digit number contains two 1's, two 2's, two 3's, and two 4's. The 1's are separated by one digit. The 2's are separated by two digits. The 3's are separated by three digits, and the 4's are separated by four digits.
What is the number?

2. How many strokes of a keyboard are required to type the page numbers in a 415 page book?

3. A 60 cm by 40 cm rectangular piece of tin has a 5 cm by 5 cm square cut out of each corner. The sides are then folded up to make a box.
What is the volume of the box?

4. Your plane for Fredericton leaves at 13:05. The airline requires that you check in one-half hour before your flight. The trip to the airport will take forty minutes. You should allow twenty minutes for parking and getting the shuttle bus to the terminal. On the way to the airport you will need ten minutes to get gasoline.
At what time should you leave for the airport?

5. The number 196 is a three-digit number that is also a perfect square since

$$14^2 = 196$$

The sum of the digits of 196 is 16 which is also a perfect square.
Find ten other three-digit numbers with these properties.

6. At a store you are given a 10% discount and you pay 7% sales tax.
Does it matter which is calculated first?

7. What is the smallest possible sum of two whole numbers whose product is 144?

8. How many of the twenty-six capital letters are symmetrical with respect to a vertical line?

9. Three tennis balls are packed snugly in a cylindrical can.
Which is greater, the volume of the balls or the volume of the air around the balls?

10. Between midnight and noon, how many times are the minute hand and the hour hand of a clock at right angles to each other?

11. The total number of angles in two regular polygons is thirteen. The total number of diagonals is twenty-five.
How many angles are there in each polygon?

12. What is the cross-sectional area of the largest square beam that can be cut from a log with a diameter of 80 cm?

13. In how many different ways can you make change for a $10 bill using $1, $2, and $5 bills?

14. A printing press can print 920 pages in ten minutes.
How long will it take to print 56 780 pages?

15. Paula has written three math tests and her average is 82.
What mark will she have to get on the next test to raise her average to 85?

16. Each of the six members of the winter carnival committee talked to the other five by phone.
How many phone calls were made?

17. The Eastmount community pool measures 25 m by 15 m. It has been decided to build a 3 m wide deck around the pool.
What is the area of the deck?

18. Which of the wheels, if any, turn counter-clockwise?

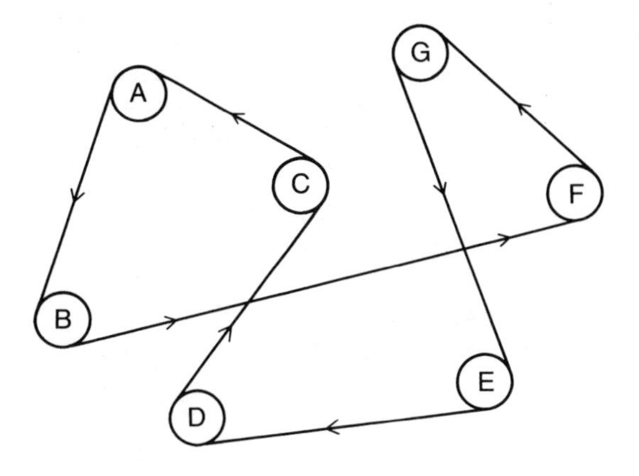

19. The numbers in the circles are found by adding the numbers in the adjacent squares.
What numbers are in the squares?

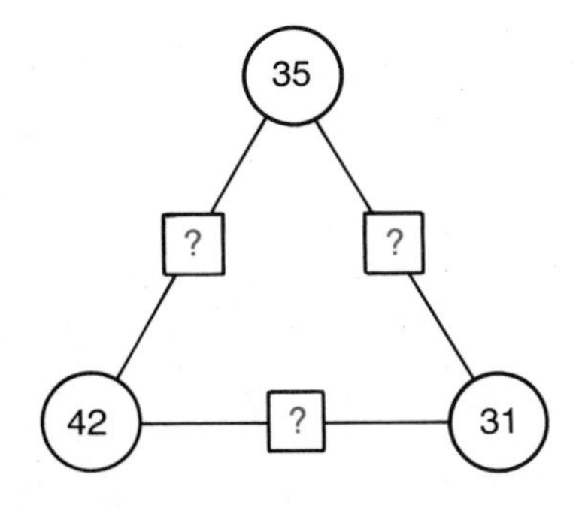

EXTRA

CAR RALLIES

The Cannonball Run is actually a car rally called the Cannonball Baker Sea-to-Shining-Seas Memorial Trophy Dash. The diagram shows the cities the cars must pass through.

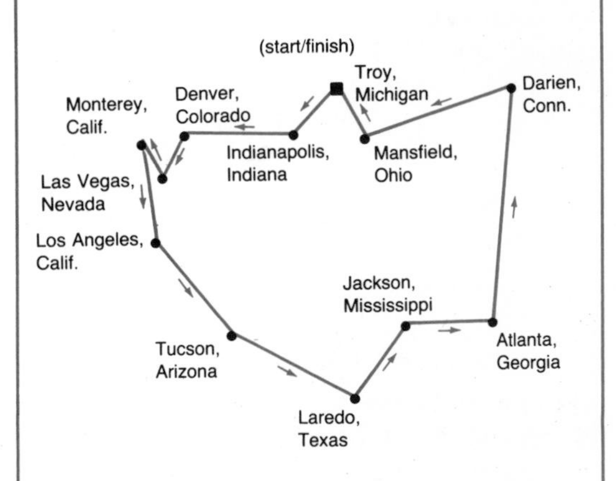

(a) Use a scale map to determine the approximate distance from start to finish.
(b) The drivers must average 77 km/h for the entire trip.
How long would it take to complete the trip?
(c) In order to qualify for the event you must have driven 5 000 000 km without an accident.
How many hours would it take you to drive 5 000 000 km if you drove 25% of the distance in 50 km/h areas, 40% of the distance in 90 km/h areas, and the rest of the distance in 100 km/h areas?
(d) Design a Canadian car rally that passes through each provincial capital.
(i) What distance is the rally?
(ii) How long would it take to complete the trip?

6.11 REVIEW EXERCISE

1. (a) Calculate the perimeter and area of a square of side 2.5 m.
(b) To the nearest tenth, what is the area of a circle with the same perimeter as the square in part (a)?

2. Suppose the radius of the hemispherical tank is (i) 1.5 m, (ii) 2 m.
Calculate each of the following to the nearest tenth.

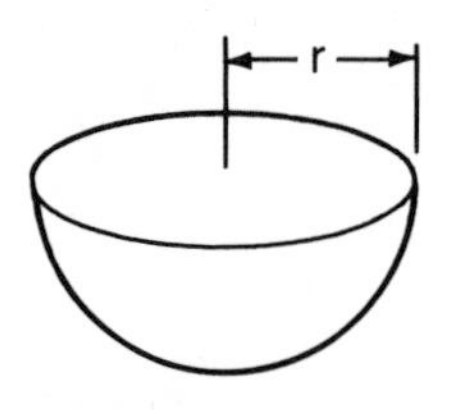

(a) the perimeter of the lip of the tank
(b) the area of the face of the tank
(c) the volume of the tank (expressed in cubic metres)
(d) the number of litres of water the tank will hold

3. Calculate each of the following to the nearest tenth.
(a) the perimeter of a square with an area of 1000 m^2
(b) the perimeter of a circle with an area of 1000 m^2
(c) the surface area of a sphere with a volume of 2974.3 m^3

4. How many litres of juice will a cylindrical container hold if the diameter is 12 cm and the height is 22.5 cm?

5. An aquarium is 16 cm wide and has circular ends 26 cm in diameter.
Calculate the capacity of the tank to the nearest tenth of a litre.

6. A cross section of a drainage ditch is a trapezoid 2 m wide at ground level and 1 m wide at the bottom. The ditch is 1.5 m deep.
How many cubic metres of earth are excavated from a ditch 400 m long?

7. A perfume atomizer is in the shape of a triangular prism with a height of 6 cm. A cross section parallel to the base is an equilateral triangle with perimeter 12 cm.
To the nearest millilitre, what is the capacity of the atomizer?

8. A sectional concrete highway divider is in the shape of a trapezoid.
If each section is 3.5 m long, how many cubic metres of concrete are needed for each section?

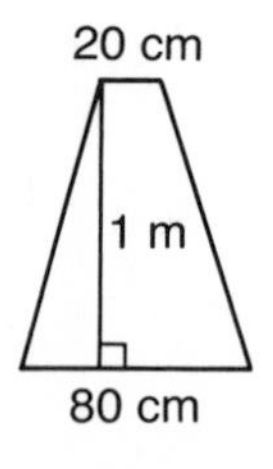

9. Calculate the capacity of the conical glass to the nearest millilitre.

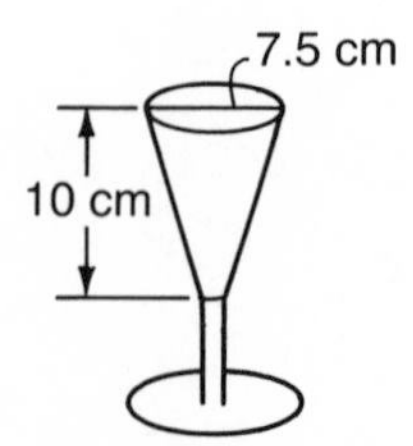

10. (a) Calculate the area of the fence to the nearest metre.
(b) How much will it cost to paint one side of the fence, if paint costs $21.40 a can and covers 16 m²?

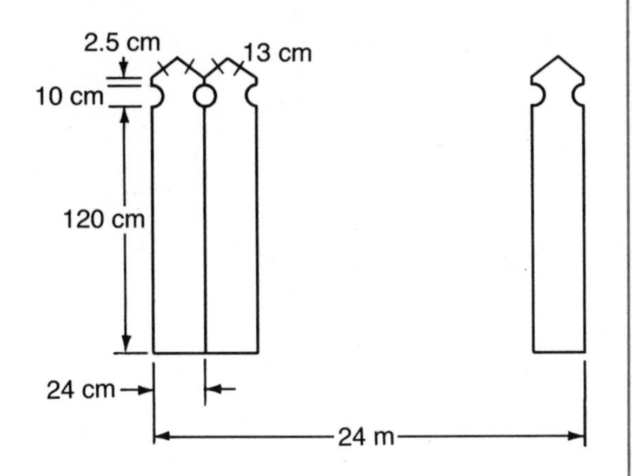

11. A circular flower bed is to have a diameter of 5 m. Tulip bulbs are to be planted around the perimeter of the bed and on equally spaced concentric circles within the bed. The tulips are to be spaced as in the diagram.

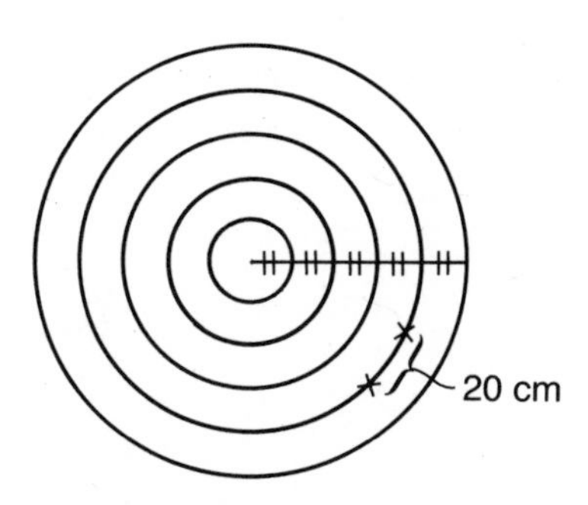

(a) How many bulbs are required?
(b) How much will the bulbs cost if packages of 16 bulbs cost $4.98 and 7% sales tax is charged?
(c) What are the dimensions of a square that could be bordered by the number of bulbs in part (a) spaced 20 cm apart?

12. (a) Express in lowest terms the ratio of area to perimeter of a square of side length s.
(b) For what side length is the area (in square units) equal to the perimeter?

13. (a) Express in lowest terms the ratio of area to perimeter of a circle of radius r.
(b) For what radius is the area of the circle equal to the perimeter?

14. (a) Express in lowest terms the ratio of volume to surface area of a cube of side length s.
(b) For what side length is the volume (in cubic units) equal to the surface area (in square units)?

15. (a) Express in lowest terms the ratio of volume to surface area of a sphere of radius r.
(b) For what radius is the volume equal to the surface area?

16. A grapefruit with a diameter of 12 cm has a skin 0.5 cm thick (the skin is included in the diameter).
(a) What is the approximate volume of the skin?
(b) What percentage of total volume is skin?

17. Calculate the surface area of the lamp shade to the nearest ten square centimetres.

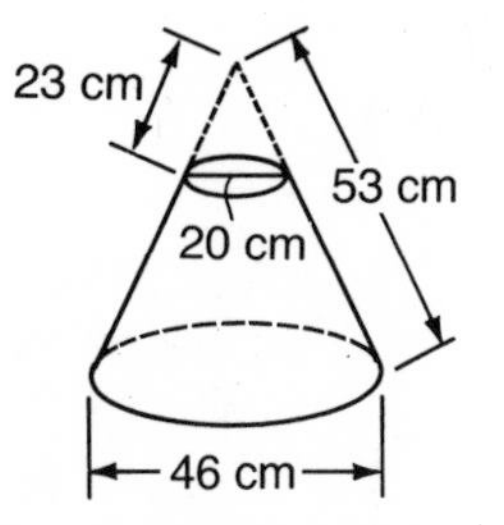

6.12 CHAPTER 6 TEST

Give all answers to the nearest tenth.

1. Calculate the perimeter of the following figures.

(a) (b) (c)

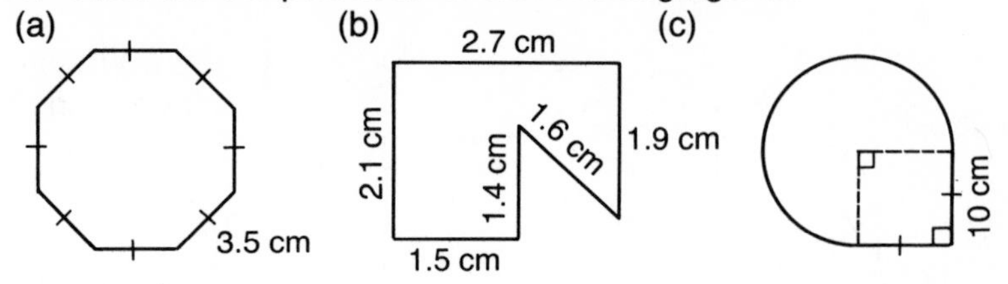

2. Calculate the area of the following figures.

(a) (b) (c)

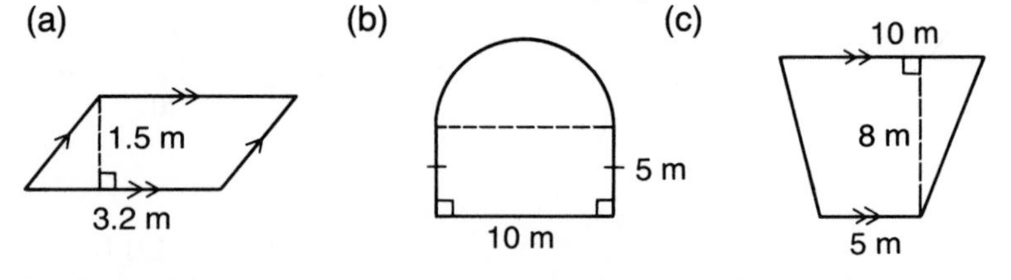

3. Calculate the surface area of the following figures.

(a) (b) (c)

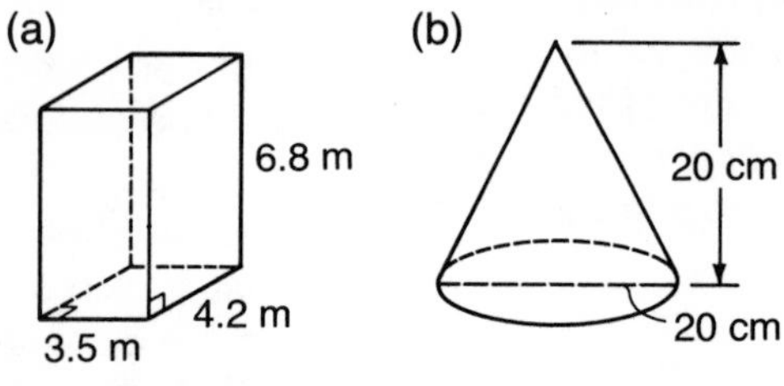

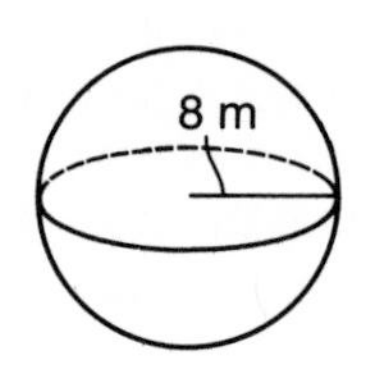

4. Calculate the volume of the following figures.

(a) (b) (c)

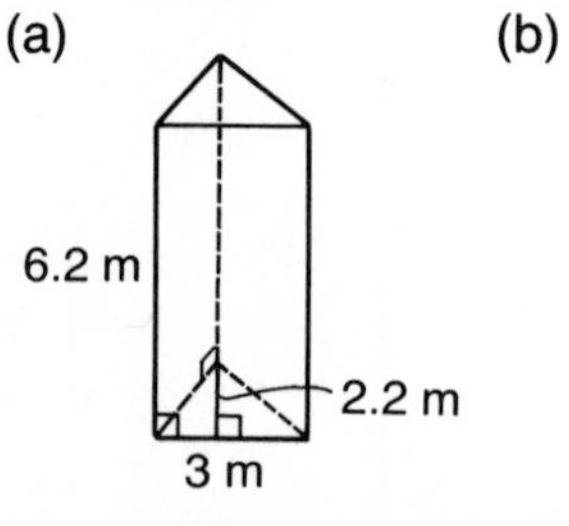

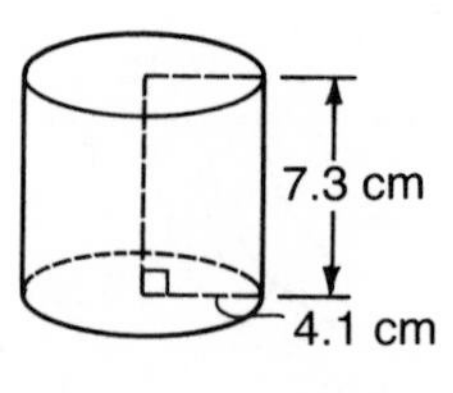

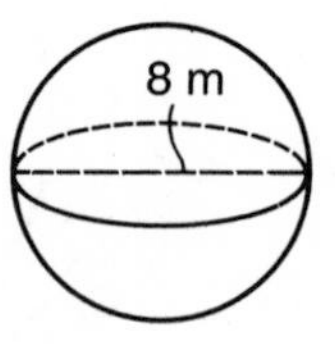

5. There are 12 cans of soup in a box with a rectangular base 40 cm by 30 cm. The diameter of each can is 10 cm.

(a) Calculate the exposed area of the base.

(b) What percentage of the total base area is exposed?

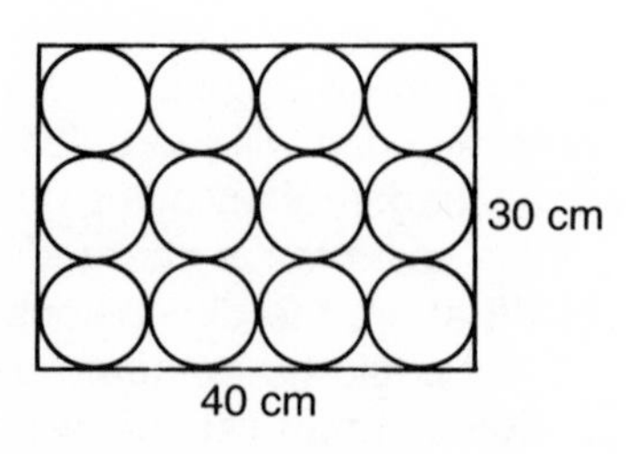

GEOMETRY

REVIEW AND PREVIEW TO CHAPTER 

BASIC TERMS IN GEOMETRY

The chart summarizes the basic terms in geometry.

Term	Labelled Diagram	Description	Symbol
Point	A •	Point A	A
Line	A ℓ B	Line $\overleftrightarrow{AB}$ or $\overleftrightarrow{BA}$ or Line ℓ	$\overleftrightarrow{AB}$ or $\overleftrightarrow{BA}$ or ℓ
Line Segment	A B	Line segment AB or BA, where A and B are the end points of the line segment	AB or BA
Ray	A B	Ray $\overrightarrow{AB}$	$\overrightarrow{AB}$
Angle	A B C A B C	Angle ABC or Angle CBA, where BA and BC are the rays (arms) of the angle and B is the vertex of the angle	∠ABC or ∠CBA or ∠B
Triangle	A B C	Triangle ABC, where AB, BC, and AC are sides of the triangle and A, B, and C are vertices	△ABC

We classify angles by their measures.

Acute Angle	Right Angle	Obtuse Angle	Straight Angle	Reflex Angle
Less than 90°	Equal to 90°	Greater than 90° but less than 180°	Equal to 180°	Greater than 180° but less than 360°

We classify pairs of angles by their sums.

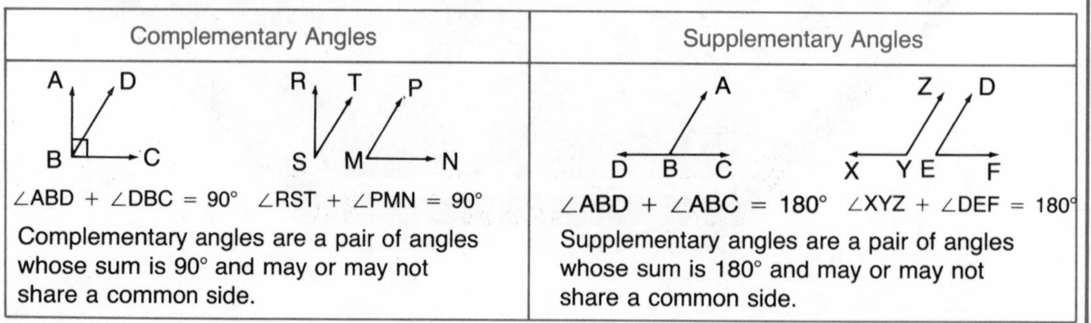

Complementary Angles	Supplementary Angles
∠ABD + ∠DBC = 90° ∠RST + ∠PMN = 90°	∠ABD + ∠ABC = 180° ∠XYZ + ∠DEF = 180°
Complementary angles are a pair of angles whose sum is 90° and may or may not share a common side.	Supplementary angles are a pair of angles whose sum is 180° and may or may not share a common side.

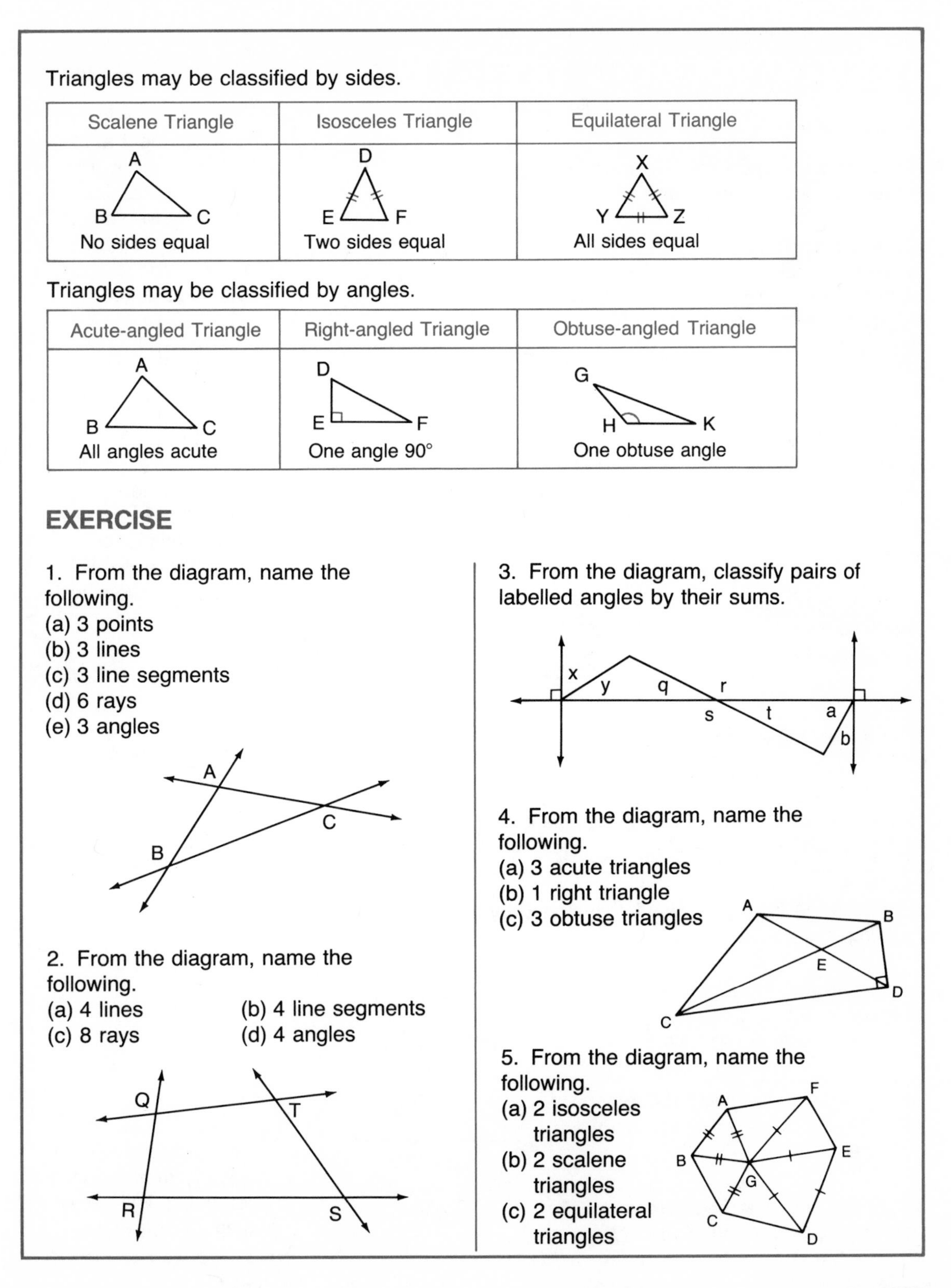

Triangles may be classified by sides.

Scalene Triangle	Isosceles Triangle	Equilateral Triangle
A, B, C No sides equal	D, E, F Two sides equal	X, Y, Z All sides equal

Triangles may be classified by angles.

Acute-angled Triangle	Right-angled Triangle	Obtuse-angled Triangle
A, B, C All angles acute	D, E, F One angle 90°	G, H, K One obtuse angle

EXERCISE

1. From the diagram, name the following.
(a) 3 points
(b) 3 lines
(c) 3 line segments
(d) 6 rays
(e) 3 angles

2. From the diagram, name the following.
(a) 4 lines
(b) 4 line segments
(c) 8 rays
(d) 4 angles

3. From the diagram, classify pairs of labelled angles by their sums.

4. From the diagram, name the following.
(a) 3 acute triangles
(b) 1 right triangle
(c) 3 obtuse triangles

5. From the diagram, name the following.
(a) 2 isosceles triangles
(b) 2 scalene triangles
(c) 2 equilateral triangles

7.1 ANGLE PROPERTIES

Because of their usefulness, triangles are found in many places.

The following experiment illustrates one of the most important ideas in geometry.

Draw a triangle on a piece of paper. Join the midpoints of AB and AC to form DE.

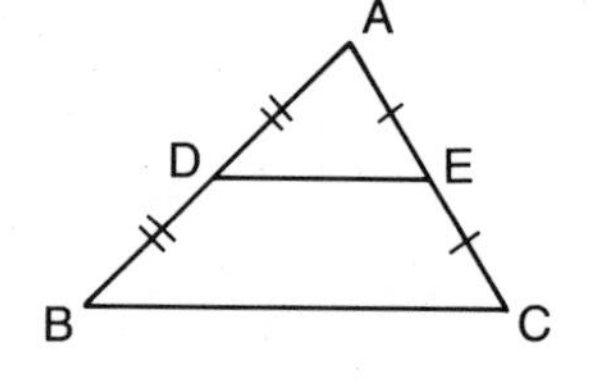

Fold the triangle along DE to place A on BC.

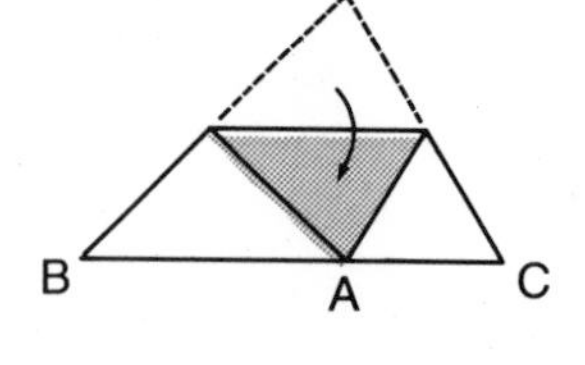

Fold the triangle again so that B and C meet at A.

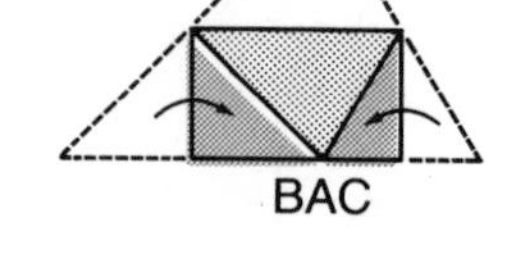

The angles appear to form a straight angle.

This experiment at the left is not a proof. The following optical illusion shows why we should rely more on logical reasoning and less on visual information.

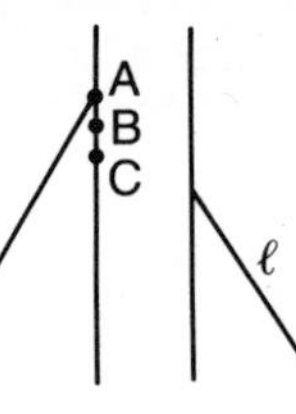

Will line ℓ, when extended, meet point A, point B, point C, or none of these points? Answer, and check with a ruler.

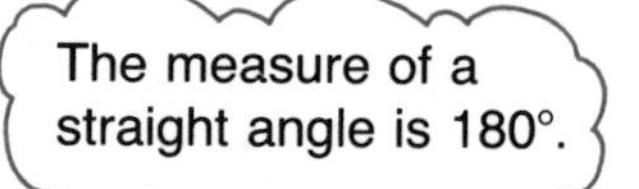

The sum of the angles of any triangle is 180°. $\angle A + \angle B + \angle C = 180°$

The following facts may also be illustrated by similar "folding" experiments.

In an equilateral triangle each angle is equal to 60°.

$$\angle A = \angle B = \angle C = 60°$$

In an isosceles triangle the angles opposite the equal sides are equal.

$$\angle B = \angle C$$

When two lines intersect, the vertically opposite angles are equal.

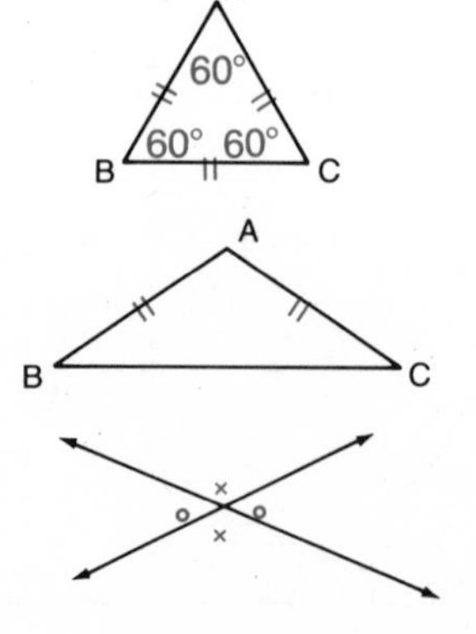

Two nonadjacent angles formed by two intersecting lines are called vertical angles.

READ

Example 1. Show that the sum of the angles of a quadrilateral is 360°.

PLAN

Solution:
Draw a quadrilateral and label the vertices.

Draw the diagonal AC to form two triangles. The sum of the angles in any triangle is 180°.

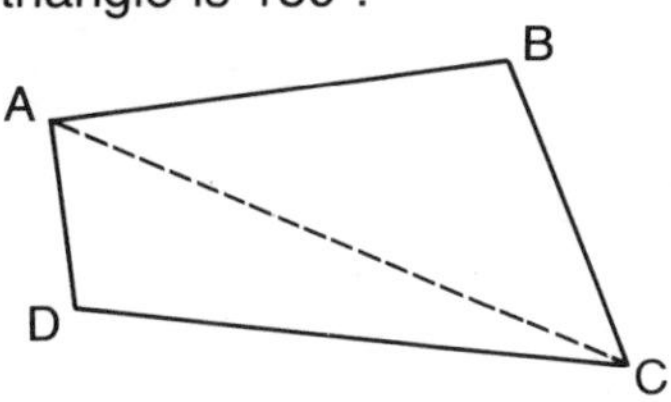

SOLVE

In $\triangle ABC$: $\angle BAC + \angle B + \angle ACB = 180°$
In $\triangle ACD$: $\angle CAD + \angle D + \angle ACD = 180°$
Add: $\underbrace{(\angle BAC + \angle CAD)}_{\angle A} + \angle B + \angle D + \underbrace{(\angle ACB + \angle ACD)}_{\angle C} = 360°$

$$\angle A + \angle B + \angle C + \angle D = 360°$$

$\angle A = \angle BAC + \angle CAD$
$\angle C = \angle ACB + \angle ACD$

ANSWER

The sum of the angles of a quadrilateral is 360°.

READ

Example 2. A window frame is to be built in the shape of a regular octagon.
At what angle should the sides be cut?

PLAN

Solution:
Draw a diagram.
Draw the diagonals to determine the lines of cut. Since all eight triangles formed by the diagonals are identical, consider only $\triangle ABC$.

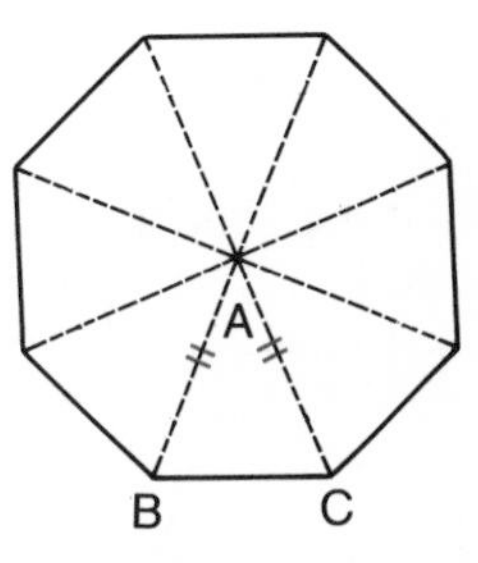

SOLVE

In $\triangle ABC$: $8 \times \angle A = 360°$
$$\angle A = \frac{360°}{8}$$
$$= 45°$$

Since $\angle A + \angle B + \angle C = 180°$
$45° + \angle B + \angle C = 180°$
$\angle B + \angle C = 135°$

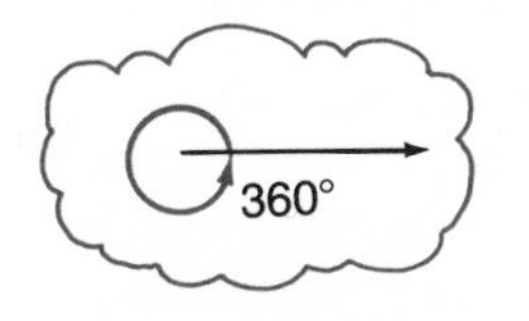

Since $\triangle ABC$ is isosceles, $\angle B = \angle C$.
$\therefore 2 \times \angle B = 135°$
$\angle B = 67.5°$

Octagon — a plane figure with eight sides and eight angles.
Regular octagon — all sides are equal in length and all angles are equal in measure.

The angle of cut should be 67.5°.

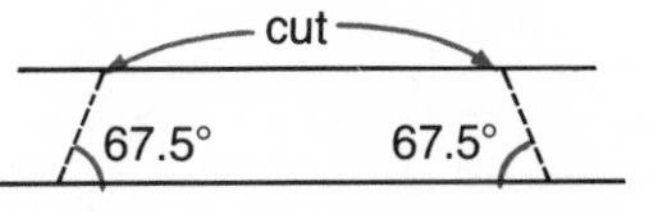

EXERCISE 7.1

A

1. Determine the measure of the indicated angles in each of the following.

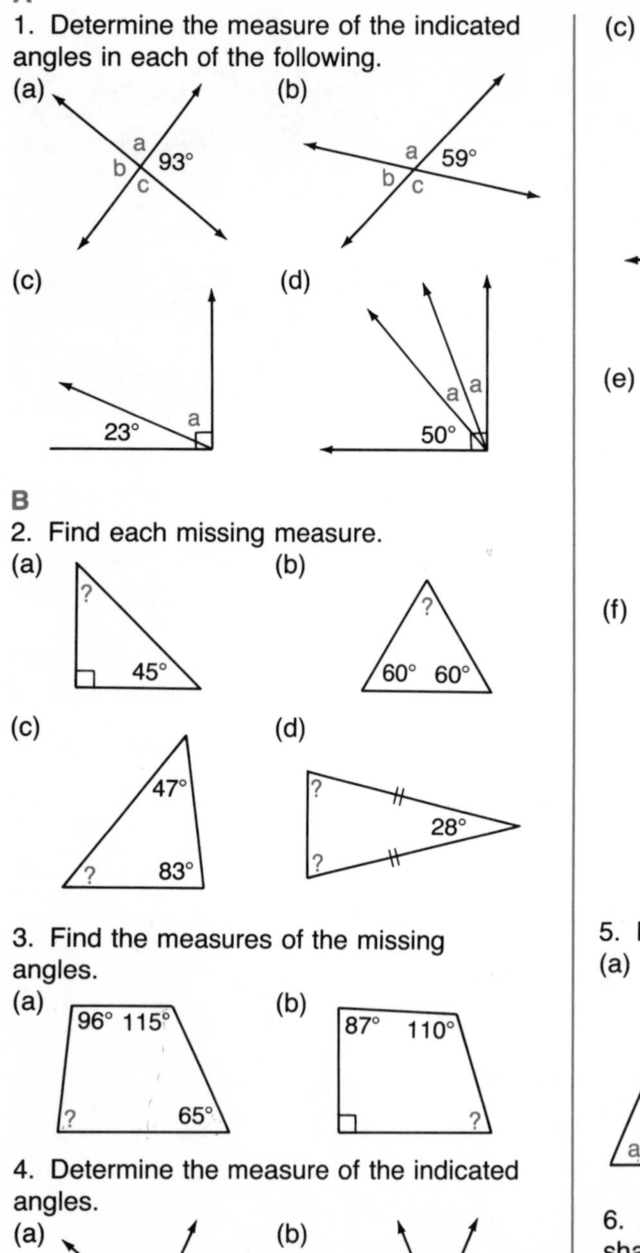

B

2. Find each missing measure.

3. Find the measures of the missing angles.

4. Determine the measure of the indicated angles.

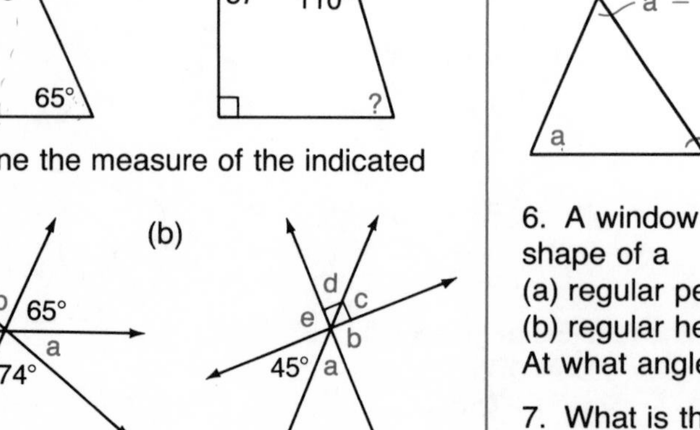

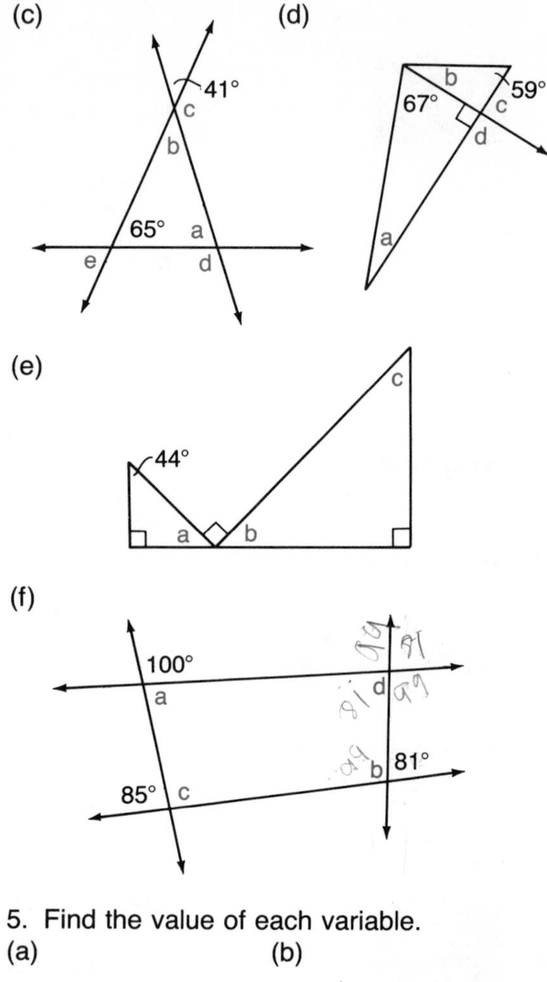

5. Find the value of each variable.

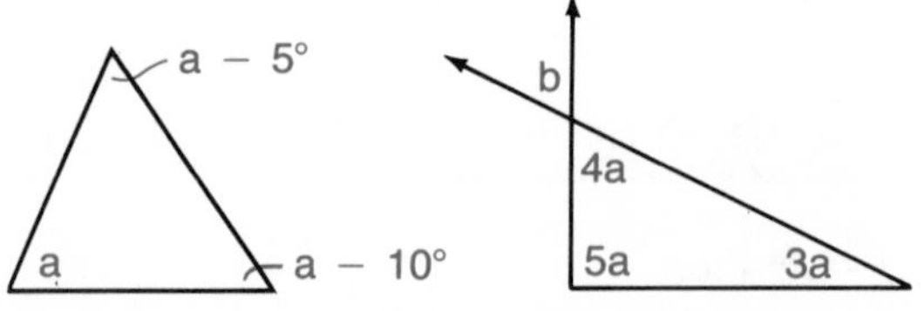

6. A window frame is to be built in the shape of a
(a) regular pentagon,
(b) regular hexagon.
At what angle should the sides be cut?

7. What is the sum of the angles in a pentagon?

7.2 PARALLEL LINES

Parallel lines are lines in the same plane that do not meet.

When line ℓ_1 is parallel to line ℓ_2, we write $\ell_1 \parallel \ell_2$.

A transversal is a line that intersects two or more lines.

In the figure at the right the transversal cuts two lines making eight angles: a, b, c, d, e, f, g, h.

We name these as follows.

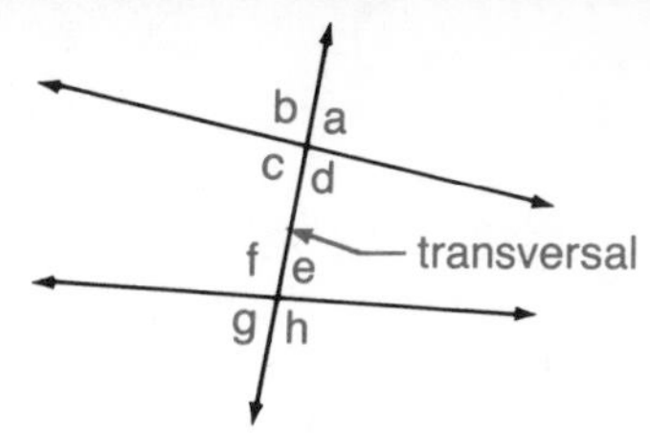

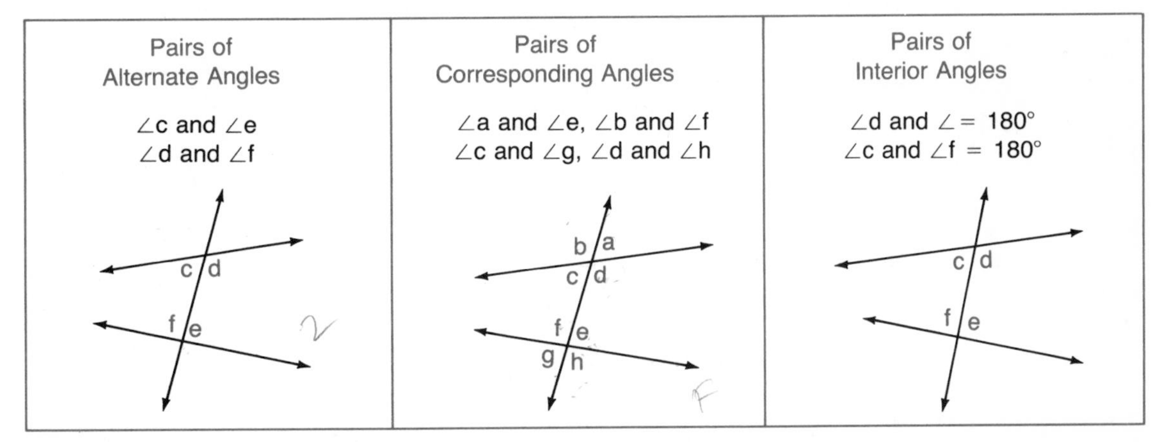

Pairs of Alternate Angles	Pairs of Corresponding Angles	Pairs of Interior Angles
$\angle c$ and $\angle e$ $\angle d$ and $\angle f$	$\angle a$ and $\angle e$, $\angle b$ and $\angle f$ $\angle c$ and $\angle g$, $\angle d$ and $\angle h$	$\angle d$ and $\angle = 180°$ $\angle c$ and $\angle f = 180°$

When a transversal meets two parallel lines:

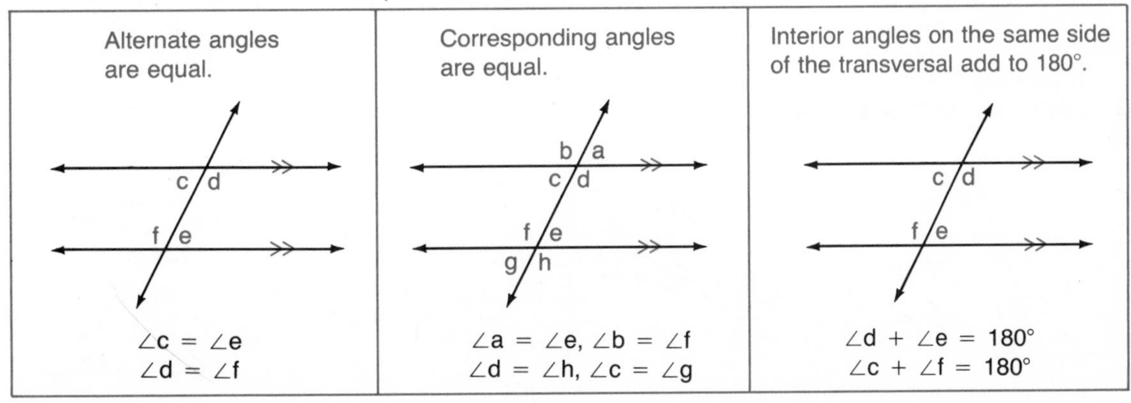

Alternate angles are equal.	Corresponding angles are equal.	Interior angles on the same side of the transversal add to 180°.
$\angle c = \angle e$ $\angle d = \angle f$	$\angle a = \angle e$, $\angle b = \angle f$ $\angle d = \angle h$, $\angle c = \angle g$	$\angle d + \angle e = 180°$ $\angle c + \angle f = 180°$

We can remember the angle pairs by thinking of the Z, F, C patterns.

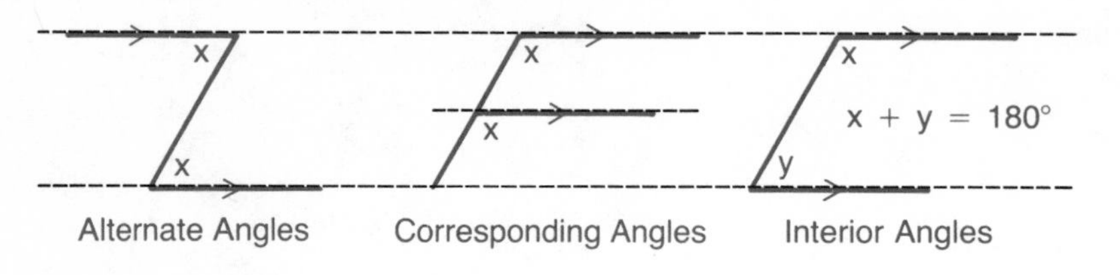

EXERCISE 7.2

A

1. In the following diagrams, name the
(a) pairs of alternate angles
(b) pairs of corresponding angles
(c) interior angles on the same side of the transversal.

(i) (ii)

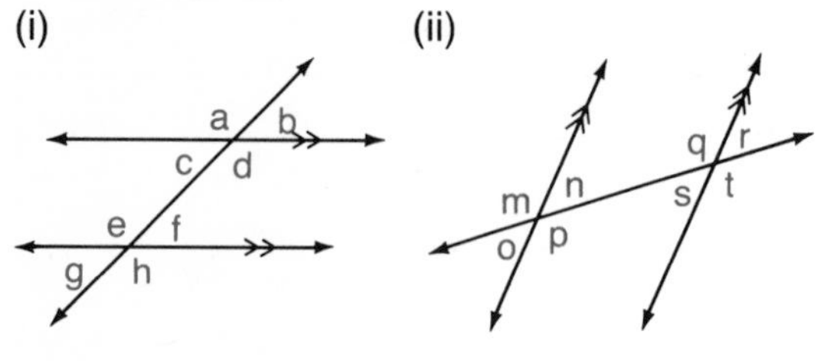

B

2. Determine the measure of the indicated angles.

(a) (b)

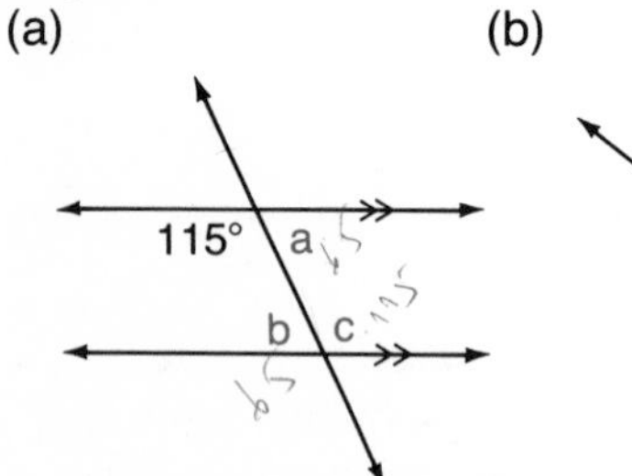

3. Calculate the missing values.

(a) (b)

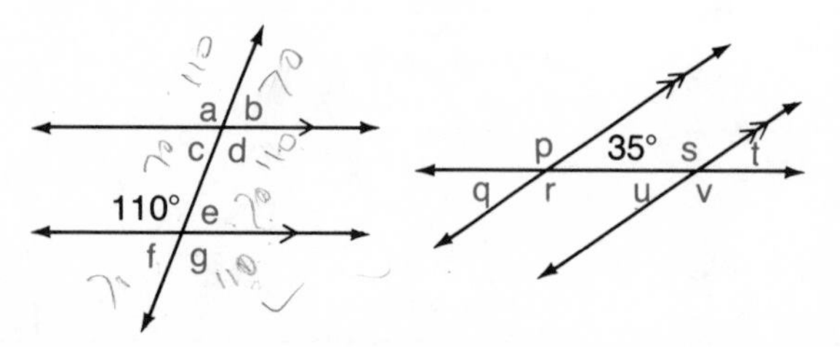

4. Calculate the missing measures.

(a) (b)

(c) (d)

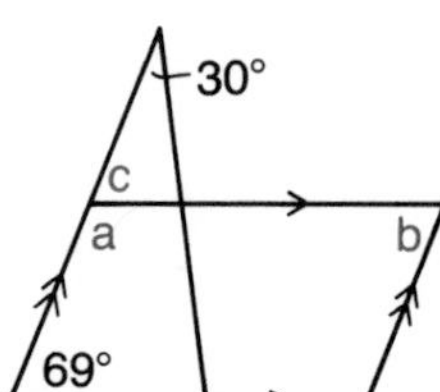

(e) (f)

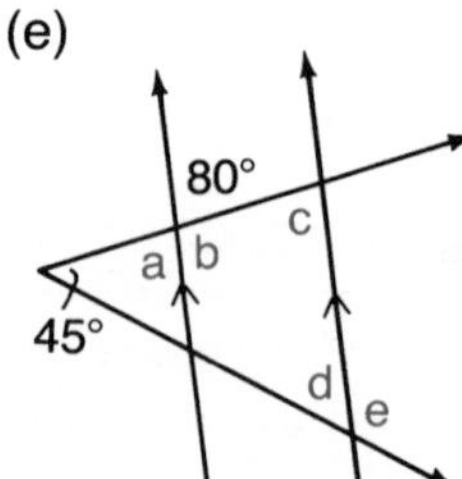

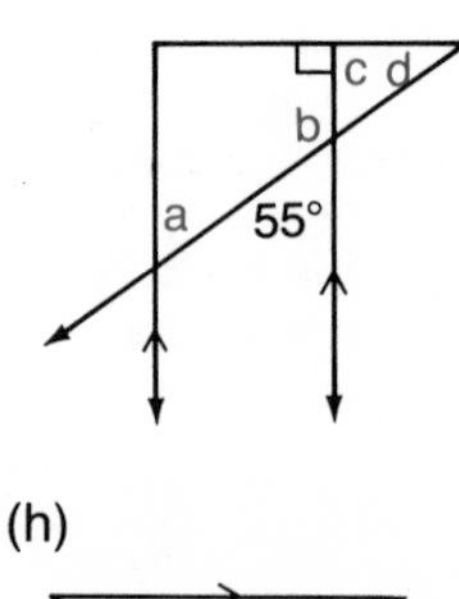

(g) (h)

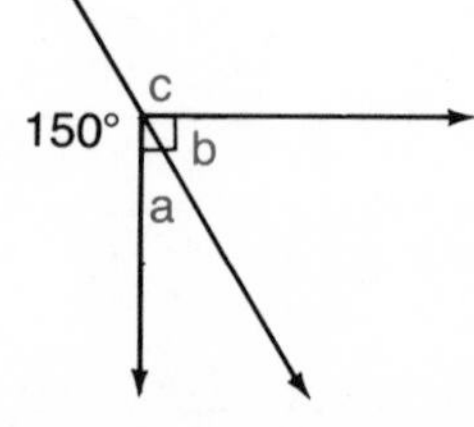

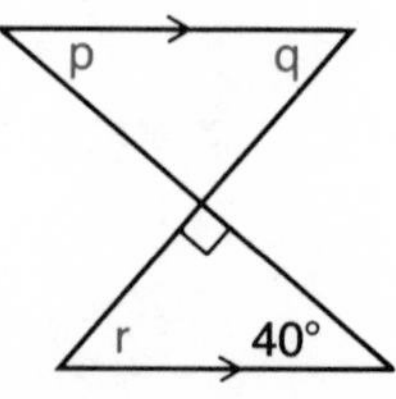

5. The diagram shows the intersection of two streets.

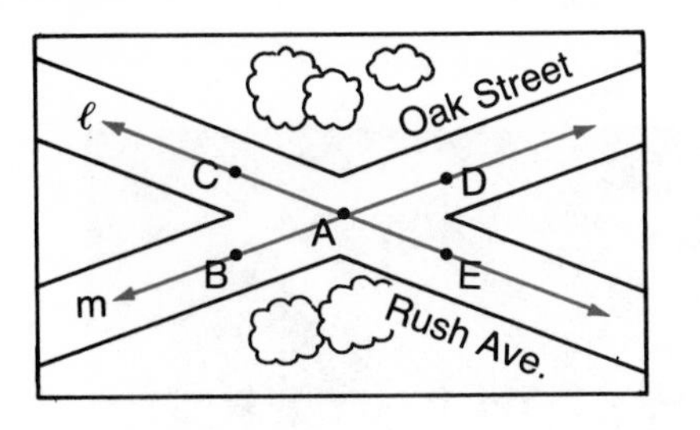

If $\angle CAB$ is 40°, what are the measures of the angles formed at the other three corners?

6. To determine the angle between the slanted ceiling and the wall, a carpenter uses a protractor and a plumbline (a string with a weight attached).

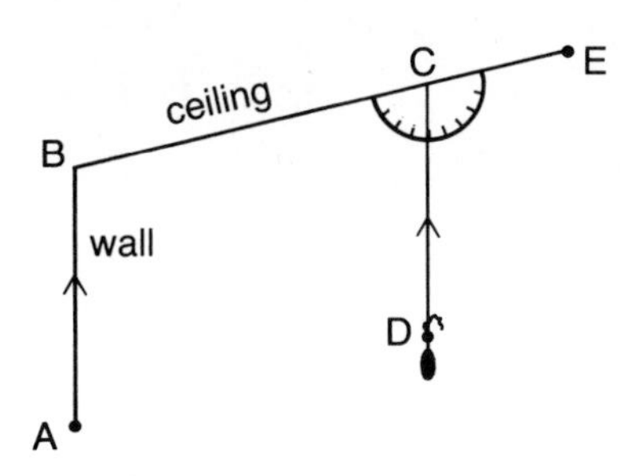

If the protractor indicates that $\angle BCD = 78°$, what is the measure of $\angle ABC$?

7. A board is cut in half to be used as two rafters in constructing a roof.

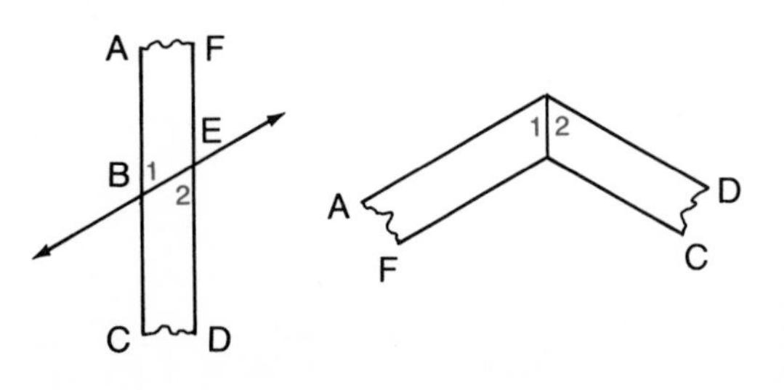

Explain why $\angle 1$ and $\angle 2$ are equal.

8. A staircase has been built up to a stage.

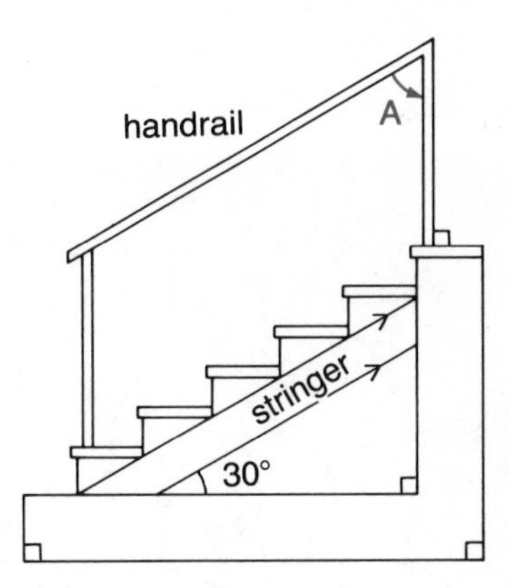

(a) If the steps are parallel to the floor, what angle do they make with the stringer?
(b) If the handrail is parallel to the stringer, what is the measure of $\angle A$?

9. In a periscope two mirrors are mounted parallel to each other.

Determine the measure of the indicated angle.

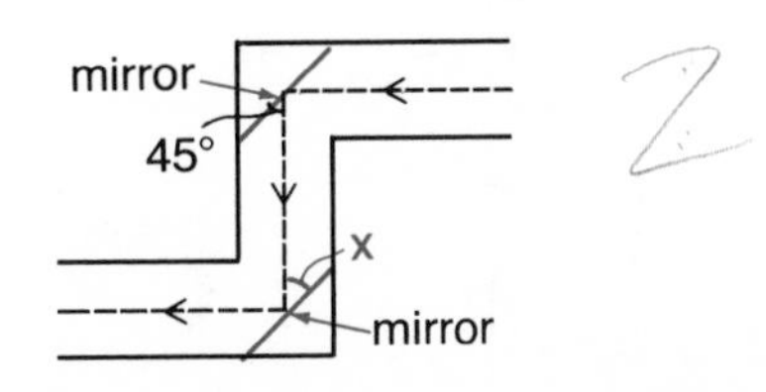

7.3 LINES AND ANGLES

A laser beam is a model of a ray. In geometry, a ray is a never-ending straight path in one direction.

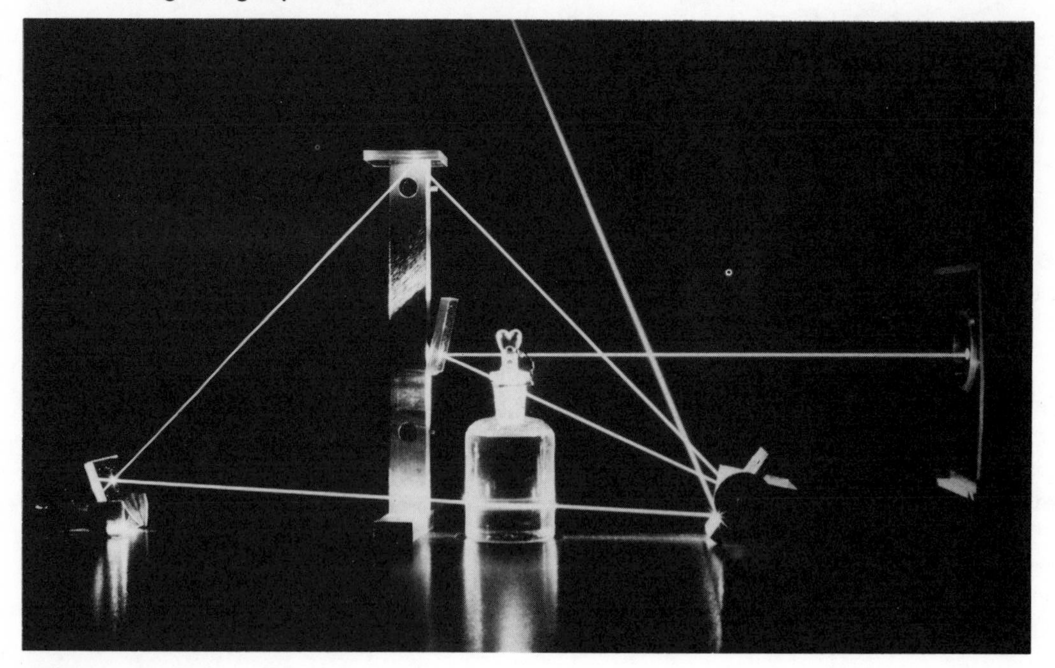

EXERCISE 7.3

B

Calculate the value of each variable in each of the following.

1.

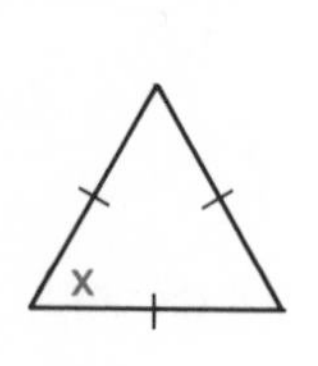

2.

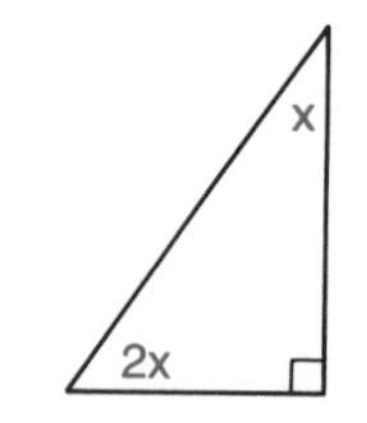

3.

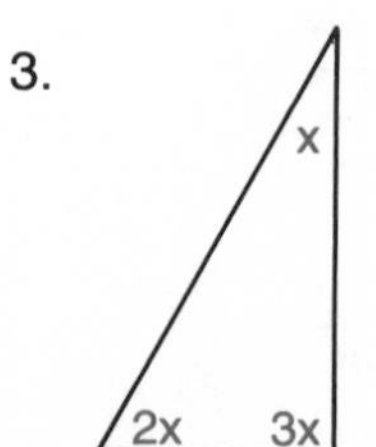

4.

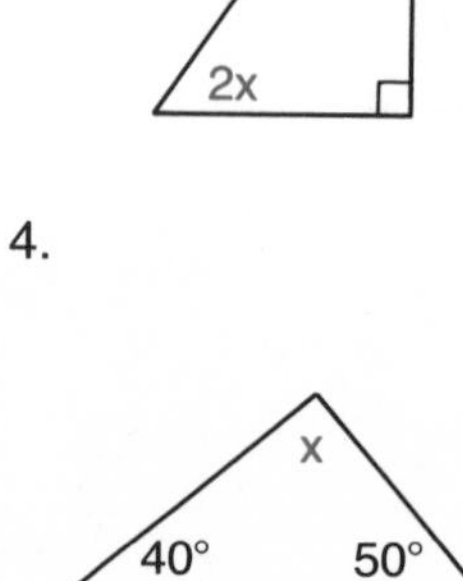

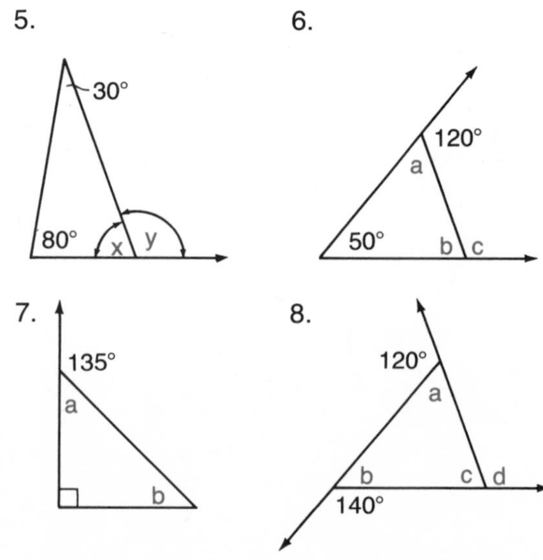

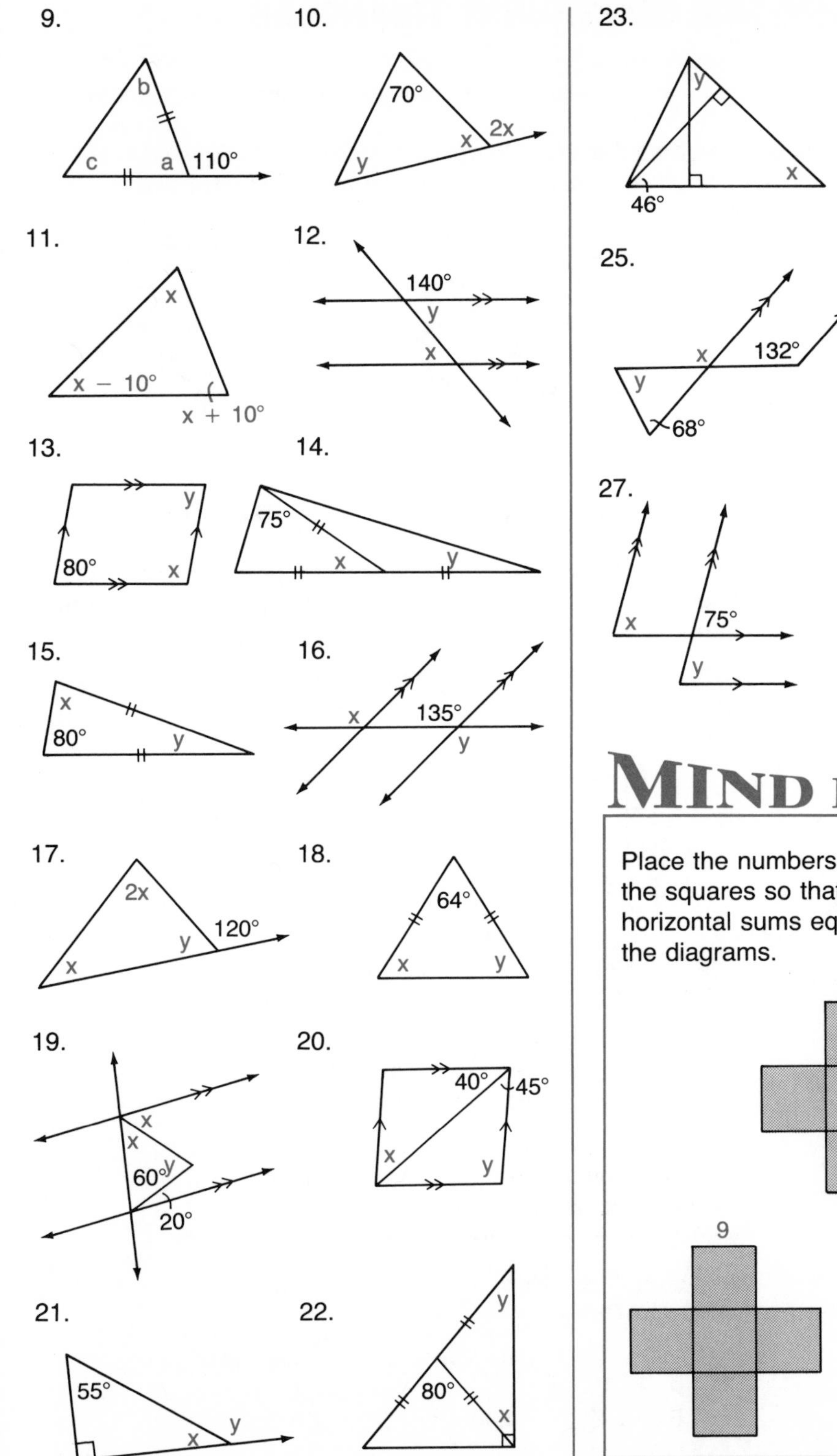

23.

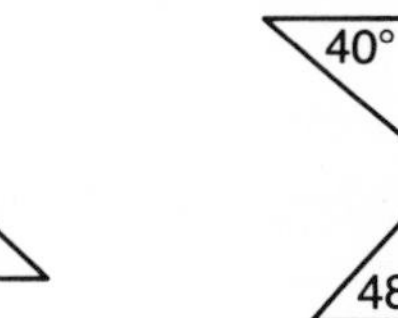

24.

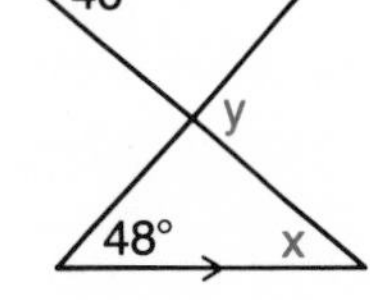

25.

26.

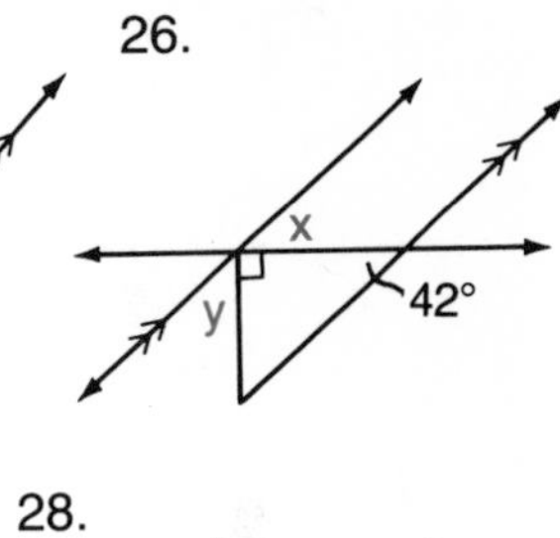

27.

x

75°

y

28.

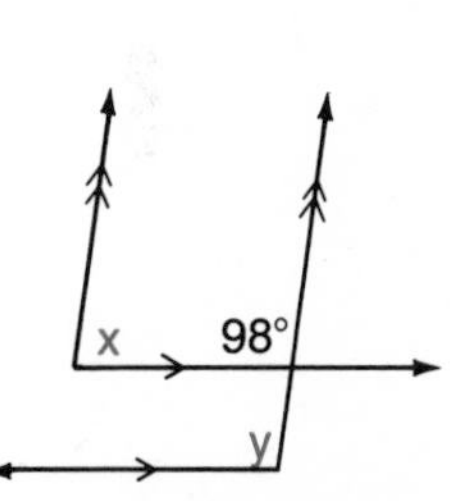

MIND BENDER

Place the numbers 1, 2, 3, 4, and 5 in the squares so that the vertical and horizontal sums equal the sum above the diagrams.

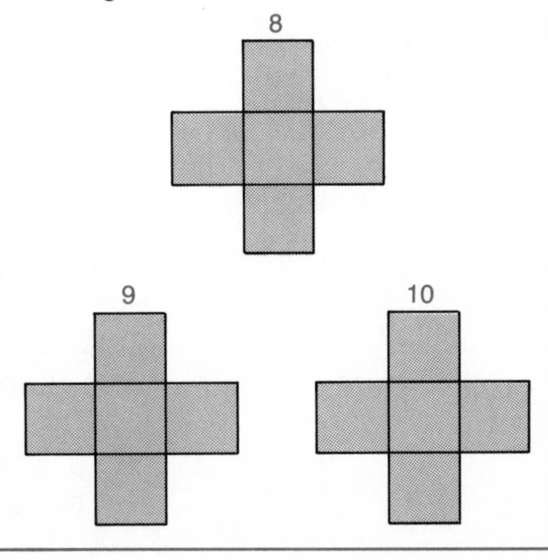

7.4 CONGRUENT TRIANGLES

When a duplicate of a key is made, the original key and a blank are held firmly in a moveable clamp. The clamp is moved so that a guide traces the edge of the key, while a cutting disk duplicates the pattern along the edge of the blank.

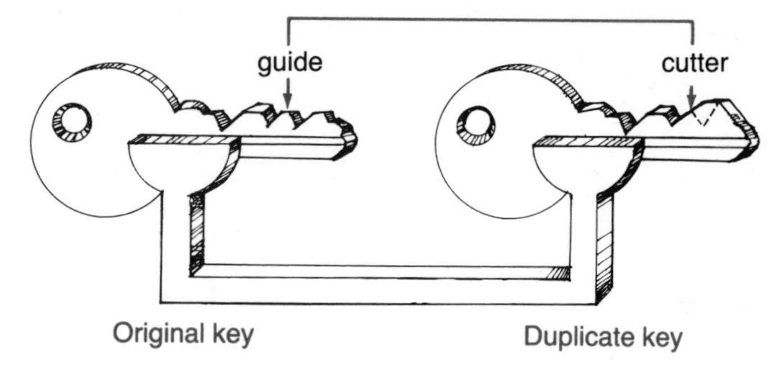

Figures that have the same size and shape are called congruent. We may always match up the points of congruent figures as we can for the congruent keys above.

△ABC and △DEF are congruent. They have the same size and shape.

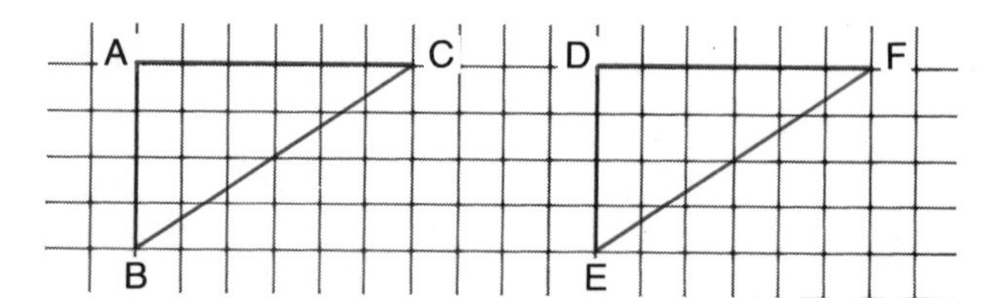

Imagine sliding △ABC over to fit on △DEF. Point B fits on point E; point A on point D; point C on point F.

When the vertices are matched in this way:
∠B and ∠E are called corresponding angles,
AB and DE are called corresponding sides.

> When triangles are congruent, corresponding angles and corresponding sides are equal.

When △ABC is congruent to △DEF, we write
△ABC ≅ △DEF

△ABC ≅ △DEF means that all of the following are true:

∠A = ∠D		AB = DE
∠B = ∠E	and	BC = EF
∠C = ∠F		AC = DF

Example. The two triangles shown are congruent.

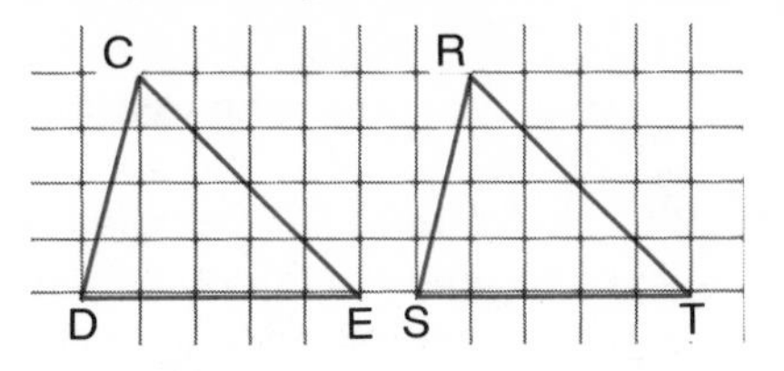

(a) Name the corresponding angles that are equal.
(b) Name the corresponding sides that are equal.

Solution:

(a) $\angle C = \angle R$
$\angle D = \angle S$
$\angle E = \angle T$

(b) $CD = RS$
$DE = ST$
$CE = RT$

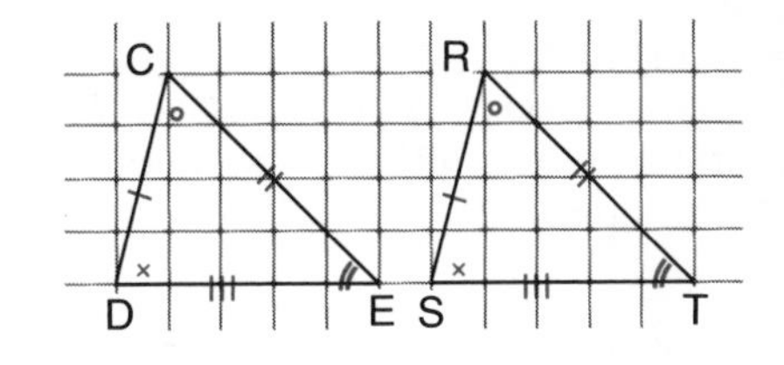

EXERCISE 7.4

A 1. The two triangles are congruent.

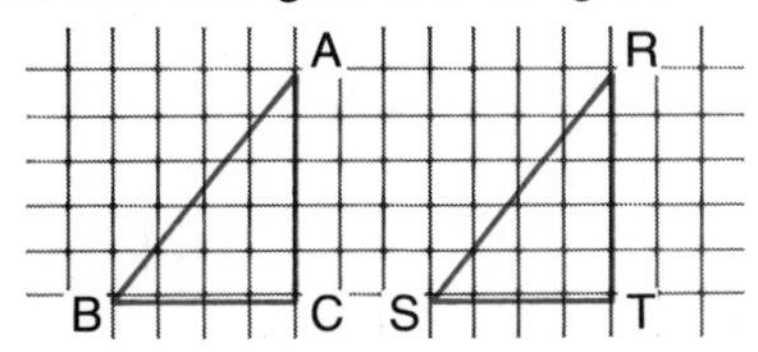

(a) Name the corresponding angles that are equal.
(b) Name the corresponding sides that are equal.

B 2. The pairs of triangles are congruent. Name the corresponding angles and sides that are equal.

(a)
(b)

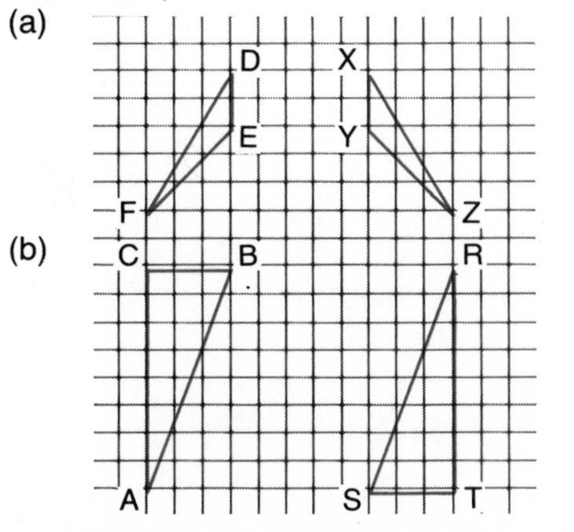

3. The pairs of triangles are congruent. Name the corresponding angles and sides that are equal.

(a)
(b)
(c)
(d)

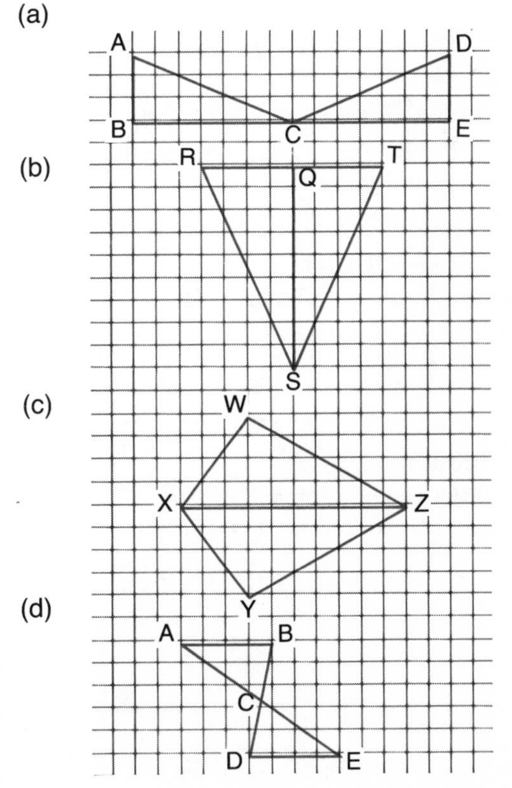

7.5 CONDITIONS FOR CONGRUENCE

When two triangles are congruent, the six parts (three sides, three angles) of one triangle are equal to the six corresponding parts of the other triangle. To determine whether two triangles are congruent, it is not necessary to compare all six pairs of parts. The following investigations show that the equality of certain combinations of three parts is sufficient to establish congruence.

Suppose you need to repair a carpet with a triangular patch. How many measurements, and of what type, would you make in order to cut out a congruent patch?

Investigation 1.
Construct at least three triangles with sides 6 cm, 7 cm, and 8 cm. You can use a ruler and compass, or cut straws with lengths 6 cm, 7 cm, and 8 cm.

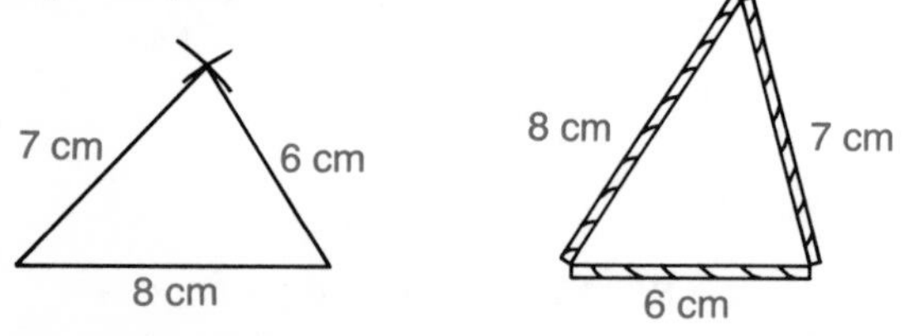

Compare the triangles by tracing or fitting one triangle on top of the other.

SSS
Side Side Side Condition for Congruence

If the three sides of one triangle are respectively equal to the three sides of another triangle, then the triangles are congruent.

In $\triangle ABC$ and $\triangle DEF$

$AB = DE$
$BC = EF$
$AC = DF$

Thus $\triangle ABC \cong \triangle DEF$ (SSS)
and $\angle A = \angle D$
$\angle B = \angle E$
$\angle C = \angle F$

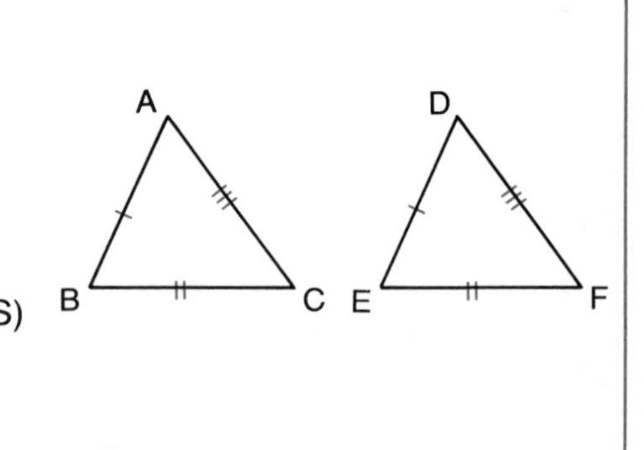

Investigation 2.
Construct at least three triangles with sides 5 cm and 6 cm that contain an angle of 60°.

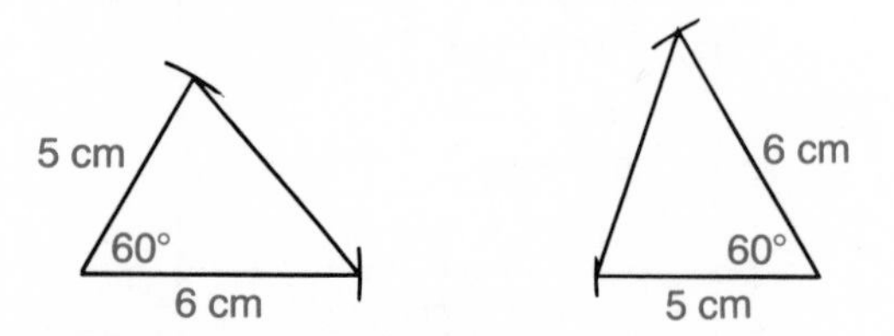

Compare the triangles by matching.

SAS

Side Angle Side Condition for Congruence

If two sides and the contained angle of one triangle are respectively equal to two sides and the contained angle of another triangle, then the triangles are congruent.

A D B C E F

In $\triangle ABC$ and $\triangle DEF$

$AB = DE$
$\angle B = \angle E$
$BC = EF$

Thus $\triangle ABC \cong \triangle DEF$ (SAS)
and $AC = DF$
$\angle A = \angle D$
$\angle C = \angle F$

Investigation 3.

Construct at least 3 triangles with one side 6 cm long and angles of 45° and 60° at the ends of the line segment.

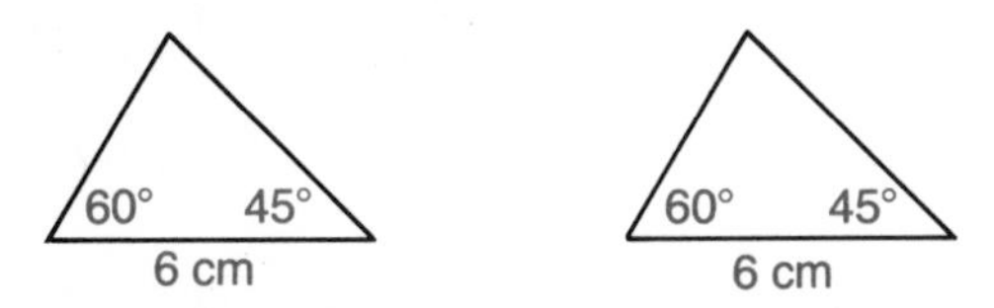

Compare the triangles by matching or tracing.

ASA

Angle Side Angle Condition for Congruence

If two angles and the contained side of one triangle are respectively equal to two angles and the contained side of another triangle, then the triangles are congruent.

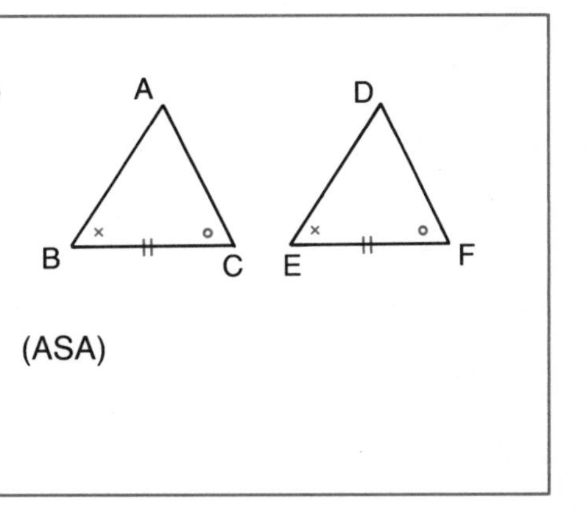

In $\triangle ABC$ and $\triangle DEF$

$\angle B = \angle E$
$BC = EF$
$\angle C = \angle F$

Thus $\triangle ABC \cong \triangle DEF$ (ASA)
and $AB = DE$
$AC = DF$
$\angle A = \angle D$

A counter example is a statement or diagram that shows that a given statement is not always true. The pictures show two **noncongruent** triangles that can be formed with sides of length 19 cm and 14 cm and a **noncontained** angle of 40°. Thus SSA (side, side, angle) cannot be used to prove that triangles are congruent.

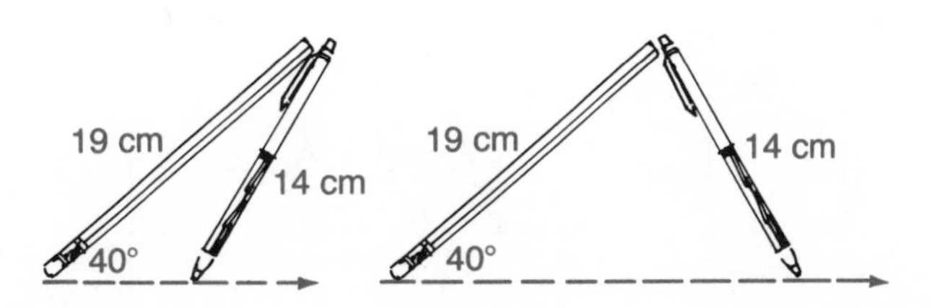

EXERCISE 7.5

B

1. (a) List the triangles that are congruent. Give reasons for your answers.
(b) Write the sides and angles that are equal as a result of the congruence.

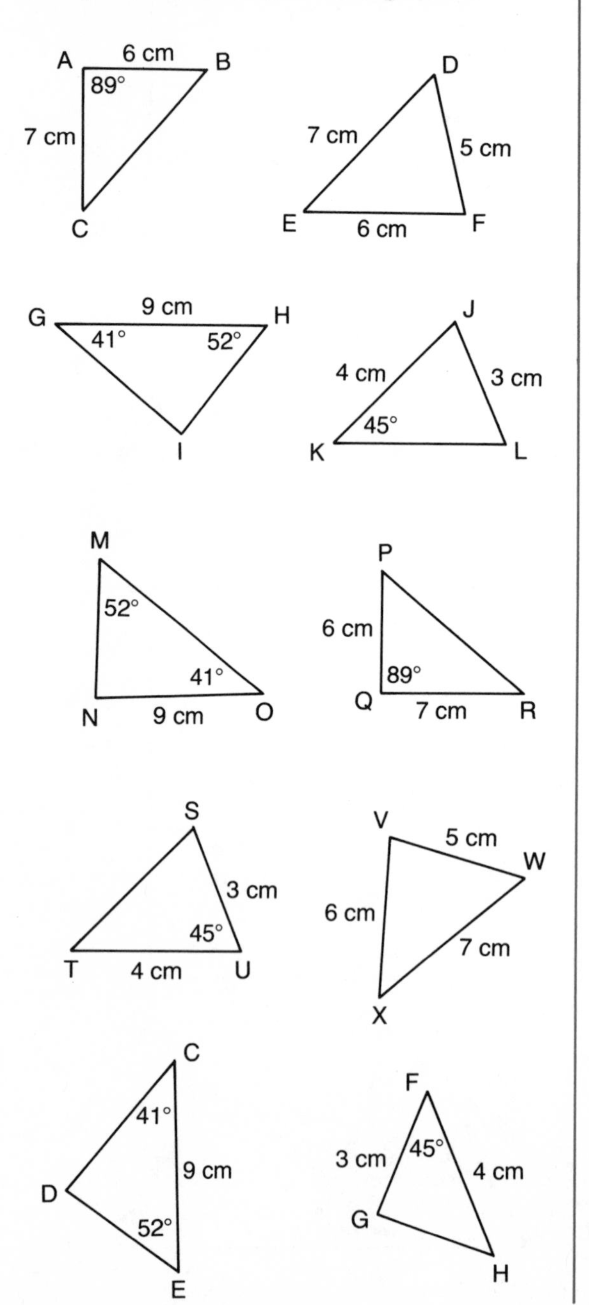

2. In each diagram
(a) select 2 congruent triangles,
(b) give the reason for the congruence,
(c) state the equal sides and angles.

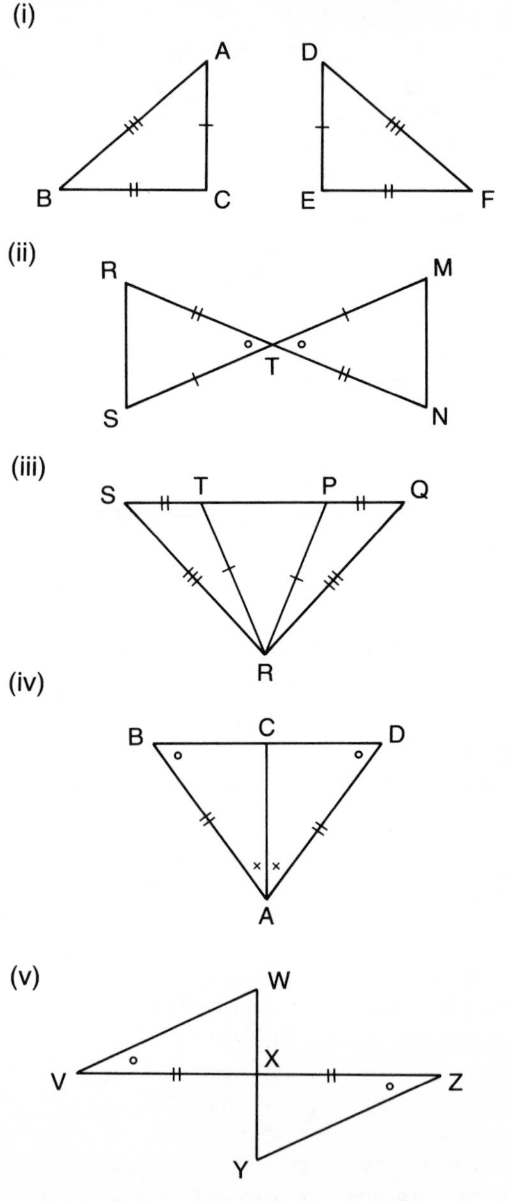

3. Provide a counter example to show that AAA (angle, angle, angle) cannot be used to prove that triangles are congruent.

7.6 WORKING WITH CONGRUENT TRIANGLES

The following summarizes the conditions for congruence.

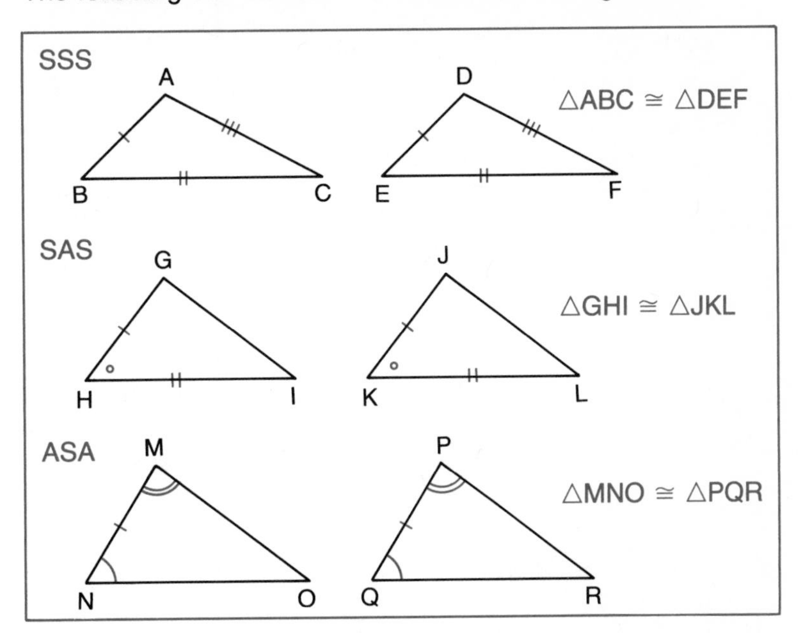

We will now use these conditions to prove triangles congruent.

READ

Example. Find DE, the width of the river.

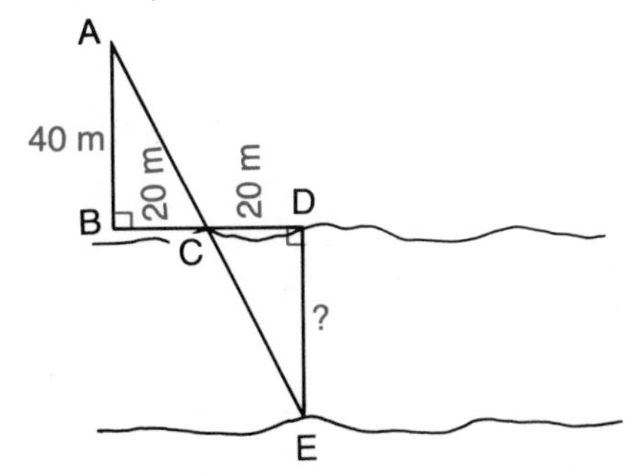

PLAN

Solution: Show that the triangles are congruent.

SOLVE

In △ABC and △EDC,

∠B = ∠D = 90°	A
BC = CD = 20	S
∠ACB = ∠ECD (opposite angles)	A
△ABC ≅ △EDC	(ASA)
AB = ED = 40	

ANSWER

The river is 40 m wide.

EXERCISE 7.6

B

1. Find the values of the unknowns.

(a)

(b)

(c)

(d)

(e)

(f)

(g)

(h)

(i)

(j)

2. Two cottages are located across a lake from each other.

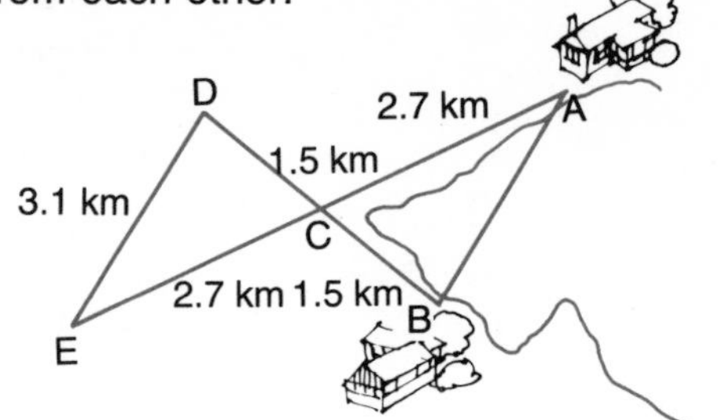

Find the distance AB between the two cottages and justify your answer.

3. The diagram shows an ancient method of determining the distance of a ship from the shore.

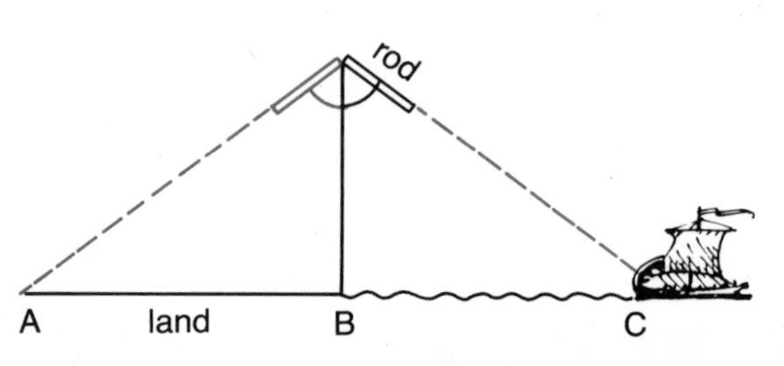

The rod is adjusted to sight the ship and then rotated to sight a point on land.
(a) If AB = 5.3 km, how far is the ship from shore?
(b) Why does this method work?

4. The legs of the director's chair are attached at their midpoints.
How wide should the material for the seat be if there is no sag in the seat and 3 cm are allowed on either side for fastening?

7.7 INVESTIGATING SIMILAR TRIANGLES

Similar triangles have the same shape, but not necessarily the same size. In this section the properties of similar triangles are investigated.

Investigation 1.

(a) Construct $\triangle ABC$ with $\angle B = 60°$, $\angle C = 45°$, $BC = 8$ cm.
(b) Construct $\triangle DEF$ with $\angle E = 60°$, $\angle F = 45°$, $EF = 4$ cm.
(c) Determine the measures of $\angle A$ and $\angle D$.
(d) Measure AB, AC, DE, and DF.
(e) Calculate the following ratios.

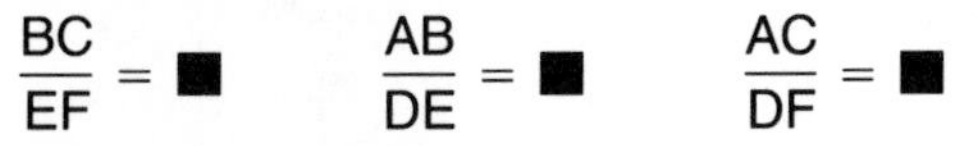

$\frac{BC}{EF} = \blacksquare \quad \frac{AB}{DE} = \blacksquare \quad \frac{AC}{DF} = \blacksquare$

(f) Construct $\triangle GHK$ with $\angle H = 60°$, $\angle K = 45°$, and $HK = 12$ cm.
(g) Compare $\triangle GHK$ to $\triangle ABC$ using angles and the ratios of the corresponding sides.
(h) Draw a conclusion about the ratios of corresponding sides of triangles that have corresponding angles equal.

Investigation 2.

(a) Construct $\triangle ABC$ with $AB = 5$ cm, $BC = 4$ cm, $AC = 3$ cm. Measure the angles.
(b) Construct $\triangle DEF$ with $DE = 10$ cm, $EF = 8$ cm, $DF = 6$ cm. Measure the angles.
(c) The corresponding sides are in a ratio of 1 : 2 and

$$\frac{AB}{DE} = \frac{BC}{EF} = \frac{AC}{DF} = \frac{1}{2}.$$

How do the angles compare?
(d) Construct $\triangle GHK$ with $GH = 7.5$ cm, $HK = 6$ cm, and $GK = 4.5$ cm.
(e) Compare $\triangle GHK$ with $\triangle ABC$ according to the ratios of corresponding sides and the measures of corresponding angles.
(f) Draw a conclusion about the corresponding angles when the ratios of the corresponding sides are equal.

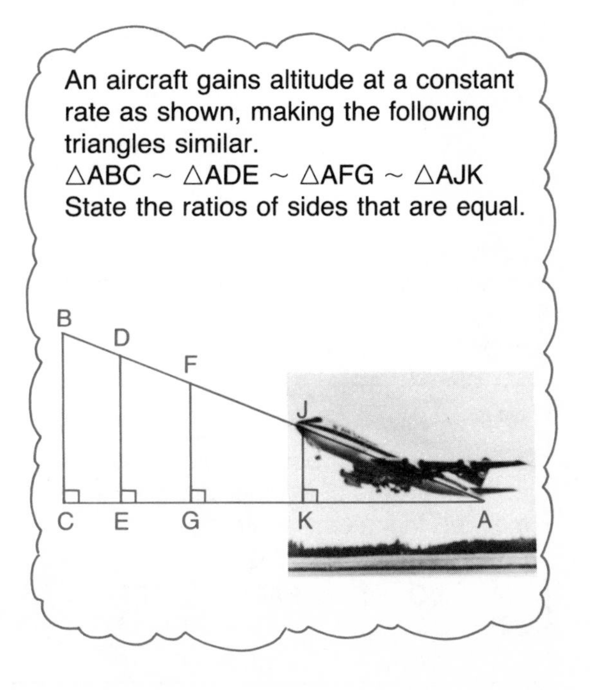

7.8 SIMILAR TRIANGLES

Enlargements of a photograph are shown.

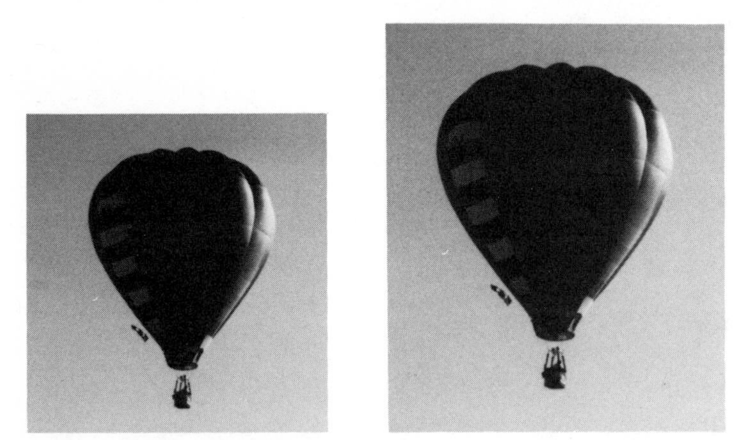

In geometry, figures that have the same shape but differ in size are called similar figures.
$\triangle ABC$ is similar to $\triangle DEF$.

In similar figures, the corresponding angles are equal and the measures of corresponding sides are proportional.

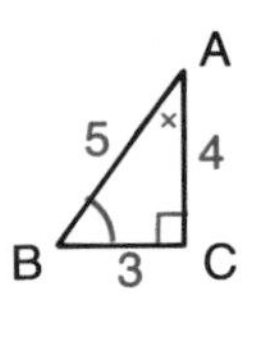

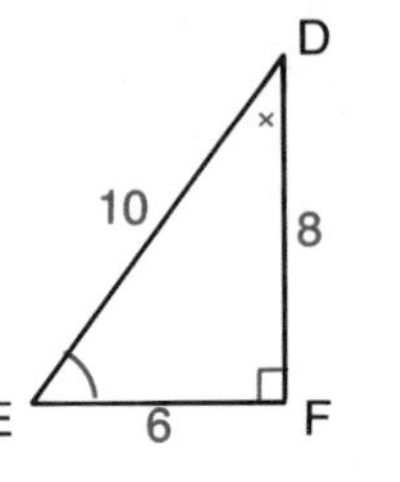

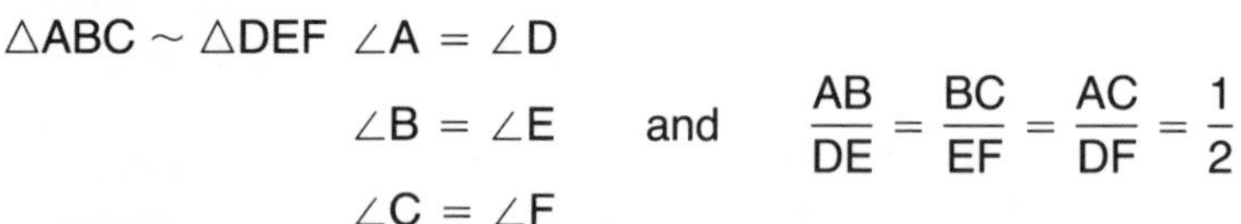

$\triangle ABC \sim \triangle DEF$ $\angle A = \angle D$

$\angle B = \angle E$ and $\dfrac{AB}{DE} = \dfrac{BC}{EF} = \dfrac{AC}{DF} = \dfrac{1}{2}$

$\angle C = \angle F$

The ratio of the lengths of the corresponding sides of $\triangle ABC$ to $\triangle DEF$ is 1 : 2

In order to show that two triangles are similar, it is not necessary to show that all three angles are equal and that all three pairs of sides are proportional. In this section we will use one condition for similarity.

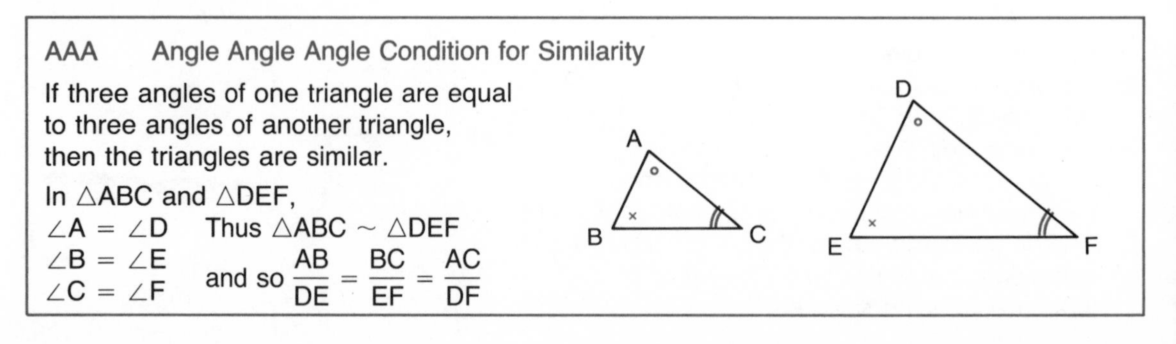

AAA Angle Angle Angle Condition for Similarity

If three angles of one triangle are equal to three angles of another triangle, then the triangles are similar.

In $\triangle ABC$ and $\triangle DEF$,

$\angle A = \angle D$ Thus $\triangle ABC \sim \triangle DEF$

$\angle B = \angle E$

$\angle C = \angle F$ and so $\dfrac{AB}{DE} = \dfrac{BC}{EF} = \dfrac{AC}{DF}$

Example 1. Prove $\triangle RST$ and $\triangle XYZ$ are similar.

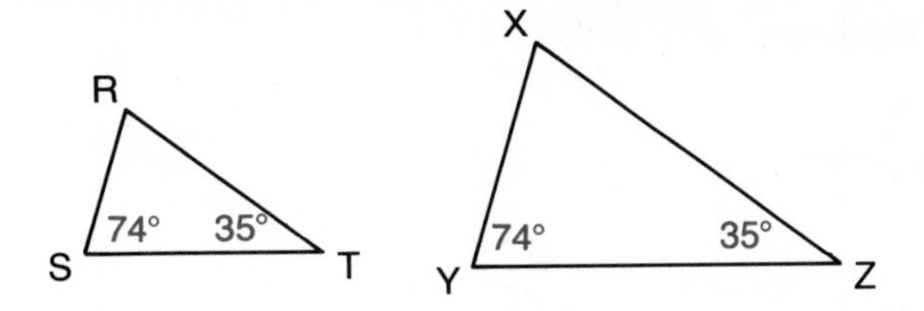

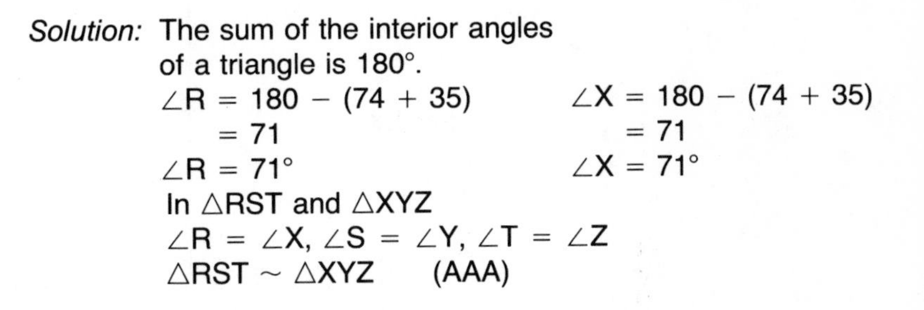

Solution: The sum of the interior angles of a triangle is 180°.

$\angle R = 180 - (74 + 35)$
$\quad = 71$
$\angle R = 71°$

$\angle X = 180 - (74 + 35)$
$\quad = 71$
$\angle X = 71°$

In $\triangle RST$ and $\triangle XYZ$
$\angle R = \angle X$, $\angle S = \angle Y$, $\angle T = \angle Z$
$\triangle RST \sim \triangle XYZ$ (AAA)

We generalize the result as follows.

AA Angle Angle Condition for Similarity
If two angles of one triangle are equal to two angles of another triangle, the triangles are similar.

Example 2. Find the value of x.

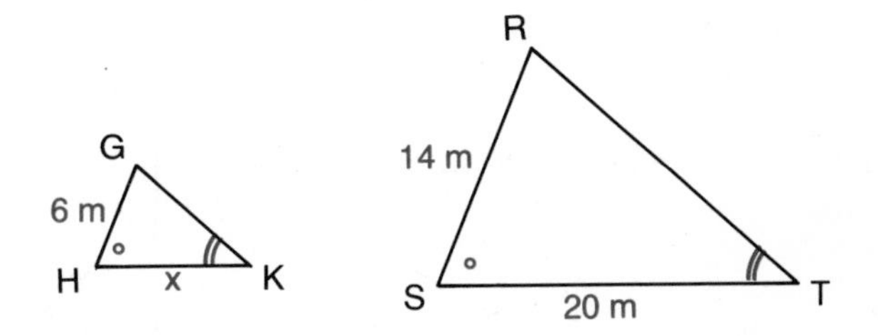

Solution: In $\triangle GHK$ and $\triangle RST$,

$$\angle H = \angle S$$
$$\angle K = \angle T$$
$$\therefore \triangle GHK \sim \triangle RST \quad \text{(AA)}$$
$$\therefore \frac{x}{20} = \frac{6}{14}$$
$$x = \frac{6 \times 20}{14}$$
$$= 8.6 \text{ to the nearest tenth.}$$

x is 8.6 m to the nearest tenth of a metre.

EXERCISE 7.8

A 1. Find the value of the variable.

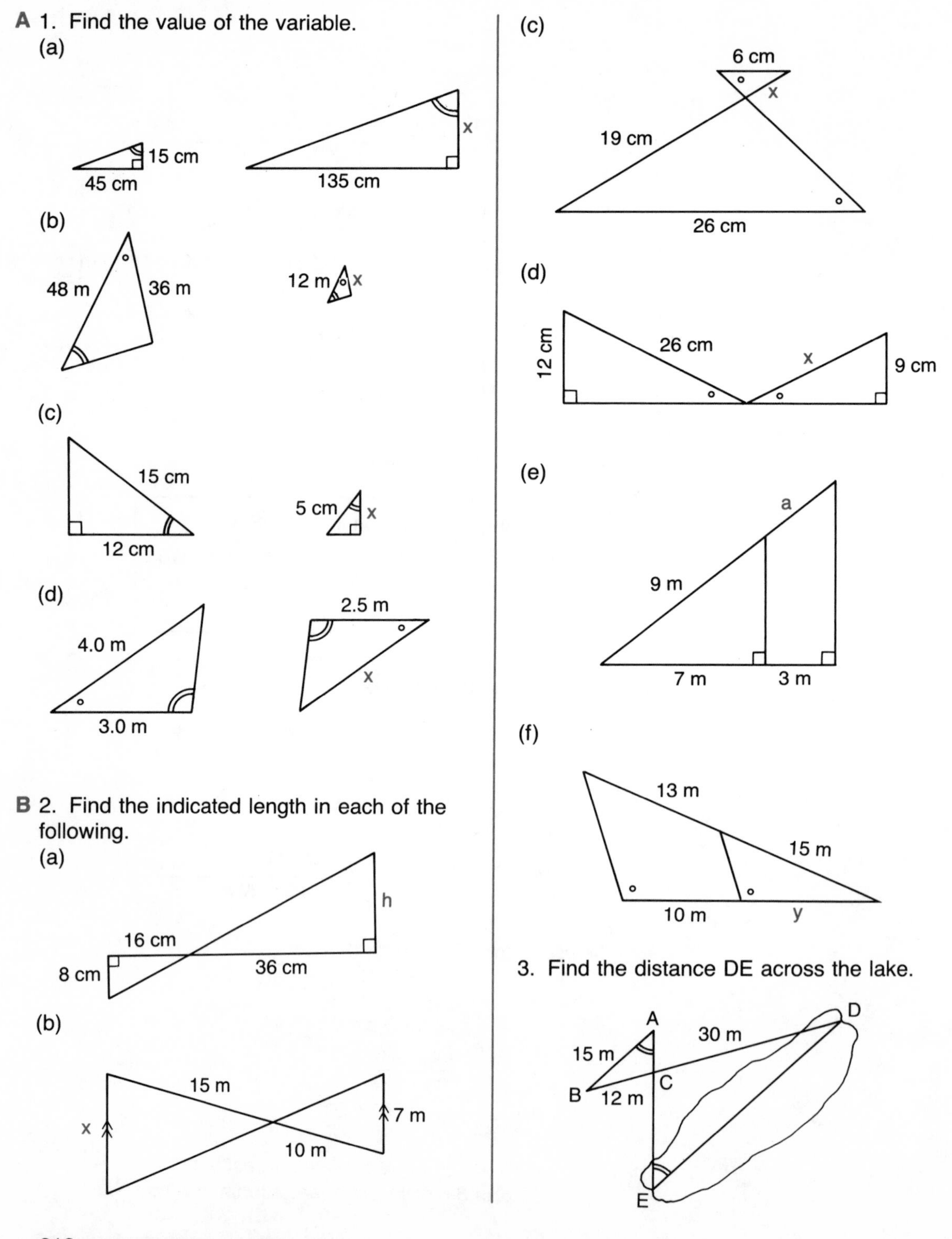

4. Find the width of the river.

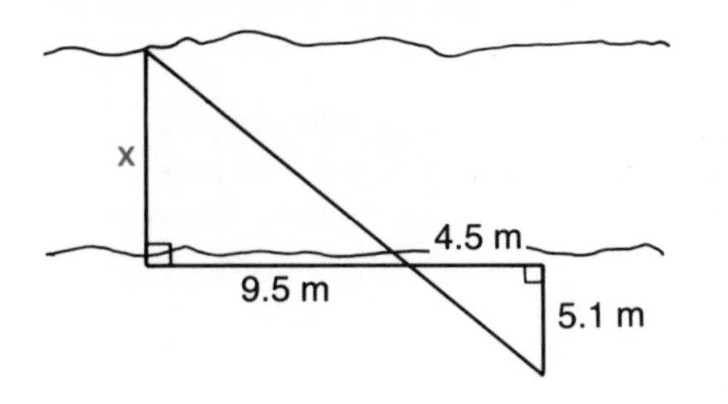

5. A pole is 5 m tall and casts a shadow of 3 m. A monument casts a shadow of 47 m.

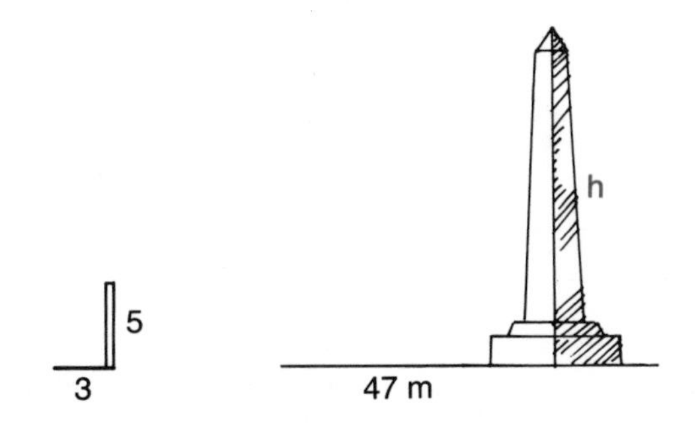

Find the height of the monument.

6. The top of a building lines up with the top of a 10 m pole when the pole is 43 m from the building and an observer 1.6 m tall is 7 m from the pole.
How tall is the building?

7. To calculate the width of a valley the following measurements were taken.

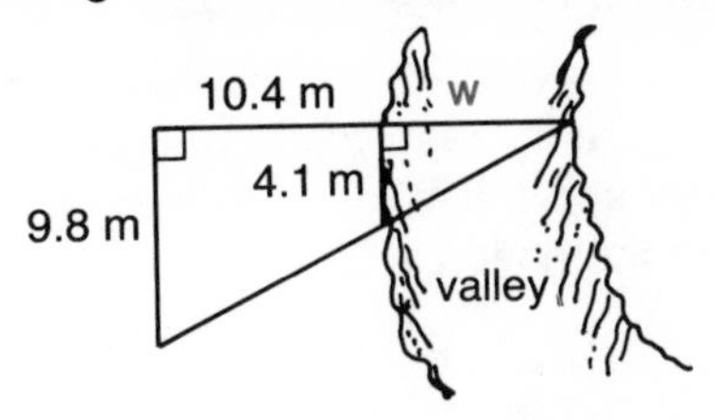

What is the width of the valley?

8. The following image is formed by a concave mirror.
Calculate the height of the image.

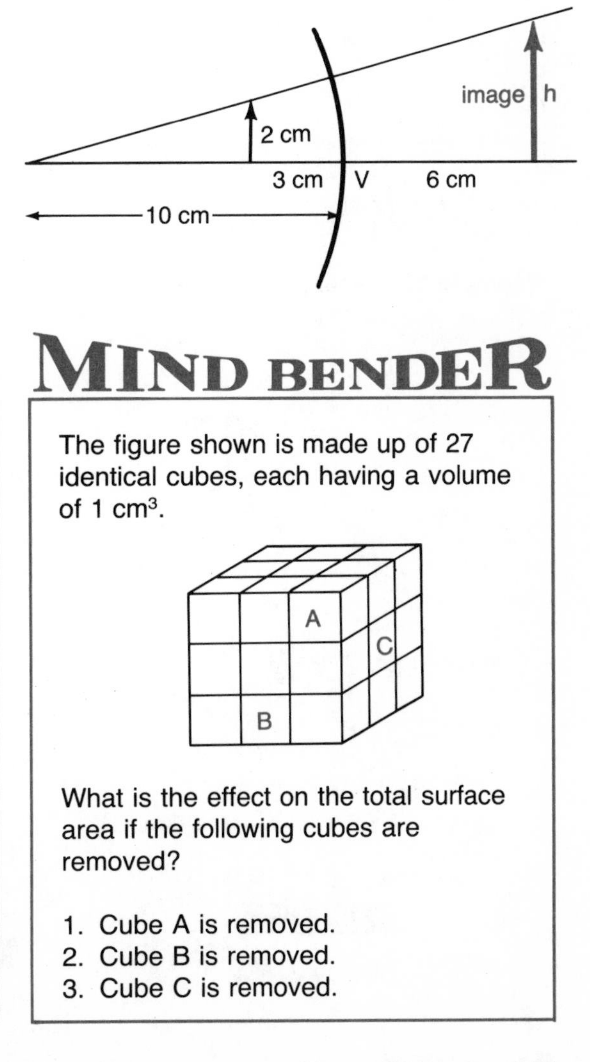

MIND BENDER

The figure shown is made up of 27 identical cubes, each having a volume of 1 cm^3.

What is the effect on the total surface area if the following cubes are removed?

1. Cube A is removed.
2. Cube B is removed.
3. Cube C is removed.

7.9 APPLYING THE PYTHAGOREAN THEOREM

The Pythagorean Theorem is one of the best known and most useful theorems in all of mathematics.

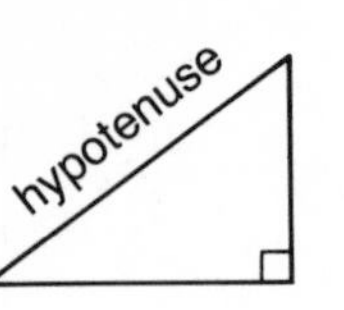

In a right-angled triangle, the side opposite to the right angle is called the hypotenuse.

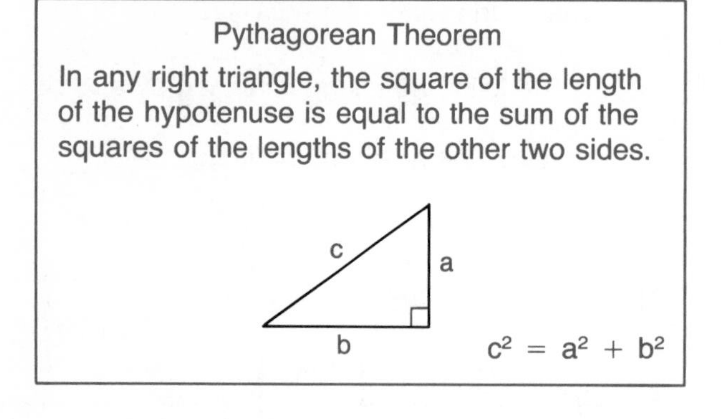

Pythagorean Theorem

In any right triangle, the square of the length of the hypotenuse is equal to the sum of the squares of the lengths of the other two sides.

$$c^2 = a^2 + b^2$$

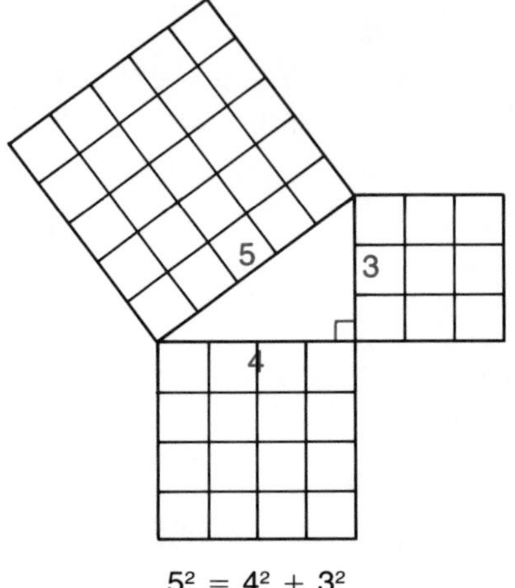

$5^2 = 4^2 + 3^2$
$25 = 16 + 9$

Example 1. Calculate the length of the third side in each diagram.

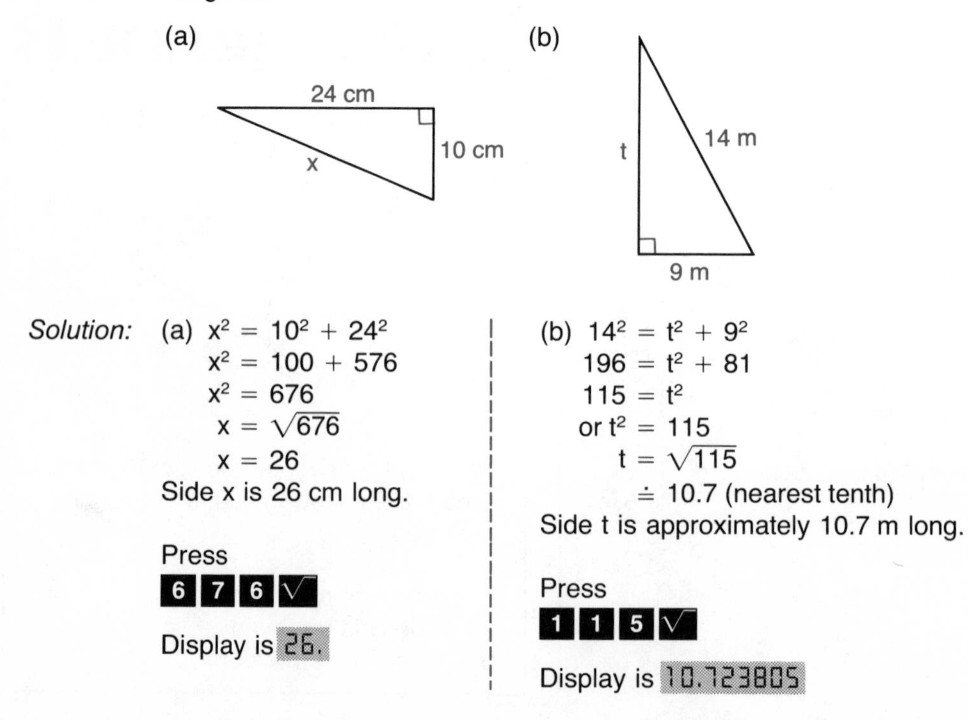

Solution:

(a)
$$x^2 = 10^2 + 24^2$$
$$x^2 = 100 + 576$$
$$x^2 = 676$$
$$x = \sqrt{676}$$
$$x = 26$$
Side x is 26 cm long.

Press

6 7 6 √

Display is 26.

(b)
$$14^2 = t^2 + 9^2$$
$$196 = t^2 + 81$$
$$115 = t^2$$
$$\text{or } t^2 = 115$$
$$t = \sqrt{115}$$
$$\doteq 10.7 \text{ (nearest tenth)}$$
Side t is approximately 10.7 m long.

Press

1 1 5 √

Display is 10.723805

READ

Example 2. Three pipes are stacked as shown. Find the height h of the stack if the diameter of each pipe is 20 cm.

PLAN

Solution:
Draw a larger picture in order to make constructions. Connect radii of the pipes to form an equilateral triangle of side 20 cm (the radius of each pipe is 10 cm). The height can then be seen to be equal to the sum of two radii plus the altitude, a, of the equilateral triangle.

SOLVE

To determine the altitude of the triangle, use the Pythagorean Theorem.

$$a^2 + 10^2 = 20^2$$
$$a^2 + 100 = 400$$
$$a^2 = 300$$
$$a = \sqrt{300}$$
$$\doteq 17.3 \text{ (nearest tenth)}$$

The sum of two radii plus the altitude equals

$$10 + 10 + 17.3 = 37.3$$

Press

3 0 0 √

Display is 17.320508

ANSWER

The height of the stack is approximately 37.3 cm.

EXERCISE 7.9

B 1. Find the value of each variable to the nearest tenth.

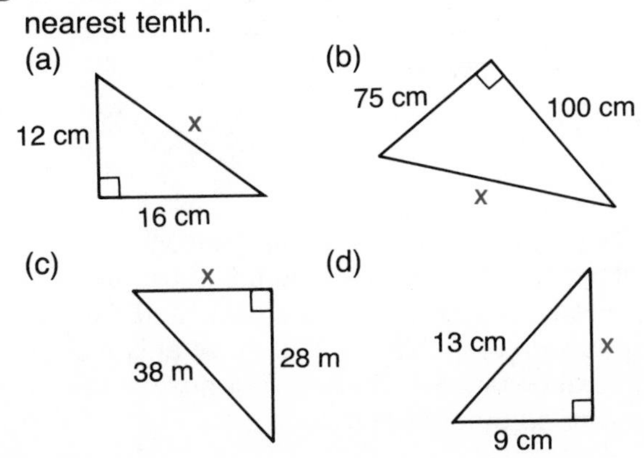

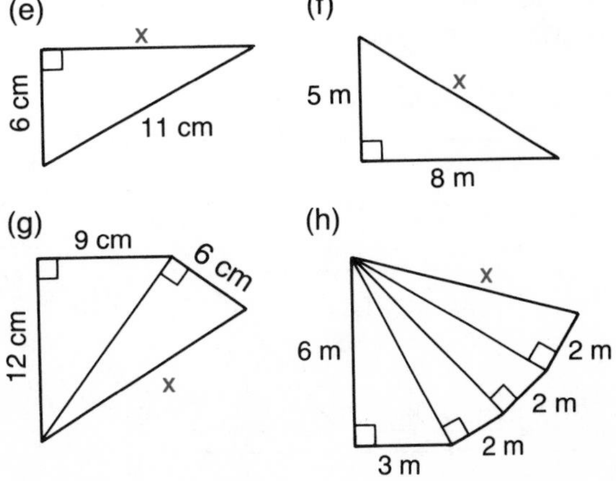

2. A plane flies 600 km due north and then 400 km due east.
How far is the plane from the starting point?

3. The front of an A-frame house is in the shape of an equilateral triangle. The base of the house is 8 m long.
How tall is the front of the house?

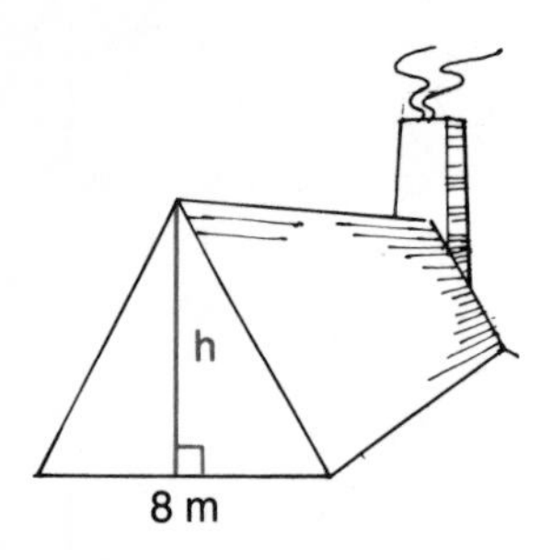

4. The diagram shows a truss for a roof. The rise of the roof is 3 m.

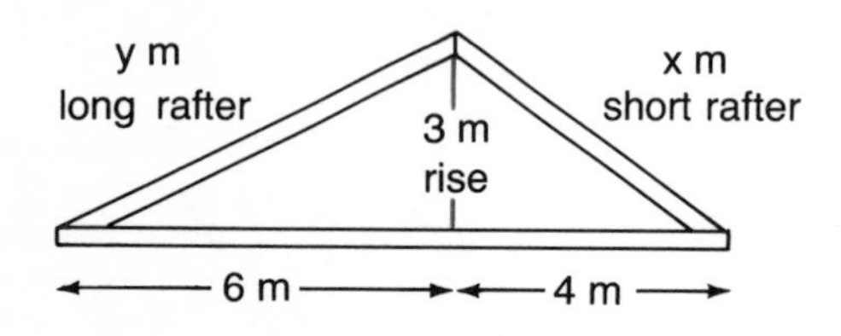

Find the lengths of both the long and short rafters to the nearest tenth.

5. Find the dimensions missing on the drawing of the two lots.

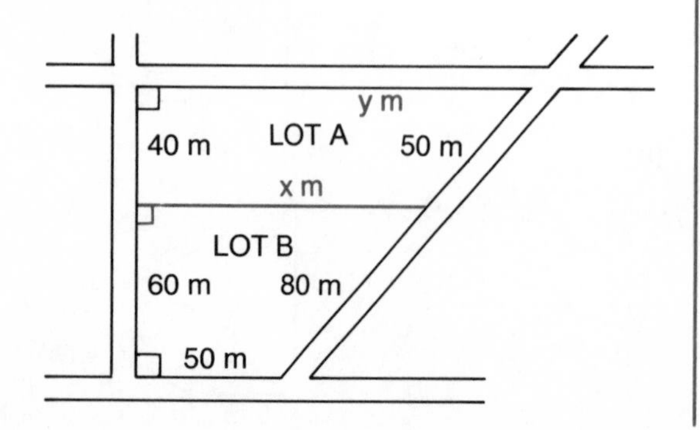

6. Six pipes are stacked as shown.
Find the height of the stack if the diameter of each pipe is 15 cm.

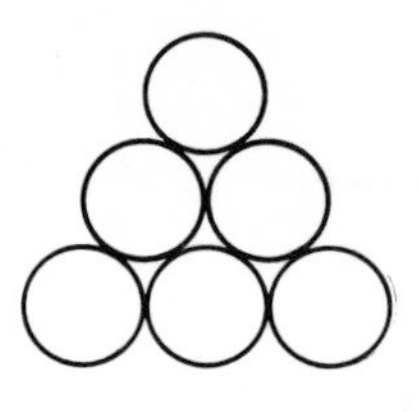

7. A door is 198 cm tall and 91 cm wide.

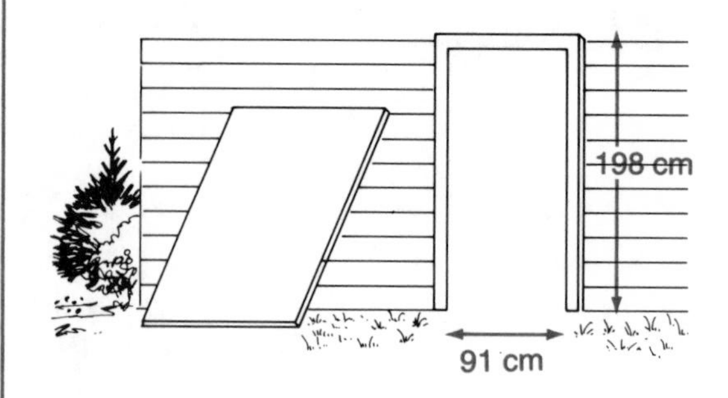

What is the widest sheet of plywood that can be carried through the door?

8. Surveyors want to measure the distance between points A and B on rough land.

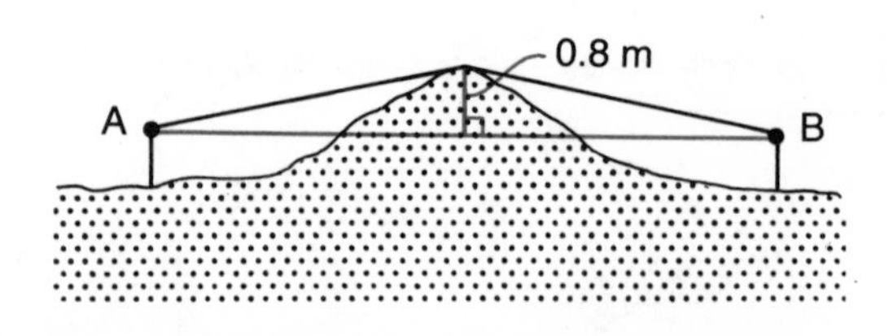

They want to find the actual horizontal distance AB. If the earth is 0.8 m higher midway between the two stakes, and if the measuring tape reads 27.0 m, what is the actual distance AB? Give your answer to the nearest tenth of a metre.

9. A shoe box is 26.5 cm by 13.0 cm by 8.8 cm.

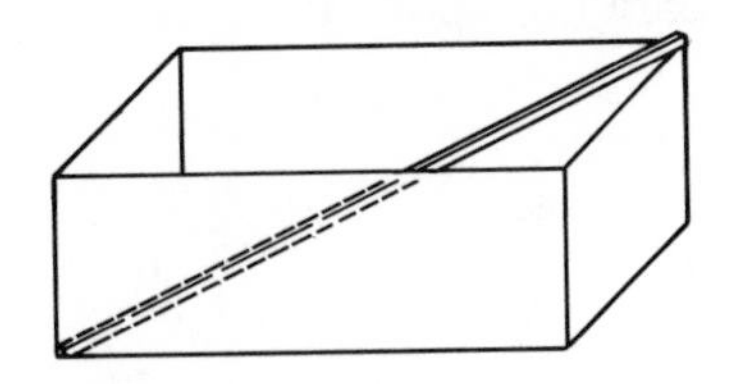

What is the length of the longest object that can be placed in the box?

10. Suppose that ABCD is a flexible wire. A is a fixed point and C is a fixed pulley. B is a weight that slides freely along the wire so that AB and CB are always equally inclined to the vertical.
Find, to the nearest tenth of a metre, how far B rises if D is pulled down 2 m.

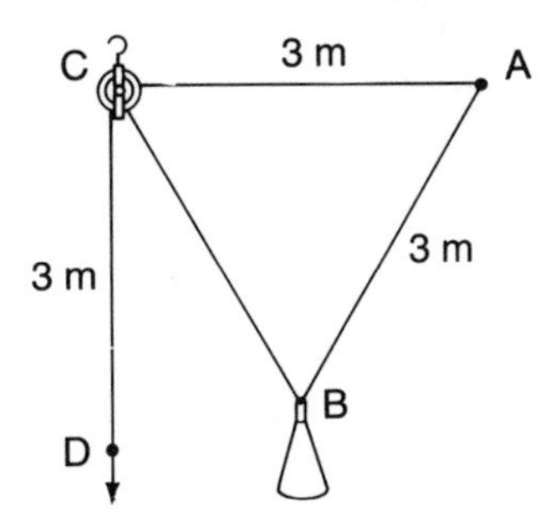

11. A ladder is 5 m long when fully extended. The foot of the ladder is 1.5 m from the building.
How high up the wall will the ladder reach?

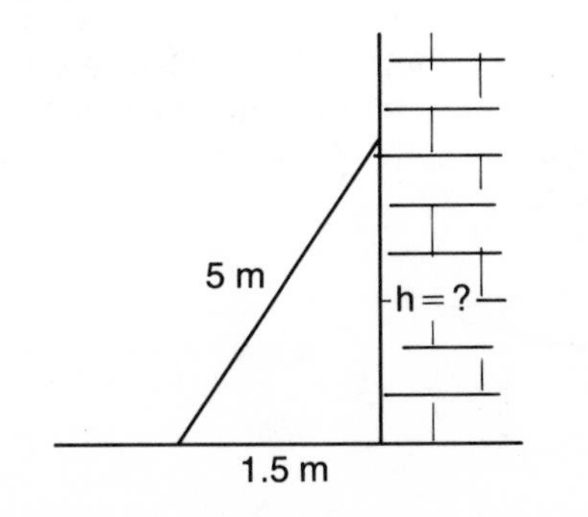

12. A ladder reaches 4 m up a wall when the foot of the ladder is 1.4 m from the building. The ladder slips down the wall until the foot of the ladder is 1.9 m from the building.
How far up the wall does the ladder reach after slipping?

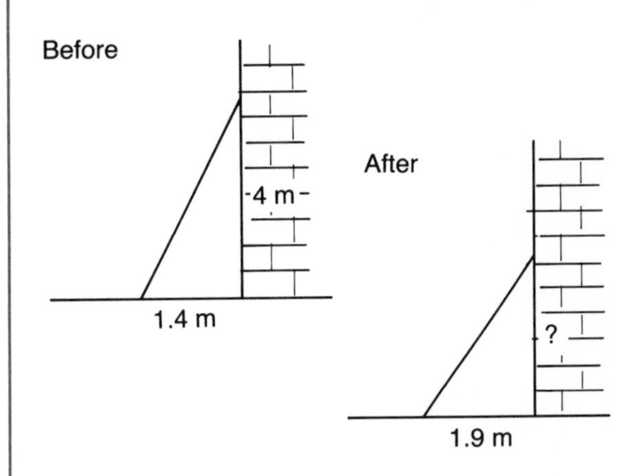

MICRO MATH

The following program calculates the length of the hypotenuse when you enter the lengths of the sides containing the right angle.

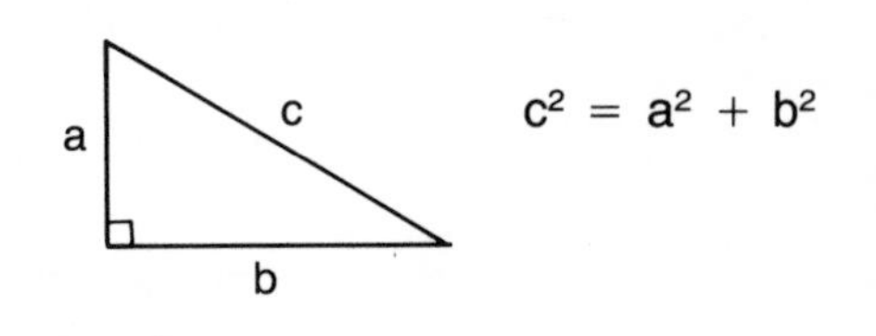

$c^2 = a^2 + b^2$

```
NEW
10 PRINT "HYPOTENUSE CALCULATOR"
20 INPUT "FIRST SIDE";A
30 INPUT "SECOND SIDE";B
40 C=SQR(A*A+B*B)
50 PRINT "THE HYPOTENUSE IS";C
60 END
RUN
```

7.10 VISUALIZING FIGURES

In a room 3 m wide, 3 m high, and 5 m long a fly crawls from point A to point B.
What is the length of the shortest path from point A to point B that the fly may crawl?

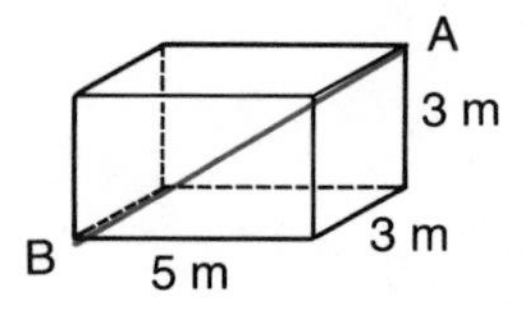

The shortest path is the diagonal AB through the air. Since the fly must crawl, this path is not available. However, if we imagine the room to be a box that can be cut apart and flattened, we can draw the straight line from A to B.

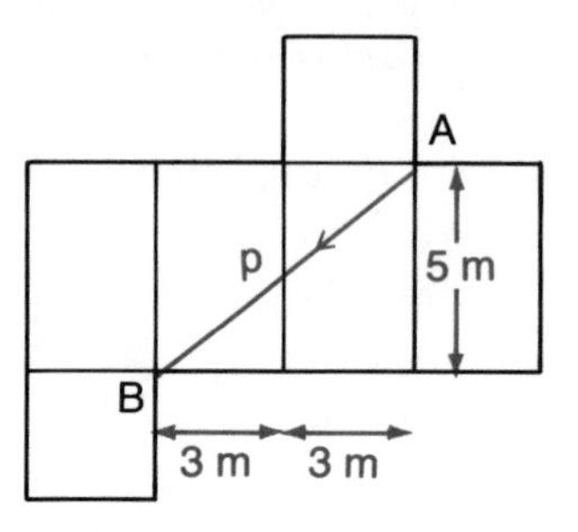

To calculate the length, p, of the path, use the Pythagorean Theorem.

$$p^2 = 5^2 + (3 + 3)^2$$
$$= 25 + 36$$
$$= 61$$
$$P = \sqrt{61}$$
$$= 7.8 \text{ (nearest tenth)}$$

Press

Display is 7.8102497

The length of the path is approximately 7.8 m. Before cutting the box apart and flattening, verify that the diagonal AB measures 6.6 m to the nearest tenth. To visualize the path, reconstruct the box as shown.

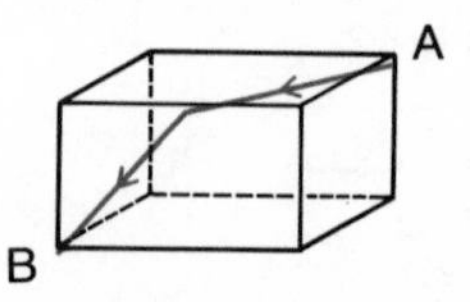

Although we **have** found the shortest path, we must be careful. The number of different "straight line" paths possible depends on the location of the points A and B. The following diagram shows another way that a box model may be flattened to yield a straight line path.

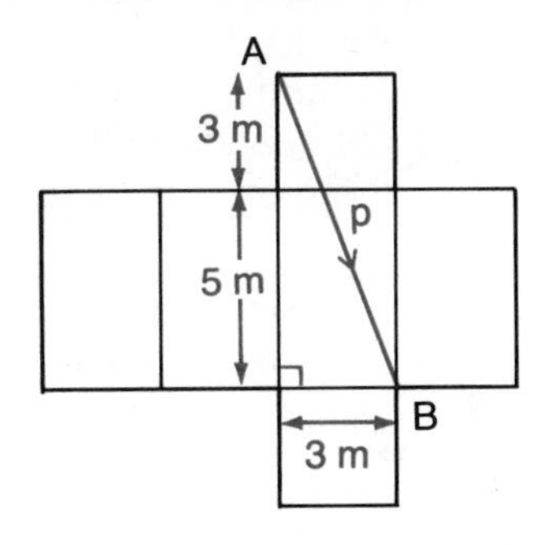

Show that the length of this path is 8.5 m, to the nearest tenth. To visualize this path, we reconstruct the box as shown.

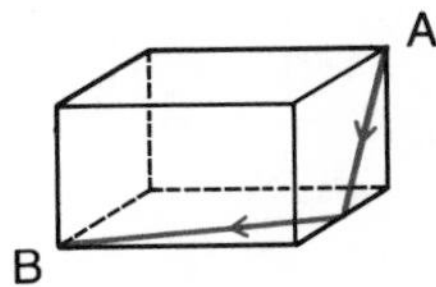

EXERCISE 7.10

In a room 4 m wide, 4 m high, and 8 m long, a fly crawls from the middle of the front wall, 1 m above the floor, to the middle of the back wall, 1 m below the ceiling.

1. Order each of the paths below from shortest to longest by guessing.

(a)

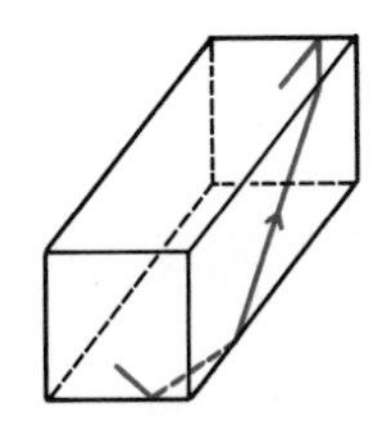

(b)

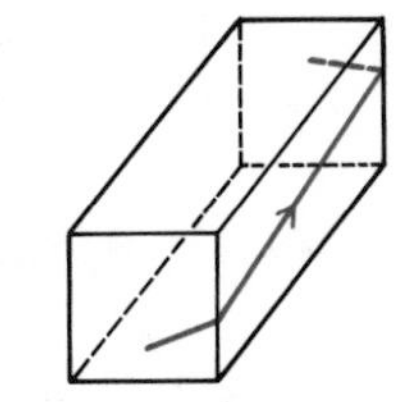

(c)

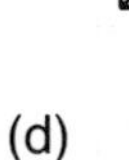

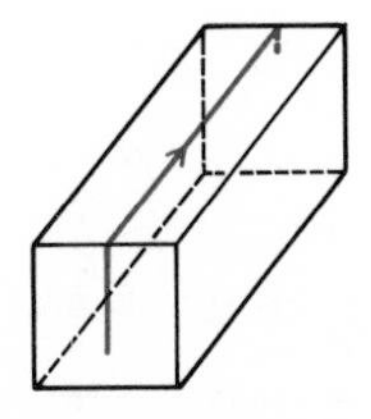

(d)

2. Imagine that the boxes in question 1 have been cut apart and flattened out. Match each of the four paths of the fly shown above with one of the diagrams below. Notice that **each** of these is a straight line path.

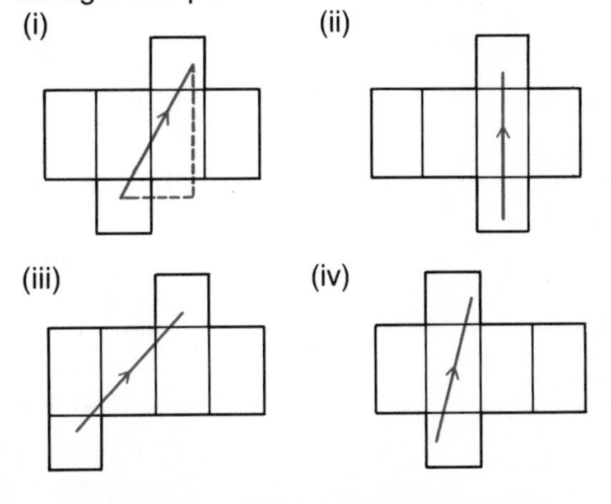

3. Complete a right triangle as in figure (i), if necessary, to determine the length of each path. Order the paths from shortest to longest.

7.11 LOGO

LOGO is a computer language that allows us to study properties and relationships of geometric figures. This language allows us to study geometric properties in creative ways.

A "turtle" or "pencil" is moved on the screen by typing in commands to draw geometric figures. Following are some of the more fundamental commands.

■ represents a numerical value

Command	Meaning	Example	Explanation
FD ■	move forward	FD 100	The turtle moves 100 units forward.
BK ■	move backward	BK 100	The turtle moves 100 units backward.
RT ■	right turn	RT 90	The turtle turns 90° clockwise.
LT ■	left turn	LT 90	The turtle turns 90° counter-clockwise.

Example. Provide the LOGO commands to draw an equilateral triangle with sides 100 units.

Solution: Each interior angle of the equilateral triangle has a measure of 60°. Hence, the measure of each exterior angle is $180° - 60° = 120°$. After drawing one side, the turtle must turn 120° before drawing the next side.
The commands are

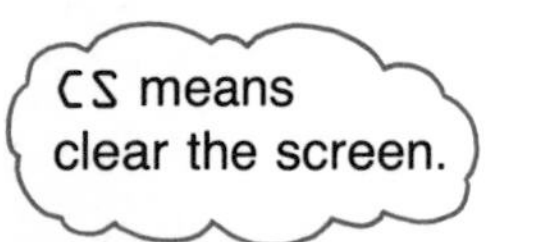


```
CS
FD 100
RT 120
FD 100
RT 120
FD 100
RT 120
```

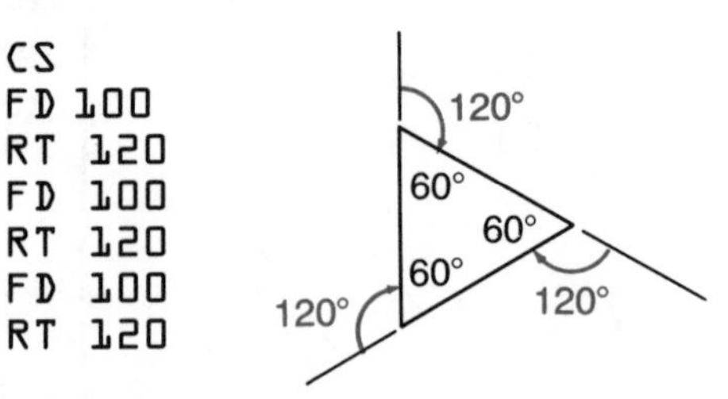

The corresponding moves of the turtle are shown in the figure above.
In the example, the commands FD 100 and RT 120 are repeated three times. The three pairs of commands can be shortened into one "repeat" command as follows.

```
REPEAT 3 [FD 100 RT 120]
```

REPEAT 3	[FD 100 RT 120]
Number of repetitions.	The group of commands to be repeated.

We can also draw the equilateral triangle using the command

```
REPEAT 3 [FD 100 LT 120]
```

In a regular polygon all sides are equal and all angles are equal. In the equilateral triangle in the example, each turn was 120° and the length of each side was 100 units. There are three equal turns and three equal sides in the program and the total number of degrees turned is 360°. This is called the "Total Turtle Turn Theorem."

The following table shows the commands used to draw regular polygons.
How is the Total Turtle Turn Theorem used?

Figure	Number of Sides and Vertices	Degree Measure of Each Turn	Total Number of Degrees Turned	LOGO Command
Equilateral Triangle	3	120°	360°	`REPEAT 3 [FD 100 RT 120]`
Square	4	90°	360°	`REPEAT 4 [FD 100 RT 90]`
Regular Pentagon	5	72°	360°	`REPEAT 5 [FD 100 RT 72]`
Regular Hexagon	6	60°	360°	`REPEAT 6 [FD 100 RT 60]`
Regular Octagon	8	45°	360°	`REPEAT 8 [FD 100 RT 45]`
Regular Polygon (n sides)	n	$\frac{360°}{n}$	360°	

EXERCISE 7.11

1. (a) Identify the figure that will be produced on a screen by the following LOGO program.

```
CS
FD 100
RT 90
FD 100
RT 90
FD 100
RT 90
FD 100
RT 90
```

(b) Write a single LOGO command to draw the figure in part (a).

2. Write a LOGO command to draw the following regular polygons.
(a) 90 sides each of length 1 unit
(b) 180 sides each of length 1 unit
(c) 360 sides each of length 1 unit
Run each of these commands on a computer.

3. (a) Write the LOGO command to draw a square with sides 50 units.
(b) Write the command that will turn the turtle 30° clockwise.
(c) Write a command that will repeat (a) and (b) twelve times.
Run this command on a computer.

4. (a) Enter the following LOGO command on a computer and RUN it.

```
REPEAT 5 [FD 100 RT 144]
```

(b) Copy the figure formed onto paper and identify congruent triangles.

5. (a) Enter the following LOGO command on a computer and RUN it.

```
REPEAT 8 [FD 100 RT 45]
```

(b) Copy the figure formed onto paper and identify congruent triangles.

7.12 PROBLEM SOLVING

1. If you take a number, add 11, then multiply by 2, and finally subtract 5, you get 23.
What is the number?

2. Don has 21 stamps to put in three packages. He wants to put an odd number of stamps in each package.
In how many different ways can he do this?

3. What is the greatest amount of money you can have in coins and not be able to give change for a dollar?

4. Place 6 dots in the following figure so that there will be no more than one dot in each row, column, or diagonal.

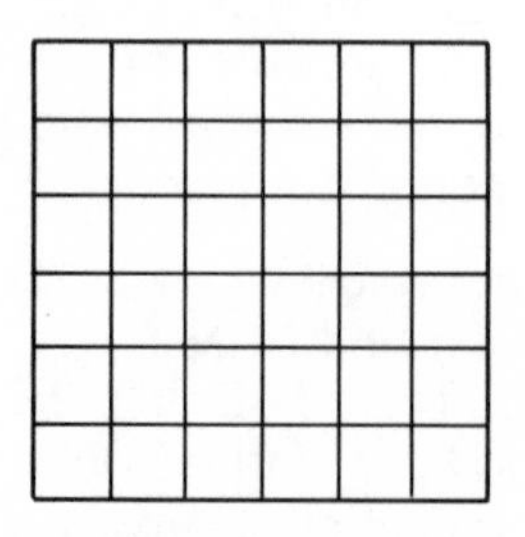

5. How old will you be when your heart beats for the billionth time?

6. The usual amount of tip on a meal in a restaurant is 15% of the cost of the meal. Approximately how much tip should you leave for a meal that cost $65.00?

7. 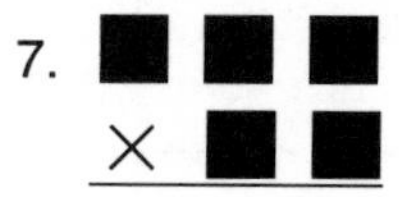

(a) Place the digits 2, 3, 4, 5, and 6 in the boxes so that the product is a maximum.

(b) Place the digits 2, 3, 4, 5, and 6 in the boxes so that the product is a minimum.

8. A lawn measures 10 m by 20 m. The mower being used is capable of mowing a strip 0.5 m wide.
There are two ways to mow the lawn. One is to mow lengthwise, then make a complete turn of 180°, and then mow lengthwise again.

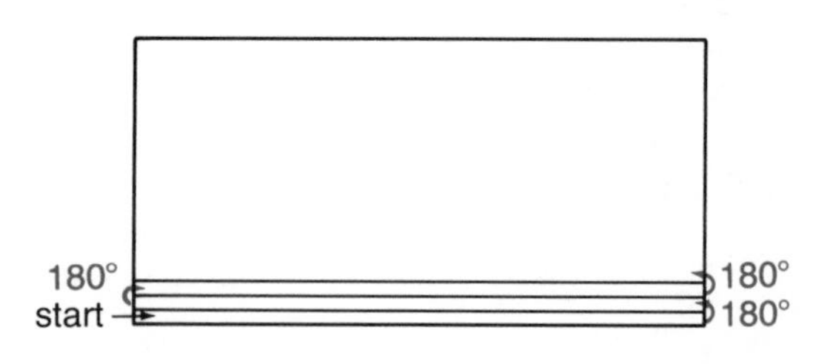

The other is to mow around the perimeter, turning 90° at each turn.

Which method is faster?

9. If you subtract 9 from a number, then divide by 2, and finally multiply by 6, you get 60.
What is the number?

10. Twenty-six fence posts are evenly spaced around a rectangular field. There are six posts along the width.
How many posts are along the length?

11. Find four consecutive numbers whose sum is 162.

12. If New Year's Day is on a Wednesday, how many Mondays are there in the year?

13. Sam left the service centre and travelled west at 90 km/h. Sandra left the same service centre one-half hour later and travelled west at 100 km/h.
How long will it take Sandra to overtake Sam?

14. Each triangle was drawn by joining the midpoints of the sides of the triangle larger than it.
What is the perimeter of the smallest triangle?

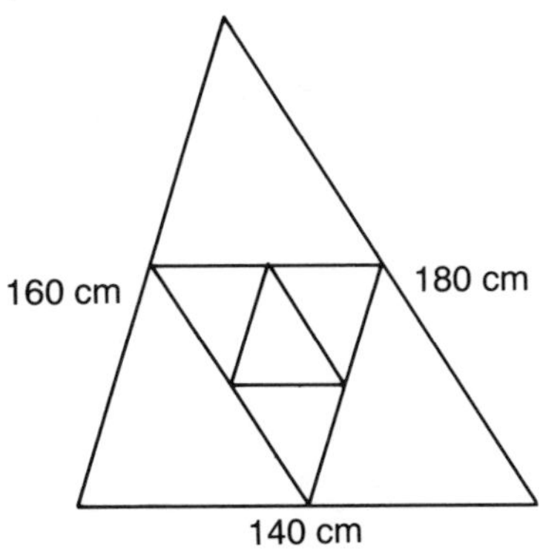

15. The figure is made up of six squares. The area of the figure is 486 cm^2.
Calculate the perimeter of the figure.

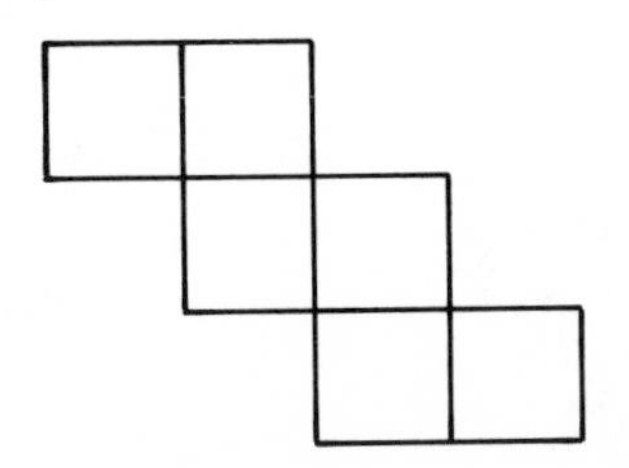

CAREER

FASHION DESIGNER

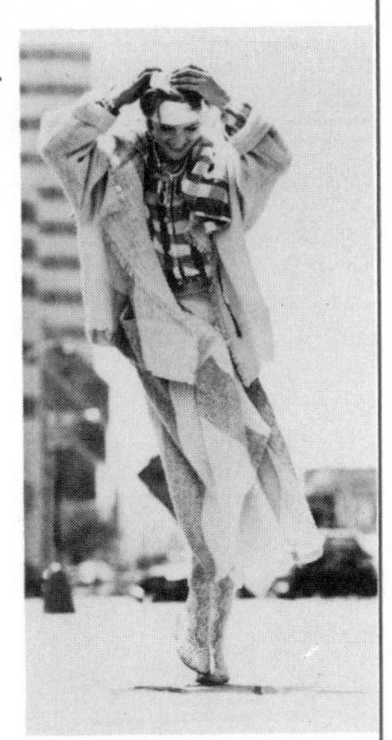

A fashion designer creates patterns for all kinds of clothing and jewellery.
Some of the skills required are sketching, pattern making, colour coordinating, cutting, sewing, and altering.
The ability to transform a flat, flexible piece of material into an object of fashion often requires proportional thinking and three-dimensional thinking, as found in geometry.

EXERCISE

1. Fabrics come in widths of 90 cm, 115 cm, 140 cm, or 150 cm.
What is the minimum number of metres of material needed to make the skirt shown below for each of the common widths?

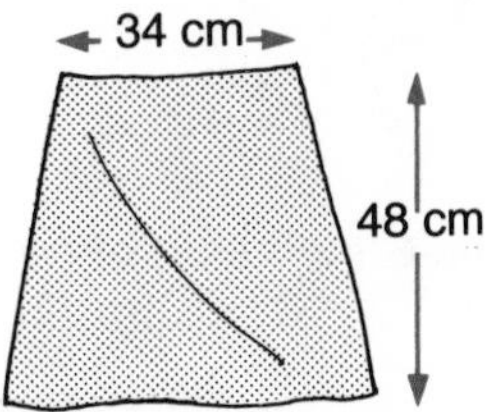

2. In industrial garment production, 10 000 m of thread are on each spool, or "cone." It takes 16 m of thread to make one skirt.
How many cones of thread are needed to make 7500 skirts?

7.13 REVIEW EXERCISE

1. Determine the measure of the indicated angles in each of the following.

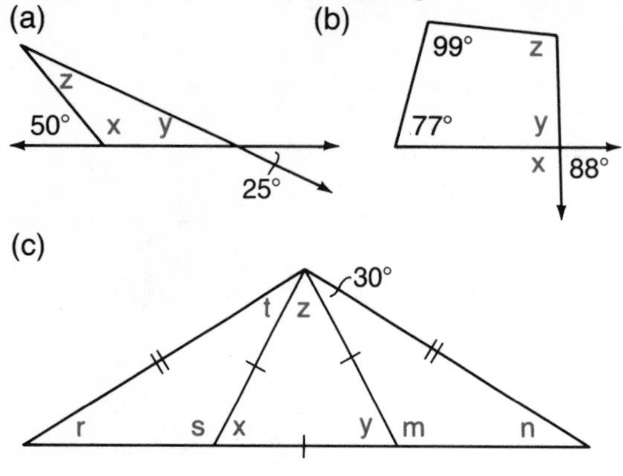

2. Find the value of each variable.

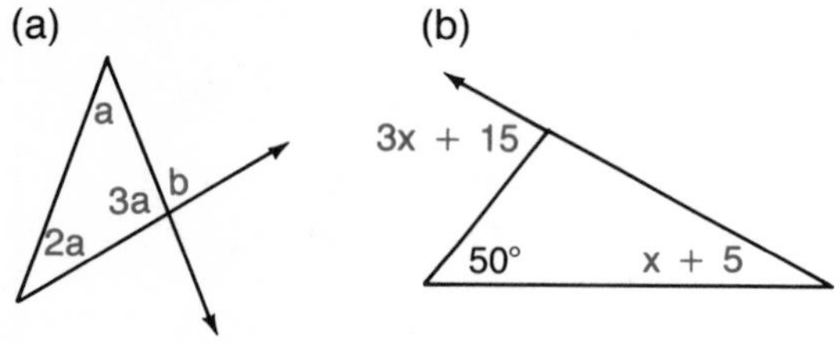

3. Determine the value of the indicated angles.

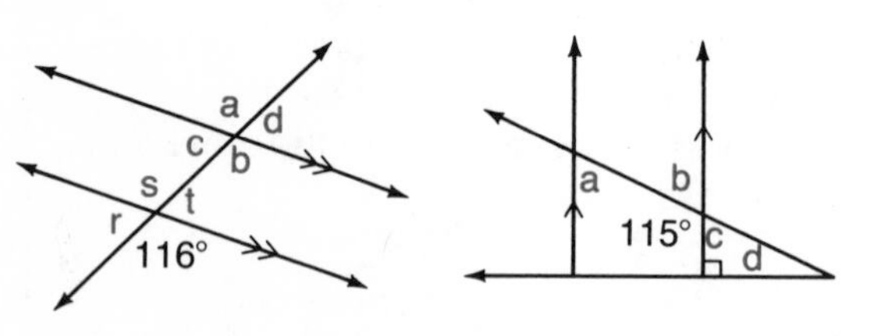

4. Calculate the value of each variable.

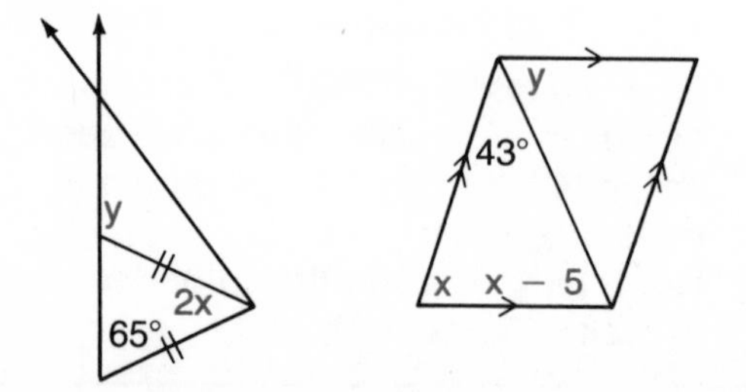

5. In each diagram
(a) select 2 congruent triangles,
(b) give the reason for congruence,
(c) state the equal sides and angles.

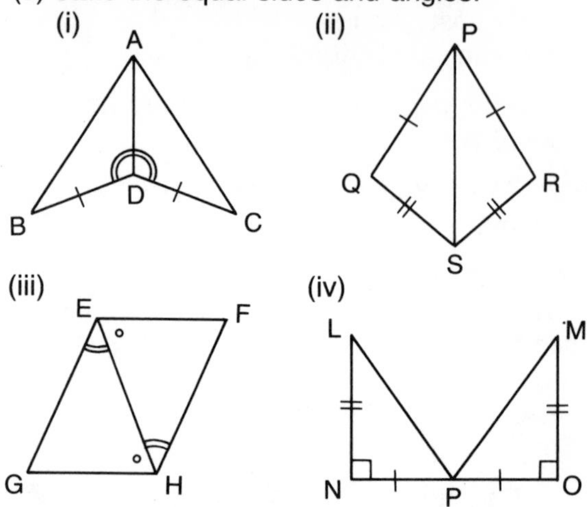

6. Find the value of the variable in each of the following.

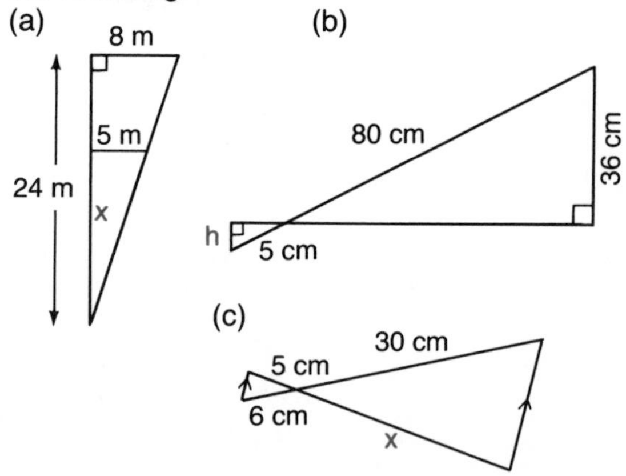

7. Find the value of each variable to the nearest tenth.

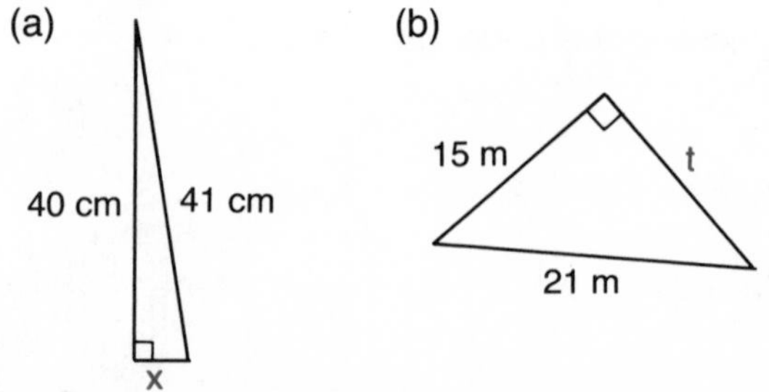

8. To measure ∠SPU, a machinist places angle gauge blocks as shown.

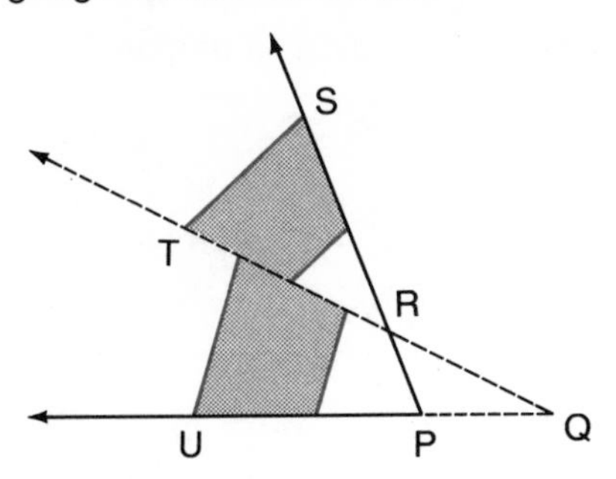

The blocks used in the diagram indicate that ∠SRT = 41° and ∠TQU = 27°. What is ∠SPU?

9. The pitch (∠BAD) of the roof is 35°.

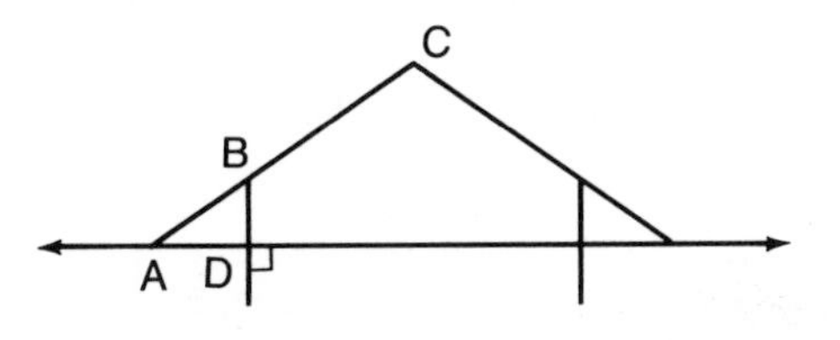

What is the measure of the angle (∠CBD) that the attic ceiling makes with the outside wall of the house?

10. One end of a support brace was cut at an angle (∠1) of 115°.

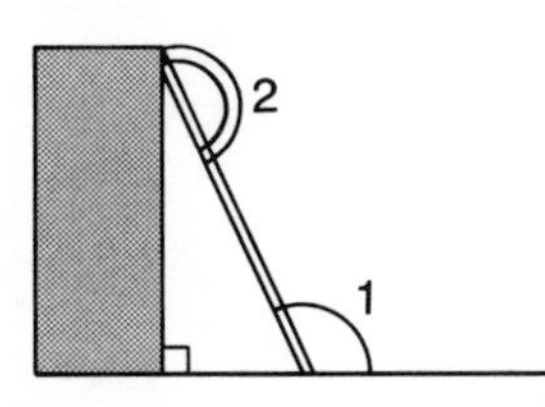

At what angle should the other end of the brace be cut (∠2)?

11. Find the measure of the angle formed at the peak P of the roof and the length of the crossbeam QR.

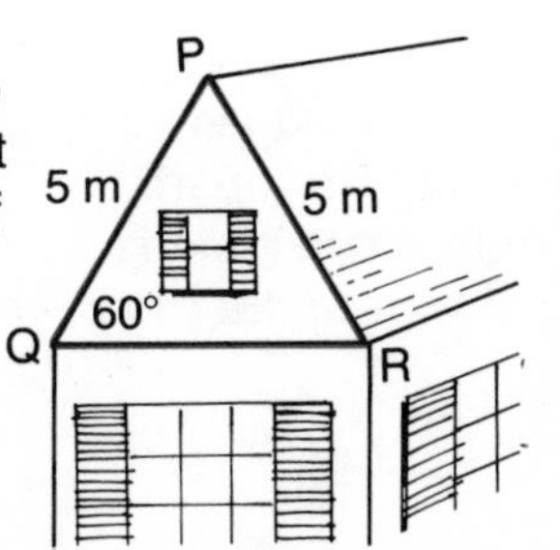

12. To find the distance from B to A across an expressway, you could use the brim of a hat.
Sight point A along the brim of the hat. Then, without raising or lowering your head, turn to sight point C. Explain why BA = BC.

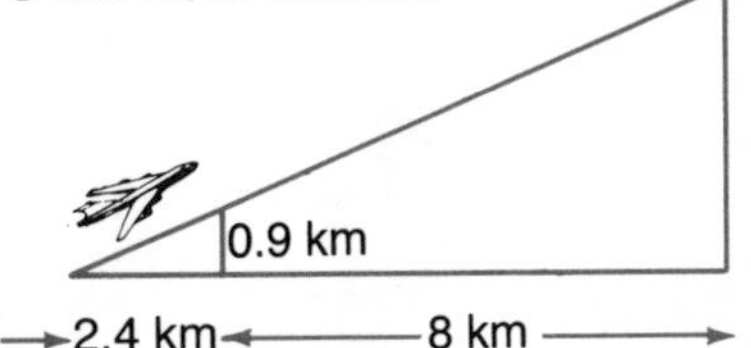

13. At a ground distance of 2.4 km from takeoff, a plane's altitude is 0.9 km. Assuming a constant angle of ascent, find its altitude 8 km from takeoff.

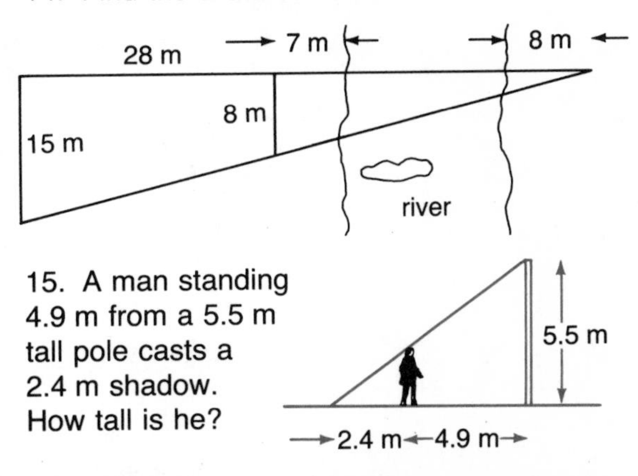

14. Find the width of the river.

15. A man standing 4.9 m from a 5.5 m tall pole casts a 2.4 m shadow. How tall is he?

16. In a rectangular container 3 m × 4 m × 12 m, all pairs of intersecting edges are perpendicular.
What is the length of the longest rod that would fit inside the container?

17. A stop sign is in the shape of a regular octagon of side 30 cm. Find the dimensions of the square sheet of metal from which the stop sign was cut.

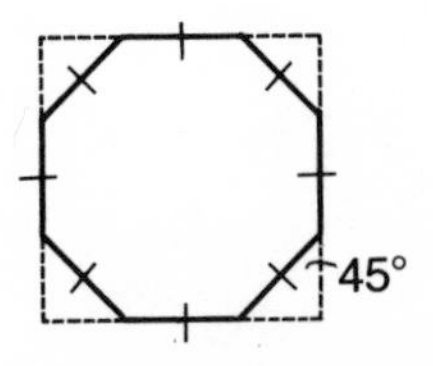

7.14 CHAPTER 7 TEST

1. Determine the measures of the indicated angles.

(a)

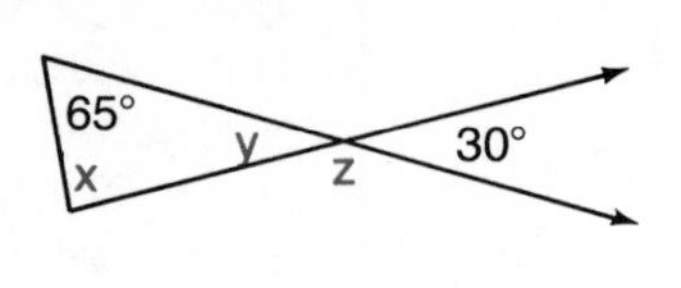

(b)

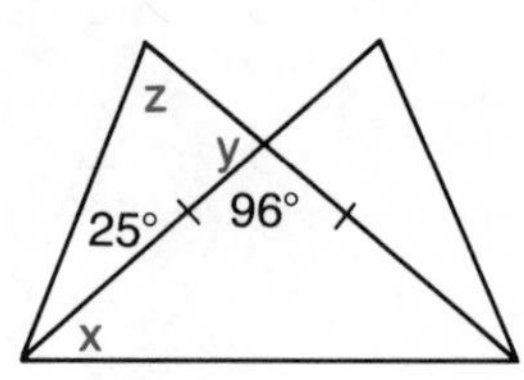

2. Calculate the missing measures.

(a)

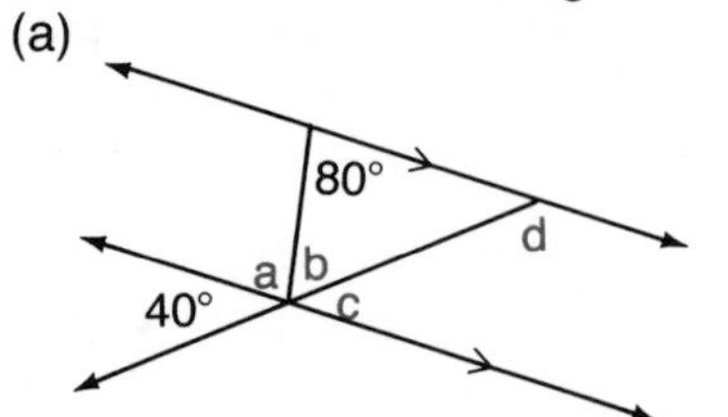

(b)

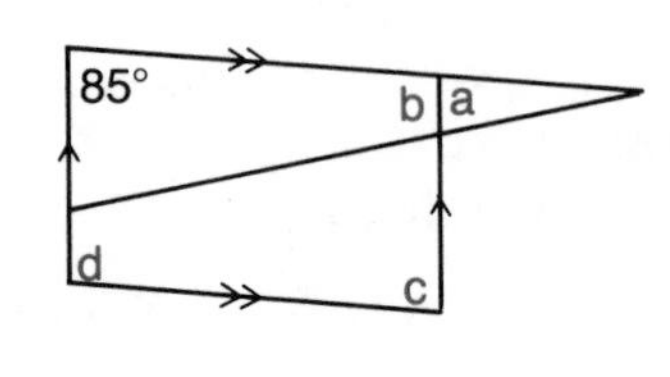

3. Select two pairs of congruent triangles and give the reason for congruence.

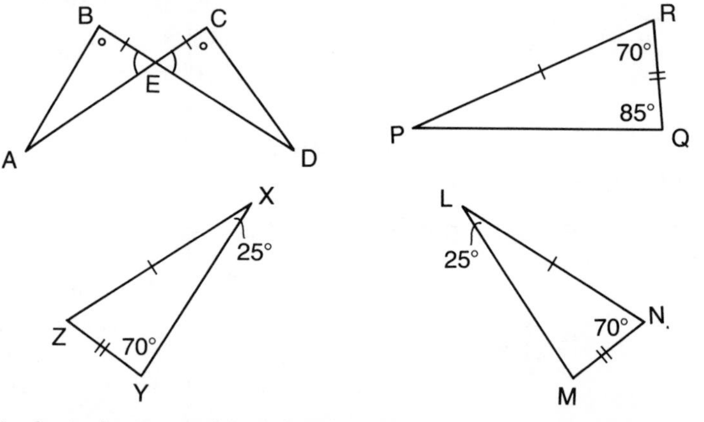

4. A student stands so that her shadow and that of the flagpole are in line and have the same tip. The student's height is 178 cm and her shadow is 267 cm long when the pole's shadow is 921 cm long. How tall is the flagpole?

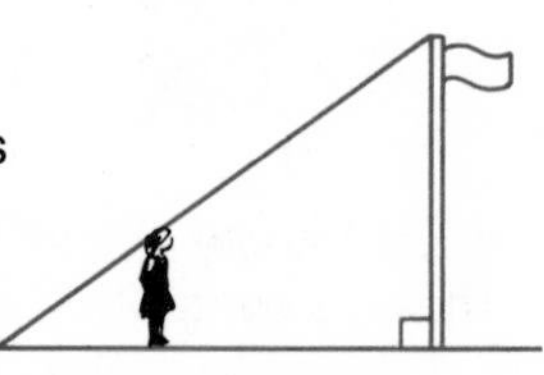

5. Consecutive bases of a square-shaped baseball diamond are 27.5 m apart. Find the distance from home plate to second base. Round your answer to the nearest metre.

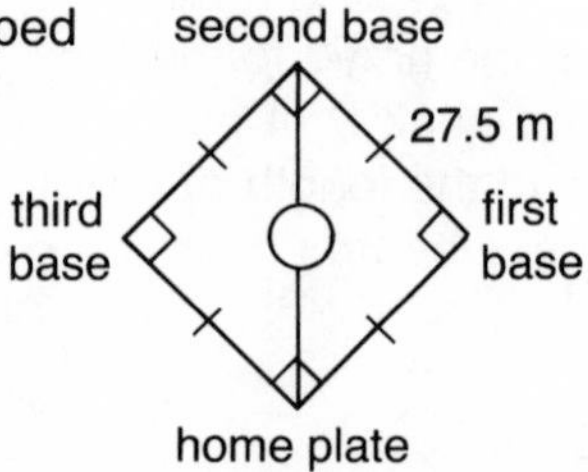

TRIGONOMETRY

REVIEW AND PREVIEW TO CHAPTER 8

RATIOS AND SIMILAR TRIANGLES

EXERCISE

1. Simplify to three significant figures.

(a) $\frac{5}{13}$ (b) $\frac{7}{24}$

(c) $\frac{5.5}{8}$ (d) 3.5×2.7

(e) 4.2×8.1 (f) 1.73×1.41

(g) $\frac{7}{25}$ (h) $\frac{28}{4.5}$

(i) 6.8×4.6 (j) 3.8^2

2. Solve the following equations to three significant figures.

Example.

$$\frac{x}{3.5} = \frac{4.7}{1.8}$$

$$3.5\left(\frac{x}{3.5}\right) = 3.5 \times \frac{4.7}{1.8}$$

Press

3 · 5 × 4 · 7 ÷ 1 · 8 =

The display is 9.138888889

$\therefore x \doteq 9.14$ (to three significant digits)

(a) $\frac{a}{5.7} = \frac{8.2}{12.5}$ (b) $\frac{h}{2.7} = \frac{6.5}{2.3}$

(c) $\frac{d}{140} = \frac{4}{3}$ (d) $\frac{x}{53} = \frac{2.7}{4.1}$

(e) $\frac{n}{58} = 0.246$ (f) $\frac{p}{62} = 0.331$

(g) $\frac{h}{2.6} = 0.866$ (h) $\frac{h}{6.2} = \frac{37}{44}$

(i) $\frac{h}{135} = 1.73$ (j) $\frac{m}{6.5} = 0.337$

3. Calculate the measure of x in each of the following right triangles.

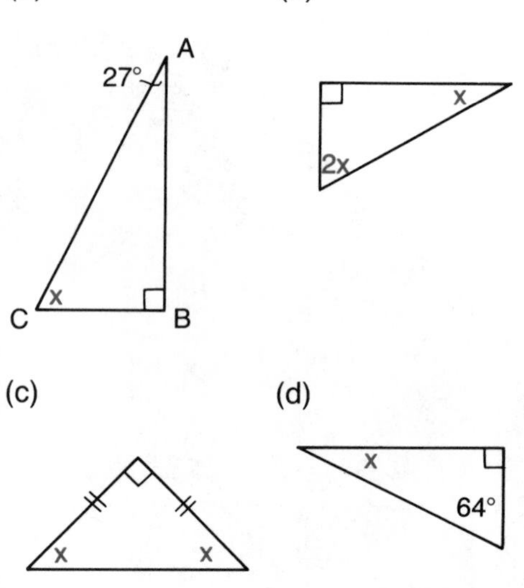

4. Find pairs of similar right triangles to calculate the value of the indicated variables.

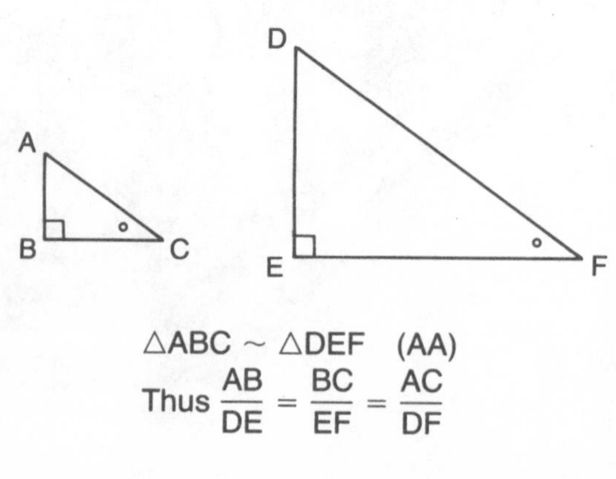

$\triangle ABC \sim \triangle DEF$ (AA)

Thus $\frac{AB}{DE} = \frac{BC}{EF} = \frac{AC}{DF}$

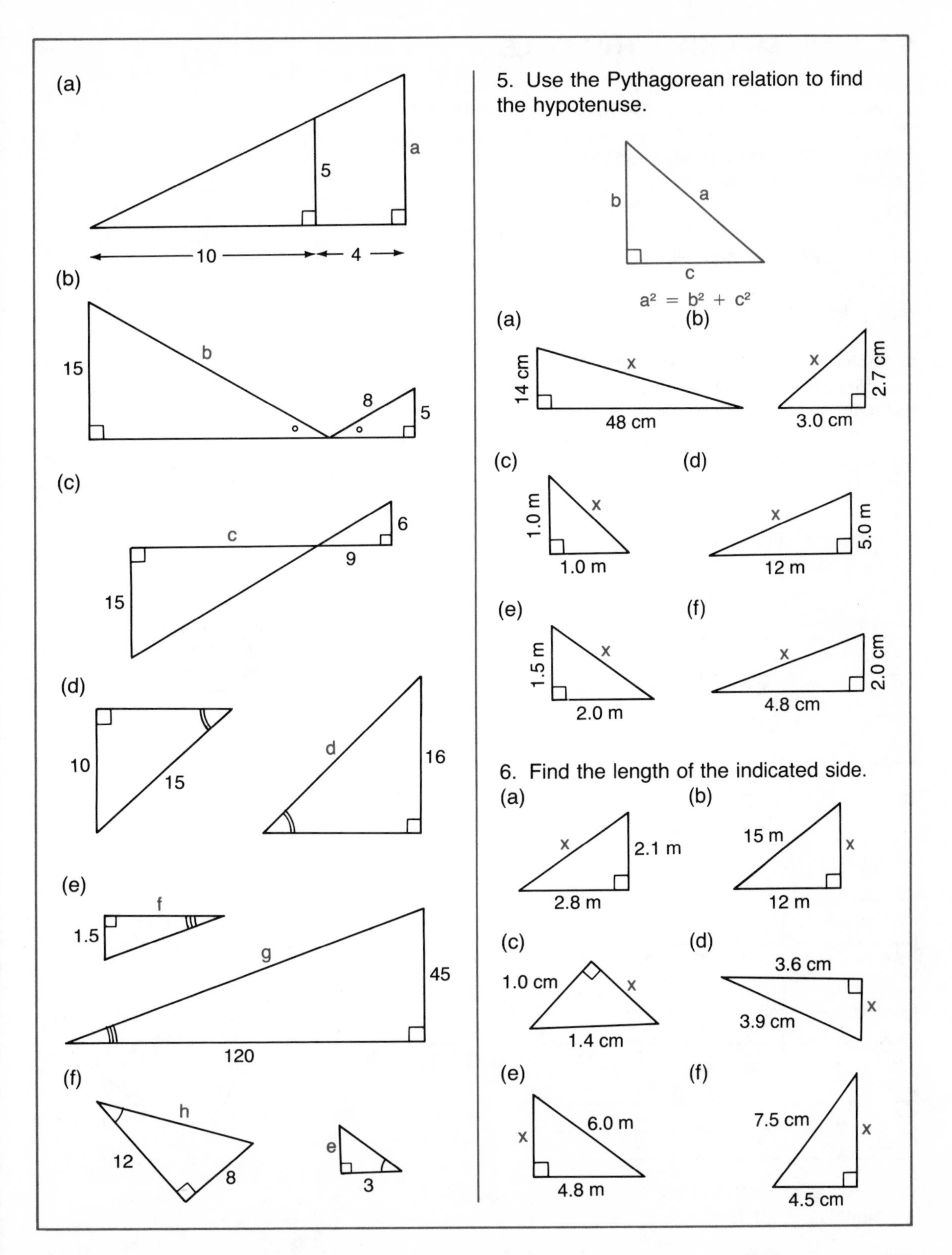
(a)
a
5
10
4
(b)
15
b
8
5
(c)
c
6
9
15
(d)
10
15
d
16
(e)
f
1.5
g
45
120
(f)
h
12
8
e
3
5. Use the Pythagorean relation to find the hypotenuse.
b
a
c
a² = b² + c²
(a)
14 cm
x
48 cm
(b)
x
2.7 cm
3.0 cm
(c)
1.0 m
x
1.0 m
(d)
x
5.0 m
12 m
(e)
1.5 m
x
2.0 m
(f)
x
2.0 cm
4.8 cm
6. Find the length of the indicated side.
(a)
x
2.1 m
2.8 m
(b)
15 m
x
12 m
(c)
1.0 cm
x
1.4 cm
(d)
3.6 cm
x
3.9 cm
(e)
x
6.0 m
4.8 m
(f)
7.5 cm
x
4.5 cm

8.1 SIMILAR RIGHT TRIANGLES

Trigonometry is a branch of mathematics used more than 2000 a ago by astronomers, navigators, and surveyors to determine distances to inaccessible objects and to determine unmeasurable heights. Today, trigonometry continues to grow in importance not only in the space program but also in the day-to-day work of skilled machinists, draftsmen, and other modern day technologists.

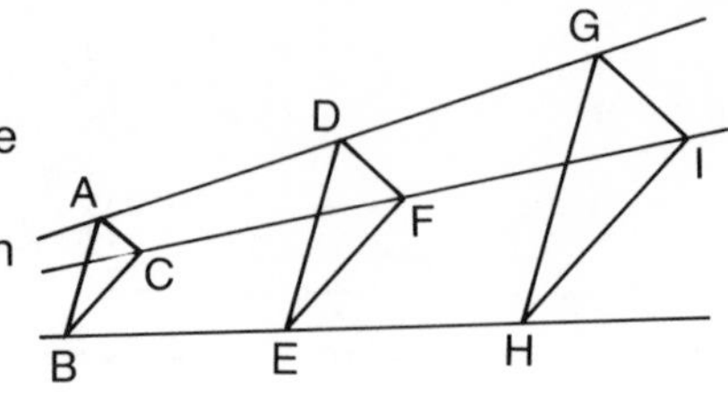

A colour slide and its image on a projection screen are examples of similar figures.

1. In the accompanying diagram, several similar right triangles are drawn on squared paper so that the lengths of the sides can be read in terms of units (AB = 10 units). From the geometry of the figure, state the relation between the angles at C, E, G, I, and K.

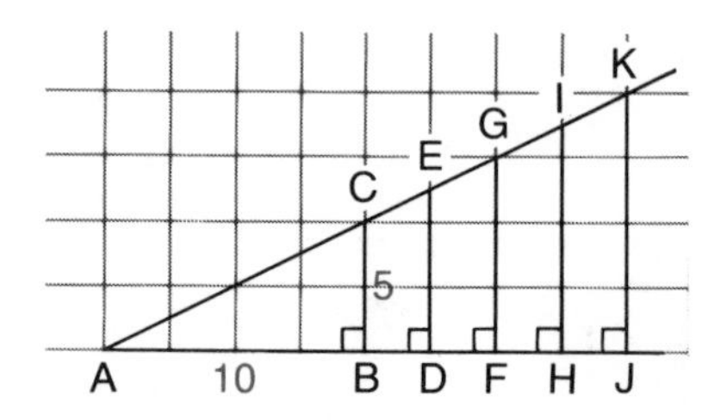

2. (a) Complete the following table in your notebook by filling in the lengths.

△ABC	△ADE	△AFG	△AHI	△AJK
AB = 10 units	AD = ■	AF = ■	AH = ■	AJ = ■
BC = 5 units	DE = ■	FG = ■	HI = ■	JK = ■
$\frac{BC}{AB} = \frac{5}{10} = \frac{1}{2}$	$\frac{DE}{AD}$ = ■	$\frac{FG}{AF}$ = ■	$\frac{HI}{AH}$ = ■	$\frac{JK}{AJ}$ = ■

(b) How are the ratios of the corresponding sides related?

3. (a) Complete the following table as in question 2 above.

△ABC	△ADE	△AFG	△AHI	△AJK
AB = 10	AD = ■	AF = ■	AH = ■	AJ = ■
BC = 5	DE = ■	FG = ■	HI = ■	JK = ■
AC = 11.2	AE = ■	AG = ■	AI = ■	AK = ■
$\frac{BC}{AC}$ = ■	$\frac{DE}{AE}$ = ■	$\frac{FG}{AG}$ = ■	$\frac{HI}{AI}$ = ■	$\frac{JK}{AK}$ = ■
$\frac{AB}{AC}$ = ■	$\frac{AD}{AE}$ = ■	$\frac{AF}{AG}$ = ■	$\frac{AH}{AI}$ = ■	$\frac{AJ}{AK}$ = ■

Use your compasses to measure AC, AE, AG, AI, AK.

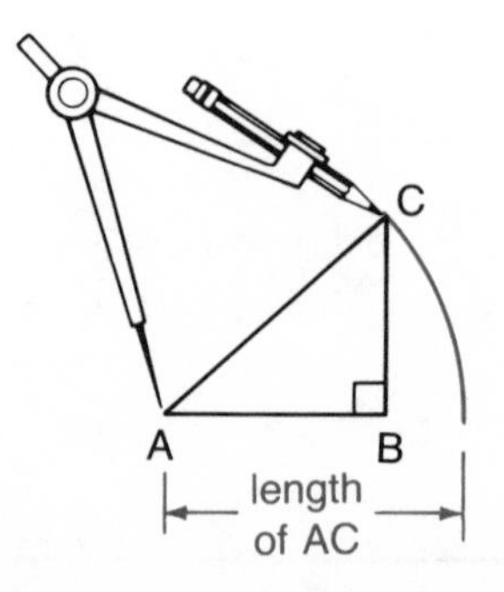

(b) How are the ratios of the corresponding sides of the triangles related?

4. The indicated angle in each of the following right triangles is equal to 55°.

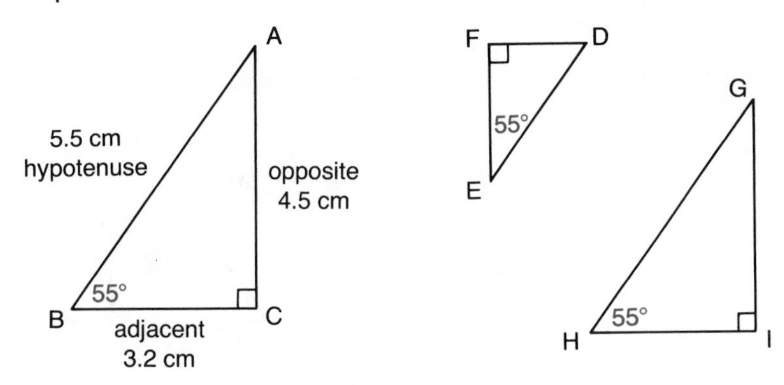

(a) Measure the side of the triangle opposite to the 55° angle and the side adjacent to the 55° angle.

Copy the following table and record your results.

$\triangle$	Opposite side to 55°	Adjacent side to 55°	Hypotenuse	Ratios $\frac{\text{opposite}}{\text{hypotenuse}}$	$\frac{\text{adjacent}}{\text{hypotenuse}}$	$\frac{\text{opposite}}{\text{adjacent}}$
$\triangle$ABC	4.5 cm	3.2 cm	5.5 cm	$\frac{4.5}{5.5} \doteq 0.8$	$\frac{3.2}{5.5} \doteq 0.6$	$\frac{4.5}{3.2} \doteq 1.4$
$\triangle$DEF						
$\triangle$GHI						

(b) (i) How are the ratios $\frac{\text{opposite}}{\text{hypotenuse}}$ related?

(ii) How are the ratios $\frac{\text{adjacent}}{\text{hypotenuse}}$ related?

(iii) How are the ratios $\frac{\text{opposite}}{\text{adjacent}}$ related?

(c) Repeat parts (a) and (b) using the following right triangles where $\angle A = \angle D = \angle G$.

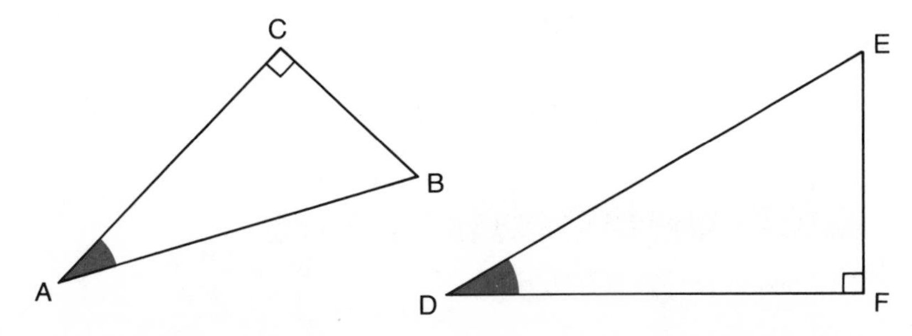

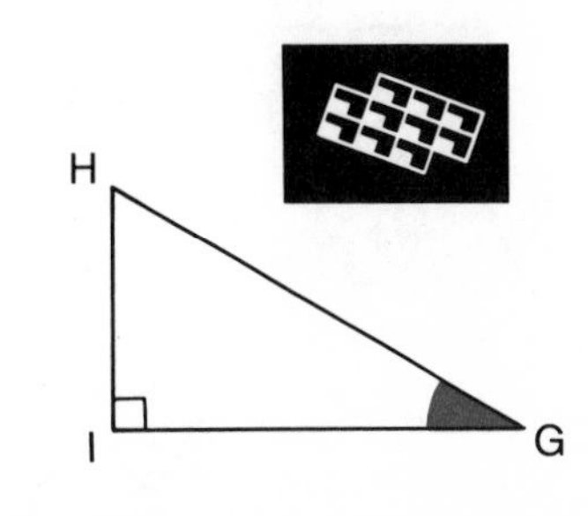

(d) What conclusions can you make from this investigation?

Example 1. The shadow of a tree is 9.25 m at the same time of day that the shadow of a 1.96 m man is 1.47 m. Find the height of the tree.

Solution: We express the data in diagrams.

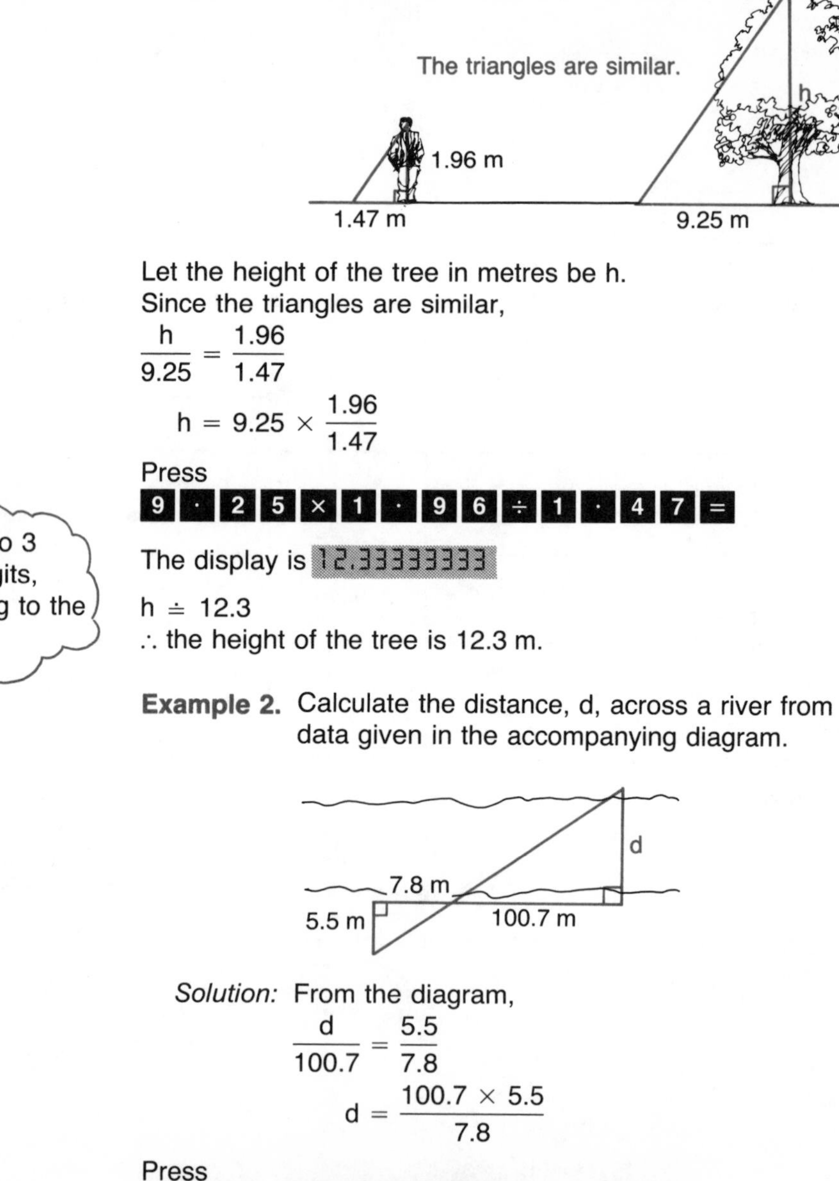

Let the height of the tree in metres be h.
Since the triangles are similar,

$$\frac{h}{9.25} = \frac{1.96}{1.47}$$

$$h = 9.25 \times \frac{1.96}{1.47}$$

Press

9 · 2 5 × 1 · 9 6 ÷ 1 · 4 7 =

The display is 12.33333333

We round h to 3 significant digits, corresponding to the given data.

$h \doteq 12.3$

∴ the height of the tree is 12.3 m.

Example 2. Calculate the distance, d, across a river from data given in the accompanying diagram.

d
7.8 m
5.5 m
100.7 m

Solution: From the diagram,

$$\frac{d}{100.7} = \frac{5.5}{7.8}$$

$$d = \frac{100.7 \times 5.5}{7.8}$$

Press

1 0 0 · 7 × 5 · 5 ÷ 7 · 8 =

The display is 71.00641026

We round d to 2 significant digits.

$d \doteq 71$

∴ the river is 71 m wide.

EXERCISE 8.1

A

1. State the proportions between sides in the following pairs of similar triangles.

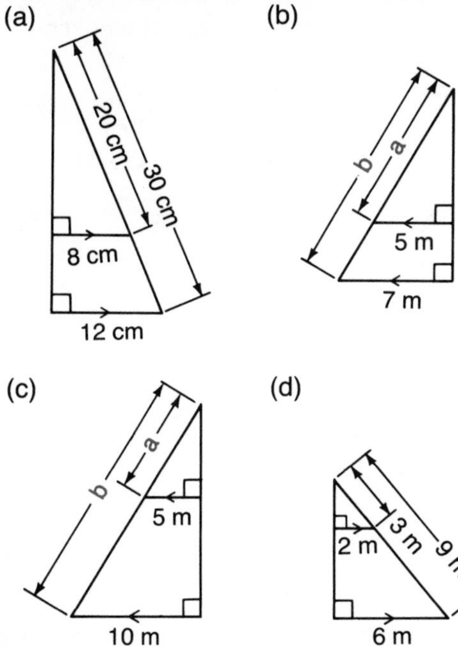

B

2. Calculate the values, in units, of the variables in the following pairs of similar triangles.

(a)

7 cm, 5 cm, 35 cm, x

(b) (c)

4 cm, 3 cm, y, 12 cm

20 cm, 30 cm, a, 24 cm

3. Find the values, in units, of f and i if $\triangle DEF$ and $\triangle GHI$ are similar to $\triangle ABC$.

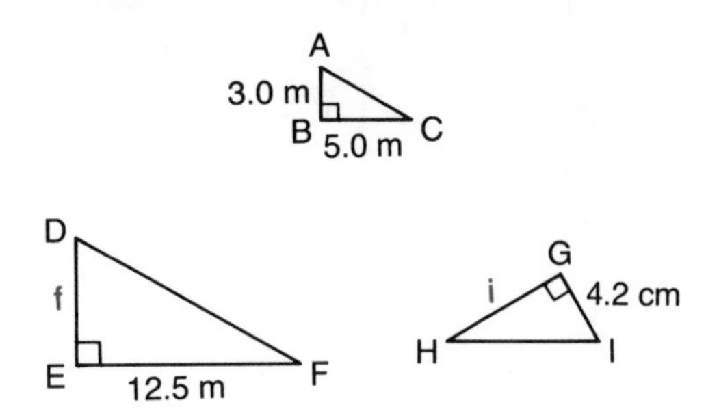

4. Calculate the values of a and b given that all three triangles are similar.

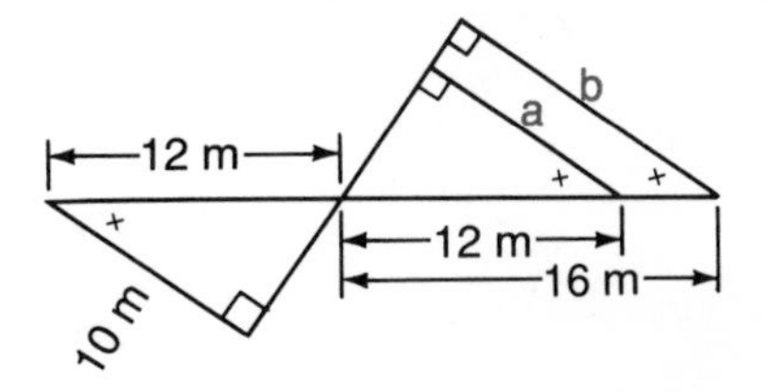

5. A flagpole casts a 12 m shadow when a man 1.8 m tall casts a 2.4 m shadow. Calculate the height of the flagpole.

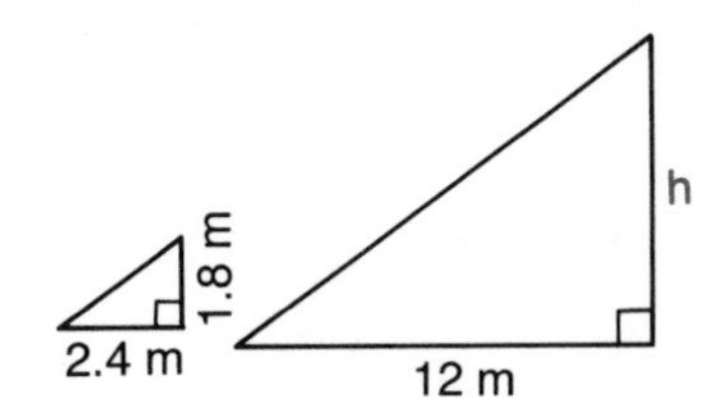

6. In the accompanying diagram, a carpenter's square is shown in two positions forming a pair of similar right triangles.
Calculate
(a) the dimension marked x,
(b) the hypotenuse of both triangles.

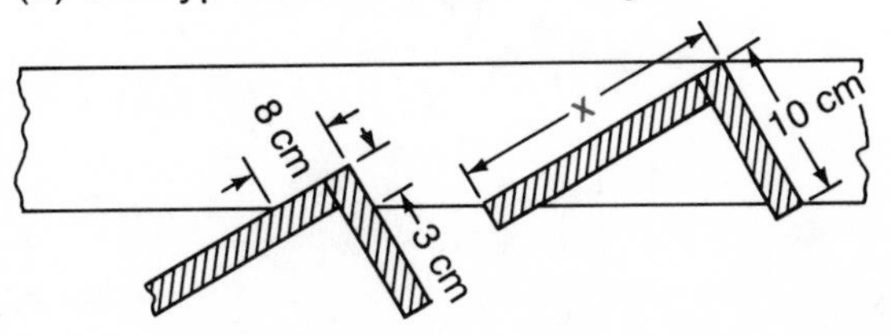

8.2 THE TANGENT RATIO

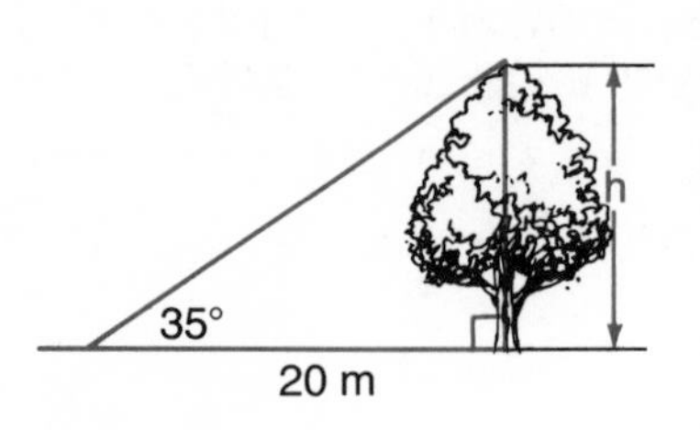

In the previous section, you were able to calculate lengths, heights, and distances, given two triangles, by setting up a proportion. How would you calculate the height of a tree which casts a shadow 20 m long when the angle of elevation of the sun is 35°?

This problem cannot be solved by the method of the previous section. In order to perform such calculations, mathematicians have developed a branch of mathematics called trigonometry.

The sides of a right triangle are labelled as follows.

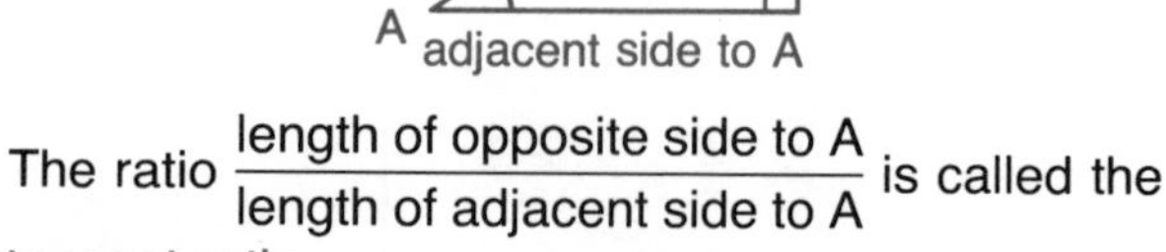

The ratio $\frac{\text{length of opposite side to A}}{\text{length of adjacent side to A}}$ is called the tangent ratio.

We write tangent of A $= \frac{\text{length of opposite side}}{\text{length of adjacent side}}$

or simply

$$\tan A = \frac{\text{opposite}}{\text{adjacent}}$$

Example 1. Calculate the tangent ratio of the indicated angle in the following.

(a)

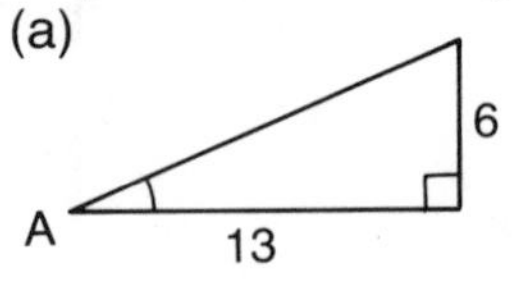

(b)

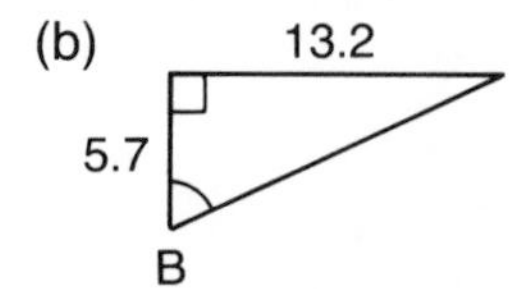

Solution:

(a) The length of the side opposite to A is 6 units. The length of the side adjacent to A is 13 units.

$\tan A = \frac{\text{opp}}{\text{adj}}$ Press 6 ÷ 1 3 =

$\therefore \tan A = \frac{6}{13}$ The display is 0.461538461

$\doteq 0.462$

(b) $\tan B = \frac{\text{opp}}{\text{adj}}$ Press 1 3 · 2 ÷ 5 · 7 =

$\tan B = \frac{13.2}{5.7}$ The display is 2.315789474

$\doteq 2.32$

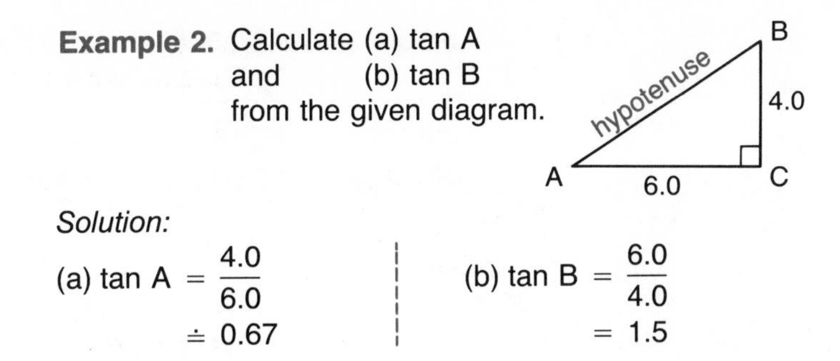

Example 2. Calculate (a) tan A
and (b) tan B
from the given diagram.

Solution:

(a) $\tan A = \dfrac{4.0}{6.0}$
$\doteq 0.67$

(b) $\tan B = \dfrac{6.0}{4.0}$
$= 1.5$

Note that side BC is opposite to ∠A, and adjacent to ∠B.

Similarly AC is opposite to ∠B, and adjacent to ∠A.

The tangent ratio depends only on the measure of the acute angle and not on the size of the right triangle. For three similar right triangles, tan 30° is always the same.

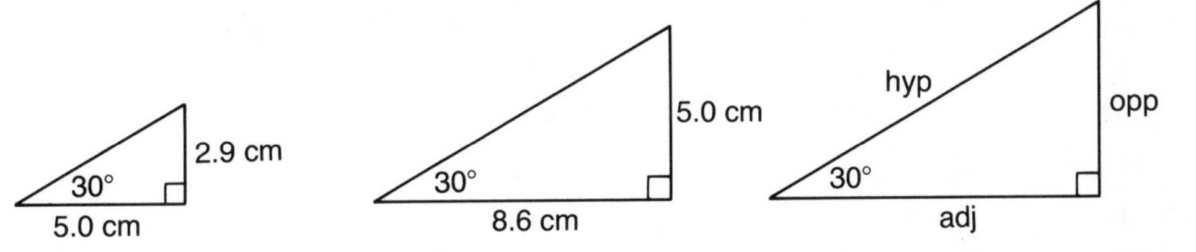

From the above triangles, we see that

$$\tan 30^\circ = \frac{2.9}{5.0} = \frac{5.0}{8.6} = \frac{opp}{adj}$$

$\frac{2.9}{5.0}$ and $\frac{5.0}{8.6}$ equal 0.58 to 2 significant digits

0°	tan θ
0	0.0000
1	0.0175
2	0.0349
3	0.0524
4	0.0699
5	0.0875
6	0.1051
7	0.1228
8	0.1405
9	0.1584
10	0.1763
11	0.1944
20	0.3640
21	0.3839
22	0.4040
23	0.4245
24	0.4452
25	0.4663
26	0.4877
27	0.5095
28	0.5317
29	0.5543
30	0.5774

A table of values for the tangent ratio for acute angles may be found in the Appendix. Most of the values in the table are approximations to four significant figures.

In order to find tan 27° using the table, we locate 27° in the angle column and read:

tan 27° = 0.5095

Using a calculator,
press

The display is 0.509525449

When an acute angle and the adjacent side of a right triangle are known, you can find the length of the opposite side using the tangent ratio.

Example 3. Calculate the height of a tree which casts a 35 m shadow when the angle of elevation of the sun is 27°.

Solution: Let the height of the tree, in metres, be h.

$$\frac{h}{35} = \tan 27°$$

$$h = 35 \times \tan 27°$$

$$\doteq 35 \times 0.5095$$

$$\doteq 17.8325$$

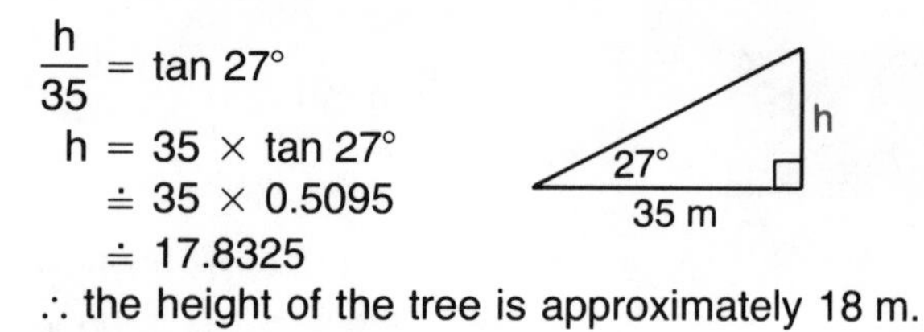

$\therefore$ the height of the tree is approximately 18 m.

Press

3 5 × 2 7 tan =

The display is 17.83339073

EXERCISE 8.2

A

1. Identify each side of the following triangles as the hypotenuse, or as the side opposite or adjacent to the indicated angle.

θ is the Greek letter theta, which is often used to denote the measure of an angle.

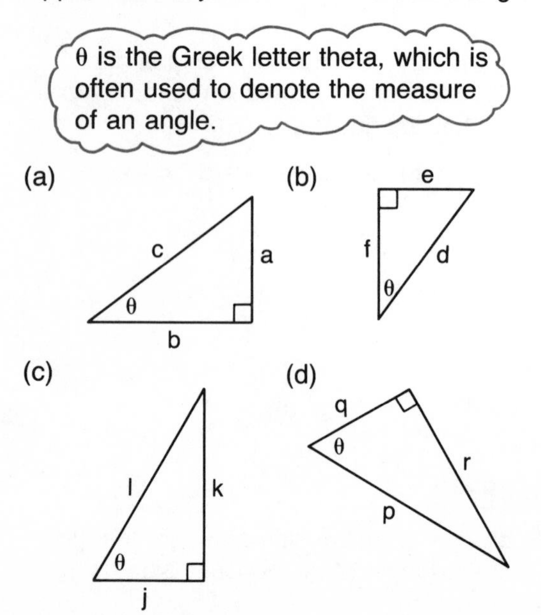

2. State the tangent ratio of the indicated angle in each of the following.

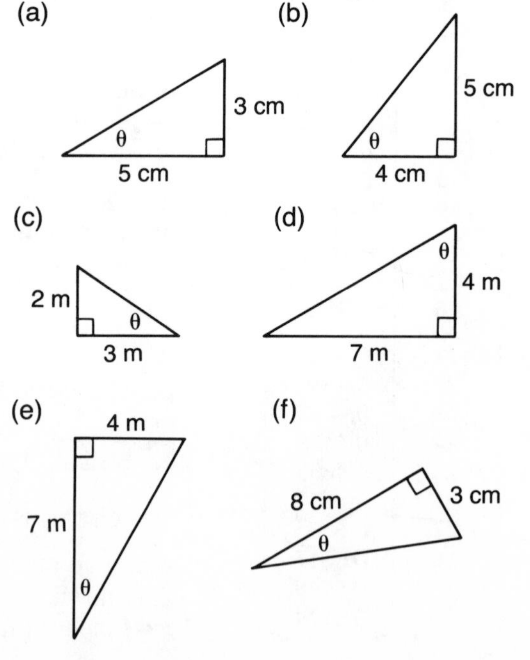

B

3. Calculate the lengths of the indicated sides using the tangent ratio.

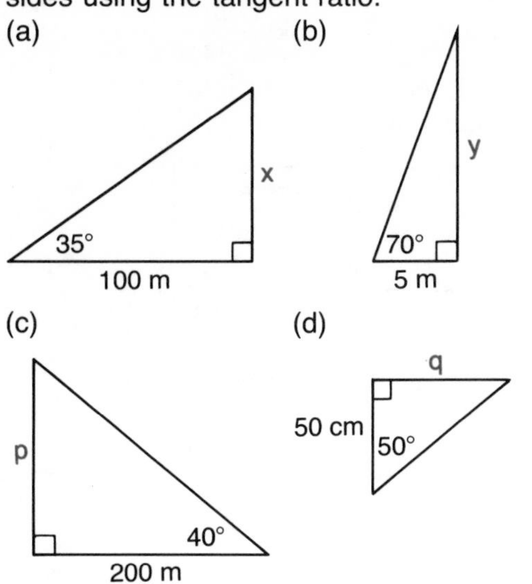

4. Calculate the values of the variables.

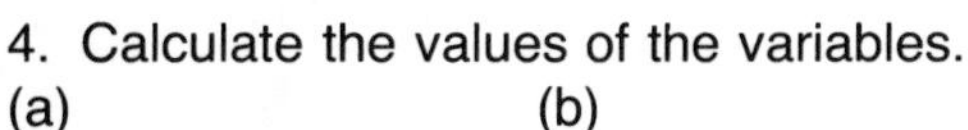

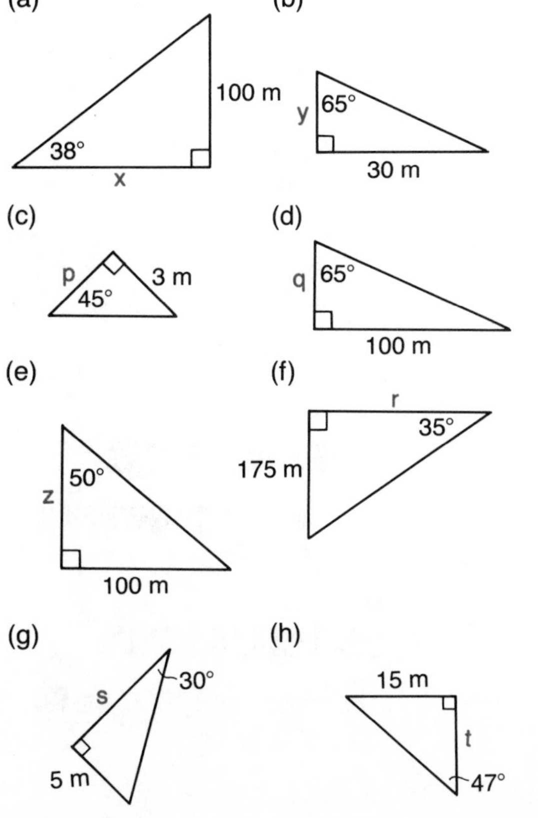

5. Calculate the value of tan θ in each of the following triangles, and then read the value of θ to the nearest degree from the table.

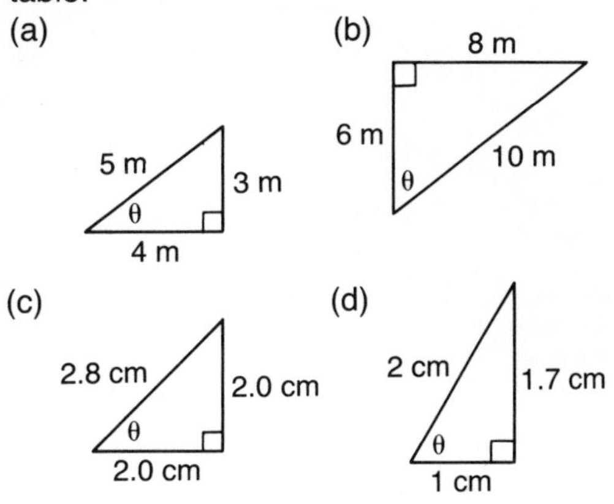

6. A building 11.5 m high casts a 27.7 m shadow.
Calculate the angle of elevation of the sun.

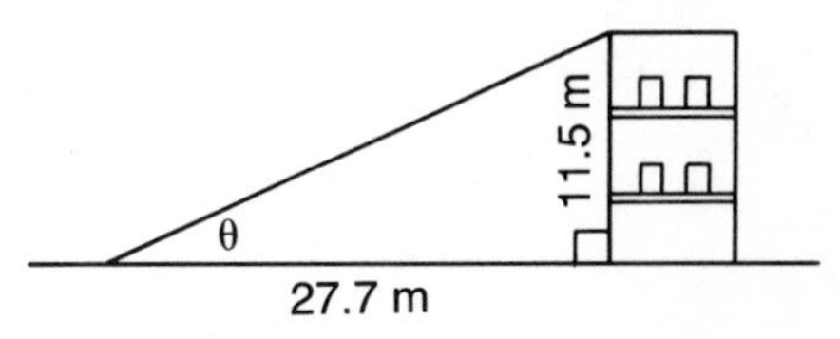

7. A flagpole casts a shadow of 22.4 m when the angle of elevation of the sun is 38°.
Calculate the height of the flagpole.

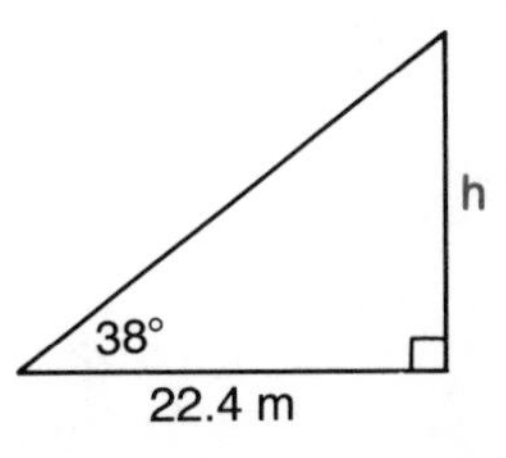

8. Calculate the distance AB from the data given in the diagram. Hint: find AD and BD separately.

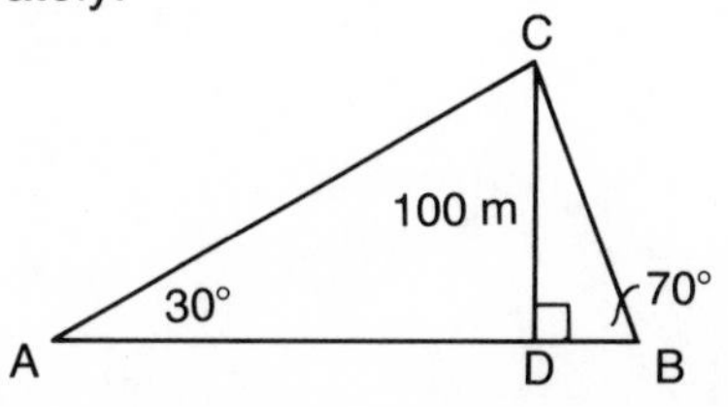

8.3 THE SINE AND COSINE RATIOS

In the previous section, we formed the ratio $\frac{\text{opposite side}}{\text{adjacent side}}$ and called it the tangent of θ (tan θ). We now define two more ratios, sine and cosine, as follows.

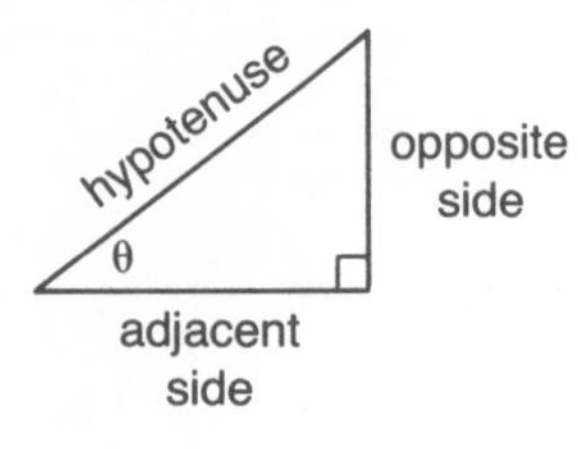

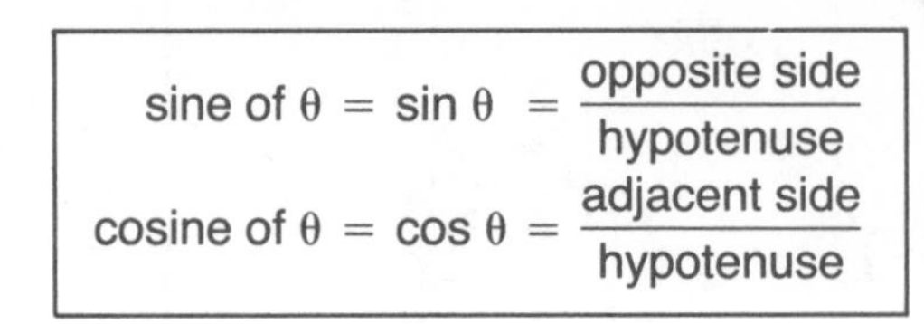

$$\text{sine of } \theta = \sin\theta = \frac{\text{opposite side}}{\text{hypotenuse}}$$
$$\text{cosine of } \theta = \cos\theta = \frac{\text{adjacent side}}{\text{hypotenuse}}$$

Example 1. State sin θ and cos θ from the given diagram.

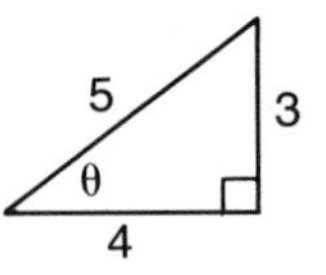

Solution:

$$\sin\theta = \frac{\text{opposite side}}{\text{hypotenuse}} \qquad \cos\theta = \frac{\text{adjacent side}}{\text{hypotenuse}}$$
$$\sin\theta = \frac{3}{5} \qquad \cos\theta = \frac{4}{5}$$

Example 2. Calculate a and b to the nearest centimetre from the data in the diagram, given that sin 25° ≐ 0.4226 and cos 25° ≐ 0.9063.

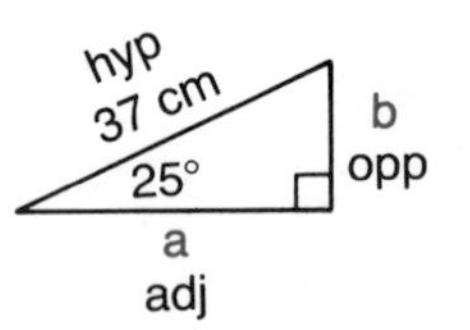

Solution:

$$\frac{b}{37} = \sin 25°$$
$$b = 37 \times \sin 25°$$
$$\doteq 37 \times 0.4226$$
$$\doteq 15.6$$

Press 3 7 × 2 5 sin =

The display is 15.63687568

$$\frac{a}{37} = \cos 25°$$
$$a = 37 \times \cos 25°$$
$$\doteq 37 \times 0.9063$$
$$\doteq 33.5$$

Press 3 7 × 2 5 cos =

The display is 33.53338812

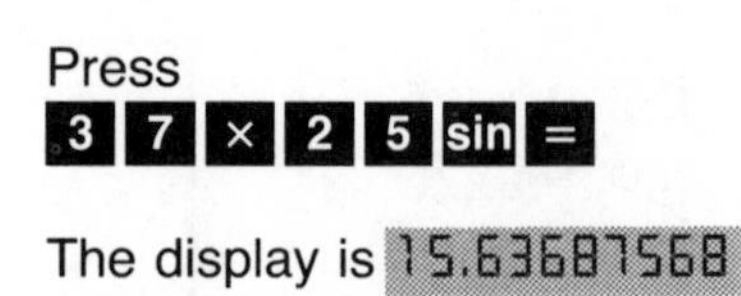

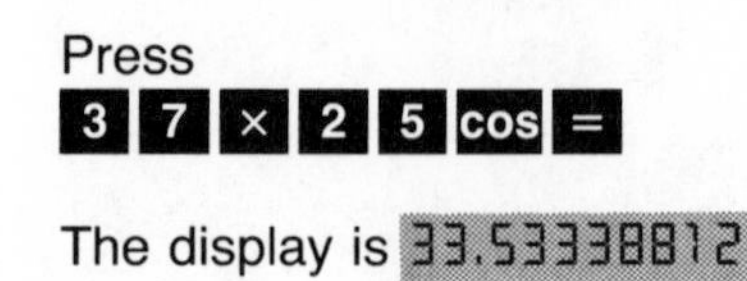

∴ in the given triangle, a is 34 cm and b is 16 cm.

EXERCISE 8.3

A

1. State the value of
(i) $\sin \theta$, (ii) $\cos \theta$, and (iii) $\tan \theta$.

(a) (b)

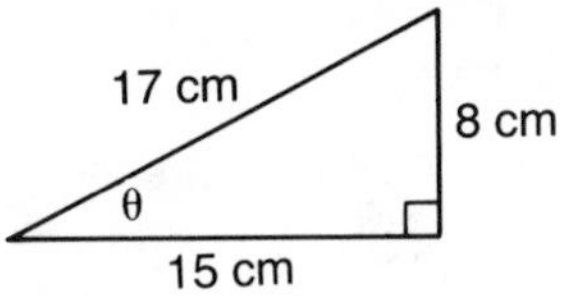

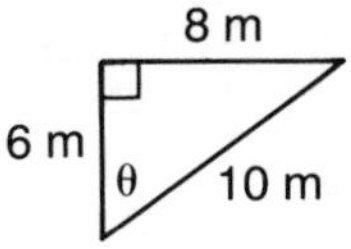

(c) 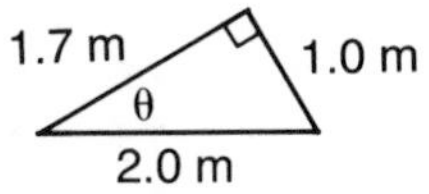 (d)

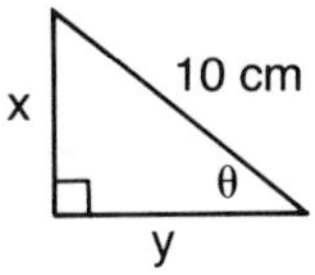

(e) 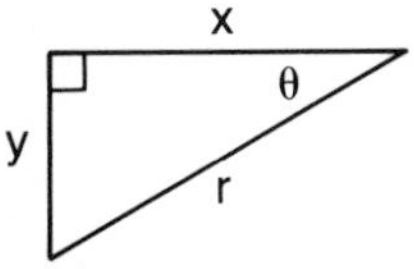 (f)

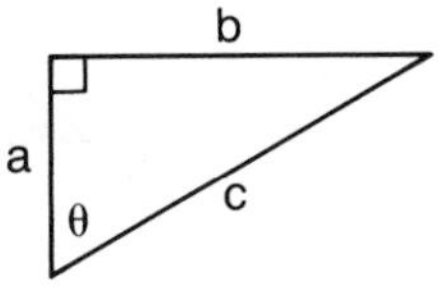

2. State the value of
(i) $\sin \theta$, (ii) $\cos \theta$, and (iii) $\tan \theta$.

(a) (b)

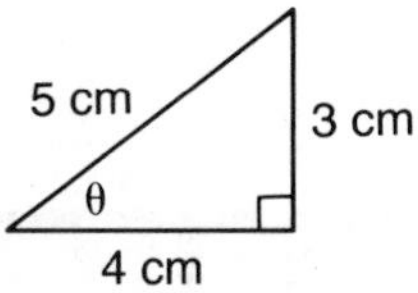

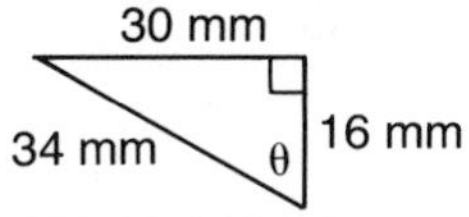

(c) 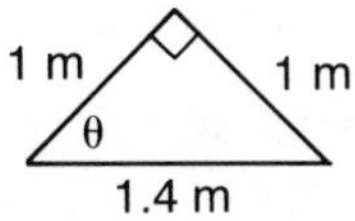 (d)

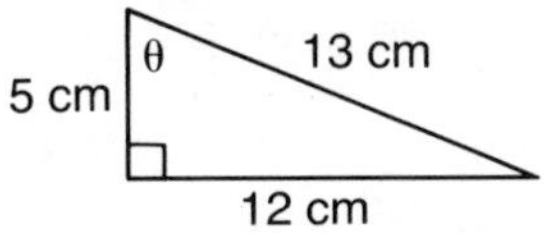

(e) 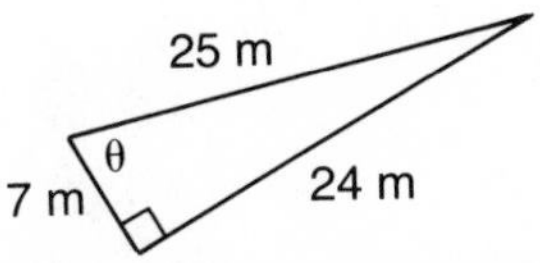 (f)

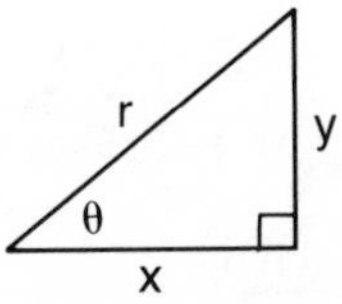

B

3. Calculate the length of the indicated side using the data given in each case.

(a) $\sin 35° \doteq 0.574$

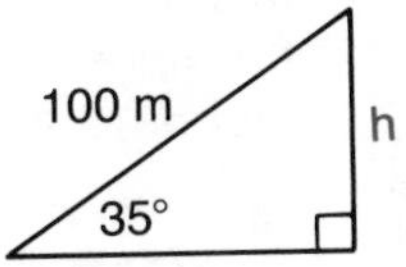

(b) $\cos 28° \doteq 0.883$

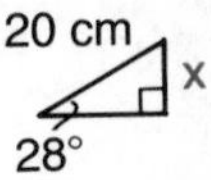

(c) $\sin 40° \doteq 0.643$, $\cos 40° \doteq 0.766$

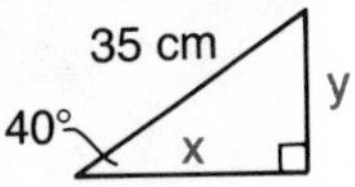

(d) $\cos 35° \doteq 0.819$

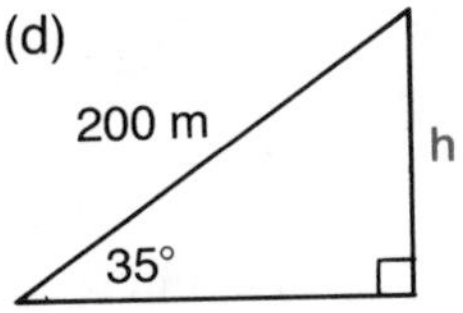

(e) $\cos 43° \doteq 0.731$, $\cos 65° \doteq 0.423$

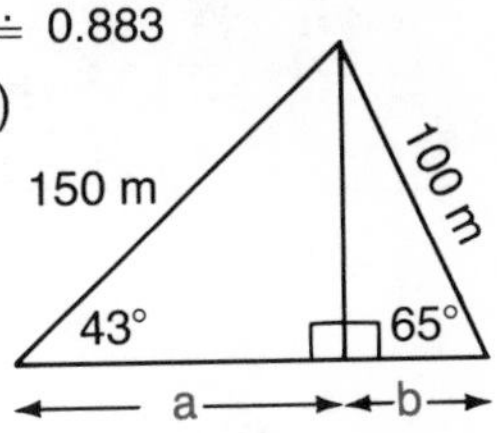

4. State the value of
(a) $\sin 45°$
(b) $\cos 45°$
(c) $\tan 45°$
using the given diagram.

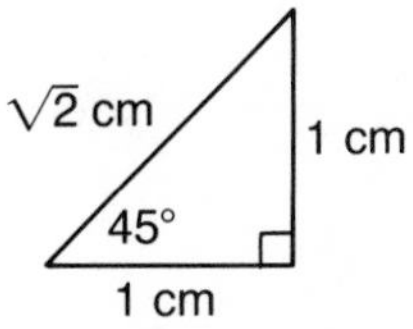

5. State the value of
(a) $\sin 30°$
(b) $\cos 30°$
(c) $\tan 30°$
using the given diagram.

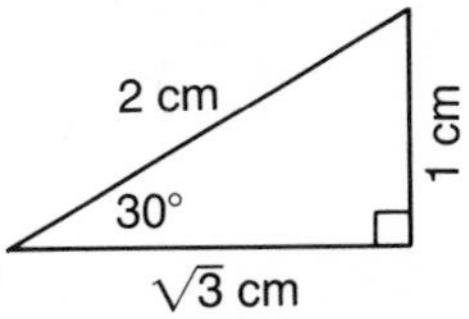

6. State the value of
(a) $\sin 60°$
(b) $\cos 60°$
(c) $\tan 60°$
using the given diagram.

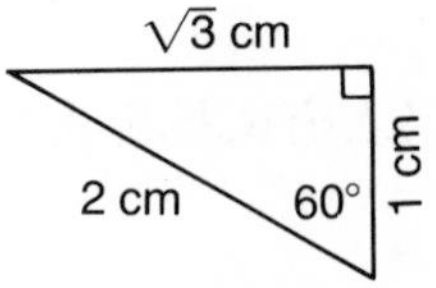

7. A guy wire 40 m long runs from the ground to the top of a pole. It makes a 63° angle with the line drawn to the foot of the pole.
(a) Find the height of the pole.
(b) How far from the pole is the wire fastened?

$\sin 63° \doteq 0.891$
$\cos 63° \doteq 0.454$

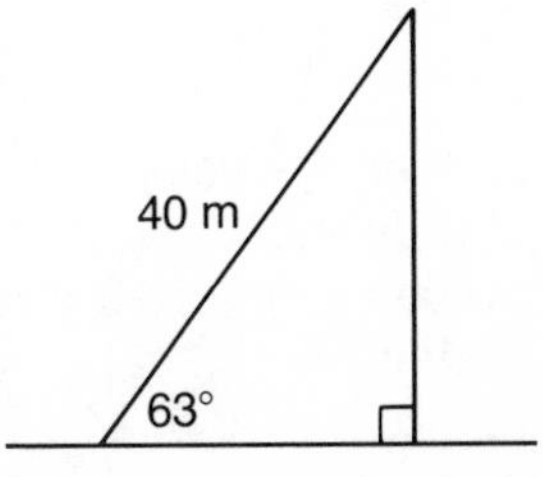

8.4 TRIGONOMETRIC RATIOS ON A CALCULATOR

In the previous sections, we used a scientific calculator as well as a trigonometric table to find the values of trigonometric ratios. Given the angle measure in degrees, the value of the corresponding trigonometric ratio can be found using a scientific calculator as follows.

(a) To find tan 48°, press

4 **8** **tan**

The display is

`1.110612515`

(b) To find sin 67°, press

6 **7** **sin**

The display is

`0.920504853`

There are several ways to find an unknown angle measure, given the value of a trigonometric ratio, depending on the calculator.

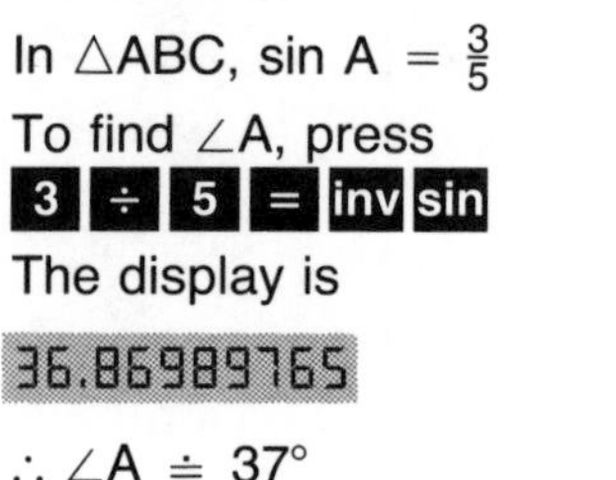

In $\triangle ABC$, $\sin A = \frac{3}{5}$

To find $\angle A$, press

3 **÷** **5** **=** **inv** **sin**

The display is

`36.86989765`

$\therefore \angle A \doteq 37°$

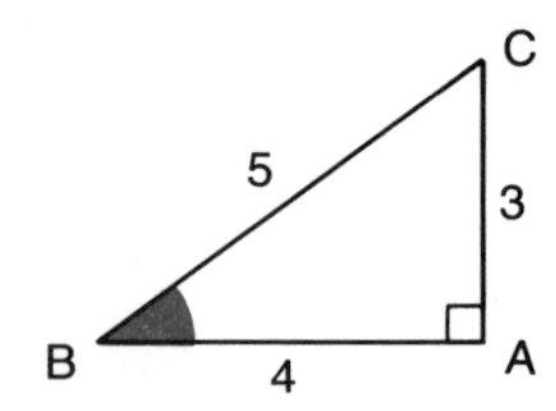

Some calculators have an **arc** or **sin⁻¹** key instead of the **inv** key. In other calculators, the **inv** **sin** is found in the second level of functions. Using this type of calculator, press

3 **÷** **5** **=** **2nd** **sin**

and the same display appears.

EXERCISE 8.4

B

1. Find the following values using a calculator. Round answers to the nearest ten thousandth.

(a) sin 25° (b) cos 36°
(c) tan 55° (d) cos 66°
(e) tan 63° (f) sin 55°

2. Find the value of θ to the nearest tenth of a degree using a calculator.

(a) $\cos \theta = 0.2545$ (b) $\sin \theta = 0.6253$
(c) $\tan \theta = 1.1125$ (d) $\sin \theta = 0.6524$
(e) $\cos \theta = 0.6524$ (f) $\tan \theta = 1.7500$

MICRO MATH

The following program prints the values of the sine, cosine, and tangent ratios.

```
NEW
10 PRINT"ENTER THE ANGLE IN DEGREES."
20 INPUT A
25 R = A*0.017453293
30 PRINT"SIN";A;"=";SIN(R)
40 PRINT"COS";A;"=";COS(R)
50 PRINT"TAN";A;"=";TAN(R)
60 PRINT"ANOTHER ANGLE? Y OR N"
70 INPUT Z$
80 IF Z$="Y" THEN 10
90 END
RUN
```

EXTRA

8.5 THE MAP COLOURING QUESTION

To colour a map, we shall follow some simple rules.

Rule 1: Use as few colours as possible.

Rule 2: Regions with a common border must have different colours.

Rule 3: A point where borders meet is not considered part of the border.

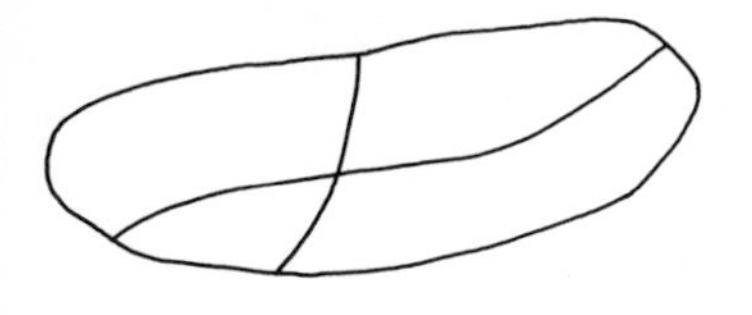

The map at the left requires only two colours to obey our rules, as shown at the right.

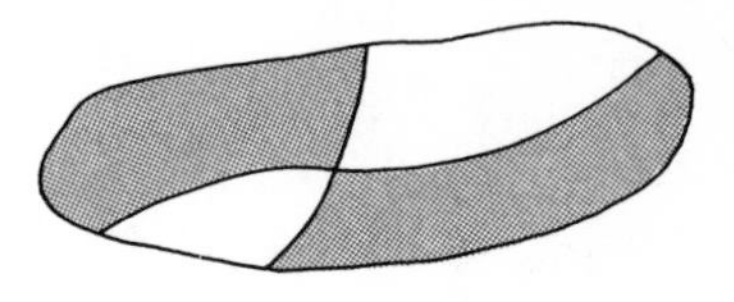

1. What is the least number of colours needed to colour each of the following maps and obey our three rules?

(a)

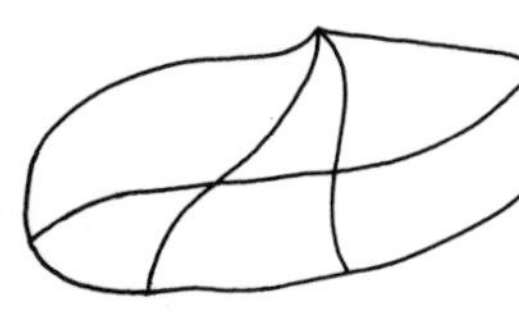

(b)

(c)

(d)

(e)

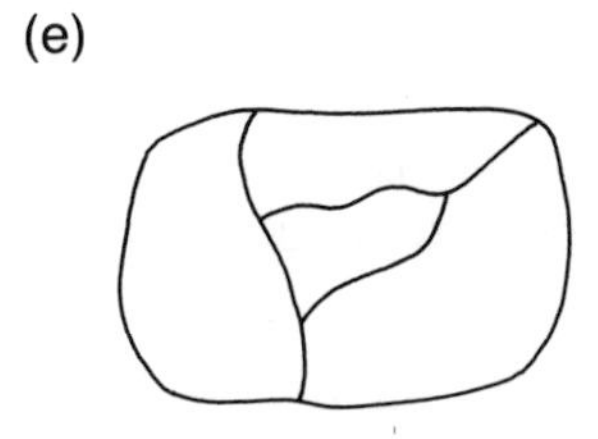

(f)

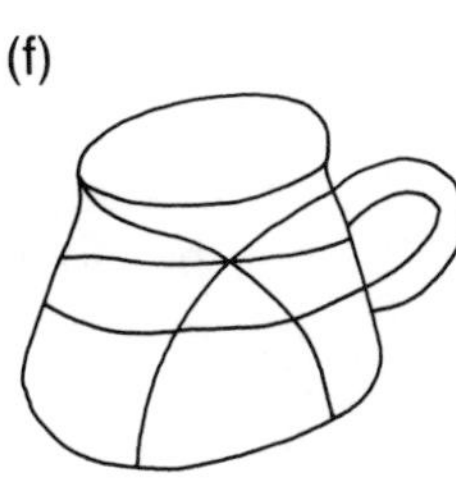

(g)

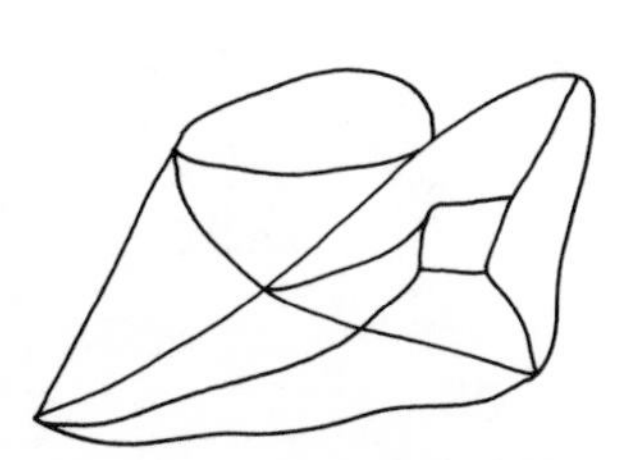

(h)

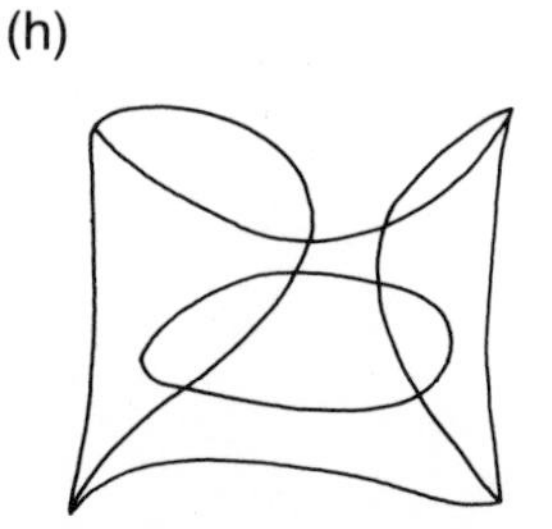

(i)

2. What is the least number of colours needed to colour any of the above maps?
3. Can you draw a map that requires at least five colours?

8.6 RIGHT TRIANGLES

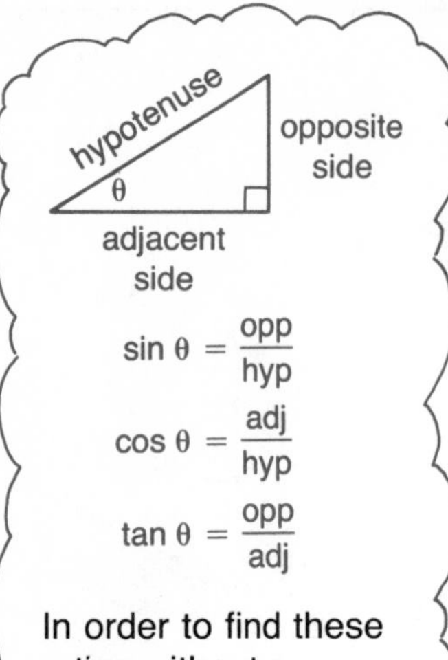

$\sin \theta = \dfrac{\text{opp}}{\text{hyp}}$

$\cos \theta = \dfrac{\text{adj}}{\text{hyp}}$

$\tan \theta = \dfrac{\text{opp}}{\text{adj}}$

In order to find these ratios without a calculator, tables of values of $\sin \theta$, $\cos \theta$, and $\tan \theta$ have been prepared and may be found in the Appendix.

We have defined the trigonometric ratios sine, cosine, and tangent as ratios of the sides of a right triangle. In △ABC, the side opposite ∠A is a units long, the side opposite ∠B is b units long, and the side opposite ∠C is c units long. When the meaning is clear, the letter corresponding to the vertex can mean the measure of the angle at that vertex.

From the diagram,

$\sin A = \dfrac{a}{c} \qquad \sin B = \dfrac{b}{c}$

$\cos A = \dfrac{b}{c} \qquad \cos B = \dfrac{a}{c}$

$\tan A = \dfrac{a}{b} \qquad \tan B = \dfrac{b}{a}$

and $a^2 + b^2 = c^2$

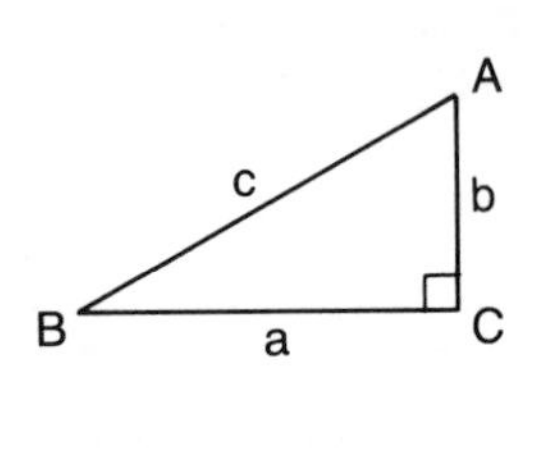

Example 1. Calculate a and b using data given in the diagram.

Solution:

$$\frac{a}{35} = \sin 29^\circ \qquad a = 35 \times \sin 29^\circ \doteq 35 \times 0.4848 \doteq 17.0 \text{ cm}$$

$$\frac{b}{35} = \cos 29^\circ \qquad b = 35 \times \cos 29^\circ \doteq 35 \times 0.8746 \doteq 30.6 \text{ cm}$$

We say that a triangle is solved when we can state the measure of the three angles and the lengths of the three sides.

Example 2. Solve △ABC, given ∠A = 90°, b = 35 m, and c = 45 m.

Solution:

(i) $\tan B = \dfrac{35}{45} \doteq 0.7778$

$\angle B \doteq 38^\circ$

(ii) $\angle C = 90^\circ - 38^\circ = 52^\circ$

(iii) $\dfrac{35}{a} = \sin 38^\circ$

$35 = a \times \sin 38^\circ$

$\dfrac{35}{\sin 38^\circ} = a$

$\dfrac{35}{0.6157} = a$

$56.8 \doteq a$

$\therefore a = 56.8$ m, ∠B = 38°, and ∠C = 52°.

EXERCISE 8.6

B

1. Using tables or calculators, find the following values.

(a) sin 25° (b) tan 80°
(c) sin 45° (d) cos 45°
(e) cos 38° (f) sin 20°
(g) tan 45° (h) cos 30°
(i) tan 28° (j) cos 32°
(k) sin 30° (l) sin 50°
(m) cos 60° (n) tan 12°
(o) sin 65° (p) tan 87°

2. Find the measure of each angle to the nearest degree.

(a) tan A = 0.6009 (b) sin B = 0.9903
(c) sin D = 0.250 (d) sin E = 0.695
(e) sin G = 0.707 (f) cos H = 0.809
(g) tan H = 0.250 (h) cos K = 0.707
(i) cos M = 0.309 (j) tan N = 11.400
(k) cos C = 0.2590 (l) sin L = 0.500
(m) tan F = 0.810 (n) sin θ = 1.000
(o) tan I = 1.600 (p) tan θ = 0.2045

3. Use the sine ratio to find the length of the indicated side.

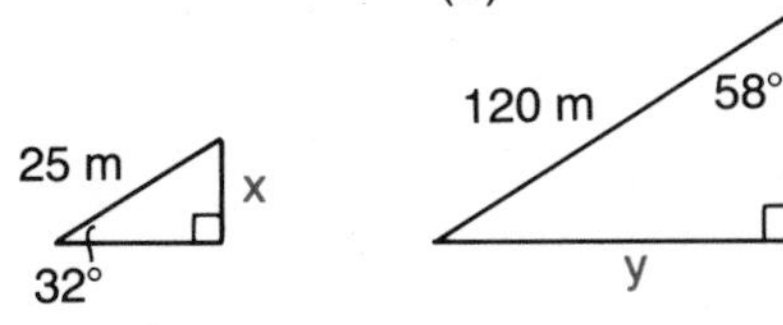

4. Use the cosine ratio to find the length of the indicated side.

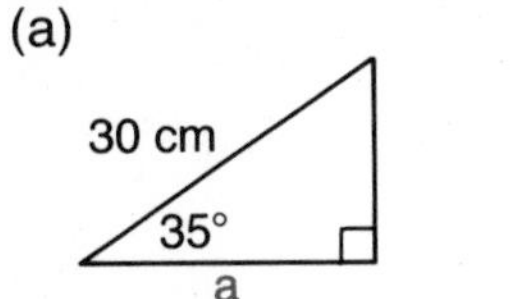

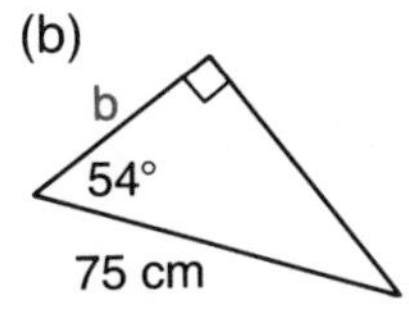

5. Use the tangent ratio to find the indicated side.

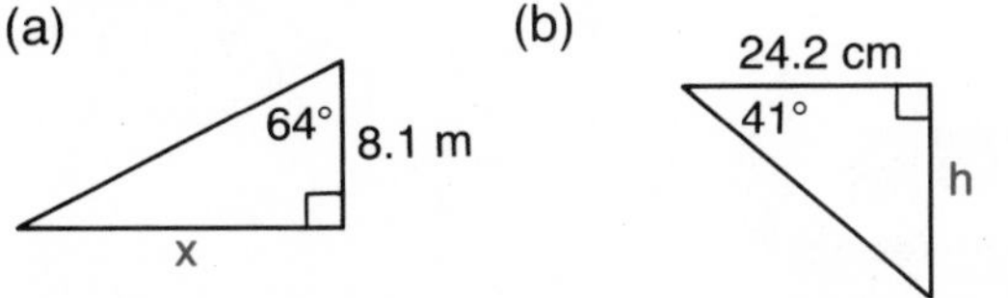

6. Find the length of the indicated side in each of the following.

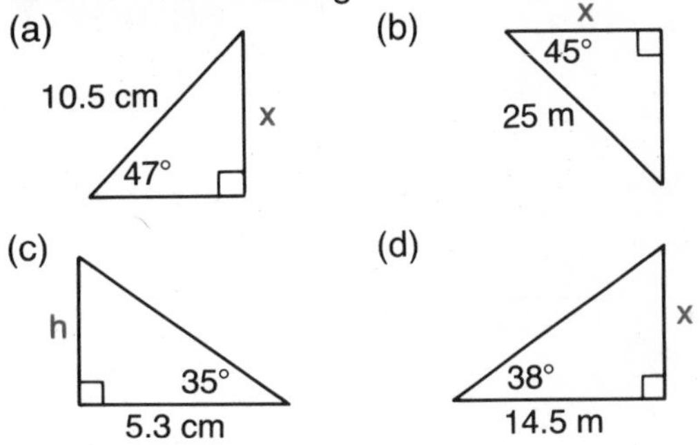

7. Find the measure of ∠θ to the nearest degree.

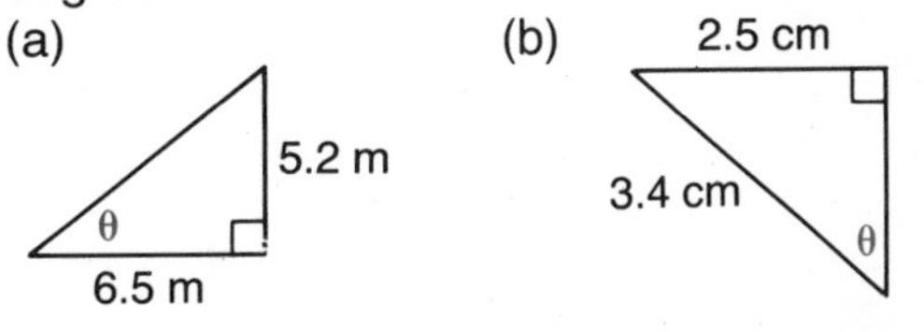

8. Solve the following triangles.

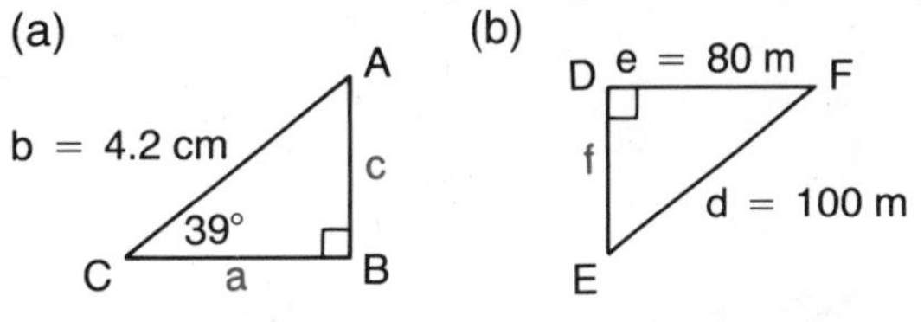

9. Solve △ABC, given
∠A = 90°, b = 7.0 m, c = 3.0 m

10. Solve △DEF, given
∠D = 35°, ∠E = 90°, e = 20 m

11. A tree is broken by the wind. The top of the tree touches the ground 13 m from the base and makes an angle of 30° with the ground.
Find the original height of the tree.

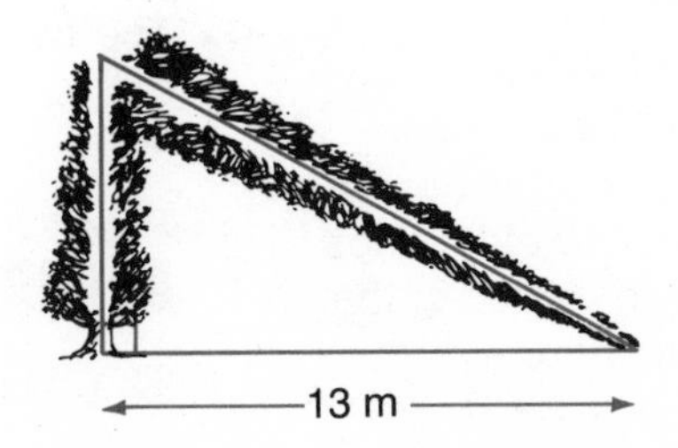

8.7 RECIPROCAL TRIGONOMETRIC RATIOS

Many problems in trigonometry are solved using the reciprocals of the primary trigonometric ratios.

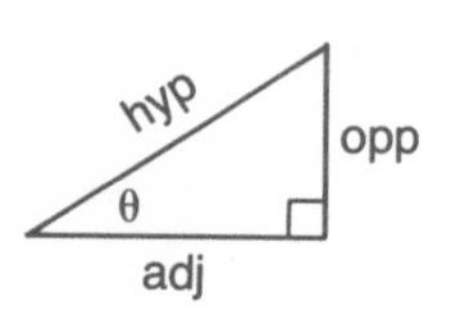

Primary Ratios	Reciprocal Ratios
$\sin\theta = \dfrac{\text{opp}}{\text{hyp}}$	$\text{cosecant}\ \theta = \csc\theta = \dfrac{\text{hyp}}{\text{opp}}$
$\cos\theta = \dfrac{\text{adj}}{\text{hyp}}$	$\text{secant}\ \theta = \sec\theta = \dfrac{\text{hyp}}{\text{adj}}$
$\tan\theta = \dfrac{\text{opp}}{\text{adj}}$	$\text{cotangent}\ \theta = \cot\theta = \dfrac{\text{adj}}{\text{opp}}$

Example 1. State the six trigonometric ratios of the angle θ in △ABC.

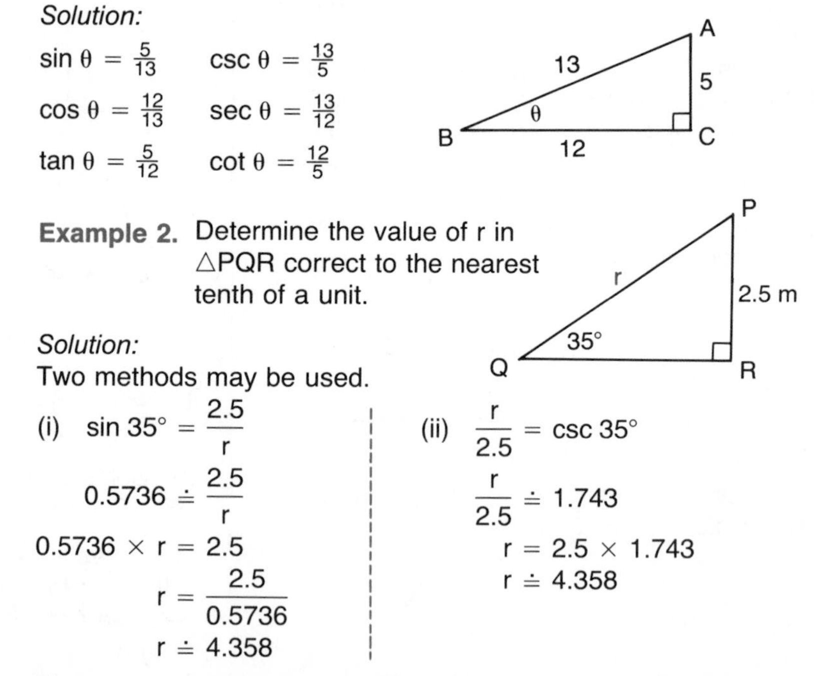

Solution:

$\sin\theta = \frac{5}{13}$ $\quad \csc\theta = \frac{13}{5}$

$\cos\theta = \frac{12}{13}$ $\quad \sec\theta = \frac{13}{12}$

$\tan\theta = \frac{5}{12}$ $\quad \cot\theta = \frac{12}{5}$

Example 2. Determine the value of r in △PQR correct to the nearest tenth of a unit.

Solution:

Two methods may be used.

E=mc²

(i)
$$\sin 35° = \frac{2.5}{r}$$
$$0.5736 \doteq \frac{2.5}{r}$$
$$0.5736 \times r = 2.5$$
$$r = \frac{2.5}{0.5736}$$
$$r \doteq 4.358$$

(ii)
$$\frac{r}{2.5} = \csc 35°$$
$$\frac{r}{2.5} \doteq 1.743$$
$$r = 2.5 \times 1.743$$
$$r \doteq 4.358$$

The value of r is approximately 4.4 m.

The calculation using cosecant θ involves less manipulation.

Using a calculator, $\sin 35° = \dfrac{2.5}{r}$ and so $r = 2.5 \div \sin 35°$.

Press

2 · 5 ÷ 3 5 sin =

The display is 4.358616989

For convenience, tables of values for trigonometric ratios are provided in the Appendix.

EXERCISE 8.7

A 1. Using tables or calculators, find the following values:

(a) csc 46°	(b) cot 89°
(c) tan 30°	(d) csc 45°
(e) sin 55°	(f) csc 90°
(g) sec 5°	(h) cot 72°
(i) sec 18°	(j) cot 90°
(k) sec 80°	(l) cot 8°

2. Find the measure of the angle θ to the nearest degree.

(a) $\sec\theta = 2.559$	(b) $\csc\theta = 1.325$
(c) $\cot\theta = 57.2900$	(d) $\csc\theta = 2.669$
(e) $\cot\theta = 0.7265$	(f) $\tan\theta = 11.4209$
(g) $\tan\theta = 0.5317$	(h) $\sec\theta = 1.0263$

B 3. Determine the length of the indicated side in each triangle to the nearest tenth of a unit.

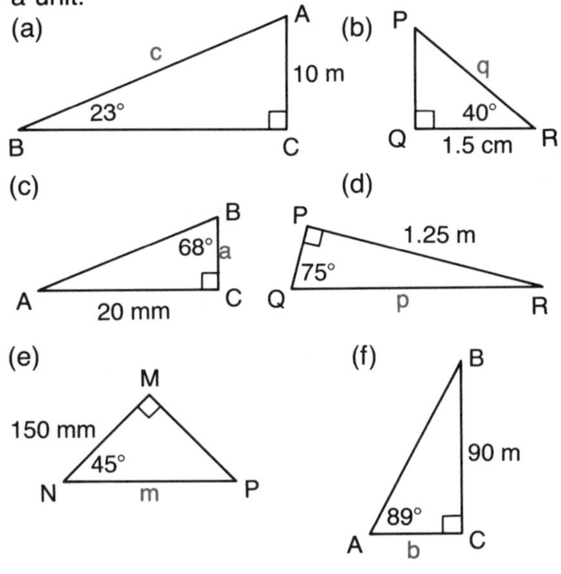

4. A supporting guy wire makes an angle of 39° with the ground. If the height of the tower is 95 m, calculate the length of the guy wire to the nearest tenth of a metre.

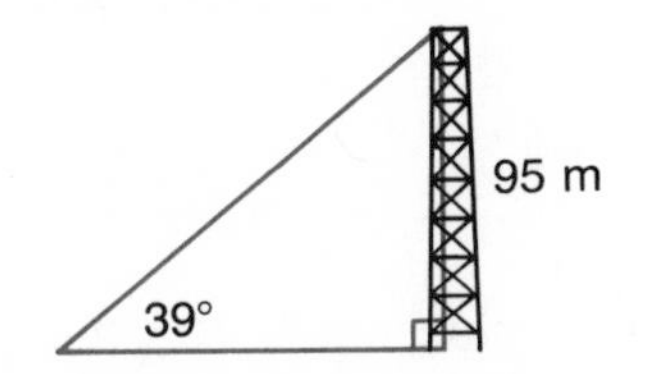

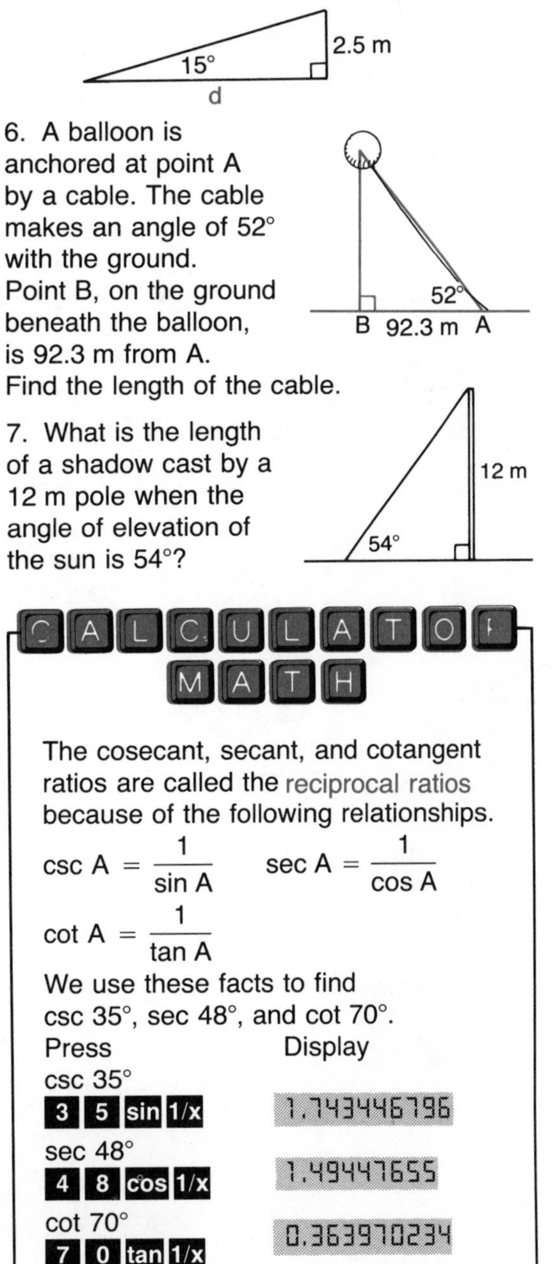

5. A ramp to a loading platform must reach a height of 2.5 m.
If the ramp angle is 15°, calculate the horizontal distance the ramp must extend, correct to the nearest tenth of a metre.

6. A balloon is anchored at point A by a cable. The cable makes an angle of 52° with the ground.
Point B, on the ground beneath the balloon, is 92.3 m from A.
Find the length of the cable.

7. What is the length of a shadow cast by a 12 m pole when the angle of elevation of the sun is 54°?

CALCULATOR MATH

The cosecant, secant, and cotangent ratios are called the reciprocal ratios because of the following relationships.

$$\csc A = \frac{1}{\sin A} \qquad \sec A = \frac{1}{\cos A}$$

$$\cot A = \frac{1}{\tan A}$$

We use these facts to find csc 35°, sec 48°, and cot 70°.

Press	Display
csc 35°	
3 5 sin 1/x	1.743446796
sec 48°	
4 8 cos 1/x	1.49447655
cot 70°	
7 0 tan 1/x	0.363970234

8.8 APPLICATIONS OF TRIGONOMETRY

Trigonometry can be used to solve problems which can be expressed as a diagram containing triangles. As we saw in earlier sections, we can calculate the height of a flagpole without actually climbing the pole. The figure shows some of the terminology which will be used in the work which follows.

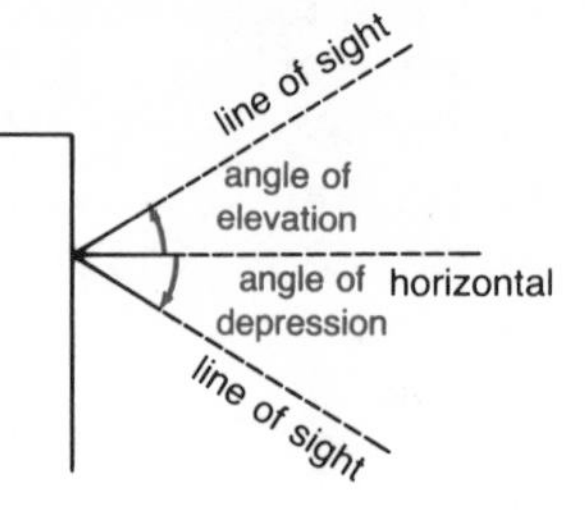

When measuring angles, a surveyor uses an instrument called a transit, or theodolite. In practice this means that the height of the instrument (HI) must be taken into account. A simple measuring device can be constructed using a blackboard protractor. Two nails serve as sights, and a plumb bob is attached to the centre. Note that the scale on the protractor has been changed so that when you are sighting along the horizontal, the angle of elevation will read 0°.

nails for sighting

90

90

0

plumb bob

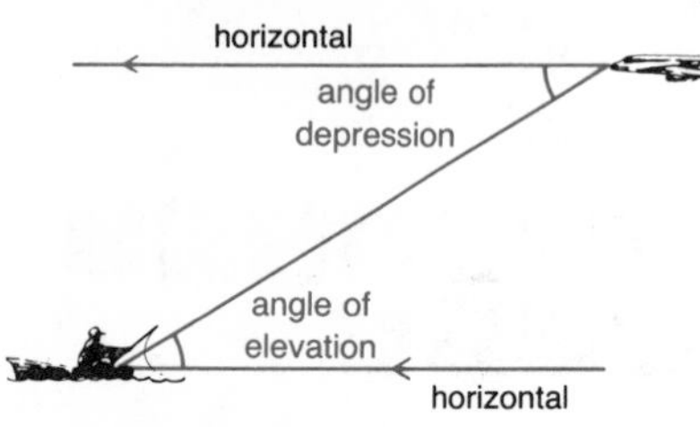

Examples 1 and 2 show how a surveyor can find the height of inaccessible objects such as tall buildings, cliffs, or flagpoles using only information which is recorded on the ground. The readings were taken using steel measuring tapes to measure the lengths and transits to measure angles.

In this illustration, the angles of elevation and depression are alternate angles and so have equal measure.

Example 1. In the given diagram, a transit was set up at T to find the height of a flagpole. The length AB was measured and found to be 14.6 m. The angle at A was measured and recorded as $\angle CAB = 32°$. The height of the instrument, HI, is 1.24 m. What is the height of the flagpole?

Solution:
Let $BC = h$, $AB = 14.6$ m
and $\angle CAB = 32°$.

$$\frac{h}{14.6} = \tan 32°$$

$$h = 14.6 \times \tan 32°$$
$$\doteq 14.6 \times 0.6249$$
$$= 9.12354$$

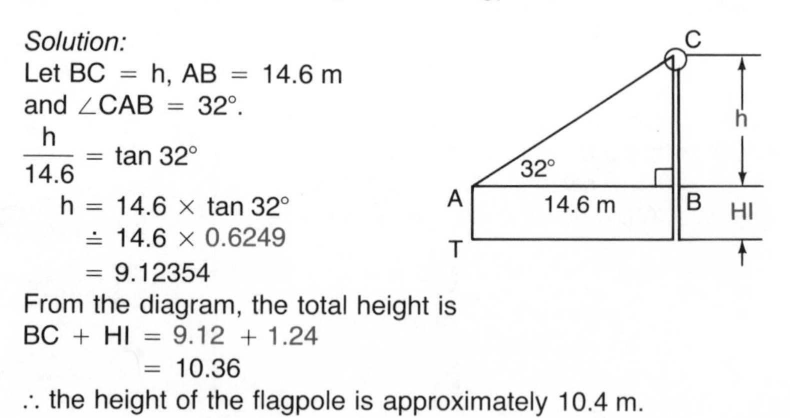

From the diagram, the total height is

$$BC + HI = 9.12 + 1.24$$
$$= 10.36$$

$\therefore$ the height of the flagpole is approximately 10.4 m.

Example 2. The accompanying diagram shows how a surveyor takes readings to find the height of an inaccessible cliff BC. The transit was set up at A and ∠CAB was measured and found to be 65°. Because AB could not be measured, it was found indirectly by laying off a baseline AD as in the diagram. With the transit set up at D, AD and ∠ADB are measured.

The following readings were recorded.

In △ABC, ∠CAB = 65°
∠ABC = 90°

In △ABD, ∠ADB = 37°
AD = 62 m
∠BAD = 90°

Find the height of the cliff.

Solution:
First find the length of AB using ∠ABD.
Use the calculated value of AB and find BC using ∠ABC.

In △ADB, $\frac{AB}{62} = \tan 37°$

$AB = 62 \times \tan 37°$
$\doteq 62 \times 0.7536$
$\doteq 46.7$

In △ABC, $\frac{BC}{AB} = \tan 65°$

$\frac{BC}{46.7} = \tan 65°$

$BC = 46.7 \times \tan 65°$
$\doteq 46.7 \times 2.1445$
$\doteq 100.1$

∴ the height of the cliff is 100 m.

To use a calculator, we substitute for AB before calculating, since AB = 62 × tan 37° and BC = AB × tan 65°
= (62 × tan 37°) × tan 65°

Press

6 2 × 3 7 tan × 6 5 tan =

The display is 100.1921163

Example 3. Each section of a sharp V thread is composed of equilateral triangles. Calculate the depth of cut, d, if the pitch of the thread is 0.250 cm.

Solution:

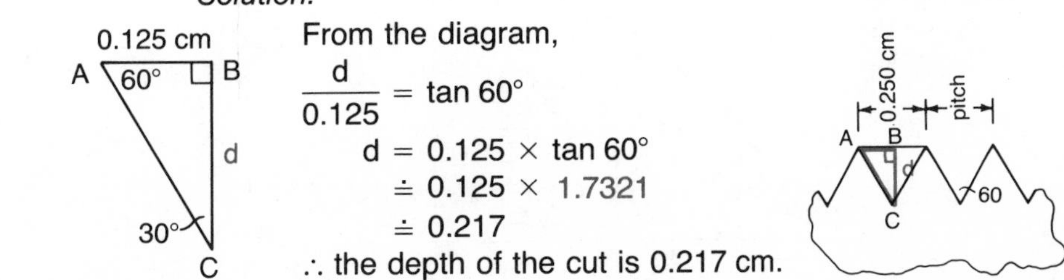

From the diagram,

$\frac{d}{0.125} = \tan 60°$

$d = 0.125 \times \tan 60°$
$\doteq 0.125 \times 1.7321$
$\doteq 0.217$

∴ the depth of the cut is 0.217 cm.

E=mc²

Example 4. Calculate the distance between the centres of the holes on a 20 cm bolt circle containing nine holes.

Solution:

The radius of the circle is 10 cm; the angle at the centre can be found when the number of holes is known.

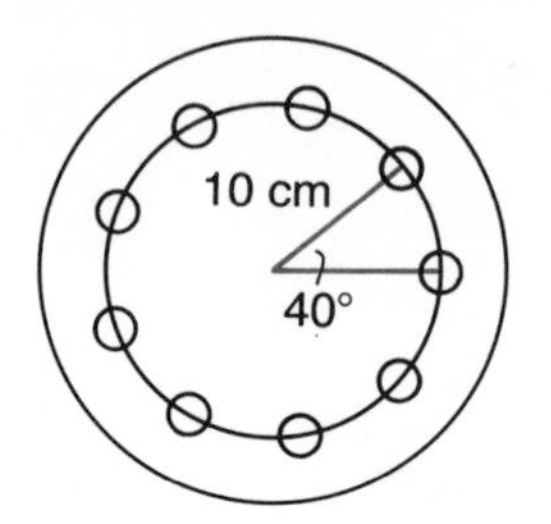

Angle at centre $= \dfrac{360°}{9} = 40°.$

If x represents one-half the distance between the holes (often called chordal distance), then

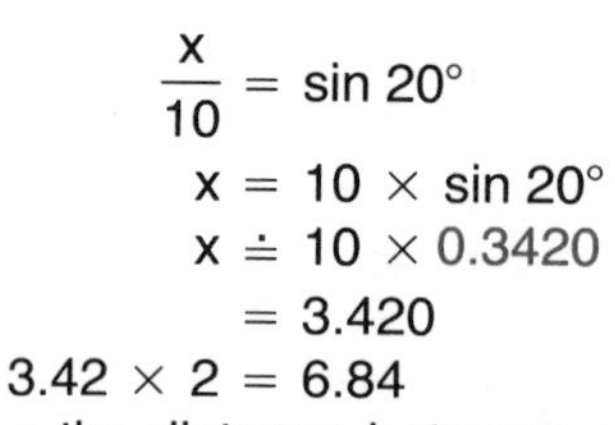

$$\frac{x}{10} = \sin 20°$$
$$x = 10 \times \sin 20°$$
$$x \doteq 10 \times 0.3420$$
$$= 3.420$$
$$3.42 \times 2 = 6.84$$

$\therefore$ the distance between centres is 6.84 cm.

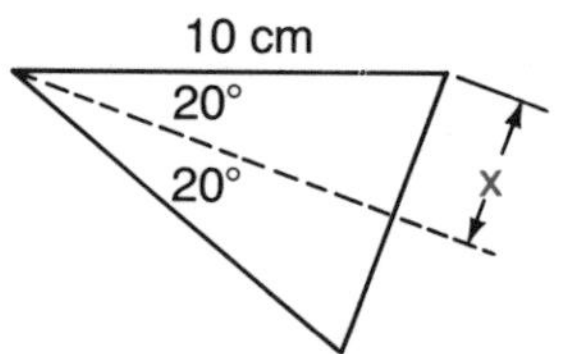

EXERCISE 8.8

B 1. From the top of a fire tower, the angle of depression of a cabin is observed to be 27°.
Find the distance from the cabin to the tower if the tower is 75 m high.

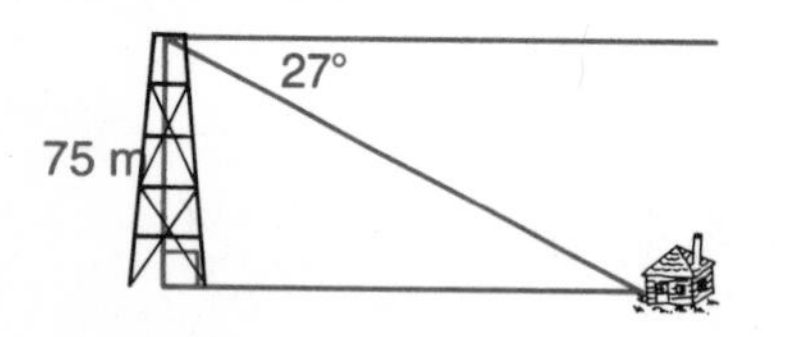

2. From a point 100 m from the foot of a building, the angles of elevation of the top and bottom of the building's flagpole are 42° and 39° respectively.
Calculate the height of:
(a) the building,
(b) the flagpole.

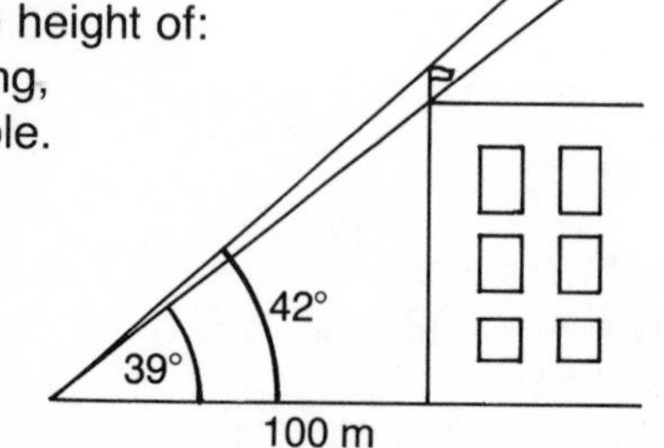

3. From the top of a cliff 70 m high the angles of depression of two small boats on the water are 8° and 13°.
Calculate the distance:
(a) from the bottom of the cliff to the closer boat
(b) between the boats.

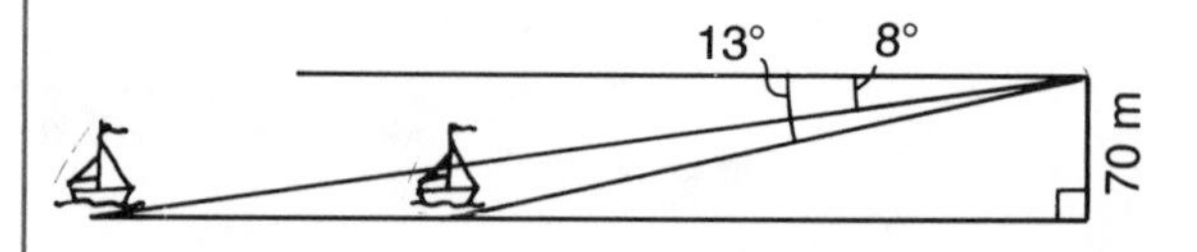

4. Ten holes are to be evenly spaced on a 20 cm bolt circle.
Calculate the distance between centres of two adjacent holes, AB.

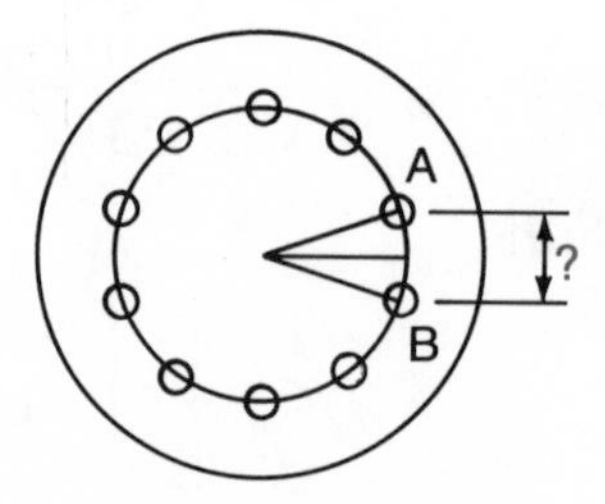

5. A pilot observes the measure of the angle of depression of a marker to be 36°. The plane is 2000 m above the ground.

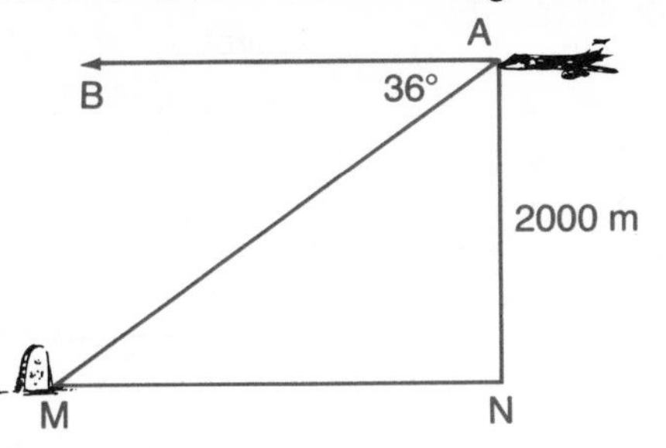

(a) How far from the marker is the point on the ground directly beneath the plane?
(b) Find the length of the line of sight to the marker.

6. Three holes are to be located in a rectangular plate as shown. When hole A has been bored, the table carrying the plate is moved horizontally the distance a so that hole C can be bored. The table is then moved vertically so that hole B can be bored.
Find the dimensions a and b (centimetres).

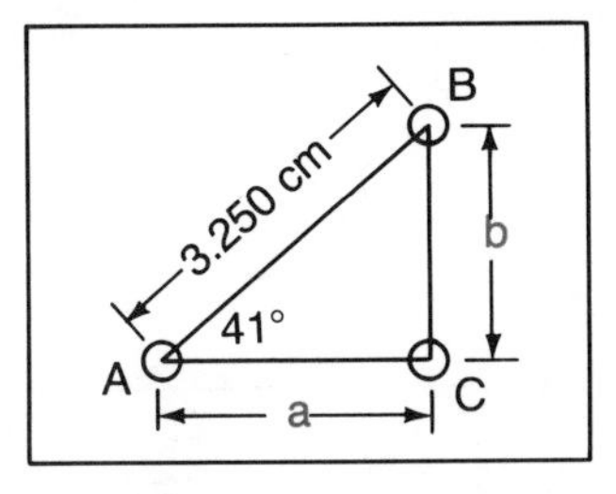

7. Find the indicated angle in the wedge as shown. Use a right triangle.

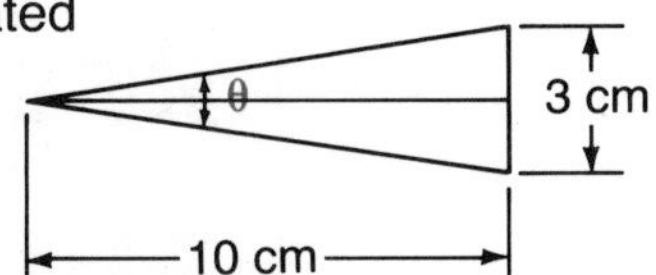

8. Calculations for tapers are similar to those for wedges.
Calculate the angles marked A and D to the nearest degree for the conical taper to be turned in a lathe.

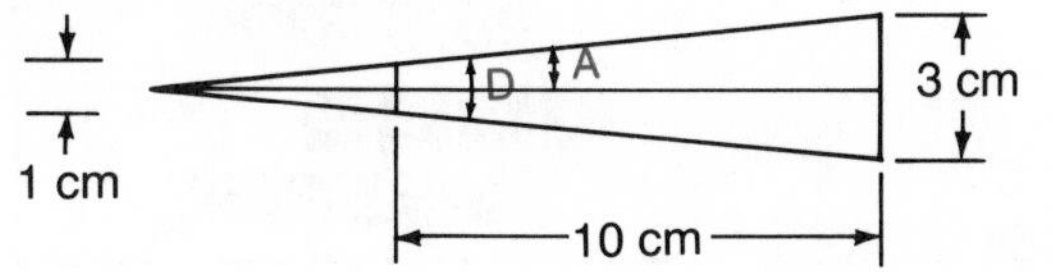

9. (a) Find the angle marked θ.
(b) Find the length marked x.

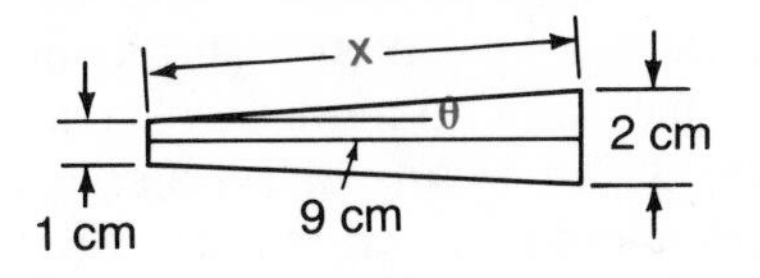

10. Calculate the measurement x in the given diagram of a template.

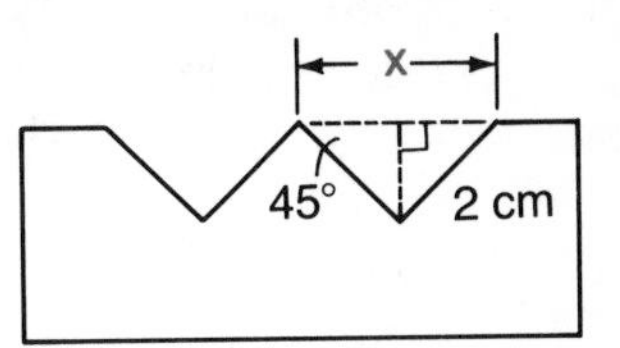

11. In the given jig-plate, two holes must be drilled as shown. Calculate the distances marked x and y if the distance between centres is 6.25 cm.

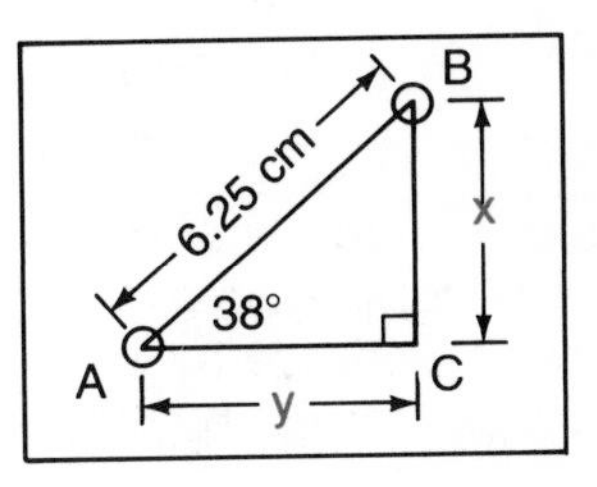

12. Calculate the distance between the centres of two adjacent holes on a five-hole bolt circle with diameter 14 cm.

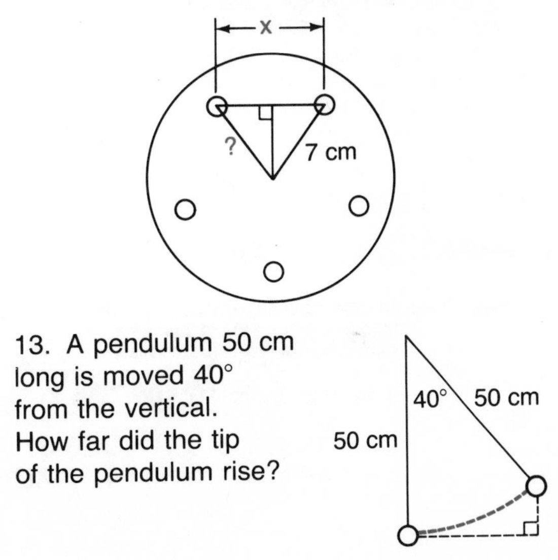

13. A pendulum 50 cm long is moved 40° from the vertical. How far did the tip of the pendulum rise?

8.9 ANGLES AND DEGREE MEASURE

Angle measure is the amount of rotation of a ray about the vertex. Rotation can be measured in degrees, which can be divided into decimal parts as on a calculator, or into 60 equal parts called minutes. Each minute can be subdivided into 60 equal parts called seconds. Note the symbols for degrees, minutes, and seconds in the table.

1 rotation = 360°
1° = 60′
1′ = 60″
degrees (°)
minutes (′)
seconds (″)

In order to convert from decimal degrees to degrees and minutes, we convert the decimal part of the measure to minutes. Since 1° = 60′, we multiply the decimal degrees by 60.

$$\begin{aligned} 36.4^\circ &= 36^\circ(0.4 \times 60)' \\ &= 36^\circ 24' \end{aligned}$$

Example 1. Express 25.64° in degrees, minutes, and seconds.

Solution:
$$\begin{aligned} 25.64^\circ &= 25^\circ(0.64 \times 60)' \\ &= 25^\circ 38.4' \\ &= 25^\circ 38'(0.4 \times 60)'' \\ &= 25^\circ 38' 24'' \end{aligned}$$

In order to convert from degrees, minutes, and seconds to decimal degrees, for use on a calculator, we convert the seconds to minutes (divide by 60), and then convert the minutes to degrees (divide by 60).

Example 2. Express 53°21′45″ in decimal degrees.

Solution:
$$\begin{aligned} 53^\circ 21' 45'' &= 53^\circ\left(21 + \frac{45}{60}\right)' \\ &= 53^\circ 21.75' \\ &= \left(53 + \frac{21.75}{60}\right)^\circ \\ &\doteq 53.3625^\circ \end{aligned}$$

Example 3. Find ∠A if sin A = 0.2657.

Solution: Using a calculator, press
[·] [2] [6] [5] [7] [inv] [sin]

The display is 15.40855105

$$\begin{aligned} \therefore \sin 15.40855105^\circ &= 0.2657 \\ 15.40855105^\circ &= 15^\circ(0.40855105 \times 60)' \\ &\doteq 15^\circ 24.51306312' \\ &= 15^\circ 24'(0.51306312 \times 60)'' \\ &\doteq 15^\circ 24' 31'' \end{aligned}$$

[·] [2] [6] [5] [7] [inv] [sin]
15.40855105
[−] [1] [5] [=]
0.408551052
[×] [6] [0] [=]
24.51306314
[−] [2] [4] [=]
0.513063144
[×] [6] [0] [=]
30.78378864

EXERCISE 8.9

B

1. Change each of the following to degrees and minutes.

(a) 53.5°	(b) 24.6°
(c) 67.8°	(d) 25.4°
(e) 48.1°	(f) 63.9°

2. Change each of the following to decimal degrees.

(a) 35°24′	(b) 55°42′
(c) 15°36′	(d) 65°54′
(e) 23°30′	(f) 45°36′

3. Change each of the following to degrees, minutes, and seconds.

(a) 35.25°	(b) 16.75°
(c) 24.27°	(d) 72.81°
(e) 46.87°	(f) 52.29°

4. Change each of the following to decimal degrees.

(a) 37°14′15″	(b) 73°25′8″
(c) 26°42′35″	(d) 27°52′16″
(e) 53°7′35″	(f) 43°54′54″

5. Using a calculator, find each of the following to 3 decimal places.

(a) sin 24°45′	(b) cos 36°24′
(c) tan 18°54′	(d) cos 53°18′
(e) sin 42°48′	(f) tan 24°24′

6. Using a calculator, find each of the following to 4 decimal places.

(a) cos 34°25′18″	(b) tan 53°25′24″
(c) cos 63°32′36″	(d) sin 45°51′42″
(e) tan 24°34′54″	(f) sin 63°45′6″

7. Find the value of the angle correct to the nearest minute.

(a) tan A = 0.8546	(b) sin B = 0.4738
(c) cos C = 0.5225	(d) tan D = 1.6424
(e) sin E = 0.4271	(f) tan F = 1.1234
(g) cos G = 0.4572	(h) sin H = 0.1375

8. Find the value of the angle correct to the nearest second.

(a) sin A = 0.7253	(b) cos B = 0.4264
(c) tan C = 1.8501	(d) tan D = 0.8501
(e) cos E = 0.6318	(f) tan F = 1.2473

9. Lighthouse C is due west from ship A. Lighthouse B, which is due north of C, is so situated that ∠CAB = 25°37′. The distance from C to B is 13.7 km.

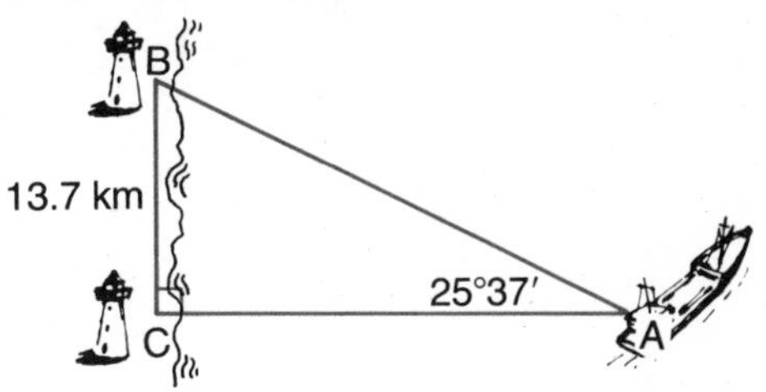

How far is the ship from C? How far is it from B?

ACCURACY AND PRECISION

When working with theoretical examples, we usually assume that the data are exact. In practical examples, calculators often give us more accuracy than is reasonable to expect. In these cases, we need to consider the implied accuracy of the answers in comparison with the numbers used. If the context of the problem does not supply information about the precision of the numbers involved, then approximations made in the process of calculation should assume that the original data were exact.

When working with angles in the degree system, the following guide is used in conjunction with our rounding rules.

Where lengths are rounded to:	The accuracy of angles is to the nearest:
1 significant digit	10°
2 significant digits	1°
3 significant digits	0.1° or 6′
4 significant digits	0.01° or 30″

8.10 PROBLEM SOLVING

1. The rectangle is divided into squares.

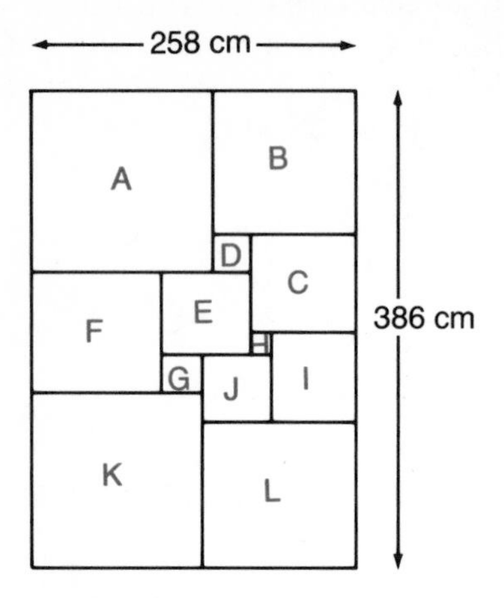

Square A has an area of 20 736 cm^2.
Square K has an area of 19 044 cm^2.
Find the area of each of the other squares.

2. When the numbers 47 and 2 are multiplied they give

$47 \times 2 = 94$

When added they give the reverse answer.

$47 + 2 = 49$

Find two more pairs of numbers, all of which are less than 25, that have this property.

3. Shawna bought a radio for $164 and paid for it with 11 bills.
What bills did she use?

4. The theatre arts class sells tickets to a play as part of the regular fund raising. If they charge $3.00 per ticket, 500 people will attend. For each $1.00 increase in the price of a ticket, the attendance will drop by 50.
Find to the nearest fifty cents, the price of the ticket that will give the greatest gross receipts.

5. Jean opened a book where the product of the two page numbers was 5256.
At what pages did she open the book?

6. A small plane dropped a water bomb on a forest fire from point F.

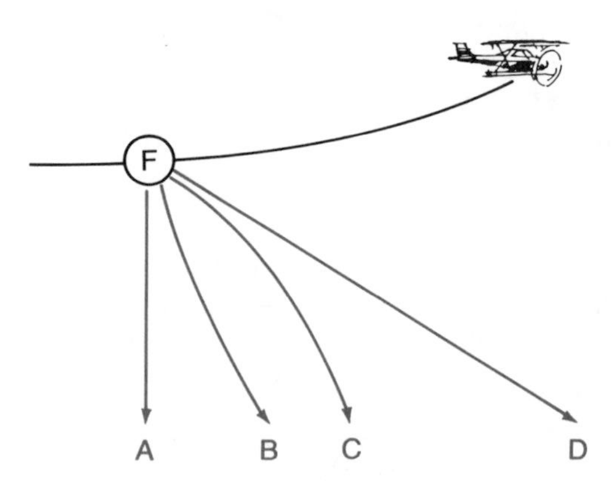

In which direction will the water bomb fall — A, B, C, or D?

7. The numbers 22 and 23 are consecutive numbers that add to 45.
What other consecutive whole numbers add to 45?

8. Three students, Brown, Black, and White, have a brown dog, a black dog, and a white dog. None of them have a dog the same colour as their name.
If White doesn't have a black dog, what colour is Black's dog?

9. The diagram below shows two ways in which four stamps can be attached.

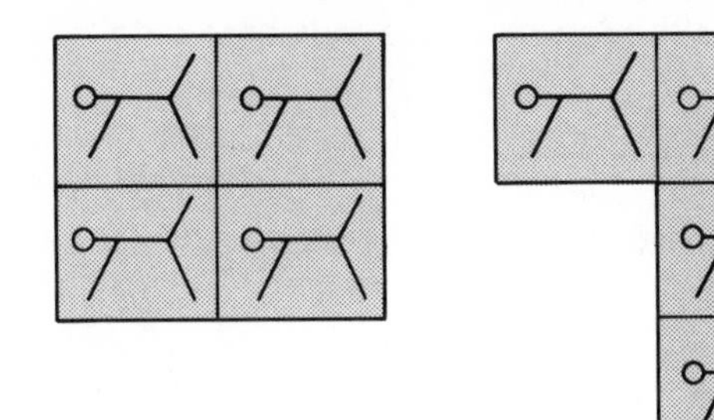

Draw diagrams to show the other possible different ways that four stamps can be attached.

10. Hot dog rolls can be bought in packages of 8 or 6. Mark bought 48 rolls in 7 packages.
How many packages of each did he buy?

11. Place 6 dots in the following figure so that there will be no more than one dot in each row, column, or diagonal.

12. (a) Find all possible solutions to the following multiplication.

$$AAAA \times AA = ABBBA$$

(b) Find all possible solutions to the following multiplication.

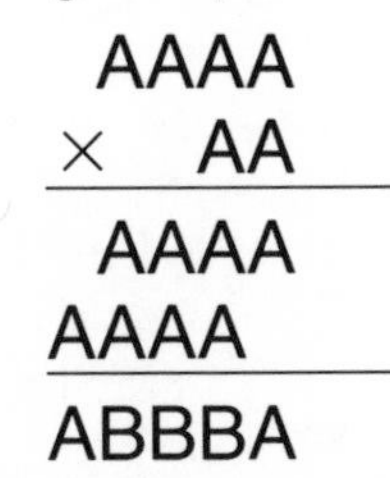

CAREER

DRAFTER

Sonja Maki is a drafter. She prepares detailed drawings based on readings, sketches, and information provided by other people. Sonja uses her knowledge of geometry, scale, and ratio along with ruler, compass, protractor, and other drafting instruments in order to prepare these drawings.

In order to provide clear, accurate drawings, drafters need to be able to draw three-dimensional objects freehand, and to work with a high degree of neatness and accuracy.

EXERCISE

1. Copy the following sketches freehand, then make accurate drawings.

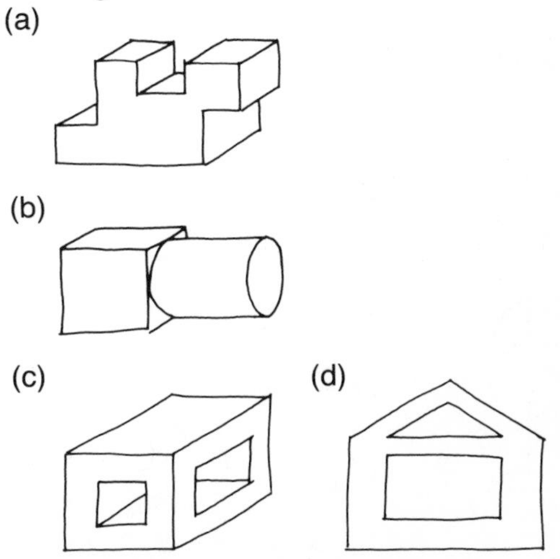

2. (a) Draw the top, bottom, and four sides of a shipping container whose dimensions are 2.4 m by 3.2 m by 8.6 m.
(b) Calculate the surface area and volume of the container.

8.11 REVIEW EXERCISE

1. Calculate the indicated lengths using similar triangles.

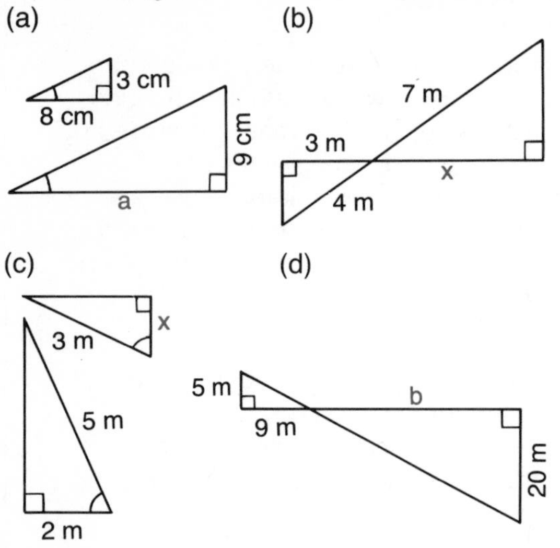

2. State the six trigonometric ratios for each of the following.

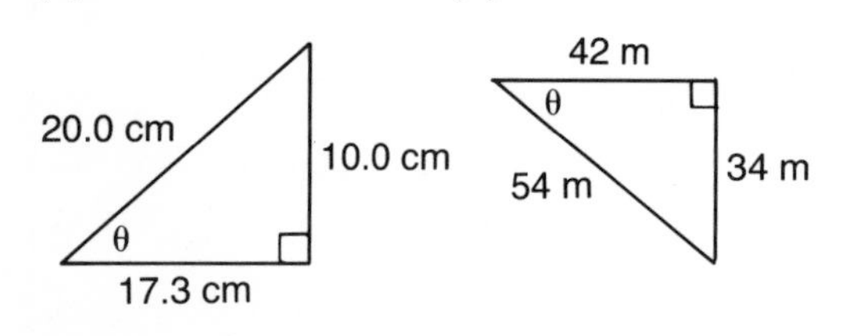

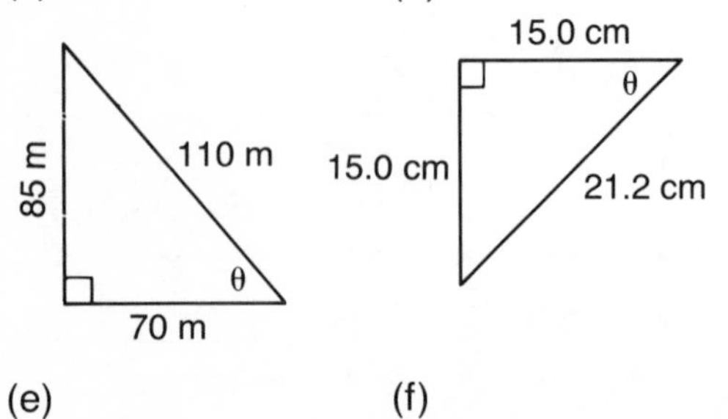

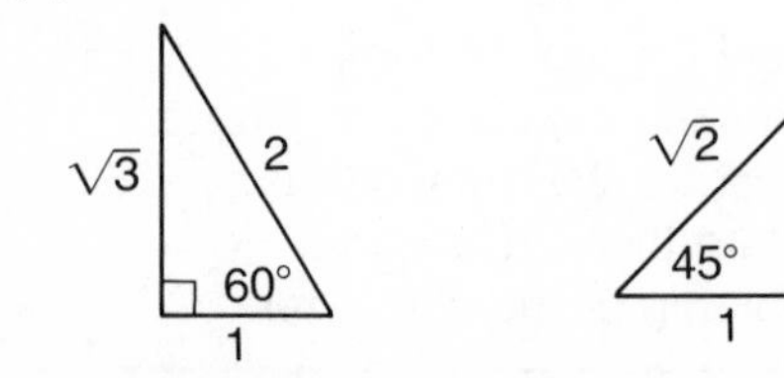

3. Find the length of the indicated side.

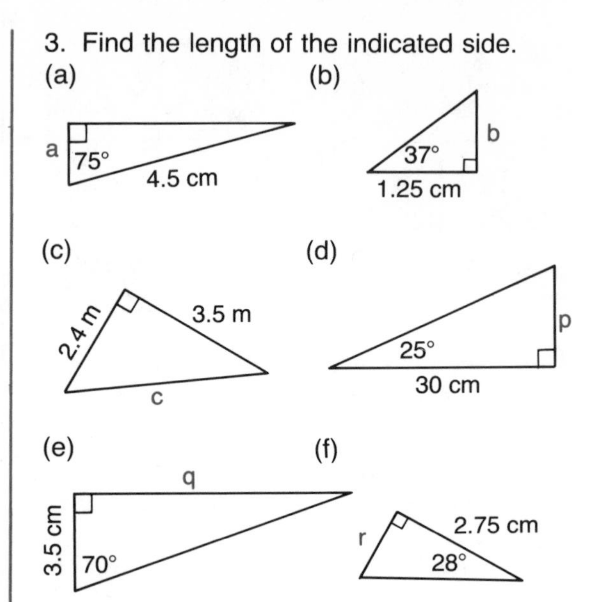

4. Find the measure of the indicated angle to the nearest degree.

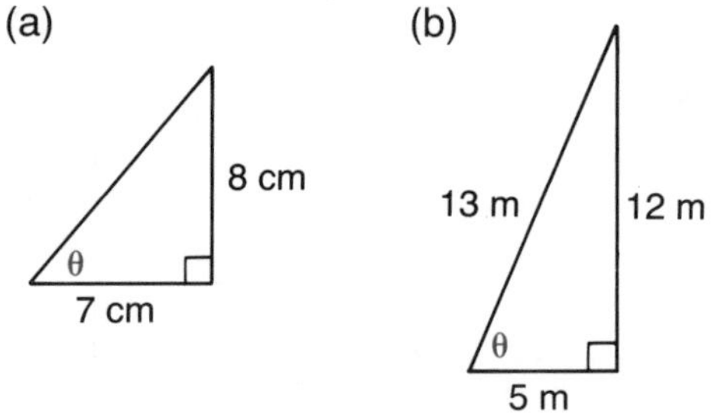

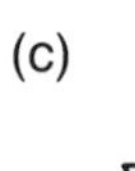

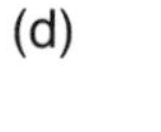

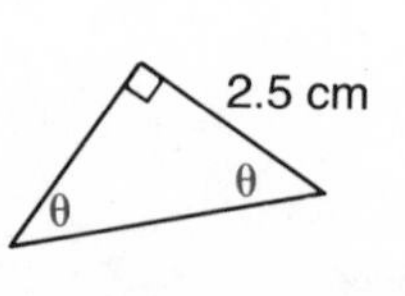

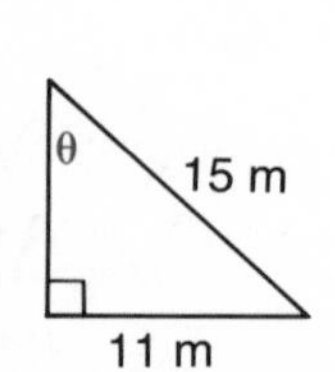

5. If the length of the hole xy is 4 cm and the hole is at an angle of 50°, calculate the thickness of the work xz.

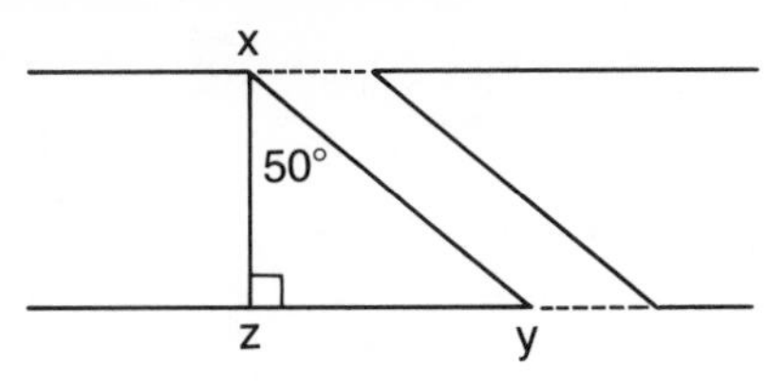

6. From the top of a cliff 300 m high, the angle of depression of a boat is 22°. Calculate the distance, x, from the boat to the foot of the cliff.

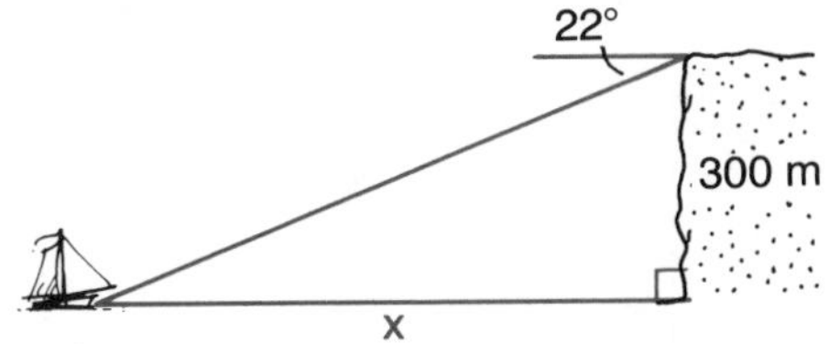

7. The shadow of a tree is 12 m when the angle of elevation of the sun is 68°. Calculate the height of the tree.

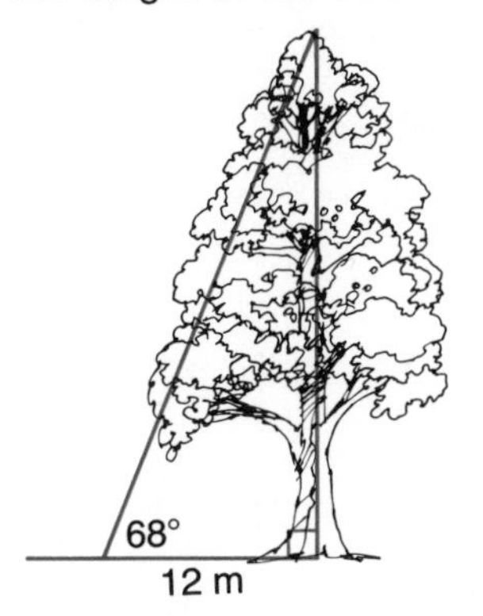

8. The diagram shows the readings which were taken to find the height of a building AD. What is the height of the building?

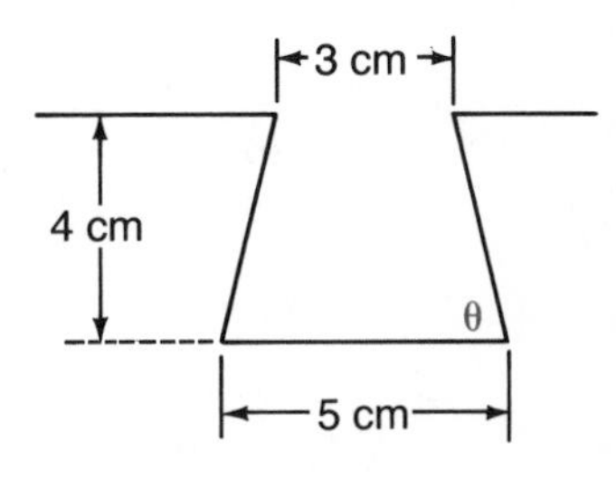

9. Calculate the distance between the centres of two adjacent holes on a nine-hole bolt circle with diameter 24.0 cm.

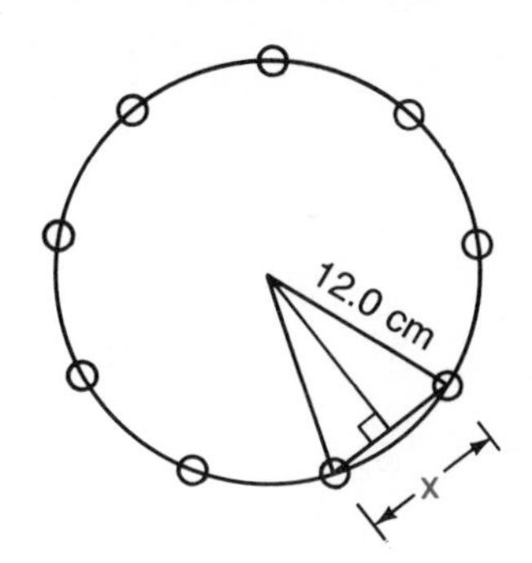

10. Calculate the angle of taper from the diagram.

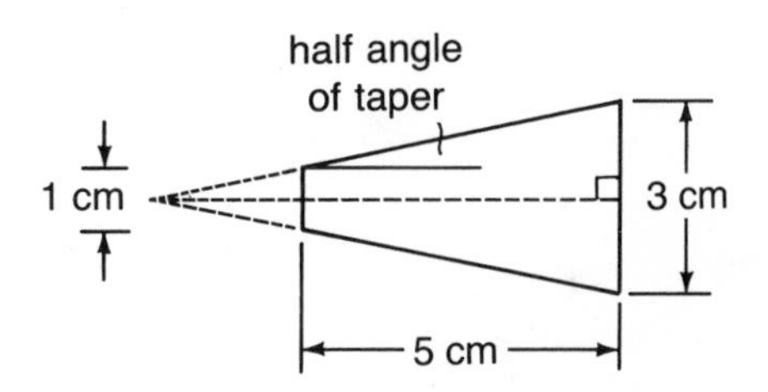

11. Calculate the angle in the dovetail in the diagram.

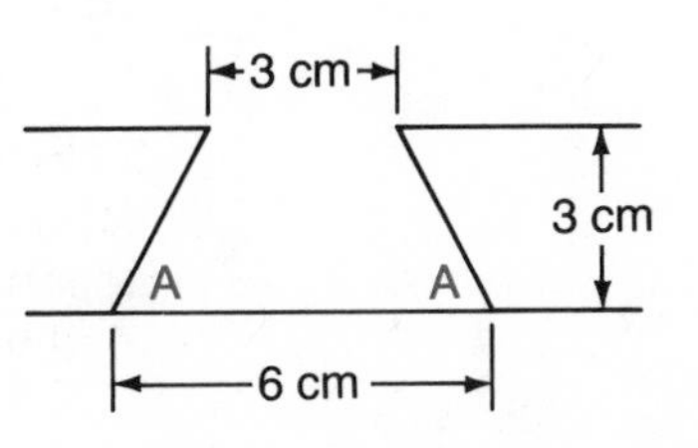

12. Find the indicated angles, A, in the dovetail slide in the diagram.

8.12 CHAPTER 8 TEST

1. State the following.

(a) $\sin \theta$

(b) $\cos \theta$

(c) $\tan \theta$

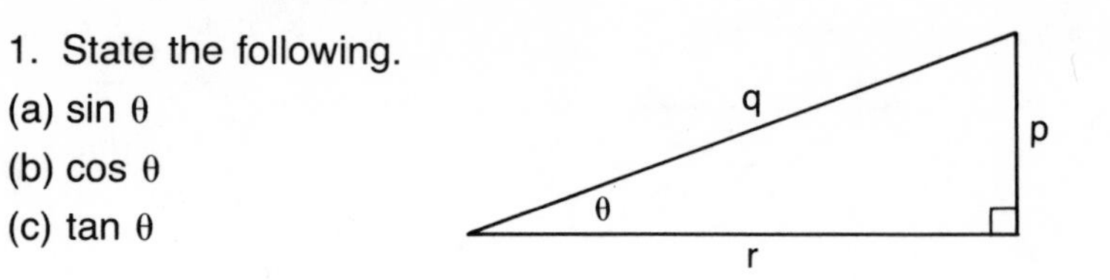

2. If $\sin \theta = \frac{5}{13}$, find

(a) $\cos \theta$

(b) $\tan \theta$

3. (a) Solve for x.

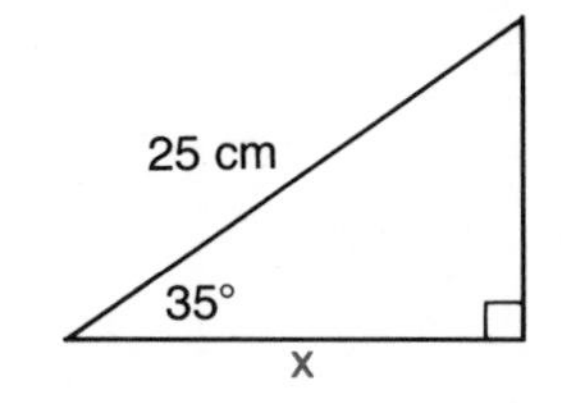

(b) Find θ to the nearest degree.

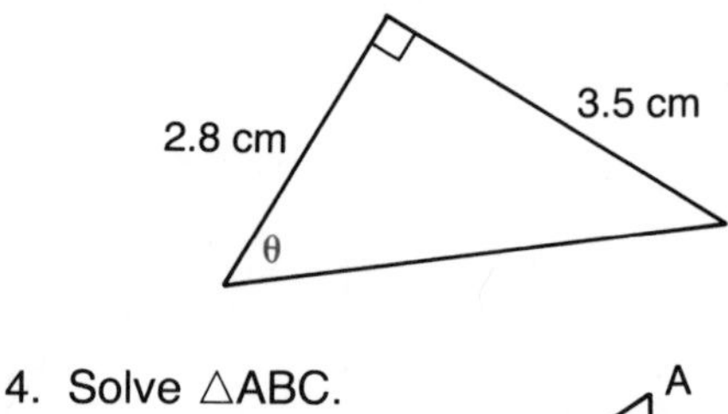

4. Solve $\triangle ABC$.

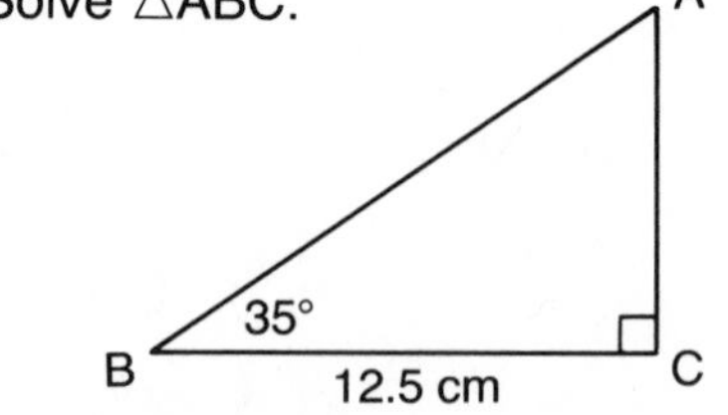

5. At a point 15.5 m from the foot of a building, the angle of elevation of the top of the building is 68°.
What is the height of the building?

6. From the top of a cliff 112 m high, the angles of depression of two boats on the water in the same line as the observer are 31° and 42°.
Find the distance between the boats.

STATISTICS

REVIEW AND PREVIEW TO CHAPTER 9

BASIC OPERATIONS

EXERCISE

1. Express the following sets of numbers from smallest to largest.
(a) 15, 22, 17, 46, 21, 9, 85, 11, 28, 20, 75
(b) 33, 24, 56, 33, 29, 85, 24, 47, 31, 83, 85, 9
(c) $\frac{1}{2}, \frac{3}{4}, \frac{5}{8}, \frac{7}{16}, \frac{1}{4}, \frac{3}{16}, \frac{5}{32}$

2. Add.

(a)
$$\begin{array}{r} 3.256 \\ 25.270 \\ 0.635 \\ \underline{21.600} \end{array}$$

(b)
$$\begin{array}{r} 325.600 \\ 61.250 \\ 45.267 \\ 312.700 \\ \underline{8.400} \end{array}$$

(c)
$$\begin{array}{r} 0.257 \\ 21.635 \\ 6.250 \\ 512.700 \\ \underline{28.732} \end{array}$$

(d)
$$\begin{array}{r} 285.700 \\ 28.350 \\ 0.275 \\ 30.010 \\ \underline{624.800} \end{array}$$

3. Subtract.

(a)
$$\begin{array}{r} 358.25 \\ \underline{211.73} \end{array}$$

(b)
$$\begin{array}{r} 6.275 \\ \underline{4.712} \end{array}$$

(c)
$$\begin{array}{r} 58.75 \\ \underline{32.97} \end{array}$$

(d)
$$\begin{array}{r} 0.03741 \\ \underline{0.01248} \end{array}$$

4. Multiply.

(a)
$$\begin{array}{r} 358.2 \\ \underline{\times 0.75} \end{array}$$

(b)
$$\begin{array}{r} 0.2175 \\ \underline{\times 3.14} \end{array}$$

(c)
$$\begin{array}{r} 26.85 \\ \underline{\times 5.75} \end{array}$$

(d)
$$\begin{array}{r} 0.625 \\ \underline{\times 0.037} \end{array}$$

5. Divide to three significant figures.
(a) 358.7 by 2.75
(b) 38.25 by 0.281
(c) 0.2753 by 4.612
(d) 3.215 by 81.6

6. Simplify.
(a) $256 + 325 \times 15$
(b) $234 \times 518 + 24$
(c) $2128 \div 56 + 72$
(d) $533 - 8804 \div 71$
(e) $51 + 28 \times 56 + 32$
(f) $1175 \div 25 \div 47$

7. Add.
(a) $\frac{1}{2} + \frac{1}{3}$
(b) $\frac{3}{4} + \frac{5}{8}$
(c) $3\frac{1}{5} + 1\frac{1}{2}$
(d) $6\frac{1}{4} + 1\frac{7}{8}$
(e) $3\frac{2}{3} + 1\frac{1}{2}$
(f) $\frac{5}{8} + 2\frac{3}{4}$

8. Subtract.
(a) $\frac{3}{4} - \frac{1}{2}$
(b) $1\frac{1}{8} - \frac{3}{8}$
(c) $3\frac{3}{4} - 1\frac{1}{2}$
(d) $2\frac{2}{3} - 1\frac{5}{6}$
(e) $5\frac{1}{4} - 2\frac{1}{3}$
(f) $3\frac{1}{2} - 1\frac{1}{4}$

9. Multiply.
(a) $\frac{3}{4} \times \frac{2}{3}$
(b) $\frac{5}{8} \times \frac{1}{2}$
(c) $1\frac{1}{2} \times 1\frac{1}{3}$
(d) $2\frac{1}{4} \times 1\frac{1}{2}$
(e) $3\frac{5}{8} \times 1\frac{1}{4}$
(f) $2\frac{1}{2} \times 4$

10. Divide.
(a) $\frac{1}{2} \div \frac{1}{4}$
(b) $\frac{3}{4} \div \frac{5}{8}$
(c) $1\frac{1}{2} \div 2\frac{1}{2}$
(d) $2\frac{3}{4} \div 11$
(e) $3\frac{5}{8} \div 1\frac{1}{4}$
(f) $5 \div 2\frac{1}{2}$

11. Simplify.
(a) $\frac{3}{4} + \frac{5}{8} \times \frac{1}{2}$
(b) $1\frac{1}{2} + 2\frac{2}{3} - 1\frac{5}{6}$
(c) $3\frac{3}{4} + 2\frac{5}{8} - 1\frac{1}{2}$
(d) $5\frac{1}{4} - 2\frac{7}{8} + 4$

CALCULATOR MATH

ROOTS

To evaluate $\sqrt{325.6}$
press 3 2 5 · 6 √

The display is 18.0443897

Alternatively, the following key sequence could be entered:
3 2 5 · 6 yˣ .5 =

The display is 18.0443897

EXERCISE

Evaluate to three significant figures.

1. $\sqrt{385.6}$
2. $\sqrt[4]{27.69}$
3. $\sqrt[8]{583.2}$
4. $\sqrt[4]{0.8176}$
5. $\sqrt[8]{6.8173}$
6. $(\sqrt{81.76})^3$
7. $(\sqrt[4]{156.8})^3$
8. $\sqrt{(94.32)^2}$
9. $\sqrt{(0.5813)^3}$
10. $\sqrt[4]{(56.48)^3}$

MICRO MATH

In BASIC, the square root function may be implemented using the expression "^.5". To find the $\sqrt{x}$ we enter "x^.5". Some versions of BASIC accept the command "SQR(X)", or "x^.5" as well.

The following program computes the $\sqrt{x}$.

```
NEW
10 PRINT "SQUARE ROOT"
20 INPUT "ENTER A NUMBER "; X
30 R = X^.5
40 PRINT "THE SQUARE ROOT IS  "; R
50 END
RUN

SQUARE ROOT
ENTER A NUMBER ? 625
THE SQUARE ROOT IS 25
```

SUMMATION NOTATION

$\sum_{n=3}^{7} n$ is read

"The sum of all n from n = 3 to 7."

$$\sum_{n=3}^{7} n = 3 + 4 + 5 + 6 + 7$$
$$= 25$$

Σ is the Greek letter "sigma" and corresponds to "s", the first letter of the word "sum."

EXERCISE

1. Write each of the following summations as additions.

(a) $\sum_{n=1}^{8} n$
(b) $\sum_{n=1}^{4} 2n$
(c) $\sum_{n=2}^{8} (3n + 1)$
(d) $\sum_{n=3}^{6} (4n - 3)$
(e) $\sum_{n=1}^{5} n^2$
(f) $\sum_{n=2}^{6} 3n^2$

2. Evaluate each of the following summations.

(a) $\sum_{n=1}^{5} n$
(b) $\sum_{n=2}^{6} (2 - n)$
(c) $\sum_{n=0}^{4} 2^n$
(d) $\sum_{n=1}^{7} (-1)^n$
(e) $\sum_{n=1}^{4} n^2$
(f) $\sum_{n=1}^{4} 5n^2$

3. Use the summation sign to write each of the following.

(a) $2 + 4 + 6 + 8 + 10 + 12$
(b) $2 + 4 + 8 + 16 + 32$
(c) $0 - 1 - 2 - 3 - 4 - 5$
(d) $\frac{1}{2} + \frac{1}{3} + \frac{1}{4} + \frac{1}{5}$
(e) $4^2 + 5^2 + 6^2 + 7^2 + 8^2 + 9^2$
(f) $\frac{1}{2^2} + \frac{1}{3^2} + \frac{1}{4^2} + \frac{1}{5^2} + \frac{1}{6^2}$

9.1 DATA GATHERING METHODS

The branch of mathematics called statistics is concerned with the collection of numerical facts, called data, the organization and presentation of these facts, and finally the interpretation of the data.

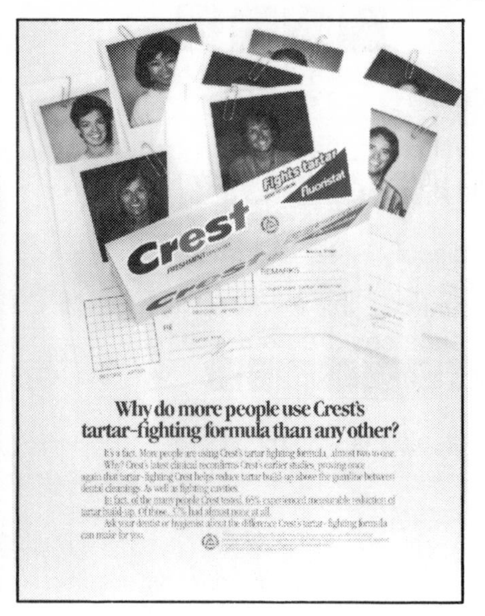

SAMPLING

It may be possible to test every item in a shipment of light bulbs, because after the test the bulb remains intact. In the case of explosives, it is not practical to test every item, because the explosive is consumed in the test. When it is either impossible or impractical to test all the items, data may be taken from a small representative group. A sample is a small group of individuals (or objects) selected to stand for a larger group called the population. When sampling a population, we must ensure that the sample is representative of the population.

There are several different ways to select a sample. Two of the most common are as follows.

Simple Random Sample: In a simple random sample, a percentage of the population is taken, using a method that gives each member of the population the same chance of being selected.

Stratified Sample: In a stratified sample, the population is divided by characteristics such as people aged 20 or under, people from 21 to 40, people over 40. These kinds of characteristics are called layers or strata and a sample is taken from each.

Data for the simple random and the stratified samples may be gathered through surveys, news articles or journals, or by recording the results of an experiment.

Example 1. The School Dance

(a) The dance committee at Meadowbank Secondary School decides to carry out a survey in order to estimate the number of students who will attend the next school dance. What is the population?

(b) A member of the committee proposes to go out and question the first 60 students encountered for the sample. Is this a simple random sample?

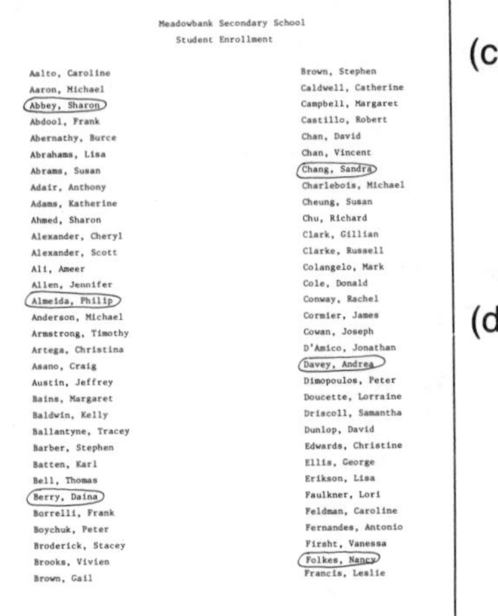
Meadowbank Secondary School
Student Enrollment

Aalto, Caroline
Aaron, Michael
Abbey, Sharon
Abdool, Frank
Abernathy, Burce
Abrahams, Lisa
Abrams, Susan
Adair, Anthony
Adams, Katherine
Ahmed, Sharon
Alexander, Cheryl
Alexander, Scott
Ali, Ameer
Allen, Jennifer
Almeida, Philip
Anderson, Michael
Armstrong, Timothy
Artega, Christina
Asano, Craig
Austin, Jeffrey
Bains, Margaret
Baldwin, Kelly
Ballantyne, Tracey
Barber, Stephen
Batten, Karl
Bell, Thomas
Berry, Daina
Borrelli, Frank
Boychuk, Peter
Broderick, Stacey
Brooks, Vivien
Brown, Gail
Brown, Stephen
Caldwell, Catherine
Campbell, Margaret
Castillo, Robert
Chan, David
Chan, Vincent
Chang, Sandra
Charlebois, Michael
Cheung, Susan
Chu, Richard
Clark, Gillian
Clarke, Russell
Colangelo, Mark
Cole, Donald
Conway, Rachel
Cormier, James
Cowan, Joseph
D'Amico, Jonathan
Davey, Andrea
Dimopoulos, Peter
Doucette, Lorraine
Driscoll, Samantha
Dunlop, David
Edwards, Christine
Ellis, George
Erikson, Lisa
Faulkner, Lori
Feldman, Caroline
Fernandes, Antonio
Firsht, Vanessa
Folkes, Nancy
Francis, Leslie

(c) Since the office keeps an alphabetical list of all 688 students attending the school, another member of the committee proposes to choose a number at random from 1 to 12, count that far down the list, taking that name and every 12th name after it for the sample. Is this a simple random sample?

(d) A third member of the committee suggests putting 688 equally sized tickets, numbered from 1 to 688, in a box. Then, after the tickets are mixed, 60 tickets are drawn and students are chosen from the list according to the numbers on the tickets. (For example, if the ticket numbered 37 is drawn then the 37th student on the list is selected for the sample.) Is this a simple random sample?

Solution:

(a) The population consists of all students attending the school.

(b) This is not a simple random sample. There is no way to calculate the chance that a particular person will get into the sample, and so there is no way of knowing if every person has the same chance of being selected. For instance, suppose the interviewer goes and stands at a definite place at a definite time. What is the chance that a particular student passes by? It is difficult or impossible to say.

(c) This is not a simple random sample. While nobody has any discretion as to who gets in the sample, this method is still not a simple random sample. For instance, two people whose names are adjacent on the list have no chance to get into the sample together. Chance enters into this sample in a planned way.

(d) This is a simple random sample. Every student has an equally likely chance of being selected. The selection of any particular student does not affect the chance of any other student being selected.

It should be pointed out that if the dance committee wants to ensure that all grade levels are adequately represented, then a stratified sample should be used.

Example 2. Information about the student population at Meadowbank Secondary School is given below.

	Grade 9	Grade 10	Grade 11	Grade 12	Total
Females	93	117	78	68	356
Males	87	89	85	71	332
Total	180	206	163	139	688

The dance committee decides to use a stratified sample of 60 students. The student population is divided according to grade level and sex, and the number of students surveyed from each group is to be proportional to the percentage of the school's students in that group.

(a) How many female students in grade 10 should be surveyed?

(b) How many grade 12 students, in total, should be surveyed?

(c) How many male students, in total, should be surveyed?

Solution:

(a) There are 117 female students in grade 10. The fraction of these students to total students is $\frac{117}{688}$, and the percentage is $\frac{117}{688} \times 100\% \doteq 17\%$. Since 60 students are to be surveyed, we calculate the number of female grade 10 students to be surveyed as 17% of 60.

$$60 \times \frac{17}{100} = 10.2$$
$$\doteq 10$$

$17\% = \frac{17}{100}$

$\therefore$ 10 female students in grade 10 should be surveyed.

(b) There are 139 students in grade 12.
As a percentage of total students this is

$$\frac{139}{688} \times 100\% \doteq 20.2\%$$

Multiplying by 60 we obtain:

$$60 \times \frac{20.2}{100} = 12.12$$
$$\doteq 12$$

$\therefore$ 12 students, in total, from grade 12 should be surveyed.

(c) There are 332 male students enrolled.
As a percentage of total students this is

$$\frac{332}{688} \times 100\% \doteq 48.3\%$$

Multiplying by 60 we obtain:

$$60 \times \frac{48.3}{100} = 28.98$$
$$\doteq 29$$

$\therefore$ 29 male students, in total, should be surveyed.

EXERCISE 9.1

B

1. One way to collect data is to take a survey.
What are some of the survey methods that can be used?

2. Sometimes when you take a sample of a population, and test the sample, the sample is destroyed.
List three examples of sampling where this would happen.

3. List three situations where the entire population would be sampled.

4. Data on meteorological observations may be found in a library. The following table shows the number of thunderstorms in Thunder Bay, by month, for two consecutive years.
(a) Which year had the most thunderstorms?
(b) Which months had no thunderstorms in both years?
(c) Which month had the most thunderstorms in
(i) year 1? (ii) year 2?
(d) Using the information provided in the table, which month would you go to Thunder Bay to observe the most thunderstorms?

Month	Year 1	Year 2
January	0	0
February	0	0
March	1	0
April	0	1
May	2	2
June	7	4
July	4	6
August	4	3
September	2	3
October	0	1
November	0	1
December	0	0

5. Discuss the validity of the following sampling techniques.
(a) To determine the popularity of a new video, a certain number of people entering a record shop are interviewed.
(b) A pollster surveyed people getting off a plane to determine the popularity of an election candidate.
(c) To determine the most popular of three brands of potato chips, every one-hundredth person in the telephone book was phoned.

6. Information about the members of a fitness club is given below.

Club Members by Age Group				
	25 or Under	26 to 40	Over 40	Total
Females	66	84	39	189
Males	75	79	47	201
Total	141	163	86	390

To determine what new equipment acquisitions would be preferred, a stratified sample of 70 members is to be taken. The number of members surveyed from each group is to be proportional to the percentage of members in that group.
(a) How many 26- to 40-year-old female members should be surveyed?
(b) How many members aged 25 or under, in total, should be surveyed?
(c) How many male members, in total, should be surveyed?

7. Outline a data collection strategy that would allow you to predict the winner in the next provincial election in your riding.

C

8. For maximum flight of a golf ball, or bounce of a basketball, the ball must have resilience, or bounce. The simplest method of determining resilience is to drop the ball from a specific height onto a hard surface, and measure the height of its rebound. If a ball bounces to 7 m after being released from a height of 10 m, it has resilience of 70%. (The remaining 30% is the energy converted into heat.)
(a) Measure the height of the first rebound of a ball when dropped from various heights. Tabulate the results.
(b) If the initial height is represented by x, and the bounce by h, calculate the quotient $\frac{h}{x}$ in each case. What do you observe?
(c) What is the resilience?

Initial Height (cm)	Rebound Height (cm)	$\frac{h}{x}$
25		
50		
75		
100		
125		
150		

MIND BENDER

How many different routes are there for the 6-segment trip from A to B. (No backtracking is allowed.)

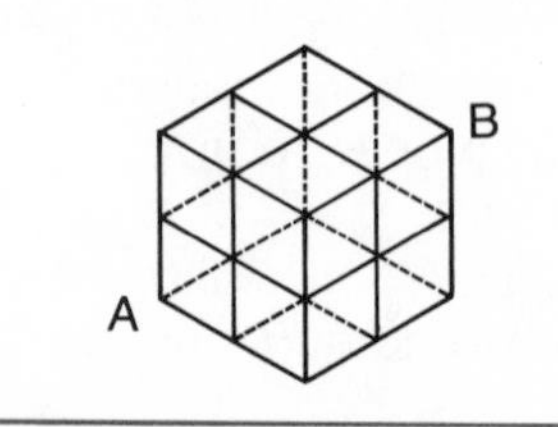

EXTRA

9.2 MAKING PREDICTIONS FROM A RANDOM SAMPLE

Suppose you ask a chemist to determine the chemical composition of a drop of a liquid. If the liquid from which the drop was taken was well mixed, the chemical composition of the drop would reflect quite faithfully the composition of the liquid — and it really wouldn't matter if the drop was taken from a test tube or a ten litre jug.

Example. From a bag of 2500 marbles, 150 marbles are drawn at random and the colours of the marbles are recorded as: 84 red, 30 blue, 36 yellow. Predict the number of marbles of each colour in the bag.

Solution:
The percentage of marbles in the sample which have the same colour is called the sample percentage. The sample percentage of red marbles is

$$\frac{84}{150} \times 100\% = 56\%$$

We use the sample percentage to estimate the population percentage.

Thus, we estimate the population percentage of red marbles as 56%.

And so, the number of red marbles in the bag is estimated as 56% of 2500.

$$\begin{aligned} 56\% \text{ of } 2500 &= 0.56 \times 2500 \\ &= 1400 \end{aligned}$$

We predict the number of red marbles to be 1400.

The sample percentage of blue marbles is

$$\frac{30}{150} \times 100\% = 20\%$$

Estimating the population percentage as the sample percentage, we calculate

$$\begin{aligned} 20\% \text{ of } 2500 &= 0.2 \times 2500 \\ &= 500 \end{aligned}$$

We predict the number of blue marbles to be 500. The sample percentage of yellow marbles is

$$\frac{36}{150} \times 100\% = 24\%$$

Similarly, we estimate the number of yellow marbles as

$$\begin{aligned} 24\% \text{ of } 2500 &= 0.24 \times 2500 \\ &= 600 \end{aligned}$$

We predict there are 600 yellow marbles.

Check: $1400 + 500 + 600 = 2500$

EXERCISE 9.2

1. A bottle manufacturer produces 5000 bottles of a certain type in one day. A sample of 50 bottles is selected at random and 3 bottles are found to have defects.
Estimate the number of defective bottles in the batch of 5000.

2. A pollster surveyed 150 eligible voters before an election. The sample was chosen at random and all persons in the sample were asked how they would vote. The results are as follows.

Candidate	Frequency
Burns	36
Lewchuck	52
O'Callaghan	41
Ramsay	21

If there are 340 000 eligible voters, prepare a table predicting the number of votes for each candidate.

9.3 ORGANIZING DATA

Once collected, data must be organized in order to be understood and properly interpreted.

CLASS AND TALLY SHEET

Raw data are information that has been collected for a specific reason but not yet organized in a meaningful way. Numerical raw data may be organized in an array in ascending (smallest to largest) or descending (largest to smallest) order.
When the data include a large number of observations, it may be more efficient to group the information into classes that define an upper and lower limit. The information may then be tallied using a tally sheet divided by class intervals.

Example 1. A small auto parts store has a special order service which allows customers to order specific parts for classic cars. Since each special order, no matter what the value of the part, costs the store $20.00 to process, the store wants to determine if this order service is cost effective. The raw data of the amount charged for each order processed in one month is listed in the following table.

A1 Auto Parts: Special Order Charges for September					
$ 28.45	$ 8.98	$ 43.65	$ 89.90	$120.10	$ 74.80
5.78	23.44	12.35	132.25	33.45	23.99
114.78	67.33	15.85	7.50	17.65	145.10
32.88	45.90	34.00	19.75	102.00	9.50
33.22	5.75	123.45	107.80	45.50	23.50
88.95	73.50	22.95	7.50	11.75	100.00
40.90	125.50	27.80	11.75	64.00	18.95
155.75	34.75	90.00	7.85	134.50	106.98

Order and display the data in a frequency table so that the store owner can draw conclusions about profit in the special order department.

Solution:
We begin by finding the spread, or range, of the data. The largest value is $155.75 and the smallest value is $5.75. The range is $150.00.

Range = Largest value − Smallest value

In order to set up the classes, we need to determine
(i) the number of classes,
(ii) the limits of each class.
General practice is to use no fewer than 5 or more than 15 classes. With a range of $150, an interval length of twenty would yield 8 classes as indicated below.
The data are now displayed in a frequency distribution table.

A1 Auto Parts Special Order Charges for September		
Classes	Tally	Frequency
$0.00 to $19.99	~~////~~ ~~////~~ ////	14
$20.00 to $39.99	~~////~~ ~~////~~ /	11
$40.00 to $59.99	////	4
$60.00 to $79.99	////	4
$80.00 to $99.99	///	3
$100.00 to $119.99	~~////~~	5
$120.00 to $139.99	~~////~~	5
$140.00 to $159.99	//	2

The frequency is the number of occurrences in each class. In this example it is the number of special order charges that fall into each class.

Conclusions Based on Data

Although it costs the store $20.00 to process a special order, it can be seen from the arrangement of data that the special order department loses money only on those orders in the first class. The frequency in that class is almost offset by the frequency in the class from $20 to $40. From these data the store owner can see that while orders under $20 are not profitable, they are more than offset by gains in the remaining classes.
Continuing to process small orders is good customer relations and does not represent a significant loss to the store.

EXERCISE 9.3

B

1. The following frequency distribution table gives the speed of 50 vehicles passing through an intersection.

Speed Through the Intersection (km/h)		
Class	Tally	Frequency
35 to 39	卌 /	6
40 to 44	卌 卌	10
45 to 49	卌 卌 /	11
50 to 54	卌 卌 ///	13
55 to 59	卌	5
60 to 64	///	3
65 to 69	//	2

(a) Into how many classes are the data divided?

(b) What is the frequency in each of the following classes:
  (i) 40 to 44?
  (ii) 50 to 54?
  (iii) 65 to 69?

(c) How many vehicles had speeds of 55 km/h or more?

2. The table below gives the masses of the Blue Jays players in kilograms.

74	80	83	91	84	79
78	85	90	77	77	86
93	75	88	70	96	89
81	87	83	82	86	84

(a) What is the range?

(b) Divide the information into classes with an interval length of 5.

(c) Using the classes selected above, record the information on a tally sheet and give the frequency in each class.

Spreadsheet activities related to this topic are found in section 15.2.

3. A computer manufacturer puts each display screen through a "burn test" that calculates the time for each screen to reach a given heat level. The faster the screen reaches the given heat level, the more likely it is to fail when used by a customer. The table below shows the time in seconds for 140 computer display screens to reach this level.

33	21	20	32	59	47
12	22	68	55	69	67
54	67	14	34	35	70
23	69	45	35	45	60
80	80	43	56	45	65
67	34	32	34	23	45
23	56	52	75	56	55
14	45	49	31	12	60
44	56	17	12	18	28
61	67	26	67	80	67
23	35	63	30	69	75
12	73	78	67	43	67
23	78	45	47	50	41
10	39	56	45	56	32
20	29	21	48	25	54
33	45	33	67	45	45
24	6	72	50	67	29
79	12	65	33	34	17
50	78	36	25	28	19
55	54	29	12	56	78
45	81	30	26	23	71
34	85	34	79	54	30
34	21	35	66		
25	25	56	28		

(a) What is the range?

(b) Divide the information into classes with an interval length of 5.

(c) Using the classes selected above, record the information on a tally sheet and give the frequency in each class.

(d) If a computer display screen is acceptable for sale only if the given heat level is reached in a minimum of 30 s, how many of the 140 computers tested will be shipped?

9.4 GRAPHIC REPRESENTATION OF DATA

Information may be pictured by constructing a bar graph, broken line graph, circle graph, or pictograph. Graphic representation of information helps us interpret the data quickly and easily.

> Each graph must have
> a title to explain the data being represented, and
> a vertical and horizontal scale, when appropriate.
> Each scale must have
> a title to explain what is being reported, and
> units of measure, when appropriate.

The *bar graph* is primarily used to compare size of quantities.

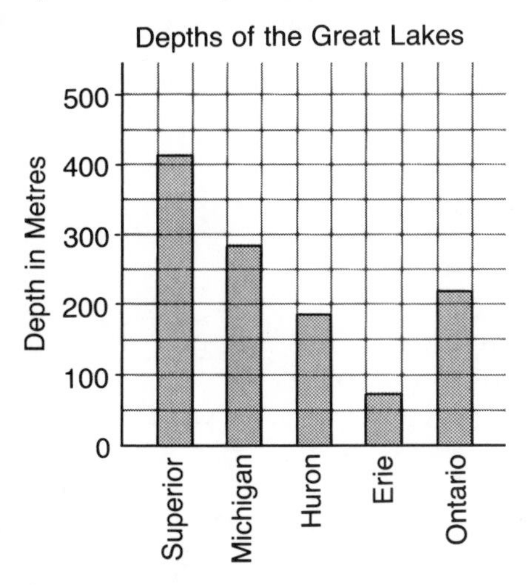

Lake Ontario is approximately 3 times as deep as Lake Erie.

The *circle graph* is used to show the relation of the parts to the whole and to each other.

Grades in Mathematics

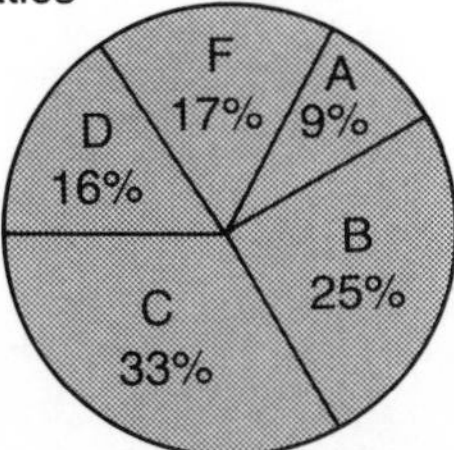

25% of the students obtained the grade B.

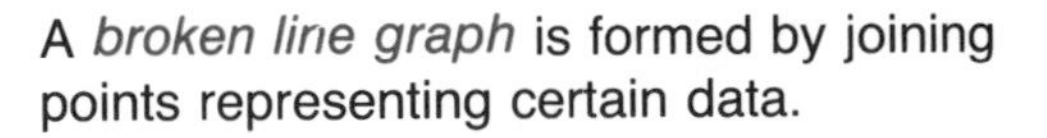

A *broken line graph* is formed by joining points representing certain data.

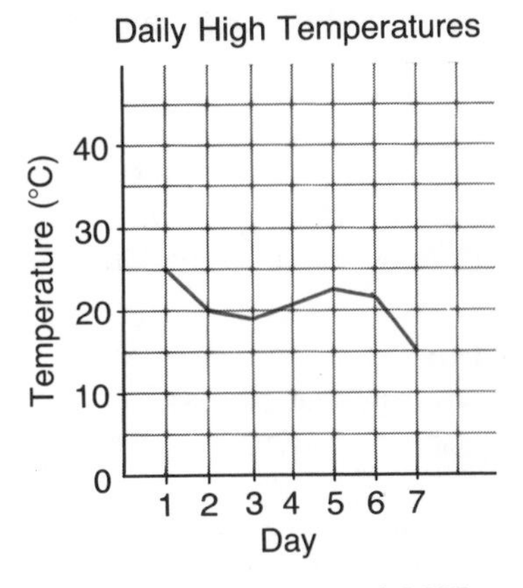

Day 2 had a temperature of 20°C.

A *pictograph* is used for special emphasis. A key or legend shows what each figure represents.

Population of Canadian Cities

Toronto
Montreal
Vancouver
Ottawa
Edmonton
Winnipeg
Halifax
St. John's

Population of Metropolitan Area
(= 100 000 people)

The population of Edmonton is 150 000 greater than the population of Winnipeg.

If a picture is worth a thousand words, then a pictograph may be worth a hundred thousand words.

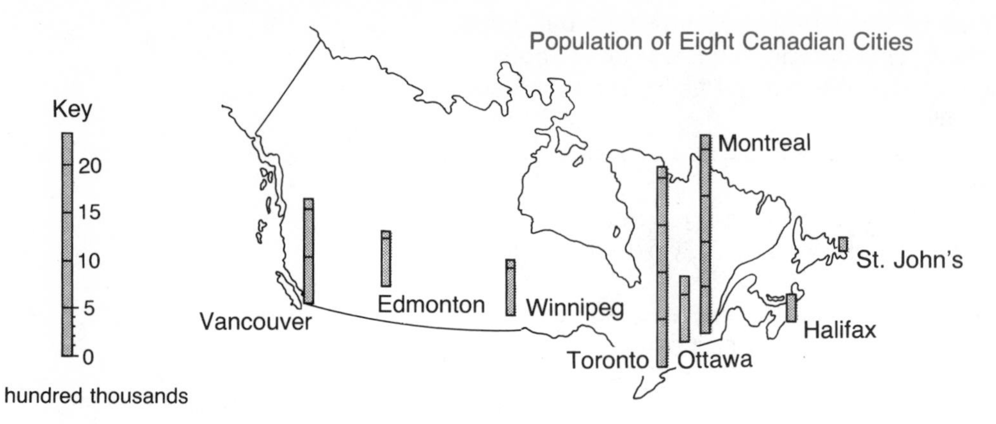

Comparing sizes of bars compares sizes of populations.

Example. There are four blood types: O, A, B, and AB. In Canada, 46% of the people are Group O, 43% are Group A, 8% are Group B, and 3% are AB. Display this information on a circle graph.

Solution: Since we are given the percentages of the whole, we now find the size of each central angle. Write each percent as a decimal and multiply by 360°.

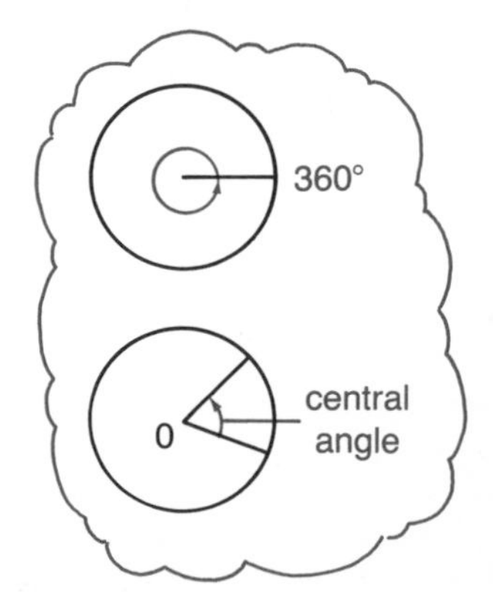

Group O: $0.46 \times 360° = 165.6°$
Group A: $0.43 \times 360° = 154.8°$
Group B: $0.08 \times 360° = 28.8°$
Group AB: $0.03 \times 360° = 10.8°$

Draw a circle and construct each central angle. Label each section and give the graph a title.

Blood Type Distribution

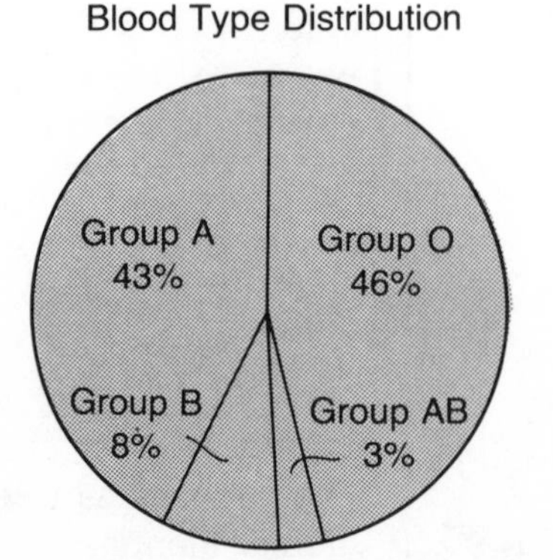

EXERCISE 9.4

A

1. The bar graph shows the maximum speeds of several mammals.

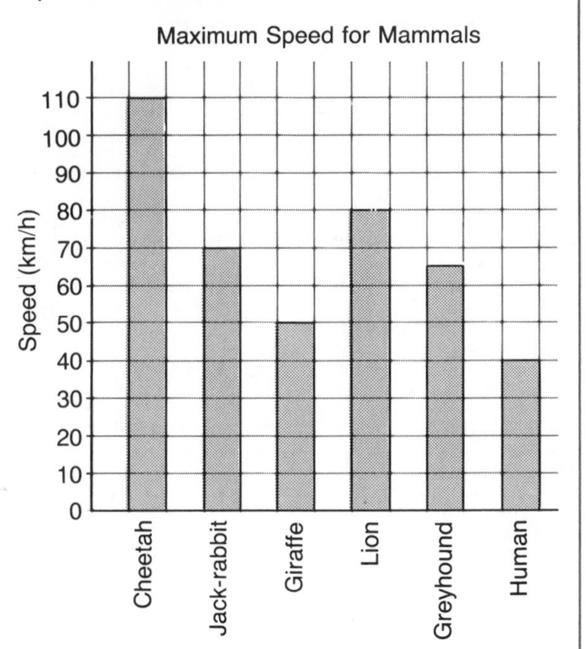

(a) Rank the mammals from fastest to slowest.
(b) Which mammals have a maximum speed greater than 60 km/h?
(c) How many times faster than a human is a lion?
(d) Do you have to use the vertical scale to answer part (c)?

B

2. The line graph following shows the number of houses sold, by month, during one year by the Gibraltar Realty Company.

(a) During which month were the sales the highest?
(b) During which months were the sales the same?
(c) By how many did sales in September exceed those in February?
(d) Which month had the fewest sales?
(e) What were the total sales for the year?

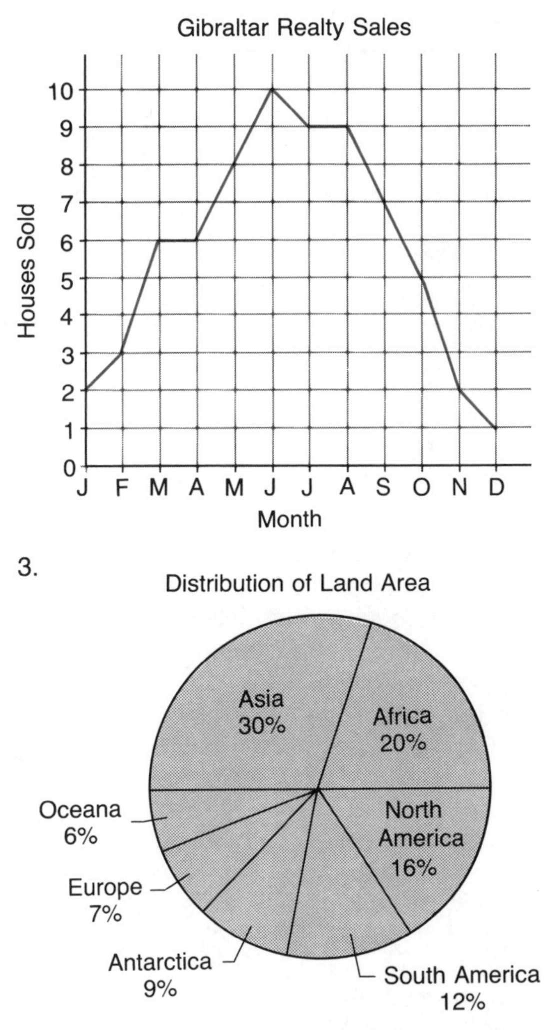

3. The circle graph shows the distribution of the earth's land area by continent.

(a) Which continent has the largest land area?
(b) Which two continents comprise approximately 50% of the land area of the earth?
(c) Which two continents comprise approximately the same land area as Asia?
(d) Which three continents comprise approximately the same land area as Africa?

4. Seven of the planets that orbit the sun have moons. The following table gives the number of moons for these planets.

Planet	Number of Moons
Earth	1
Mars	2
Jupiter	16
Saturn	17
Uranus	15
Neptune	2
Pluto	1

Display the data on a bar graph.

5. The pictograph shows how much a young man would have to eat if he were to obtain his required daily intake of 10 000 kJ from eating only one type of food. (The symbol for kilojoule is kJ.)

(a) How many kilograms of each of the following types of food are required for an intake of 10 000 kJ?
(i) Cheddar cheese (ii) lamb
(iii) spaghetti (iv) potatoes
(v) bananas

(b) How many kilojoules are contained in 1 kg of Cheddar cheese?

Amounts of a Food
Containing 10 000 kJ

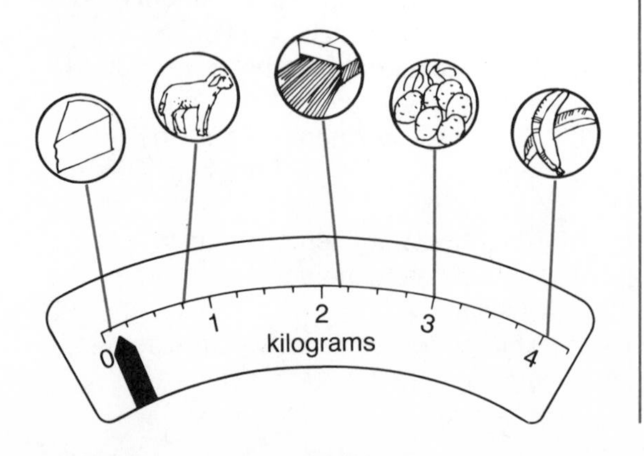

6. The average monthly temperatures for Toronto and Vancouver are given below. Display the data on a broken line graph. Use a solid line to represent Toronto and a dotted line to represent Vancouver.

Temperature (°C)		
Month	Toronto	Vancouver
January	−4	2
February	−11	1
March	−3	8
April	10	12
May	15	14
June	19	16
July	22	17
August	20	18
September	15	12
October	4	10
November	−1	8
December	−3	3

7. The following data show the types and number of each type of book found in a private collection.
Construct a pictograph to represent the data.

Biography	200
Humour	5000
Mystery	3500
Romance	500
Sports	1500
Travel	2500
Science	4000
Other	1000

8. For every 100 people, 28 have black hair, 36 have brown hair, 24 have blonde hair, and 12 have red hair.
Construct a circle graph to illustrate this information.

C

9. Information can be *distorted* and lead to false impressions or conclusions. For the following graphs, find the distortion and re-construct the graph appropriately.

(a) TV Sets in Homes

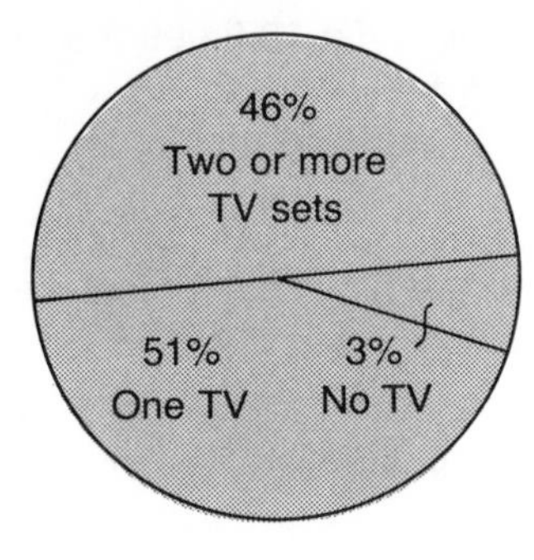

(b) Percent of Income Spent on Food

Canada 19%

England 26%

Africa 55%

(c) Sales at Hamburg Haven for Five Months

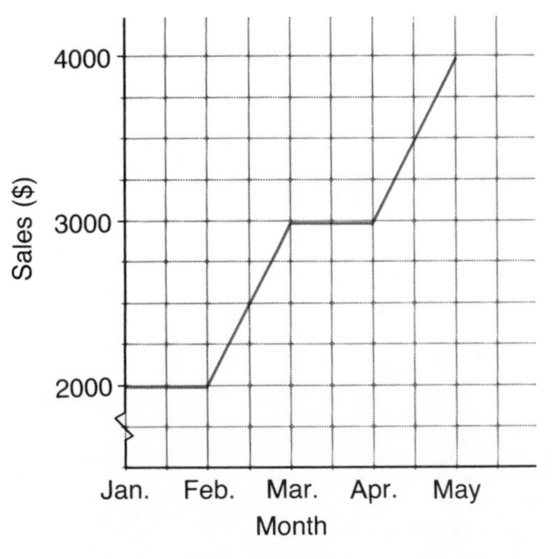

(d) Points Earned at a Track and Field Contest

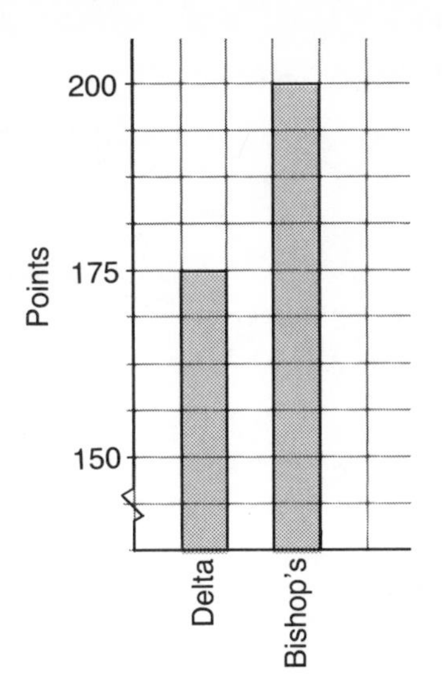

10. For each of the distortions in question 9 above, state a possible motive for presenting the data as shown.

In the seventeenth century, mazes like the one shown below were designed using hedges.

What rule can you follow to enter or exit most mazes?

9.5 HISTOGRAMS AND FREQUENCY POLYGONS

The histogram is a graph that is similar to a bar graph. The frequency of a value or a class interval can be presented in a histogram.

Example 1. The results of casting a die 10 times are as follows: 3, 4, 1, 3, 3, 5, 1, 3, 6, 2.
Record the results in a histogram.

Solution: On the horizontal axis we list the possible outcomes of rolling the die. The vertical axis records the frequency.

Unlike a bar graph, a histogram does not have spaces between the bars.

Results of Casting a Die

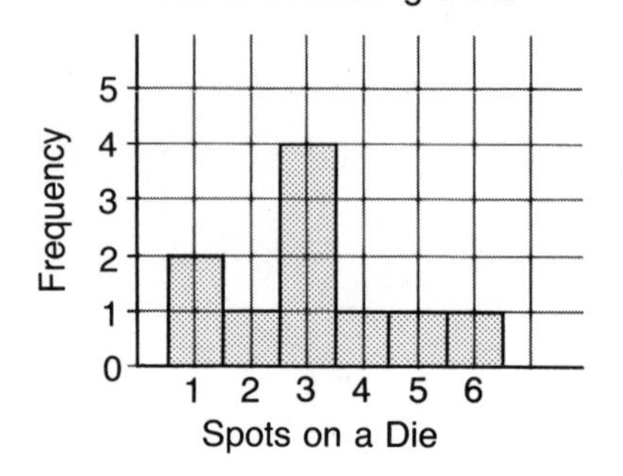

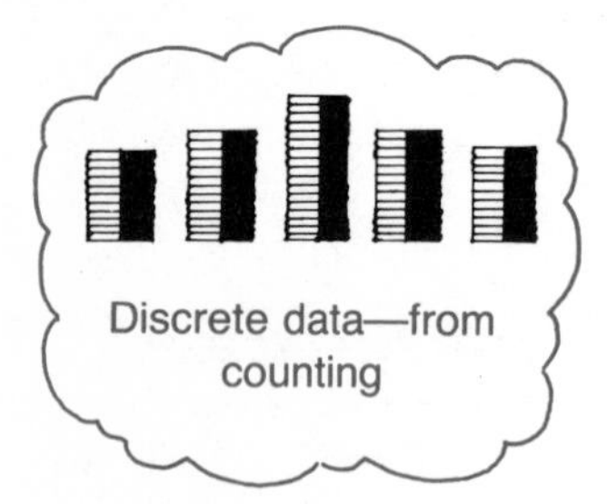

Data such as that of example 1 are called discrete. Discrete data can differ only by fixed amounts and result from counting. Family size is discrete. Two families can differ in size by 0 or 1 or 2, and so on. Nothing in between is possible. When plotting a histogram for discrete data, we centre the bars over the possible values. Discrete data may also be grouped into classes. If, in example 1, the possible outcomes are grouped into the classes 1-2, 3-4, 5-6, a histogram of the results is as follows.

Results of Casting a Die

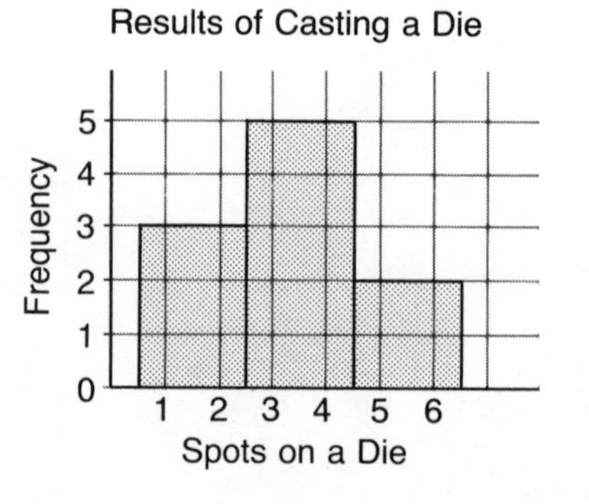

In 10 rolls of the die, either ⚀ or ⚂ were seen 3 times.

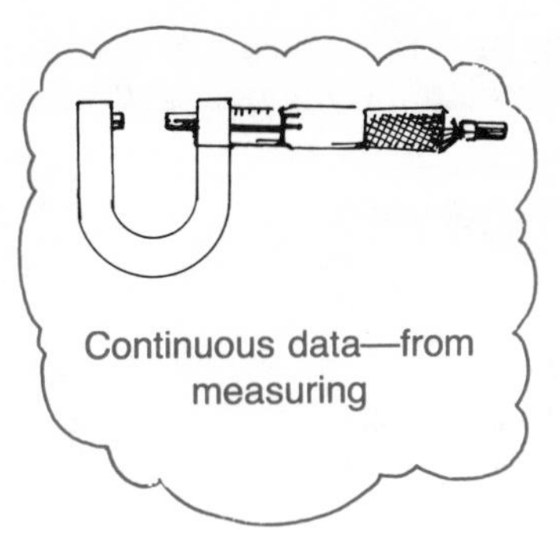

Data, such as temperature readings, that are the result of measurement are called continuous data. The change in temperature is continuous, and cannot be counted as in the case of discrete data.

When plotting a histogram for continuous data, we must decide what to do with cases that fall on the boundary of the classes. General practice is illustrated in the following example.

Example 2. The heights, in centimetres, of some students were measured and recorded in the following frequency distribution table.

This interval includes all heights from 160 cm up to but *not* including 165 cm.

Height of Students		
Class	Tally	Frequency
150 – 155	/	1
155 – 160	𝍸	5
160 – 165	𝍸 𝍸	10
165 – 170	𝍸 𝍸 //	12
170 – 175	𝍸 𝍸 𝍸 ///	18
175 – 180	𝍸 𝍸 ///	13
180 – 185	𝍸 /	6
185 – 190	///	3

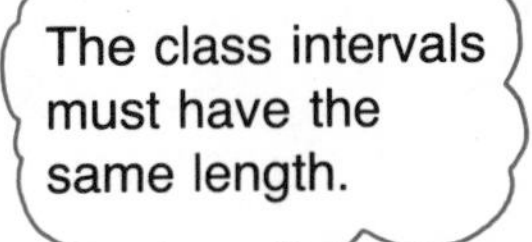

Display the data in a histogram.

Solution. We display the class intervals on the horizontal axis. The endpoints of each bar coincide with the endpoints of the class it represents. The tally for the right hand endpoint is not included in the bar size.

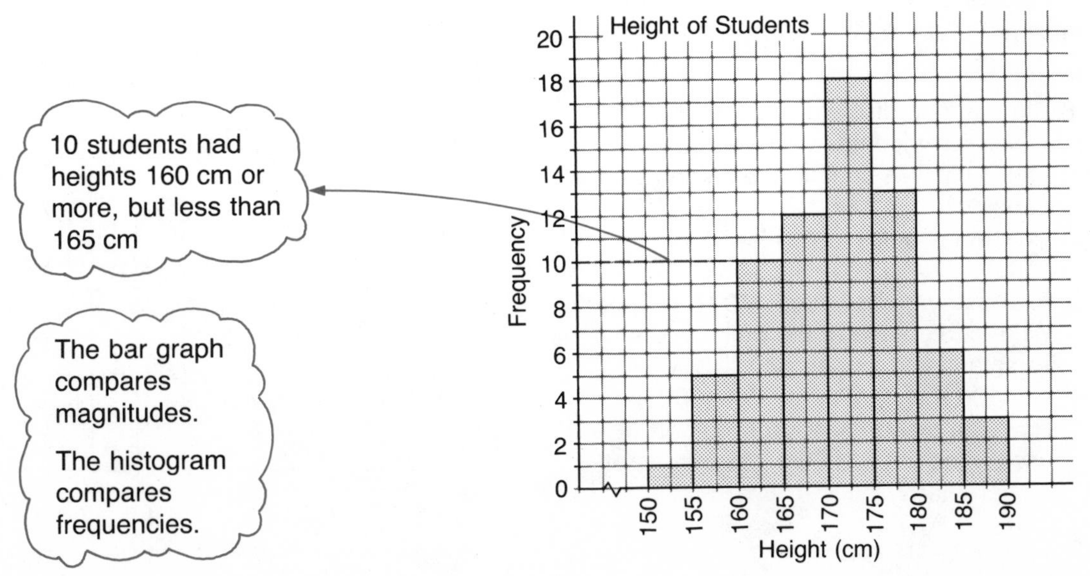

A histogram is sometimes replaced by a frequency polygon. A frequency polygon is formed by joining the midpoints at the top of each class.

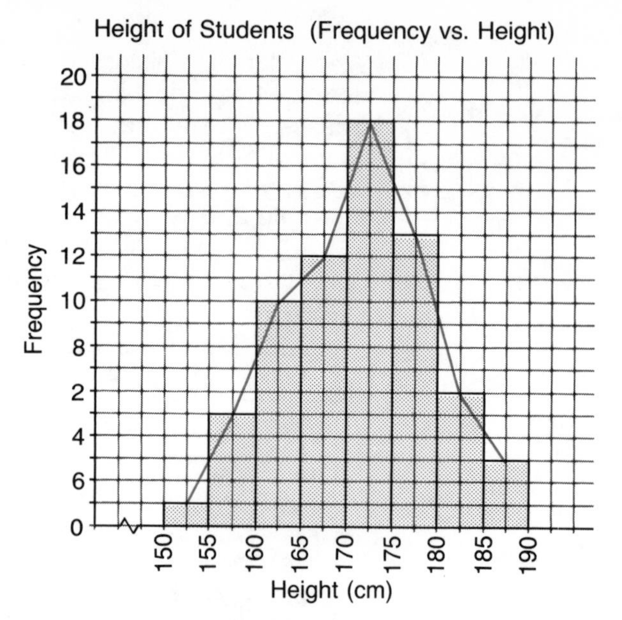

Both the histogram and the frequency polygon provide a method of viewing the shape of the data and a pictorial look at the frequency of occurrence in each class.

EXERCISE 9.5

A

1. The life lengths of a sample of 100 light bulbs are recorded in the following histogram.

(a) Are the data discrete or continuous?
(b) Which class contains the most bulbs?
(c) Which classes contain the same number of bulbs?
(d) How many bulbs lasted less than 1300 h?
(e) How many bulbs lasted 1700 h or more?
(f) What percentage of the bulbs in the sample lasted longer than (i) 1000 h? (ii) 1100 h? (iii) 1500 h? (iv) 1900 h?
(g) How can the information from part (f) be used if the manufacturer decides to offer a guarantee?

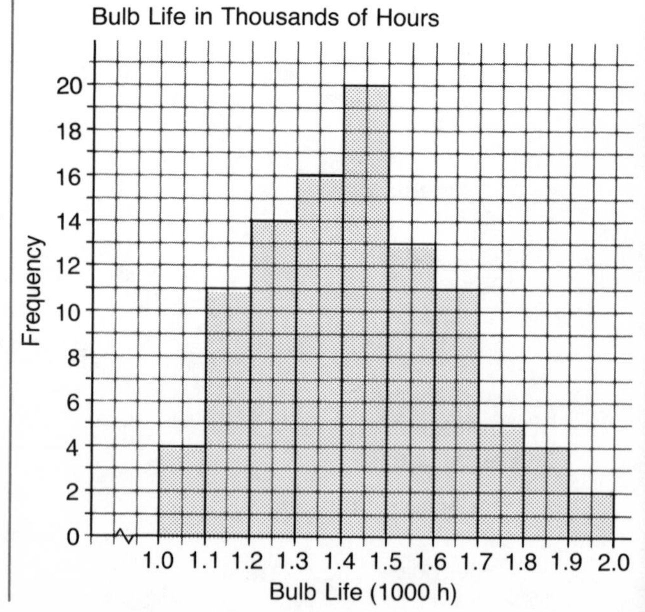

B

2. The tally sheet below records the marks on a chapter test, out of 35 possible marks, for a grade 11 math class.

Chapter Test, Grade 11 Mathematics Class		
Mark	Tally	Frequency
0–3		0
4–7	//	2
8–11	///	3
12–15	~~////~~ ////	9
16–19	~~////~~ ~~////~~ ///	13
20–23	~~////~~ ~~////~~ //	12
24–27	~~////~~ ///	8
28–31	////	4
32–35	//	2

(a) Are the data discrete or continuous?
(b) Draw a histogram.
(c) Draw the frequency polygon on the same axes.

3. The table below shows the masses, in kilograms, of the players on the Trojan football team.

84.6	88.2	92.0	97.1	109.4	81.5
84.2	104.3	96.9	91.2	86.0	83.0
87.1	100.4	95.8	90.9	82.4	86.5
82.3	85.3	85.7	98.4	90.7	93.2
105.2	98.9	88.4	92.5	77.4	84.5
79.3	84.0	98.6	82.4	89.8	92.3

(a) Are the data discrete or continuous?
(b) What is the range of the data?
(c) Prepare a frequency distribution table using a class interval length of 5.
(d) Display the data on a histogram and, on the same graph, superimpose a frequency polygon.

4. A pair of dice are rolled 50 times and the spots appearing are totalled after each throw. The results are given in the following table.

6	11	7	2	8	6	12	5	3	7
7	2	4	8	10	6	6	10	9	7
9	3	5	6	7	7	9	8	7	4
8	10	3	8	6	11	11	9	8	6
7	8	6	11	7	7	6	4	12	8

(a) Are the data discrete or continuous?
(b) Prepare a frequency distribution table giving the frequency of each value.
(c) Draw the frequency polygon on the same axes.

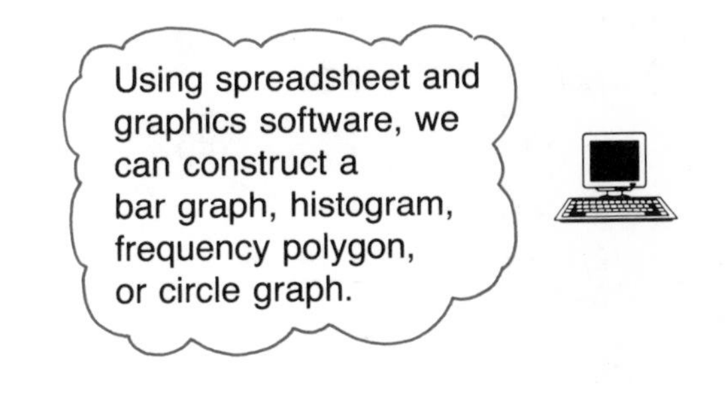

MICRO MATH

```
NEW
100 REM THIS PROGRAM ROLLS TWO DICE
110 PRINT "TYPE NUMBER OF ROLLS"
120 PRINT "TO BE MADE"
125 INPUT N
130 PRINT
140 FOR A =1 TO N
150 D1=INT (6*RND(1))+1
160 D2=INT (6*RND(1))+1
170 T= D1 + D2
180 PRINT " FIRST DIE=" D1
190 PRINT "SECOND DIE=" D2
200 PRINT "       TOTAL=" T
210 PRINT "   "
220 NEXT A
RUN
```

9.6 CUMULATIVE FREQUENCY

When preparing a frequency distribution table, we may include a column giving the cumulative frequency. The cumulative frequency helps us to answer questions about the data quickly. It is obtained by adding frequencies consecutively from the first class to the last.

Example. The frequency distribution table records the results of a test, out of 35 possible marks, given to a group of students taking a scuba diving course. The table includes a column giving the cumulative frequency.

(a) How many students scored less than 20?
(b) How many students scored 16 or more?

Scuba Diving Test Results			
Score	Tally	Frequency	Cumulative Frequency
0–3		0	0
4–7	//	2	2
8–11	////	4	6
12–15	~~////~~ //	7	13
16–19	~~////~~ ////	9	22
20–23	~~////~~ ~~////~~ //	12	34
24–27	~~////~~ ~~////~~ ~~////~~ /	16	50
28–31	~~////~~ ///	8	58
32–35	//	2	60

0 + 2
2 + 4
6 + 7
Total number of students tested

Solution:

(a) The number of students that scored less than 20 is the sum of the frequencies in the classes

0–3, 4-7, 8-11, 12-15 and 16-19.

This sum appears in the cumulative frequency column across from the 16-19 class.

∴ 22 students scored less than 20.

(b) The number of students that scored 16 or more equals the total number of students minus the number of students that scored 15 or less. Reading from the cumulative frequency column, we obtain:

$60 - 13 = 47$

∴ 47 students scored more than 16.

We may construct a histogram showing cumulative frequency. The bar height for each class is now given in the **cumulative** frequency column.

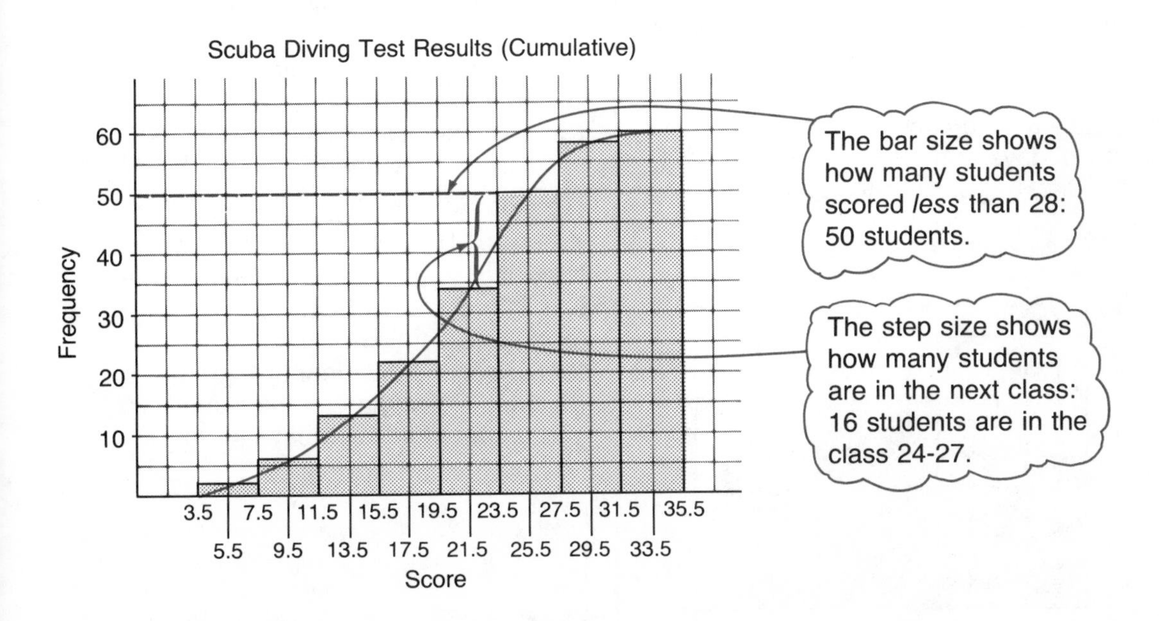

A cumulative frequency polygon has been superimposed.

EXERCISE 9.6

A 1. The following frequency table shows the marks of 100 students on an English test.

Class	Frequency	Cumulative Frequency
45–49	6	6
50–54	4	10
55–59	5	15
60–64	12	27
65–69	17	44
70–74	23	67
75–79	9	76
80–84	13	89
85–89	8	97
90–94	3	100

(a) How many students had a mark lower than 65?
(b) How many students had a mark lower than 80?
(c) How many students had a mark lower than 75?
(d) How many students had a mark of 70 or more?

B 2. The histogram gives the number of days with precipitation (rain or snow) in Ottawa, each month, for a given year. Using these data, draw a histogram of the cumulative number of days with precipitation in Ottawa for the year, beginning with January.

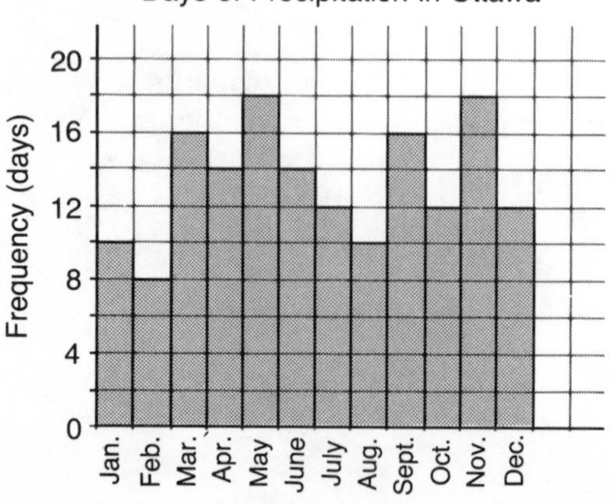

3. The table below shows the hourly wages of 70 high school students who have part-time jobs after school or on weekends.

\$5.60	\$7.20	\$6.60	\$6.10	\$8.50
6.00	8.00	6.40	6.30	9.23
6.10	8.00	8.75	8.10	5.80
6.30	5.50	6.90	8.10	9.70
5.80	8.34	6.00	7.50	6.71
6.67	9.20	6.50	8.50	8.50
5.45	5.80	7.10	6.75	6.00
6.10	5.90	5.60	6.15	7.10
7.50	6.10	6.30	8.25	7.23
8.00	7.20	6.20	8.75	6.60
5.73	9.10	5.70	6.10	5.75
8.40	8.50	8.50	6.15	6.10
5.70	9.30	5.90	7.75	8.00
6.00	8.10	5.75	10.80	9.30

(a) Using the classes 5.00 – 6.00, 6.00 – 7.00, ..., 10.00 – 11.00, record the information on a tally sheet and give the frequency and cumulative frequency in each class. (Include the left hand endpoint in each class, but not the right hand endpoint.)
(b) How many students earned less than \$8.00 per hour?
(c) How many students earned \$7.00 or more per hour?
(d) How many students earned \$8.00 or more but less than \$9.00 per hour?
(e) Display the data in a histogram.

4. The table below shows the number of "freezing days" (days with temperatures less than 0.0°C) in Saint John, each month, for a particular year.
(a) Display the data in a histogram.
(b) Draw a histogram of the cumulative number of freezing days for the year.

Jan.	31	July	0
Feb.	28	Aug.	0
Mar.	30	Sept.	0
April	22	Oct.	9
May	3	Nov.	16
June	0	Dec.	24

9.7 MEASURES OF CENTRAL TENDENCY

Statistics is the process of collecting and analysing data. Numerical data can be analysed using the measures of central tendency — mean, median, and mode.

MEAN

The mean or average of a set of numbers is found by adding them together and dividing the total by the number of numbers added. For the set of values $x_1, x_2, x_3, ..., x_n$ the mean is

$\bar{x}$ is commonly used to denote the mean of a set of values.

$$\bar{x} = \frac{x_1 + x_2 + x_3 + ... + x_n}{n}$$

If a newspaper wanted to know how much paper to order, the mean or average number of pages per paper per day is the most meaningful value.

MEDIAN

When a set of numbers is arranged in order (smallest to largest), then the middle number is the median. If there is an even number of numbers, then the median is the average of the middle two numbers.

The median income of families in Canada is usually more meaningful for decision making than is the mean because very high and very low incomes tend to distort the mean.

MODE

The mode of a set of numbers is the value that occurs most frequently. If each number of the set occurs only once, then there is no mode. On the other hand, there may be more than one mode in a set of numbers.

A shoe store is more interested in the mode of shoe sizes purchased than the mean. They need to know which shoe size sells the most and order accordingly.

RANGE

The range of a set of numbers is found by subtracting the smallest number from the largest.

Example. Find the mean, median, mode, and range of the following data:
14, 25, 17, 15, 21, 20, 18, 20, 16, 23

Solution:

Mean: $\bar{x} = \dfrac{x_1 + x_2 + x_3 + ... + x_n}{n}$

There are 10 values.

$\therefore n = 10$

$$\therefore \bar{x} = \frac{14 + 25 + 17 + 15 + 21 + 20 + 18 + 20 + 16 + 23}{10}$$

$$= \frac{189}{10}$$

$$= 18.9$$

The mean is 18.9.

Median: To find the median the values must be ordered, usually from smallest to largest.

14, 15, 16, 17, 18, 20, 20, 21, 23, 25

Since there is an even number of values, the median is the average of the middle two: 18 and 20.

$\therefore$ the median is $\dfrac{18 + 20}{2} = 19$.

The median is 19.

Mode: Since 20 occurs more frequently than any other value (twice), the mode is 20.

Range: The largest value is 25.
The smallest value is 14.
$\therefore$ The range is calculated as $25 - 14 = 11$.
The range is 11.

EXERCISE 9.7

B

1. Find the mean, median, and range for the following sets of data. Find the mode where one exists.
(a) 12, 17, 24, 13, 16
(b) 3, 9, 8, 4, 7, 6, 4
(c) 5, 7, 7, 8, 8, 8, 9, 9, 10, 10, 10
(d) 42, 58, 64, 65, 53, 71, 66, 47
(e) 135, 256, 191, 241, 176, 204
(f) 58.3, 57.6, 58.2, 58.0, 57.9
(g) 0.040, 0.070, 0.095, 0.080, 0.055, 0.045, 0.070, 0.090, 0.075, 0.065
(h) 5.2, 3.1, 7.6, 5.9, 4.7, 4.8, 6.5, 5.7, 3.4, 7.7, 5.9, 6.3

2. A class of 20 students has the following marks out of 25 questions on a test.
22, 25, 20, 19, 12, 16, 20, 17, 23, 19, 18, 16, 13, 10, 15, 17, 21, 18, 16, 23
(a) Find the median mark, mean, range.
A second class of 19 students has the following marks on a similar test.
20, 19, 17, 18, 13, 14, 16, 18, 22, 17, 18, 16, 24, 14, 16, 21, 15, 19, 15
(b) Find the median mark, mean, range.
(c) If you were asked to decide which class did better on the test, how would you do it?

CALCULATOR MATH

STATISTICAL FUNCTIONS

Many calculators have statistical functions. Data may be entered into the statistics register and analysed by these calculators. On some calculators the data entry key is Σ+.

Example. To enter the data 3, 5, 9 press 3 Σ+ 5 Σ+ 9 Σ+

Display 9. or 3.

The display, after each pressing of Σ+ in the above sequence, varies from calculator to calculator. After pressing Σ+ some calculators may continue to display the data point just entered, while others will display the number of data points that have thus far been entered.

To find the mean of these data, locate the key displaying $\bar{x}$. (Usage of this key generally must be preceded by pressing 2nd or INV)

Continuing from above, press 2nd $\bar{x}$

Display 5.666666667

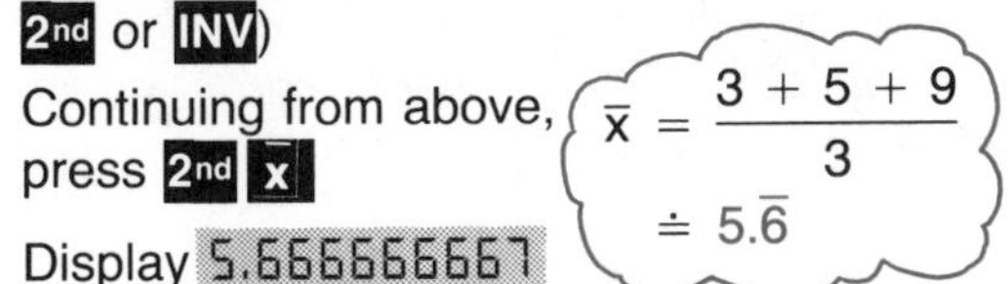

To find or recall the number of data points entered, continuing from above press 2nd n

Display 3.

3 data points (3,5, and 9) have been entered.

To find the sum of the values entered we may multiply the mean ($\bar{x}$) by the number of data points (3). Continuing from above, press

2nd $\bar{x}$ × 3 =

Display 17.

Some calculators have the keys Σx and Σx²

To find the sum of the values entered on calculators such as these, continuing from above, we may press 2nd Σx

Display 17.

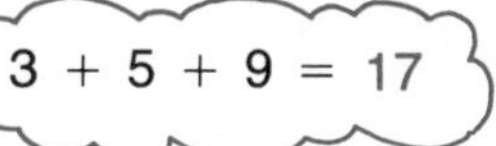

To find the sum of the squares of the values, continuing from above, press 2nd Σx²

Display 115.

$3^2 + 5^2 + 9^2 = 115$

Note that when entering data into the statistics register, we may delete an incorrect entry rather than start over. For example, suppose when entering the data 3, 5, 9 we press the following keys.

3 Σ+ 5 Σ+ 8 Σ+

The data 3, 5, 8 have been entered.

To delete the incorrect entry (8) proceed as follows. Continuing, press

8 2nd Σ−

8 has been deleted from the statistics register.

Then, continuing, press 9 Σ+

9 has been entered.

The correct data 3, 5, 9 have now been entered.

Some calculators retain data in the statistics register even after having been turned off. Before entering data it may be necessary to first clear the statistics register. Check your handbook to find how to clear the register.

9.8 WEIGHTED MEAN

The weighted mean is calculated on data that are grouped by class for group comparisons or because the sample is large.

Example 1. The grade 11 students at a high school all took the same test, out of a possible 20 marks. The raw data are shown below.
Group the marks to find the weighted mean.

Test Marks out of 20
12, 15, 10, 5, 10, 11, 12, 7, 8, 11, 13, 14, 11, 8, 10, 9, 11, 11, 10, 10, 14, 20, 12, 13, 6, 9, 12, 13, 8, 12, 11, 12, 9, 11, 8, 11, 11, 10, 9, 6, 19, 13, 19, 18, 17, 18, 18, 17, 16, 20, 16, 10, 17, 19, 7, 9, 7, 10, 10, 11, 10, 8, 12, 9, 13, 15, 11, 13, 15, 16, 18, 11, 16, 14, 12, 15, 12, 14, 11, 9, 11, 8, 14, 12, 13, 10, 7, 11, 8, 15, 13, 6, 9, 9, 10, 12

Solution:
The most efficient way to organize the data is to group the data. We must determine the classes and tally the raw data. Since there are 21 possible values, 0 to 20, a grouping of three values per class is convenient. The class mid-value is the value in the middle of each class. It is calculated by adding class limits and dividing by 2:

$$\frac{(\text{class lower limit} + \text{class upper limit})}{2}$$

Class Values	Tally	Class Mid-values x	Frequency f	Frequency × Mid-values f × x
0–2		1	0	0
3–5	/	4	1	4
6–8	~~////~~ ~~////~~ ////	7	14	98
9–11	~~////~~ ~~////~~ ~~////~~ ~~////~~ ~~////~~ ~~////~~ ~~////~~ /	10	36	360
12–14	~~////~~ ~~////~~ ~~////~~ ~~////~~ ////	13	24	312
15–17	~~////~~ ~~////~~ ///	16	13	208
18–20	~~////~~ ///	19	8	152

$n = 96 \quad \Sigma(f \times x) = 1134$

$\Sigma(f \times x)$ means the sum of all values in the $f \times x$ column.

The weighted mean or average for the students is calculated as follows.

$$\bar{x} = \frac{\Sigma f \times x}{n}$$

$$\bar{x} = \frac{1134}{96}$$

$$\doteq 11.8$$

Using a calculator, calculate the mean of the raw data. Has there been a significant loss of accuracy through grouping?

Example 2. The Store, a tuck shop run by the Student Council, wants to know the average value of the books, pens, and miscellaneous supplies sold in a month.
Calculate the weighted averages of books, pens, and miscellaneous items using the following sales information.

Books	No. Sold(f)	Price/Item(x)	Total (f × x)
note	11	$1.75	$19.25
binder	5	3.50	17.50
steno	9	1.30	11.70
Total (N) = 25			Σ(f × x) = 48.45

Solution:
Weighted Mean ($\bar{x}$)

$$\bar{x} = \frac{48.45}{25}$$

$$\bar{x} \doteq \$1.94$$

Pens	No. Sold(f)	Price/Item (x)	Total (f × x)
ballpoint	27	$ .30	$ 8.10
school	33	1.00	33.00
erasable	11	1.75	19.25
Total (N) = 71			Σ(f × x) = 60.35

$$\bar{x} = \frac{60.35}{71}$$

$$\bar{x} = \$0.85$$

Misc.	No. Sold (f)	Price/Item (x)	Total (f × x)
T-shirt	6	$8.50	$51.00
button	32	.50	16.00
cap	5	5.50	27.50
Total (N) = 43			Σ(f × x) = 94.50

$$\bar{x} = \frac{94.50}{43}$$

$$\bar{x} \doteq \$2.20$$

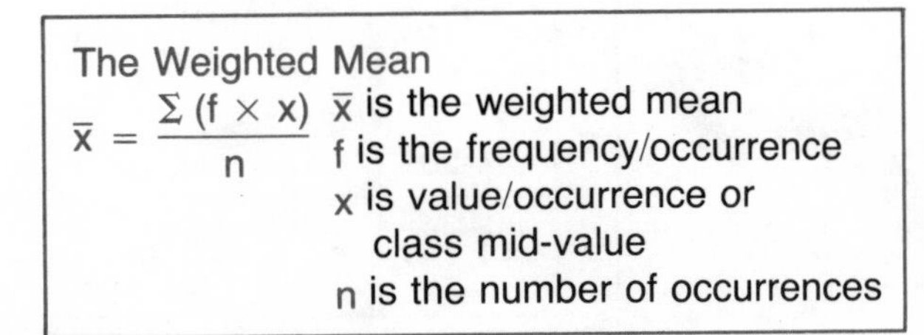

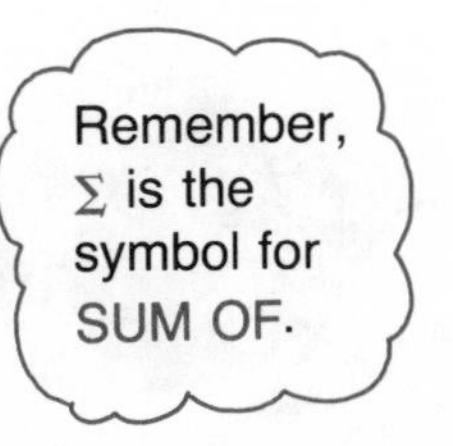

EXERCISE 9.8

B

1. The life length of a sample of 100 light bulbs is recorded in the following frequency table.

Bulb Life in Hours			
Class Values	Class Mid-values x	Frequency f	f × x
0–999		0	0
1000–1099	1050	4	4 200
1100–1199	1150	11	12 650
1200–1299	1250	14	17 500
1300–1399	1350	16	21 600
1400–1499	1450	20	29 000
1500–1599	1550	13	20 150
1600–1699	1650	11	18 150
1700–1799	1750	5	8 750
1800–1899	1850	4	7 400
1900–1999	1950	2	3 900

Find the weighted mean life length.

2. The handspans of grade 11 students were measured. Construct a frequency distribution table. Compare the weighted mean for the handspan of girls and handspan of boys and the mean of all handspans.

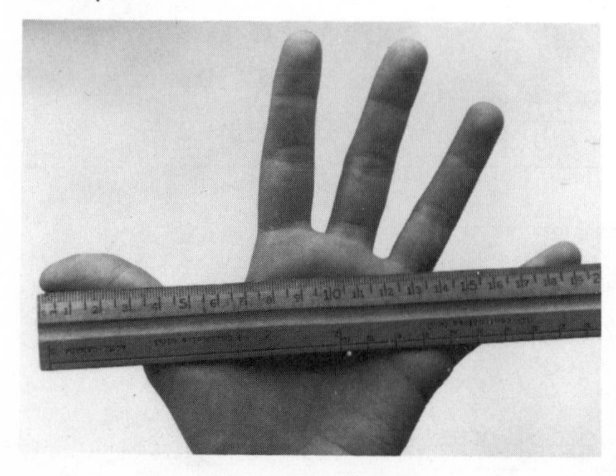

Handspans of Students in Centimetres					
Handspan (cm)	Frequency		Cumulative Frequency		
	Girls	Boys	Girls	Boys	Total
17	3	1			
18	5	3			
19	11	8			
20	15	12			
21	10	12			
22	5	8			
23	1	4			
24	2	2			
25	0	1			

3. Using the data in question 2, find the median and mode of the handspan of girls, boys, and the total of girls and boys.

4. Complete the following frequency distribution table. Calculate the weighted mean and construct a histogram.

Push-ups by High School Boys in 5 min			
Class Values	Class Mid-values x	Frequency f	f × x
0–4		3	
5–9		5	
10–14		24	
15–19		40	
20–24		21	
25–29		4	
30–34		2	
35–39		1	

5. Throw three dice 50 times and record the totals of each throw in a frequency distribution with classes 3–4, 5–6, ... 17–18. Calculate the mean. Construct a histogram of the results.

Class Values	Tally	Class Mid-values x	Frequency f	f × x
3–4	///	3.5	(Sample only)	

6.

Construct a frequency distribution table for the number of cars offered for sale by year. Find the mean age. Consider 1986 cars to be one year old.

Cars for Sale by Year	
Year	Frequency
1986	21
1985	101
1984	111
1983	81
1982	87
1981	105
1980	65
1979	50
1978	29
1977	29
1976	13
1975	8
1974	2

C

7. The table gives cottage prices in $1000's from the advertisements of a daily newspaper. Construct a frequency distribution with classes 25.0–34.9, 35.0–44.9, 45.0–54.9, ... 125–134.9. Calculate the mean price and construct a histogram. Round off the mid-value to a whole number.

Cottage Prices in $1000's				
62.5	50.9	52.0	56.5	53.5
80.0	114.9	49.9	29.9	85.9
45.0	66.9	66.9	67.9	45.9
47.5	53.9	72.9	74.5	39.0
54.5	39.9	37.9	63.9	42.9
109.5	66.5	39.5	39.0	41.5
39.0	45.9	48.0	108.0	69.9
46.9	37.5	38.5	55.9	44.9
43.9	48.0	72.9	39.5	37.9
64.9	74.5	69.9	66.5	68.5
52.5	55.9	54.0	39.5	42.9
69.0	82.5	64.9	53.9	39.9
35.9	74.9	39.5	39.5	62.9
56.9	53.9	54.5	65.5	58.9
99.5	42.9	25.9	110.0	35.9
49.5	82.9	88.5	63.9	62.9
47.9	47.9	51.0	35.9	81.9
75.0	67.9	74.9	49.9	55.9
66.9	60.0	99.5	79.6	65.9
46.5	125.0	56.0	38.9	107.0
54.5	43.9	64.9	49.5	51.0
53.9	44.9	79.9	79.9	72.9
61.9	41.0	87.0	55.9	72.0
57.9	53.5	56.9	45.9	53.9
76.9	85.0	53.9	53.9	52.9

9.9 CUMULATIVE MEAN AND MOVING MEAN

When data are recorded over a period of time, changes or trends can be analysed using the cumulative mean and the moving mean.

> Cumulative Mean:
> The mean of a selected group of cumulative data

Example 1. Calculate the cumulative mean for each month based on the monthly sales for the first year of operation for Maxwell Records, a retail record store. The year's sales by month are given in the table below.

Solution:
Cumulative mean is calculated by dividing the cumulative sum by the number of months cumulated.

Month	Sales	Cumulative Total Sales	Cumulative Mean
January	$1500.00	$ 1500.00	$1500.00
February	1350.00	2850.00	1425.00
March	1800.00	4650.00	1550.00
April	2100.00	6750.00	1687.50
May	1950.00	8700.00	1740.00
June	1800.00	10500.00	1750.00
July	2050.00	12550.00	1792.86
August	2200.00	14750.00	1843.75
September	2000.00	16750.00	1861.11
October	2200.00	18950.00	1895.00
November	2800.00	21750.00	1977.27
December	2950.00	24700.00	2058.33

$\frac{1500}{1}; \frac{2850}{2}; \frac{4650}{3}; \frac{6750}{4};$ etc.

Cumulative mean shows the changes in sales as the year progresses. Business decisions can be made relative to the information. Taken over a longer period of time, further sales comparisons year to year can be made.

The following line graph compares the sales per month (solid line) with the cumulative mean of sales by month (dotted line). The graph of the cumulative mean shows the trend as a smoother curve than the graph of the sales. By continuing this curve, predictions of future sales can be made.

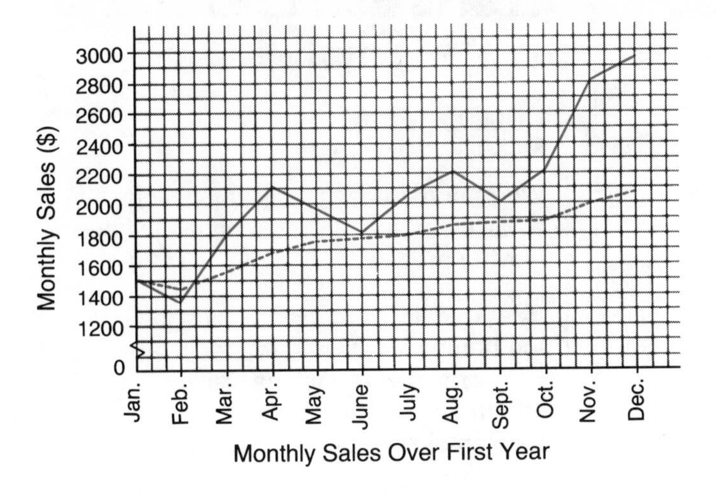

> Moving Mean:
> The mean of a selected group of consecutive data

Example 2. Using the data in Example 1, calculate a 4-month moving mean.

Solution:
The 4-month moving mean is calculated by adding the sales over the first 4 consecutive months, dividing by 4, and then moving month by month, calculating the mean of the next four consecutive months to the end of the year.

Month	Sales ($)	4-Month Moving Mean
January	1500.00	
February	1350.00	
March	1800.00	
April	2100.00	$1687.50
May	1950.00	1800.00
June	1800.00	1912.50
July	2050.00	1975.00
August	2200.00	2000.00
September	2000.00	2012.50
October	2200.00	2112.50
November	2800.00	2300.00
December	2950.00	2487.50

Mean for January, February, March, and April

$$\frac{\$1500 + \$1350 + \$1800 + \$2100}{4} = \$1687.50$$

Mean for February, March, April and May

$$\frac{\$1350 + \$1800 + \$2100 + \$1950}{4} = \$1800.00$$

and so forth to December.

EXERCISE 9.9

B 1. A farmer charted the mass, in kilograms, of a prize calf over two years. The results are given below. Calculate the cumulative means and 3-month moving means over the two-year period. For comparison, graph the cumulative mean and the monthly masses on the same line graph.

	Year 1	Year 2
May	75	542
June	93	550
July	114	553
August	153	564
September	197	560
October	230	569
November	275	572
December	311	574
January	412	572
February	440	575
March	492	580
April	520	578

2. World population figures since 1650:

1650–555 000 000	1850–1 200 000 000
1700–600 000 000	1900–1 500 000 000
1750–725 000 000	1950–3 400 000 000
1800–900 000 000	2000–5 500 000 000 (projected)

Make a table showing the 50 a cumulative means and 100 a moving means.

C 3. Land-speed records for the car have increased dramatically since 1890.
(a) Calculate the cumulative means from the information given.
(b) Construct a histogram of the speeds.
(c) On the same graph, construct a line graph of the cumulative means.

Land-Speed Records (km/h)			
1900	63	1950	634
1910	211	1960	863
1920	327	1970	966
1930	484	1980	1002
1940	634	1990	1034

CUMULATIVE AND MOVING MEANS

We may use the statistical functions on a calculator to calculate cumulative and moving means.

Example 1. The table below shows the number of days with precipitation (rain or snow) in Victoria, each month, in a particular year. Calculate the cumulative mean for each month.

Month	Days With Precipitation	Cumulative Mean
January	26	26
February	19	22.5
March	10	18.3
April	11	16.5
May	7	
June	6	
July	7	
August	6	
September	8	
October	14	
November	16	
December	15	

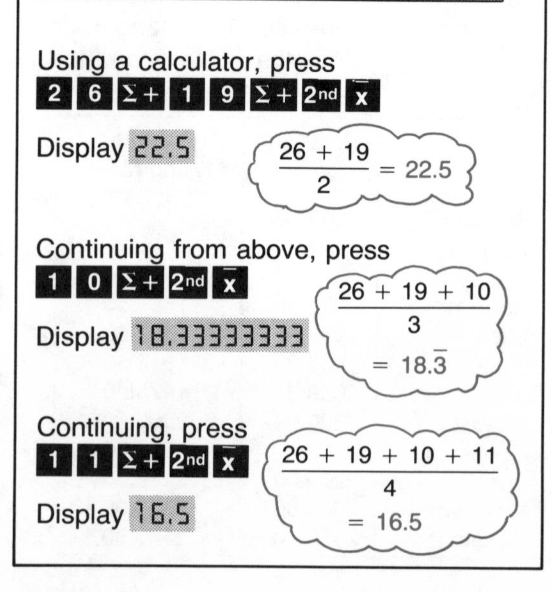

Notice that, when using a calculator with statistical functions, we did not first have to find a cumulative sum. If the cumulative total days with precipitation for a particular month is desired, we may multiply the cumulative mean for that month by the number of months. For example, to find the cumulative total days with precipitation up to and including April, we multiply the cumulative mean for April (16.5) by the number of months (4).

$16.5 \times 4 = 66$

$26 + 19 + 10 + 11 = 66$

For the first 4 months of this year there were 66 days with precipitation in Victoria.

EXERCISE 1

1. Copy and complete the above table.
2. How many days of precipitation did Victoria have in this year?

Example 2. Using the data in Example 1, calculate a 3-month moving mean.

Month	Days With Precipitation	3-Month Moving Mean
January	26	
February	19	
March	10	18.3
April	11	13.3
May	7	9.3
June	6	
July	7	
August	6	
September	8	
October	14	
November	16	
December	15	

Did you clear the statistics register before entering new data?

Some calculators may use the "INV" key to replace the "2ND" key.

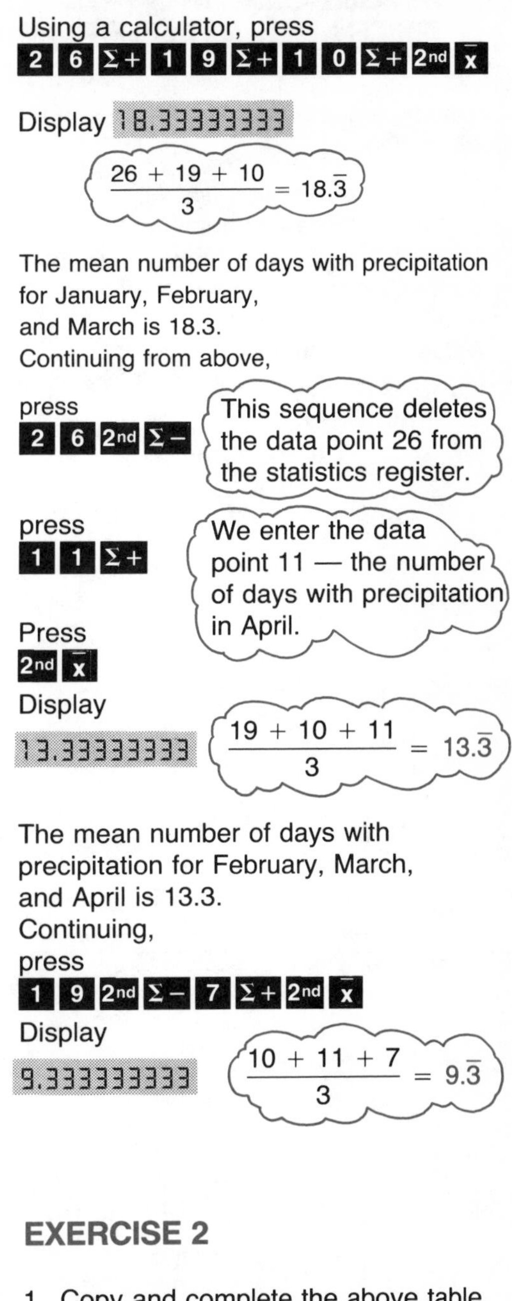

EXERCISE 2

1. Copy and complete the above table.
2. What is the mean number of days with precipitation for the months June, July, and August? (Read the value directly from the table after completing part (a).)

9.10 INTERPOLATING AND EXTRAPOLATING FROM GRAPHS

Information is gathered so it can be used to help make decisions, or predictions, or to confirm beliefs.

Graphs compare one quantity with another, and show the relationship between them. For every change in the first quantity, there is a corresponding change in the second. The shape of the graph shows clearly the type of the relationship. As in algebraic functions, the horizontal quantity (x) is compared to the vertical quantity (y).

Constantly Increasing Relationship
(Linear Relationship)

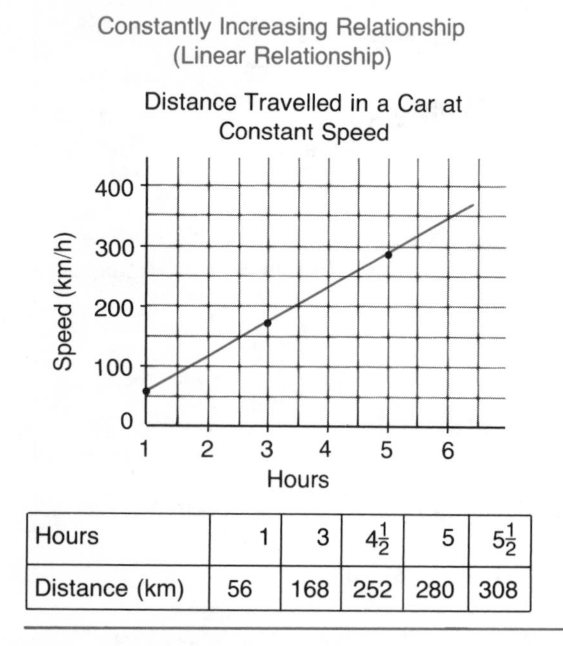

Hours	1	3	$4\frac{1}{2}$	5	$5\frac{1}{2}$
Distance (km)	56	168	252	280	308

Increasing Relationship

Property Tax Due to Assessment

Assessment ($)

9000
8000
7000
6000
5000

250 300 350 400

Tax ($)

Assessment ($)	5100	5900	6800	7600	8600
Tax ($)	250	281	324	362	410

Decreasing Relationship

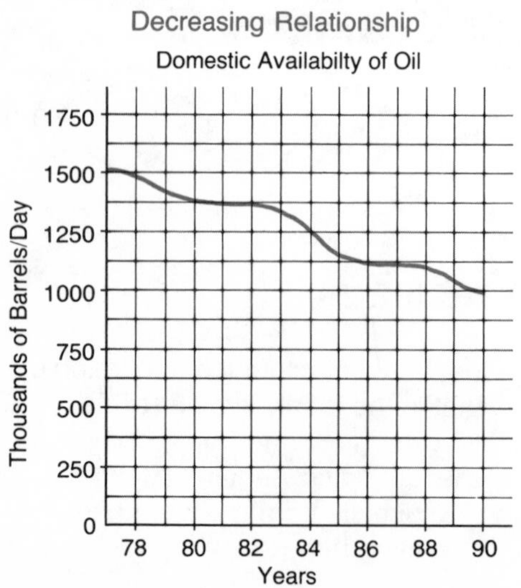

Increasing to Maximum and then
Decreasing Relationship

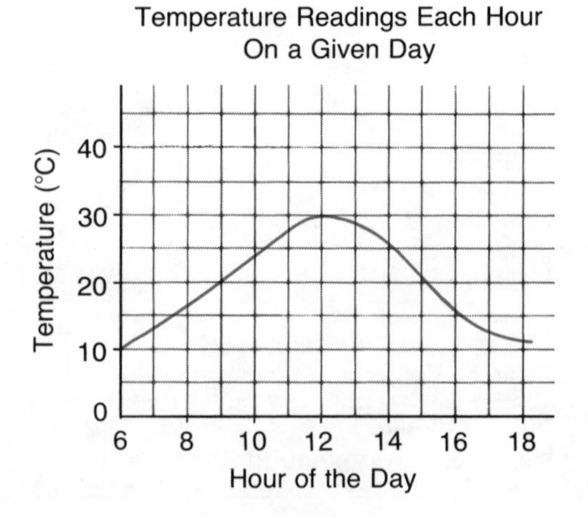

A relationship which graphs a straight line is called a linear relationship. The graph of Distance Travelled in a Car at Constant Speed is a linear relationship. The distance travelled after two hours can be read directly from the graph.

> Approximating values which were not included in the original data, but lie within the limits of the data, is known as interpolation.

From the graph Property Tax Due to Assessment, we can interpolate the tax on an \$8100 assessment as approximately \$385.

Trends can also be seen and predictions made from graphs by extending the line or curve of the graph beyond the limits of the data.

> Approximating values beyond the limits of the original data is known as extrapolation.

We can better approximate by interpolation or extrapolation the values on graphs which are non-linear by drawing a curve of best fit.

Example. Canada's growth in population from 1959 to 1968 is indicated in the following table.

Year	1959	1960	1961	1962	1963	1964	1965	1966	1967	1968
Population (millions)	17.5	17.9	18.2	18.6	18.9	19.2	19.6	20.0	20.4	20.7

(a) Represent these data on a graph by drawing a curve of best fit.
(b) If the census figure in the table was for June 1 in each case, from your graph give the approximate population of Canada on:
(i) January 1, 1964
(ii) January 1, 1961
(iii) June 1, 1970
(iv) June 1, 1972

Solution:

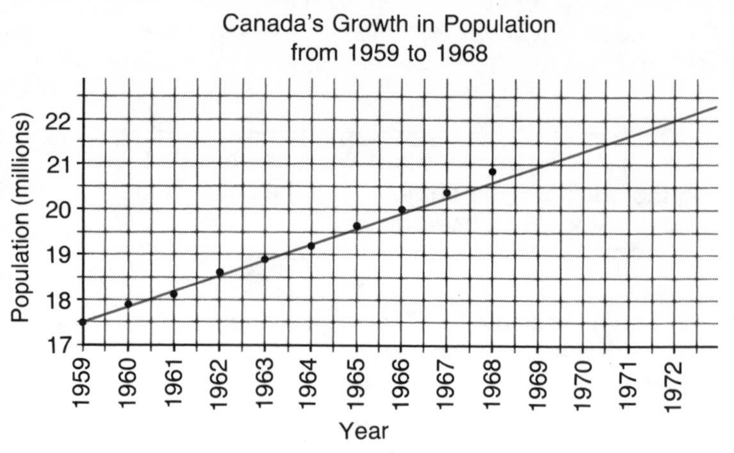

The curve of best fit is drawn as close to all points as possible. In this example the best approximation is a straight line.

(i) The population as of January 1, 1964 is approximately 19 000 000 by interpolation.

(ii) The population as of January 1, 1961 is approximately 18 000 000 by interpolation.

(iii) The predicted population, if the factors remain the same, as of June 1, 1970 is approximately 21 400 000 by extrapolation.

(iv) The predicted population, if the factors remain the same, as of June 1, 1972 is approximately 22 100 000 by extrapolation.

EXERCISE 9.10

B

1. For each description, sketch a graph that illustrates the event.

(a) A candle burning: horizontal axis, time; vertical axis, length.

(b) A rock rolling down a hill: horizontal axis, time; vertical axis, speed.

(c) A car, travelling at a constant speed, hitting a wall: horizontal axis, time; vertical axis, speed.

(d) A dragster from starting line to finish line: horizontal axis, time; vertical axis, speed.

(e) A ball thrown in the air and landing: horizontal axis, time; vertical axis, height.

(f) A car going around an "S" curve: horizontal axis, time; vertical axis, speed.

2. The graph below shows the enrolment figures from 1973 to 1985 for Woodland High School on the first day of semester 1, September of each year.

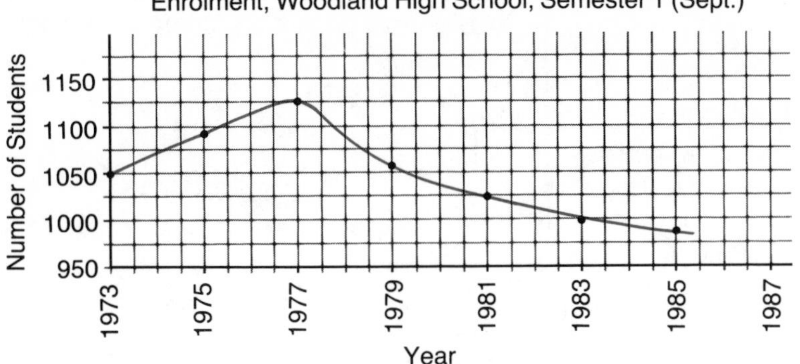

(a) What is the enrolment in September 1975?
(b) Approximately what was the enrolment in 1976?
(c) Approximately what was the enrolment at the end of semester 1, January 1979?
(c) Draw a curve of best fit.
(d) Predict the enrolment in September 1986.
(e) Predict the enrolment at the end of semester 1, January 1987.

3. The table below shows the number of albums of "Life is Strange," by The Soaring, that were sold during the weeks listed.

Album "Life is Strange" by The Soaring	
Week Ending	Number Sold
June 7	4 000
June 14	12 000
June 28	20 000
July 12	32 000
July 26	41 000

(a) Construct a frequency polygon using the data on "Life is Strange" record sales.

(b) Approximately how many albums were sold on June 21?

(c) How many records, given the rise, would you predict will be sold the week of August 2?

4. Draw a frequency polygon using the data below, which gives the altitudes we have attained through the years by mechanical means. Plot time on the horizontal axis, and height in metres on the vertical axis.

Means of Transportation	Height (m)	Year
Hot air balloon	274	1783
Hydrogen balloon	6 096	1803
Coal gas balloon	7 620	1837
Coal gas balloon	8 519	1875
Aircraft	11 145	1923
Aircraft	13 157	1930
Hydrogen balloon	18 665	1933
Helium balloon	22 066	1935
Skyrocket	24 262	1951
Rocket plane	28 346	1954

(a) Draw a curve of best fit on the frequency polygon.
(b) Predict the height reached by 1962.

5. Using the data from question 4, construct a pictograph which represents the data. Be creative and artistic.

9.11 PROBLEM SOLVING

1. If you divide a number by 6, multiply by 4, and finally subtract 22, you get 2. What is the number?

2. Place the numbers from 1 to 10 in the circles of the pentagon so that the sum of the three numbers on each side is 14. The number 5 has been placed to get you started.

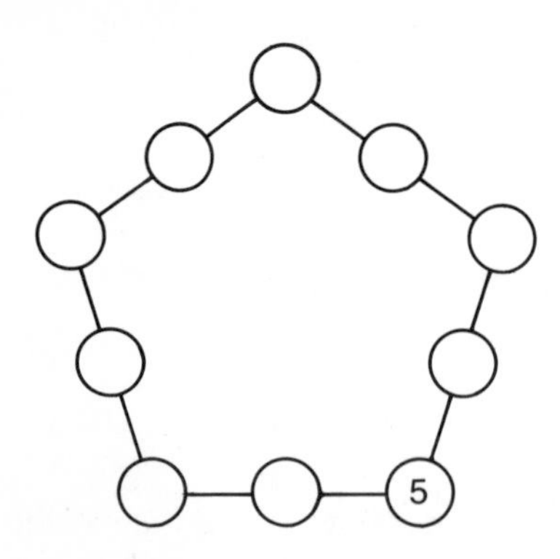

3. The area of the top of a rectangular box is 108 cm^2. The area of one side of the box is 96 cm^2. The area of one end of the box is 72 cm^2.
What is the volume of the box?

4. The Marshalls want to travel from Winnipeg to Halifax. On the way they want to stop in Toronto and Montreal to visit friends.
There are two flights and one train they can take from Winnipeg to Toronto.
There are three flights, one train, and one bus they can take from Toronto to Montreal.
There are two flights and two trains they can take from Montreal to Halifax.
How many different travel plans can they make?

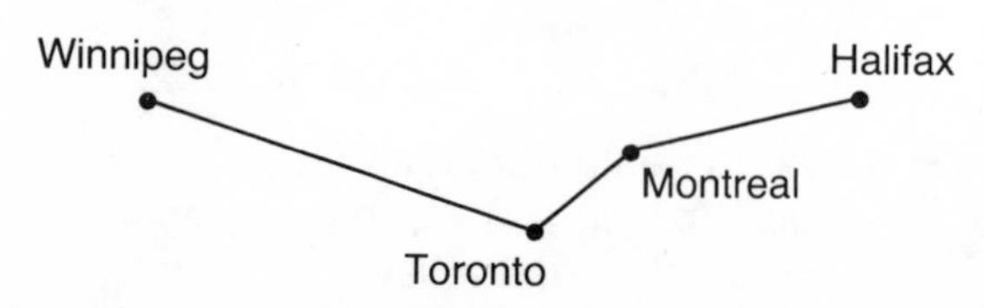

5. How many page numbers in Chapters 1 to 15 in this book have at least one digit that is a 7?

77 77 77 77
77 77 77 77

6. Sam was expecting a package so he put the following note on his door.

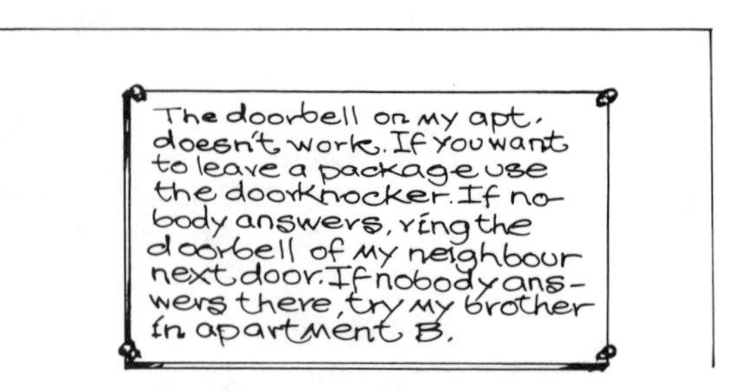

When a postman arrived with a package, the note had fallen on the floor, yet he was able to deliver the package to Sam.
Which apartment is Sam's?

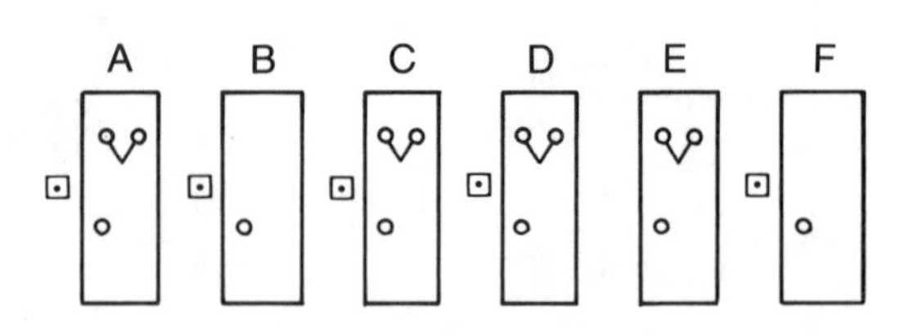

7. A lifeguard job pays \$18.50/h.
For overtime, the pay is time-and-a-half.
For working on a holiday, the pay is double time-and-a-half.
If, during one month, you worked 305 regular hours, 23 overtime hours, and 15 holiday hours, how much would you get paid?

8. What must your average speed be if you plan to drive 715 km in 9 h?

9. A famous mathematical problem states that any map can be coloured with at most 4 colours, so that any two countries that share a common boundary are coloured differently.
Trace the following map in your notebook and colour it using only 4 colours.

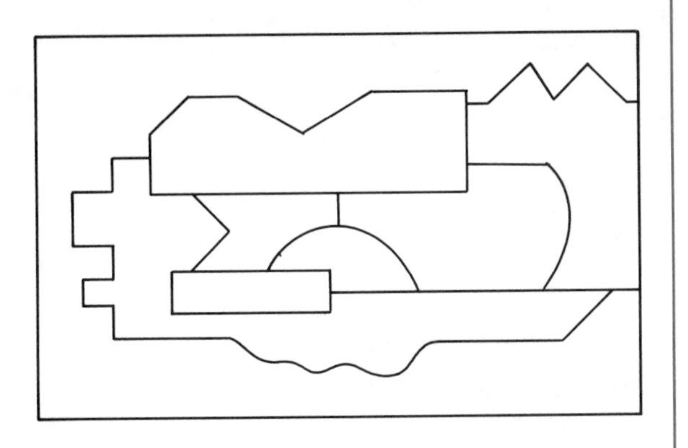

10. Place 8 dots in the following figure so that there will be no more than one dot in each row, column, or diagonal.

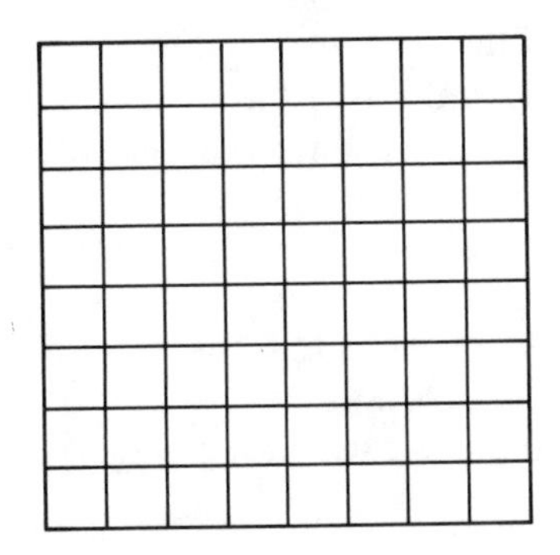

11. Geno had two purchase options when buying his twelve-speed racing bicycle. Stan's Cycle offered a plan of $135.00 down payment and $61 per month for twelve months, or $155.00 down and $58 per month for twelve months.
Which is the less expensive option, and by how much?

EXTRA

SUPERNOVA SHELTON 1987A

A supernova is an exploding star, rarely seen from Earth. In 1572, the astronomer Tycho Brahe saw a supernova explode. In 1604, Brahe's famous pupil Johannes Kepler saw another supernova explode. Both Brahe and Kepler made their discoveries without telescopes.

On the night of February 23, 1987, Canadian astronomer Ian Shelton discovered the next exploding star, which now bears his name. He made his discovery in northern Chile while working on a team from the University of Toronto.

EXERCISE

1. Supernova Shelton is 170 000 light years from Earth. A light year is the distance light travels in one year at a speed of 300 000 km/s. How far is Supernova Shelton from Earth?
2. Eighteen hours before the light reached his telescope, Supernova Shelton bombarded every square centimetre of the earth with ten billion particles called neutrinos. The bombardment started on February 23 at 7:35:41.37 Universal Time.
What time was that in your time zone?

9.12 REVIEW EXERCISE

1. The data below estimates the expenditures on advertising in the U.S.A. and Canada.

Newspaper	$15 000 000 000
Television	11 000 000 000
Direct mail	7 800 000 000
Magazine	3 500 000 000
Radio	4 800 000 000
Miscellaneous	11 400 000 000

(a) Construct a bar graph of the information.
(b) Construct a circle graph of the information using percentages of the total amount spent on advertising in the U.S.A. and Canada.

2. Find the mean, median, and mode.
(a) 109, 45, 86, 86, 34, 109, 56, 93, 86, 108
(b) 1, 2, 3, 4, 5, 6, 7, 8, 9, 10
(c) −9, −8, −7, −6, −5, −4, −3, −2, −1, 0, 0, 0, 0, 1, 2, 3, 4, 5, 6, 7, 8, 9
(d) 1.2, 2.3, 4.5, 1.2, 4.5, 2.3, 2.3, 4.7, 4.8, 4.9
(e) 1, 1, 1, 1, 1, 1, 1, 1, 1, 2
(f) $8000, $8000, $4000, $2000, $1000

3. The table below shows the hourly wages of 70 high school students, selected at random, who have part-time jobs after school or on weekends.

$4.49	$8.20	$9.00	$6.30	$4.50	$4.71
6.00	6.00	8.50	8.77	12.50	8.50
4.49	7.20	9.00	5.20	8.25	5.00
5.10	9.00	4.75	8.50	4.75	8.45
5.80	8.00	5.64	8.90	4.50	7.23
4.67	5.50	4.34	4.75	6.59	5.60
4.45	8.34	8.75	6.25	5.72	4.75
6.10	4.20	8.90	5.43	12.80	7.00
7.50	5.20	9.00	8.10	8.50	4.35
2.00	5.10	4.50	7.45	9.23	5.10
4.46	8.40	4.50	7.50	4.80	
8.40	9.50	4.65	8.50	4.78	

(a) What is the range?
(b) Select classes for division of the information.
(c) Using the classes selected above, tally the information on a tally sheet and give the frequency in each class.

4. Maximum temperatures in degrees Celsius were recorded for 50 consecutive days. The data are given in the table.

12	13	10	9	10	9	11	10	8	7
3	−2	−4	0	2	−2	−4	−1	0	3
5	7	2	2	6	2	0	−3	−9	−8
−11	−10	−9	−8	−4	0	0	3	4	−1
4	3	7	6	3	2	7	7	5	0

(a) Tally the data in a frequency distribution table using a class interval of 3. Include the cumulative frequency.
(b) Find the midpoint of each class.
(c) What is the weighted mean?
(d) What is the median?
(e) What is the mode?
(f) From the frequency table, construct a histogram.
(g) Draw a line on the graph at the mean, median, and mode.
(h) On the same graph, superimpose a frequency polygon.
(i) On the same graph, using a different type or coloured line, superimpose a cumulative frequency polygon.

5. Survey your class to determine each person's age in months.
(a) List the data in a descending array.
(b) Tally the data in a frequency distribution table by number of months. Include the cumulative frequency.
(c) What is the mean?
(d) What is the mode?
(e) What is the median?
(f) Which of the measures of central tendency best describes the ages of the students in the class? Why?

6. The City Summer Exposition ran for ten days in August. The number of people who attended is given first, and the average temperature each day, in degrees Celsius, is given in the last column.

City Summer Exposition		
Day	Number Attending	Average Temperature (°C)
Friday (Day 1)	8000	27
Saturday (Day 2)	10 000	28
Sunday (Day 3)	9500	26
Monday (Day 4)	7000	22
Tuesday (Day 5)	6000	21
Wednesday (Day 6)	8000	24
Thursday (Day 7)	9000	23
Friday (Day 8)	12 000	26
Saturday (Day 9)	13 000	27
Sunday (Day 10)	10 000	30

(a) For the data in the table continue the table by calculating cumulative frequency, the cumulative mean, and the moving mean over two days for the attendance *and* the temperature.
(b) On a graph, construct a histogram of the attendance and a frequency polygon for the cumulative mean attendance.
(c) On a graph, construct a histogram of the temperature and a frequency polygon for the cumulative mean temperature.
(d) On a graph, construct two frequency polygons using two different types or coloured lines, of the cumulative frequency of attendance and temperature.
(e) From the data and graphs, can you draw conclusions about the relationship between the attendance and the temperature?
(f) What factors, other than weather, could influence attendance at the Exposition?

7. Pick-Your-Own Strawberry Patch sells strawberries at three different prices. The sign at the entrance reads:

You pick them in your containers
33¢/kg

You pick them in our containers
35¢/kg

We pick them in our containers
55¢/kg

On opening day the Patch sold:
8500 kg at 33¢/kg
2750 kg at 35¢/kg
900 kg at 55¢/kg

(a) What is the unweighted mean price of a box of strawberries?
(b) What is the weighted mean price of a box of strawberries on opening day?
(c) Which mean is more of an indicator of the profitability of Pick-Your-Own Strawberry Patch?

9.13 CHAPTER 9 TEST

1. Find the mean, median, mode, and range for the following sets of data.
(a) 4, 6, 10, 3, 5, 9, 5
(b) 2.5, 7.8, 1.0, 12.3, 8.9, 2.5, 0.6, 2.5, 7.8, 9.1
(c) -1, 0, 0, 1

2. Calculate the weighted mean of the following data.

Class Values	Class Mid-values x	Frequency f	Frequency × Mid-values f × x
10-12		11	
13-15		8	
16-18		12	
19-21		15	
22-24		8	

3. The table below shows the number of days with precipitation (rain or snow) in Halifax, each month, for a particular year.
(a) Complete the table, giving the cumulative days with precipitation, the cumulative means, and the 4-month moving means.
(b) Display the data in a histogram and, on the same graph, superimpose a frequency polygon for the cumulative mean days with precipitation.

Month	Days With Precipitation	Cumulative Total Days With Precipitation	Cumulative Mean	4-Month Moving Mean
January	23			
February	16			
March	16			
April	15			
May	12			
June	11			
July	8			
August	10			
September	14			
October	8			
November	16			
December	19			

BORROWING MONEY

REVIEW AND PREVIEW TO CHAPTER 10

PERCENTAGES

Most work with finance involves percentages in some form.

To find $6\frac{1}{2}$ % of 80 using a calculator, press

8 0 × 6 · 5 %

The display is

5.2

EXERCISE

1. Calculate the following using a calculator.

(a) 2% of $15 (b) 3% of $169
(c) 4% of $9640 (d) 1% of $274
(e) 5% of $43 (f) 7% of $971
(g) 8% of $536 (h) 9% of $634
(i) 12% of $864 (j) $10\frac{1}{4}$% of $579
(k) 5% of $805 (l) 15% of $1650
(m) 3% of $534 (n) $4\frac{1}{2}$% of $71
(o) 6% of $753 (p) $3\frac{1}{2}$% of $654
(q) 8% of $846 (r) $12\frac{1}{2}$% of $395

2. Express the following percents as decimals.

(a) 6% (b) 8%
(c) 10% (d) 11%
(e) $5\frac{1}{2}$% (f) $6\frac{3}{4}$%
(g) $12\frac{1}{2}$ (h) $7\frac{3}{4}$%
(i) $9\frac{1}{4}$% (j) $10\frac{1}{8}$%
(k) $11\frac{5}{8}$% (l) $17\frac{3}{4}$%

FRACTIONS OF A YEAR

Since interest is usually given in per annum rates, time must be expressed as a fraction of a year. The table shown on the next page shows selected numbers of days as decimal fractions of a year. The complete table appears in the Appendix. Where the time is given in months, assume 30 d/month.

EXERCISE

Express the following as fractions of a year.

1. 33 d
2. 63 d
3. 93 d
4. 5 months
5. 2 months
6. 7 months
7. 12 weeks
8. 26 weeks
9. 60 d
10. 90 d
11. 120 d
12. 3 weeks, 2 d
13. 5 weeks, 2 d
14. 4 weeks, 2 d
15. 8 weeks
16. 6 weeks, 3 d
17. 10 months
18. 48 h
19. 30 months
20. 72 h

DAYS AND DATES

The same table can be used to find the number of days, and hence the fraction of a year, between two dates.

Example 1. Find the number of days between April 24 and June 16. Express your answer as a fraction of a year.

Solution:

June 16: day 167 (from table)
April 24: day 114 (from table)
Number of days = 167 − 114
= 53
53 d = 0.1452 a (from table)

Example 2. A loan is made on April 23 and is to be repaid in 93 d. Find the due date.

Solution:
April 23: day 113

$113 + 93 = 206$

day $206 =$ July 25

The due date is July 25.

EXERCISE

1. Find the number of days between the following dates. Express your answer as a fraction of a year. All dates are in the same or successive years.

For convenience, a complete table of days is provided in the Appendix.

(a) January 6 and March 16
(b) February 14 and May 30
(c) February 28 and July 19
(d) March 7 and September 21
(e) April 22 and November 1
(f) May 12 and September 8
(g) July 15 and December 20
(h) October 3 and November 17
(i) November 17 and March 18
(j) October 29 and March 13
(k) December 20 and May 6
(l) November 1 and January 8

2. Find the following dates.
(a) 30 d after February 6
(b) 63 d after March 4
(c) 25 d after April 28
(d) 93 d after May 17
(e) 120 d after June 8
(f) 57 d after August 11
(g) 75 d after November 7
(h) 150 d after December 15

	March		April		May		June	
Day of Month	Day of Year	Decimal Equivalent	Day of Year	Decimal Equivalent	Day of Year	Decimal Equivalent	Day of Year	Decimal Equivalent
1	*60*	0.1644	*91*	0.2493	*121*	0.3315	*152*	0.4164
2	*61*	0.1671	*92*	0.2521	*122*	0.3342	*153*	0.4192
3	*62*	0.1699	*93*	0.2548	*123*	0.3370	*154*	0.4219
4	*63*	0.1726	*94*	0.2575	*124*	0.3397	*155*	0.4247
5	*64*	0.1753	*95*	0.2603	*125*	0.3425	*156*	0.4274
6	*65*	0.1781	*96*	0.2630	*126*	0.3452	*157*	0.4301
7	*66*	0.1808	*97*	0.2658	*127*	0.3479	*158*	0.4329
8	*67*	0.1836	*98*	0.2685	*128*	0.3507	*159*	0.4356
9	*68*	0.1863	*99*	0.2712	*129*	0.3534	*160*	0.4384
10	*69*	0.1890	*100*	0.2740	*130*	0.3562	*161*	0.4411
11	*70*	0.1918	*101*	0.2767	*131*	0.3589	*162*	0.4438
12	*71*	0.1945	*102*	0.2795	*132*	0.3616	*163*	0.4466
13	*72*	0.1973	*103*	0.2822	*133*	0.3644	*164*	0.4493
14	*73*	0.2000	*104*	0.2849	*134*	0.3671	*165*	0.4521
15	*74*	0.2027	*105*	0.2877	*135*	0.3699	*166*	0.4548
16	*75*	0.2055	*106*	0.2904	*136*	0.3726	*167*	0.4575
17	*76*	0.2082	*107*	0.2932	*137*	0.3753	*168*	0.4603
18	*77*	0.2110	*108*	0.2959	*138*	0.3781	*169*	0.4630
19	*78*	0.2137	*109*	0.2986	*139*	0.3808	*170*	0.4658
20	*79*	0.2164	*110*	0.3014	*140*	0.3836	*171*	0.4685
21	*80*	0.2192	*111*	0.3041	*141*	0.3863	*172*	0.4712
22	*81*	0.2219	*112*	0.3068	*142*	0.3890	*173*	0.4740
23	*82*	0.2247	*113*	0.3096	*143*	0.3918	*174*	0.4767
24	*83*	0.2274	*114*	0.3123	*144*	0.3945	*175*	0.4795
25	*84*	0.2301	*115*	0.3151	*145*	0.3973	*176*	0.4822
26	*85*	0.2329	*116*	0.3178	*146*	0.4000	*177*	0.4849
27	*86*	0.2356	*117*	0.3205	*147*	0.4027	*178*	0.4877
28	*87*	0.2384	*118*	0.3233	*148*	0.4055	*179*	0.4904
29	*88*	0.2411	*119*	0.3260	*149*	0.4082	*180*	0.4932
30	*89*	0.2438	*120*	0.3288	*150*	0.4110	*181*	0.4959
31	*90*	0.2466			*151*	0.4137		

March 6 is the 65th day of the year.

June 20 is the 171st day of the year.

10.1 SIMPLE INTEREST

When someone needs money to purchase goods, a home, a car, or to make an investment, the money may be borrowed. When a sum of money is lent or borrowed, the rent for the use of the money is called interest. Interest is the charge, over and above what is borrowed, for using the money that belongs to other people or institutions.

Throughout this chapter, we will be using the following definitions.

Principal (P):	the sum of money deposited or borrowed
Interest (I):	the money charged for the use of the principal
Rate per annum (r):	the interest charged per year expressed as a percentage of the principal
Time (t):	the length of time on which interest is charged
Amount (A):	the sum of money to be repaid, including interest and principal

If you borrow \$100 for 3 a at 12% interest, you are agreeing to pay 12% of \$100 each year. 12% of \$100 is \$12. If you must pay this for 3 a, you pay \$12 × 3 = \$36.

We may find the interest in one calculation:

$I = Prt$
$I = 100 \times 0.12 \times 3$
$= 12 \times 3$
$= 36$

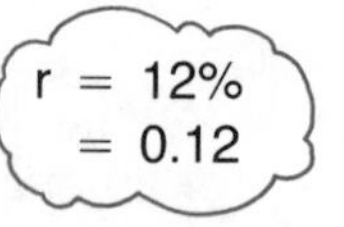

You must repay the interest, \$36, plus the original \$100 at the end of the 3 a term.

The sum of money to be repaid, A, is found as

$A = P + I$
$A = 100 + 36$
$= 136$

The total to be repaid is \$136.

Two equations are used in simple interest.

Amount = Principal + Interest
$A = P + I$

Interest = Principal × Rate × Time
$I = Prt$

They may be combined, by substitution, to yield:

$$\boxed{A = P + Prt}$$

Example 1. Jane borrows $500 for 2 a at 10% interest. How much must be repaid at the end of the term?

Solution: $A = P + Prt$
$P = 500,\ r = 0.1,\ t = 2$ (10% = 0.1)
$A = 500 + 500 \times 0.1 \times 2$
$= 500 + 100$
$= 600$
At the end of the term Jane must pay $600.

Example 2. Find the amount to be repaid if $570 is borrowed for 63 d at 12% interest.

Solution: Express 63 d as a fraction of a year and use the formula for the amount.

METHOD I
Using the table "Days Expressed in Decimal Equivalents of a Year — 365 d Basis" in the Appendix,
$A = P + Prt$
$P = 570,\ r = 0.12,\ t = 63 \text{ d}$
$= 0.1726 \text{ a}$
$A = 570 + 570 \times 0.12 \times 0.1726$
$\doteq 570 + 11.81$
$\doteq 581.81$ (to the nearest cent)

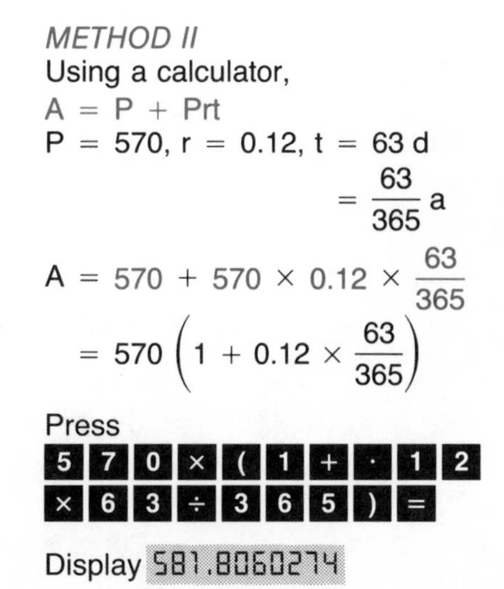

METHOD II
Using a calculator,
$A = P + Prt$
$P = 570,\ r = 0.12,\ t = 63 \text{ d}$
$= \frac{63}{365} \text{ a}$
$A = 570 + 570 \times 0.12 \times \frac{63}{365}$
$= 570\left(1 + 0.12 \times \frac{63}{365}\right)$
Press
5 7 0 × (1 + · 1 2 × 6 3 ÷ 3 6 5) =
Display 581.8060274

The amount to be repaid is $581.81.

The simple interest equations may be rearranged to yield formulas for the rate, the time, or the principal.

Example 3. A deposit of \$350 earned \$42 interest in 18 months.
Find the rate of interest.

Solution: Solve the equation $I = Prt$ for the rate, r.

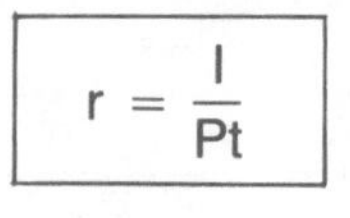

$$r = \frac{I}{Pt}$$

$I = 42$, $P = 350$, $t = 18$ months
$= 1.5$ a

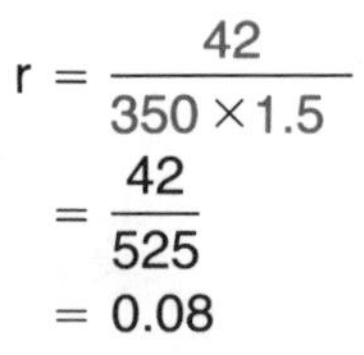

$$r = \frac{42}{350 \times 1.5} = \frac{42}{525} = 0.08$$

Using a calculator, press
4 2 ÷ 3 5 0 ÷ 1 · 5 =

Display 0.08

The rate of interest was 8%.

Example 4. How much should be deposited now at 12% annual interest to have an amount of \$8000 in 5 a?

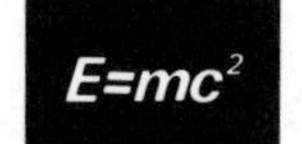

Solution: In the equation $A = P + Prt$,
$A = 8000$, $r = 0.12$, $t = 5$.

$$\begin{aligned} 8000 &= P + P \times 0.12 \times 5 \\ &= P + P(0.6) \\ &= P(1 + 0.6) \\ &= P(1.6) \end{aligned}$$

P is a common factor.

Solve for P:

$$P = \frac{8000}{1.6} = 5000$$

A principal of \$5000 must be deposited now.

A formula to determine principal, when the amount A is known, may be found using the method in example 4.

$$\begin{aligned} A &= P + Prt \\ &= P(1 + rt) \end{aligned}$$

P is a common factor.

Solve for P:

$$P = \frac{A}{1 + rt}$$

EXERCISE 10.1

A 1. (a) Define:
(i) amount (ii) interest
(iii) principal (iv) rate (v) time
(b) Give three formulas which describe relations between the quantities defined in (a).

B 2. Solve the formula I = Prt for r and t.

3. Calculate the interest and the amount repaid in each case.
(a) \$4000 at 7% for 6 months
(b) \$520 at 8% for 3 months
(c) \$5280.00 at 9% for 256 d
(d) \$750 at 9% for 8 months
(e) \$429.65 at $5\frac{1}{2}$% for 5 weeks
(f) \$2500 at 10% for 7 months

4. Find the missing quantity in each line.

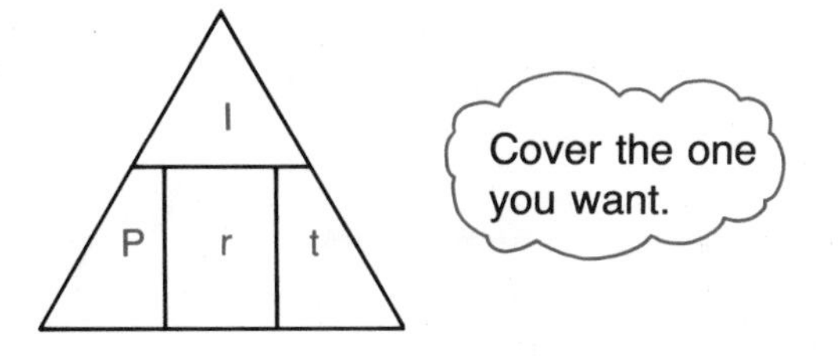

	I	P	r	t
(a)	■	\$200	6%	6 months
(b)	■	\$1200	$5\frac{1}{2}$%	1 a
(c)	\$65	■	5%	3 months
(d)	\$90	■	12%	1 a
(e)	\$640	\$16 000	■	6 months
(f)	\$31.50	\$350	■	9 months
(g)	\$2.25	\$90	6%	■
(h)	\$3750	\$50 000	$7\frac{1}{2}$%	■

5. Calculate the amounts to be repaid to the nearest cent.
(a) \$375.00 at 6% for 40 d
(b) \$539.00 at 8% for 60 d
(c) \$7348.00 at $8\frac{1}{4}$% for 150 d
(d) \$125.25 at $6\frac{1}{2}$% for 93 d

6. The Cedar-wood Canoe Company borrowed working capital at 7% to keep the plant producing over the slack winter months. After 170 d they repaid the total loan with a payment of \$10 326.06.
How much had they borrowed?

7. What principal must be lent out at $5\frac{1}{2}$% to give a return of \$5000 after 195 d?

8. The Extension Rule Company borrowed \$15 000 for 130 d and repaid \$15 293.84. What rate of simple interest was charged?

9. J. P. Howard endowed his alma mater with a scholarship which amounted to the annual income from \$25 000 invested at $6\frac{3}{4}$%.
What was the annual cash value of the scholarship?

10. South Western Trust pays $5\frac{1}{2}$%/a on deposits in its savings accounts. At the end of 6 months the interest is calculated and added to the account. The interest for the next period is calculated on the new balance.
If you deposit \$500 in an account and leave it for 2 a, what balance will be in the account?

11. A loan of \$500 was taken out on June 15 and repaid on August 30, the same year.
If interest was charged at 12%, how much was repaid?

12. \$1500 was borrowed for 93 d on April 23.
If interest was charged at $9\frac{1}{2}$%, what amount was repaid?
When was it due?

C 13. \$750.00 was borrowed on March 3 and \$755.42 was repaid on April 5.
(a) How much interest was charged?
(b) What rate of interest was charged?

10.2 COMPOUND INTEREST

When interest is compounded, interest is being calculated not only on the principal, but on the principal and the interest being accumulated. When major purchases are made such as cars, homes, or businesses, the cost of borrowing increases because interest is compounded. This means that interest is calculated on the amount plus any accumulated interest.

Example 1. On a loan of \$100, compare the interest accrued and the total owed at the end of a two-year term at the following rates.
(a) 12%/a
(b) 12%/a compounded semi-annually

Solution:

(a) $I = Prt$ and $A = P + I$

$I = 100 \times 0.12 \times 2 = 24$

$A = 100 + 24 = 124$

The interest accrued is \$24 and the amount owed at end of term is \$124.

(b) Since the interest is calculated twice per year (semi-annually), we say that the conversion period is six months or one-half year. The interest rate per conversion period is 6%. Over a two-year period there will be four conversion periods.

(Note that the amount at the end of one conversion period becomes the principal for the next.)

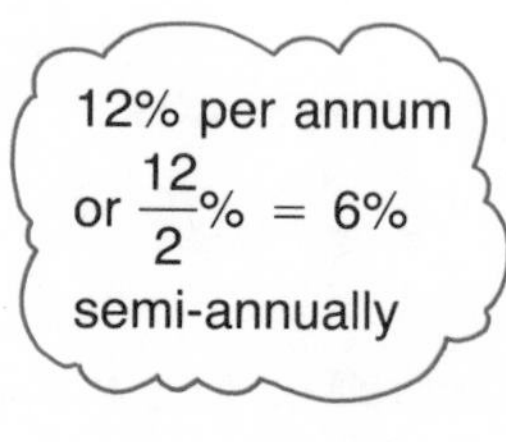

$I = Prt \quad A = P + I$	
1. After 1 conversion period $I = \$100(0.12)(\frac{1}{2})$ $= \$100(0.06)$ $= \$6$ $A = \$100 + \$6$ $= \$106$	2. After 2 conversion periods $I = \$106(0.12)(\frac{1}{2})$ $= \$106(0.06)$ $= \$6.36$ $A = \$106 + \$6.36$ $= \$112.36$
Note in each case rate per conversion period is 0.06	
3. After 3 conversion periods $I = \$112.36(0.06)$ $= \$6.74$ $A = \$112.36 + \$6.74$ $= \$119.10$	4. After 4 conversion periods $I = \$119.10(0.06)$ $= \$7.15$ $A = \$119.10 + \$7.15$ $= \$126.25$

The interest for the same loan, same term, same rate at simple interest is \$24.00, and at compound interest is \$26.25. The amount repaid is \$124 at simple interest and \$126.25 at compound interest.

To lessen the work when computing compound interest, we look for a pattern which will lead to a compound interest formula.

Example 2. Examine the amount of the following loan after each conversion period to find a pattern. A sum of \$100 is lent for 2 a at 8% compounded semi-annually.

Solution:
Since the interest is being calculated twice per year, the interest rate per conversion period is $\frac{8\%}{2} = 4\%$. At the beginning of the first conversion period the principal is \$100. For each conversion period, $r = 0.04$ per period and $t = 1$ period.

After 1 period:

$$\begin{aligned} \text{Amount} &= P + Prt \\ \text{Amount} &= 100 + 100 \times 0.04 \times 1 \\ &= 100 + 100(0.04) \\ &= 100[1 + 0.04] \\ &= 100(1.04) \end{aligned}$$

(Common factor) (1 + 0.04 = 1.04)

The principal for the second period is the amount after the first period: 100(1.04).

After 2 periods:

$$\begin{aligned} \text{Amount} &= P + Prt \\ \text{Amount} &= 100(1.04) + 100(1.04) \times 0.04 \times 1 \\ &= 100(1.04)[1 + 0.04] \\ &= 100(1.04)(1.04) \\ &= 100(1.04)^2 \end{aligned}$$

(Common factor)

The principal for the third period is the amount after the second period: $100(1.04)^2$.

After 3 periods:

$$\begin{aligned} \text{Amount} &= P + Prt \\ \text{Amount} &= 100(1.04)^2 + 100(1.04)^2 \times 0.04 \times 1 \\ &= 100(1.04)^2[1 + 0.04] \\ &= 100(1.04)^2(1.04) \\ &= 100(1.04)^3 \end{aligned}$$

(Common factor)

Using the pattern to find the amount after the fourth period, we multiply the amount after the third period by the factor 1.04.

After 4 periods:

$$\begin{aligned} \text{Amount} &= 100(1.04)^3 \times 1.04 \\ &= 100(1.04)^4 \end{aligned}$$

The pattern suggests the following compound interest formula.

$$A = P(1 + i)^n$$

where A is the amount
P is the principal
n is the number of conversion periods
i is the interest rate **per period**

The interest rate per period may be found using the following formula.

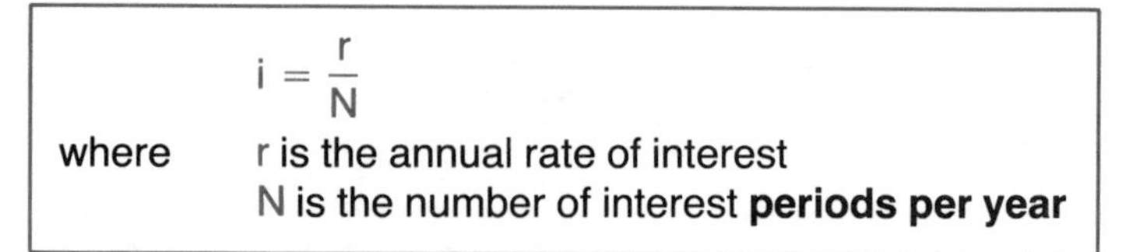

$$i = \frac{r}{N}$$

where r is the annual rate of interest
N is the number of interest **periods per year**

Example 3. A sum of \$1500 is lent for 2 a at 8% compounded quarterly.
(a) Write the amount in the form $A = P(1 + i)^n$.
(b) Evaluate the amount using a calculator.

Solution: (a) Since interest is calculated 4 times per year (quarterly), $N = 4$.

The interest rate per period: $i = \frac{r}{N}$

$$i = \frac{0.08}{4}$$
$$= 0.02$$

To find an expression for the amount:
$P = 1500$, $i = 0.02$, $n = 2 \times 4$
$= 8$

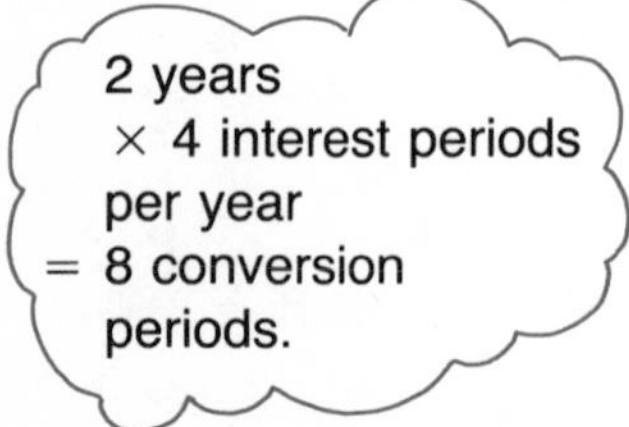

$A = P(1 + i)^n$
$A = 1500(1 + 0.02)^8$
$= 1500(1.02)^8$

An expression for the amount is
$A = 1500(1.02)^8$.

(b) Using a calculator,
press
1 5 0 0 × 1 . 0 2 y^x 8 =

Display 1757.489072

The amount is \$1757.49 (to the nearest cent).

EXERCISE 10.2

A 1. Give the rate ,i, per conversion period.

	Rate per annum (r)	Compounded
(a)	10%	Semi-annually
(b)	12%	Annually
(c)	8%	Semi-annually
(d)	7%	Semi-annually
(e)	12%	Quarterly
(f)	9%	Semi-annually
(g)	8%	Quarterly
(h)	15%	Quarterly
(i)	12%	Monthly
(j)	18%	Monthly

B 2. Write the following in the form $P(1 + i)^n$.

(a) $1000 at 9%/a, compounded annually for 10 a

(b) $325 at 12%/a, compounded monthly for 36 months

(c) $117 at 10%/a, compounded semi-annually for 18 months

(d) $200 at $11\frac{1}{4}$%/a, compounded semi-annually for $3\frac{1}{2}$ a

(e) $5000 at 8%/a, compounded quarterly for $5\frac{1}{2}$ a

(f) $4500 at 9%/a, compounded semi-annually for $9\frac{1}{2}$ a

(g) $600 at 18%/a, compounded monthly for $2\frac{1}{4}$ a

(h) $2500 at 12%/a, compounded bi-monthly for $4\frac{1}{2}$ a

3. Find the interest at the end of the first conversion period for each of the following loans.

(a) $5000 at 8% compounded semi-annually

(b) $8000 at 12% compounded quarterly

(c) $7500 at 10% compounded semi-annually

(d) $500 at 12% compounded monthly

(e) $12 000 at 18% compounded bi-monthly

4. $500 is invested at 12%/a, compounded semi-annually. The interest is added to the principal at the end of each conversion period.
Calculate the interest and the amount at the end of the first 4 conversion periods.

5. $100 is borrowed at 12%, compounded quarterly. The interest is added to the principal.
Calculate the amount required to repay the loan after 15 months.

> Unless stated otherwise it will be assumed that the interest is added to the principal at the end of each conversion period.

6. (a) Find the amount to be repaid when $5000 is borrowed at 10%/a, compounded semi-annually for 3 a.

(b) Find the amount to be repaid when $5000 is borrowed at 10%/a, simple interest for 3 a.

7. Find the amount to be repaid when $2500 is borrowed at 18%/a, compounded quarterly for 2 a.

8. Find the amount required to repay a debt of $300 when interest is charged for $1\frac{1}{2}$ a at 8%/a, compounded semi-annually.

MIND BENDER

Place the numbers from 1 to 12 in the circles so that each side adds up to 28.

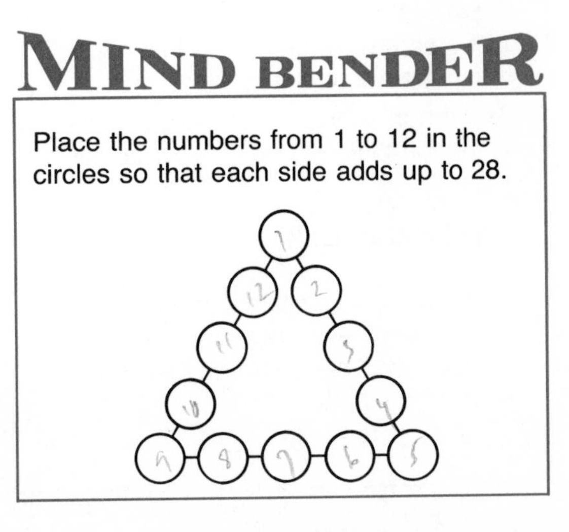

EXTRA

10.3 COMPARISON OF SIMPLE AND COMPOUND INTEREST

The tables below show what would be received from an investment of $100 at 8%/a under simple interest and under compound interest.

Simple Interest: $A = P + Prt$	
Years Invested	Amount Returned
1	$108
2	116
3	124
4	132
5	140
6	148
7	156
8	164
9	172
10	180
11	188
12	196

Compound Interest: $A = P(1 + i)^n$	
Years Invested	Amount Returned
1	$108
2	116.64
3	125.97
4	136.05
5	146.93
6	158.69
7	171.38
8	185.09
9	199.90
10	215.89
11	233.16
12	251.82

We may graph the relationships to compare the results, as shown on the following page. The black line shows the growth of the investment at 8%/a simple interest. The red curve shows the growth of the investment at 8%/a compounded annually.

The graph shows that more interest is accumulated under compound interest than under simple interest.

EXERCISE 10.3

1. How much additional interest has accumulated after 12 a at 8%/a compounded annually compared to 8% simple interest?

2. How long, to the nearest year, does it take for $100 to double when invested at
(a) 8%/a simple interest?
(b) 8%/a compounded annually?

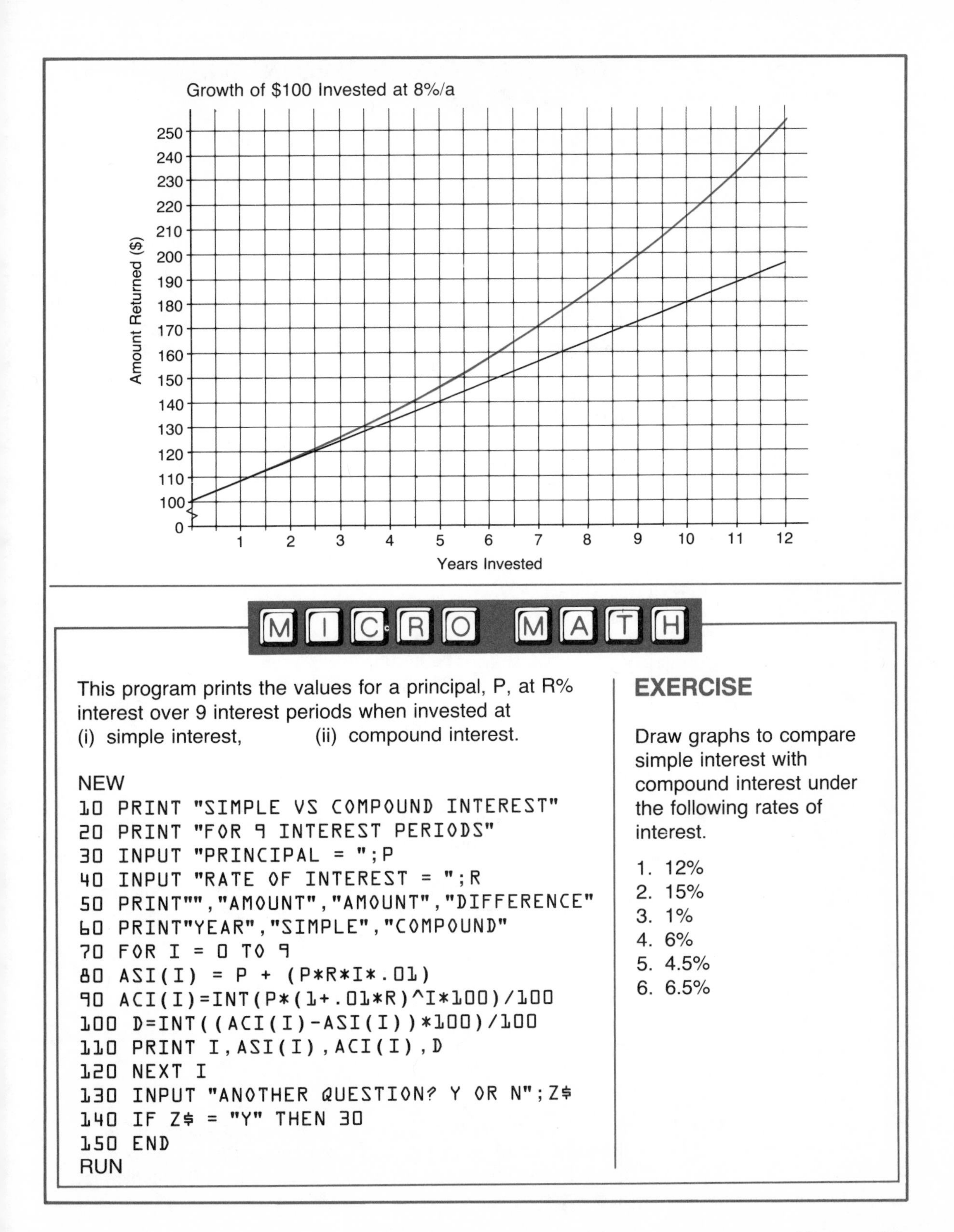

This program prints the values for a principal, P, at R% interest over 9 interest periods when invested at
(i) simple interest, (ii) compound interest.

```
NEW
10 PRINT "SIMPLE VS COMPOUND INTEREST"
20 PRINT "FOR 9 INTEREST PERIODS"
30 INPUT "PRINCIPAL = ";P
40 INPUT "RATE OF INTEREST = ";R
50 PRINT"","AMOUNT","AMOUNT","DIFFERENCE"
60 PRINT"YEAR","SIMPLE","COMPOUND"
70 FOR I = 0 TO 9
80 ASI(I) = P + (P*R*I*.01)
90 ACI(I)=INT(P*(1+.01*R)^I*100)/100
100 D=INT((ACI(I)-ASI(I))*100)/100
110 PRINT I,ASI(I),ACI(I),D
120 NEXT I
130 INPUT "ANOTHER QUESTION? Y OR N";Z$
140 IF Z$ = "Y" THEN 30
150 END
RUN
```

EXERCISE

Draw graphs to compare simple interest with compound interest under the following rates of interest.

1. 12%
2. 15%
3. 1%
4. 6%
5. 4.5%
6. 6.5%

10.4 USING COMPOUND INTEREST TABLES

To reduce the work required to find the amount of a loan or investment, tables of values for $(1 + i)^n$ have been calculated for various values of i and n.

Since: $A = P(1 + i)^n$,

to find the amount for a given investment it is only necessary to multiply the appropriate value in the table by the principal invested. A part of the table is shown. The complete table, "Amount of $1(1 + i)^n$", is given in the Appendix.

n \ i	4%	5%
1	1.040 00	1.050 00
2	1.081 60	1.102 50
3	1.124 86	1.157 63
4	1.169 86	1.215 51
5	1.216 65	1.276 28
6	1.265 32	1.340 10
7	1.315 93	1.407 10
8	1.368 57	1.477 46
9	1.423 31	1.551 33
10	1.480 24	1.628 89
11	1.539 45	1.710 34
12	1.601 03	1.795 86
13	1.665 07	1.885 65
14	1.731 68	1.979 93
15	1.800 94	2.078 93
16	1.872 98	2.182 87
17	1.947 90	2.292 02
18	2.025 82	2.406 62
19	2.106 85	2.526 95
20	2.191 12	2.653 30
21	2.278 77	2.785 96
22	2.369 92	2.925 26
23	2.464 72	3.071 52
24	2.563 30	3.225 10
25	2.665 84	3.386 35

Example 1. Find the amount to be repaid on a \$1000 loan at 10%/a, compounded semi-annually for 12 a.

Solution: $A = P(1 + i)^n$

$P = 1000, \quad i = \frac{r}{N}, \quad n = 12 \times 2$

$= \frac{0.1}{2} \quad = 24$ (semi-annually)

$= 0.05$

$A = 1000(1 + 0.05)^{24}$
$= 1000(1.05)^{24}$
$= 1000(3.225\ 10)$
$= 3225.10$

The amount is \$3225.10.

Example 2. A sum of money is lent at 16% compounded quarterly.
How long will it take for the amount to double the principal?

Solution: We find the number of conversion periods first. Since interest is calculated 4 times per year, N = 4. Therefore,

$i = \frac{r}{N}$

$i = \frac{0.16}{4}$
$= 0.04$

From the formula $A = P(1 + i)^n$, the amount will be twice the principal ($A = 2P$) when $(1 + i)^n = 2$. Since $i = 0.04$, scan the column under 4% to find a value of $(1.04)^n$ which is at least 2.

We see that $(1.04)^n = 2.025\,82$ when $n = 18$. Since n is the number of conversion periods and since there are 4 conversion periods per year, we calculate the number of years as $\frac{18}{4} = 4.5$.

It will take 4.5 a (or 4 a 6 months) for the amount to double the principal.

EXERCISE 10.4

A

1. Find i and n for each of the following.
(a) 12% compounded semi-annually for 6 a
(b) 18% compounded quarterly for 8 a
(c) 8% compounded annually for 10 a
(d) 7% compounded semi-annually for 5 a
(e) 12% compounded monthly for 3 a
(f) 11% compounded semi-annually for 9 a
(g) 10% compounded quarterly for $4\frac{1}{2}$ a
(h) 9% compounded bi-monthly for $5\frac{1}{2}$ a

2. Read from the tables.
(a) $(1.015)^4$ (b) $(1.04)^{12}$
(c) $(1.08)^{20}$ (d) $(1.035)^{18}$
(e) $(1.05)^{35}$ (f) $(1.06)^{24}$
(g) $(1.03)^{11}$ (h) $(1.055)^{33}$
(i) $(1.07)^{16}$ (j) $(1.025)^{36}$
(k) $(1.005)^{25}$ (l) $(1.045)^{14}$
(m) $(1.07)^{20}$ (n) $(1.03)^{11}$

B

3. Use the tables to find the following amounts.
(a) $100(1.025)^{14}$ (b) $25(1.04)^8$
(c) $500(1.07)^{12}$ (d) $500(1.035)^{15}$
(e) $150(1.025)^{15}$ (f) $1000(1.015)^{24}$
(g) $450(1.07)^{12}$ (h) $1500(1.08)^{25}$
(i) $700(1.055)^{30}$ (j) $500(1.045)^{16}$

4. Find the amount of the following.
(a) $700 invested at 8% for 2 a, compounded annually
(b) $125 invested at 7% for 2 a, compounded annually
(c) $600 invested at 12% for 3 a, compounded quarterly
(d) $5000 invested at 7% for 12 a, compounded annually
(e) $3000 invested at 10% for 4 a, compounded quarterly
(f) $12 000 invested at 11% for 15 a, compounded semi-annually
(g) $25 000 invested at 9% for 20 a, compounded semi-annually

5. (a) How long must money be invested at 8% compounded annually to double? (To the nearest year.)
(b) How long must money be invested at 8% compounded semi-annually to double? (To the nearest half year.)
(c) How long must money be invested at 8% compounded quarterly to double? (To the nearest quarter year.)

6. In order to double an investment in 10 a, at what rate compounded annually must the money be invested? (To the nearest percent.)

7. When Joe Smith was born, his grandfather invested $100 in Joe's name at 10%, compounded semi-annually.
(a) If Joe cashed in the investment when he was 19 a old, how much did he get?
(b) If Joe waited until he was 20 a old, how much did he get?
(c) How much did he gain by waiting the extra year?

Spreadsheet activities related to this topic are found in section 15.3.

10.5 THE COST OF BORROWING MONEY

When you need to borrow money, you should consider not only whether you can afford the monthly payment, but also the rate of interest being charged. When you know the effective annual rate you can "comparison shop" for money in the same way that you would shop for other consumer goods.

Money may be borrowed from chartered banks, credit unions, trust companies, or finance companies. When you go shopping for a loan, you should compare the effective annual rate of all of these major lending institutions.

EFFECTIVE ANNUAL RATES

Example 1. Paul borrowed $1500 for camping equipment. The loan is to be repaid in 24 equal payments of $72 beginning the month after the loan was made.
What rate of interest was charged?

Solution:
We can reason the approximate rate of interest by considering that at the time the loan was made the principal was $1500 and at the time of the last payment the principal was $72. Therefore:

AVERAGE PRINCIPAL METHOD

Average Principal $P_{av} = \dfrac{\$1500 + \$72}{2}$

$= \$786$

Interest

$I = A - P$

$I = 24 \times \$72 - \$1500$

$= \$1728 - \$1500$

$= \$228$

Rate

$r = \dfrac{I}{P_{av} \times t}$

$r = \dfrac{228}{786 \times 2}$

$\doteq 0.145$

The interest rate was 14.5%.

FORMULA METHOD

The following formula gives the effective annual rate of interest.

$$r = \frac{2NI}{P(n + 1)}$$

where r is the effective annual rate
N is the number of payment periods in 1 a
I is the interest charged
P is the principal
n is the total number of payments

When buying financing services, you should shop as carefully as you do for the articles you buy. The way to check the cost of finance is to compare the effective annual rates.

In this case $r = \frac{2(12)(228)}{1500 \times 25}$

$\doteq 0.146$

The rate was 14.6%.

Example 2. Ms. Seward borrowed $2500 from the bank for a vacation. The loan was to be repaid by 30 monthly instalments of $95.
Calculate the effective annual rate being charged.

Solution:

n = 30   A = 30 × $95 = $2850
I = $350   N = 12   P = $2500

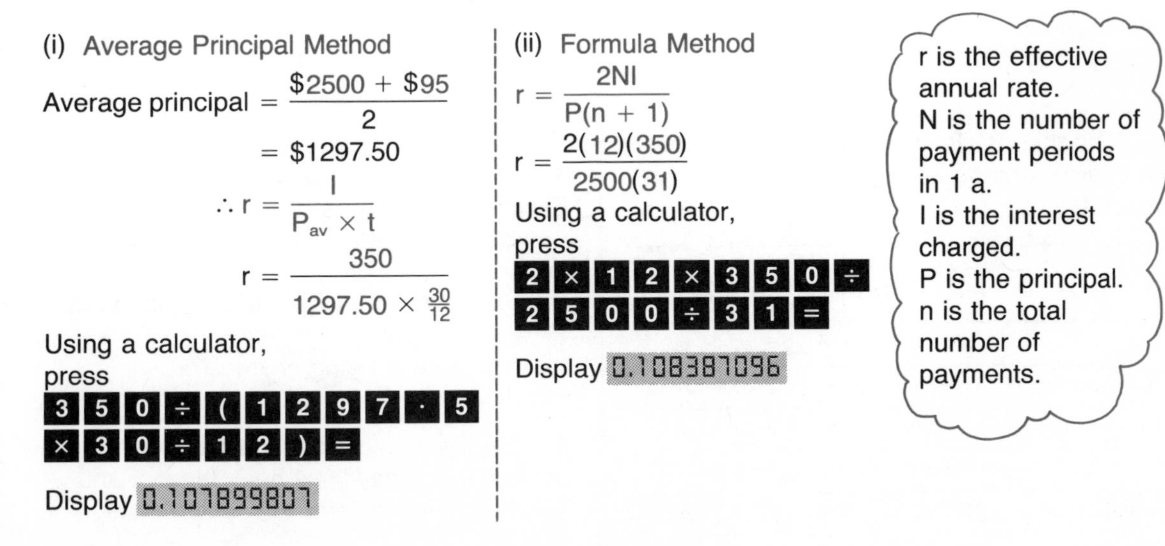

(i) Average Principal Method

$$\text{Average principal} = \frac{\$2500 + \$95}{2}$$
$$= \$1297.50$$
$$\therefore r = \frac{I}{P_{av} \times t}$$
$$r = \frac{350}{1297.50 \times \frac{30}{12}}$$

Using a calculator, press

3 5 0 ÷ (1 2 9 7 · 5 × 3 0 ÷ 1 2) =

Display 0.107899807

(ii) Formula Method

$$r = \frac{2NI}{P(n + 1)}$$
$$r = \frac{2(12)(350)}{2500(31)}$$

Using a calculator, press

2 × 1 2 × 3 5 0 ÷ 2 5 0 0 ÷ 3 1 =

Display 0.108387096

r is the effective annual rate.
N is the number of payment periods in 1 a.
I is the interest charged.
P is the principal.
n is the total number of payments.

The effective annual rate is 10.8% (to the nearest tenth).

Example 3. A sign in a music store advertises portable cassette players. On inquiring, you are told that there will be 35 weekly payments.
Find
(a) the instalment price;
(b) the instalment charges;
(c) the effective annual rate.

The principal, P, is the amount financed. If there is a down payment, then
P = cash price − down payment.

PORTABLE CASSETTE PLAYERS

Regular Price $550
Down Payment $100
$15.00 per week

Solution:

(a) Instalment price = $100.00 + (35 × $15.00)
= $625.00

(b) Instalment charge = $625.00 − $550.00
= $75.00

(c) Amount financed = $550.00 − $100.00
= $450.00

$$\text{Effective annual rate} = \frac{2NI}{P(n+1)}$$

$$= \frac{2(52)(75.00)}{450.00(36)}$$

$$\doteq 0.48$$

$$\therefore r = 48\%$$

EXERCISE 10.5

B 1. Find the instalment charges and the rate of interest charged on each of the following articles.

	Article	Cash Price	Down Payment	Monthly Payments
(a)	Radio	$68.50	$10	10 of $6.50
(b)	Camera	$344.95	$0	24 of $18
(c)	Boat	$762.50	$80	24 of $30
(d)	Car	$13 789.50	$3000	30 of $417.72
(e)	Coat	$125.80	$25	12 of $9.80
(f)	VCR	$565.90	$50	36 of $16.50

2. Easy-built Furniture Company advertises: "Five-piece kitchen suite. Exciting styling, great value, $499.50. Only $50 down and $25.50 a month for 20 months."
(a) What service charge is being added to the cash price?
(b) What rate is being charged?

3. Mrs. Cartwright bought a tricycle for her son's birthday. She paid $9 cash and $5/month for 6 months. The cash price was $37.95.
What rate of interest was charged?

4. A chain saw costs $185.60. It can be bought for $45.60 down and 12 monthly payments of $12.25.
(a) What are the finance charges?
(b) What rate of interest is being charged?

5. What service charge is being paid on an electronic typewriter, cash price $379.50, selling for $99.50 down and 30 monthly payments of $10.50?

6. A sewing machine sells for $279 cash or $30 down and 12%/a service charge on the total balance financed.
What amount will discharge the debt in 12 monthly payments?

7. Find the interest charged and the effective annual rate of interest to the nearest $\frac{1}{2}$% for each of the following.

	Principal	Monthly Payments
(a)	$100	12 of $8.79
(b)	$500	18 of $30.00
(c)	$1 000	24 of $47.00
(d)	$3 000	36 of $96.84
(e)	$12 500	26 of $500.00
(f)	$20 000	120 of $250.00

8. Easy Loan Company advertised a loan of $500 repaid by 12 easy payments of $45. Cash-4-U advertised a loan of $600 repaid by 12 payments of $54.
Calculate the interest rate charged by each company.

9. A "Fly now, pay later" plan offered a $375 air fare at $22.50/month for 18 months.
What interest rate was being charged?

10. Ms. Plaunt borrowed $600 to pay dental bills. Interest was charged at 6%/a on the total amount borrowed for 9 months. The loan was repaid by nine equal monthly payments beginning 1 month after the loan was made.
Calculate:
(a) the amount of each payment;
(b) the effective annual rate.

11. Mr. Fortin purchased an automobile on time payments. Mr. Fortin's payments fell in arrears when he was laid off temporarily. Now that he is back at work he feels the only way he can catch up is to consolidate his debts and pay them off by means of a single loan which will reduce monthly payments, but extend the time of the debt. To do this he borrows $3000 to be repaid over 30 months with payments of $113.80. What interest rate is he being charged?

C 12. (a) A house is advertised at $97 900 with $9500 down.
How much is being financed?
If the effective annual rate is 9% and there are 240 monthly payments (a 20 a mortgage), use the formula
$r = \frac{2NI}{P(n + 1)}$ to calculate the total interest charged.
(b) A loan of $2500 is repaid by 30 monthly payments. If the effective annual rate is 10.5% use the formula to calculate I, the total interest charged. Add the interest to the principal borrowed and divide by 30 to find the monthly payment.

MIND BENDER

Determine the pattern and find the missing number

8	9	15	3
5	7	13	
7	5	9	2

10.6 CONSUMER CREDIT

RETAIL CREDIT

If you purchase an item and agree to pay for it at a later date, you are using consumer credit. If you agree to pay for it later, you will probably pay more for the item than if you paid cash, because of interest charges.

Type of Credit	Description
Standard Charge Account (Department Store)	Expect to pay balance by a specific date. No interest charged if paid by that date.
Credit Card (Bank or Trust Company)	May pay minimum balance or payment in full. High interest is charged on unpaid balance. Can be used in many stores, and in many countries.
Instalment Credit (Small shop or Department Store)	Specific number of equal payments must be made. Contract must be signed. Used for a specific purchase. Relatively high interest rate.
Budget Account (Small shop or Department Store)	Usually paid for on short term, 6 months or less. Interest rate is low. Contract must be signed.

CREDIT CARD

The credit card is a very popular form of consumer credit. It is easy to use and gives an accurate record of purchases. Because of the convenience of the credit card, the interest rate is higher than most consumer loans at major lending institutions. The credit card company earns money in two ways: receiving interest from the borrower, and charging the store a fee for the credit service.

The effective rate of interest on a credit card is difficult to calculate because additional charges are being made from time to time, and payment is being received that reduces the balance. Most credit cards give the option of paying the total balance owing or making a minimum payment. If the total balance owing is paid within the due date, and there is no previous balance, then no interest is charged. If only a partial payment is made towards the total balance, service charges are generally a certain percentage of the previous month's balance.

Example. For the following credit statement, calculate the amount of interest charged for the statement period, total debits, the new balance, and the minimum payment due. Interest is charged at 1.5% of the previous month's balance and the minimum payment is 10% of the new balance, to the next dollar.

CHARGE-IT-CARD COMPANY

Date Posted	Transactions	Purchases Debits	Payments Credits
04Aug■■	Payment Received -- Thank You		40.00
10Aug■■	Empire Books Ottawa On	20.00	
04Sep■■	Interest		

Account No.	Previous Balance	Total Credits	Total Debits	New Balance
45 128 851	388.00	40.00		
Statement Date	**Date Payment Due**	**Past Due**	**Minimum Payment**	**Credit Limit**
Sep04, ■■	Oct04, ■■	.00		1000

Solution:
Since only a partial payment of $40 was made towards the previous balance of $388, interest is calculated on the entire previous balance.

$$\text{Interest charges} = (388)(0.015) = \$5.82$$

$$\text{Total debits} = (\text{purchases}) + (\text{interest charged}) = 20.00 + 5.82 = \$25.82$$

$$\text{The new balance} = (\text{previous balance}) - (\text{total credits}) + (\text{total debits}) = 388.00 - 40.00 + 25.82 = \$373.82$$

$$\text{The minimum payment due} = (373.82)(0.1) \doteq 37.38 = \$38.00 \text{ (to the next dollar)}$$

Total Debits	New Balance
25.82	373.82
Minimum Payment	**Credit Limit**
38.00	1000

DECIDING TO USE YOUR CREDIT

Before you make a purchase using credit, you should ask yourself the following questions.

1. Is having and using the item now worth the extra cost?
2. Is the item needed now?
3. Can the payment be met within my current budget?
4. Have I shopped wisely for the best interest rate?
5. Is the interest rate or carrying charge too high?
6. Have I been treated in a reasonable way by the lender?

EXERCISE 10.6

A

1. Why is the use of credit considered a convenience to the consumer?

2. Explain why the credit consumer is apt to get good service from the retailer.

3. Why is overspending one of the dangers of credit buying?

4. Why does the consumer tend to shop in those places extending credit?

5. Consider the following statements. Explain why you agree or disagree.
(a) Never pay cash when you can charge it.
(b) By using credit the consumer is able to build a credit rating.
(c) Always shop in those stores that accept credit cards.

B

6. List three ways that credit cards assist the consumer, and three ways that they can be abused.

7. For the credit card statements below, calculate the missing information. Interest charges are 1.5% of the previous month's balance and the minimum payment is 10% of the new balance, to the next dollar.

(a)

CHARGE-IT-CARD COMPANY

Date Posted	Transactions	Purchases Debits	Payments Credits
01Apr■■	Bookworm Book Store Toronto On	30.00	
07Apr■■	Payment Received -- Thank You		60.00
28Apr■■	Great Toy Company Vancouver BC	26.00	
07May■■	Interest		

Account No.	Previous Balance	Total Credits	Total Debits	New Balance
45 128 851	520.00			
Statement Date	**Date Payment Due**	**Past Due**	**Minimum Payment**	**Credit Limit**
May 07, ■■	Jun 07, ■■	.00		1000

(b)

CHARGE-IT-CARD COMPANY

Date Posted	Transactions	Purchases Debits	Payments Credits
02Jul■■	Johnny's Good Eats Windsor On	34.00	
06Jul■■	Payment Received -- Thank You		120.00
07Jul■■	Value Inn Calgary Alta	75.00	
08Jul■■	Fast Service Centre Edmonton Alta	20.00	
16Jul■■	First Fiddle Ltd. Ottawa On	24.75	
07Aug■■	Interest		

Account No.	Previous Balance	Total Credits	Total Debits	New Balance
45 128 851	432.56			
Statement Date	**Date Payment Due**	**Past Due**	**Minimum Payment**	**Credit Limit**
Aug 07, ■■	Sep 07, ■■	.00		1000

10.7 PROBLEM SOLVING

1. Sixty-four identical cubes are placed in a cubical box with no top.

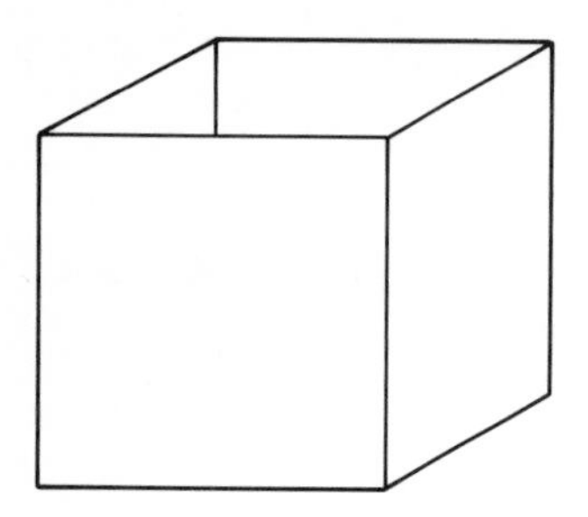

The sixty-four cubes fill the box completely.
(a) How many cubes are visible if you look down on the box?
(b) How many cubes are touching the sides of the box?
(c) How many cubes are not visible from the top and do not touch the sides or the bottom of the box?

2. Books with pages numbered from 1 to 250 are side by side on a book shelf. The book on the right is upside down.
If you add the page number on the extreme right-hand side of this book to the page number at the extreme left-hand side of the book on the left, what is the sum?

3. Find the smallest number, which when it is
(a) divided by 2, gives a remainder 1.
(b) divided by 3, gives a remainder 2.
(c) divided by 4, gives a remainder 3.
(d) divided by 5, gives a remainder 4.
(e) divided by 6, gives a remainder 5.

4. Match each sleuth to his or her helper.

1. The Saint — (a) Jolly
2. Perry Mason — (b) Archie Goodwin
3. Laura Holt — (c) Marybeth Lacey
4. Nero Wolfe — (d) Dr. Watson
5. Christine Cagney — (e) Hoppy
6. Peter Wimsey — (f) R. Steele
7. The Toff — (g) Della Street
8. Sherlock Holmes — (h) Bunter

5. Fence posts are placed 4 m apart around a lot.
What is the area of a lot that is enclosed by a fence that requires 20 posts?

6. Eight steel balls are hanging in a row and touching each other.
What will happen when ball no. 1 hits ball no. 2?

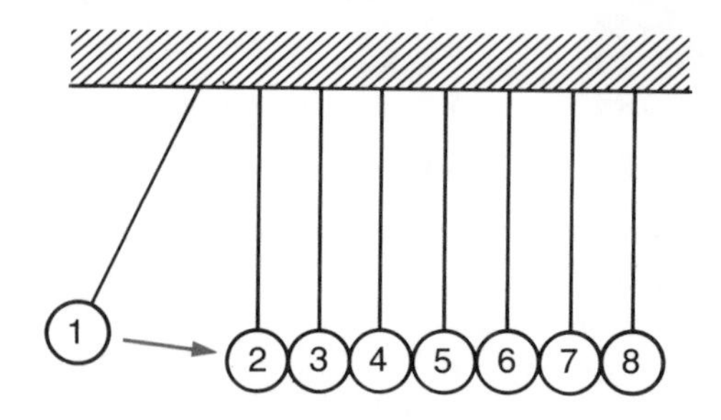

7. The product of two whole numbers is 200. Their sum is less than 60.
What are the possibilities for the two numbers?

8. (a) In week one of a bowling league, Tony bowled games of 179, 186, and 175.
What was his average at the end of the first week?
(b) In week two he bowled games of 194, 200, and 152.
What was his average after the second week?
(c) In week three he bowled games of 221, 196, and 180.
What was his average after the third week?

9. If New Year's Day falls on a Tuesday,
(a) how many more Tuesdays are there in the year?
(b) on what day of the week will July 1 fall?

10. Place the numbers from 1 to 9 in the boxes to make each statement true.

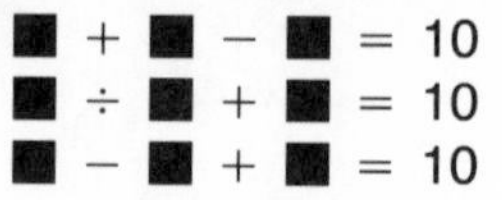

11. A square is formed by joining the centres of four identical circles, as shown.

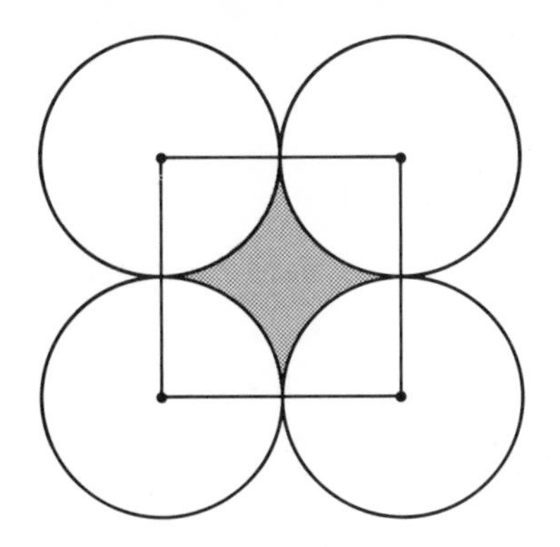

If the radius of each circle is 6 cm, what is the area of the shaded region?

12. Mary bought some golf club cleaner for \$4.33 including tax. Her change from a five-dollar bill was 10 coins consisting of quarters, nickels, and pennies.
Did she get the correct change? Explain.

13. If you take a certain number, subtract 12, then add 4, and finally multiply by 3, you get 36.
What is the number?

CAREER

WILDLIFE CONSERVATION OFFICER

Wildlife conservation officers protect either designated animals or all animals within a designated area. These officers enforce the laws for hunting to ensure that hunting takes place only in season and that hunters do not exceed limits. In addition to law enforcement, wildlife conservation officers act as resource managers. They gather data on various species of wildlife to assist in determining the animal and fish population and to ensure that appropriate numbers are maintained. Calculations using unknown quantities are applied in estimating changes in population using the capture–recapture method as described in the exercise below.

EXERCISE

1. In a small lake, 200 fish are caught and tagged, then released. One week later, 240 fish are caught in the same lake, and 12 are found to be tagged. Complete the following steps to find an estimate of the fish population of the lake.

$\frac{12}{200}$ of the population is 240 fish

$\frac{1}{200}$ of the population is ■ fish

All of the population is ■

= ■ fish

2. In a large game reserve, 120 deer are captured, tagged, and released. Three weeks later, 96 deer are captured in the same reserve, and 7 are found to be tagged.
Find an estimate of the deer population of the reserve.

10.8 REVIEW EXERCISE

1. Evaluate.

(a) $3\frac{1}{2}\%$ of \$122.28

(b) $33\frac{1}{3}\%$ of \$474.80

(c) 25% of \$437.25

(d) $12\frac{1}{2}\%$ of \$643.50

(e) $16\frac{2}{3}\%$ of \$1257.80

(f) $22\frac{1}{2}\%$ of \$4750.18

(g) 17% of \$3375.95

(h) $8\frac{3}{4}\%$ of \$84 900.00

(i) $9\frac{1}{4}\%$ of \$2487.49

(j) $12\frac{1}{2}\%$ of \$1649.99

2. Find the interest when \$100 is invested at the following rates per annum.

(a) 1 a at 5%

(b) 1 a at 9%

(c) 1 a at 12%

(d) 1 a at 8%

(e) 1 a at $10\frac{1}{2}\%$

(f) 1 a at $7\frac{1}{4}\%$

(g) 1 a at $16\frac{3}{4}\%$

(h) 1 a at $12\frac{1}{2}\%$

(i) $\frac{1}{2}$ a at 8%

(j) $\frac{1}{4}$ a at 10%

(k) $\frac{3}{4}$ a at 12%

(l) $1\frac{1}{2}$ a at 18%

3. Find the amount if \$100 is invested at the following rates per annum.

(a) 1 a at 6%

(b) 1 a at 8%

(c) 1 a at 9%

(d) 1 a at 7%

(e) 1 a at 12%

(f) $\frac{1}{2}$ a at 6%

(g) $\frac{1}{4}$ a at 8%

(h) $\frac{1}{3}$ a at 7%

(i) $\frac{1}{2}$ a at 7%

(j) $\frac{1}{12}$ a at 12%

4. Find the amount to be repaid for each of the following loans.

(a) \$256 at $6\frac{1}{2}\%$ for 8 months

(b) \$1594 at 8% for 30 d

(c) \$750 at 12% for 90 d

5. A curb-side loan shark will lend \$9 on Monday to be repaid by \$10 on payday, Friday.
What interest rate is he charging?

6. The interest charged on a loan taken for six months at 12%/a is \$219.
What principal was borrowed?

7. The interest paid on a loan of \$1500 borrowed at 8%/a is \$30.
Find the time period of the loan.

8. The interest charged on \$2400 borrowed for three months is \$126.

(a) What monthly interest rate is charged?

(b) What is the annual interest rate charged?

9. What principal must be lent at $9\frac{1}{2}\%$ to give a return of \$8000 after 230 d?

10. Determine the number of time intervals for each of the following.

(a) $\frac{1}{2}$ a intervals in $3\frac{1}{2}$ a

(b) $\frac{1}{4}$ a intervals in $10\frac{1}{2}$ a

(c) $\frac{1}{2}$ a intervals in 5 a

(d) $\frac{1}{3}$ a intervals in $7\frac{2}{3}$ a

(e) 2 month intervals in $8\frac{1}{2}$ a

(f) $\frac{1}{4}$ a intervals in 25 a

11. Find the compound amount of the following.

(a) \$3500 at 7% for 3 a, compounded semi-annually
(b) \$100 at 1%/month, compounded monthly for 10 months
(c) \$1200 at 10%/a, compounded semi-annually for 18 months
(d) \$2400 at 7%/a, compounded semi-annually for 36 months
(e) \$4500 at 9%/a, for 12 a compounded semi-annually
(f) \$900 at $1\frac{1}{2}$%/month, compounded monthly for 30 months

12. Find the compound amount of the following.

(a) \$500 for $3\frac{1}{2}$ a at 5%/a, compounded semi-annually
(b) \$100 at $2\frac{1}{4}$ a at 6%/a, compounded quarterly
(c) \$1500 for 4 a at 8%/a, compounded annually
(d) \$325 for 48 months at 12%/a, compounded quarterly
(e) \$600 for $3\frac{3}{4}$ a at 8%/a, compounded quarterly
(f) \$750 for 730 d at 9%/a, compounded semi-annually

13. Banks and businesses usually calculate the interest at the end of a conversion period so that the graph is not a smooth curve but a series of steps. The following graph is an example of this type of step function.

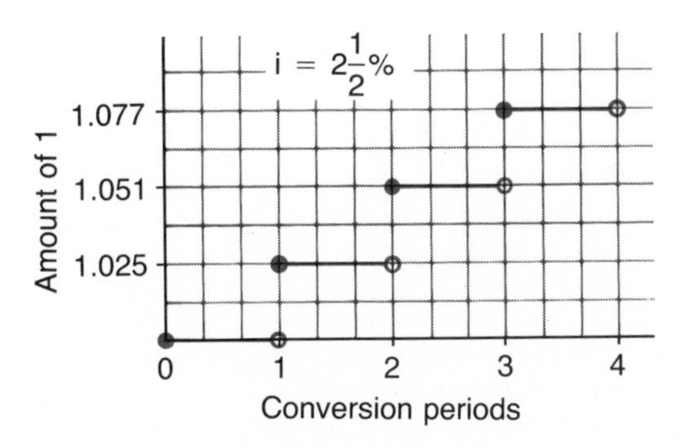

Prepare step graphs to show the amount of \$1 invested:

(a) for 3 a at 10%, compounded semi-annually;
(b) for 1 a at 12%, compounded monthly.

14. A loan for \$653 is to be repaid in 12 equal instalments over the next year. The interest charged is $5\frac{1}{2}$% of the full principal for one year.

(a) How much will each payment be?
(b) Find the effective annual rate.

15. A personal bank loan, with life insurance included, for \$3000 may be repaid by 24 monthly payments of \$138.51 or 36 monthly payments of \$96.84.

(a) Compare the effective annual rates (including insurance costs).
(b) Compare the total amounts of the charges.

16. A vacuum cleaner costs \$375 cash or \$75 down and \$11/month for 30 months (service charge of \$1/month).
Find the effective annual rate being charged.

17. A colour television set will cost \$562 cash. It can be bought with a \$50 allowance for a trade-in in any condition and \$22.50/month for 24 months.

(a) What is the cash price with a trade-in?
(b) What are the instalment charges?

18. Modern Furniture Company advertises a bed and dresser set for \$50 down and \$17.50/month for 30 months. On inquiring, you find there is a 7% discount for cash purchases.
What is the cash price?

19. Mr. Saunders has a revolving credit account at Diamond Department Store. His previous month's balance was \$79.50, and his monthly purchases have amounted to \$276.80. Service charges are $1\frac{1}{4}$% of the previous month's balance and the minimum payment is 20% of the new balance, to the next dollar.
Find the amount due this month.

10.9 CHAPTER 10 TEST

1. Find the amount to be repaid for each of the following loans at simple interest.

(a) \$2500 at $7\frac{1}{2}\%$ for 2 a

(b) \$1400 at 14% for 150 d

2. The simple interest charged on a loan taken for 15 months at 10%/a is \$250.
What principal was borrowed?

3. Find the amount to be repaid when \$3000 is borrowed at 6%/a for 3 a compounded
(a) semi-annually,
(b) quarterly,
(c) monthly.

4. A mountain bike may be bought for \$59.50 down and \$15/month for 18 months.
If the finance charges are \$30.55, what is the cash price?

5. Find the total cost and finance charges on a motorcycle sold for \$300 down and \$45/month for 30 months. The cash price is \$1500.
What rate of interest is being charged?

SAVING MONEY

REVIEW AND PREVIEW TO CHAPTER 11

SIMPLE INTEREST

EXERCISE 1

1. Write as a decimal.

(a) 17% (b) 9% (c) $16\frac{1}{2}$%
(d) 6.75% (e) $\frac{1}{4}$% (f) $\frac{2}{5}$%

2. Find the interest when $200 is invested at the following rates per annum.

$$I = Prt$$

(a) 1 a at 6% (b) 1 a at 9%
(c) 1 a at 13% (d) 1 a at 7%
(e) 1 a at $10\frac{1}{2}$% (f) 1 a at $7\frac{1}{4}$%
(g) 1 a at $16\frac{3}{4}$% (h) 1 a at $12\frac{1}{2}$%
(i) $\frac{1}{2}$ a at 8% (j) $\frac{1}{4}$ a at 10%
(k) $\frac{3}{4}$ a at 11% (l) $1\frac{1}{2}$ a at 17%

3. Find the amount if $200 is invested at the following rates per annum.

$$A = P + Prt$$

(a) 1 a at 6% (b) 1 a at 5%
(c) 1 a at 9% (d) 1 a at 7%
(e) 1 a at 14% (f) $\frac{1}{2}$ a at 6%
(g) $\frac{1}{4}$ a at 9% (h) $\frac{1}{3}$ a at 7%
(i) $\frac{1}{2}$ a at 7% (j) $\frac{1}{12}$ a at 16%

4. A loan of $700 is to be repaid at the rate of $100 plus accrued interest per month. Interest is being charged at $\frac{3}{4}$% per month.
Find the total interest charges.

CHEQUES

EXERCISE 2

1. Write the amount in words as it would appear on a cheque.

(a) $101.40 (b) $5.67
(c) $14.99 (d) $1026.42
(e) $34.75 (f) $75.20

2. Find the total and balance carried forward for each cheque stub.

(a)

BALANCE FORWARD	345	86
DEPOSITS	25 372	00 25
SUB TOTAL		
CHEQUE AMOUNT	145	86
BALANCE		

(b)

BALANCE FORWARD	684	21
DEPOSITS	104	76
SUB TOTAL		
CHEQUE AMOUNT	162	86
BALANCE		

(c)

BALANCE FORWARD	132	14
DEPOSITS	459 200	74 00
SUB TOTAL		
CHEQUE AMOUNT	372	30
BALANCE		

(d)

BALANCE FORWARD	795	86
DEPOSITS	1 300	00
SUB TOTAL		
CHEQUE AMOUNT	752	87
BALANCE		

COMPOUND INTEREST

EXERCISE 3

1. Determine the number of time intervals for each of the following.

(a) $\frac{1}{2}$ a intervals in $2\frac{1}{2}$ a

(b) $\frac{1}{4}$ a intervals in $11\frac{1}{2}$ a

(c) $\frac{1}{3}$ a intervals in 5 a

(d) $\frac{1}{3}$ a intervals in $4\frac{2}{3}$ a

(e) 2 month intervals in $7\frac{1}{2}$ a

(f) $\frac{1}{5}$ a intervals in 25 a

2. Find the amount of the following loans.

	Principal	Annual Rate	Conversion Period	Term
(a)	\$100	8%	annual	4 a
(b)	\$1000	9%	semi-annual	$6\frac{1}{2}$ a
(c)	\$100	12%	quarterly	5 a
(d)	\$10 000	6%	annual	10 a
(e)	\$100	10%	quarterly	33 months
(f)	\$100	11%	semi-annual	20 a
(g)	\$100 000	9%	semi-annual	18 months
(h)	\$1 000 000	12%	quarterly	3 months

CALCULATOR MATH

Perform the following calculations.

1. 71.52 − 9.32
2. 182 216 − 902
3. \$12.45 + \$123.96 + \$12.45 + \$56.78 + \$43.57 + \$78.97 − \$12.45
4. 6.75% × 7.86
5. \$43.86 − \$23.75 + \$87.76 + \$4.76
6. (\$123.87) × 7% − \$45.86
7. 12 × \$1224.78
8. \$4.56 × 20 + \$5.78 × 30
9. 7.85 − 12.76 − 7.87 + 14.87 + 23.87 − 1.23
10. $(14\frac{4}{5}\%) \times \$93\,876.54$
11. $9200(1.0935)^{10}$
12. $1600(1.1275)^{12}$
13. $44\,900(1.1125)^{7}$
14. $55\,700(1.135)^{6}$
15. $66\,900(1.0635)^{8}$
16. $7300 \times \frac{1}{(1.125)^4}$
17. $1575 \times \frac{1}{(1.0675)^6}$
18. $7760 \times \frac{1}{(1.095)^8}$
19. $8150 \times \frac{1}{(1.1275)^6}$
20. $17\,250 \times \frac{1}{(1.025)^{10}}$

11.1 BANK ACCOUNTS

When we earn money we rarely receive it as cash. Our earnings are usually moved by computer transfer from our employer to a bank, trust company, or credit union. Each of these institutions offers a variety of accounts. Chequing accounts, chequing/savings accounts, and savings accounts enable us to manage our money and to transfer it from place to place. Many people have more than one type of bank account because there are times when money can be set aside to earn interest, and other times when it must be readily available.

CHEQUING ACCOUNT

Features:

Money can be conveniently withdrawn, transferred, or deposited by writing a cheque or using an automated banking machine.

A complete record of all transactions, credits (deposits), and debits (withdrawals) is available on a monthly basis.

Money usually does not earn interest in a chequing account.

A monthly service charge, which is either a flat fee or based on the number of transactions, is deducted from your balance.

Example 1. Roberta opened a chequing account at the Provincial Bank. She had the choice of a flat service charge of $6.00 per month or $0.50 per transaction, which included withdrawals and deposits by cheque or banking machine. She chose the flat rate of $6.00 per month. Her first month's bank statement follows.

PROVINCIAL BANK

Description	no.	Debits/Cheques	Deposits/Credits	Date	Balance
		$	$	m d	$ 00.00
machine dep			455.87	7 6	455.87
cheque	001	76.45		7 8	379.42
machine wd		25.00		7 9	354.42
cheque	002	150.00		7 10	204.42
dep			120.00	7 15	324.42
cheque	003	95.65		7 17	228.77
machine wd		125.00		7 23	103.77
service charge		6.00		7 31	97.77

no. debits	total amount debit	no. credits	total amount credit
6	$478.10	2	$575.87

(a) Was the choice of a flat rate a wise one?

Solution:

5 debits + 2 credits = 7 transactions
(The service charge does not count as a debit.)

At $0.50 each, the service charge would have been
$7 \times 0.50 = 3.50$

It would have cost Roberta less to select $0.50 per transaction. Since this was the first month of the account, it may not be representative of later months.

(b) Roberta received this statement of her chequing account on August 10. On August 1 she made a deposit of $200 and wrote three cheques, #004 on July 20 for $45.00, #005 on July 30 for $25.00, and #006 on August 7 for $34.56.
Reconcile the cheque register with the bank statement on page 338.

Solution:

CHEQUE REGISTER

date	no.	Description	✓	deposit	withdr.	Balance
7/6		deposit	✓	455.87		455.87
7/6	1	Price Rite Foods	✓		76.45	379.42
7/9		machine wd	✓		25.00	354.42
7/9	2	cash	✓		150.00	204.42
7/10	3	Mary Clark	✓		95.65	108.77
7/15		deposit	✓	120.00		228.77
7/20	4	Nice Clothes			45.00	183.77
7/22		machine wd	✓		125.00	58.77
7/30	5	Woodland H.S.			25.00	33.77
8/1		deposit		200.00		233.77
8/7	6	Price Rite Food			34.56	199.21
7/31		Service charge	✓		6.00	193.21

Reconciliation

Balance shown on Bank statement 97.77
97.77

Add all deposits not on statement 200.00

Total + 200.00
Subtotal 297.77

Subtract all cheques not on statement 45.00
25.00
34.56

Total - 104.56
Balance/Register 193.21

CHEQUING/SAVINGS ACCOUNTS

Features:

Money can be conveniently withdrawn, transferred, and deposited by completing a bank transaction slip, writing a cheque, or using an automated banking machine.

Interest is earned either on an average daily balance or based on a minimum balance, although the interest rate is low.

A complete record of all transactions, credits (deposits), and debits (withdrawals) is available on a monthly basis.

A monthly service charge, which is either a flat fee or based on the number of transactions, is deducted from your balance. If you go below your minimum balance or average daily balance, the service charge is high.

Example 2. Jeff has a Chequing/Savings Account which pays 5%/a simple interest if the average daily balance does not fall below \$500. Otherwise there is a service charge. His May bank statement is given below.
How much interest does he earn in May?

PROVINCIAL BANK

Description	no.	Debits/Cheques	Deposits/Credits	Date	Balance
		\$	\$	m d	\$1200.00
machine dep			230.00	5 3	1430.00
cheque	123	500.00		5 12	930.00
machine wd		400.00		5 20	530.00
dep			300.00	5 25	830.00
interest			4.27	5 31	834.27

no. debits	total amount debit	no. credits	total amount credit
2	\$900.00	3	\$534.27

Solution:

The balance is \$1200 for 2 d (May 1, 2)
The balance is \$1430 for 9 d (May 3 to May 11)
The balance is \$930 for 8 d
The balance is \$530 for 5 d
The balance is \$830 for 7 d (May 25 to May 31)

$$\text{Average daily balance} = \frac{(1200 \times 2) + (1430 \times 9) + (930 \times 8) + (530 \times 5) + (830 \times 7)}{31}$$

$$\doteq 1005.48 \text{ (to the nearest cent)}$$

$$I = Prt$$

$$I = (1005.48)(0.05)\left(\tfrac{31}{365}\right)$$

$$\doteq 4.27 \text{ (to the nearest cent)}$$

The interest is \$4.27. This is added to Jeff's balance on his statement on the final day of the month, provided this is a business day. If the average daily balance had fallen below \$500, a service charge would have been deducted.

EXERCISE 11.1

B 1. List the advantages and disadvantages of a chequing account.

2. List the advantages and disadvantages of a chequing/savings account.

3. A chequing/savings account requires a minimum average daily balance of $500. If the average daily balance is above $500, you earn interest of 7%/a on the average daily balance. If the average daily balance is below $500, a service charge of $0.50 per transaction is deducted. The January statement is given below.

PROVINCIAL BANK					
Description	no.	Debits/Cheques	Deposits/Credits	Date	Balance
		$	$	m d	$1000.00
machine dep			100.00	1 3	
cheque	523	500.00		1 9	
machine wd		400.00		1 11	
dep			200.00	1 22	
service charge/ interest				1 31	

no. debits	total amount debit	no. credits	total amount credit
	$		$

(a) Calculate the average daily balance.
(b) Will the bank pay you interest or will you pay a service charge?
(c) What is the amount of the interest or service charge?
(d) Complete the bank statement.

4. Repeat question 3 assuming that the initial balance was $900, rather than $1000.

5. Bob's chequing account statement is given below. It does not include cheque #453 for $76.50 written on Feb. 23, or cheque #454 for $27.89 on March 2, or a deposit of $300.00 on March 1. Bob must pay a service charge of $0.75 for each transaction.
(a) What is the service charge?
(b) Complete the bank statement.
(c) What is the balance in Bob's cheque book?

PROVINCIAL BANK					
Description	no.	Debits/Cheques	Deposits/Credits	Date	Balance
		$	$	m d	$123.89
machine dep			154.13	2 2	
cheque	450	12.45		2 8	
machine wd		30.00		2 10	
cheque	451	150.00		2 10	
dep			345.76	2 15	
cheque	452	95.65		2 17	
machine wd		125.00		2 23	
service charge/ interest				2 28	

no. credits	total amount debit	no. debits	total amount credit
	$		$

11.2 SAVINGS ACCOUNTS AND TERM DEPOSITS

When you deposit money in a bank, trust company or credit union, you are investing your money in that financial institution. These institutions offer accounts with many different features. The account you choose will depend on how flexible you want to be. If you want an account which will give ready access to your money, a savings account is a good choice, but the interest rate will be low. If you are willing to leave your money in an account for a longer or set period of time, interest rates will be higher.

SAVINGS ACCOUNTS

The main difference among savings accounts is the method of calculating interest. The sign in a credit union, bank, or trust company may read as follows:

Daily Interest
Interest Compounded Quarterly
Interest Paid Semi-Annually
Interest Paid on Minimum Monthly Balance

When you select a savings account you want to know:

What is the interest rate? When is it paid or compounded?
How is it calculated? Is there a service charge?

Example 1. Paul has a savings account at the credit union which calculates interest on a daily basis and pays it monthly at a rate of 8%/a based on the minimum daily balance. A page of his savings book is shown below.
Calculate the interest paid for October.

CITY CENTRE CREDIT UNION				
DATE	ITEM	WITHDRAWAL	DEPOSIT	BALANCE
OCT 1	DP		400.00	750.00
OCT 10	WD	100.00		650.00
OCT 15	WD	100.00		550.00
OCT 15	DP		300.00	850.00
OCT 16	DP		100.00	950.00
OCT 28	WD	300.00		650.00
OCT 31	INT		■	■

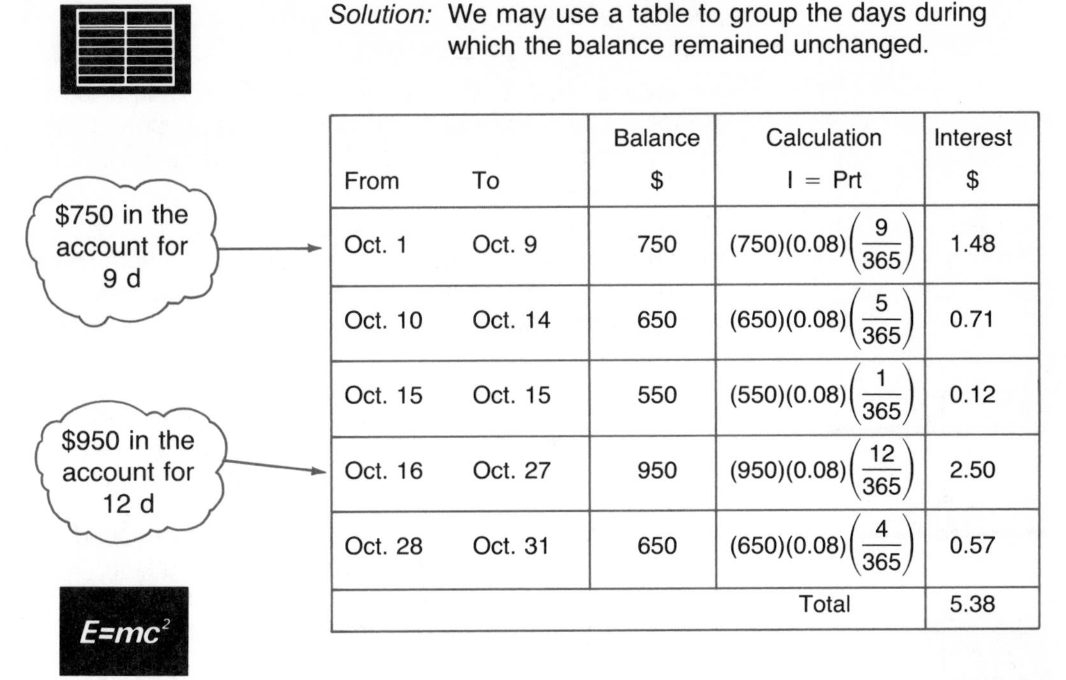

Solution: We may use a table to group the days during which the balance remained unchanged.

From	To	Balance $	Calculation $I = Prt$	Interest $
Oct. 1	Oct. 9	750	$(750)(0.08)\left(\frac{9}{365}\right)$	1.48
Oct. 10	Oct. 14	650	$(650)(0.08)\left(\frac{5}{365}\right)$	0.71
Oct. 15	Oct. 15	550	$(550)(0.08)\left(\frac{1}{365}\right)$	0.12
Oct. 16	Oct. 27	950	$(950)(0.08)\left(\frac{12}{365}\right)$	2.50
Oct. 28	Oct. 31	650	$(650)(0.08)\left(\frac{4}{365}\right)$	0.57
			Total	5.38

Over the 31 d in October, Paul's money earned $5.38.

Example 2. If the savings account in Example 1 paid 8.5%/a on the minimum monthly balance, calculate the interest.
How do the two savings acccunts compare?

Solution: The minimum balance during the month is $550. (Oct. 15 to Oct. 26)

$$I = (550 \times 0.085)\left(\frac{31}{365}\right)$$

$$\doteq 3.97 \text{ (to the nearest cent)}$$

Although the interest rate is higher, the interest paid is lower because of frequent deposits and withdrawals. If a balance can be left undisturbed for the month, the account based on the minimum monthly balance is preferable because of the higher interest rate.

> The savings account you need depends on how you will use your account.

TERM DEPOSITS

When you have a sum of money and you can foresee no immediate need for it, the funds can be placed in a term deposit. A term deposit pays a higher rate of interest over a fixed period of time. However, the money may not be available until the end of the term.

When you put your money in a term deposit, you are guaranteeing the financial institution the use of your money for the term. Since money you deposit is lent to others, it is important that the financial institution have guaranteed funds to lend.

READ

Example 3. Nadine placed $5000 in a one-year term deposit at a rate of 10%/a, compounded quarterly. What is the amount at the end of the term?

PLAN

Solution: $A = P(1 + i)^n$, where A is the compound amount, P is the initial principal, n is the number of conversion periods, and i is the interest rate per conversion period.

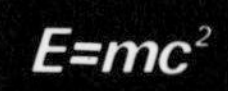

$P = 5000, \quad n = 4, \quad i = \frac{0.10}{4}$ or 0.025

$A = P(1 + i)^n$
$A = 5000(1.025)^4$

SOLVE

Using a calculator, press

5 0 0 0 × 1 · 0 2 5 yˣ 4 =

ANSWER

The display is 5519.064453

The term deposit yields $5519.06 (to the nearest cent).

EXERCISE 11.2

B

1. Calculate the interest you would earn.
(a) $450 in a savings account for three days at 7%/a
(b) $734.85 in a savings account for one month at 8%/a
(c) $45.50 in a savings account for one day at 8.5%/a
(d) $195.85 in a savings account for six months at 9.25%/a

2. What is the interest and the amount in the savings account at the end of the term for each of the following?

	Amount Invested	Term	Rate
(a)	$1000	30 d	10%
(b)	$3456	1 a	7%
(c)	$100	10 d	6.5%
(d)	$7567	90 d	7.5%
(e)	$1 000 000	1 a	9.5%
(f)	$500	9 months	10%

3. The following is a page from a savings book.

COMMUNITY TRUST				
DATE	ITEM	WITHDRAWAL	DEPOSIT	BALANCE
DEC 1	DP		330.00	650.00
DEC 7	WD	250.00		
DEC 11	WD	50.00		
DEC 15	DP		458.00	
DEC 15	DP		222.00	
DEC 28	WD	240.00		
DEC 31	INT			

(a) Complete the balance column.
(b) What is the interest if the account pays 7%/a on the minimum monthly balance, credited monthly?
(c) What is the interest if the account pays 6.5%/a on the minimum daily balance, credited monthly?
(d) What is the interest if the account pays 6.75%/a on the average daily balance, credited monthly?

4. When their first grandchild was born, Mr. and Mrs. Fournier put $100 in a 3-month term deposit at 10%/a, compounded quarterly.
(a) If their grandchild cashed in the investment at age 19, what was the amount received?
(b) If their grandchild waited until age 20, what was the amount received?
(c) How much was gained by waiting the extra year?

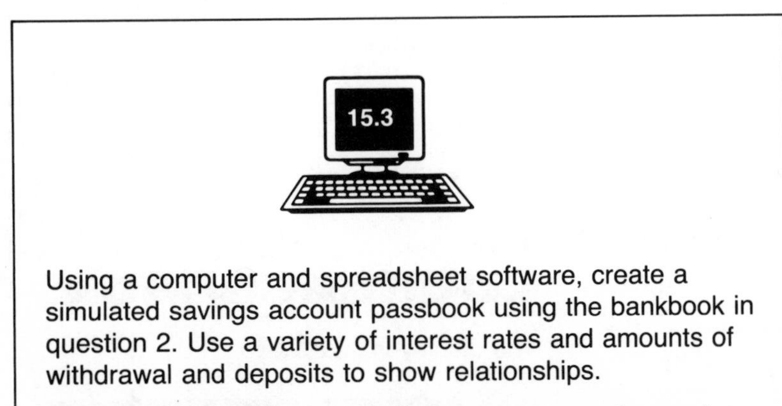

Using a computer and spreadsheet software, create a simulated savings account passbook using the bankbook in question 2. Use a variety of interest rates and amounts of withdrawal and deposits to show relationships.

Additional applications of savings accounts can be made using the concepts of Chapter 15, section 15.3, on spreadsheets.

EXTRA

11.3 FRACTIONAL PARTS OF A TIME PERIOD

The formula $A = P(1 + i)^n$, for compound amount, is derived on the assumption that n is a whole number and that the money will be invested for a whole number of conversion periods. There may be occasions when it is convenient to calculate the amount for a fractional part of a period. When computing compound interest for a fraction of a conversion period, simple interest is used.

Example 1. Find the amount of \$100 in $3\frac{1}{2}$ a at 7%/a, compounded annually.

Solution:

For the first 3 a,

$A = P(1 + i)^n, \quad P = 100, \quad i = 0.07, \quad n = 3$

$A = 100(1.07)^3$

$\quad = 100(1.225\ 04) \qquad \text{(from table)}$

$\quad = 122.504$

The compound amount for the first 3 a is \$122.50 (to the nearest cent).

For the remaining $\frac{1}{2}$ a the principal is \$122.50.

$A = P + Prt, \quad P = 122.50, \quad r = 0.07, \quad t = \frac{1}{2}$

$A = 122.50 + 122.50(0.07)(\frac{1}{2})$

$\quad = 122.50 + 4.2875$

$\quad = 126.7875$

The amount after $3\frac{1}{2}$ a is \$126.79 (to the nearest cent).

This calculation can be completed in one step using a calculator.

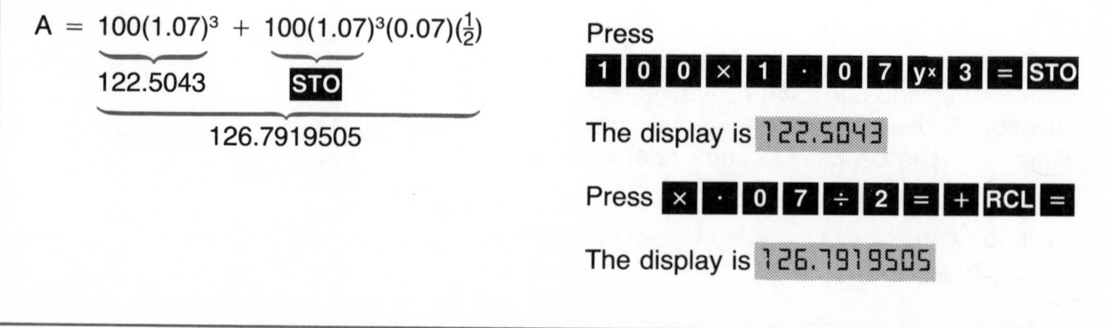

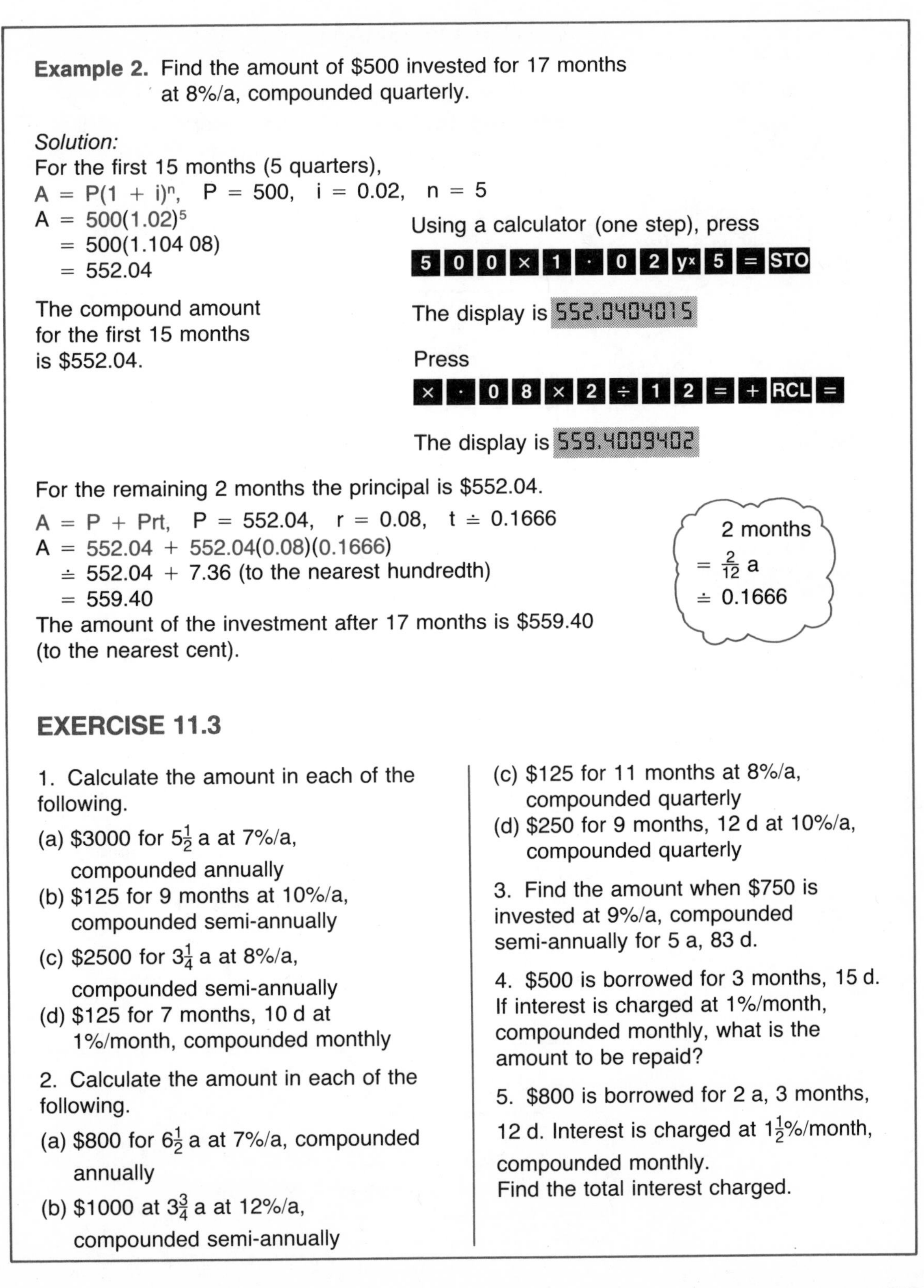

Example 2. Find the amount of $500 invested for 17 months at 8%/a, compounded quarterly.

Solution:

For the first 15 months (5 quarters),

$A = P(1 + i)^n$, $P = 500$, $i = 0.02$, $n = 5$

$A = 500(1.02)^5$
$= 500(1.104\ 08)$
$= 552.04$

The compound amount for the first 15 months is $552.04.

Using a calculator (one step), press

5 0 0 × 1 · 0 2 y^x 5 = STO

The display is 552.0404015

Press

× · 0 8 × 2 ÷ 1 2 = + RCL =

The display is 559.4009402

For the remaining 2 months the principal is $552.04.

$A = P + Prt$, $P = 552.04$, $r = 0.08$, $t \doteq 0.1666$

$A = 552.04 + 552.04(0.08)(0.1666)$
$\doteq 552.04 + 7.36$ (to the nearest hundredth)
$= 559.40$

The amount of the investment after 17 months is $559.40 (to the nearest cent).

2 months
$= \frac{2}{12}$ a
$\doteq 0.1666$

EXERCISE 11.3

1. Calculate the amount in each of the following.
   (a) $3000 for $5\frac{1}{2}$ a at 7%/a, compounded annually
   (b) $125 for 9 months at 10%/a, compounded semi-annually
   (c) $2500 for $3\frac{1}{4}$ a at 8%/a, compounded semi-annually
   (d) $125 for 7 months, 10 d at 1%/month, compounded monthly

2. Calculate the amount in each of the following.
   (a) $800 for $6\frac{1}{2}$ a at 7%/a, compounded annually
   (b) $1000 at $3\frac{3}{4}$ a at 12%/a, compounded semi-annually
   (c) $125 for 11 months at 8%/a, compounded quarterly
   (d) $250 for 9 months, 12 d at 10%/a, compounded quarterly

3. Find the amount when $750 is invested at 9%/a, compounded semi-annually for 5 a, 83 d.

4. $500 is borrowed for 3 months, 15 d. If interest is charged at 1%/month, compounded monthly, what is the amount to be repaid?

5. $800 is borrowed for 2 a, 3 months, 12 d. Interest is charged at $1\frac{1}{2}$%/month, compounded monthly. Find the total interest charged.

11.4 TIME DIAGRAMS

Spreadsheet activities related to this topic are found in section 15.3.

$i = 8\%$ $\quad n = 1,2,3,4$
$= 0.08 \quad 5,6,7$
$A = 75(1.08)^n$

The growth of money, period by period, can be illustrated on a time diagram. The following time diagram shows the amount of $75 at 8%/a, compounded annually for 7 interest periods.

Time Diagram — $75 at 8%/a Compounded Annually

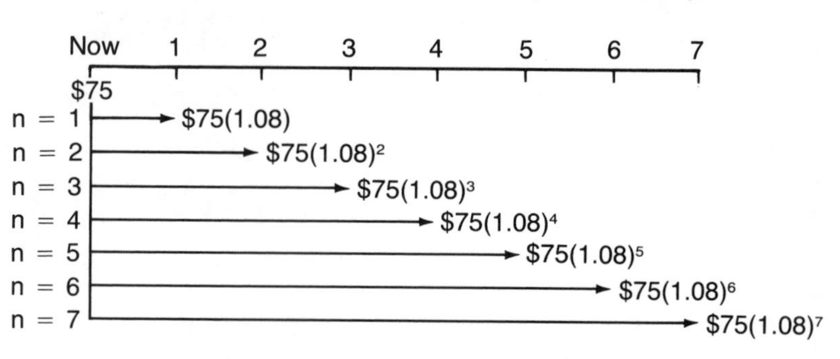

From the table "Amount of $1(1 + i)^n$" in the Appendix, for 8%, the amount $\$75(1.08)^n$ may be found.

n	$1(1 + 0.08)^n$	$P(1 + 0.08)^n$	A ($)
1	1.08	75(1.08)	81.00
2	1.166 4	75(1.166 4)	87.48
3	1.259 71	75(1.259 71)	94.48
4	1.360 49	75(1.360 49)	102.04
5	1.469 33	75(1.469 33)	110.20
6	1.586 87	75(1.586 87)	119.02
7	1.713 82	75(1.713 82)	128.54

The growth of the investment can be seen on the time diagram. Time diagrams are often used by financial institutions to illustrate how, over time, the amount you deposit in your savings account grows.

Time Diagram — $75 at 8%/a Compounded Annually

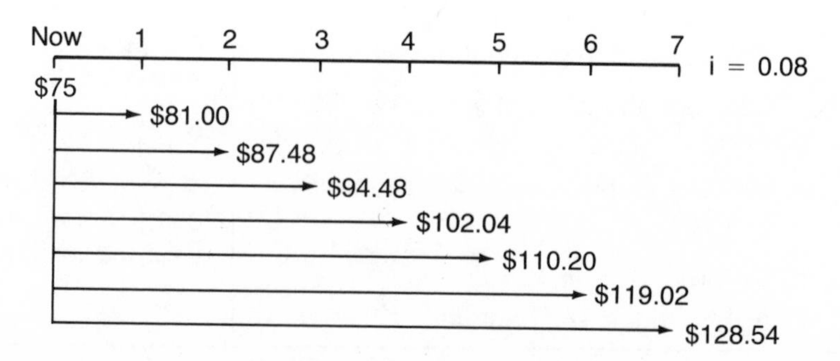

READ

Example 1. Draw a time diagram and find, to the nearest cent, the compound amount of $2000 invested at 9%/a, compounded semi-annually over a three-year period.

PLAN

Solution:
Since interest is being compounded semi-annually, the conversion period is 6 months, or 0.5 a, and i = 0.045 per conversion period.

$i = \frac{0.09}{2}$
$= 0.045$

$A = P(1 + i)^n$
$A = 2000(1.045)^n$, where n = 1, 2, 3, 4, 5, 6

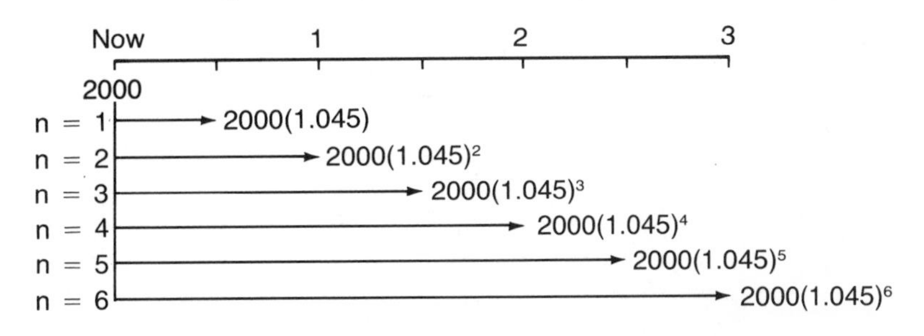

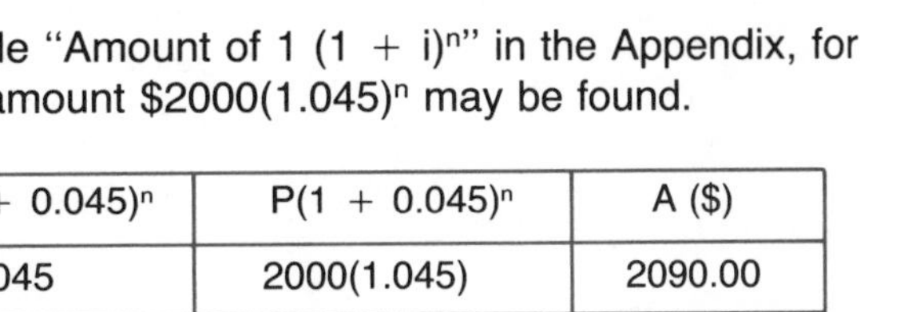

From the table "Amount of 1 $(1 + i)^n$" in the Appendix, for 4.5%/a, the amount $\$2000(1.045)^n$ may be found.

SOLVE

n	$1(1 + 0.045)^n$	$P(1 + 0.045)^n$	A ($)
1	1.045	2000(1.045)	2090.00
2	1.092 03	2000(1.092 03)	2184.06
3	1.141 17	2000(1.141 17)	2282.34
4	1.192 52	2000(1.192 52)	2385.04
5	1.246 18	2000(1.246 18)	2492.36
6	1.302 26	2000(1.302 26)	2604.52

ANSWER

The compound amount is $2604.52.

A time diagram is often helpful in determining the total value of investments made at different times.

Note that there may be slight discrepancies between using tables and calculators due to rounding.

Example 2. Makema invested \$6000 on June 1, 1984 at 9%, compounded semi-annually, and \$12 000 on December 1, 1986 at 7%, compounded semi-annually.
How much will her investments be worth on June 1, 1995?

Solution:
Regard June 1, 1984 as "now." Then, December 1, 1986 is 2.5 a from now, and June 1, 1995 is 11 a from now.
Draw a time diagram to illustrate this.

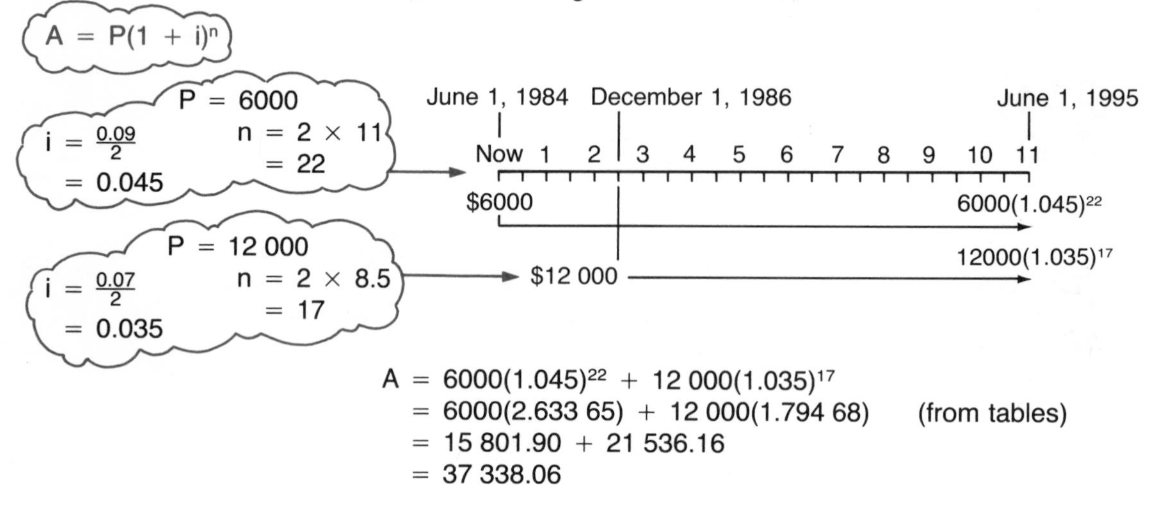

$$\begin{aligned} A &= 6000(1.045)^{22} + 12\,000(1.035)^{17} \\ &= 6000(2.633\,65) + 12\,000(1.794\,68) \quad \text{(from tables)} \\ &= 15\,801.90 + 21\,536.16 \\ &= 37\,338.06 \end{aligned}$$

The total amount of the investments will be \$37 338.06.

EXERCISE 11.4

B

1. Make time diagrams to show the compound amount for each of the following. Calculate the amount.
(a) \$400 in 5 a at 8%, compounded annually
(b) \$550 in 2 a at 7%/a, compounded semi-annually
(c) \$75 in 18 months at 12%/a, compounded monthly
(d) \$1200 in 2 a at $3\frac{1}{2}$% per half-year, compounded semi-annually
(e) \$100 in 12 months at 1%/month, compounded monthly

2. Petra borrows \$2000 from the bank at 7%/a, compounded semi-annually.
Find the amount she must pay in 36 months.

3. On her fourteenth birthday, Julie's grandfather left her \$25 000 invested at 8%/a, compounded semi-annually until her twenty-first birthday.
How much does she receive on that birthday?

4. An aunt leaves $100 000 to be divided equally between her two nephews, who are 13 a and 15 a old. Instead of giving each $50 000, the money is invested at 9%/a, compounded semi-annually.
How much does each receive at the age of 18?

5. (a) Find the compound amount to the nearest 10¢ at the end of 18 a if a principal of $1000 is invested over the first half of the term at 8%/a, compounded semi-annually, and over the second half of the term at 11%/a, compounded semi-annually.

(b) Find the compound amount to the nearest 10¢ if the principal of $1000 had been invested at 10%/a, compounded semi-annually over the 18 a term.

6. On her son's first birthday, a woman invests $2000 at 8%/a, compounded semi-annually, to provide for the boy's education. How much money will the boy have on his eighteenth birthday?

7. When Mia was born, her father invested $1000 at 7%/a, compounded semi-annually, to provide for her education. If he invested $1000 again on each of her first, second, and third birthdays, how much will she have at the age of 18? Begin with a time diagram.

8. A bank pays 8%/a, compounded semi-annually, on its deposits, and adds interest to a depositor's account on June 1 and December 1 of each year. On June 1, 1985 Kurt deposited $1200.
If no further deposits or withdrawals were made, how much was on deposit on December 1, 1987?

9. A financial concern which pays 9%/a, compounded semi-annually, on the minimum half-yearly balance, adds interest to deposits on January 1 and July 1 of each year. Lionel deposited $500 on July 1, 1987 and $300 on December 29, 1987.
How much did he have on deposit on January 1, 1989 if he made no further deposits or withdrawals?

C

10. Colleen opened a savings account February 1 and deposited $500. On March 1 she deposited $300 and on April 1 she withdrew $200.
If interest is credited on June 1 and December 1 at the annual rate of 5%, compounded semi-annually on the minimum balance for the preceding six months, how much is credited by the bank to Colleen's account on December 1?

11. If $150 is deposited in an account every three months for 3 a (12 deposits, starting now), what is the value of the investment at the time of the last deposit? Interest is paid at the rate of 8%, compounded quarterly.

MICRO MATH

The following program computes the amount of a principal, P, invested at I% for N interest periods.

```
NEW
10 PRINT "COMPOUND AMOUNT"
20 PRINT "ENTER P, I, N"
30 INPUT P, I, N
40 A = P*(1 + I)^N
50 PRINT "THE AMOUNT IS";A
60 END
RUN
```

11.5 ORDINARY ANNUITIES

When you are saving or investing towards a goal, you may not have a large sum of money to invest at one time. The ordinary annuity allows you to make regular deposits over a period of time.

Example 1. Jill is saving to buy a sailboat. She deposits \$1500 now and each year for 3 a into an ordinary annuity at 10%/a, compounded semi-annually.

(a) Illustrate the annuity on a time diagram.
(b) What is the term of the annuity?
(c) How much is the annuity worth at the end of the term or at maturity?

Solution:

(a) Time Diagram — Ordinary Annuity 10%/a Compounded Semi-Annually

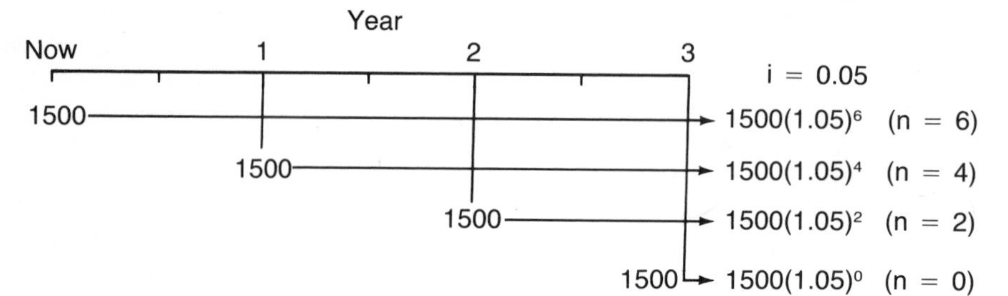

(b) The term of the annuity is the time interval from the beginning of the first to the end of the last interval.
The term is 3 a.

(c) First deposit, 1500 earns interest over 6 conversions
$1500(1.05)^6 = 1500(1.340\ 10)$
$= 2010.15$
Second deposit, 1500 earns interest over 4 conversions
$1500(1.05)^4 = 1500(1.215\ 51)$
$= 1823.27$
Third deposit, 1500 earns interest over 2 conversions
$1500(1.05)^2 = 1500(1.10250)$
$= 1653.75$
Fourth deposit, 1500 has just been deposited and earns no interest $= 1500$
At maturity, the annuity is worth
\$2010.15 + \$1823.27 + \$1653.75 + \$1500 = \$6987.17

Annuities may be purchased from a broker or from a financial institution. Many insurance plans that require an annual premium are annuities.

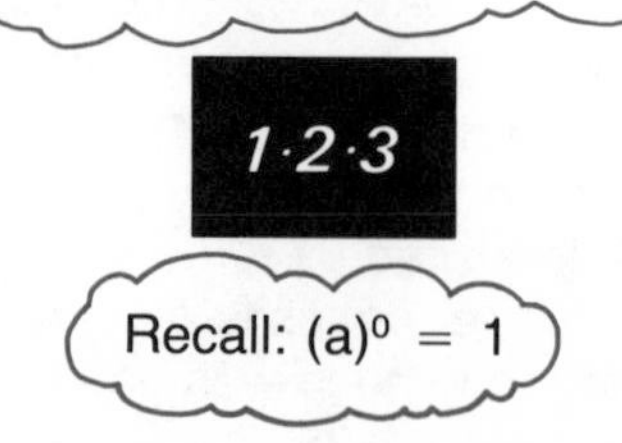

An ordinary annuity is a sequence of equal payments which earn interest at a fixed rate over a specific period of time.

EXERCISE 11.5

B 1. Give reasons why a person would purchase an annuity instead of an ordinary savings account or term deposit.

2. Complete the time diagram.

Time Diagram — Ordinary Annuity 8%/a Compounded Annually

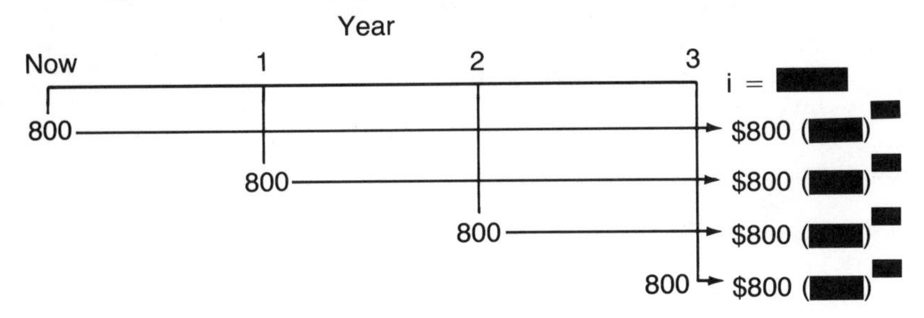

(a) What is the term of the annuity?
(b) What is the amount of the annuity at the end of the term or at maturity?

3. For each of the following annuities:
(a) Construct a time diagram.
(b) Calculate the amount at maturity. Assume payments are made at the beginning of each interval, but not at the end of the term.

	Payment	Interval	Term	Rate of Interest
(i)	$1000	yearly	3 a	6%/a, compounded annually
(ii)	$876	monthly	1 a	6%/a, compounded monthly
(iii)	$500	quarterly	2 a	12%/a, compounded quarterly
(iv)	$10 000	semi-annually	5 a	10%/a, compounded semi-annually

4. Find the amount of an annuity of $156 payable at the end of every six months for $3\frac{1}{2}$ a, if the interest rate is 9%, compounded semi-annually.

5. Angelo deposited $250 every six months in a fund earning interest at 10%/a, compounded quarterly. The first deposit was made when he turned 20 a and the last deposit was made when he turned 24. If he leaves the fund intact, how much will he have when he turns 30?

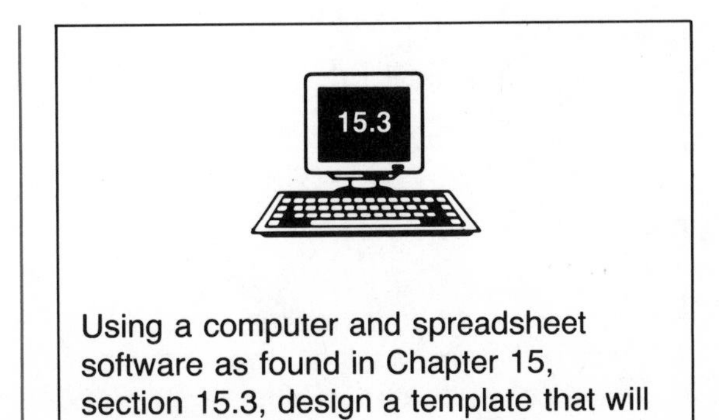

Using a computer and spreadsheet software as found in Chapter 15, section 15.3, design a template that will calculate the annuities in question 3.

EXTRA

11.6 TIME DIAGRAMS AND FRACTIONAL PERIODS

Suppose that payments are made into a savings plan more frequently than interest is compounded. To determine the amount at the end of a term we may combine the ideas from time diagrams and fractional periods.

Example. Cecile pays \$500 now and at each quarter for $1\frac{1}{2}$ a into a savings plan which pays 12%/a, compounded semi-annually. What is the amount in the plan at the end of the term?

Solution: Construct a time diagram to illustrate the plan. Interest is calculated and added to the plan every $\frac{1}{2}$ a.

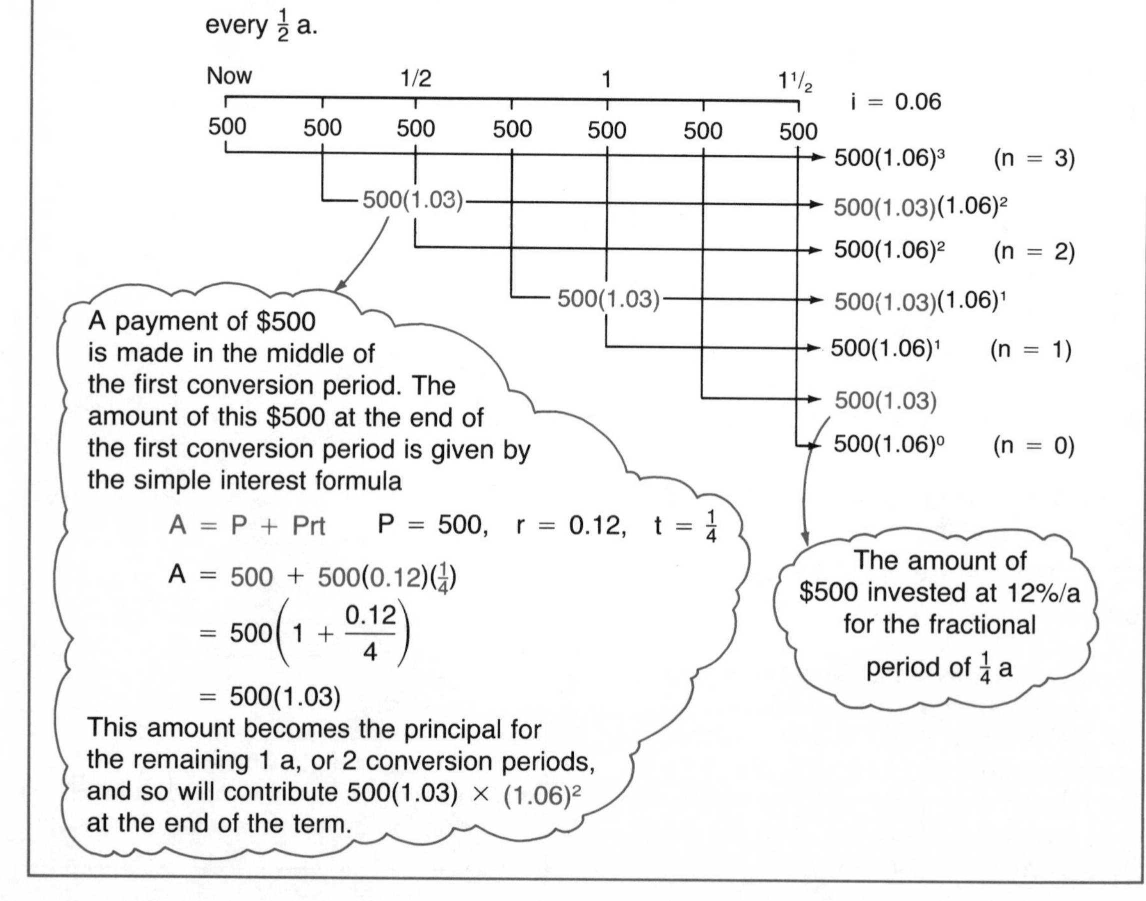

The sum of the amounts of the payments is

$$500(1.06)^3 + 500(1.03)(1.06)^2 + 500(1.06)^2 + 500(1.03)(1.06)$$
$$+ 500(1.06) + 500(1.03) + 500$$
$$= 3826.86$$

The amount in the plan at the end of the term is $3826.86.

EXERCISE 11.6

1. (a) Tom deposited $750 now and every 6 months into a fund earning interest at 8%/a, compounded annually for 3 a. Find the amount at the end of the term. Begin with a time diagram.
(b) Compare the amount in (a) with the amount obtained by depositing $750 now and $1500 each year into the same fund for 3 a.

2. Calculate the amount of each savings plan at maturity. Assume payments are made at the beginning of each interval, but not at the end of the term.

	Payment	Interval	Term	Rate of Interest
(a)	$250	quarterly	2 a	10%/a, compounded semi-annually
(b)	$100	monthly	1 a	8%/a, compounded quarterly

3. Calculate the amount of $1000 deposited now, and $500 at each quarter, for $2\frac{1}{2}$ a, into a savings plan that pays 14%/a, compounded semi-annually.

4. Compare the amount of $500 deposited now, and $200 at each quarter, for 4a, into a savings plan that pays 10%/a, compounded
(a) quarterly,
(b) semi-annually.

11.7 PRESENT VALUE OF AN AMOUNT

It is often necessary to plan your savings or investments to reach a particular goal, such as a future purchase. It is possible to determine the amount you must save or invest now to attain a specific amount of return.

> Present Value of an Amount
>
> The amount of money, or principal, P, which must be saved or invested now at a specific rate of interest to produce the required amount, A, after a specified time is called the present value.

We have already established the formula for compound amount: $A = P(1 + i)^n$

Solving for P, we have $P = \dfrac{A}{(1 + i)^n}$

In these applications we represent present value with PV so that $PV = \dfrac{A}{(1 + i)^n}$

where: PV is the principal which must be invested now,
A is the required amount,
i is the interest rate per period,
n is the number of periods.

The values of $\dfrac{1}{(1 + i)^n}$ can be found in the table in the Appendix.

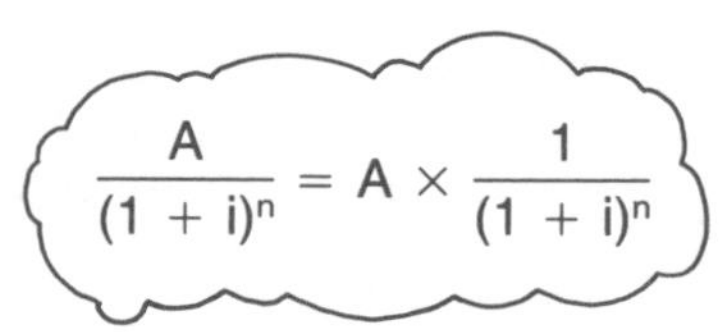

Example 1. Find the sum which must be invested today in order to accumulate an amount of $1000 in 10 a if the interest rate is 5%/a, compounded annually.

Solution:
Let the present value in dollars be PV. The required amount is A = 1000 where i = 0.05 and n = 10.

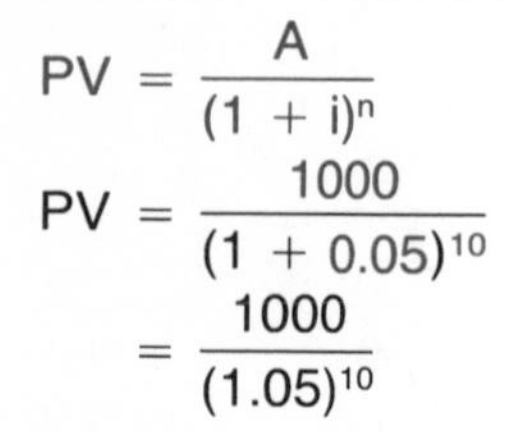

$$PV = \frac{A}{(1 + i)^n}$$

$$PV = \frac{1000}{(1 + 0.05)^{10}} = \frac{1000}{(1.05)^{10}}$$

Year n = 10
Now 1 2 3 4 5 6 7 8 9 10
A = 1000
$\dfrac{1000}{(1.05)^{10}}$ ←

METHOD I
Using the table in the Appendix,

$$PV = 1000 \times \frac{1}{(1.05)^{10}}$$
$$= 1000 \times 0.61391$$
$$= 613.91$$

METHOD II
Using a calculator, press

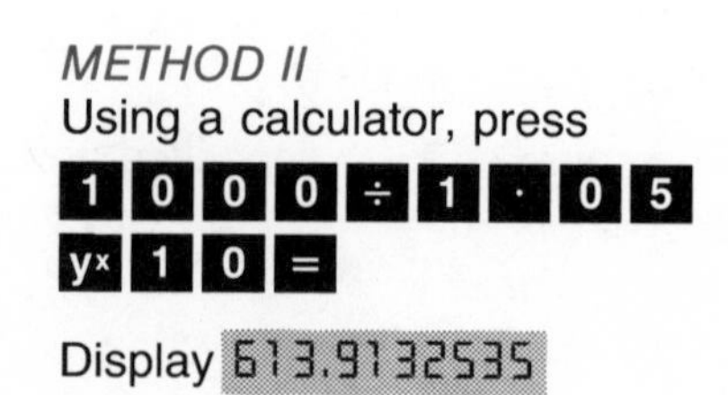

The sum of $613.91 must be invested today.

READ

Example 2. On the birth of a child, what sum of money should a family invest at 9%/a, compounded semi-annually, to provide the child with \$10 000 on the sixteenth birthday?

PLAN

Solution:
Since interest is being calculated twice per year, the interest rate per period is $\frac{0.09}{2} = 0.045$.

$A = 10\,000, \quad i = 0.045, \quad n = 16 \times 2$
$\qquad\qquad\qquad\qquad\qquad\quad = 32$

E=mc²

$$PV = \frac{A}{(1 + i)^n}$$

$$PV = \frac{10\,000}{(1.045)^{32}}$$

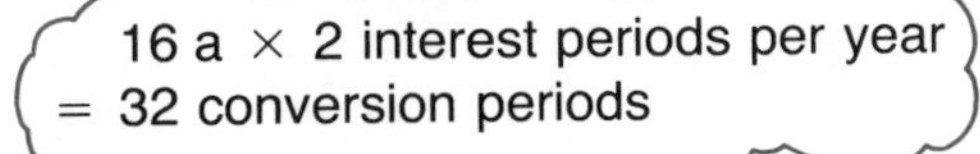

SOLVE

Using a calculator, press

Display 2444.999112

ANSWER

The family should invest \$2445.00 (to the nearest cent).

Example 3. Calculate and compare the amounts to be invested today in order to have
(a) \$1000 in 2 a, invested at 13%/a, compounded semi-annually,
(b) \$1200 in 6 a, invested at 11%/a, compounded annually.

Solution:

(a) Present value of \$1000 due in 2 a where $i = 0.065, \quad n = 4$:

$$PV = \frac{A}{(1 + i)^n}$$

$$PV = 1000 \times \frac{1}{(1.065)^4}$$
$$= 1000 \times 0.777\,32$$
$$= 777.32$$

∴ the present value is \$777.32.

(b) Present value of \$1200 due in 6 a where $i = 0.11, \quad n = 6$:

$$PV = \frac{A}{(1 + i)^n}$$

$$PV = 1200 \times \frac{1}{(1.11)^6}$$
$$= 1200 \times 0.534\,64$$
$$= 641.57$$

∴ the present value is \$641.57.

Hence \$1000 due in two years at 13%, compounded semi-annually, is worth more today than \$1200 due in six years at 11%/a, compounded annually.

EXERCISE 11.7

B 1. Using tables or a calculator, evaluate each of the following expressions to the nearest hundredth.

(a) $\frac{100}{(1.08)^5}$ (b) $\frac{100}{(1.045)^{20}}$ (c) $\frac{1500}{(1.06)^{10}}$

2. Find the present value of each of the following.
(a) $1000 due in 5 a at 7%/a, compounded annually
(b) $4000 due in 6 a at 8%/a, compounded semi-annually
(c) $180 due in 2 a at 12%/a, compounded quarterly
(d) $180 due in 2 a at 12%/a, compounded monthly
(e) $5000 due in 10 a at 8%/a, compounded quarterly

3. (a) What sum of money should a family invest on the birth of a child to provide $5000 at the age of 18 if the money is to be invested at 9%, compounded semi-annually?
(b) If bank interest is 9%/a, compounded semi-annually, what sum should you deposit today to have $15 000 in 10 a?
(c) If money is worth 8%, compounded quarterly, what sum must be invested now to purchase an automobile worth $14 650 in four years?

4. Which is worth more today, $100 due in 4 a at 8%/a, compounded annually, or $125 due in 8 a at 12%/a, compounded semi-annually? By how much?

5. (a) Which has the greater present value?
(i) an investment at 8%, compounded annually, worth $3000 in 7 a
(ii) an investment at 9%, compounded semi-annually, worth $5000 in 10 a
(b) By how much is it greater?

6. How much money must be invested at 9%, compounded semi-annually to give an amount of $6000 in 5 a?

7. A company holds investments in the amounts of $3000 due in 3 a at 7%/a, compounded semi-annually; $5000 in 7 a at 9%/a, compounded semi-annually; and $4000 in 5 a at 8%/a, compounded semi-annually.
(a) How much money does the company have today?
(b) If the present value of the three investments were reinvested at 10%/a, compounded semi-annually, how much would it have in: (i) 2 a? (ii) 5a?

8. (a) William Saxon received a legacy worth $10 000 on his 21st birthday. If money is worth 9%, compounded semi-annually, what was the legacy worth on his 18th birthday?
(b) How much will the legacy be worth if he leaves it invested at the same rate until his 30th birthday?

9. How much should a family invest at the birth of a child to provide $1500 at the age of 18 and $3000 at the age of 20 if money is worth 8%/a, compounded semi-annually? (Hint: Calculate the present value of $1500 and $3000 for the required terms.)

10. What sum of money paid in 5 a is equivalent to $3000 paid in one year if money is worth 12%/a, compounded semi-annually?

MICRO MATH

The following program computes the present value of an amount, $A, invested at I% for N interest periods.

```
NEW
10 PRINT "PRESENT VALUE"
20 PRINT "ENTER A, I, N"
30 INPUT A, I, N
40 PV=A/(1+I)^N
50 PRINT "THE PRESENT VALUE IS";PV
60 END
RUN
```

EXTRA

11.8 PRESENT VALUE OF AN ANNUITY

We may amalgamate the ideas from time diagrams, annuities, and present value to determine the amount to be invested now to meet a payment schedule.

Example. A company wishes to set up a college scholarship of \$2000/a for the next four years.
How much should the company invest now at 12%/a, compounded semi-annually, to meet the payments?

Solution: Draw a time diagram to illustrate the situation. Calculate the present value of each payment.

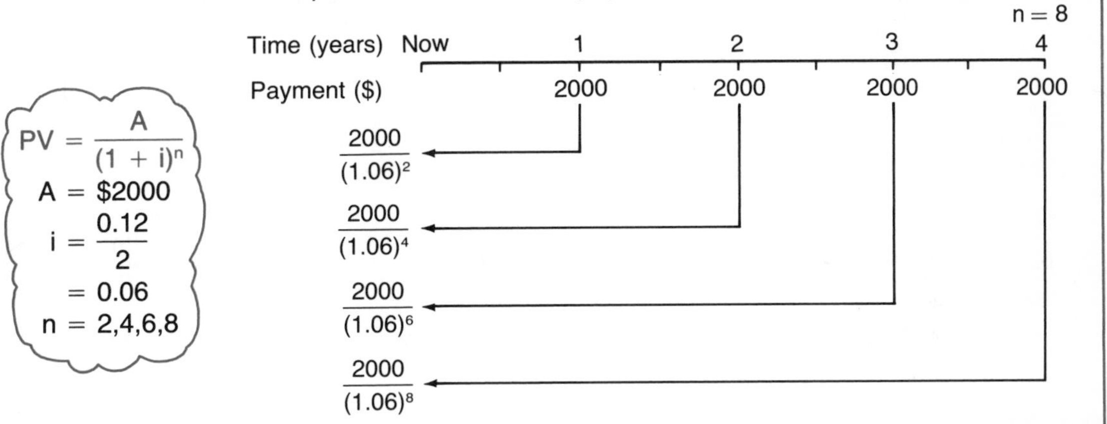

The sum of the present values of each payment

is: $\frac{2000}{(1.06)^2} + \frac{2000}{(1.06)^4} + \frac{2000}{(1.06)^6} + \frac{2000}{(1.06)^8}$

$= 1780 + 1584.18 + 1409.92 + 1254.82$

$= 6028.92$

The company should invest \$6028.92 now to support the fund for four years.

EXERCISE 11.8

1. Find the present value of an annuity if each payment is \$800 payable at the end of the month for 4 months at an interest rate of 12%/a, compounded monthly.

2. A student will require \$2000/a for three years for further education. What amount must be invested now at 10%, compounded semi-annually, if the first payment will be required in four years.

11.9 PROBLEM SOLVING

1. The cross section of a concrete highway support is shown in the diagram.
If the support is 10 m long, what is the volume of concrete in the support?

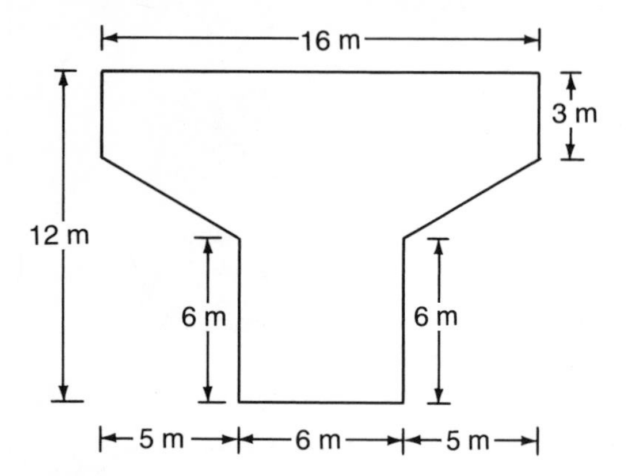

2. The value of 45 coins consisting of quarters and nickels is $6.45.
How many nickels and quarters are there?

3. The product of two consecutive whole numbers is 9702.
What is the sum of the numbers?

4. The digits from 1 to 9 have been used to write three numbers.
The number in the second row is twice the number in the first row.
The number in the third row is three times the number in the first row.

219
438
657

There are three other possible solutions to this same problem. One solution contains the number 576. Another solution contains the number 654.
Find all three other solutions.

5. What is the largest possible product of two whole numbers whose sum is 80?

6. Eighteen trees are evenly spaced around a rectangular field. Five trees form the width.
How many trees form the length?

7. How many squares can you draw with open circles at the corners so that each square contains the solid circle? One has been drawn for you.

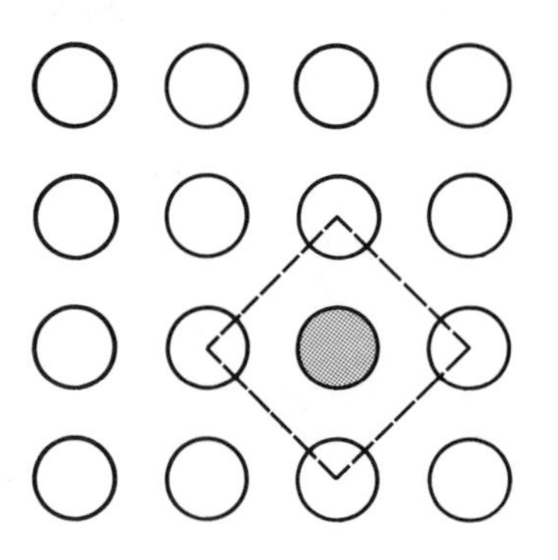

8. The amount of water in a container triples every minute. The container is completely filled at 14:13.
What fraction of the container was filled at 14:12?

9. Two runners are 4000 m apart. They start running towards each other. One runner runs at a rate of 250 m/min. The other runs at a rate of 150 m/min.
After how many minutes will the runners meet?

10. Is it possible to pass through all the rooms and pass through each door only once?

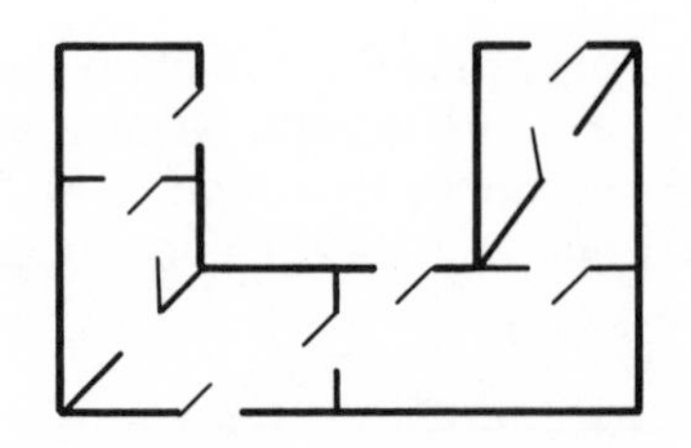

11. How many squares are in the design?

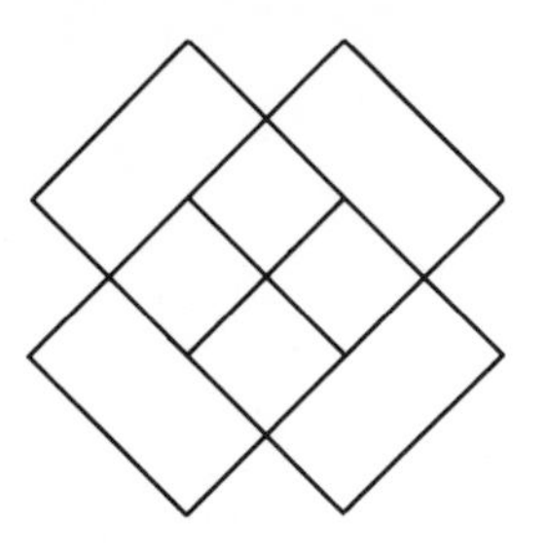

12. Find four consecutive odd numbers whose sum is 288.

13. Three rolls of steel are held together by a band.

The diameter of each roll of steel is 1 m. What is the length of the band?

14. A store buys a suit at a wholesale cost of $175.00. The store then marks up the price by 30%. When the suit does not sell after 6 months, it is sold at a 30% discount. What is the selling price of the suit?

15. A store buys a dress at a wholesale cost of $150.00. The store then marks up the price by 40%. When the dress is not sold after 6 months, it is sold at a discount. What should the percentage discount be to break even?

EXTRA

THE BOSTON MARATHON

The Boston Marathon is a difficult race because the competitors are running downhill most of the time. This puts stress on the upper thigh muscles.
The table gives the elevation above sea level at several points along the route.

Distance (km)	Elevation (m)
Start	150
8	63
16	52
24	49
32	46
40	5
42.3	3

(a) Draw a graph of elevation (vertical axis) versus distance from the start.

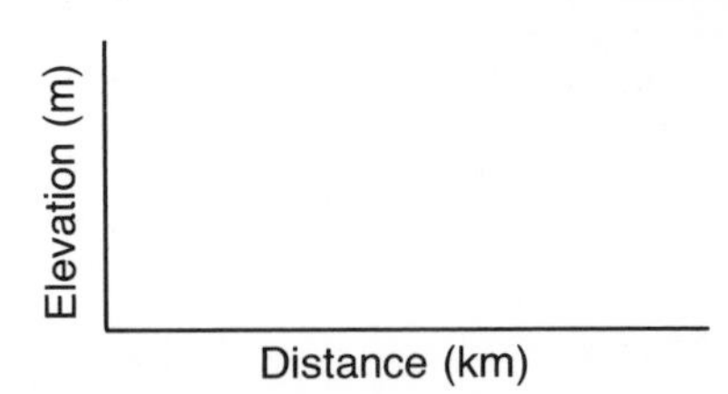

(b) A good time for a marathon is 2 h 10 min.
What is this speed in kilometres per hour?

(c) What is the origin of the word *marathon*?

11.10 REVIEW EXERCISE

1. Bernard's credit union chequing account statement is shown below. Complete the balance. The credit union has a service charge of $0.50 per transaction unless a minimum average daily balance of $500 is maintained. Calculate the service charge, if applicable.

CITY CO-OPERATIVE CREDIT UNION						
Description	no.	Debits/Cheques	Deposits/Credits	Date		Balance
		$	$	m	d	$800.00
machine wd		200.00		3	8	
dep			400.00	3	8	
machine wd		25.00		3	9	
cheque	122	55.00		3	10	
dep			120.00	3	15	
cheque	124	90.00		3	17	
machine wd		125.00		3	23	
service charge				3	31	

no. debits	total amount debit	no. credits	total amount credit
	$		$

2. Using the statement above and the following information, copy and complete Bernard's cheque register below. Reconcile the cheque register with the bank statement. On April 2 he made a deposit of $100 and wrote three cheques — #123 on March 10 for $45.00, #125 on March 30 for $75.00, and #126 on April 7 for $80.00.

CHEQUE REGISTER						
date	no.	Description		deposit	withdr.	Balance
3/1		Balance Forward				800.00

Reconciliation

Balance shown on Bank statement ______

______

Add all deposits not on statement ______

Total ______
Subtotal ______

Subtract all cheques not on statement ______

______

______

______

______

Total ______
Balance/ Register ______

3. Construct time diagrams to show the compound amount for each of the following. Calculate the amount.
(a) $675 in 9 months at 18%/a, compounded monthly
(b) $750 in 15 months at 10%/a, compounded quarterly
(c) $1500 in 3 a at 9%/a, compounded semi-annually

4. Simone invested $2000 on January 1, 1984 at 10%/a compounded quarterly, and $2500 on July 1, 1985 at 9%/a, compounded semi-annually.
Construct a time diagram and calculate how much her investments will be worth on July 1, 1990.

5. What is the amount of an annuity if the payments are $250 payable at the end of each quarter for one year at an interest rate of 8%/a, compounded quarterly?

6. What is the amount of an annuity of $1200 payable at the end of each year for 4 a at an interest rate of 9%/a, compounded semi-annually?

7. Calculate the amount at maturity for each of the following annuities. Assume that payments are made at the beginning of each interval, but not at the end of the term.

	Payment	Interval	Term	Rate of Interest
(a)	$2500	yearly	4 a	7%/a, compounded annually
(b)	$750	quarterly	2 a	10%/a, compounded quarterly
(c)	$350	monthly	0.5 a	12%/a, compounded monthly

8. Find the present value of the following.
(a) $1000 due in 3 a at 7%/a, compounded semi-annually
(b) $3000 due in 2 a at 5%/a, compounded semi-annually
(c) $1200 due in 2 a at 8%/a, compounded quarterly
(d) $500 due in 24 months at 1%/month, compounded monthly

9. Which has the greater present value and by how much?
(a) $600 due in 5 a at 8%/a, compounded quarterly
(b) $600 due in 6 a at 7%/a, compounded annually

10. How much would it cost now to settle debts of $1800 due in 3 a and $2600 due in 4 a if money is worth 9%/a, compounded semi-annually?

11. What sum of money should a family invest at the birth of a child to provide $600 at the age of 18 and $1000 at the age of 20? The money is to be invested at 7%/a, compounded semi-annually.

12. What sum of money paid 5 a from today is equivalent to payments of $1500, 2 a from now and $3500 paid 7 a from now, if money is worth 8%/a, compounded semi-annually?

13. Find the present value of 5 annual payments of $500 if the first payment is made 1 a from now and money is worth 8%, compounded semi-annually.

14. Find the present value of 6 semi-annual payments of $100 if the first payment is made 2 a from now and money is worth 9%, compounded semi-annually.

15. $50/month is placed in an account for 6 months. Interest at 1%/month is added to the account at the end of each month after the first deposit.
(a) How much is in the account at the time of the last deposit?
(b) One month after the last deposit, withdrawals of $50/month are made for 6 months. How much is in the account after the last withdrawal?

11.11 CHAPTER 11 TEST

1. A chequing/savings account requires a minimum average daily balance of $500. If the average daily balance is above $500, interest of 8%/a on the average daily balance is earned. If the average daily balance is below $500, a service charge of $0.50 per transaction is deducted. The September statement is given below.
(a) Complete the balance.
(b) Calculate the average daily balance.
(c) What is the amount of interest or service charge?

PROVINCIAL BANK					
Description	no.	Debits/Cheques	Deposits/Credits	Date	Balance
		$	$	m d	$713.60
machine dep			500.00	9 3	
cheque	010	435.00		9 7	
machine wd		300.00		9 13	
cheque	011	250.65		9 20	
dep			350.00	9 23	
cheque	012	568.73		9 25	
service charge/ interest					

no. debits	total amount debit	no. credits	total amount credit
	$		$

2. An investment of $1000 is made on January 1, 1984 at 8%/a, compounded semi-annually. Eighteen months later another investment of $1000 at 9%/a, compounded semi-annually, is made.
Draw a time diagram and find, to the nearest cent, the total value of the investments on January 1, 1989.

3. Find the amount of an annuity of $700 payable at the end of every six months for 3 a if the interest rate is 10%/a, compounded quarterly.

4. Which is worth more today, $1500 due in 4 a at 6%/a, compounded semi-annually, or $2000 due in 6 a at 8%/a, compounded quarterly? By how much?

VEHICLE COSTS

REVIEW AND PREVIEW TO CHAPTER 12

ABBREVIATIONS

EXERCISE 1

AC	— air conditioning	HT	— hardtop
auto	— automatic transmission	int	— interior
cert	— certified safety checked	km	— kilometres
cyl	— cylinder	PB	— power brakes
dr	— door	PS	— power steering
EC	— excellent condition	PW	— power windows
ext	— exterior	spd	— speed
gd	— good	std	— standard transmission

1. Read each used car ad below.
2. Which car does the seller say is in excellent condition?
3. Which car would you buy and why?
4. Which car would you avoid and why?
5. What are the laws on safety certification in your province?

Newyorker 2dr turbo, well equipped, 24 000 km, cert, asking $13 750 firm, 555-1400 after 6.

MGB, under 48 000 km, no winters, asking $5800, 555-1122.

Buick Riviera, the ultimate Riv, fully loaded/digital dash, pushbutton - air, all leather, moonroof etc. $16 900, 824-9065.

Parisienne wagon, fully equipped, AC, PS, Mike, 555-6745.

Volkswagen Rabbit, 4 dr, std, AM/FM cass, no rust, EC, PB, PS, must be seen, moving, 555-1346.

Chev Malibu Classic, 120 000 km, 2dr, 305, ext gd, will cert, $2600, or $75/mo. 555-4567.

Buick LeSabre, collector's edition, Florida car, 33 000 km, P/seat, P/recliner, vanity mirror, Radio with autoscan, $14 500. Immac. 459-9632 after 6.

Volvo, 6 cyl, auto, AC, gd ext, cert, $3700, 555-5074.

Toyota Celica GTS, h-back, blue, 15 000 km, warranty, like new, $17 500. 671-9610.

GREAT BUY!
Cadillac Fleetwood Brougham d'Elegance, fully loaded, new tires/brakes, non-smoker, 62 000 km. Mint cond. $19 500. Days, 482-8030 or evgs. & wkends., 314-7612.

Honda Accord, LX, 4 dr., sedan, auto., P/S, P/B, AM/FM, cruise, low mi., 1 owner, fully cert. Call 752-1143.

ORDER OF OPERATIONS

EXERCISE 2

1. 7.85 + 14.98(0.09) + 7.85
2. 1234.85(1.08) + 458.98(2.23)
3. 5.89(0.08) − 1.83(0.06)
4. 0.009 + 0.09 + 0.9
5. 89.98(1.009)(0.98)
6. 23.45 + 78.987 − 29.87
7. (4.9 + 4.8)(12.8 − 70.82)
8. 78.98 − 34.89(0.78)
9. 100 − 10 − 1 − 0.1 − 0.01
10. (0.5 − 0.3)(0.05 − 0.03)

PERCENT

EXERCISE 3

1. 5% of 89
2. 4.5% of 129
3. 124% of 12
4. 34% of 1234
5. 1.4% of 1
6. 50% of 127
7. 103% of 234
8. 98% of 98
9. 0.09% of 23
10. 1.09% of 23
11. 24 is what percent of 56?
12. 100 is what percent of 10?
13. 10 is what percent of 100?
14. 456 is what percent of 1238?
15. 1 is what percent of 9?
16. 24 is what percent of 24?
17. 24 is what percent of 1?
18. 234 is what percent of 235?
19. 98 is what percent of 998?
20. 998 is what percent of 98?

ESTIMATION

EXERCISE 4

Estimate the value of each. Check your estimate using a calculator.

1. 12 345 ÷ 12
2. 23 438 ÷ 20
3. (11 985)(11)
4. (43 823)(0.04)
5. (12 834) ÷ 0.4
6. 12 345 ÷ 0.12
7. (17 834)(21)
8. 23 234 ÷ 0.5
9. (17 875)(0.07)
10. (8456)(0.4)
11. 234.89 + 12.48 + 123.89
12. 12.34 + 123.34 + 234.89
13. 176.89 + 17.98 + 45.89
14. 4.50 + 7.75 + 1.95 + 6.34
15. 234.45 + 834.93 + 345.86
16. 789.23 + 123.89 + 45.78
17. 8.98 + 7.89 + 45.89 + 7.12
18. 101.98 + 103.45 + 105.78
19. 34.56 + 78.45 + 101.76 + 3.45
20. 234.89 + 34.45 + 189.89
21. You want to buy a new car for $21 450 with optional extras costing the following: $123.34,
    $423.85,
    $123.95,
    $45.87, and
    $20.99.

    You also want a 5-year extended service contract which costs 1% of the purchase price, before taxes, per year of extended service. Taxes are 7% of the total purchase price and your licence will cost $55.00.

    (a) Estimate the total amount the car will cost.

    (b) What is the actual cost of the car?

12.1 OPERATING EXPENSES

Whether you own or lease a car, there are operating expenses. Some of these, such as licence plates, are fixed expenses regardless of how much you drive. Other expenses, such as gasoline and oil, are variable and depend on how much you drive.

FIXED COSTS	VARIABLE COSTS
Car registration fee	Gasoline and oil
Driver's licence fee	Repair and maintenance
	Parking fees
	Insurance

The car registration fee and the driver's licence fee have several purposes.

Identification of the car and the driver

Tax for the privilege of owning and driving a car

Control to ensure that the car is insured and the driver drives safely

GASOLINE

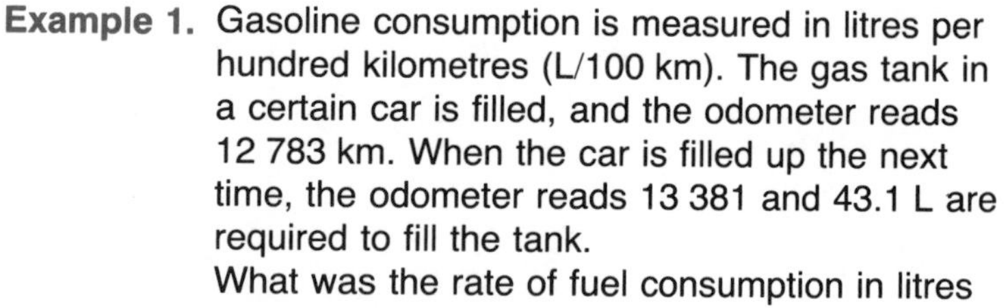

Example 1. Gasoline consumption is measured in litres per hundred kilometres (L/100 km). The gas tank in a certain car is filled, and the odometer reads 12 783 km. When the car is filled up the next time, the odometer reads 13 381 and 43.1 L are required to fill the tank.
What was the rate of fuel consumption in litres per hundred kilometres?

Solution:

The distance driven between fill-ups is

13 381 km − 12 783 km = 598 km.

The number of litres consumed is 43.1 L.

$\frac{\text{n L}}{\text{100 km}}$ is the rate of fuel consumption.

$$\frac{n}{100} = \frac{43.1}{598}$$
$$598n = 4310$$
$$n \doteq 7.2$$

The rate of consumption is 7.2 L/100 km.

Determine the number of litres, n, per 100 km that is equivalent to 43.1 L in 598 km.

OIL

Example 2. The owner's manual for a new car recommends that the oil be changed after the first 5000 km and every 6000 km thereafter.
If each oil change costs an average of \$28.50, and the car will be driven 24 000 km in the first year, how much will oil changes cost in the first year?

Solution:
1 oil change the first 5000 km

$24\,000 - 5000 = 19\,000$

$19\,000 \div 6000 \doteq 3$

4 oil changes are needed at an average cost of \$28.50 each.

$4 \times 28.50 = 114.00$

The oil changes will cost approximately \$114.00/a.

READ

Example 3. Find the yearly cost of gasoline and oil changes for a car that will be driven 30 000 km in one year. The average rate of fuel consumption is 6.8 L/100 km. Oil changes are required every 6000 km. An oil change costs \$28.50 and the price of gasoline is 62.9¢/L on the average.

PLAN

Rule of Three

Solution:

SOLVE

Cost of oil changes:
Number of oil changes is

$$\frac{30\,000}{6000} = 5$$

1 oil change costs \$28.50
5 oil changes cost $5 \times \$28.50$
$= \$142.50$

Cost of gasoline:
100 km requires 6.8 L

30 000 km require $\frac{6.8}{100} \times 30\,000$
$= 2040$

1 L of gasoline costs 62.9¢
2040 L of gasoline cost
$2040 \times 62.9¢$
$= \$1283.16$

ANSWER

The yearly cost for gasoline and oil changes is
$\$142.50 + \$1283.16 = \$1425.66$

MAINTENANCE

To keep a car in top running condition regular service is necessary. It is important to know when a car needs a major or minor repair. If minor problems are not taken care of, they become major repairs and can be more costly.

Routine maintenance is important and should not be neglected. This includes:

oil change, lubrication, new oil filter, engine tune-up, changing spark plugs, engine timing, tire rotation.

As a car gets older, the expenses for maintenance are likely to increase.

> It is estimated that maintenance and repairs on a car will average $500/a, increasing by $200/a through a 5 a life of a car. After 5 a repairs are not predictable.

Mechanical protection plans, which are like large-repair insurance, are available but they do not cover servicing or routine maintenance, and usually do not cover brakes, exhaust system, or tires. They will also be voided if damage is caused by lack of proper maintenance.

SIGNALS CHECKLIST

INSTRUCTION: Check As Many As Necessary With Pencil

1. **WHAT IS IT DOING?** **Description**
   - □ Noise ______
   - □ Odour ______
   - □ Visual ______
   - □ Performance ______
   - □ Handling ______

2. **WHERE DOES IT COME FROM?**

A □ Inside Car

	LEFT	RIGHT	FRONT	REAR	CENTRE
• Instrument Panel	□	□	□	□	□
• Seat	□	□	□	□	□
• Door	□	□	□	□	□
• Window	□	□	□	□	□
• Roof	□	□	□	□	□
• Floor	□	□	□	□	□
• Trunk	□	□	□	□	□
• Rear Fender	□	□	□	□	□

B □ Outside Car
- □ Under car
- □ Under Hood
- □ Front
- □ Rear
- □ Right
- □ Left

3. **WHEN DOES IT HAPPEN?**

A □ Car not moving and engine stopped

B □ When car is moving and mostly:
- □ During braking
- □ During turning
- □ While accelerating (increasing load)
- □ While decelerating (coasting)
- □ During change from acceleration to coasting
- □ At ___km/h
- □ At any speed
- □ When shifting from forward to reverse
- □ On rough roads
- □ In ___gear or range

C □ Mostly when using:
- □ Brakes
- □ Steering wheel
- □ Clutch
- □ Heater/ air conditioning
- □ Windshield wiper/washer
- □ Radio/power antenna
- □ Rear window defogger
- □ Starter
- □ Other ______

D □ When engine is:
- □ Idling
- □ Cold
- □ Hot
- □ Warming-up
- □ Being started

4. **DOES IT:**
   - □ Vary with car speed?
   - □ Vary with trunk load?
   - □ Vary with engine speed?
   - □ Vary with engine load (acceleration)?

5. **HOW DOES IT HAPPEN?**
   - □ Always
   - □ Comes and goes
   - □ After ___km

EXERCISE 12.1

B

1. (a) Copy the following table in your notebook.
(b) Fill in the current cost of gasoline per litre.
(c) Find the total yearly cost of gasoline and parking for the cars described below.

Type	Sedan	Convertible	Station Wagon
Age of Car	1	4	3
Distance (km)	14 500	20 000	17 876
L/100 km	6.8	5.7	6.1
Gas cost/L			
Parking	$4 /weekday	$50 /month	no charge

2. For the cars in question 1, use current registration fee and driver's licence fee. What are the total yearly operating costs for each car?

3. The information below is recorded in a Car Cost book. Assume that the gas tank was filled at each purchase.
Find the gasoline consumption (L/100 km) for each entry, if possible.
Find the average gasoline consumption for the month of May.

Date	Cost	Litres	Odometer Reading
May 1	58.8	45	18 326
May 9	61.5	40	18 946
May 20	60.9	43	19 461
May 31	59.9	37	19 949

4. A new 4-door Roadhandler sedan is purchased in June for $35 336.63. The car is serviced according to the following schedule.

Maintenance Schedule/Cost/City Automotive			
Service	Frequency	Parts	Labour
Servicing	3000 km	none	$9.40
Oil change and oil filter	12 000 km	$2.80/L $14.00	$14.50
Lubrication	12 000 km	no charge	no charge
Air filter	18 000 km	$18.75	no charge
Gas filter	12 000 km	$3.20	$12.00
Tune-up and spark plugs	18 000 km	$2.20 each	$61.00
Winterizing and coolant	1/a (fall) (Sept., Oct.)	$3.20/L	$42.00

The car requires 5 L of oil, 6 spark plugs, and 7 L of coolant.

(a) In October the car is taken in to be serviced. The odometer reads 6123. Determine the service cost.

(b) In June the car is taken in to be serviced. The odometer reads 24 098. Determine the service cost for the first year.

(c) In September the car is taken in to be serviced. The odometer reads 36 010. Determine the service cost.

(d) The following June, the odometer reads 45 528 km. The car also gets a "brake job" for $288.00.
What is the total charge for maintenance and repairs for this second year?

Throughout this chapter we will accumulate the cost of ownership of the Roadhandler. Retain your answers to question 4.

12.2 DEPRECIATION

A car is a major investment. Unlike most investments, however, it loses value from year to year. This loss of value is called depreciation.

Depreciation may not seem "real" but it is part of the true cost of owning a car.

The table below shows the percentage of depreciation each year on a typical car and on a typical pick-up truck.

Age of Car (a)	Current Value as a Percentage of Original Value	Age of Truck (a)	Current Value as a Percentage of Original Value
1	77%	1	83%
2	65%	2	68%
3	42%	3	45%
4	25%	4	27%
5	10%	5	17%

Example. A car was purchased three years ago for \$22 789.
(a) What is the current value of the car?
(b) What is the average loss per year due to depreciation?

Solution:

(a) The car is 3 a old. According to the current value table, the current value is 42% of the original value.
$22\,789(0.42) = 9571.38$
The current value of the car is \$9571.38.

1·2·3

(b) The loss due to depreciation may be found in two ways.

METHOD I
Purchase price − Current value
$= 22\,789.00 - 9571.38$
$= 13\,217.62$

METHOD II
The current value is 42% of the original price.
The percent loss due to depreciation is
$100\% - 42\% = 58\%$.
$22\,789(0.58) = 13\,217.62$

The loss due to depreciation is \$13 217.62.
The average loss per year due to depreciation

is $\dfrac{13\,217.62}{3} \doteq \$4405.87$

EXERCISE 12.2

B

1. Give reasons why a truck would depreciate less than a typical car.

2. A car was bought new for $21 789.
(a) What will its current value be in 5 a?
(b) What is the mean loss per year after 5 a?
(c) What is the mean loss per month after 5 a?
(d) What is the mean loss per day after 5 a?

3. A truck was bought new for $23 789.
(a) What will its current value be at the end of 1 a?
(b) What is the loss per month in the first year?
(c) What is the loss per day in the first year?
(d) What will its current value be at the end of the second year?
(e) What is the loss per month in the second year?
(f) What is the loss per day in the second year?
(g) What is the mean loss per year after 5 a?
(h) What is the mean loss per month after 5 a?
(i) What is the mean loss per day after 5 a?
(j) On a bar graph, graph the value of the car over the first five years.

4. A truck and a car each cost $22 000. How much more will the car cost per day in depreciation than the truck over a 2 a period?
What factors other than depreciation would influence your decision to buy a car or a truck?

5. A 3 a old car is purchased for $7892. The original cost of the car was $15 983. From the current value table, was the price approximately correct?
What other factors must be taken into consideration when buying a used car besides the current market value?

6. A car dealership offers a customer $10 200 for a car which is 2 a old and had an original purchase price of $17 000.
(a) How much has the car depreciated?
(b) What amount of depreciation, in percent, is the dealership applying?
(c) What is a fair price according to the current value table?

7. Cumulative cost for the Roadhandler (See p. 371.)

(a) What is the value of the Roadhandler after 2 a?
(b) What is the depreciation cost for the second year?
(c) What is the mean monthly depreciation for the second year?
(d) What is the mean daily depreciation for the second year?

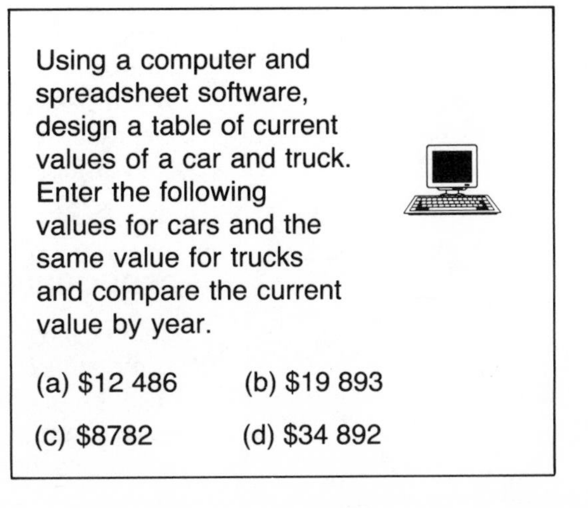

Using a computer and spreadsheet software, design a table of current values of a car and truck. Enter the following values for cars and the same value for trucks and compare the current value by year.

(a) $12 486 (b) $19 893

(c) $8782 (d) $34 892

12.3 AUTOMOBILE INSURANCE

In most provinces the law requires that automobile owners have specific types of insurance on their vehicles.

TYPES OF INSURANCE COVERAGE

There are several types of benefits available when you purchase automobile insurance.

Public liability — protects the insured against claims for injuries or death caused by the insured.

Property damage — protects the insured when another person's property, including the car, is damaged by the insured.

Medical services benefits — protect the insured and those riding in the insured's car; protect the insured when riding in a car belonging to someone else; protect the insured if struck by a car, no matter who is at fault.

Collision — pays for damages from a collision to a car owned by the insured and caused by the insured, up to the value of the car.

Comprehensive — pays for the loss of, or for damages to, the insured car caused by fire, theft, weather, flood, etc.

Motorist coverage — ensures payment to the insured who is injured or killed through the fault of another motorist who has no insurance, or whose policy limits are not high enough.

Which insurance company pays for the damages, medical or funeral expenses depends on the type of coverage and which party is at fault. Some provinces have "no fault" insurance which does not require the assessment of who was at fault.

DEDUCTIBLES

Both collision and comprehensive insurance involve damage to the insured car caused by the owner, by an act of chance, or by an act of nature. For this reason, both types of coverage may require the insured to assume some financial responsibility for the damage.

With collision and comprehensive coverage there is usually an amount of money that the insured is required to pay before collecting from the insurance company. This money is called the deductible amount. It is deducted by the insurance company from the amount paid to the insured for damages or loss.

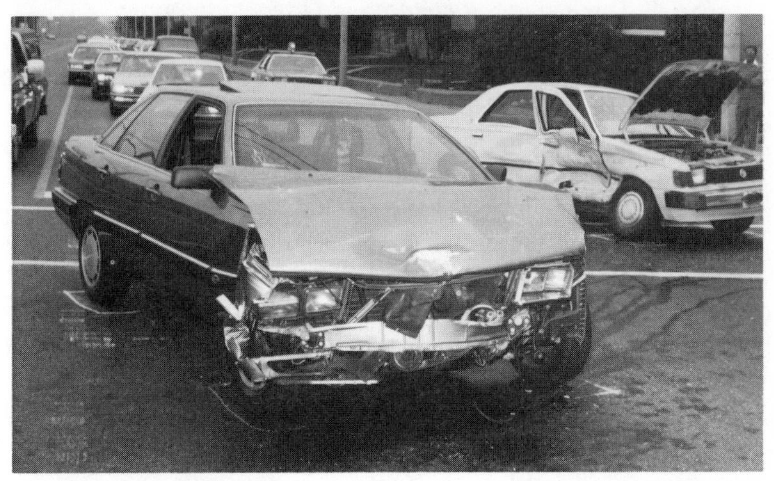

INSURANCE RATES

The rate that is charged for insurance coverage depends on:

- Types of coverage purchased
- Maximums placed on payment of a claim
- Amount of the deductibles
- Age
- Sex
- Accident and driving record
- Number of cars insured with the company

Young drivers may receive a discount for being good students or for having completed driver education courses.

The insurance industry sets rates according to the accident and damage claim history of the various categories of drivers. If you fall into a group with a history of good driving, your rates will be lower than for drivers in high risk groups. For example, people who have taken driver training have fewer accidents than those who have not; drivers over 25 a old have fewer claims than those under 25; females have fewer and lower claims than males; good students have fewer accidents than poor students.

Insurance rates depend not only on the record of the individual, but on the record of the group to which the individual belongs. Insurance companies rely on statistics to determine their rates.

Example. A table of insurance rates follows. What is the insurance premium on the Roadhandler for the following driver?

Female student, 18 a, has been driving for 2 a with no accidents, has a 66% grade average, and has passed a driver training course.

The insurance coverage is to include public liability ($500 000 maximum), property damage, medical services, $200 deductible collision, and $75 deductible comprehensive.

Favourable Vehicle Insurance Company Rates Table/Year			
Type of vehicle: Roadhandler			Age of driver: 18
Type of Coverage	Premium		Discount Available (percent of premium)
	Male	Female	
Public liability ($500 000 max.)	945	375	10% 2 a accident free 3% passed driver training
Property damage	110	88	10% 2 a accident free 3% passed driver training
Medical services	34	12	10% 2 a accident free 3% passed driver training
Collision ($100 ded.)	509	314	12% good student (over 70%) 15% each add. $100 ded. to $500
Comprehensive ($25 ded.)	189	189	18% each add. $25 ded. to $200

Solution:

Public liability for a female is $375 discounted 13% for accident-free driving and passing driver education.

$375 - (375)(0.13) = 375 - 48.75$ *or* $375(0.87) = 326.25$

Public liability = $326.25

100% − 13% = 87%

Property damage liability for a female is $88 discounted 13% as above

$88 - (88)(0.13) = 88 - 11.44$ *or* $(88)(0.87) = 76.56$

Property damage = $76.56

Medical services for a female is $12 discounted 13% as above

$12 - (12)(0.13) = 12 - 1.56$ *or* $12(0.87) = 10.44$

Medical services = $10.44

Collision for a female is $314 discounted 15% because $200 deductible

$314 - (314)(0.15) = 314 - 47.10$ *or* $314(0.85) = 266.90$

$200 deductible collision = $266.90

Comprehensive for a female is $189, discounted 36% because $75.00 deductible

$189 - (189)(0.36) = 189 - 68.04$ *or* $189(0.64) = 120.96$

$75 deductible comprehensive = $120.96

The total premium is $326.25 + 76.56 + 10.44 + 266.90 + 120.96$
$= \$801.11$ for one year.

EXERCISE 12.3

A

1. Why is it essential to have liability insurance on your car?

2. Which types of automobile insurance cover
(a) other people and their property?
(b) you, your family and passengers, and your property?

3. When is it not absolutely necessary to have collision and comprehensive automobile insurance?

4. Why do insurance companies prefer that you have an automobile insurance policy with a deductible amount for collision and comprehensive?

5. If you finance your car through a bank, why is it a condition of the loan that you have full insurance coverage?

6. What factors, other than those mentioned, affect the premium on comprehensive and collision automobile insurance?

B

7. Complete the following table to calculate the insurance premium for Ben Simpson who is 18 a old, attending community college with an 85% average. Two years ago, Ben passed driver education and has never been involved in an accident. Use the rates of the Favourable Vehicle Insurance Company.

PREMIUM FOR: Ben Simpson	
Public liability Property damage Medical services Collision ($300 ded.) Comprehensive ($100 ded.)	
Total	

8. Using the rates of the Favourable Vehicle Insurance Company, calculate the premiums for the insurance coverage for the following drivers. In each case the insurance table purchased covers public liability and property damage, medical services, collision and comprehensive, both with $100 deductible.
(a) Male, 18, 80% average in school, passed driver education, has driven for two years accident free
(b) Male, 18, 55% average in school, never took driver education, has had two accidents in first year of driving
(c) Female, 18, 80% average in school, passed driver education, has driven for two years accident free
(d) Female, 18, 55% average in school, never took driver education, has had two accidents in first year of driving

9. Cumulative cost for the Roadhandler (See p. 371.)

Calculate the insurance premium if you purchase *full* coverage from Favourable Vehicle Insurance Company. Assume you are 18 a of age. Use the rates for your own sex. Assume also that you have passed driver education and are accident free. Use your own overall average in school, and assume you want $200 deductible collision and $100 deductible comprehensive.

Using a computer and spreadsheet software as described in Chapter 15, design a table of insurance coverage. Repeat question 8, using your spreadsheet design.

12.4 BUYING A NEW OR USED CAR

There are many decisions you must make when buying a car. First, do you want a new or used car? Because cars depreciate greatly in value during the first two to three years, a used car is less expensive than a new car. However, a used car may not have been well-maintained, and therefore could be unreliable and require expensive repairs. New cars, although usually more reliable, are also much more expensive.

Whether buying a new or used car, you will need to ask yourself, "What do I want?" and "What am I prepared to pay?" Here are some factors to consider.

Car —foreign or domestic, maker, model (two-door, four-door, convertible, hardtop, sedan, station wagon), size (compact, subcompact, full-size), options

Van —foreign or domestic, maker, size (mini, full-size), interior (standard, camping, luxury), options

Truck —foreign or domestic, maker, model (panel, pick-up), size (long or short bed, small or large cab, heavy or light duty), options

Motorbike —foreign or domestic, maker, model (sport, cruising, trail), size (large, small, moped)

BUYING A NEW CAR

New cars are sold through dealerships. When a new car is delivered to a dealer, a sticker on the window of the car gives the list price and the prices of the optional equipment. The sticker price is the manufacturer's suggested retail price. It includes the dealer's markup at a percentage agreed upon by the manufacturer and the dealer. The dealer, through the salesperson, can offer a price lower than the suggested price.

The sticker shows the price of all available options. Some options have no charge attached, which means that they are standard on the model.

The destination charge is the cost of transporting the car from the manufacturing plant to the dealer.

You can buy a car "off the lot," which means that the dealer has a car in stock equipped with options you find satisfactory, or you can order a car with exactly the options you want, provided they are offered on the model you select.

Model		Manufacturer's Suggested Retail Price	
3NT69	ROADHANDLER SEDAN	28 325	00
This is not an invoice. It provides tentative price information only. Please check this confirmation carefully.	Destination Charges	645	00
	Subtotal	28 970	00

Options and Accessories		
82C TRIM, CLOTH/VINYL-GREY	N/C	
13U COLOUR CODE ONE-PLATINUM	N/C	
AR9 SEAT, BUCKET FRONT RECLINING	N/C	
A31 POWER WINDOWS	873	45
A90 POWER TRUNK LID RELEASE	52	70
B34 MATS, FLOOR W/CARPET INSERTS-FRT	24	15
B35 MATS, FLOOR W/CARPET INSERTS-RR	19	75
B67 CONTAINER-RADIO CASSETTE TAPES	N/C	
CD4 WINDSHIELD WIPER SYSTEM, PULSE	165	90
C49 DEFROSTER, REAR WINDOW	N/C	
DW1 STRIPE	N/C	
D55 CONSOLE, FLOOR-SHIFTING	N/C	
D68 MIRRORS, O/S SPORT LH-RH REMOTE	41	75
K05 HEATER, ENGINE BLOCK	56	35
K34 CRUISE CONTROL, ELECTRONIC	230	65
LN7 ENGINE, 3.8 LITRE MFI-181 CID	722	75
MX1 TRANSMISSION, 3-SPEED AUTOMATIC	818	40
N33 STEERING WHEEL, TILT-AWAY	149	40
PX1 WHEELS, STYLED ALUMINUM	262	50
QCS TIRES, P205/70RX13 S/B RADIAL WS	236	15
UM6 RADIO, AM/FM ETR STEREO W/CASS	494	40
U19 INSTRUMENTATION, CANADIAN KILO	N/C	
U66 RADIO EQUIP, 4 SPEAKER/S-EXTEND	N/C	
W93 COMMEMORATIVE PACKAGE	70	30
Z31 ADVANCE PRICE SHEET	N/C	
CANADIAN MANDATORY BASE EQUIPMENT	N/C	
Subtotal	4 218	60
TOTAL AMOUNT (Does not include Provincial or Municipal Taxes)	33 188	60

Example 1. From the sticker price list for the Roadhandler sedan, what is the cost of transporting the car from the plant to the dealer, and how much will the car cost without power windows, cruise control, or tilt-away steering?

Solution:

From the sticker, the Destination Charges are $645.00.

The cost of options not desired:

power windows	$873.45
cruise control	$230.65
tilt-away steering	$149.40
Total	$1253.50

The cost without these options is $33 188.60 − $1253.50
= $31 935.10

The cost for the Roadhandler without power windows, cruise control, or tilt-away steering is $31 935.10.

TRADE-IN

If you already have a car, you may trade it in, and the amount the dealer offers you for your old car is then deducted from the price of the new car. To determine the amount they will allow for a trade-in, dealers check the condition of the interior and exterior, the mechanical reliability, and the number of kilometres the vehicle has been driven. They also may refer to the Black Book.

The Black Book lists wholesale values for dealers, banks, and finance companies. A sample page of the 1986 Black Book is shown below.

THE BLACK BOOK (1986)

80 CAMARO	**(Prices Inc. AC at PS)**
· Add ·	· Deduct ·
200 Rally Sport	450 Without F/Air
	400 W/O Auto Trans
	150 V6
1P87 3430 2D Coupe	4090 3810 2910 2010
1S87 3880 2D Berlinetta CPE	4610 4310 3310 2310
1P87 4725 2D Coupe Z28	5550 5250 4140 3050

81 CAMARO	**(Prices Inc. AC at PS)**
· Add ·	· Deduct ·
250 Rally Sport	500 Without F/Air
	450 W/O Auto Trans
	200 V6
1FP87 3860 2D Coupe	4640 4290 3400 2490
1FS87 4490 2D Berlinetta CPE	5350 4990 4000 2990
1FP87 5400 2D Coupe Z28	6360 6000 4910 3800

82 CELEBRITY	**(Prices Inc. AC at PS)**
· Add ·	· Deduct ·
50 Power Windows	550 Without F/Air
50 Power Seat	Diesel V6
150 6 Cyl	
1AW19 4870 4D Sedan	5800 5410 4510 3610
1AW27 4870 2D Coupe	5810 5410 4490 3600

83 MALIBU	**(Prices Inc. AC at PS)**
· Add ·	· Deduct ·
75 Cruise Control	600 Without F/Air
75 Power Windows	Diesel V6
100 Sport Wheels	Diesel V8
75 Stereo	400 V6
Malibu	
1GW69 5635 4D Sedan	6690 6260 5350 4450
1GW35 5705 4D Station Wagon	6800 6340 5400 4440

83 CELEBRITY	**(Prices Inc. AC at PS)**
· Add ·	· Deduct ·
75 Cruise Control	600 Without F/Air
75 Power Windows	Diesel V6
75 Power Seat	
100 Sport Wheels	
75 Stereo	
200 6 Cyl	
1AW19 5670 4D Sedan	6740 6300 5410 4490
1AW27 5670 2D Coupe	6740 6300 5410 4510

84 CELEBRITY	**(Prices Inc. AC at PS)**
· Add ·	· Deduct ·
100 Cruise Control	650 Without F/Air
100 Power Windows	600 W/O Auto Trans
100 Power Seat	Diesel V6
125 Sport Wheels	
100 Stereo	
200 Eurosport	
250 6 Cyl	
1AW19 6470 4D Sedan	7700 7190 6290 5390
1AW27 6490 2D Coupe	7700 7210 6300 5400
1AW35 6670 4D Station Wagon	7890 7410 6460 5500

85 CELEBRITY	**(Prices Inc. AC at PS)**
· Add ·	· Deduct ·
125 Cruise Control	700 Without F/Air
125 Power Windows	650 W/O Auto Trans
125 Power Seat	Diesel V6
150 Sport Wheels	
125 Stereo	
300 Eurosport	
300 6 Cyl	
1AW19 7515 4D Sedan	8890 8350 7460
1AW27 7515 2D Coupe	8910 8350 7440
1AW35 7695 4D Station Wagon	9090 8550 7590

Example 2. What is the maximum and minimum the dealer would have offered in 1986 on an '83 Malibu 4-door sedan with cruise control but without air conditioning?

Solution:

The Black Book gives a range from \$6690 to \$4450. Cruise control adds \$75 but \$600 is deducted for no air conditioning.

$$75 - 600 = -525$$

The range is (6690 − 525) to (4450 − 525).
The dealer would offer from $6165 to $3925.
The dealer may offer more than the book value of a trade-in as a bargaining tactic to sell a new car. A dealer who does so is really giving a discount on the sticker price of the new car.

In addition to the sticker price less the trade-in less any dealer discount, you also must pay sales tax and licence transfer fee or new licence fee.

BUYING A USED CAR

A used car may be purchased from a dealer, privately or through an advertisement in a newspaper. Most provinces require a safety certificate before a used car can be licensed. A safety certificate verifies that the vehicle has been safety checked, that any necessary repairs have been completed, and that the car is roadworthy. A car for which a safety certificate has been issued is said to be "certified."
In addition to the agreed price of the used car, you will have to pay sales tax and a licence transfer fee or new licence fee.

EXERCISE 12.4

B 1. A used truck is advertised in the newspaper.
What is the total cost if the price agreed on is $12 500, sales tax is 8%, and transfer and licence fees are $45?

2. A new car is listed at $12 785.67. The dealer gives a 2% "end of the model year" discount.
What is the total cost if sales tax is 9%, and registration and licence fees are $72?

3. From the sticker for the Roadhandler sedan, p. 379, what is the base price of the car, what options are standard, and what is the total cost of the other options available?

4. From the Black Book, p. 380, what is the maximum and minimum value of a 1985 Celebrity 2-door coupe with cruise control, power seats and windows, stereo, and standard transmission?

5. Assume that sales tax is 9%. The registration fee is $15 and licence transfer fee is $48 but you pay for only the 3 months before your licence expires.
Calculate the cost of each car.

Newyorker 2dr turbo, well equipped, 24 000 km, cert, asking $13 750 firm, 555-1400 after 6.	**Chev** Malibu Classic, 120 000 km, 2dr, 305, ext gd, will cert, $2600, or $75/mo, 555-4567.
Volvo, 6 cyl, auto, AC, gd ext, cert, $3700, 555-5074.	**MGB,** under 48 000 km, no winters, asking $5800, 555-1122.

6. Cumulative cost for the Roadhandler (See p. 371.)

What will you pay for the Roadhandler, p. 379, without power windows, cruise control or tilt-away steering? Include a 4 a warranty for $355 and have Deepgloss and Fabricguard for $429. The sales tax is 8%.

12.5 FINANCING A VEHICLE: BUYING AND LEASING

Once you have decided that you need a car and can afford to buy one, you can choose among several ways of financing the purchase. The money can be borrowed from a financial institution, or a financial plan offered by the vehicle manufacturer may be used. Instead of buying, you may decide to lease a car over a period of time.

BUYING AND FINANCING A VEHICLE

Example 1. The cash price of a car is \$20 889.53. Taxes are 7%. A down payment of \$5000 is made. The dealer finances the car at 36 payments of \$563 per month.
What is the cost of financing the car, and what is the effective rate of interest?

$E=mc^2$

Formula for the Effective Annual Rate of Interest

$$r = \frac{2NI}{P(n+1)}$$

r is the effective annual rate
N is the number of payments in 1 a
I is the interest charged
P is the principal
n is the total number of payments

Solution:

Taxes: (20 889.53)(0.07)
= \$1462.27

Cash price:	\$20 889.53
plus taxes:	1 462.27
	22 351.80
less down payment:	5 000.00
Total principal (P) financed:	\$17 351.80

Amount paid through 36 payments of \$563 each
(36)(563) = 20 268.00

Interest paid is 20 268.00 − 17 351.80
= 2916.20

The interest on the \$17 351.80 financed is \$2916.20.

The effective rate is
$$r = \frac{2(12)(2916.20)}{(17\,351.80)(36+1)} \doteq 0.109$$

The effective rate of interest is 10.9% to the nearest tenth.

LEASING A VEHICLE

When you need a car, leasing a vehicle over 1 a, 2 a, or 3 a is one option.

> Leasing a Vehicle
> When you lease a car, you, the lessee, agree to make monthly payments to a leasing company, the lessor, over a given period of time, the term. At the end of the term the car is returned to the company. Most leases offer a buy back, which means that the car may be purchased at the end of the term of the lease at a price usually under the Black Book price.

There are several advantages to leasing.

Convenience — The leasing company pays for licensing but bills the customer. If the car becomes disabled, the lessor usually provides a replacement.

Capital — A lease does not tie up the customer's capital or credit limit since it is not a loan.

Taxes — If you own a business, or must use your car as a requirement for employment, you may be able to deduct more from your income tax because you do not own the car.

Buy Back — You may purchase the used car for less than market value. If you do so, you know the condition and performance of the car.

Here are the disadvantages to leasing.

Actual Cost — The total cost is usually greater with leasing than with buying a car. In most agreements, the lessee is responsible for insurance, licence fees, and maintenance.

Equity — At the end of the lease period you do not own the car. You are really paying for the privilege of driving a new, dependable car for the period of the lease.

Limits — Most leases limit the total number of kilometres you may accumulate over the life of the lease. Above this limit you are charged an additional per kilometre fee.

Example 2. The cash price of a vehicle, including taxes, is \$34 955.40. The car is leased over 2 a at \$885 per month. At the end of the lease period, the car may be returned, or purchased for a cash price of \$16 800, including taxes.

(a) What is the total cost of driving the car for 2 a?

(b) What is the equivalent effective annual rate of interest paid if the car is purchased, less the buy back value?

Solution:

(a) Amount paid through 24 payments of \$885 each.

$$(24)(885) = 21\ 240$$

The total amount paid for driving the car for 2 a is \$21 240.

(b) Since the buy back price includes taxes, the amount actually financed is the difference between the cash price and the buy back price.

$$\text{Principal (P)} = 34\ 955.40 - 16\ 800$$
$$= 18\ 155.40$$

$$\text{Interest paid (I)} = \text{amount paid} - \text{amount financed}$$
$$I = 21\ 240.00 - 18\ 155.40$$
$$= 3084.60$$

Interest equivalent to \$3084.60 is paid on the \$18 155.40 expenditure (the amount financed).

$$r = \frac{2NI}{P(n + 1)}$$

$$r = \frac{2(12)(3084.60)}{(18\ 155.14)(24 + 1)}$$
$$\doteq 0.1631$$

The effective rate of interest is 16.3%, rounded to the nearest tenth.

Compare this effective rate with the effective rate in Example 1.

EXERCISE 12.5

B1. Why would private companies prefer to lease rather than purchase their fleet of vehicles?

2. Write a paragraph explaining why you would prefer to purchase or to lease.

3. Using the table at the side, calculate:
(i) the price after taxes,
(ii) the principal financed after down payment,
(iii) the effective rate of interest.

	Cash Price ($)	Tax Rate (%)	Down Payment ($)	Payment per Month ($)	Number of Payments (months)
(a)	24 957.60	8	2400	2240	12
(b)	36 978.00	9	4000	1260	36
(c)	20 957.80	10	800	620	48
(d)	48 916.20	9.5	6000	1600	36
(e)	19 968.90	9	200	560	60

4. Define the following using a dictionary.
(a) lease
(b) equity
(c) lessor
(d) lessee
(e) interest
(f) principal
(g) term
(h) afford

5. For each lease in the table below, calculate the equivalent effective rate you would pay if you were purchasing an equivalent car, less the buy back value. Add 7% sales tax.

	Cash Price ($)	Lease Payment per Month ($)	Term (months)	Buy Back Value ($)
(a)	24 957.60	900	12	15 912.40
(b)	36 978.00	845	36	13 468.00
(c)	20 957.80	560	48	2 000.00
(d)	48 916.20	1250	36	15 790.00
(e)	19 968.90	495	60	200.00

6. Use the following depreciation table to answer this question.
(a) Calculate the value, after depreciation, of each of the leased cars in question 5.
(b) By what amount is the buy back amount of the leased car above or below the depreciated value?

Age of Car (a)	Current Value as a Percent of Original Value
1	77%
2	65%
3	42%
4	25%
5	10%

7. Cumulative cost for the Roadhandler (See p. 371.)

Use your answer to Exercise 12.4, question 6, page 381. If you make a $5000 down payment and finance the rest over 36 months with a payment of $975 per month,
(a) What is the interest over 3 a?
(b) What is the mean interest per year?
(c) What is the mean interest per month?
(d) What is the mean interest per day?
(e) What is the effective rate of interest?

12.6 THE TOTAL COST OF OWNING A VEHICLE

COST FACTORS IN OWNING OR LEASING A VEHICLE	
Operating Expenses:	
Fixed costs	Variable costs
Car registration fee	Gasoline and oil
Driver's licence fee	Repairs and maintenance
	Parking fees and parking tickets
Depreciation: Percentage loss each year of ownership	
Insurance: Liability, Medical, Collision, Comprehensive	
Financing: Monthly payments if financed or leased	

Example. You drive your car an average of 24 000 km/a. Your car is 2 a old.
Considering the factors below, what is the cost per year, month, day, and kilometre of owning and operating your car for the third year?

Insurance — full coverage	\$789/a
Car registration fee	\$ 56/a
Driver's licence fee	\$ 17/a
Maintenance and repairs	\$566/a
Gasoline	7.8 L/100 km at \$0.619/L (61.9¢/L)
Parking fees	\$120/a

Purchased car new for \$32 862 including taxes
Financed purchase by paying \$1500 down payment and 48 payments of \$824.37

Solution:

1. Add insurance, car registration and driver's licence fee, maintenance, and parking.
   789 + 56 + 17 + 566 + 120
   = \$1548

2. Let x represent the number of litres of gasoline used.
   $\frac{7.8}{100} = \frac{x}{24\,000}$; x = 1872 L
   Cost of gasoline = (1872)(0.619)
   = 1158.77 (to the nearest cent)

3. Depreciation
   From the table, page 374, the car is worth 65% of its original value after 2 a, and 42% after 3 a. This means that the car has lost 23% of its original value (65 − 42 = 23) in the third year.
   Loss due to depreciation = 23% of 32 862
   = 0.23 × 32 862
   = 7558.26

4. Car payments $= (824.37)(12)$
$= 9892.44$

Total cost per year:

1. Insurance, fees, parking, maintenance	$1548.00
2. Cost of gasoline	1158.77
3. Depreciation	7558.26
4. Car payments	9892.44
Total cost per year =	$20 157.47

Cost per month $= 20\ 157.47 \div 12$
$\doteq 1679.79$

The cost per month is $1679.79.

Cost per day $= 20\ 157.47 \div 365$
$\doteq 55.23$

The cost per day is $55.23.

Cost per kilometre $= 20\ 157.47 \div 24\ 000$
$\doteq 0.840$

The cost per kilometre is $0.84.

The costs for the first year would include the down payment.

EXERCISE 12.6

B

1. A 3 a old used car is purchased for $4500 with a bank loan. The car payment is $250 per month for 24 months. The car is driven an average of 18 500 km/a.
Use the following information to determine the total cost per year, per month, per day, and per kilometre of owning and operating the car for the next year.

Insurance — full coverage	$1277/a
Car registration fee	$42/a
Driver's licence fee	$19/a
Maintenance and repairs	$893/a
Gasoline	6.1 L/100 km at $0.945/L
Parking fees	No charge

Assume that the value of the car when new was $10 714.29.

2. Cumulative cost for the Roadhandler (See p. 371.)

Using the following information, determine the cost per year, month, day, and kilometre of your new Roadhandler during the second year. You drove 21 430 km at an average of 6.5 L/100 km. Gasoline cost an average of $0.619/L, and licence and registration fees totalled $55.

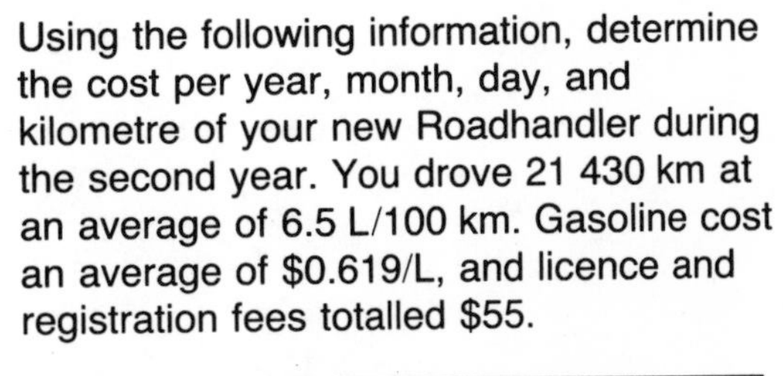

Cumulative Cost for the Roadhandler Sedan Second Year of Ownership

Cost Factors	Amount
Maintenance and repairs (question 4d, Section 12.1)	
Depreciation (question 7b, Section 12.2)	
Insurance (question 9, Section 12.3)	
Payments (question 7, Section 12.5)	

12.7 THE COST OF ALTERNATIVE MODES OF TRANSPORTATION

It is not essential to own a car. There are alternative means of transportation. In an urban area it is usually very convenient, and in many cases more convenient, to use public transportation than to own, operate, park, and maintain a car. If you live in a rural area, public transportation may not be readily available but commercial bus transportation and trains can be used.

PUBLIC TRANSPORTATION

Public transportation is, in part, financed by provincial and federal taxes. It is considered an essential service. Public transportation includes:

Urban bus and subway system
Commuter train
Intercity train
Airline

In each case we pay a fare but the revenue from the fare is subsidized, or supported, by additional funds from taxes.

PRIVATE TRANSPORTATION

Taxi
Car rental

Example. Lee travels to work every weekday and shops downtown on Saturday. Bus fare is \$1.00 per trip or \$38.00 per month for a bus pass. It would cost Lee about \$0.37 per kilometre to operate a car. He travels approximately 40 km a day on the average.
Which is the least expensive way for Lee to travel?

Solution: In an average week Lee makes 12 bus trips, 10 to work and 2 for shopping.

Bus fare	\$12.00 per week
Bus passes cost	$\$38.00 \div 4 = \$9.50$ per week
Distance travelled	$(40)(7) = 280$ km per week
Car cost	$280(0.37) = \$103.60$ per week

Since $\$9.50 < \$12.00 < \$103.60$, it is least expensive to buy a bus pass each month.

EXERCISE 12.7

B

1. The Beam family is planning a trip, and wants to know the least expensive form of transportation. There are four people travelling — 2 adults, and 2 children under 12. They plan to stay for three full days. They are travelling from Hilton to Carlisle, which is 550 km away.
Calculate the travel cost for the family for each of the following modes of travel.

(a)

$54 return each

(b)

Adult: $129 Child under 12: $\frac{2}{3}$ fare

(c)

Family car: $0.39/km

(d)

Rental: $30/d, plus $0.19 for each kilometre

2. Sarah can take the commuter train to work or buy a car. Her office is 34 km from her home. The return fare on the train is $9.50. If she takes her car, the parking fee is $5/d and the car costs $0.27/km to operate.
Which method of transportation is less expensive? By how much?

3. The bus fare is $45 for a trip of 342 km. What is the cost per kilometre of taking the bus?

4. The following figures show the odometer readings of a car.
Before: 34 782 After: 35 124
It took 32 L of gasoline at $0.609/L to refill the tank. Assume fixed costs of $0.17/km. What is the cost per litre of driving the car?

5. Compare the costs of the trip by bus in question 3 with the trip by car in question 4.

6. Last year City Transport carried an average of 2 789 232 passengers per day. This year they carried 3 456 896 per day. The fare is $1.05 for a single trip and $36 per month for a bus pass.
(a) What is the percentage increase in riders?
(b) If 25% of the passengers pay by single fare and 75% use a bus pass, estimate the revenue for each year? (Assume each person makes 2 trips per day.)

12.8 PROBLEM SOLVING

1. Find the sum of the indicated angles in the five points of the star.

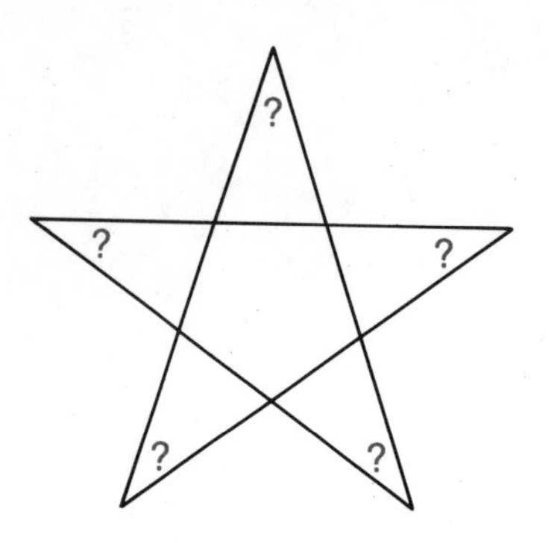

2. Which wheels, if any, turn clockwise in the diagram?

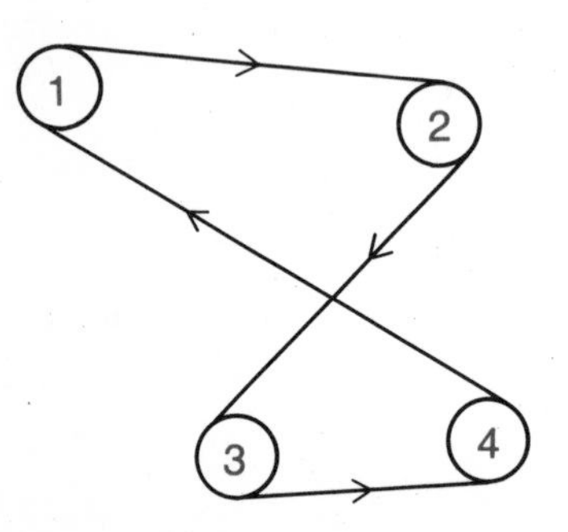

3. The length of one of the equal sides of an isosceles triangle is 33 cm. If the perimeter of the triangle is 108 cm, what is the length of the base?

4. In how many ways can you make change for fifty cents if at least one coin is a dime?

5. What is the temperature that has the same numerical value on both the Celsius and Fahrenheit scales?

6. The number 17 and its reverse, 71, are both prime numbers.
Find three other 2-digit prime numbers whose digits, when reversed, give prime numbers.

7. Select a month from a calendar.
Select any square of 16 d.

S	M	T	W	T	F	S
			1	2	3	4
5	6	7	8	9	10	11
12	13	14	15	16	17	18
19	20	21	22	23	24	25
26	27	28	29	30	31	

(a) Find the sum of each diagonal.
(b) Find the sum of the four corners.
(c) Find the sum of the four inside numbers.
(d) What is the pattern?
(e) What other combinations of four numbers give the same sum?
(f) Represent the numbers in each cell of a 16 d square algebraically, and explain the results of (a), (b), (c), (d), and (e).

8. Continue the pattern.

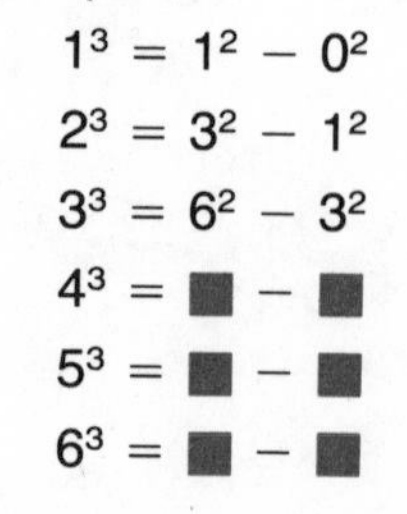

$$1^3 = 1^2 - 0^2$$
$$2^3 = 3^2 - 1^2$$
$$3^3 = 6^2 - 3^2$$
$$4^3 = \blacksquare - \blacksquare$$
$$5^3 = \blacksquare - \blacksquare$$
$$6^3 = \blacksquare - \blacksquare$$

9. The tower is made of 35 cubes in 5 layers.

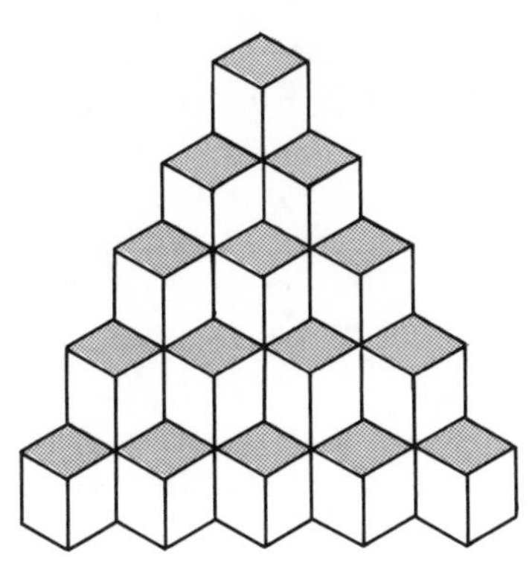

How many cubes are needed to make a similar tower with 10 layers?

10. A clothing store buys neckties from a factory for $16 each, and then sells them for $20.
(a) What is the profit as a percent of the cost price?
(b) If the selling price of one of these neckties is reduced by 25%, what is the profit or loss on the sale?

11. The opening balance for the month in a bank account was $563.77.
The following transactions were made.

	DEBITS	CREDITS	BALANCE
MAY 1			$563.77
MAY 3	$ 22.56		
MAY 4		$123.98	
MAY 10		$ 33.75	
MAY 11	$322.67		
MAY 17	$ 8.90		
MAY 20		$ 43.43	
MAY 22	$ 66.80		
MAY 24		$101.00	

Find the balance at the end of each transaction.

12. Find four consecutive even numbers whose sum is 364.

CAREER

AUTOMOBILE SERVICE ADVISOR

An automobile service advisor at a car dealership is the link between the customer and the mechanic.

When a customer brings a car to a dealer for repair work or service, the service advisor, often after a test drive, writes up the order for the mechanic, with a brief description of what needs to be done. The customer is also told what work is needed and an estimate of the cost is given, as well as a time when the car will be ready. Service records for individual customers are kept on computers.

In order to be an automobile service advisor, some knowledge of automobiles is essential, along with the skill to describe the service required in a concise manner.

EXERCISE

1. The cost of a brake job consists of $264.78 for parts, and 3 h of labour at $35.00/h.
What is the total cost of the work, including 7% sales tax on both parts and labour?

2. A customer complains that his car's gasoline consumption is high. The expected gasoline consumption should be 7.4 L/100 km. The service advisor finds that this car takes 52.4 L of gasoline to travel 600 km on the highway.
What is the rate of gasoline consumption for this car?

12.9 REVIEW EXERCISE

1. You buy a new car for $20 450 with optional extras costing $223.34, $235.85, $23.95, $845.87, $120.99, and a five-year extended service contract which costs 1% of the purchase price, before taxes, per year of extended service. Taxes are 8.5% of the total purchase price and your licence will cost $55.
What is the total amount the car will cost?

2. Naomi paid a fair market price of $9180 for a three-year-old used car. Using the depreciation table on page 372,
(a) what was its approximate value new?
(b) what was its approximate value after one year?
(c) what is the mean loss after 3 months?
(d) what is the mean loss per day after 2 a?

3. A family has four teenagers, twin boys aged 16, a girl 17, and a boy 19. They all are in high school and each has a driver's licence and wants to drive the family car. The yearly insurance premium before the teenagers started to drive was $458 per year, full coverage. The insurance company charges an additional 20% for each boy under 18, 12% for each girl under 18, and 15% for each boy over 18 but under 25.
What is the total premium for the family?

4. Terry wants to buy a supersports car with all the options. The total price is $35 890.
How much tax would he pay at a rate of 7%?

5. Kit purchased a new compact car for $9348.87. Taxes are 8%, and his down payment was $300. He financed the car through the credit union at $232 per month for 48 months.
What is the effective rate of interest charged by the credit union?

6. Larry is buying a used car through the newspaper for $5700, including taxes, and no down payment. He wants to borrow money to pay for the car. He compared the lending terms offered by three trust companies.
Which has the best effective rate of interest?
(a) City Trust
$188 per month for 36 months
(b) Town Trust
$266 per month for 24 months
(c) Provincial Trust
$510 per month for 12 months

7. Irene owns a car and drives an average of 15 000 km/a.
Assuming the factors below remain the same, what is the total cost per year, per month, per day, and per kilometre of owning and operating the car for
(a) the first year?
(b) the second year?

Insurance — full coverage	$910/a
Car registration fee	$23/a
Driver's licence fee	$19/a
Maintenance and repairs	$1066/a
Gasoline consumption	6.7 L/100 km at $0.619/L
Parking fees	$240/a

Purchased car new for $25 684.50, including taxes
Financed purchase by paying $9000 down, and 48 payments of $430.68 per month

8. How much more does it cost per day to drive the car in question 7(b) than to take the bus every day on a bus pass which costs $63.00 per month?

9. For each of the vehicles described below, find the total yearly variable operating cost for the year corresponding to the age of the vehicle. Assume that maintenance and repairs will average \$300/a, increasing \$200/a through a five-year life of a vehicle. Use the current cost of unleaded gasoline.

Type	Age of Car	km/a	L/100 km	Gasoline/L	Parking
4-wh. drive	3 a	24 000	7.8		\$9/weekday
convertible	2 a	21 000	5.7		\$45/month
station wagon	5 a	18 123	6.7		no charge

10. Using a computer and spreadsheet software, enter the formula for effective rate of interest.
Check how the interest rate changes if you purchase a \$24 000 car and finance it over 48 months for the following monthly payments.

(a) 500 (b) 510
(c) 520 (d) 530
(e) 540 (f) 550
(g) 560 (h) 570
(i) 580 (j) 590
(k) 600 (l) 610
(m) 620 (n) 630
(o) 640 (p) 650

11. Repeat question 10 for 36 months and payments.

(a) 680 (b) 685
(c) 690 (d) 695
(e) 700 (f) 705
(g) 710 (h) 715
(i) 720 (j) 725
(k) 730 (l) 735
(m) 740 (n) 745
(o) 750 (p) 755

12. Place 8 queens on a chessboard so that no queen attacks another queen.

MIND BENDER

Place the numbers from 1 to 12 in the circles so that the numbers along each side add to 26.

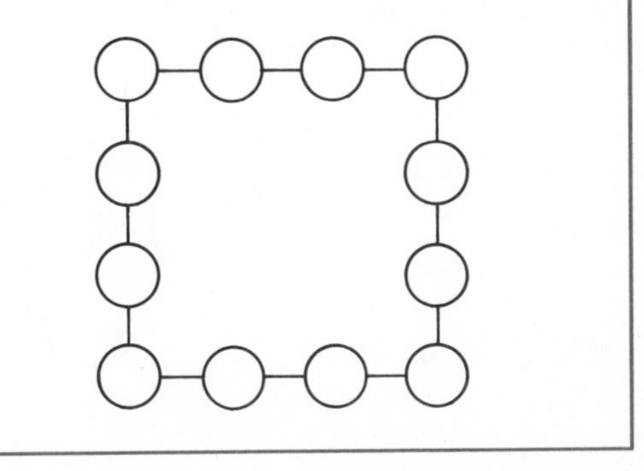

12.10 CHAPTER 12 TEST

1. When the gas tank in a car was filled the odometer read 36 432 km. To fill the tank the next time it required 34.3 L and the odometer read 36 855 km.
What was the rate of fuel consumption in litres per hundred kilometres?

2. A car dealership is asking $9875 for a used car which is 3 a old. The car had an original purchase price of $21 061.70.
(a) How much has the car depreciated?
(b) What percent depreciation is the dealership applying?

3. The cash price of a vehicle, including taxes, is $24 853.10. The car is leased over 2 a at $650 per month. At the end of the lease period the car is purchased for a cash price of $11 600, including taxes.
Calculate the equivalent effective rate of interest if you were purchasing an equivalent car, less the buy back value. Use the formula $r = \frac{2NI}{P(n + 1)}$

4. You have owned your car for one year. You drive an average of 21 000 km/a.
Considering the factors below, what will be the cost per month, and per kilometre, of owning and operating your car for the second year?

Insurance — full coverage	$850/a
Car registration fee	$30/a
Driver's licence fee	$42/a
Maintenance and repairs	$500/a
Gasoline consumption	8.3 L/100 km at $0.875/L
Parking fees	$244/a

Purchased car new for $37 795.26 including taxes
Financed purchase by paying $3000 down payment and 48 payments of $792 per month
Depreciation during the second year is 12% of the total purchase price.

BUYING AND SELLING

REVIEW AND PREVIEW TO CHAPTER 13

EXERCISE 1

1. Complete the table.

	a	b	a × b	a ÷ b	b ÷ a	b% of a	a% of b
(a)	45	12					
(b)	105		735				
(c)		1.4		6.5			
(d)	0.1				9		
(e)		6				12	
(f)	5						15

EXERCISE 2

1. Find the price of each item after the discount.

	Item	Original Price ($)	Discount	Sale Price
(a)	Jeans	$55.00	25%	
(b)	Shoes	28.99	30%	
(c)	Knit dress	45.98	50%	
(d)	Purse	30.00	20%	
(e)	Sweatsuit	75.00	50%	
(f)	Shirt	17.00	10%	

CALCULATING SKILLS

EXERCISE 3

1. Add.

(a) $ 25.36
471.59
8.75
97.31

(b) $199.84
364.17
801.42
83.20

(c) $823.65
251.43
562.14
547.28

(d) $3429.15
517.34
842.75
84.27

(e) \$279.21
610.44
934.82
106.39

(f) \$873.62
84.13
156.21
273.94

(g) \$647.52
485.29
146.24
735.91

(h) \$721.16
9.43
17.50
479.32

(i) \$5295.60
1029.36
3500.14
721.18

(j) \$410.23
528.16
476.04
859.36

2. Subtract.

(a) \$784.63
281.42

(b) \$645.83
423.51

(c) \$532.71
311.50

(d) \$1756.43
893.52

(e) \$824.59
643.75

(f) \$239.84
178.15

(g) \$573.24
185.12

(h) \$746.15
538.42

(i) \$284.15
97.86

(j) \$943.20
215.12

3. Multiply. Answer to the nearest cent.

(a) \$37.24
1.07

(b) \$57.34
0.065

(c) \$29.14
0.93

(d) \$152.84
0.0825

(e) \$97.50
0.925

(f) \$74.31
1.085

(g) \$193.40
1.12

(h) \$473.21
1.0875

(i) \$631.40
0.9125

(j) \$1764.23
0.125

4. Divide. Answer to the nearest cent.

(a) $\frac{\$57.38}{0.94}$ (b) $\frac{\$28.42}{0.88}$

(c) $\frac{\$163.20}{0.90}$ (d) $\frac{\$47.15}{0.075}$

(e) $\frac{\$6.29}{0.1025}$ (f) $\frac{\$84.14}{0.98}$

Answer to the nearest $\frac{1}{10}\%$.

(g) $\frac{\$73.20}{\$850.00}$ (h) $\frac{\$25.63}{\$195.00}$

(i) $\frac{\$84.50}{\$985.00}$ (j) $\frac{\$7.24}{\$538.40}$

(k) $\frac{\$9.15}{\$239.42}$ (l) $\frac{\$221.54}{\$225.00}$

5. Calculate to the nearest cent.

(a) 6% of \$48.30
(b) $9\frac{1}{2}\%$ of \$34.20
(c) $8\frac{3}{4}\%$ of \$93.40
(d) 12% of \$83.52
(e) 18% of \$475.80
(f) $12\frac{1}{2}\%$ of \$593.28
(g) $16\frac{3}{4}\%$ of \$384.70
(h) 24.5% of \$259.74
(i) 107% of \$582.30
(j) 118% of \$375.25
(k) $112\frac{1}{2}\%$ of \$168.43
(l) $108\frac{3}{4}\%$ of \$437.95

13.1 PROFIT AND LOSS

Before setting up a business, it is important to study the market for the goods or services being offered. Is the product or service wanted or needed by the customer? What is the competition? A price must be set that is as good as or better than the competitors'. The price chosen must cover the cost of doing business, and provide a reasonable profit.

The financial basis of the retail trade consists of buying goods at a cost price and then performing a service to the customer, such as display or delivery, which justifies the retailer's charging a higher selling price. This results in a gross profit on the transaction.

Example 1. Frank has a stall at the market where he sells apples that he buys from local farmers. One Saturday he bought 200 baskets at \$2.50 per basket, and offered them for sale at \$3.50 per basket. He is charging \$1.00 for the service of convenient shopping.

(a) During the morning, Frank sold 165 baskets.
What was his gross profit on these sales?

(b) Late in the afternoon, he found that some apples were bruised. To sell the remaining 35 baskets quickly, he dropped the price to \$1.75 a basket.
What was Frank's loss on these sales?

(c) What was his gross profit for the day?

Solution:

(a)

$$\begin{aligned} \text{Sales} &= 165 \times 3.50 \\ &= 577.50 \\ \text{Total cost of goods sold} &= 165 \times 2.50 \\ &= 412.50 \\ \text{Gross profit} &= 577.50 - 412.50 \\ &= 165.00 \end{aligned}$$

1·2·3

$\therefore$ Frank's gross profit was \$165.00.

(b)

$$\begin{aligned} \text{Sales} &= 35 \times 1.75 \\ &= 61.25 \\ \text{Total cost of goods sold} &= 35 \times 2.50 \\ &= 87.50 \\ \text{Loss} &= 87.50 - 61.25 \\ &= 26.25 \end{aligned}$$

$\therefore$ Frank's loss was \$26.25.

(c) *METHOD I*

From the previous calculations:

$$\begin{aligned} \text{Gross profit} &= 165.00 - 26.25 \\ &= 138.75 \end{aligned}$$

METHOD II

As a complete question:

$$\begin{aligned} \text{Sales} &= (165 \times 3.50) + (35 \times 1.75) \\ &= 577.50 + 61.25 \\ &= 638.75 \\ \text{Total cost of goods sold} &= 200 \times 2.50 \\ &= 500.00 \\ \text{Gross profit} &= 638.75 - 500.00 \\ &= 138.75 \end{aligned}$$

$\therefore$ Frank's gross profit for the day was \$138.75.

This example illustrates the following relation.

$$\text{Sales} - \text{Cost of goods sold} = \begin{cases} \text{Gross profit (if positive)} \\ \text{Loss (if negative)} \end{cases}$$

NET PROFIT AND INVENTORY

In determining the cost of goods sold it is not sufficient for the retailer to know how much has been bought. Many of the previously purchased articles may still be in stock. The value of the merchandise in stock is called the inventory.

$$\text{Cost of goods sold} = \begin{cases} + \text{ Inventory at the beginning of the period} \\ + \text{ Purchases} \\ - \text{ Inventory at the end of the period} \end{cases}$$

[illegible] store had an inventory [illegible] .0. During June it [illegible] th $58 750.00. On July 1, [illegible] $75 962.00.

(a) What was the cost of goods sold?
(b) Sales for the month of June were $79 315.00. Find the gross profit.

PLAN

1·2·3

SOLVE

ANSWER

Solution:

(a) Cost of goods sold
= 75 963.50 + 58 750.00 − 75 962.00
= 58 751.50

The total cost was $58 751.50.

(b) Gross profit = sales − cost of goods sold
= 79 315.00 − 58 751.50
= 20 563.50

The gross profit was $20 563.50.

Note: The gross profit does not represent the store owner's gain for the month of June. From it must be paid store rent (or upkeep, taxes, and insurance if the store is the owner's property), services, wages, and other amounts, all of which we shall call operating expenses.

$$\text{Gross profit} - \text{Operating expenses} = \text{Net profit}$$

If the operating expenses of the Bits and Pieces Variety Store for June were $13 400.00, what was the net profit?

Net profit = 20 563.30 − 13 400.00
= 7163.50

The net profit was $7163.50.

EXERCISE 13.1

B

1. Find the missing quantities.

	Number of Units Sold	Unit Cost Price ($)	Unit Selling Price ($)	Cost of Goods Sold ($)	Total Sales ($)	Profit (+) or Loss (−) ($)
(a)	50	1.25	1.65	■	■	■
(b)	15	■	■	82.50	131.25	■
(c)	144	0.09	■	■	17.28	■
(d)	3	265.30	■	■	■	+92.07
(e)	20	32.40	■	■	560.00	■

2. (a) Northland Lumber sold 1000 sheets of particle board at $12.50 per sheet on the understanding that unused sheets might be returned if unmarked. After the job was completed, 45 sheets were returned. What was the net sale of particle board?
(b) Northland Lumber bought the sheets from Wabi Manufacturing at $8.46 per sheet.
Find the gross profit on the sale.

3. King Book Stores Limited had gross sales of $25 000 with returns of $3750. The cost of goods sold was $13 500.
Find the gross profit.

4. Walkon Shoes Limited had $87 460 gross sales of shoes during their fall sale. They had returns amounting to $5120 and made a gross profit of $23 460.
What was the cost of goods sold?

5. A shipment of 96 blouses was purchased at $16.50 each for the Christmas trade. Sales were as follows.
52 at regular price of $33.00
19 at "Last Shopping Day" sale (10% discount on regular price)
16 at "Boxing Day Specials" (40% discount)
The remainder at "Counter Soiled" sale (sale price of $15.00)
Find the gross profit on the sales.

6. Find the cost of goods sold in each case.

	Inventory at Beginning of Period ($)	Purchases for Period ($)	Inventory at End of Period ($)
(a)	6275.00	30 500.00	5760.00
(b)	25 472.00	139 760.00	32 420.00
(c)	2195.00	12 090.00	3260.00
(d)	4934.00	5620.00	1498.00

7. Find the net profit for each of the following periods.

	Net Sales ($)	Cost of Goods Sold ($)	Operating Expenses ($)
(a)	42 760.00	34 076.00	7620.00
(b)	9425.00	6792.00	1240.00
(c)	96 500.00	75 400.00	5850.00
(d)	27 850.00	22 480.00	2150.00

8. During the period July 1 to December 31, Acme Tool had net sales of $257 572. The cost of the goods sold was $146 750 and the operating expenses were $135 308. What was the net loss?

9. Tandem Corporation bought $1 365 000 worth of goods and sold them for $2 047 500.
If the net profit was $417 300, find the expenses.

10. Work-Rite Tools had a March 1 inventory of $56 495 and an April 1 inventory of $47 800. Purchases for the period were $135 870. For the same period sales were $253 000 with operating expenses of $57 200.
Find
(a) the cost of goods sold, (b) gross profit for the period,
(c) net profit for the period.

11. Uni-Hold Fasteners had the following sales and inventory for four quarters.

	A	B	C	D	E	F
1	19 –	Inventory	Purchases	Sales	Operating	
2		as of	Previous	Previous	Expenses	
3		Date	Quarter	Quarter	Previous	
4					Quarter	
5	Jan 01	12400				

(a) Find the net profit for the year.
(b) Find the net profit for the year as a percentage of sales.

12.

	A	B	C	D	E	F
1	19 –	Inventory	Semi-annual	Semi-annual	Semi-annual	
2			Purchases	Sales	Operating	
3					Expenses	
4	Mar 01	7450				
5	Sep 01	6230	25940	46800	7120	
6	Mar 01	8190	32860	40650	6090	

(a) Find the net profit for each half-year.
(b) Find the year's profit as a percentage of the year's sales.

13. Using a computer and spreadsheet software as in section 15.1, enter the data in question 11. Enter formulas that will give you
(a) the net profit for the year,
(b) the net profit for the year as a percentage of sales.

Spreadsheet activities related to this topic are found in section 15.1.

14. Using a computer and spreadsheet software as in section 15.1, enter the data in question 12. Enter formulas that will give you
(a) the net profit for the year,
(b) the net profit for the year as a percentage of sales.

13.2 MARGIN AND MARKUP

Gross profit is often given two different names, margin and markup. Two names for the same quantity arise from two needs of the merchant.

From an estimate of future sales and expenses, the merchant can calculate what margin in the selling price is required to give an acceptable level of profit. Margin may be expressed as a percentage of the selling price or it may refer to the amount of money involved. We shall use the term "rate of margin" to refer to the percentage.

The rate of margin is the rate of gross profit based on the selling price.

$$\text{Margin} = \text{Selling price} - \text{Cost price}$$

$$\text{Rate of margin} = \frac{\text{Margin}}{\text{Selling price}} \times 100\%$$

When goods are bought, the merchant must be able to quickly set the price at which they are to be sold. Since the cost price is known, the fastest method of setting the selling price is to know the amount by which the cost price is to be raised or "marked up."

The rate of markup is the rate of gross profit based on the cost price.

$$\text{Selling price} = \text{Cost price} + \text{Markup}$$

$$\text{Markup} = \text{Selling price} - \text{Cost price}$$

$$\text{Rate of markup} = \frac{\text{Markup}}{\text{Cost price}} \times 100\%$$

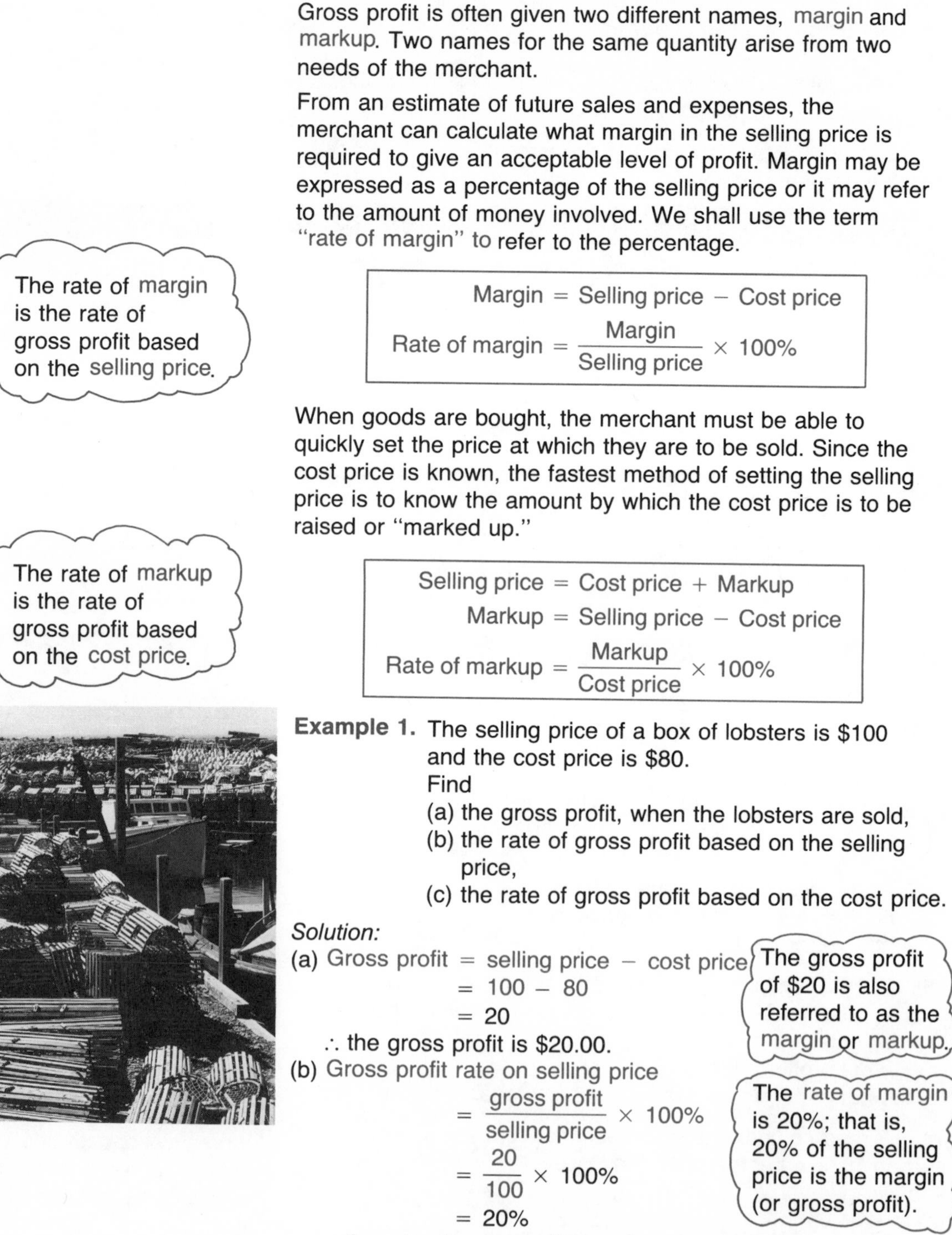

Example 1. The selling price of a box of lobsters is \$100 and the cost price is \$80.
Find
(a) the gross profit, when the lobsters are sold,
(b) the rate of gross profit based on the selling price,
(c) the rate of gross profit based on the cost price.

Solution:

(a) Gross profit = selling price − cost price
= 100 − 80
= 20

∴ the gross profit is \$20.00.

The gross profit of \$20 is also referred to as the margin or markup.

(b) Gross profit rate on selling price

$$= \frac{\text{gross profit}}{\text{selling price}} \times 100\%$$

$$= \frac{20}{100} \times 100\%$$

$$= 20\%$$

∴ the rate of gross profit based on the selling price is 20%.

The rate of margin is 20%; that is, 20% of the selling price is the margin (or gross profit).

(c) Gross profit rate on cost price $= \dfrac{\text{gross profit}}{\text{cost price}} \times 100\%$

$= \dfrac{20}{80} \times 100\%$

$= 25\%$

The rate of markup is 25%; that is, 25% of the cost price is the markup (or gross profit).

Example 2. The Pro Shop can sell a pair of running shoes for \$27.95 and meet the competitive price. It has been found that a margin of 35% is required to operate the business and give a reasonable profit.
How much could the Pro Shop owner pay a wholesaler for the running shoes?

Solution:

METHOD I

Margin = 35% of selling price
$= 0.35 \times 27.95$
$\doteq 9.78$ (to the nearest cent)

METHOD II

Margin = 35% of selling price
Cost price = selling price − margin
= 100% of selling price

Example 3. If the rate of markup on a pen is 45% and the cost price is \$4.80, find the selling price.

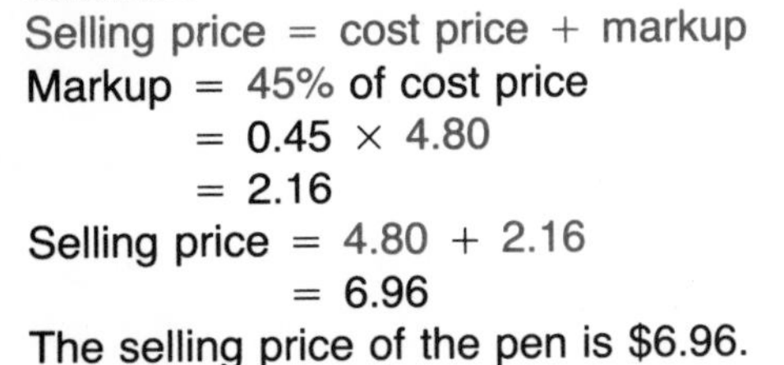

Solution:

Selling price = cost price + markup
Markup = 45% of cost price
$= 0.45 \times 4.80$
$= 2.16$
Selling price $= 4.80 + 2.16$
$= 6.96$
The selling price of the pen is \$6.96.

E=mc²

Example 4. Northern Ski Shop must make a margin of 40% on sales to make a profit.
What should be the selling price of skis with a cost price of \$300.00?

Solution:

Let the selling price in dollars be x.
The margin is 40% of the selling price, or 0.4x.
Selling price − margin = cost price

$$x - 0.4x = 300.00$$
$$0.6x = 300.00$$
$$x = \frac{300.00}{0.6}$$
$$= 500.00$$

The selling price of the skis should be \$500.00.

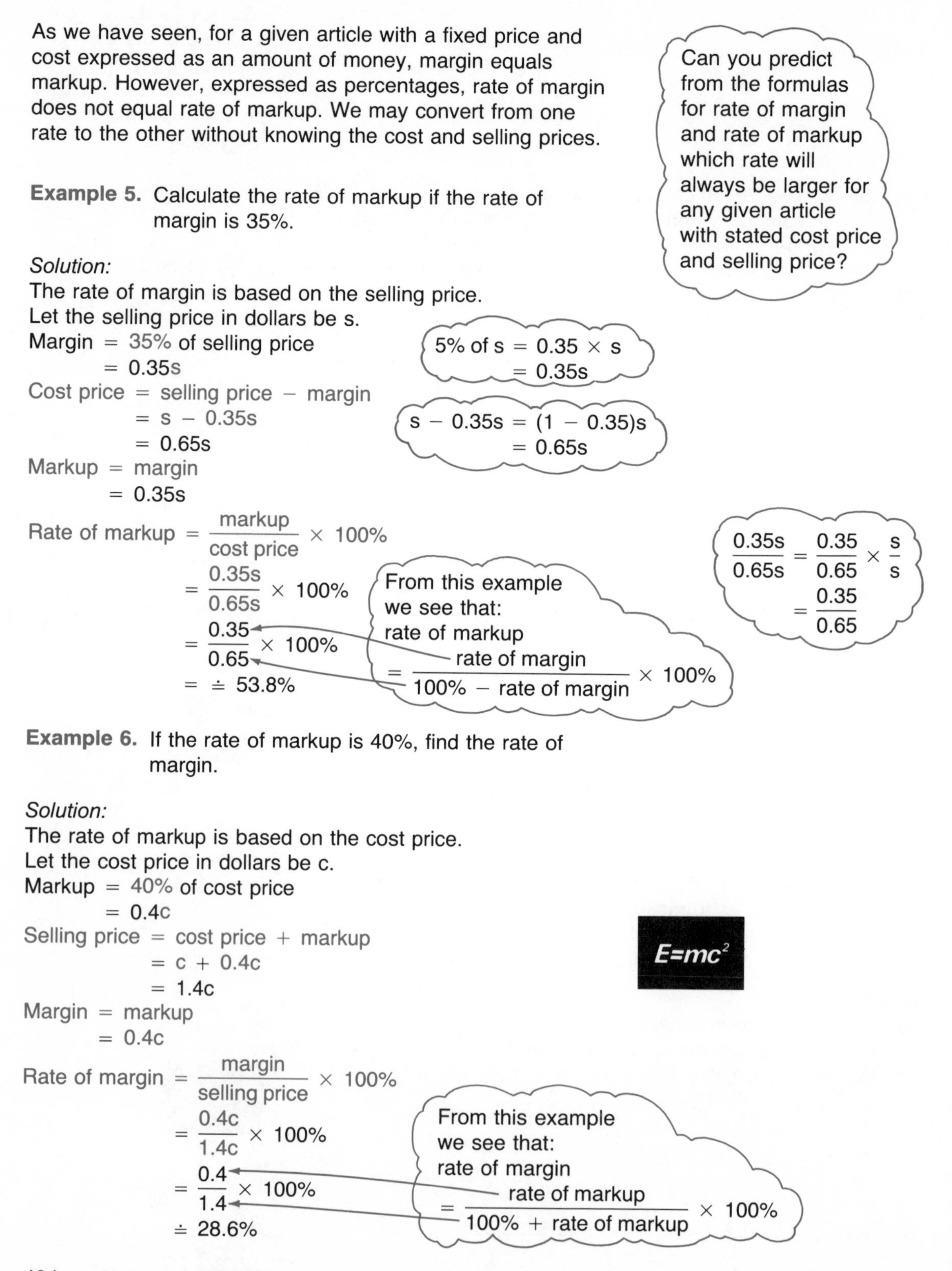

As we have seen, for a given article with a fixed price and cost expressed as an amount of money, margin equals markup. However, expressed as percentages, rate of margin does not equal rate of markup. We may convert from one rate to the other without knowing the cost and selling prices.

Can you predict from the formulas for rate of margin and rate of markup which rate will always be larger for any given article with stated cost price and selling price?

Example 5. Calculate the rate of markup if the rate of margin is 35%.

Solution:

The rate of margin is based on the selling price.
Let the selling price in dollars be s.

Margin = 35% of selling price
$= 0.35s$

5% of s $= 0.35 \times s$
$= 0.35s$

Cost price = selling price − margin
$= s - 0.35s$
$= 0.65s$

$s - 0.35s = (1 - 0.35)s$
$= 0.65s$

Markup = margin
$= 0.35s$

$$\text{Rate of markup} = \frac{\text{markup}}{\text{cost price}} \times 100\%$$
$$= \frac{0.35s}{0.65s} \times 100\%$$
$$= \frac{0.35}{0.65} \times 100\%$$
$$= \doteq 53.8\%$$

$$\frac{0.35s}{0.65s} = \frac{0.35}{0.65} \times \frac{s}{s} = \frac{0.35}{0.65}$$

From this example we see that:
$$\text{rate of markup} = \frac{\text{rate of margin}}{100\% - \text{rate of margin}} \times 100\%$$

Example 6. If the rate of markup is 40%, find the rate of margin.

Solution:

The rate of markup is based on the cost price.
Let the cost price in dollars be c.

Markup = 40% of cost price
$= 0.4c$

Selling price = cost price + markup
$= c + 0.4c$
$= 1.4c$

Margin = markup
$= 0.4c$

$$\text{Rate of margin} = \frac{\text{margin}}{\text{selling price}} \times 100\%$$
$$= \frac{0.4c}{1.4c} \times 100\%$$
$$= \frac{0.4}{1.4} \times 100\%$$
$$\doteq 28.6\%$$

From this example we see that:
$$\text{rate of margin} = \frac{\text{rate of markup}}{100\% + \text{rate of markup}} \times 100\%$$

$E=mc^2$

EXERCISE 13.2

In the following questions, cash values are to be correct to the nearest cent and rates are to be correct to one decimal place.

B 1. Complete the given table.

	Cost Price	Markup	Selling Price
(a)	$22.43	$1.15	■
(b)	$26.80	$5.90	■
(c)	$8.30	■	$10.50
(d)	$164.00	■	$205.00
(e)	■	$32.60	$174.60
(f)	■	$3.40	$24.60

(a)	$48.50	$12.25	■
(b)	$65.30	$15.20	■
(c)	$152.10	■	$121.00
(d)	$94.20	■	$42.15
(e)	■	$9.80	$17.20
(f)	■	$17.30	$38.40

3. Find the selling price.

	Cost Price	Rate of Markup	Selling Price
(a)	$4.00	10%	■
(b)	$25.00	20%	■
(c)	$15.00	30%	■
(d)	$100.00	75%	■
(e)	$80.00	25%	■
(f)	$120.00	40%	■

4. Find the cost price.

	Selling Price	Rate of Margin	Cost Price
(a)	$7.00	20%	■
(b)	$12.00	25%	■
(c)	$50.00	40%	■
(d)	$140.00	50%	■
(e)	$60.00	30%	■
(f)	$90.00	10%	■

5. Find the missing quantities.

	Cost Price	Markup	Rate of Markup	Selling Price
(a)	$36.40	$16.38	■	■
(b)	$9.20	■	40%	■
(c)	■	$2.50	■	$6.00
(d)	$1793.00	■	■	$2546.06

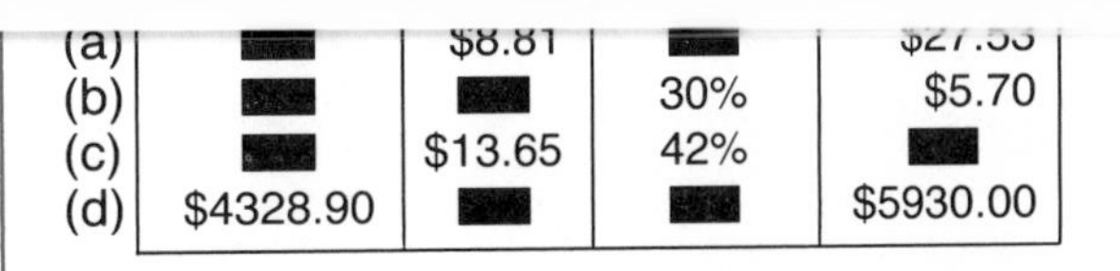

(a)	■	$8.81	■	$27.53
(b)	■	■	30%	$5.70
(c)	■	$13.65	42%	■
(d)	$4328.90	■	■	$5930.00

7. A.B.C. Stores require a margin of $33\frac{1}{3}\%$ to operate at a profit. They can sell a line of toy trucks for $4.65 each.
How much can they afford to pay for them?
Calculate the rate of markup.

8. Lo-Cost Store has annual operating expenses budgeted at $75 000. The owner expects a net profit of 12% on estimated annual sales of $280 000.
(a) If the sales and expenses estimated are correct, what will be the cost of goods sold?
(b) What rate of markup is used?
(c) What rate of margin is used?

9. Smith's Hardware sells hockey sticks which cost the store $8.12 each.
If the margin is 35%, at what price should the sticks be sold?

10. If outboard motors bought for $486 are sold at a margin of 28%, find the selling price.

11. A graph is useful to convert margin and markup quickly.
Complete the following table and plot the values with *margin* on the horizontal axis and *markup* on the vertical axis. Calculate all values to one-tenth of 1%.

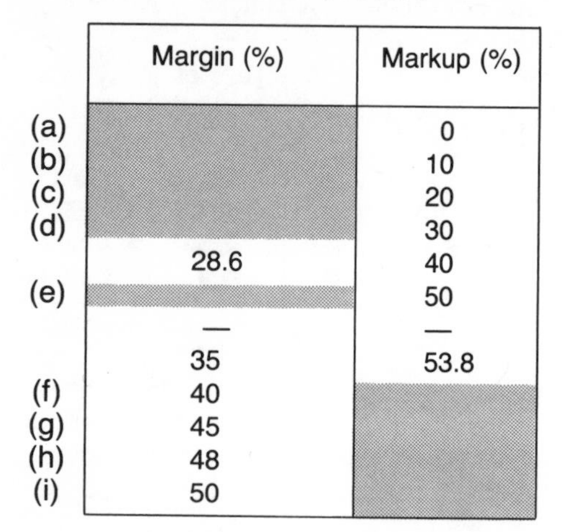

	Margin (%)	Markup (%)
(a)		0
(b)		10
(c)		20
(d)		30
	28.6	40
(e)		50
	—	—
	35	53.8
(f)	40	
(g)	45	
(h)	48	
(i)	50	

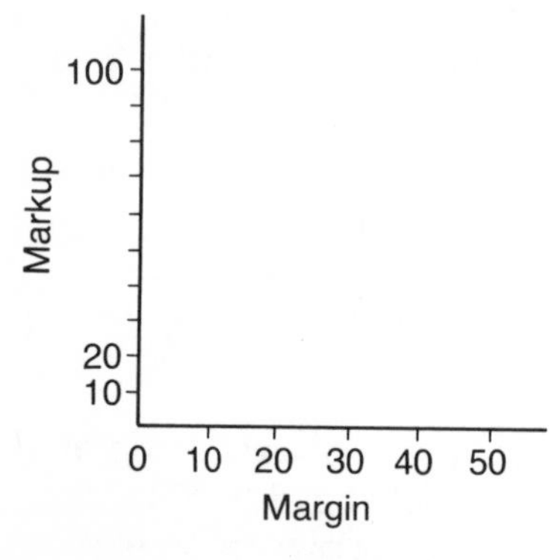

12. Use the graph from question 11 to make the following conversions.
(a) margin of 24% to markup
(b) margin of 32% to markup
(c) markup of 48% as margin
(d) markup of 65% as margin

13. A store works on a margin of 37%. What is the markup on a wet suit which wholesales at $165?

14. A toy store buys trucks at $3.50 and sells them with a markup of 46%.
Find the margin and the selling price.

15. Watches bought for $7 are sold at $12.50, with a 12% discount during the Christmas sale.
What are the sale price and the rate of margin?

16. A store owner estimates that the year's sales will be $150 000. From his estimates of costs and expenses, he calculates that he must work on a margin of 27%.
(a) What is his rate of markup?
(b) What is the selling price of an article costing $76.80?
(c) Find his gross profit for the year if his estimate is correct.

C

17. A store owner estimates his operating expenses to be $125 000 for the coming year. In addition, he wishes to pay himself $35 000 salary for his work plus 8% on his investment of $250 000 in stock and equipment.
(a) What gross profit must the business produce?
(b) If the store can operate competitively on a margin of 18%, what sales must there be for the business to fulfill the owner's expectations?

18. A store owner invests $65 000 in stock. The store works on a margin of 20% with operating expenses of $21 000/a.
(a) If the stock turns over in 4 months, find his annual net profit.
(b) If he reduced his turnover time to 3 months, what would the net profit be?

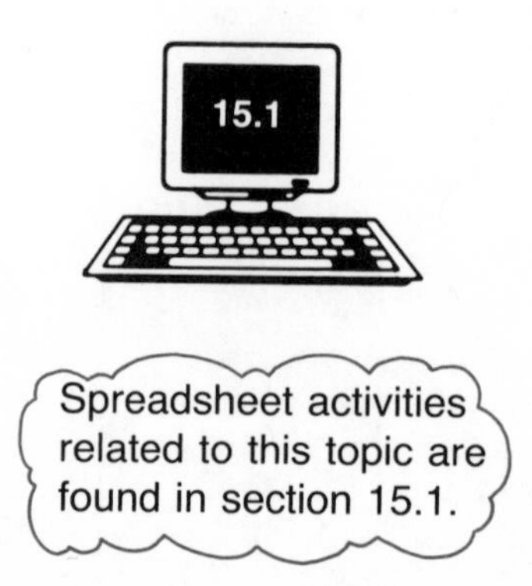

EXTRA

13.3 RATE OF MARKDOWN

Retailers often reduce, or mark down, the prices of their merchandise. These sales allow the retailer to clear existing inventory and make room for new stock. The retailer may advertise these sales by making use of eye-catching advertisements stating the rate of markdown.

Example. This advertisement appeared in a flyer from a department store.
What is

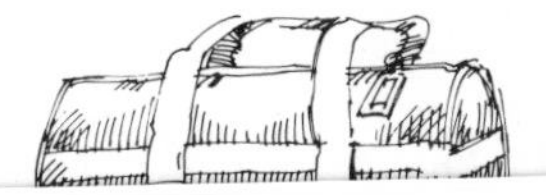

Is the advertisement correct?

SAVE OVER 35%
Heavy-duty Nylon Roll Bag
Acrylic-coated with reinforced polypropylene grips, adjustable shoulder strap.
$15.55
Reg. $24.99

Solution:
(a) \$24.99
(b) \$15.55
(c) The reduction in price is
$24.99 - 15.55$
$= 9.44$
(d) The rate of markdown is based on the regular selling price.

$$\text{rate of markdown} = \frac{\text{reduction in price}}{\text{regular selling price}} \times 100\%$$
$$= \frac{9.44}{24.99} \times 100\%$$
$$\doteq 37.8\%$$

The advertisement states that savings are over 35%. They are actually 37.8%. The advertisement is correct.

SATURDAY ONLY

EXERCISE 13.3

1. Refer to the advertisement. What is
(a) the regular selling price?
(b) the sale price?
(c) the reduction in price?
(d) the rate of markdown?

2. Is the advertisement correct?

SAVE 40%
3-Pair Pack Work Socks
Machine-washable wool blend.
$11.97/pack
Reg. $19.95

13.4 DISCOUNTS

TRADE DISCOUNTS

Building contractors do not usually pay the list price for materials bought in quantity. Instead, there is a reduction in price, called a trade discount, which the contractor receives. The price paid for the materials is the net price.

Net price = List price − Discount

The rate of trade discount is expressed as a percentage of the list price.

Example 1. Find the net price of floor tiles with a list price of $475.60 and a trade discount of 30%.

Solution:

METHOD I

Trade discount = 30% of list price
= 0.3 × 475.60
= 142.68

Net price = list price − discount
= 475.60 − 142.68
= 332.92

METHOD II

Trade discount = 30% of list price

Net price = list price − discount
= 100% of list price − 30% of list price
= 70% of list price
= 0.7 × 475.60
= 332.92

The net price is $332.92.

To give special consideration to customers who buy large quantities, a second discount may be applied to the net price after the first discount has been taken.

Example 2. Find the net price of lighting fixtures with a list price of $927 after applying trade discounts of 25% and 15%.

Solution:

METHOD I

First discount = 927.00 × 0.25
= 231.75

First discounted price = 927.00 − 231.75
= 695.25

Second discount = 695.25 × 0.15
≐ 104.29

Net price = 695.25 − 104.29
= 590.96

METHOD II

First discount = 25% of list price

First discounted price = (100% − 25%) of list price
= 75% of list price

Second discount = 15% of first discount price

Net price = (100% − 15%) of first discount price
= 85% × 75% of list price
= 0.85 × 0.75 × 927.00
≐ 590.96

The net price is $590.96.

SINGLE DISCOUNT EQUIVALENT

To make it easier to compare competitive offers, we may express a series of trade discounts as a single discount equivalent.

Example 3. Find the single discount equivalent to successive discounts of 20% and 15%.

Solution:

First discount = 20% of list price
First discounted price = list price − first discount
= (100% − 20%) of list price
= 80% of list price

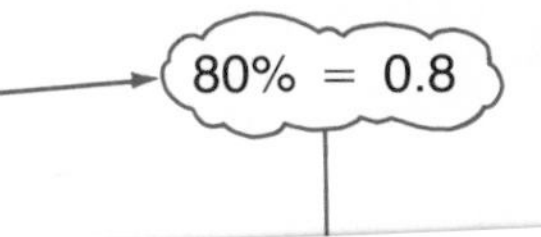

Second discount = 15% of first discounted

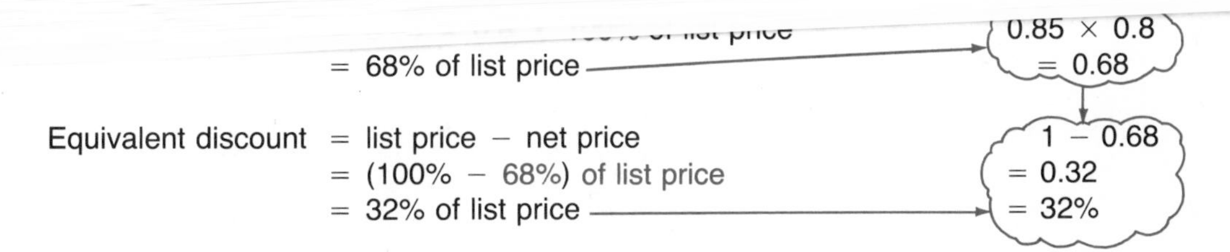

= 68% of list price

0.85 × 0.8 = 0.68

Equivalent discount = list price − net price
= (100% − 68%) of list price
= 32% of list price

1 − 0.68 = 0.32 = 32%

The single discount equivalent is 32%.

Observe that the single equivalent discount (32%) is not equal to the sum of the discounts (35%).

Example 4. Find the single discount equivalent to successive discounts of 25%, 15%, and 10%.

Solution:

100% − 25% = 75% = 0.75
100% − 15% = 85% = 0.85
100% − 10% = 90% = 0.9

0.75 × 0.85 × 0.9
= 0.57375
= 57.375%
The net price is 57.375% of the list price.
∴ the discount is 100% − 57.375%
= 42.625%

The single discount equivalent is 42.625%.

EXERCISE 13.4

B

1. Find the net price after applying the following discounts.

	List Price ($)	First Discount (%)	Second Discount (%)
(a)	75.40	8	nil
(b)	189.20	6.5	nil
(c)	527.80	8	3
(d)	1857.00	10	2.5
(e)	5163.00	12	1.5

2. Alpha Printing gives trade discounts of 8% and 3% to Beta Stationery Store on all printing orders handled in the shop.
Find the net price on a $375 order.

3. Acme Plumbers can buy pipe from Copper Tube Company at $3.20/m with discounts of 15% and 2%, or from Alloy Pipe Company at $2.80/m with discounts of 10% and $1\frac{1}{2}$%.
Compare the list and net prices on an order for 12 000 m of pipe.

4. In each of the following, find the lower net price.
(a) $12.65 list with discounts of 22% and 5%, or $13.05 list with discounts of 25% and 4%.
(b) $475 list with discounts of 30% and 12%, or $496 list with discounts of 35% and 8%.

5. A radio which lists at $34.50 is sold with discounts of 25% and 10%.
(a) Find the net price.
(b) Calculate the net price with a single discount of 35%.
(c) Are the two equivalent? Which gives a lower net price, successive discounts or a total rate of discount?

6. A saw lists for $24.75 with a trade discount of 20% to a carpenter.
(a) What is the net price of the saw?
(b) If a sale discount of 11% is also offered, find the sale price.

7. (a) Hot Shot Hardware offers a trade discount of 15% with a second sale discount of 10%.
Find the net price of an article listing for $76.40.
(b) Homeway Hardware offers a trade discount of 10% with a second sale discount of 15%.
Find the net price of an article listing for $76.40.
(c) Does the order of discounts affect the net price?

8. Find the single discount equivalent to the following successive discounts.
(a) 20% and 15%
(b) 25% and 16%
(c) 17% and 8%
(d) 25%, 16%, and 9%
(e) 35%, 20%, and 5%
(f) 22%, 12%, and 6%

9. It is convenient to use a single discount equivalent to a series of discounts when the discounts are to be applied to a number of articles.
Find the net price corresponding to the following list prices if they are subject to discounts of 30%, 14%, and 2%.
(a) $729.30
(b) $82.95
(c) $17.24
(d) $1097
(e) $4.95
(f) $27.40

10. Playfair Company allows trade discounts of 28% and 12%. Axiom Inc. gives discounts of 25%, 14%, and 2%.
If the list prices for similar products are the same, compare net prices by showing each series of discounts as a single equivalent discount.

11. Compare the effective discounts offered under the following plans.
(a) 12%, 8%, and 4%; or 15%, 5%, and 5%
(b) 30%, 10%, and 2%; or 25%, 10%, and 6%

12. An order from two suppliers is compared using a spreadsheet.
Company A gives discounts of 20% and 4%.
Company B gives discounts of 15% and 8%.

		A	B	C	D	E	F	G	H
	1	Item	Company	Company					
	2		A List	B List					
	3		Price	Price					
	4	1	47.20	45.30					
	5	2	172.00	160.00					
	6	3	14.50	15.10					
	7	4	493.00	487.00					
	8	5	8.43	8.25					
	9	6	15.30	17.20					
	10	7	4.85	4.85					
	11	8	17.80	16.40					
	12	9	85.90	86.20					
	13	10	581.00	576.00					
(a)	14	Total	(i)	(ii)					
(b)	15	Disc 1	(i)	(ii)					
(c)	16	Disc 2	(i)	(ii)					
(d)	17	Net	(i)	(ii)					
	18								
	19								
	20								

To add the values in cells B4 to B13, use the SUM function of the spreadsheet. In cell B14, enter @ SUM (B4 .. B13)

(a) Enter the formulas to find the sums for
(i) company A (ii) company B
(b) What formulas will calculate the first rate of discounts?
(c) What formulas will calculate the second rate of discounts?
(d) What formulas will calculate the net cost of each order?
(e) Compare the net prices of each company.

Spreadsheet activities related to this topic are found in Chapter 15.

13.5 RATE OF DISCOUNT

The rate of discount is based on the list price.

Example 1. Top Tap Company lists standard sink faucets at \$24.60 each. Their chief competitor, Fine Faucets Inc., sells the same grade of tap to the trade for \$22.76.
What rate of trade discount should Top Tap offer to match their competitor?

Solution:

$$\begin{aligned} \text{List price} &= \$24.60 \\ \text{Net selling price} &= \$22.76 \\ \text{Discount} &= 24.60 - 22.76 \\ &= \$1.84 \\ \text{Rate of trade discount} &= \frac{\text{discount}}{\text{list price}} \times 100\% \\ &= \frac{1.84}{24.60} \times 100\% \\ &\doteq 7.5\% \end{aligned}$$

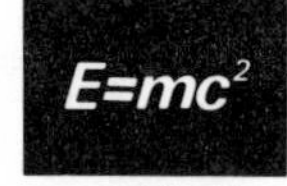

Example 2. A manufacturer of paint sells flat wall paint at a list price of \$15.20/L with a trade discount of 25%. To meet competition, the price must be reduced to \$10.26.
What additional successive discount should be given?

Solution:

$$\begin{aligned} \text{List price} &= \$15.20 \\ \text{First discounted price} &= 75\% \times 15.20 \\ &= 11.40 \\ \text{Net price} &= 10.26 \\ \text{Second discount} &= 1.14 \\ \text{Rate of second discount} &= \frac{1.14}{11.40} \times 100\% \\ &= 10\% \end{aligned}$$

Since we are calculating successive discounts, the second discount is found as a percentage of the first discount price.

CASH DISCOUNT

Many companies give a discount to encourage prompt payment of accounts. If payment is delayed beyond an allowed time, the company may charge interest on the overdue account. A commonly used discount plan is 2/10, n/30 which indicates that a discount of 2% is given on accounts paid within 10 d, and the net price must be paid within 30 d or interest will be charged.

Example 3. On June 19, Corner Groceries purchased 5 cases of ketchup for \$24.50 each and 3 cases of hot dog relish at \$18.40 each.
Find the net cash price if the invoice was paid June 26 with terms of 2/10, n/30.

Solution: $5 \times 24.50 = 122.50$
$3 \times 18.40 = 55.20$
Net price = 177.70
Since payment has been made within 10 d,
Rate of cash discount = 2%
Net cash price = $98\% \times 177.70$
$\doteq 174.15$ (to the nearest cent)
The net cash price is \$174.15.

Date: June 19, 19–
Terms: 2/10, n/30

To: Corner Groceries
Whitefield, Alta.

Cases	Description	Price	Amount
5	Ketchup 750 mL 12's	24.50	122.50
3	Hot dog relish 341 mL 24's	18.40	55.20

Often a cash discount is offered in conjunction with other discounts.

Example 4. Builders' Supply Company sells Home Construction Company 200 bags of cement at \$7.85 each with trade discounts of 15% and 5%, terms 2/10, n/30.
Find the net cash price if the invoice was paid within 10 d.

Solution:
Gross amount: $200 \times 7.85 = \$1570$
Net cash price: $1570 \times 0.85 \times 0.95 \times 0.98 \doteq 1242.42$
The net cash price is \$1242.42.

100% − 15% = 85%
100% − 5% = 95%
100% − 2% = 98%

1·2·3

EXERCISE 13.5

B Give all rates accurate to one decimal place unless otherwise stated.

1. Find the single discount rate required to reduce each list price to the net price.

	List price	Net price
(a)	576.50	449.67
(b)	1073.00	912.05
(c)	5872.00	4815.04
(d)	3.75	3.15
(e)	94.20	89.96

2. Standard Brick sells tiles at 42¢ each with a trade discount of 8% on orders over 1000 tiles.
What successive discount rate must be offered to meet a competitive price of 36¢ per tile?

3. What successive discount rate should be given after a discount of 15% in order to reduce a price of \$36.80 to \$29.72?

4. What discount rate must follow a discount of 26% if the successive discounts are to be equivalent to discounts of 30% and 15%?

5. A shower stall unit sells for $225.00 with a trade discount of 20%.
(a) What is the net price of the unit?
(b) What second discount rate must be offered to meet a competitor's sale price of $163.80?

6. A fireplace unit has a list price of $565.00 with a trade discount of 25%. What second discount rate is required to reduce the price to $389.95?

7. A carpet store has three classes of customers: casual customers, contractors spending less than $10 000/a, and contractors spending more than $10 000/a. The first class of customer pays list price, the second receives a trade discount, and the third receives the trade discount and a second "quantity purchase" discount. Find the rates of discount if the three prices on the same rug are as follows.
(a) $16.20, $14.58, and $13.85
(b) $18.50, $16.65, and $16.15
(c) $20.40, $17.34, and $16.47
(d) $22.10, $20.11, and $18.50

8. Joan's power bill reads:

Payment by final due date	54.16
Amount payable after due date	56.87

Determine to two decimal places, the rate of discount offered for early payment.

9. Find the net cash price for the following amounts if paid within the discount period.

	Gross Amount ($)	Trade Discount (%)	Terms
(a)	523.60	15	2/10, n/30
(b)	7846.00	8	3/10, n/30
(c)	5800.00	12, 4	$1\frac{1}{2}$/10, n/30
(d)	24.60	20	2/10, n/30
(e)	129.30	10, 5	3/10, n/30

10. Omega Electronics Limited sells to Corner Appliances Limited; three television sets at $489.00, six compact disc players at $219.00, and twenty mini-cassette players at $19.00. Apply a trade discount of 20% and a cash discount of 2% to the total sale. What was the cash discount price?

11. Find the cash price for an order listing at $5280.00 with a trade discount of 20% and a cash discount of 2%.

12. John's Plumbing sells to the trade at 23% trade discount with terms 2/10, n/30, and 18%/a interest charged on overdue accounts. An order to a tradesman for $674.00 list is charged on June 26. Find the amount due.
(a) June 30 (b) July 16 (c) August 30

13. A company has annual purchases of $250 000.
(a) If the average discount offered for payment within 10 d is $1\frac{3}{4}$%, how much can they save in a year?
(b) If money is worth 12%/a, how much can the company earn by consistently not paying until the tenth day?

C14. A company buys $56 000 worth of goods with terms 2/10, n/30. The company will not have funds available to pay for the goods until the thirtieth day. How much would it save if the money to pay the account was borrowed from the bank at 12% on the tenth day (in order to take advantage of the discount), and repaid to the bank on the thirtieth day?

MIND BENDER

How many different squares are in this picture?

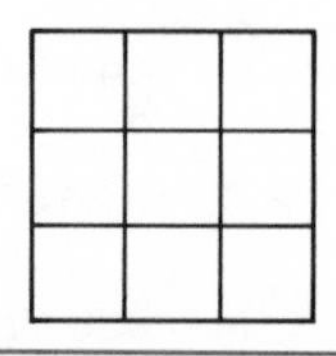

13.6 FEDERAL AND PROVINCIAL SALES TAXES

FEDERAL SALES TAX

When certain goods are manufactured in Canada, the manufacturing company is licensed by the Federal Government to collect a 12% sales tax and pay these taxes to the government monthly. Federal sales tax is paid on the wholesale price after any applicable discounts have been taken. Since this tax is collected by the manufacturer, it is included in the price of the article. Some classes of goods are exempt from federal sales tax.
Many provinces also have a sales tax. Since the provincial sales tax is collected by the retailer, it is not included in the marked price but is paid in addition to it.

Example 1. Auto Game Company sells 50 videos at $35 with a trade discount of 15% and a cash discount of 2%. Federal sales tax is 12%. Find the invoiced amount.

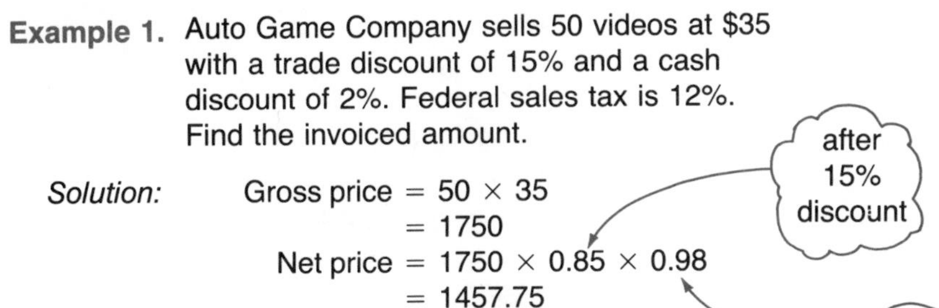

Solution:

Gross price $= 50 \times 35$
$= 1750$
Net price $= 1750 \times 0.85 \times 0.98$
$= 1457.75$
Sales tax $= 1457.75 \times 0.12$
$= 174.93$
Invoiced amount $= 1457.75 + 174.93$
$= 1632.68$

after 2% discount

The invoiced amount is $1632.68.

PROVINCIAL SALES TAX

Provincial sales tax is charged on an item at the time of purchase. The difference between federal and provincial taxes is that the provincial tax is a *sales* tax and is added at the point of retail sale, whereas federal tax is charged by the manufacturer when goods are sold to the wholesaler or dealer.

Example 2. Toy, Toys, Toys Company sells 45 race car sets at a cost of $50 each.
What provincial sales tax would the company pay if the sales tax is 5%?

Solution: Total of retail sales $= 45 \times 50$
$= 2250$
Sales tax $= 2250 \times 0.05$
$= 112.50$
The company would pay $112.50.

Provincial sales tax is calculated on the price with federal tax added.

EXERCISE 13.6

B

1. Find the price to the retailer (including sales tax) for the following sales direct from the manufacturer. Federal sales tax is 12%.
(a) $478.54 (b) $7372.50
(c) $5016 (d) $895
(e) $7492 (f) $651.20

2. Find the retail price, plus tax, for the following sales made directly from manufacturer to customer. Federal sales tax is 12% and the provincial sales tax is 7%.
(a) $72.50 (b) $486
(c) $183 (d) $2.40
(e) $16.50 (f) $6.46

3. Playtime Manufacturing Company Limited produces Buildblocks for $2.50 per set, including profit. The blocks are sold to Toy Distributing Limited for $2.50 plus 12% sales tax. Toy Distributing sells them to retail outlets after adding a markup of 15%. To meet the "suggested retail price," the retailer marks his cost up 50%. When you buy Buildblocks, you pay the retail price plus 7% provincial sales tax.
How much do you pay?

4. During the month of June, a store collected $13 700.61, which includes sales and sales taxes. The sales tax rate is 8%.
(a) Find the amount of sales.
(b) Find the sales tax.

5. Find the final price, including tax, of the following purchases.

	List Price ($)	Discounts (%)	Federal Sales Tax (%)
(a)	76.50	20	12
(b)	135.20	15, 2	12
(c)	5163.00	40, 2	7
(d)	39.20	35, 15	7
(e)	394.00	25, $1\frac{1}{2}$	7
(f)	87.50	12, 2	12
(g)	245.00	18, 7	11
(h)	24.50	20, 3	12

6. Using the final price from question 5(a), find the sales tax if the item is sold retail in the following provinces.
(a) New Brunswick
(b) Alberta
(c) Ontario
(d) Prince Edward Island
(e) Nova Scotia
(f) British Columbia
(g) Quebec
(h) Saskatchewan
(i) Newfoundland
(j) Manitoba

Table of Provincial Sales Taxes	
New Brunswick	11%
Quebec	9%
Newfoundland	12%
Nova Scotia	10%
Ontario	7%
Prince Edward Island	10%
British Columbia	7%
Manitoba	6%
Saskatchewan	5%
Alberta	0%

13.7 INSTALMENT BUYING

Buying an item by paying for it with regular monthly payments is called instalment buying.

Example. The cash price of a wind surfer, including sales tax, is \$967.50.
How much more than the cash price would Nora pay if she bought the wind surfer for \$200 down and \$75 per month for 12 months?

Solution:

Down payment =	200.00
Instalment payments (12 × \$75) =	900.00
Instalment price =	1100.00
Cash price =	967.50
Difference =	132.50

Nora would pay \$132.50 more than the cash price.

It costs more to buy an article on instalments than to pay by cash. The additional cost is called finance charges.

Instalment price = Down payment + Instalment payments

Finance charges = Instalment price − Cash price

The difference between the instalment price and the cash price can be expressed as a percentage of the cash price.

Finance charges = 132.50
Cash price = 967.50

$$\frac{\text{Finance charges}}{\text{Cash price}} \times 100\% = \frac{132.50}{967.50} \times 100\%$$
$$\doteq 13.7\%$$

The cost of Nora's financing the wind surfer is 13.7% of the cash price.

EXERCISE 13.7

B

1. Find the instalment price for each of the following instalment terms.
(a) $20 down and $25.12/month for 6 months
(b) $50 down and $47.50/month for 12 months
(c) $65 down and $53.15/month for 18 months

2. Find the down payment on each of the following purchases.
(a) bookshelf, $599 at 10% down
(b) dishwasher, $649 at 15% down
(c) camera, $439 at 25% down

3. Find the instalment price and the finance charges for each of the following.
(a) a weight bench that sells for $289, with $50 down and payments of $41.83/month for 6 months
(b) a ring that sells for $499, with $75 down and payments of $38.15/month for 12 months
(c) a garden tractor that sells for $2798, with $450 down and payments of $93.20/month for 30 months

4. An electronic keyboard is advertised for $399.99. Sales tax is calculated at 7%. Paul makes a down payment of 15% on the keyboard, and pays off the balance at $23.21/month for 18 months.
(a) Calculate the cash price.
(b) What is the instalment price?
(c) What are the finance charges?
(d) By what percent is the instalment price greater than the cash price?

5. The sticker price on a laptop computer is $1800. The rate of sales tax is 7%.
(a) Calculate the cash price.
(b) Calculate the instalment price and the finance charges if there is a down payment of $500 and the monthly payments are $140 for 12 months.
(c) Calculate the instalment price and the finance charges with a down payment of $600 and $250/month for 6 months.

6. The price of a stereo is $1329.99 plus 5% provincial sales tax. The stereo can be bought with 20% down and monthly payments of $69.33.
(a) How many months will it take to pay for the stereo, if the instalment price is $1527.24?
(b) By what percent is the instalment price greater than the cash price?

SALES TAX CALCULATOR

The following BASIC program computes the amount of sales tax on a purchase.

```
NEW
10 PRINT "SALES TAX CALCULATOR"
20 INPUT "TAX RATE"; R
30 INPUT "PURCHASE AMOUNT"; A
40 T=A*.01*R
50 PRINT "SALES TAX $"; T
60 INPUT "ANOTHER AMOUNT? Y OR N"; Z$
70 IF Z$="Y" THEN 30
RUN
```

13.8 EFFECTIVE RATE OF INTEREST

When you buy an item on the instalment plan, you are really borrowing money from the store. The borrowed money makes up the difference between the cash price of the item and the down payment.

Interest is paid on this borrowed money just as on any other loan. A wise shopper knows how to calculate the effective rate of interest when buying on the instalment plan.

The following formula calculates the effective annual rate of interest.

$$r = \frac{2NI}{P(n + 1)}$$

where r is the effective rate of interest per annum (expressed as a decimal)
N is the number of payments per year
I is the finance or instalment charge
P is the principal (cash price − down payment)
n is the total number of payments

Example.

Caroline bought a motor scooter.
The cash price was $4000.
Caroline paid $1000 down and $175/month for 24 months.
Calculate the effective rate of interest.

Solution:

$$r = \frac{2NI}{P(n + 1)}$$

$N = 12$

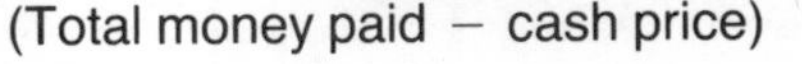

$I = (24 \times 175 + 1000) - 4000$ (Total money paid − cash price)

$= 1200$

$P = 4000 - 1000$ (Cash price − down payment)

$= 3000$

$n = 24$

$$r = \frac{2(12)(1200)}{3000(24 + 1)}$$

$$= \frac{2 \times 12 \times 1200}{3000 \times 25}$$

$$= 0.384$$

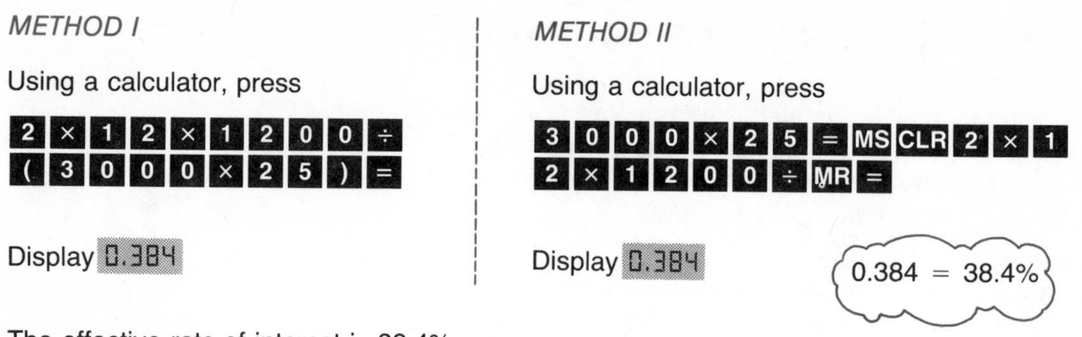

The effective rate of interest is 38.4% per annum.

EXERCISE 13.8

B 1. Calculate the effective interest rate on each of the following purchases.

	Cash Price	Instalment Plan
(a)	$550	$50 down, $31.20/month for 18 months
(b)	$575	$75 down, $46.20/month for 12 months
(c)	$386	no down payment, $37.96/ month for 12 months
(d)	$625	$100 down, $27.56/month for 24 months
(e)	$2950	$500 down, $101.92/month for 30 months

2. A microwave oven sells for $639.99 plus 7% sales tax. With $50 down, payments are spread over 24 months.
What is the effective interest rate if the monthly payments are $31.99?

3. A clothes washer and dryer set has a cash price of $1168, including sales tax. A down payment of $200 is required. Finance charges are $119.20, paid in 18 equal monthly payments.
What is the effective annual interest rate?

4. A TV set is advertised at two different stores for $617.40, including sales tax.
Store A: $65 down, $49.88/month for 12 months
Store B: $70 down, $34.43/month for 18 months
Which store offers the better effective rate of interest?

This program calculates the effective rate of interest.

NEW

```
10 PRINT"EFFECTIVE INTEREST RATE"
20 INPUT"NUMBER OF PAYMENTS PER YEAR";N
30 INPUT"FINANCE (INSTALMENT) CHARGE";I
40 INPUT"PRINCIPAL";P
50 INPUT"TOTAL NUMBER OF PAYMENTS";M
60 R=2*N*I*100/(P*(M+1))
70 PRINT"EFFECTIVE ANNUAL RATE IS";R;"%"
80 INPUT"ANOTHER QUESTION? Y OR N";Z$
81 IF Z$ = "Y" THEN 20
90 END
```

RUN

The previous example is verified below.

```
EFFECTIVE INTEREST RATE
NUMBER OF PAYMENTS PER YEAR? 12
FINANCE (INSTALMENT) CHARGE? 1200
PRINCIPAL? 3000
TOTAL NUMBER OF PAYMENTS? 24
EFFECTIVE ANNUAL RATE IS 38.4 %
```

13.9 CALCULATING THE INSTALMENT PAYMENT

When something is purchased on an instalment plan, a store employee has to calculate the amount of the monthly payments. To make the calculations easy and accurate, a table of monthly payments for financing $100 over various terms at various effective rates is used. A part of the table is shown.

For convenience, the complete Monthly Payment Table for Financing $100 is provided in the Appendix.

Monthly Payment Table for Financing $100		
Effective Rate	Term in Months	Monthly Payment ($)
16%	6	$17.44
	12	9.06
	18	6.26
	24	4.86
	30	4.02
	36	3.46
17%	6	17.49
	12	9.10
	13	6.30
	24	4.90
	30	4.07
	36	3.51
18%	6	17.54
	12	9.15
	18	6.35
	24	4.95
	30	4.11
	36	3.55

The table shows that the monthly payment for financing $100 for 30 months at an interest rate of 17% is $4.07.

Example 1. Calculate the amount of the monthly payment if $500 is financed for 24 months and the effective rate of interest is 18%.

Solution: From the table of monthly payments, the monthly payment for financing $100 for 24 months at 18% is $4.95.

For $500, the monthly payment is
5×4.95
$= \$24.75$

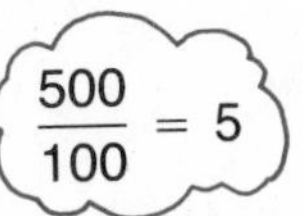

The following formula can be used to determine the monthly payment required for financing amounts other than $100.

$$\text{Monthly payment} = \frac{\text{Amount financed}}{100} \times \text{Monthly payment for \$100}$$

Example 2. The Robertson Furniture Company sells furniture to its customers on the instalment plan. It is considering what effective rate of interest to charge.
On a sofa selling for $1000, how much will the company earn in interest over 12 months of payments at the following rates of interest: 19%, 18%, 17%, and 16%?

Solution: From the table, the monthly payment for $100 at 19% interest over 12 months: $9.19/month.

$$\text{Monthly payment for \$1000} = \frac{1000}{100} \times 9.19$$
$$= 91.90$$
$$\text{Interest paid over cost of sofa} = (91.90 \times 12) - 1000$$
$$= \$102.80$$

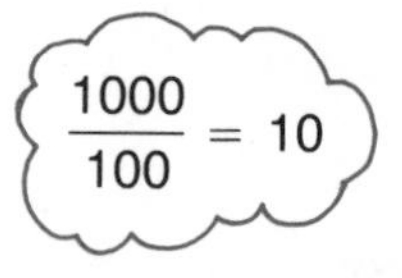

From the table, the monthly payment for $100 at 18% interest over 12 months: $9.15/month.

$$\text{Monthly payment for \$1000} = \frac{1000}{100} \times 9.15$$
$$= 91.50$$
$$\text{Interest paid over cost of sofa} = (91.50 \times 12) - 1000$$
$$= \$98.00$$

The monthly payment for $100 at 17% interest over 12 months: $9.10/month.

$$\text{Monthly payment for \$1000} = 10 \times 9.10$$
$$= 91.00$$
$$\text{Interest paid over cost of sofa} = (91.00 \times 12) - 1000$$
$$= \$92.00$$

The monthly payment for $100 at 16% interest over 12 months: $9.06/month.

$$\text{Monthly payment for \$1000} = 10 \times 9.06$$
$$= 90.60$$
$$\text{Interest paid over cost of sofa} = (90.60 \times 12) - 1000$$
$$= \$87.20$$

Although the range of interest earned from the highest rate to the lowest is only from \$102.80 to \$87.20, or \$15.60 on a \$1000 purchase, over an inventory of \$1 000 000, this difference is \$15 600.

In order to make a profit, a company offering instalment buying must charge a rate of interest that covers the cost of maintaining a sufficient inventory, and the cost of administering the instalments, billing, and paperwork. It must also cover the cost of those customers who fail to make the required payment each month.

Example 3.

A set of dining room furniture costs \$1500. The Furniture Company charges 19% interest and offers a choice of 6, 12, 18, or 24 monthly payments.
What would the monthly payments be; how much would the furniture cost, including interest, over each payment term; and how much more would you pay for the furniture over each payment schedule?

Solution:
From the table, the monthly payment for \$100 at 19% interest:

\$17.59 per month over 6 months
\$9.19 per month over 12 months
\$6.39 per month over 18 months
\$4.99 per month over 24 months

Monthly payment for \$1500 $= 15 \times$ monthly payment for \$100

Over 6 months: monthly payment $= 15 \times 17.59$
$= 263.85$

Total cost over 6 months $= 6 \times 263.85$
$= 1583.10$

You would pay an additional \$83.10 for \$1500 worth of furniture.

Over 12 months: monthly payment $= 15 \times 9.19$
$= 137.85$

Total cost over 12 months $= 12 \times 137.85$
$= 1654.20.$

You would pay an additional \$154.20 for \$1500 worth of furniture.

Over 18 months: monthly payment $= 15 \times 6.39$
$= 95.85$

Total cost over 18 months $= 18 \times 95.85$
$= 1725.30$

You would pay an additional $225.30 for $1500 worth of furniture.

Over 24 months: monthly payment $= 15 \times 4.99$
$= 74.85$

Total cost over 24 months $= 24 \times 74.85$
$= 1796.40$

You would pay an additional $296.40 for $1500 worth of furniture.

Shorter payment periods mean larger payments but a smaller additional cost.

EXERCISE 13.9

B 1. Find the missing cells in the table using the Monthly Payment Table for Financing $100 in the Appendix.

	A	B	C	D
1	Amount Financed	Term	Effective	Monthly
2	($)	(Months)	Rate (%)	Payment ($)
3	100.00	24	20	
4	500.00	18	18	
5	1000.00	30	25	
6	499.85	12	26	
7	2640.00	12	23	
8	2640.00	24	23	
9	1000.00	36		38.50
10	950.00	6		168.53
11	2850.00		27	128.25
12		36	10	112.35

2. A coat manufacturer ships 100 coats at $500 each to the Warm-up Coat Store. The store has 12 months to pay for the coats at 14% interest. After a markup of 100%, the store sells coats to 50 customers for cash; to 25 customers on an instalment plan, charging 23% interest over 6 months; and to 25 customers on an instalment plan paying 23% interest over 12 months. At the end of the year:
(a) How much has the store paid the manufacturer for the coats?
(b) How much has the store collected from the sale of the coats?
(c) What is the store's gross profit on the coats?

3. Complete the table for $100 financed over a term of 36 months.

	A	B	C	D	E
1	Effective	Monthly	Total	Interest	Percent Increase
2	Rate	Payment	Paid	Paid	Over Original
3	(%)	($)	($)	($)	Price
4	10				
5	12				
6	14				
7	16				
8	18				
9	20				
10	22				
11	24				
12	26				

MICRO MATH

MONTHLY PAYMENTS

The interest paid, I, can be expressed in terms of the principal, P, the monthly payment, p, and the total number of payments, n.

$$I = np - P$$

Substituting for I in the effective interest rate formula, we have

$$r = \frac{2NI}{P(n + 1)}$$

$$r = \frac{2N(np - P)}{P(n + 1)}$$

Solving for p, the result is

$$p = \frac{P[2N + (n + 1)r]}{2Nn}$$

For monthly payments, N = 12, and

$$p = \frac{P[24 + (n + 1)r]}{24n}$$

This formula is incorporated into the following BASIC program to calculate monthly payments, when the principal, P, total number of payments, n, and annual interest rate, r, are known.

NEW

```
10 PRINT"EQUAL MONTHLY PAYMENTS"
20 INPUT"PRINCIPAL";P
30 INPUT"TOTAL NUMBER OF PAYMENTS";M
40 INPUT"ANNUAL RATE OF INTEREST (%)";R
50 MP = P*(24+(M+1)*.01*R)/24/M
60 PRINT"THE MONTHLY PAYMENT IS $";MP
70 INPUT"ANOTHER QUESTION? Y OR N";Z$
71 IF Z$ = "Y" THEN 20
80 END
```

RUN

The following output confirms the factor used in Example 1 of this section. Round the answer to $4.95.

```
EQUAL MONTHLY PAYMENTS
PRINCIPAL? 100
TOTAL NUMBER OF PAYMENTS? 24
ANNUAL RATE OF INTEREST (%)? 18
THE MONTHLY PAYMENT IS $4.947917
```

EXTRA

13.10 COMPARING FINANCING METHODS

It has become common for expensive items, such as cars and household appliances, to be bought on the instalment plan. In such transactions a down payment is often required and the balance is paid off in instalments, each payment including a constant amount of principal and interest. To show clearly the costs involved in an instalment plan, the following examples compare the amounts of interest paid on an instalment plan and a bank loan.

Example 1. On an instalment plan, \$1500 is to be financed over 12 months. The rate of interest charged is 12%/a.
Calculate
(a) the finance charge,
(b) the amount of each monthly payment,
(c) the amount of interest and principal paid each month.

Solution: (a) The finance charge is 12% of \$1500.

$$0.12 \times 1500 = 180$$

The finance charge is \$180.

(b) The amount to be repaid is

$$1500 + 180 = 1680$$

The amount of each monthly payment is

$$\frac{\$1680}{12} = \$140$$

(c) The amount of interest paid each month is

$$\frac{\$180}{12} = \$15$$

The amount of principal paid each month is

$$\$140 - \$15 = \$125$$

Example 2. $1500 is borrowed from a bank at 12%/a interest and payments of $140/month are made. Construct a table showing the details of this plan.

Solution: Each payment includes interest of 1%/month on the previous month's outstanding balance.

	A	B	C	D	E
1	Month	Payment	Interest	Principal	Outstanding Principal
2		($)	($)	($)	1500.00
3	1	140.00	15.00	125.00	1375.00
4	2	140.00	13.75	126.25	1248.75
5	3	140.00	12.49	127.51	1121.24
6	4	140.00	11.21	128.79	992.45
7	5	140.00	9.92	130.08	862.37
8	6	140.00	8.62	131.38	730.99
9	7	140.00	7.31	132.69	598.30
10	8	140.00	5.98	134.02	464.28
11	9	140.00	4.64	135.36	328.92
12	10	140.00	3.29	136.71	192.21
13	11	140.00	1.92	138.08	54.13
14	12	54.67	0.54	54.13	0.00
15		1594.67	94.67	1500.00	

OBSERVATIONS

At the end of the 11th month the outstanding principal is only $54.13, so a final payment of only $54.67 (including interest of $\$54.13 \times 0.01 = \$0.54$) is required to discharge the debt.

On the instalment plan, the total amount of interest is $180 or $85.33 more than with the bank loan.

On the instalment plan, the interest paid every month (excluding the 1st month) exceeded the interest actually owed, based on the outstanding principal.

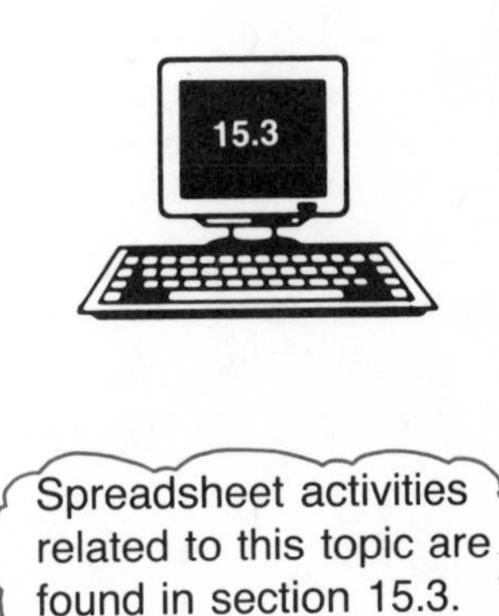

EXERCISE 13.10

1. Calculate the effective annual interest rate for the instalment plan in Example 1.
2. In Example 2, calculate the finance charge as a percentage of the amount borrowed.

13.11 PROBLEM SOLVING

1. Mathematical problems that have digits replaced by letters are called cryptic arithmetic problems. Different letters stand for different digits. The letter farthest to the left of any word cannot equal zero.
Solve the following.

(a)

$$\begin{array}{r} \text{FORTY} \\ \text{TEN} \\ +\,\text{TEN} \\ \hline \text{SIXTY} \end{array}$$

(b)

$$\begin{array}{r} \text{THIS} \\ \text{IS} \\ +\,\text{VERY} \\ \hline \text{EASY} \end{array}$$

2. A farmer has to get a fox, a goose, and a bag of corn across a river in a boat that is only big enough for her and one of the three items. If she leaves the goose alone with the corn, the goose will eat the corn. If she leaves the fox alone with the goose, the fox will eat the goose.
How does the farmer get all the items across the river?

3. Approximately how high would a stack of one million dollar coins be?

4. If the entire population of the world moved to Canada and each person was given the same amount of land, how much land would each receive?

5. You have a 7 L container and a 4 L container. How can you measure exactly 6 L of water? You can add water from a tap and you can throw out water.

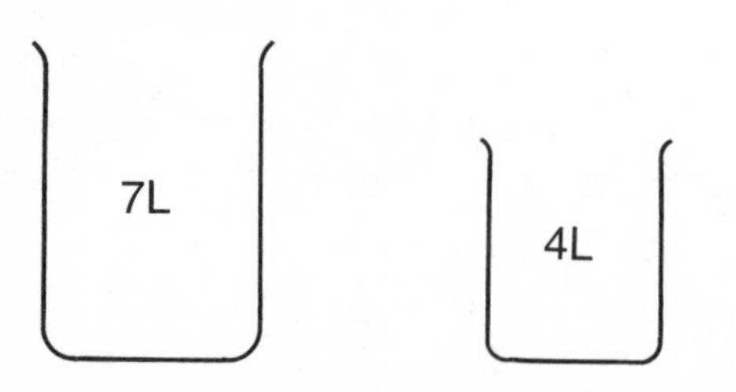

6. If you add 7 to a number, multiply by 5, and subtract 11, you get 89.
What is the number?

7. Your small car has four wheel nuts on each wheel. You have a flat tire on an isolated part of a road. You remove the four wheel nuts from the flat tire and place them in the hubcap. While you are getting the spare tire from the trunk, your dog kicks the hubcap, knocking the four wheel nuts down a sewer. You can't get down the sewer to get the nuts.
How do you get your car to the garage in the next town?

8. A word processor operator makes 3 errors for every 100 characters entered. He types one page every two minutes. There are fifty lines per page and sixty characters per line.
How many errors will be made in two and one-half hours?

9. It costs a summer theatre $1250 per day to operate, regardless of how many people attend a performance. Theatre tickets cost $10 each.
How many tickets were sold if the profit for one day was $620?

10. In the hexidecimal number system, the symbols 0, 1, 2, 3, 4, 5, 6, 7, 8, 9, A, B, C, D, E, and F represent digits.
Write the number 45 in the hexidecimal system.

11. Place 7 dots in the following figure so that there will be no more than one dot in each row, column, or diagonal.

12. The dice are identical.
What is the total of the two hidden sides that face each other?

13. Is it possible to make an entire trip through the house shown below and pass through each door once and only once?

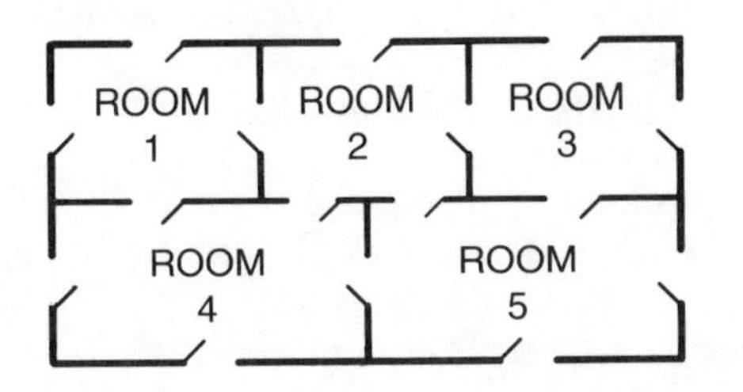

CAREER

PROPS MANAGER

A props technician manages the properties used in the production of movies, television, or theatre. Props that are saved from earlier productions are stored in warehouses and are located using a coordinate system.

EXERCISE

1. A prop is to be stored in a warehouse as follows:
   5 aisles down the centre;
   turn left to the fourth set of shelves in from the centre aisle;
   the sixth shelf from the bottom.
Design a coordinate system to record the location of the prop.

2. In a play, a small staircase is required to reach a platform 1.6 m above the stage. The height of each step is to be 20 cm, and the depth is 25 cm.
(a) How far is the platform from the bottom step of the staircase?
(b) What is the length of the stringer used to make a side of the staircase?

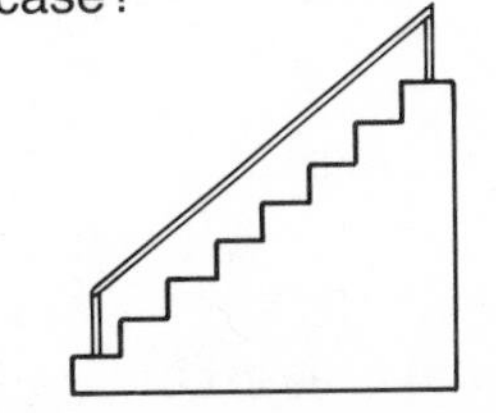

13.12 REVIEW EXERCISE

1. Find the net profit on each of the following transactions.
(a) Bought: 750 articles at $32.60 each, total sales $36 000, with operating expenses of $9000.
(b) Bought: 500 articles for a total cost of $25 600, sold at $69.20 each, operating expenses of $1200.

2. For the period of January 1 to June 30 Ace Variety Store had an opening inventory of $12 750. Goods were bought at a value of $56 000, and the closing inventory of the store was $14 850. Sales for the period were $80 000, with operating expenses of $17 000.
What was the net profit?

3. Find the cost price of an article sold for $76.40, with a margin of 25%.

4. What is the selling price of an article with a cost price of $3.65 and a rate of markup of 40%?

5. What is the markup on an article with a cost price of $23.50 and a margin of 22%?

6. (a) If a company is working on a margin of 24%, what is their rate of markup?
(b) If the rate of markup is 42%, what is the margin?

7. Find the rate of markup and rate of margin on the retail price and the rate of discount for each of the following transactions.

	Cost to Retailer ($)	Retail Price ($)	Discount Price ($)
(a)	40.00	50.00	45.00
(b)	104.00	130.00	117.00
(c)	4.71	7.85	7.22
(d)	35.50	62.13	52.81
(e)	2560.00	3840.00	3264.00

8. Give the net price of goods with a list price of $72.46 and trade discounts of 20% and 12%.

9. What is the single discount equivalent to successive discounts of 28% and 15%?

10. A tent lists for $362.50 in the sporting goods catalogue. The company offers a discount of 20% to members of a camping club.
What second discount must be given to reduce the price to $261.00?

11. An article is offered for sale with a list price of $34.20, trade discounts of 15% and 8%, and terms 2/10, n/30.
What is the net cash price if the invoice is paid within 10 days?

12. Alumstorm Company Limited makes storm windows and storm doors for home installation. A 3 cm storm door retails for $174.50 plus 12% federal sales tax and 5% provincial sales tax. A contractor is given a trade discount of 15% and terms of 2/10, n/30 applied before the calculation of the tax.
What is the net cash price plus tax?

13. A stereo lists at $545 with a trade discount of 18% and sales tax of 7%.
Find the cost to the purchaser.

14. A manufacturer fabricates toy cars at a cost of $1.73 each. The following sequence of factors determines the price:
manufacturer's markup 40%, federal sales tax 12%, retailer's markup 50%, sale discount 20%, provincial sales tax 8%.
Find the cost to the consumer.

15. A compact disc player lists at $399.00 with a trade discount of 15% and sales tax of 7%.
What is the cost to the purchaser?

16. Find the instalment price and the finance charges for each of the following.
(a) a television that sells for $574.99 with $50 down and payments of $33.33/month for 18 months
(b) a typewriter that sells for $354.88 with 10% down and payments of $29.50/month for 12 months

17. A dining room table and six chairs are advertised for $899.98. Sales tax is calculated at 8%. Maria makes a down payment of 10% and pays the balance at $43.66/month for 24 months.
(a) Calculate the cash price.
(b) What is the instalment price?
(c) What are the finance charges?
(d) By what percent is the instalment price greater than the cash price?

18. A small cottage is advertised at $47 900 with $11 975 down. The rest is paid in monthly payments of $681.08 for 6 a.
(a) How much is being financed?
(b) Calculate the total interest charged.
(c) What is the effective annual rate of interest?

19. Compare the following instalment plans to see which plan offers the better effective rate of interest for financing a $750 purchase.
(a) $50 down, $63.07/month for 12 months
(b) $100 down, $40.83/month for 18 months

20. Using the Monthly Payment Table for Financing $100, or the computer program on page 425, determine the monthly payment for each of the following instalment plans.
(a) $250 financed for 6 months at an effective rate of 20%/a
(b) $945 financed for 18 months at an effective rate of 22%/a
(c) $4800 financed for 36 months at an effective rate of 25%/a

21. From the Monthly Payment Table for Financing $100, find the total cost, original price, and finance charges on a motorcycle sold for $300 down and $66.75/month for 30 months at 26% effective rate of interest.

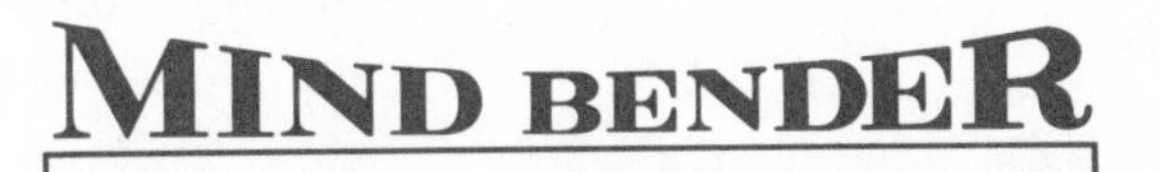

The hands of a clock directly overlap at 12:00.
In how many minutes will they be in a straight line?

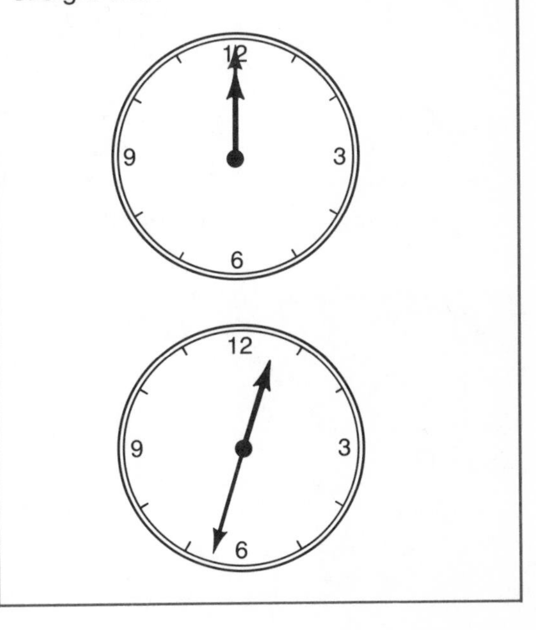

Place the numbers from 1 to 9 in the circles so that each side adds to 17.

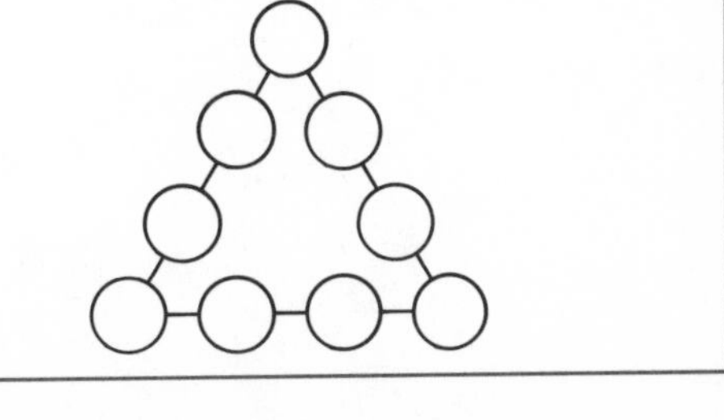

13.13 CHAPTER 13 TEST

1. Find the selling price of an article with a cost price of $14.28 and

(a) a markup of $3.92,

(b) a rate of markup of 25%,

(c) a rate of margin of 25%.

2. Give the net price of an item with a list price of $89.95 and trade discounts of 15% and 12%.

3. Find, to the nearest tenth, the single discount equivalent to successive discounts of 26% and 12%.

4. A telescope is advertised for $269.98. Sales tax is calculated at 6%. Joel makes a down payment of $50 and pays the rest at $41.60/month for 6 months.

(a) Calculate the cash price.

(b) Calculate the instalment price.

(c) What are the finance charges?

(d) What is the effective annual interest rate?

5. Determine from the Monthly Payment Table for Financing $100, the monthly payment for the following instalment plan:

> $1350 financed for 18 months at an effective rate of 23%/a.

WAGES AND COMMISSIONS

REVIEW AND PREVIEW TO CHAPTER 14

ADVERTISEMENTS FOR EMPLOYMENT

TERMS
Income—the money you receive in return for the work you do or the services you perform.
Remuneration package—income plus benefits such as life insurance, medical and dental insurance, long-term disability, stock options.
Annual salary—total salary paid per year. Usually paid monthly, biweekly (once every two weeks), or weekly.
Hourly wage—amount paid per hour. Usually paid weekly, based on the total number of hours. Overtime wage—amount paid beyond hourly wage for working more than a set number of hours per day or per week.
Commission—amount earned based on a percentage of total sales.
Fees—amount earned based on amount charged for services. These are usually professional services by lawyers, dentists, doctors, or consultants.

ASSEMBLY
Immediate openings on afternoon shifts. Need dependable person with reliable transportation. Call Norrell Services.

Artist Representative
Position with performing artist management. Experience required in sales, classical music, creative and technical writing, and typing. Send resume to: GL/PAA.

Auto Technician
Certification helpful, but not necessary. We will train. Immediate opening. Pay commensurate with experience.

BOOK COVER STRIPPER
Must have color experience. Needs to be self-motivated and able to work independently. Days or afternoons, full or part-time.

BICYCLE SERVICE DEPT.
needs experienced, qualified mechanics. Apply at Student Bike Shop.

For Prime System. Knowledge of information helpful, but not necessary. Send resume and salary requirements.

The Graduate School of Journalism is searching for an experienced journalist to teach in its print program. The person we are looking for has an outstanding record in the industry, perhaps some teaching experience, a commitment to good journalism and an interest in issues affecting journalists, particularly in the role of women in news media. A graduate degree is preferable but not absolutely essential. Academic rank, salary, and length of contract all open to negotiation. This is a challenging job for an experienced newspaper journalist interested in developing new skills in a congenial setting. Deadline for applications Oct. 1, for an appointment starting January.
An Equal Opportunity Employer

CAB DRIVERS WANTED
Chauffers license and city cab license needed.

Licensed Physical Therapist
Modern suburban out-patient physical therapy-rehabilitation agency is expanding. Seeking LPT with orthopedic interest. Contact J. Vincent, Tues.-Fri.

Red Lake Board of Education
requires
SCIENCE/ MATHEMATICS TEACHER
Send resume by special delivery.
Application deadline: August 22.

RETAIL SALES PART-TIME
Must have one year sales experience. Hourly wage + bonus.

WORD PROCESSING SECRETARY
$17 000. Fee Paid.
Sallie Hamilton

Activists
DESPERATELY SEEKING STUDENTS
PIRGIM is hiring college students (and others) from across the country for its summer campaign, promoting toxic waste legislation. Earn $170-$225 per week. Rapid advancement.

PROGRAMMER/ ANALYST For Vancouver Office
Environment is HP3000-48 using Speedware, Adager, HP products and Cobol. REQUIREMENTS: three-five years programming and analysis. Excellent interpersonal and communication skills. Ability to work independently on projects with minimum supervision. Minimum two years using HP3000 software. References required and must be bondable.

EXERCISE 1

1. Which of the jobs advertised probably pay an hourly wage?

2. Which of the jobs advertised probably pay on a yearly basis?

3. Which of the jobs advertised probably pay commission?

4. Which of the jobs advertised probably pay commission plus wages?

5. Which of the jobs advertised would a student probably apply for?

6. Which of the jobs advertised are career opportunities?

7. Which of the jobs advertised require experience?

8. Which of the jobs advertised are semi-skilled?

9. Which of the jobs advertised are professional jobs?

TIME PERIODS

EXERCISE 2

How long, in hours and minutes, is each time period?

1. 8:15 to 16:56
2. 6:15 to 14:09
3. 7:35 to 17:10
4. 10:23 to 18:35
5. 9:00 to 21:30
6. 14:00 to 3:55
7. 7:56 to 19:34
8. 8:73 to 23:47
9. 1:10 to 13:40
10. 23:34 to 8:43

CALCULATIONS WITH MONEY

EXERCISE 3

1. 2 × $45.89 + 2.5 × $55.98
2. 87.9 × 34.8 × $1.23
3. 1.5 × $4.89 × 36
4. 0.12 × $456.89 + 8 × $45.98
5. 4.8 × 8.9 × $0.98 × 23.8
6. 0.23 × $567 + 39 × $4.35

7. 45% of $897
8. 78% of $123
9. $456 is what percent of $1789?
10. $89 is what percent of $890?
11. 123% of $438
12. 0.89% of $89

13. ($89.8 + $43.89) − (0.89 × $12.89)
14. $34.89 + $24.95 + $38.89 + $23.98
15. $456.89 − $4.56
16. $567.89 − $8.75
17. 0.12 × $12 123
18. 0.11 × $123 489

SLOPE

EXERCISE 4

Slope of line segment joining (x_1, y_1) to (x_2, y_2):

$$m = \frac{y_2 - y_1}{x_2 - x_1}$$

Calculate the slope of the line segment joining the following pairs of points.

1. (2, 3), (4, 5)
2. (4, 3), (1, 2)
3. (1, 0), (0, 1)
4. (8, 3), (4, 9)
5. (6, −2), (−4, 8)
6. (1, 2), (−4, −1)

14.1 CALCULATING GROSS WAGES

Throughout your life, you will probably work at several different jobs, occupations, or careers. As a student you may want part-time work, while later you will be looking for full-time employment. The method of earning income depends on the type of job you have. You might be paid by the hour, day, week, month, or year. It is also possible to be paid based on commission, tips, profits, fees, bonus, or dividends. It is important to know enough about the method and the rate of pay so that you can decide if you are being paid a fair wage for your work or services.

Gross wages are the amount earned before any deductions, such as income tax, unemployment insurance, or medical insurance, are subtracted from the pay.

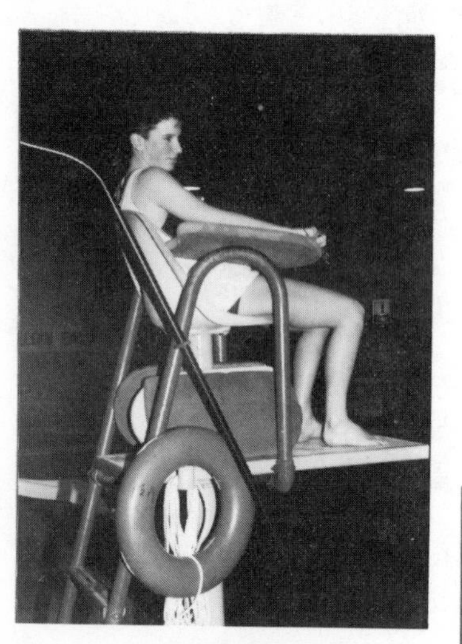

Example 1. A lifeguard is paid weekly at $15.50/h, with time and a half for overtime. Overtime is paid for any time over the usual eight-hour day. During one week, the lifeguard worked the following hours.

Monday	7 h 30 min	Tuesday	9 h 30 min
Wednesday	8 h	Thursday	10 h 15 min
Friday	5 h 45 min		

What are the lifeguard's gross weekly wages?

Solution:

It is helpful to set the information out in a time chart.

Day	Time	Regular	Overtime
Mon.	7 h 30 min	7.5 h	
Tues.	9 h 30 min	8.0 h	1.5 h
Wed.	8 h	8.0 h	
Thurs.	10 h 15 min	8.0 h	2.25 h
Fri.	5 h 45 min	5.75 h	
Total		37.25 h	3.75 h

Wages for regular hours:

$37.25 \times 15.50 = 577.38$

Overtime rate:

$$15.50 + \tfrac{1}{2} \times 15.50 = 1.5 \times 15.50$$
$$= 23.25$$

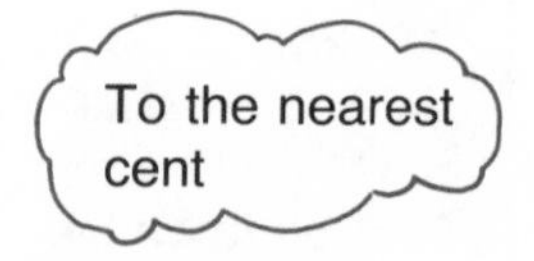

Wages for overtime:

$3.75 \times 23.25 = 87.19$

Total gross weekly wages:

$577.38 + 87.19 = 664.57$

The gross weekly wages are $664.57.

Example 2. A timecard used for "punching in" and "punching out" appears at the right. Complete the hours columns and calculate the gross weekly wages according to the following employee/employer agreement.

Regular hours are from 8:30 to 17:00.
Time and a half is paid after 8 h in a day and for weekends.
Lunch period is 0.5 h each day deducted from time.
Time for pay is calculated in 15 min intervals.
Overtime is calculated at 15 min intervals.
Punching in after 8:30 is considered late. Pay begins at the next 15 min interval.

NAME T. EVANS EMPLOYEE # 431
WEEK ENDING AUGUST 3

DAY	IN	OUT	HOURS	
			REGULAR	OVERTIME
MON	8:27	17:05		
TUE	8:25	17:01		
WED	8:23	18:16		
THU	8:50	17:07		
FRI	8:37	17:01		
SAT	10:00	15:33		
SUN				
		TOTAL		
		RATE	$17.40	
TOTAL			$	$
GROSS WAGES	$			

Solution:
To complete the timecard:

Calculate total hours per day less 0.5 h for lunch.

Calculate regular earnings.
$17.40 \times 39.25 = 682.95$

Calculate the overtime rate.
$17.40 \times 1.5 = 26.10$

Calculate overtime earnings.
$26.10 \times 6.25 = 163.12$

Calculate total gross earnings.
$682.95 + 163.12 = 846.07$

The gross weekly wages for the week ending August 3 are $846.07.

NAME T. EVANS EMPLOYEE # 431
WEEK ENDING AUGUST 3

DAY	IN	OUT	HOURS	
			REGULAR	OVERTIME
MON	8:27	17:05	8	
TUE	8:25	17:01	8	
WED	8:23	18:16	8	1.25
THU	8:50	17:07	7.5	
FRI	8:37	17:01	7.75	
SAT	10:00	15:33		5
SUN				
		TOTAL	39.25	6.25
		RATE	$ 17.40	$ 26.10
TOTAL			$682.95	$163.12
GROSS WAGES	$846.07			

EXERCISE 14.1

B

1. A computer company pays technicians \$26.87/h based on a 40 h week.
(a) What is the gross pay each payday, if the pay period is 2 weeks?
(b) What is the gross pay for 52 weeks?
(c) What is the new biweekly gross pay if the hourly rate is increased to \$28.19 h?
(d) What is the percentage increase?

2. Paula earns \$39 585/a in gross earnings teaching piano.
What is the equivalent gross hourly rate based on a 35 h week, 52 weeks per year?

3. What are the gross yearly earnings that would be produced by a salary of \$4023.04/month?

4. The gross biweekly wages for a secretarial assistant are \$987.50.
Calculate the following.
(a) gross yearly earnings
(b) gross weekly earnings
(c) gross daily earnings
(d) the hourly rate, based on a 40 h week

5. The hours of work for Joe McLean, a landscaper, are given below.

Monday	8 h 45 min
Tuesday	6 h
Wednesday	9 h
Thursday	8 h
Friday	7 h 15 min
Saturday	4 h 30 min

The rate of pay is \$19.88/h with time and a half for overtime after 8 h and for weekends.
Calculate the following.
(a) gross weekly earnings
(b) estimated gross yearly earnings based on hours worked this week, assuming an 8 month work year
(c) the new hourly rate after an increase of 8%

6. Eight people work on a crew at Burger Quick. The three junior members of the crew earn \$7.50/h, the four senior crew members earn \$8.25/h, and the crew chief earns \$10.00/h.
Each crew works a shift of 6.5 h each day, 5 d each week.
Calculate each of the following.
(a) daily gross earnings for each category on the crew
(b) total daily gross cost to the employer for each crew
(c) weekly gross earnings for each category on the crew
(d) total weekly gross cost to the employer for each crew
(e) the gross yearly earnings for each crew category if a crew works 52 weeks
(f) the gross cost to Burger Quick for one year if there are 3 crews per day

7. Complete the timecards according to the following employee/employer agreement.
Hours are 8:30 to 17:30.
Lunch is one hour per day deducted from time.
Cards with times punched after 8:30 are late.
Overtime: each 15 min interval after 17:30, Saturday, Sunday.
Overtime is paid time and a half.
Time periods for overtime and lateness are recorded in 15 min intervals.

(a)

NAME W. POWER EMPLOYEE # 314

WEEK ENDING JULY 7

DAY	IN	OUT	HOURS REGULAR	HOURS OVERTIME
MON	8:29	17:31		
TUE	8:35	17:32		
WED	8:21	17:37		
THU	8:28	17:55		
FRI	9:13	20:32		
SAT				
SUN				
		TOTAL		
		RATE	$16.12	$
TOTAL			$	$
GROSS WAGES	$			

(b)

NAME L. SHAH EMPLOYEE # 159

WEEK ENDING JULY 14

DAY	IN	OUT	HOURS REGULAR	HOURS OVERTIME
MON	8:22	17:31		
TUE	8:30	17:33		
WED	8:27	17:30		
THU	8:28	17:35		
FRI	8:20	17:32		
SAT				
SUN				
		TOTAL		
		RATE	$18.40	$
TOTAL			$	$
GROSS WAGES	$			

(c)

NAME C. O'BRIEN EMPLOYEE # 265

WEEK ENDING JULY 21

DAY	IN	OUT	HOURS REGULAR	HOURS OVERTIME
MON	8:24	17:32		
TUE	9:06	18:50		
WED	8:47	19:16		
THU	8:23	18:05		
FRI	10:00	17:33		
SAT				
SUN	11:56	17:32		
		TOTAL		
		RATE	$15.56	$
TOTAL			$	$
GROSS WAGES	$			

(d)

NAME S. THACHUCK EMPLOYEE # 473

WEEK ENDING JULY 28

DAY	IN	OUT	HOURS REGULAR	HOURS OVERTIME
MON				
TUE	8:23	19:30		
WED	8:27	17:11		
THU	8:42	17:32		
FRI	8:27	17:33		
SAT	9:56	18:02		
SUN	9:55	16:32		
		TOTAL		
		RATE	$17.08	$
TOTAL			$	$
GROSS WAGES	$			

14.2 CALCULATING COMMISSION

People who are working in sales or service jobs are often paid commission, which acts as an incentive to job performance.

Commission is the amount paid to the employee as a percentage of the total in sales or services that are credited to the employee.

Example 1. Sandra works on a straight commission basis, selling fine clothing in an exclusive shop. During her first week on the job, her sales totalled \$2456.89. Her commission is 17% of her sales. What is her gross pay for the week?

Solution:
Straight commission means that commission is your total salary.

$$\begin{aligned}\text{Gross salary} &= 17\% \text{ of } 2456.89 \\ &= 0.17 \times 2456.89 \\ &= 417.67\end{aligned}$$

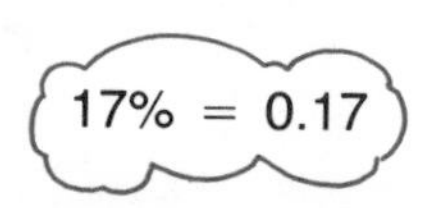

Sandra's gross salary for the first week is \$417.67.

Example 2. Peter works as a waiter at the Summer Sands Resort. He is paid salary plus gratuities, in the form of an automatic gratuity (tip) of 15% on the value of each bill. During the week of August 21, the total value of the bills was $789.45 and Peter worked a 37.5 h week.
What was his gross pay for the week if his hourly rate is $6.23?

Solution:

$$\text{Gratuities} = 789.45 \times 0.15$$
$$= 118.42$$

$$\text{Regular wages} = 6.23 \times 37.5$$
$$= 233.62$$

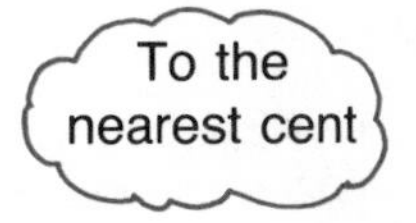

$$\text{Total gross salary} = 118.42 + 233.62$$
$$= 352.04$$

Peter's gross pay for the week was $352.04.

Example 3. Len works in a major appliance department of a large store. His monthly pay is based on a graduated commission of 10% on the first $1000 in sales, and an additional 3% for each further $1000, or part of $1000, to a maximum of 25%. For the month of February, his sales totalled $8579.72.
What is Len's gross pay for the month?

Solution:
Len earns

10% on first $1000	: 0.1 × 1000	=	$100.00
13% on next $1000	: 0.13 × 1000	=	$130.00
16% on next $1000	: 0.16 × 1000	=	$160.00
19% on next $1000	: 0.19 × 1000	=	$190.00
22% on next $1000	: 0.22 × 1000	=	$220.00
25% on remaining $3579.72	: 0.25 × 3579.72	=	$894.93
			$1694.93

Len's gross pay for February is $1694.93.

Example 4. Zella works for a local delivery company delivering letters and packages by bicycle within the city. She works on a piecework basis at a rate of $1.89 per delivery. On Tuesday, Zella delivered 45 packages and letters.
What are her gross earnings for the day?

Solution:

Gross earnings Tuesday: $45 \times 1.89 = 85.05$

Zella's gross earnings for Tuesday are $85.05.

CALCULATING GROSS EARNINGS BASED ON COMMISSION AND PIECEWORK
Earnings from Straight Commission = (value of sales/service) × (rate of commission)
Earnings from Salary plus Commission = (salary from employer) + (value of sales/service) × (rate of commission)
Earnings from Graduated Commission = (initial value of sales/service) × (initial rate of commission) + (second value of sales/service) × (second rate of commission) + ... + (nth value of sales/service) × (nth rate of commission)
Earnings from Piecework = (number of pieces) × (rate per piece)

EXERCISE 14.2

B

1. Complete the table below for earnings based on straight commission.

	Rate of Commission (%)	Total Sales ($)	Gross Earnings ($)
(a)	13	1 345.89	
(b)	2	123 678.00	
(c)	34	899.89	
(d)	1.2	56 789.00	

2. Ahmed works for straight commission at an auto dealership. He earns 4% commission on all the cars he sells. On Monday, Tuesday, Wednesday, and Thursday he worked from 12:00 to 17:00 but made no sales. On Friday he sold a used car worth $14 890, and on Saturday he sold a full-size car worth $32 897. What were his gross earnings for the week?

3. Moira sells small appliances at a local department store. The company gives her the choice of straight commission of 16% on total sales, or a salary of $5.23/h plus a commission of 6% on total sales.

(a) Which is the better choice if she works 37 h the first week and sells $1797.87 worth of merchandise?

(b) Approximately what value of merchandise would Moira have to sell, based on a 37 h week, to make the methods of payment the same?

4. Yukio operates a word processor at a community college for a rate of $1.75/page. Over the week, he types a 17-page paper for a student in social work, a 14-page paper for a student in medical technology, and a 25-page set of lecture notes for a college instructor.
What are his total gross earnings?

5. Edward waits on tables at a private club for a salary plus commission. He earns $6.98/h and 15% of the total value of the food and beverages he serves. Edward's timecard/pay envelope is shown below. His sales total was $1143.00 for the week. He is paid to the hour worked, to the closest 15 min interval.
What are his gross earnings for the week?

NAME______ EMPLOYEE#______

WEEK ENDING SEPT. 21

DAY	IN	OUT	HOURS
MON			
TUE	17:23	23:30	
WED	17:27	23:33	
THU	17:25	22:32	
FRI	19:20	1:33	
SAT	19:22	1:30	
SUN			
		TOTAL	______
		RATE	$6.98
TOTAL HOURLY RATE			$
TOTAL COMMISSION			$
TOTAL GROSS WAGES			

6. Brandon is a real estate agent. He earns 2% commission for selling a house. His sales for a year are given below, by month. What is his gross yearly income, and his average gross monthly income?

Month	Sales ($)
January	198 500
February	—
March	102 300
April	113 700
May	123 800
June	193 870
July	115 000
August	142 500
September	189 900
October	238 400
November	—
December	—

7. Kaitlin works in a video store earning graduated commission of 11% on the first $250 of sales, 15% on the next $500, and 18% on all further sales, each month. In December, she sold $12 484.20 worth of merchandise.
What were her gross earnings?

14.3 COMPARING GROSS RATES OF PAY USING GRAPHS

Gross wages and commission can be represented and compared graphically.
Gross wages may vary directly as the hours worked or service provided.

Example 1. Grant cleans swimming pools and earns \$9.50/h.
Construct a graph to represent the gross wages he would receive over an 8 h period.

Solution:

Hours worked	1	2	3	8
Earnings (\$)	9.50	19.00	28.50	76.00

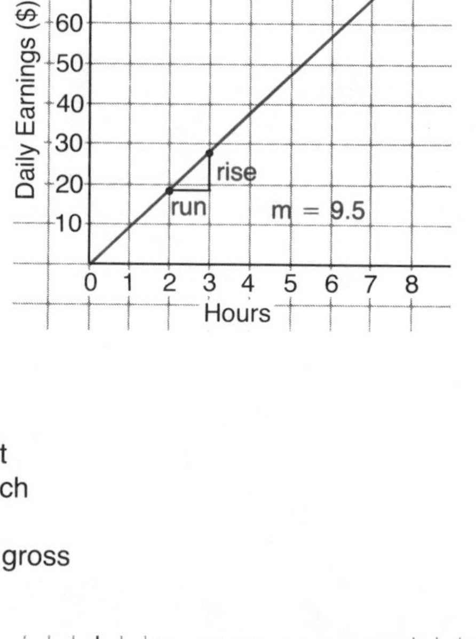

The slope of the graph is

$$m = \frac{\text{rise}}{\text{run}} \text{ or } \frac{\text{earnings}}{\text{hours worked}},$$

$$m = \frac{19.00}{2} \text{ or \$9.50, the hourly rate.}$$

For a regular hourly rate, the slope is the hourly rate.

Example 2. Holly sells furniture. She earns a straight commission of 13% of the total sales each month.
Construct a graph to show her potential gross earnings per month.

Solution:

Sales (\$)	1000	2000	10 000	15 000
Earnings (\$)	130	260	1300	1950

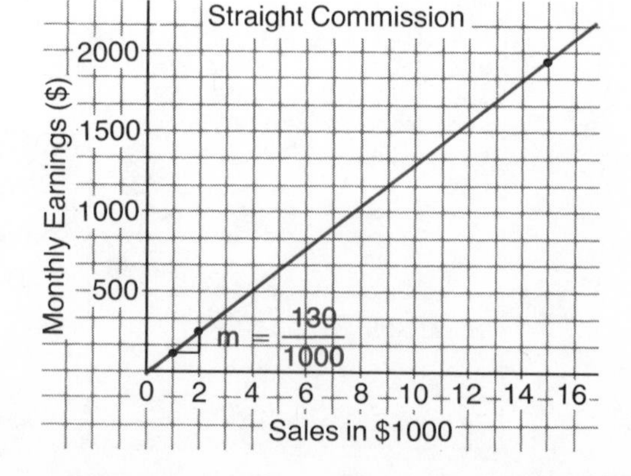

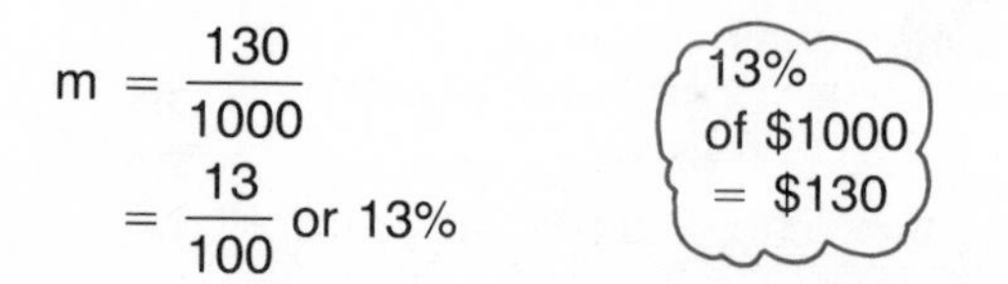

$$m = \frac{130}{1000}$$
$$= \frac{13}{100} \text{ or } 13\%$$

The slope is the rate of commission.

Example 3. Ernie sells stereo equipment. He earns a salary of \$500 per month, plus 11% commission on total sales.
Construct a graph to represent his potential gross earnings per month.

Solution:

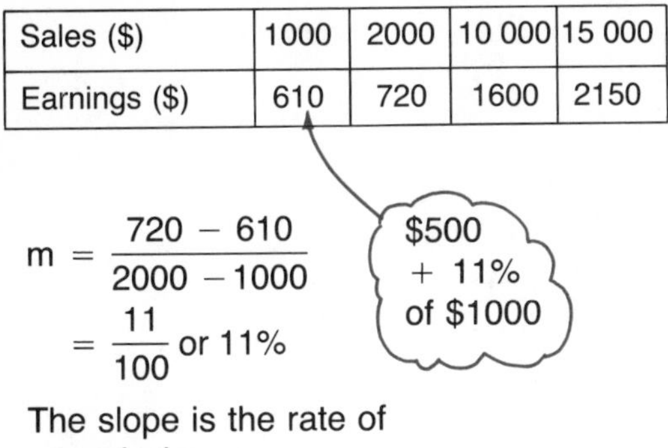

Sales (\$)	1000	2000	10 000	15 000
Earnings (\$)	610	720	1600	2150

$$m = \frac{720 - 610}{2000 - 1000}$$
$$= \frac{11}{100} \text{ or } 11\%$$

The slope is the rate of commission.
The graph intersects the y-axis at \$500. This represents Ernie's monthly salary.

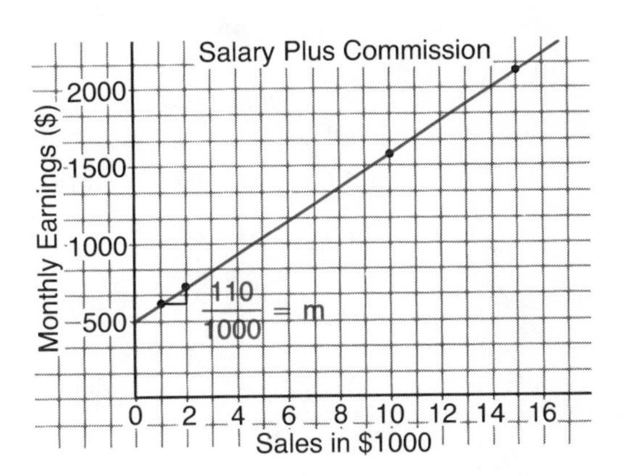

Example 4. Jackie earns a graduated commission selling cosmetics. Based on her sales for the week, Jackie receives 20% commission on the first \$500 in sales, 25% on the next \$500, and 30% on all further sales.
Construct a graph to represent her potential gross earnings per week.

Solution:

Sales (\$)	500	1000	1500	2000
Earnings (\$)	100	225	375	525

The graph is a polygon made up of 3 line segments, each with a different slope. The slope of each segment is: $m_1 = \frac{20}{100}$ or 20%, $m_2 = \frac{25}{100}$ or 25%,

$m_3 = \frac{30}{100}$ or 30%

The slope of each line segment is the commission for that level of sales.

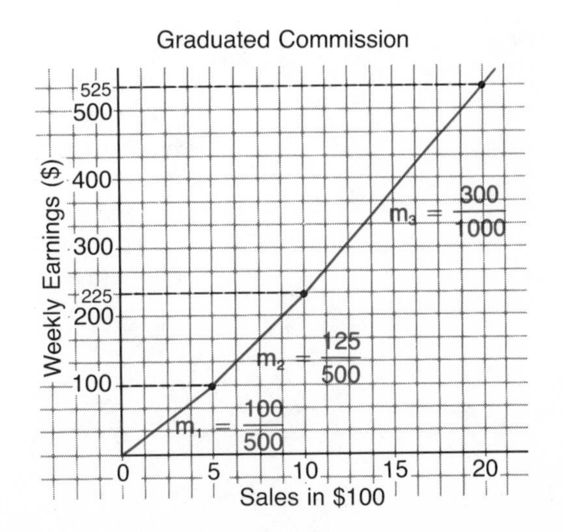

Graphs may be helpful in determining an advantageous rate of pay.

Example 5. Colin is offered a job selling for 20% commission on total sales per week, or \$600/week plus 10% commission on total sales per week.
Construct a graph to find the amount of sales necessary to make straight commission an advantage.

Solution:
The line for straight commission starts at (0, 0) with a slope of 0.20 or a rise of 20 for a run of 100.

The line for salary plus commission starts at (0, 600) with a slope of 0.10 or a rise of 10 for a run of 100.

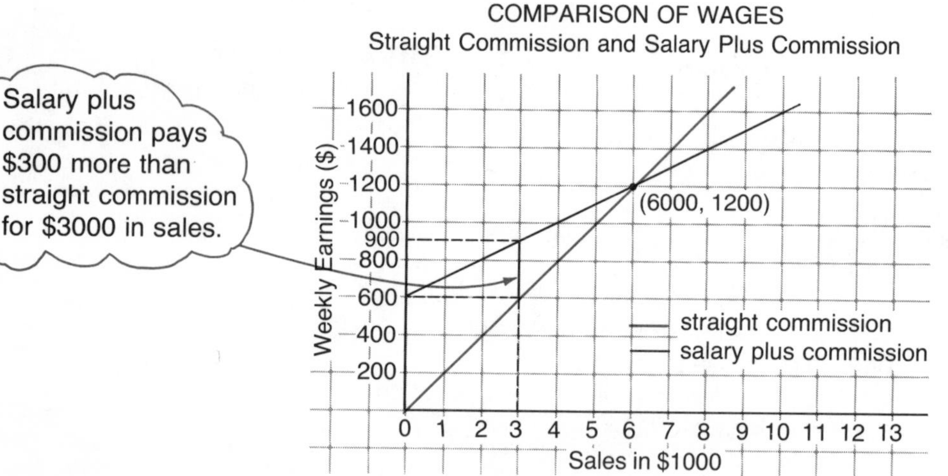

The point of intersection (6000, 1200) is the point at which the earnings are equal; Colin would earn \$1200 for \$6000 worth of sales for each method of payment. After this point it is better to work on straight commission of 20%. If Colin can make sales of more than \$6000/week, he should select straight commission as the method of payment; if not, he should select salary plus commission.

EXERCISE 14.3

A

1.

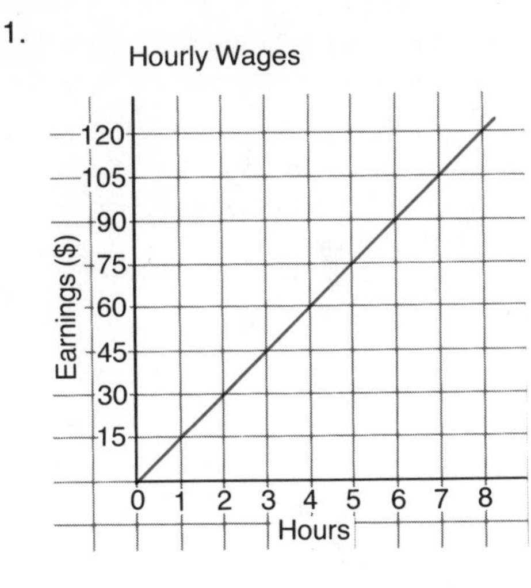

(a) What is the hourly rate of pay represented by the graph?
(b) What is the slope of the line?
(c) From the graph, how much would you earn for 6.5 h of work?

2.

Straight Commission

(a) What is the rate of commission represented by the graph?
(b) What is the slope of the line?
(c) From the graph, how much would you earn for selling $8000 worth of merchandise?

3.

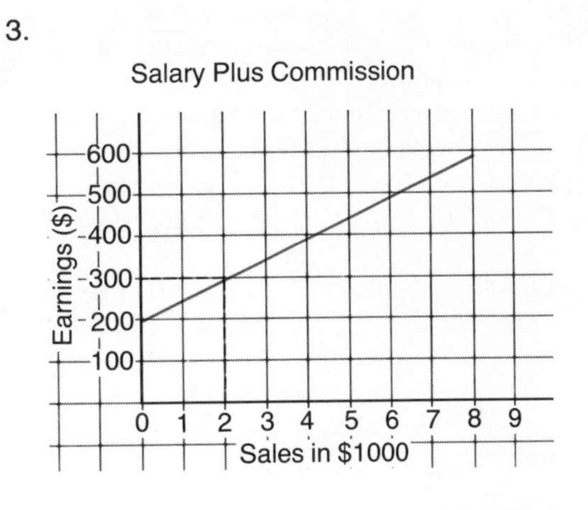

(a) What is the salary represented by the graph?
(b) What is the rate of commission in addition to salary?
(c) What is the slope?
(d) From the graph, how much would you earn for $6000 in sales?

4.

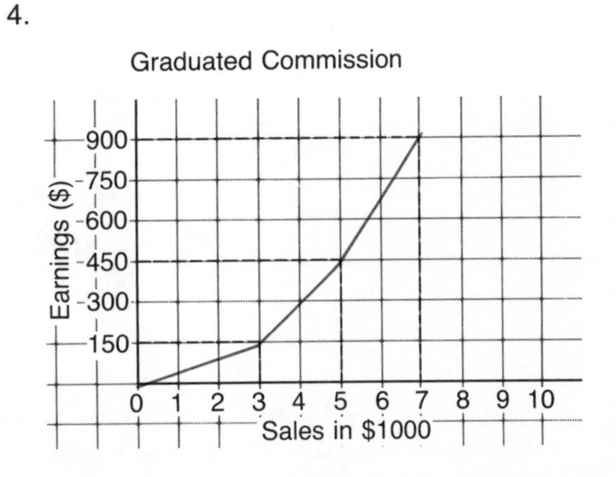

(a) What are the three rates of graduated commission represented by the graph?
(b) What is the slope of each of the three line segments?
(c) From the graph, how much would you earn for selling $6000 worth of merchandise?

B

5. Construct a graph to display each of the following methods of earning an income.
(a) hourly wage of \$9.50 to 8 h
(b) piecework sewing designs on flags at \$4.78/piece to 20 pieces
(c) piecework telephone soliciting for magazines at \$5.00 per positive response to 25 positive responses
(d) salary of \$170 plus 30% commission to \$1000 worth of sales
(e) graduated salary of 10% for first \$500, 15% for next \$500, 25% for next \$500, to \$1500 in sales
(f) fixed weekly salary of \$375/week, independent of hours worked or sales

6. Construct a graph that compares the hourly wages of a crew at Burger Quick. Junior burger-handlers earn \$7.50/h, senior burger-handlers earn \$8.25/h, and the chief burger-handler earns \$10.00/h.

7. Construct a graph to compare earnings of 30% commission with a salary of \$80 plus 15% commission.
What is the approximate difference for a sales level of \$1123?

8.

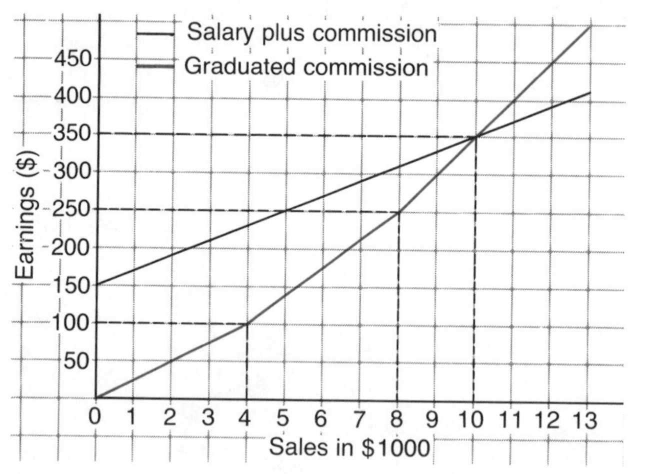

(a) What is the salary and rate of commission for an employee working on salary plus commission?
(b) What are the graduated rates of commission for an employee working on graduated commission?
(c) At what level of sales are the earnings equivalent?
(d) Which method of payment offers the best potential earnings?
(e) What is the approximate difference in salary for a sales level of
(i) \$4000? (ii) \$8000? (iii) \$12 000?

14.4 CALCULATING NET PAY: READING PAY SLIPS

Gross pay is what an employee earns. Net pay is what the employee actually receives, either by pay cheque or pay envelope. It is the amount that the employee takes home after deductions are made from gross pay.

Net pay = Gross pay − Deductions

Some deductions are required by federal or provincial law. These are called statutory deductions. Other deductions are private or employment deductions. These are for benefits required by the employee or employer.

Statutory deductions include:

Unemployment Insurance premium
Canadian Pension Plan
Income tax
Provincial medical plan

Other deductions include:

Extended medical insurance
Long-term disability insurance
Life insurance
Dental insurance
Private pension plan

PAY SLIP

An example of a pay slip for one week's earnings is shown below. The net pay is the gross pay less the sum of the deductions.

BURGER QUICK

WEEK END	EMPLOYEE	CHEQUE #	REGULAR EARNINGS	OVERTIME EARNINGS	GROSS PAY
JUNE 27	AJ 21833	123872	$ 300.00	$ 44.80	$ 344.80

EMPLOYEE DEDUCTIONS		
C.P.P.	5.64	
U.I.	8.10	
INCOME TAX	$ 61.45	
PROV. MEDICAL	13.50	
GROUP LIFE	6.75	
TOTAL DEDUCTIONS	95.44	NET PAY 249.36

CANADA PENSION PLAN (C.P.P.) CONTRIBUTION

The Canada Pension Plan contribution is really money going toward an employee's future pension. When the employee reaches the qualifying age, the government will guarantee a minimum income based on her/his contributions to the Plan.

The rates are set by statute and are presented in table form. A portion of the Canada Pension Plan Contributions table is given. Additional tables are given in the Appendix. C.P.P. contributions are listed by the number of pay periods. The table is organized by the method of payment; for example, daily (260 pay periods), weekly (52 pay periods), biweekly (26 pay periods), monthly (12 pay periods).

CANADA PENSION PLAN CONTRIBUTIONS

WEEKLY PAY PERIOD

199.39 — 350.96

Remuneration *Rémunération* From-*de*	To-*à*	C.P.P. *R.P.C.*	Remuneration *Rémunération* From-*de*	To-*à*	C.P.P. *R.P.C.*	Remuneration *Rémunération* From-*de*	To-*à*	C.P.P. *R.P.C.*	Remuneration *Rémunération* From-*de*	To-*à*	C.P.P. *R.P.C.*
227.81 -	228.33	3.42	265.71 -	266.22	4.14	303.60 -	304.12	4.86	341.50 -	342.01	5.58
228.34 -	228.85	3.43	266.23 -	266.75	4.15	304.13 -	304.64	4.87	342.02 -	342.54	5.59
228.86 -	229.38	3.44	266.76 -	267.28	4.16	304.65 -	305.17	4.88	342.55 -	343.06	5.60
229.39 -	229.91	3.45	267.29 -	267.80	4.17	305.18 -	305.70	4.89	343.07 -	343.59	5.61
229.92 -	230.43	3.46	267.81 -	268.33	4.18	305.71 -	306.22	4.90	343.60 -	344.12	5.62
230.44 -	230.96	3.47	268.34 -	268.85	4.19	306.23 -	306.75	4.91	344.13 -	344.64	5.63
230.97 -	231.49	3.48	268.86 -	269.38	4.20	306.76 -	307.28	4.92	344.65 -	345.17	5.64
231.50 -	232.01	3.49	269.39 -	269.91	4.21	307.29 -	307.80	4.93	345.18 -	345.70	5.65
232.02 -	232.54	3.50	269.92 -	270.43	4.22	307.81 -	308.33	4.94	345.71 -	346.22	5.66
232.55 -	233.06	3.51	270.44 -	270.96	4.23	308.34 -	308.85	4.95	346.23 -	346.75	5.67
233.07 -	233.59	3.52	270.97 -	271.49	4.24	308.86 -	309.38	4.96	346.76 -	347.28	5.68
233.60 -	234.12	3.53	271.50 -	272.01	4.25	309.39 -	309.91	4.97	347.29 -	347.80	5.69
234.13 -	234.64	3.54	272.02 -	272.54	4.26	309.92 -	310.43	4.98	347.81 -	348.33	5.70
234.65 -	235.17	3.55	272.55 -	273.06	4.27	310.44 -	310.96	4.99	348.34 -	348.85	5.71
235.18 -	235.70	3.56	273.07 -	273.59	4.28	310.97 -	311.49	5.00	348.86 -	349.38	5.72
235.71 -	236.22	3.57	273.60 -	274.12	4.29	311.50 -	312.01	5.01	349.39 -	349.91	5.73
236.23 -	236.75	3.58	274.13 -	274.64	4.30	312.02 -	312.54	5.02	349.92 -	350.43	5.74
236.76 -	237.28	3.59	274.65 -	275.17	4.31	312.55 -	313.06	5.03	350.44 -	350.96	5.75

Example 1. Using the table, find the C.P.P. contribution deducted from a gross weekly pay of $344.80 for an employee at Burger Quick.
What is the total contribution over the year?

Solution: From the table, $344.80 is between $344.65 and $345.17 and would require a contribution of $5.64 each week. If earnings continued for one full year, January to January, at the same rate, the total contribution would be $5.64 from 52 pays, one for each week.

$$\text{Expected annual contribution} = 52 \times 5.64$$
$$= 293.28$$

$293.28 would be deducted annually for C.P.P.

UNEMPLOYMENT INSURANCE (U.I.) PREMIUM

U.I. is an insurance plan, supported both by the employee who is contributing and the government. If a person who has made the minimum number of contributions required loses a job, he or she can collect a sum of money while unemployed.

A portion of the Unemployment Insurance Premiums table is given. Additional U.I. tables are given in the Appendix.

Unlike the Canada Pension Plan Contribution tables, U.I. is based on weekly contributions, even though they may be collected monthly or biweekly. It is done this way because eligibility to receive benefits is based on the number of weeks of contribution. If the pay is not weekly, the premiums are converted to biweekly or monthly premiums.

UNEMPLOYMENT INSURANCE PREMIUMS

Remuneration *Rémunération* From-*de*	To-*à*	U.I. Premium *Prime d'a.-c.*	Remuneration *Rémunération* From-*de*	To-*à*	U.I. Premium *Prime d'a.-c.*	Remuneration *Rémunération* From-*de*	To-*à*	U.I. Premium *Prime d'a-c.*	Remuneration *Rémunération* From-*de*	To-*à*	U.I. Premium *Prime d'a.-c.*
245.32 -	245.74	5.77	275.96 -	276.38	6.49	306.60 -	307.02	7.21	337.24 -	337.65	7.93
245.75 -	246.17	5.78	276.39 -	276.80	6.50	307.03 -	307.44	7.22	337.66 -	338.08	7.94
246.18 -	246.59	5.79	276.81 -	277.23	6.51	307.45 -	307.87	7.23	338.09 -	338.51	7.95
246.60 -	247.02	5.80	277.24 -	277.65	6.52	307.88 -	308.29	7.24	338.52 -	338.93	7.96
247.03 -	247.44	5.81	277.66 -	278.08	6.53	308.30 -	308.72	7.25	338.94 -	339.36	7.97
247.45 -	247.87	5.82	278.09 -	278.51	6.54	308.73 -	309.14	7.26	339.37 -	339.78	7.98
247.88 -	248.29	5.83	278.52 -	278.93	6.55	309.15 -	309.57	7.27	339.79 -	340.21	7.99
248.30 -	248.72	5.84	278.94 -	279.36	6.56	309.58 -	309.99	7.28	340.22 -	340.63	8.00
248.73 -	249.14	5.85	279.37 -	279.78	6.57	310.00 -	310.42	7.29	340.64 -	341.06	8.01
249.15 -	249.57	5.86	279.79 -	280.21	6.58	310.43 -	310.85	7.30	341.07 -	341.48	8.02
249.58 -	249.99	5.87	280.22 -	280.63	6.59	310.86 -	311.27	7.31	341.49 -	341.91	8.03
250.00 -	250.42	5.88	280.64 -	281.06	6.60	311.28 -	311.70	7.32	341.92 -	342.34	8.04
250.43 -	250.85	5.89	281.07 -	281.48	6.61	311.71 -	312.12	7.33	342.35 -	342.76	8.05
250.86 -	251.27	5.90	281.49 -	281.91	6.62	312.13 -	312.55	7.34	342.77 -	343.19	8.06
251.28 -	251.70	5.91	281.92 -	282.34	6.63	312.56 -	312.97	7.35	343.20 -	343.61	8.07
251.71 -	252.12	5.92	282.35 -	282.76	6.64	312.98 -	313.40	7.36	343.62 -	344.04	8.08
252.13 -	252.55	5.93	282.77 -	283.19	6.65	313.41 -	313.82	7.37	344.05 -	344.46	8.09
252.56 -	252.97	5.94	283.20 -	283.61	6.66	313.83 -	314.25	7.38	344.47 -	344.89	8.10

Example 2. Using the table, find the U.I. premium deducted from a gross weekly pay of \$344.80 for a Burger Quick employee.
What is the total yearly U.I. contribution?

Solution: From the table, \$344.80 is between \$344.47 and \$344.89 and would require a contribution of \$8.10 each week. If earnings continued for one full year, January to January, at the same rate, the total contribution would be \$8.10 from 52 pays, one for each week.

$$\begin{aligned}\text{Expected annual premium} &= 52 \times 8.10 \\ &= 421.20\end{aligned}$$

\$421.20 would be deducted annually for U.I.

INCOME TAX DEDUCTION

The rate of income tax you must pay depends on two things: the amount of money earned, or income, and the number of exemptions claimed. Income tax is calculated on gross pay, less the contributions to C.P.P. and U.I. because these contributions are not taxable.

On first taking a job the employee is required, within seven days, to fill in a TD1 Form declaring tax exemptions. If the worker is single, the claim is for only one person. A married worker may claim a spouse who is not earning a certain minimum income. Each child not earning a certain minimum income may also be claimed. Under certain circumstances other people, who are also dependent for support, may be claimed.

This portion of the table from Revenue Canada Taxation shows how the two factors, income and exemptions, determine the amount of tax deducted from each pay so that your annual income tax will be paid by the end of the year. Additional tables are given in the Appendix.

INCOME TAX DEDUCTIONS AT SOURCE

WEEKLY TAX DEDUCTIONS
Basis — 52 Pay Periods per Year

WEEKLY PAY Use appropriate bracket — **PAIE PAR SEMAINE** Utilisez le palier approprié	IF THE EMPLOYEE'S "NET CLAIM CODE" ON FORM TD1 IS – SI LE «CODE DE DEMANDE NETTE» DE L'E								
	1	**2**	**3**	**4**	**5**	**6**	**7**	**8**	**9**
	DEDUCT FROM EACH PAY – *RETENEZ SUR CHAQUE P*								
296.00 – 300.99	51.30	49.15	45.25	41.40	40.10	34.05	32.05	29.00	24.80
301.00 – 305.99	52.75	50.60	46.70	42.85	41.55	35.40	33.40	30.35	26.20
306.00 – 310.99	54.20	52.05	48.15	44.30	43.00	36.85	34.80	31.75	27.55
311.00 – 315.99	55.65	53.50	49.60	45.75	44.45	38.30	36.20	33.15	28.95
316.00 – 320.99	57.10	54.95	51.05	47.20	45.90	39.75	37.65	34.50	30.30
321.00 – 325.99	58.55	56.40	52.50	48.65	47.35	41.20	39.10	35.90	31.70
326.00 – 330.99	60.00	57.85	53.95	50.10	48.80	42.65	40.55	37.35	33.05
331.00 – 335.99	61.45	59.30	55.40	51.60	50.25	44.10	42.00	38.80	34.45
336.00 – 340.99	62.90	60.75	56.85	53.05	51.70	45.55	43.45	40.25	35.85
341.00 – 345.99	64.40	62.20	58.30	54.50	53.15	47.00	44.90	41.70	37.30
346.00 – 350.99	65.85	63.70	59.75	55.95	54.60	48.45	46.40	43.15	38.75
351.00 – 355.99	67.40	65.15	61.20	57.40	56.10	49.95	47.85	44.60	40.20
356.00 – 360.99	68.90	66.65	62.65	58.85	57.55	51.40	49.30	46.05	41.65
361.00 – 365.99	70.45	68.20	64.15	60.30	59.00	52.85	50.75	47.50	43.10
366.00 – 370.99	72.00	69.70	65.60	61.75	60.45	54.30	52.20	49.00	44.55

The numbers at the top of the table indicate the number of exemptions. The column at the left shows the pay levels.

Example 3. A Burger Quick employee earns a weekly gross pay of \$344.80. Using the table, find the income tax deducted from each pay, after U.I. and C.P.P. contributions are deducted as in Examples 1 and 2. The employee claims a personal exemption only.
What is the expected annual tax due at the end of the year?

Solution:
We must deduct U.I. and C.P.P. from the gross pay.

$$\begin{aligned}\text{Taxable income} &= 344.80 - (8.10 + 5.64)\\ &= 344.80 - 13.74\\ &= 331.06\end{aligned}$$

From the table, \$331.06 is between \$331.00 and \$335.99. With one dependent, the tax per weekly pay would be \$61.45. If earnings continued at the same rate for one full year, January to January, the tax due would be 52 payments of \$61.45, one each week.

$$\begin{aligned}\text{Expected annual tax} &= 52 \times 61.45\\ &= 3195.40\end{aligned}$$

\$3195.40 would be deducted to pay income tax. The actual tax due should be approximately the same amount.

EXERCISE 14.4

B 1. Cindy works part-time as a computer operator for Hi-High Tech Company.
Complete the pay slip below including C.P.P., U.I., and income tax, and calculate net pay. Only the personal exemption was claimed.

HI-HIGH TECH COMPANY					
WEEK END	EMPLOYEE	CHEQUE #	REGULAR EARNINGS	OVERTIME EARNINGS	GROSS PAY
JULY 21	763 8422	234561	\$ 298.50	V	\$ 298.50
EMPLOYEE DEDUCTIONS					
C.P.P. U.I. INCOME TAX			\$		
TOTAL DEDUCTIONS				NET PAY	

2. The net claim codes table is as follows.

Table of Net Claim Codes

Net Claim - *Demande nette* Exceeding - Not exceeding *Excédant - N'excédant pas*	Net Claim Code *Code de demande nette*	Net Claim - *Demande nette* Exceeding - Not exceeding *Excédant - N'excédant pas*	Net Claim Code *Code de demande nette*
For use re: Tables 11 and 12 *Utilisation: Tables 11 et 12*	0	7,890 – 8,660	8
4,219 – 4,270	1	8,660 – 9,470	9
4,270 – 4,940	2	9,470 – 10,360	10
4,940 – 5,670	3	10,360 – 11,230	11
5,670 – 6,310	4	11,230 – 12,060	12
6,310 – 7,140	5	12,060 – 12,710	13
7,140 – 7,510	6	12,710 and up – *et plus*	X
7,510 – 7,890	7	No tax withholding required *Aucune retenue d'impôt requise*	E

The following tax exemptions may be claimed:

4220 as a personal exemption

3700 for a dependent spouse

560 for each non-income-earning child under 18 a

1200 for each non-income-earning child 18 a or over

Find the weekly deduction for a weekly taxable income of $442.40 for each of the following conditions.

(a) a taxpayer who has a spouse with no income and 3 children under 8 a

(b) a taxpayer with only the personal exemption

(c) a taxpayer with a spouse who works full-time and has 2 children with no income, one 18 a and the other 16 a

3. Sherry has a weekly income of $308.34.

(a) What is her C.P.P. contribution per week?

(b) What is her annual contribution to C.P.P.?

(c) What percent of her gross weekly income is the weekly C.P.P. deduction?

(d) What is her U.I. premium per week?

(e) What is her annual U.I. contribution?

(f) What percent of her gross weekly income is the weekly U.I. deduction?

4. Find the amount of the income tax deducted weekly from each gross pay. (Remember that U.I. and C.P.P. contributions are non-taxable.) Only a personal exemption is claimed.

(a) $297.00 (b) $250.00
(c) $314.75 (d) $342.50

5. You are married and your spouse has no income. You have a taxable income of $461.53 per week. Assume that your income stays the same and there is no change in the tax rate.
What is the percentage decrease in income tax deducted per week after each of the following?

(a) the birth of one child

(b) the birth of a second child two years after the first

(c) the birth of a third child three years after the second

6. What is the approximate taxable income if the following weekly deductions are made for income tax purposes for a taxpayer who claims only the personal exemption?

(a) $18.05 (b) $36.75
(c) $68.90 (d) $116.75

7. A single student attending a community college lives on her own and works part-time for an hourly rate of $9.82/h.
What is her net pay for a week in which she worked 25 h?

14.5 CASE STUDIES FOR PERSONAL INCOME TAX

Because tax rates, tax credits, and allowable deductions vary, worked examples of completed tax forms are not provided. Current tax forms are available at any branch of the Post Office or from the District Taxation Office. The following exercises provide data for the completion of sample tax forms. Assume that the taxpayer lives in your province.

Since Canada Pension Plan payments and Unemployment Insurance premiums vary from year to year, values are not provided in the questions. The word "maximum" should be taken to mean the greatest amount that can be deducted from one job without overpayment. In cases where a person held more than one job, overpayment is possible. When the overpayment is claimed through completing the tax form, it is refunded.

EXERCISE 14.5

B

1. Jose Perez was born on 1960 09 03. He is single. His address is
   1104 King St.
   Apartment 1102

Jose is employed as a computer operator by Information Link Limited.

He is also a part-time student at Seneca College and his tuition fees were $825.00 this year.

In the taxation year, Jose had the following financial data.

Total Earnings Before Deductions	$21 500.00
Deductions	
Income tax	$4210.00
Registered pension plan	$457.00
Canada Pension Plan	maximum
Unemployment Insurance	maximum

(a) Complete the T4 slip that the employer gives to Jose Perez.
(b) Complete an income tax return for Jose Perez.

2. Alison Nashiki was born on 1961 10 07, and is employed as a research supervisor by the First Canadian Electronics Company. She shares an apartment for $1150.00/month with a girlfriend at
   1307 Queen St.
   Apt 1A

In the taxation year, Alison had the following financial data.

Total Earnings Before Deductions	$34 700.00
Deductions	
Income tax	$4720.00
Union/association dues	$180.00
Registered pension plan	$694.00
Canada Pension Plan	maximum
Unemployment Insurance	maximum

As well, Alison had charitable donations amounting to $242.50.

(a) Complete the T4 slip that the employer gives to Alison Nashiki.
(b) Complete an income tax return for Alison Nashiki.

3. Yvette Gagnon was born on 1960 04 03 and is employed as a dietitian by the Memorial Medical Centre. She lives with her husband, who is self-employed, in an apartment at

2156 Rue St. Aubin

As a part-time student at the University of Ottawa, Yvette paid tuition of $610.00. Her charitable donations were $305.00, and professional dues were $254.56.

Her T5 slips show the following income from investments.

Royal Bank of Canada	$126.73
Civil Service Credit Union	$486.32

In the taxation year, Yvette had the following financial information from her employer.

Total Earnings Before Deductions	$38 655.00
Deductions	
Income tax	$5926.00
Registered pension plan	$772.11
Canada Pension Plan	maximum
Unemployment Insurance	maximum

(a) Complete the T5 information slips that Yvette would receive.
(b) Complete the T4 slip that Yvette Gagnon would receive.
(c) Complete a tax return for Yvette Gagnon.

4. John Eagle, born 1958 09 05, is married and lives with his wife at

2465 Roselawn Ave.

He is employed by the Ford Motor Company as an engineer. During the year, his wife, Sarah, worked part-time and earned $1474.00. The property taxes on their home are $1857.50.

T5 slips show the following investment income.

Canada Trust (interest) $1245.00

In the taxation year, John Eagle had the following financial information from his employer.

Total Earnings Before Deductions	$64 150.00
Deductions	
Income tax	$21 285.00
Registered pension plan	$1283.00
Professional dues	$360.00
Canada Pension Plan	maximum
Unemployment Insurance	maximum

(a) Complete the T5 slip that John Eagle would receive from the trust company.
(b) Complete the T4 slip that he would receive from his employer.
(c) Complete a tax return for John Eagle.

5. Phyllis Nadam, born 1952 12 07, lives with her husband, Jamil, and their three children. David is 8 a old, Sally is 11, and Jamil, Jr. is 15. They live in a rented house at

33 Pleasant Drive

Phyllis works as a shoe buyer at

Sally's Shoe Shops
121 Front Street

During the past year, Phyllis' husband, Jamil, worked part-time and earned $2250.00. The rent on the house is $1200 per month.

T5 slips showed that Phyllis received interest from the Bank of Nova Scotia in the amount of $724.80.

The financial records at the shoe company indicate the following.

Total Earnings Before Deductions	$62 261.00
Deductions	
Income tax	$12 480.00
Registered pension plan	$1245.22
Canada Pension Plan	maximum
Unemployment Insurance	maximum

(a) Complete the T5 slip from the Bank of Nova Scotia.
(b) Complete the T4 slip that the employer would give to Phyllis Nadam.
(c) Complete a tax return for Phyllis Nadam.

6. Sam Gianconna (born September 2, 1950) and his wife, Sandra, have three children. Sandra earned $1200 evaluating manuscripts for a publishing company. The ages of the children are: Paula, 19 a; Justine, 13 a; and Colleen, 11 a. Sandra receives Family Allowance payments every month for Justine and Colleen, which she deposits in a bank for college expenses. Paula is a full-time student at university. Sam paid her tuition fees which amounted to $2500.00. Paula earned $2100.00 during the summer. Sam's interest from a Canadian bank was $2367.89. Sam's total earnings as a sailboat designer were $86 700.00. Sam contributed the maximum amount to the C.P.P. and the U.I. and paid $12 170.00 into a registered pension plan. $21 266.00 was deducted from Sam's salary for income tax. Sam pays professional dues of $350.00.
Complete Sam's income tax return.

7. Deborah Sanderson (born July 19, 1952) is married to David. They have two children: Melissa, 14 a and Rocky, 12 a. David returned to university to study forestry. His tuition fees were $2500.00 and he earned $4200.00 tutoring students. Both Melissa and Rocky attend school and their parents receive Family Allowance payments. Deborah earned $96 123.78 as a stock broker and contributed the maximum amount to C.P.P. and U.I. She earned interest of $7 891.00 on deposits in a Canadian credit union. A total of $27 396.80 was deducted from Deborah's pay for income tax. She paid $5678.00 into a registered pension plan. During the year Deborah donated a painting to Canada which was valued at $2500.00.
Complete Deborah's income tax return.

8. Charles (born June 13, 1960) and Dianah Caversan (born May 2, 1961) are married. Charles works for the police department and earned $56 890.00 last year. Dianah is a dental hygienist and earned $52 700.00 last year. Charles had $12 978.00 deducted for income tax. He contributed $2345.89 to a registered pension fund and he earned interest of $345.78 from a Canadian credit union. Charles' union dues were $750.00 and he paid tuition of $400.00 to take a course at a college. Charles overpaid the C.P.P. by $5.60 and he paid the maximum U.I.

Dianah had $11 200.00 deducted for income tax. She contributed $2589.00 to a registered pension plan. Her professional dues were $700.00 and she earned $123.89 interest from Canadian bank deposits.

Living with the Caversans is Julie Smith, who is Charles' sister. Because of an illness, Julie does not work and she relies totally on her brother and sister-in-law for her support.

Complete Charles' and Dianah's income tax return and claim Julie in such a way that the total tax paid by the Caversans is a minimum.

9. Glen Wong (born February 23, 1959) is a construction engineer. Last year he earned $92 890.00 in salary and $4000.00 in bonuses. His employer deducted $22 300.75 for income tax. Glen made the maximum C.P.P. and U.I. contributions. His professional dues were $950.00. He contributed $3500.00 to a registered pension plan. Glen had interest of $1329.00 and $456.78 from Canadian sources. He also had investment interest of $567.90 from the United States. This interest was paid to Glen in U.S. funds. Glen pays family support payments of $1500 a month to his ex-wife and their children. Glen made a contribution of $1000.00 to a federal political party.
Complete Glen's income tax return.

14.6 PROBLEM SOLVING

1. In how many ways can three people be seated in the back seat of a car?

2. Place 5 dots in the following figure so that there will be no more than one dot in each row, column, or diagonal.

3. The number of square centimetres in the surface area of a certain cube is the same as the number of cubic units in its volume. What is the length of each edge of the cube?

4. The number 125 is a cubic number because

$$5^3 = 125.$$

The number 232 is a palindrome because it reads the same forward and backward.
Find a cubic number that is a palindrome.

5. There are n checkers on top of a table. Two players take turns removing the checkers. A player can remove 1, 2, or 3 checkers in one move. The winner is the player who removes the last checker or checkers from the table.
How many checkers should you leave on the board to assure that you win the game?

6. How many different triangles can be drawn so that the perimeter is 11 m and the length of each side is a whole number?

7. The small circles are tangent to each other at the centre of the large circle. What fraction of the large circle is shaded?

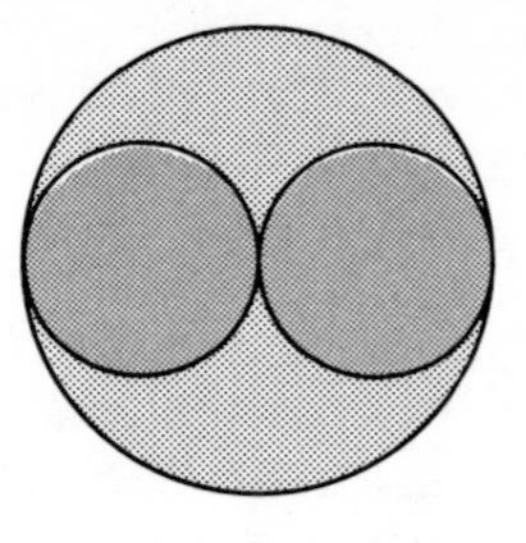

8. Make an assumption and determine the next two numbers in each.

(a) 9, 10, 12, 15, 19, ■, ■

(b) 212, 179, 146, 113, ■, ■

(c) 2, 3, 6, 11, 18, ■, ■

9. A driver's reaction time is one second. If she is driving at 85 km/h, how far will her car travel between the time danger appears and she applies the brakes?

10. An engraver will put two initials on a bracelet.
How many different pairs of initials are possible?

11. The two dice are identical.
What is the total of the two hidden sides that face each other?

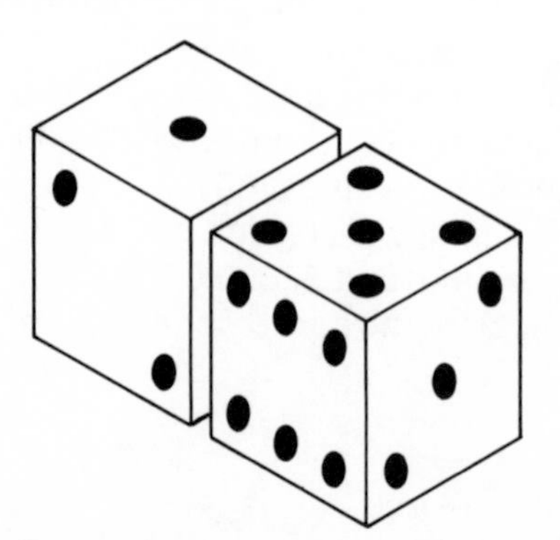

12. Divide the square into 4 congruent parts so that the numbers in each part total 45.

4	9	2	5	4	7
2	1	6	8	6	2
6	7	9	3	5	4
1	3	8	1	7	9
8	5	7	2	6	8
3	4	1	5	9	3

13. The Roman god Jupiter claimed he could do anything.
Does that mean he could make an object that he couldn't lift?

14. If you divide a number by 3, add 5, and multiply by 6, you get 54.
What is the number?

15. Name the wheels that are turning clockwise.

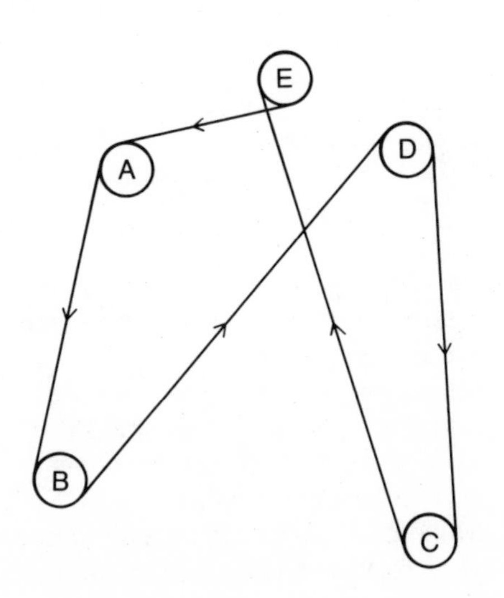

CAREER

REAL ESTATE SALESPERSON

Jim Maharaj sells real estate. When Jim sells a residential property, the vendor (the owner who sells the property) pays a real estate commission of 6%. This is divided between the agency that listed the property (3%) and Jim's agency that sold it (3%). Jim works on straight commission, and receives 1.5% of the sale, which is half of what his agency received.

For his 1.5%, Jim provides the service of locating the properties, arranging the viewings, and preparing the necessary papers when the buyers are ready to purchase.

Jim must be able to communicate well with people, and work accurately to calculate down payments and monthly payments to assist buyers with their purchase.

EXERCISE

1. A house is sold for $195 000.
(a) Calculate the commissions to be paid to the listing and selling agencies, and to the agent who sells the property.
(b) What amount of money does the vendor receive after paying real estate commissions?

2. Jim sold three houses:

bungalow	$149 500.00
two-storey	$195 000.00
duplex	$210 000.00

What is Jim's total commission for the three sales?

14.7 REVIEW EXERCISE

1. You earn an hourly wage, paid weekly, of $16.50 plus time and a half for overtime. Overtime is paid any time over the usual 8 h day. During one week, you work the following hours.

Monday	9 h 30 min
Tuesday	7 h 30 min
Wednesday	12 h
Thursday	10 h 15 min
Friday	9 h 45 min

What are your gross earnings for the week?

2. An employee's gross annual earnings are $33 123.
(a) What is the gross salary paid monthly?
(b) Based on a 40 h week, 52 weeks in the year, what is the equivalent gross hourly rate, to the nearest cent?

3. Calculate the straight commission.

	Rate of Commission (%)	Total Sales ($)	Gross Earnings ($)
(a)	15	1 890.00	
(b)	8	2 760.25	
(c)	2.5	3 889.90	
(d)	33	5 500.50	

4. Complete the table.

	Rate of Commission (%)	Total Sales ($)	Gross Earnings ($)
(a)	17.5	1 482.50	
(b)	12.5		625.00
(c)		5 660.00	481.10
(d)		17 804.00	400.59
(e)	28		623.07

5. For each of the following sales figures, calculate the gross earnings by graduated commission of 8% on the first $3000, 11% on the next $3000, and 15% on all further sales.
(a) $2500.00
(b) $3500.00
(c) $6500.00
(d) $3001.00
(e) $6000.10
(f) $7482.35

6. Construct a graph to represent gross earnings for each of the following methods of earning an income.
(a) hourly wage of $9.50 to 8 h
(b) piecework at $116/piece to 25 pieces
(c) salary of $255 plus 30% commission to $2000 worth of sales
(d) graduated salary of 8% for first $500, 16% for next $500, 32% for next $500 to $1500 in sales
(e) investment income of $375/week

7.

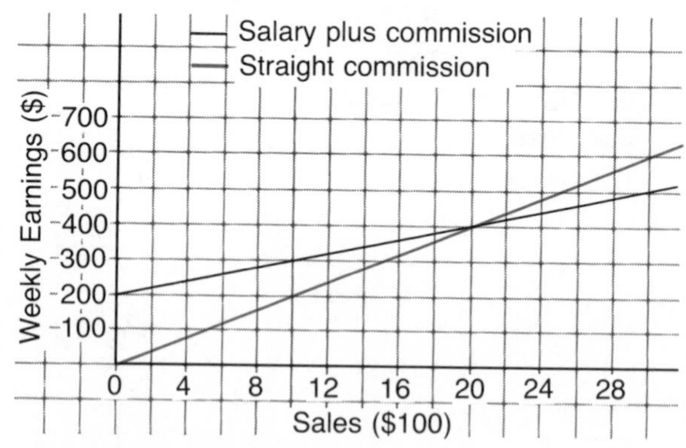

(a) For earnings by salary plus commission, determine from the graph the salary and rate of commission.
(b) For earnings by straight commission, determine the rate of commission.
(c) What sales level yields the same income for each method?
(d) Which plan yields higher earnings at a sales level of $1200? By what amount do the earnings differ?

(e) Which plan yields higher earnings at a sales level of $2600? By what amount do the earnings differ?

8. Two timecard/pay envelopes appear below.
How much will each employee's envelope contain if earnings are based on the following employee/employer agreement?

Regular hours are from 7:30 to 16:30.

Employees are paid for an 8 h day, time and a half for overtime.

Lunch period is 1 h each day, deducted from time.

Employees are late if they punch the time clock after 7:30. Pay begins at the next 15 min interval.

Overtime is calculated at 15 min intervals after 8 h and on Saturday and Sunday.

For income tax purposes, assume personal exemptions only.

(a)

NAME P. SMITH			EMPLOYEE # 141	
WEEK ENDING DEC. 23				
DAY	IN	OUT	HOURS	
			REGULAR	OVERTIME
MON	7:18	16:41		
TUE	7:23	16:30		
WED	7:27	17:38		
THU				
FRI	7:20	13:33		
SAT				
SUN				
		TOTAL		
		RATE	$11.50	
TOTAL			$	$
GROSS WAGES			$	
DEDUCTIONS				
C.P.P. U.I. INCOME TAX OTHER DEDUCTIONS				
TOTAL DEDUCTIONS				
NET EARNINGS/WEEK				

(b)

NAME N. BRETT			EMPLOYEE # 421	
WEEK ENDING DEC. 23				
DAY	IN	OUT	HOURS	
			REGULAR	OVERTIME
MON				
TUE				
WED				
THU	7:35	16:32		
FRI	7:24	19:33		
SAT	7:50	16:30		
SUN				
		TOTAL		
		RATE	$10.65	
TOTAL			$	$
GROSS WAGES			$	
DEDUCTIONS				
C.P.P. U.I. INCOME TAX OTHER DEDUCTIONS				
TOTAL DEDUCTIONS				
NET EARNINGS/WEEK				

9. (a) Determine the net pay for weekly gross pays of (i) $329, and (ii) $330.
(b) Which gross pay produces the larger net pay?

10. Explain the advantages of the following benefits and statutory deductions.
(a) Income tax
(b) Unemployment Insurance
(c) Canada Pension Plan
(d) Private pension plan
(e) Long-term disability insurance
(f) Extended medical coverage

11. (a) Using a computer and spreadsheet software, enter the formulas to calculate the amount earned over 40 h at rates of
(i) $14.57/h (ii) $15.17/h
(iii) $15.74/h (iv) $16.43/h.
(b) Graph each result on a wage graph.

14.8 CHAPTER 14 TEST

1. An advertising agency pays market researchers $19.46/h based on a 37.5 h week.
(a) What is the gross pay each payday if the pay period is biweekly?
(b) What is the gross yearly pay?
(c) Calculate the new gross yearly pay after an hourly wage increase of 4.2%.

2. Jim has a job selling appliances. The company gives him the choice of a straight commission of 18% on total sales, or a salary of $8.90/h plus commission of 8% on total sales.
(a) Which is the better choice if he worked 30 h the first week and sold $2465.90 worth of appliances? By how much?
(b) Based on a 30 h week, what level of sales would make the method of payment the same?

3. Calculate the gross earnings by graduated commission of 5% on the first $2500, 7% on the next $3500, and 10% on sales exceeding $6000, for the following sales figures.
(a) $2250.60 (b) $2600.00 (c) 7414.50

4. How much will you find in the timecard/pay envelope shown if your earnings are calculated according to the following employee/employer agreement?
Regular hours are from 7:30 to 16:30.
You are paid for an 8 h day, time and a half for overtime.
Lunch period is 1 h each day, deducted from time.
You are late if you punch the time clock after 7:30. You are not paid for time punched prior to the next 15 min interval.
Overtime is calculated at 15 min intervals after 8 h and on Saturday and Sunday.
Assume a personal exemption only.

NAME W. KNOX EMPLOYEE # 1313

WEEK ENDING NOV. 13

DAY	IN	OUT	HOURS	
			REGULAR	OVERTIME
MON				
TUE	7:21	16:33		
WED	7:25	11:30		
THU	7:25	17:46		
FRI	7:32	17:16		
SAT	13:28	15:33		
SUN				
		TOTAL		
		RATE	$10.28	
TOTAL			$	$
GROSS WAGES			$	

DEDUCTIONS	
C.P.P.	
U.I.	
INCOME TAX	
OTHER DEDUCTIONS	
TOTAL DEDUCTIONS	
NET EARNINGS/WEEK	

SPREADSHEET APPLICATIONS

REVIEW AND PREVIEW TO CHAPTER 15

BASIC COMPUTER LANGUAGE

SUMMARY OF OPERATIONS

Operation	Mathematical Symbol	BASIC Symbol
addition	+	+
subtraction	−	−
multiplication	×	*
division	÷	/
exponentiation	exponent	^ or ↑
square root	$\sqrt{\ }$	SQR

EXERCISE

1. Evaluate these expressions.
(a) 5*8
(b) −35/5
(c) 6^2
(d) 2^6
(e) 3*(7−4)
(f) SQR(25)
(g) SQR(9)+SQR(16)

2. Write these expressions in BASIC.
(a) $-15 \div 3$
(b) 7^3
(c) $\sqrt{2.25}$
(d) 5.8×2.4
(e) $6.25 + 5.8$
(f) $(-5)^2$
(g) $\dfrac{2.4 + 3.8}{5.2 \times 1.7}$

3. Evaluate these expressions.
(a) 6−3*2
(b) 5^3/10
(c) 6^2/9
(d) (5+7)*(5^2*4)
(e) (3+3)^3/3−3
(f) (2*3)^2−2*(3^2)
(g) 2*3^2−3*2^2

4. Write these expressions in BASIC.
(a) $x^2 + y^2$
(b) $x^2 \div y$
(c) $5X + 2Y$
(d) $2(L + W)$
(e) 3.14159R
(f) $(A + B)(A - B)$
(g) 2(3.14159)R
(h) LW
(i) $0.5(A + B)H$
(j) $X^2 - 2X - 6$

5. RUN the following programs to find the output.
(a)
```
NEW
10 FOR X = -10 TO 10
20 Y = X^2
30 PRINT X,Y
40 NEXT X
50 END
RUN
```
(b)
```
NEW
10 FOR X = 1 TO 10
20 Y = SQR(X)
30 PRINT X,Y
40 NEXT X
50 END
RUN
```

6. (a) RUN the following program to find the sum of 3.625 and 5.218.
```
NEW
10 INPUT A
20 INPUT B
30 C=A+B
40 PRINT A,B,C
50 END
RUN
```
(b) Modify line 30 of the program to find the product of the numbers.
(c) Modify line 30 of the program to find the quotient of the numbers.

7. N! means the product of all numbers from 1 to N:
$N! = 1 \times 2 \times 3 \times ... \times (N - 1) \times N$
The following program calculates N!.
```
NEW
10 PRINT"THE VALUES OF N!"
20 P=1
30 INPUT N
40 FOR I=1 TO N
50 P=P*I
60 NEXT I
70 PRINT"THE PRODUCT OF THE NUMBERS"
80 PRINT"FROM 1 TO N IS ";P
90 END
RUN
```

SPREADSHEET SOFTWARE

This table shows the operations which will be used in the spreadsheet applications chapter.

Operation	Operator	Order
Exponentiation	^	1
Negative, Positive	− +	2
Multiplication, Division	* /	3
Addition, Subtraction	+ −	4

The following example shows how a spreadsheet would perform a calculation.

```
             1st          3rd     4th
              ↓            ↓       ↓
275 + ((250^2 + 175)*3.25)/−8.25
    ↑            ↑             ↑
   6th          2nd           5th
```

To override this order of operations, use additional brackets. Accordingly, the spreadsheet will then apply the BEDMAS rules. Using these rules the answer is −24 435.15, to two decimal places.

EXERCISE

1. Using a spreadsheet manual and spreadsheet software, prepare a summary of the following.
(a) Cursor Movement →, ←, ↑, ↓
(b) Entering Numeric Data
(c) Entering Alpha Data
(d) Copy Command
(e) Formatting—decimal places
—column width
(f) Entering a Formula—taking the values from two or more cells and performing operations (*, /, +, −).
(g) @Functions
@SUM(...)
@INT(...)
@MEAN(...)
@SQRT(...)
@PI
@SIN(...)
@COS(...)
@TAN(...)

2. The following table shows Pier Marchand's sales for one day.
3 suits @ $349.50
2 suits @ $199.95
12 shirts @ $49.50
3 shirts @ $39.95
52 pairs of socks @ $12.50
9 ties @ $29.95
81 ties @ $14.50
14 pairs of shoes @ $79.50
Set up a spreadsheet to find Pier's total sales for the day.

3. Ravi earns $68 500 as a computer consultant. The following are Ravi's deductions and expenses.

Item	Deduction
taxes, medical, etc.	38%
accommodations	21%
transportation	6%
food	9%
entertainment	6%
insurance	3%

The balance is saved.
Design a spreadsheet to calculate the amount of money that is directed to each item.

4. (a) Design a spreadsheet with the following information.

Weekly Service Summary—Ace Auto				
Day	Tune-ups	Lube Oil	Tires (new)	Car Wash
Mon	3	12	16	45
Tues	2	14	12	32
Wed	5	11	20	0
Thurs	4	15	18	7
Fri	7	17	24	48
Sat	1	5	8	22

Tune-ups cost $49.95 each; lube/oil specials are $21.95; new tires installed cost $87.50 each; and car washes are $11.00 each.
(b) Write and enter formulas to find the total amount.

15.1 PRODUCTION COSTS

A business that is involved in producing goods to sell must be concerned with production costs. Production costs are in two parts—fixed costs such as rent, and variable costs such as labour and materials.

Production Costs = Fixed Costs + Variable Costs

Example. The Prairie Cycle and Sports Company buys bicycle parts and assembles bicycles for shipping to stores. The rent is $600 per month. Variable costs depend on the number of bicycles assembled and shipped, as in the following table.

Output Quantity	0	5	10	15	20	25
Variable Costs ($)	0	150	200	225	340	600

Set up a spreadsheet to find the total costs of assembling bicycles.

Solution:
The spreadsheet requires 4 columns. The Output Quantity column is included to identify the figures and is not used in this calculation. The Total Costs column is found by adding the previous two columns. Note the number of decimal places in each column.

	A	B	C	D	E
1					
2	Total Costs = Fixed Costs + Variable Costs				
3					
4	Output	Fixed	Variable	Total	
5	Quantity	Costs	Costs	Costs	
6	0	600.00	0.00	600.00	
7	5	600.00	150.00	750.00	
8	10	600.00	200.00	800.00	
9	15	600.00	225.00	825.00	
10	20	600.00	340.00	940.00	
11	25	600.00	600.00	1200.00	
12				↑	
13				Column B	
14				+	
15				Column C	

In production it is often necessary to know the average cost of producing an item. Using the spreadsheet, we can extend the results of the example to find the average costs.

	A	B	C	D	E	F	G
1							
2	Production Costs				Average Production Costs		
3							
4	Output	Fixed	Variable	Total	Average	Average	Average
5	Quantity	Costs	Costs	Costs	Fixed	Variable	Total
6					Cost	Cost	Cost
7	0	600.00	0.00	600.00	0.00	0.00	0.00
8	5	600.00	150.00	750.00	120.00	30.00	150.00
9	10	600.00	200.00	800.00	60.00	20.00	80.00
10	15	600.00	225.00	825.00	40.00	15.00	55.00
11	20	600.00	340.00	940.00	30.00	17.00	47.00
12	25	600.00	600.00	1200.00	24.00	24.00	48.00
13					↑	↑	↑
14					Column B	Column C	Column D
15					Column A	Column A	Column A

EXERCISE 15.1

B 1. The following table shows the production costs for the production of honey at Sweet Clover Honey Cottage.

Sweet Clover Honey Cottage		
Output (litres)	Fixed Costs ($)	Variable Costs ($)
0	450.00	0.00
20	450.00	14.00
40	450.00	27.00
60	450.00	39.00
80	450.00	50.00
100	450.00	60.00
120	450.00	70.00
140	450.00	81.00
160	450.00	93.00
180	450.00	107.00
200	450.00	120.00

(a) Set up a spreadsheet to find the total costs for each of the given outputs up to 200 L.

(b) Extend the spreadsheet in (a) to find
  (i) average fixed cost,
  (ii) average variable cost,
  (iii) average total cost.

(c) Reading from your spreadsheet, determine the number of litres of production that has the lowest average total cost.

2. (a) Set up a spreadsheet to find
  (i) the average fixed cost,
  (ii) the average variable cost,
  (iii) the average total cost

for the production of sausage at the Europa Meat and Salami Company.

Europa Meat & Salami Company		
Output (kilograms)	Fixed Costs ($)	Variable Costs ($)
0	2000.00	0.00
100	2000.00	400.00
200	2000.00	780.00
300	2000.00	1175.00
400	2000.00	1569.00
500	2000.00	1967.00
600	2000.00	2364.00
700	2000.00	2760.00
800	2000.00	3155.00
900	2000.00	3550.00
1000	2000.00	4000.00
1100	2000.00	4380.00
1200	2250.00	4000.00
1300	2250.00	4380.00
1400	2250.00	4750.00
1500	2250.00	5100.00
1600	2250.00	5460.00

(b) Reading from your spreadsheet, determine the amount of sausage that has the lowest average total cost.

15.2 DECISION MAKING WITH A SPREADSHEET

A spreadsheet is helpful in organizing information and performing calculations so that we can make intelligent decisions when solving problems. When making decisions, it is important to have an organized plan. In this section the PACED model for decision making is adapted for use with a spreadsheet. Setting up a spreadsheet in the following manner permits us to assign values to the criteria and to rate each alternative based on each criterion.

PROBLEM Identify the problem, starting in cell B4.

ALTERNATIVES List each alternative under the numerals I, II, III, IV, ...

CRITERIA List up to 7 criteria in cells A10 to A16.
Assign each criterion a value from 1 to 10 in cells B10 to B16, based on how important you think it is.
Enter the values in column B of the same row.

EVALUATE Evaluate the alternatives based on each criterion and assign a value of 0, 1, 2, ... to the number of alternatives.
Multiply the value of each of the criteria by the corresponding value for each alternative.
Add the products for each alternative, and place the sums in row 18.

DECIDE Compare the sums in row 18 and decide.

	A	B	C	D	E	F
1						
2		The PACED Decision-Making Model				
3						
4	Decision:					
5						
6				ALTERNATIVES		
7						
8		VALUES	I	II	III	IV
9	CRITERIA	1 TO 10				
10						
11	LIST	ASSIGN	← ASSIGN VALUES TO THE →			
12	CRITERIA	VALUES FROM		ALTERNATIVES		
13	HERE	1 TO 10	0	1	2	. . .
14		TO THE				
15		CRITERIA				
16						
17						
18	TOTALS		Sum	Sum	Sum	

Example. Marie and Alex used the PACED model to assist in deciding which used car to buy. As a result of good shopping, they were able to reduce the choices to 3 alternatives—a sedan, a coupe, and a convertible.

The criteria on which they planned to make their choice were the model, colour, year, condition, price, metrage, and down payment. They assigned values from 1 to 10 to the criteria and rated the alternatives in order (values 2, 1, 0) as follows:

model: 8 convertible, sedan, coupe
colour: 7 sedan, coupe, convertible
year: 5 coupe, sedan, and convertible are the same
condition: 10 sedan, convertible, coupe
price: 2 sedan, coupe, convertible
metrage: 4 sedan, convertible, coupe
down pay't: 6 convertible, sedan, coupe

Complete a spreadsheet to rate each car based on the criteria.

Solution:

P: Identify the decision needed in cell B4.

A: List the alternatives in cells C9, D9, E9.

C: List the criteria in cells A10, A11, ... A16.
List the assigned criteria values in column B.

E: Assign values 2, 1, or 0 to the alternatives and list in columns C, D, and E.
Multiply the criteria values by the alternative values.
(e.g., B10*C10, B11*C11, ... B16*C16)
Place the sum for each alternative in row 18.
(e.g., B10*C10+B11*C11+ ... +B16*C16)

D: Examine the totals in row 18 and decide.

	A	B	C	D	E	F
1						
2		The PACED Decision-Making Model				
3						
4	Decision:	Selecting and buying a used car				
5						
6			ALTERNATIVES			
7						
8		VALUES	I	II	III	IV
9	CRITERIA	1 TO 10	SEDAN	COUPE	CONVERT	
10	Model	8.00	1.00	0.00	2.00	
11	Colour	7.00	2.00	1.00	0.00	
12	Year	5.00	0.00	2.00	0.00	
13	Condition	10.00	2.00	0.00	1.00	
14	Price	2.00	2.00	1.00	0.00	
15	Metrage	4.00	2.00	0.00	1.00	
16	Down Pay't	6.00	1.00	0.00	2.00	
17						
18	TOTALS		60.00	19.00	42.00	

EXERCISE 15.2

1. Complete the following charts to determine which alternatives have the highest score.

(a)

Decision: Choose a vehicle				
Criteria/Value		Alternatives		
		I Truck	II Wagon	III Van
Cost	5	2	1	0
Work	4	0	1	2
Hauling	1	2	0	1
Vacation	2	0	2	1
Camping	3	0	1	2
Pleasure	9	0	2	1
Resale	2	2	0	1
Totals				

(b)

Decision: Select a TV-quiz team					
Criteria/Value		Alternatives			
		I Alice	II Rob	III Moe	IV Sue
History	3	2	3	0	1
Sports	5	0	1	2	3
Trivia	10	3	0	2	1
Quotes	8	1	3	2	0
Arts	6	2	0	1	3
Medicine	2	1	3	0	2
Totals					

(c)

Decision: Select a vacation spot				
Criteria/Value		Alternatives		
		I Tampa	II Banff	III Regina
Ski	10	0	2	1
Football	5	2	0	1
Sunshine	7	2	1	0
Shopping	4	0	1	2
Cost	8	0	1	2
Drive	2	0	1	2
Hotel	3	1	2	0
Totals				

2. Complete the following chart to determine the method of travel to New York that receives the highest score.

Decision: Method of travel to New York				
Criteria/Value		Alternatives		
		I Road	I Rail	III Air
Cost	6	2	1	0
Comfort	8	0	1	2
Time	4	1	0	2
Pleasure	9	0	1	2
Schedules	3	2	1	0
Stopovers	8	2	1	0
Sightseeing	7	2	1	0
Totals				

3. Complete the following chart to find which accommodations are best for a school trip: (i) motel on the edge of town at $35 per person, (ii) hotel downtown at $45 per person, (iii) tourist home in midtown at $32.
Most of the places to visit are downtown. The hotel has a heated pool. The tourist home does not have private bathrooms. Transportation costs from the edge of town and from midtown would be $6 per person for the whole trip.
Use the PACED model with a spreadsheet.
(a) Assign values from 1 to 10 to each criterion.
(b) Assign the values 0, 1, or 2 to the alternatives based on each criterion.

Decision: Accommodations for school trip			
Criteria/Value	Alternatives		
	I Motel	II Hotel	III Tourist Home
Distance			
Pool			
Cost			
Comfort			
Privacy			
Totals			

4. Set up a spreadsheet to determine your choice of a bicycle. The choices are:
a red 10-speed for $349.50,
a black mountain bike for $299.95, and
a silver motocross for $275.00.
The criteria are price, general road use, colour, durability, and resale value.
(a) Assign values from 1 to 10 to each criterion.
(b) Assign the values 0, 1, or 2 to the alternative models of bicycle based on each criterion.

Decision: Choose a bicycle			
Criteria/ Value	Alternatives		
	I 10-Speed	II Mntn.	III Mtocrs.
Price General Colour Durability Resale			
Totals			

5. Set up a spreadsheet to find your choice of camera equipment.
The choices are Disc Camera, Automatic Focus Compact, and Automatic Focus Single Lens Reflex (SLR).
The criteria are basic price, ease of use, quality of pictures, flexibility, carrying ease, and cost of film.
(a) Assign values from 0 to 10 to each criterion.
(b) Assign the values 0, 1, or 2 to each model of camera based on each criterion.

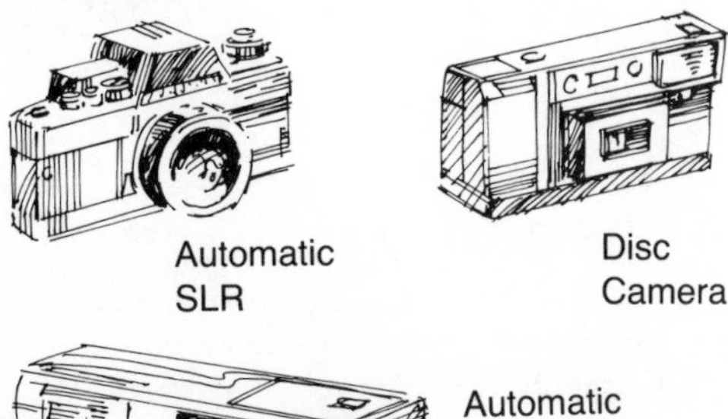

6. Set up a spreadsheet to predict the order of finish for four baseball teams.
(a) Select any four teams.
(b) Use the following criteria.
Batting
Pitching
Errors
Base stealing
Current standing

7. Set up a spreadsheet to determine your choice of college upon completion of high school.
(a) Use the criteria below.
(b) Assign your own criteria values.
(c) Select three colleges you would like to attend.

Decision: Choose a college			
Criteria/Value	Alternatives		
	I	II	III
Distance			
Cost			
Programs			
Standards			
Residence			
Athletics			
Size			
Totals			

15.3 COMPOUND INTEREST TABLES AND SPREADSHEETS

A spreadsheet can be constructed to generate a compound interest table using the formula

$A = P(1 + I)^N$

where A is the amount
P is the principal
I is the rate of interest for one interest period
N is the number of interest periods

Example. Set up a spreadsheet to generate a table of values for $1(1 + I)^N$ giving 40 interest periods for the interest rates
0.5%, 1.0%, 1.5%, 2.0%, 2.5%, 3.0%, 3.5%.

Solution:

Setting P = 1 in the formula, $A = P(1 + I)^N$, we are able to have the computer print a table of accumulation factors.

Enter the spreadsheet title in A1: Amount of 1(1 + I)^N.

Format the left column, A, of the spreadsheet with column width 3, and the number of fixed decimal places 0.

Enter the following headings in Row 3:
N 0.5% 1.0% 1.5% 2.0% 2.5% 3.0% 3.5%

Enter the numbers 1, 2, 3, ..., 40 in cells A5 to A44.

The cell entries shown in red in the table will generate the inside rows and columns of the spreadsheet.

	A	B	C	D	E	F	G	H
1	Amount of 1(1 + I)^N							
2								
3	N	.5%	1.0%	1.5%	2.0%	2.5%	3.0%	3.5%
4								
5	1	1.005^A5	1.01^A5	1.015^A5	1.02^A5	1.025^A5	1.03^A5	1.035^A5
6	2	1.005^A6	1.01^A6	1.015^A6	1.02^A6	1.025^A6	1.03^A6	1.035^A6
7	3	1.005^A7	1.01^A7	1.015^A7	1.02^A7	1.025^A7	1.03^A7	1.035^A7
8	4	1.005^A8	1.01^A8	1.015^A8	1.02^A8	1.025^A8	1.03^A8	1.035^A8

This process will generate the following table.

Amount of 1(1 + I)^n

N	0.5%	1.0%	1.5%	2.0%	2.5%	3.0%	3.5%
1	1.005	1.01	1.015	1.02	1.025	1.03	1.035
2	1.010025	1.0201	1.030225	1.0404	1.050625	1.0609	1.071225
3	1.015075	1.030301	1.045678	1.061208	1.076890	1.092727	1.108717
4	1.020150	1.040604	1.061363	1.082432	1.103812	1.125508	1.147523
			1.077284	1.104080	1.131408	1.159274	1.187686

The real power of the spreadsheet is realized even more when the COPY command is used. Our work can be simplified if we copy the formula in cell B5 (1.005^A5) to the range of cells B6..B44. In spreadsheet terminology, copying a formula from a source cell (in this case B5) to a destination cell or range of cells (in this case B6..B44) is called replication. When copying a cell which contains a formula (such as B5), some spreadsheets will ask for each value in the formula if the value is relative to the position of the cell or is a direct copy.

In the example, when we copy the formula 1.005^A5 from B5 to B6, we want the value in B6 to be based on the value in A6, and not on the value in A5. The spreadsheet will use relative values and copy 1.005^A6 into B6, and then 1.005^A7 into B7. The column can be completed in one step by copying across the range B6..B44 as follows.

Copy from B5 to B6 .. B44

Copy from C5 to C6 .. C44

Copy from H5 to H6 .. H44

	A	B	C	D	E	F	G	H
1	Amount of 1(1 + I)^N							
2								
3	N	0.5%	1.0%	1.5%	2.0%	2.5%	3.0%	3.5%
4								
5	1	1.005	1.01	1.015	1.02	1.025	1.03	1.035
6	2	1.010025	1.0201	1.030225	1.0404	1.050625	1.0609	1.071225
7	3	1.015075	1.030301	1.045678	1.061208	1.076890	1.092727	1.108717
8	4	1.020150	1.040604	1.061363	1.082432	1.103812	1.125508	1.147523
9	5	1.025251	1.051010	1.077284	1.104080	1.131408	1.159274	1.187686
10	6	1.030377	1.061520	1.093443	1.126162	1.159693	1.194052	1.229255
11	7	1.035529	1.072135	1.109844	1.148685	1.188685	1.229873	1.272279
12	8	1.040707	1.082856	1.126492	1.171659	1.218402	1.266770	1.316809
13	9	1.045910	1.093685	1.143389	1.195092	1.248862	1.304773	1.362897
14	10	1.051140	1.104622	1.160540	1.218994	1.280084	1.343916	1.410598
15	11	1.056395	1.115668	1.177948	1.243374	1.312086	1.384233	1.459969
16	12	1.061677	1.126825	1.195618	1.268241	1.344888	1.425760	1.511068
17	13	1.066986	1.138093	1.213552	1.293606	1.378511	1.468533	1.563956

It should be pointed out that discrepancies that appear between spreadsheet values and values in printed tables are often due to the number of decimal places used.

EXERCISE 15.3

B 1. (a) Print out the complete table for Example 1.
(b) Extend the table to include accumulation factors 1, 2, 3, ..., 50.

2. Set up a spreadsheet to generate a table of accumulation factors for 1(1 + I)^N giving 40 interest periods for the interest rates
4.0%, 4.5%, 5.0%, 5.5%, 6.0%, 6.5%, 7.0%.

3. Use a spreadsheet to generate a table to show how an investment of $1.00 at 1% interest per month will grow in two years if interest is compounded monthly.

4. Use a spreadsheet to generate a table to compare how a principal of $1000 will grow over a 36 month period if the monthly interest is
(a) 0.8% (b) 1.0% (c) 1.2% (d) 1.4%

5. (a) The present value, PV, of an amount, A, is found using the formula

$$PV = A(1 + I)^{-N}$$

or

$$PV = \frac{A}{(1 + I)^N}$$

Design a spreadsheet to generate a table of the present values of an amount of 1, giving values for
N = 1, 2, 3, ..., 40
and using the interest rates
0.5%, 1.0%, 1.5%, 2.0%, 2.5%, 3.0%, 3.5%.

6. Set up a spreadsheet to generate a table of present values of 1 using 1/(1 + I)^N giving 40 interest periods for the interest rates
4.0%, 4.5%, 5.0%, 5.5%, 6.0%, 6.5%, 7.0%.

7. Use a spreadsheet to generate a table to compare the present value of an amount of $1000 over 36 months if the monthly interest rates are
(a) 1.8% (b) 1.0%
(c) 1.2% (d) 1.4%

EXTRA

BURNING WOOD

Everyone knows that wood burns at a very high temperature. This burning is a chemical process that combines oxygen and carbon. The process occurs at very low temperatures as well as at very high ones. At high temperatures the process is spectacular — fire. At low temperatures (room temperature) you won't even notice it, although it is still going on. Wood is always burning.

The speed of a chemical reaction diminishes with the lowering of its temperature. For a drop of 10°C the time of the reaction is doubled.
For example, if a substance burns completely in one second at 100°C, then at 90°C it will burn completely in two seconds, at 80°C in $2^2 = 4$ s, at 70°C in $2^3 = 8$ s, and so on.

Suppose a quantity of wood burns completely in one second at 620°C. How long will it take to burn at 20°C?

By using the general law, we see that there is a drop of 600°C, or $600 \div 10 = 60$ intervals of 10° each. Therefore, it will take 2^{60} s for the wood to burn completely. To get an approximation of this time we use the fact that $2^{10} = 1024$, which is approximately equal to 1000;

$$\therefore 2^{60} = (2^{10})^6 \doteq (1000)^6$$
$$\doteq (10^3)^6 \doteq 10^{18}$$

The burning time is 10^{18} s or about 33 billion years.

Wood is constantly burning no matter what its temperature. We observe this burning only when heat speeds up the combustion.

1. A quantity of wood burns completely in one second at 600°C. How long will it take the wood to burn if it is on the sun where the temperature is 6000°C?

15.4 SPREADSHEET APPLICATIONS WITH THE QUADRATIC FORMULA

The roots of the quadratic equation $ax^2 + bx + c = 0$ can be found using the quadratic formulas

$$x = \frac{-b \pm \sqrt{b^2 - 4ac}}{2a}$$

For example, to find the roots of the quadratic equation $3x^2 - 2x - 2 = 0$, the values $a = 3$, $b = -2$, and $c = -2$ are substituted into the quadratic formulas:

$$x = \frac{-b + \sqrt{b^2 - 4ac}}{2a} \quad \text{and} \quad x = \frac{-b - \sqrt{b^2 - 4ac}}{2a}$$

When a spreadsheet is used, we place the formulas into two cells. The data for a, b, and c are placed in other cells and the roots are calculated automatically.
In this spreadsheet, the following commands are used.

Operation	Function	Example
square root exponentiation	@SQRT ^	@SQRT(A*B) means $\sqrt{a \times b}$ 2^2 means 2^2

The formulas to enter into the spreadsheet are

$(-b + \sqrt{b^2 - 4ac})/(2a)$ and $(-b - \sqrt{b^2 - 4ac})/(2a)$

(−B+@SQRT(B^2−4*A*C))/(2*A)
(−B−@SQRT(B^2−4*A*C))/(2*A)

In the following spreadsheet, the quadratic formulas are entered in cells C6 and C9. The value for a is entered in B7, for b in B8, and for c in B9. The formulas then relate the values to the cell locations as shown.

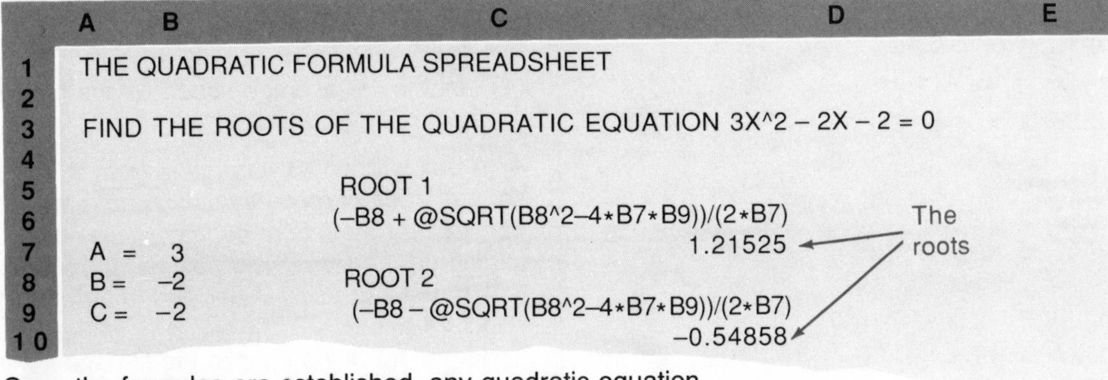

Once the formulas are established, any quadratic equation can be solved. Entering new values for a, b, and c in cells B7, B8, and B9, respectively, will generate the roots of the new equation.

EXERCISE 15.4

B

1. The following is an example of the spreadsheet from the previous page under a different format.

	A	B	C	D	E
1	THE QUADRATIC FORMULA				
2	SPREADSHEET				
3	Write the equation below.				
4					
5	3X^2 − 2X − 2 =0				
6					
7	Enter the coefficients below.				
8	A =	3			
9	B =	−2			
10	C =	−2			
11	The roots are:				
12	(−B9+@SQRT(B9^2−4*B8*B10))/(2*B8)				
13			1.21525		
14	(−B9−@SQRT(B9^2−4*B8*B10))/(2*B8)				
15			−0.54858		
16					
17					
18					
19					
20					

Use the spreadsheet to solve the following equations.

(a) $5x^2 + 3x - 2 = 0$
(b) $x^2 - 5x + 6 = 0$
(c) $4x^2 - 4x + 1 = 0$
(d) $5x^2 + x - 6 = 0$
(e) $-3x^2 + 2x + 7 = 0$
(f) $4x^2 - x - 5 = 0$
(g) $2x^2 + 3x - 4 = 0$
(h) $-x^2 + 5x - 6 = 0$
(i) $-7x^2 - 3x + 7 = 0$
(j) $4x^2 - 7x + 3 = 0$
(k) $1.25x^2 + 3.65x - 2.47 = 0$
(l) $3.05x^2 - 6.25x - 3.2 = 0$
(m) $4.50x^2 - 10.25x + 5.75 = 0$

2. A rectangular flower garden 12.7 m by 9.2 m is to be surrounded by a walk equal in area to the area of the garden.

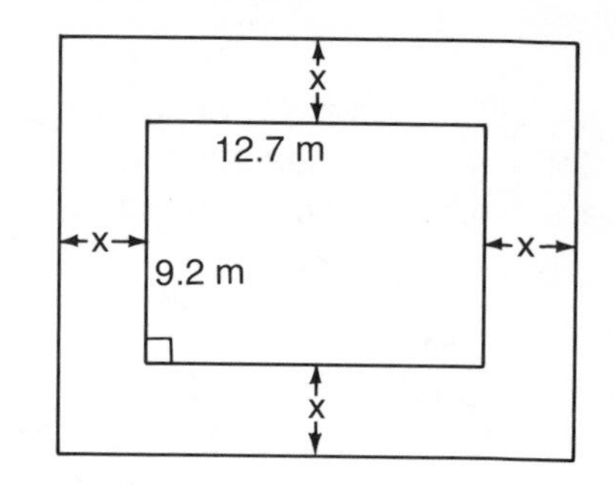

(a) Guess the width of the walk.
(b) Make an estimate by calculating with rounded numbers.
(c) Solve the following equation to find the width of the walk to the nearest tenth of a metre.
$$4.00x^2 + 43.80x - 116.84 = 0$$

3. A messenger travels a distance of 400 km by car at one speed and returns immediately by the same route at an average speed which is 10 km/h faster.
(a) Guess the speed.
(b) Use rounded numbers to estimate the average speed for the round trip.
(c) Solve the following quadratic equation to find the average speed going.
$$8.56x^2 - 714.40x - 4000 = 0$$
(d) What is the average speed for the return trip?

4. A box with no lid was made from a square piece of metal by cutting squares 4.5 cm by 4.5 cm from each corner and folding up the sides. The volume of the box was measured using water and found to be about 2485 cm³.
Solve the following equation to find the original size of the piece of metal.
$$x^2 - 18x - 471.22 = 0$$
Give your answer to the nearest tenth of a centimetre.

15.5 PERIMETER, AREA, VOLUME, AND THE SPREADSHEET

Spreadsheets can be used to calculate perimeter, area, and volume by placing a formula in a cell. When data to be substituted into the formula are placed in other cells, the output can be calculated automatically.

When entering a formula, great care must be taken to express the formula in terms of the cells where the values to be substituted are located. For example, if the value for N is located in cell B6, then the formula $S = N(N+1)/2$ must be entered as 0.5*B6*(B6+1)

Note that the formula is the same, except that N is replaced by B6. This means that the value for N is located in cell B6. In the following example, the constant "pi", $\pi = 3.1415926...$ will be used. In the spreadsheet, pi is entered using the @PI function.

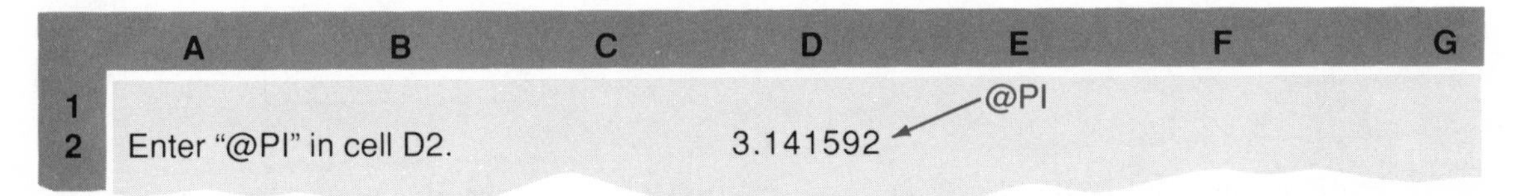

Example. (a) Set up a spreadsheet to calculate the circumference and area of a circle.
(b) Set up a spreadsheet to calculate the surface area and volume of a sphere.
(c) Find the circumference and area of a circle with radius 4.5 cm.
(d) Find the surface area and volume of a sphere with radius 7.2 cm.

Solution:

(i) Set the column width at 13 characters to accommodate some of the longer headings.
(ii) Set all figures to display 3 decimal places.
(iii) Enter the information as shown below.
(iv) Enter 4.5 in cell B5, and enter 7.2 in cell B13.

	A	B	C	D	E
1	PERIMETER, AREA, AND VOLUME SPREADSHEET				
2					
3	CIRCLE				
4				Entered	
5	Radius R =	4.500			
6	Circumference			2*@PI*B5	
7	C = 2*@PI*R	28.274			
8	Area			@PI*B5^2	
9	A = @PI*R^2	63.617			
10					
11	SPHERE				
12				Entered	
13	Radius R =	7.200		4*@PI*B13^2	
14	Surface area	651.441			
15	SA = 4*@PI*R^2			4/3@PI*B13^3	
16	Volume	1563.458			
17	V = 4/3*@PI*R^3				

EXERCISE 15.5

B

1. The formula for the perimeter of a triangle is

$$P = a + b + c$$

where a, b, c are the lengths of the three sides.

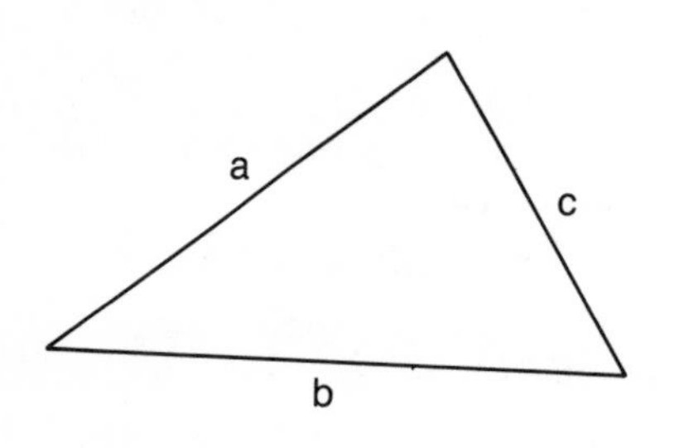

(a) Write the formula for perimeter of a triangle on a spreadsheet if the value for a is in cell B6, for b is in cell B7, and for c is in cell B8.

(b) Use your spreadsheet to find the perimeter of a triangle with sides 3.5 cm, 2.8 cm, and 4.7 cm.

2. The formula for area of a triangle is

$$A = 0.5bh$$

where b is the base of the triangle and h is the height.

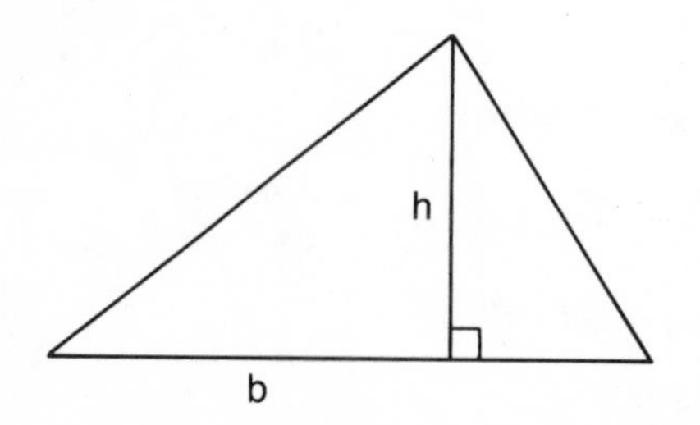

(a) Write the formula for a spreadsheet if the base, b, is in cell B6 and the height, h, is in cell B7.

(b) Use a spreadsheet to find the area of a triangle with base 8.7 cm and height 7.2 cm.

3. A square has sides, s. The formulas for perimeter and area of a square are, respectively,

$$P = 4s$$
$$A = s^2$$

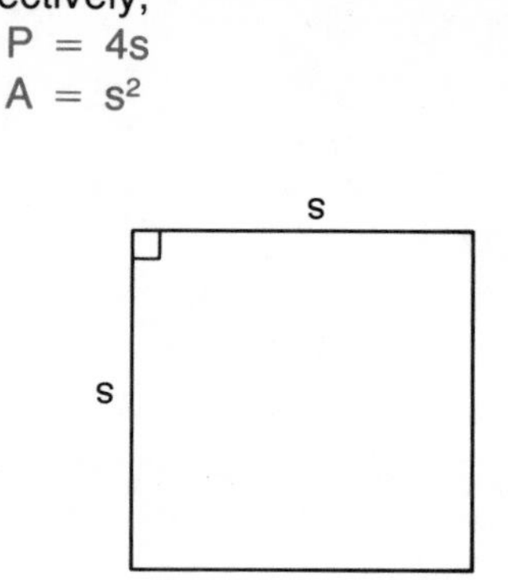

(a) Write the formulas for perimeter and area of a square if the value of s is entered in cell A3.

(b) Set up a spreadsheet to find the perimeter and area of a square having sides 12.5 cm.

4. The formulas for perimeter and area of a rectangle are, respectively,

$$P = 2(\ell + w)$$
$$A = \ell w$$

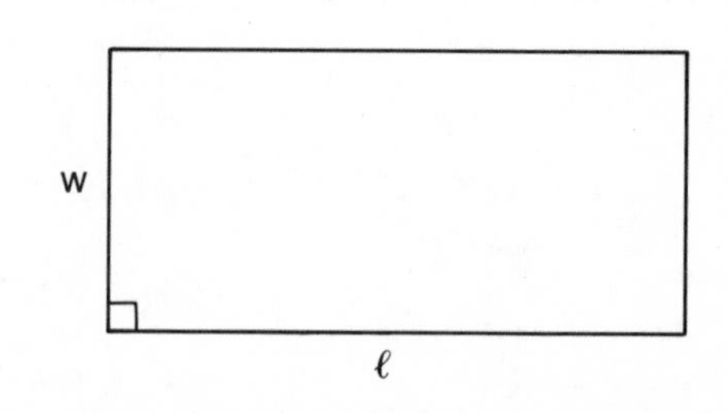

(a) Write the formulas for perimeter and area of a rectangle if the value of ℓ is entered in cell A7 and the value of w is in cell B7.

(b) Set up a spreadsheet to find the perimeter and area of a rectangle with length 7.5 cm and width 6.4 cm.

5. The formula for area of a parallelogram is

$A = bh$

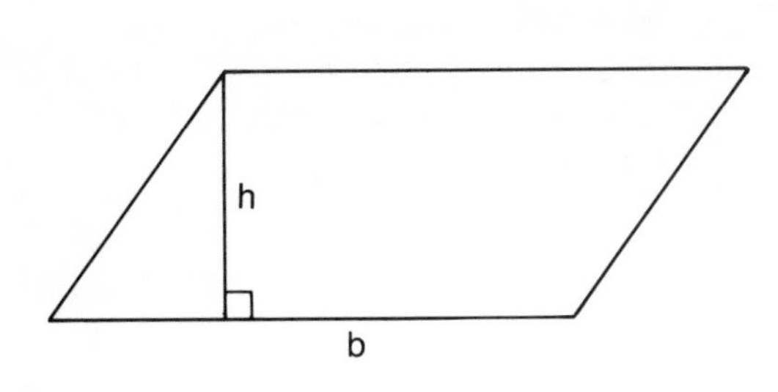

(a) Write a formula for the area of a parallelogram on a spreadsheet if the value of b is located in cell C5, and the value of h is in cell D5.

(b) Use a spreadsheet to find the area of a parallelogram with base 12.3 cm and height 8.7 cm.

6. The area of a trapezoid is given by the formula

$A = 0.5(a + b)h$

where a and b are the parallel bases, and h is the height (or distance between the parallel lines).

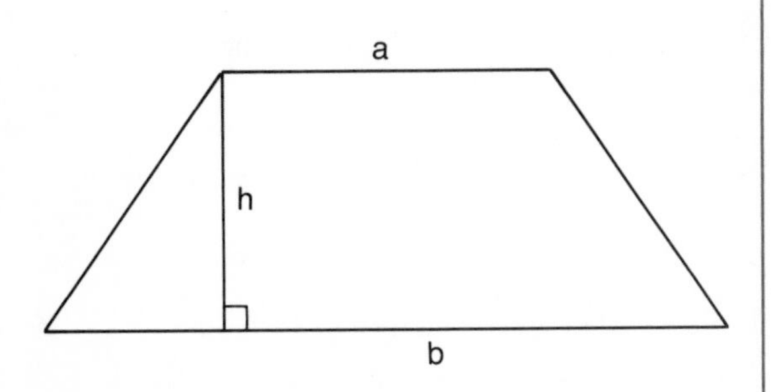

(a) Set up a spreadsheet and write the spreadsheet formula for the area of a trapezoid if the value for a is in cell B6, b is in cell B7, and h is in cell B8.

(b) Find the area of a trapezoid with bases 12.6 cm and 10.4 cm if the height of the figure is 12.2 cm.

7. The value for the edge of a cube, s, is located in cell B3. The formulas for surface area and volume are, respectively,

$SA = 6s^2$

$V = s^3$

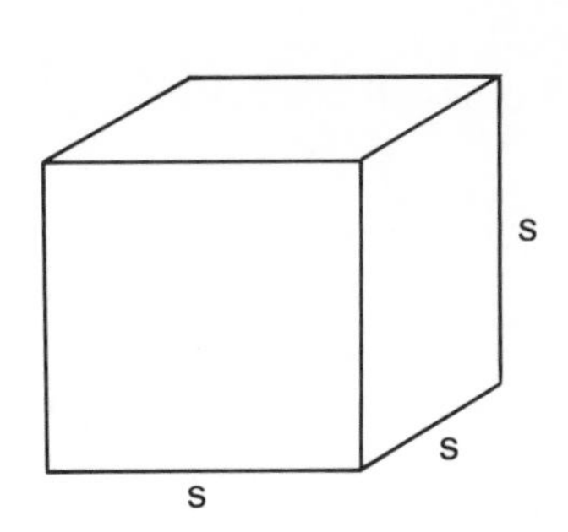

(a) Write the spreadsheet formulas for the surface area and volume of a cube.

(b) Set up a spreadsheet and find the surface area and volume of a cube having edges of 5.7 cm.

8. The formulas for a rectangular prism are

$SA = 2(\ell w + \ell h + wh)$

$V = \ell wh$

The value for ℓ is located in cell B5, w is located in cell B6, and h is located in cell B7.

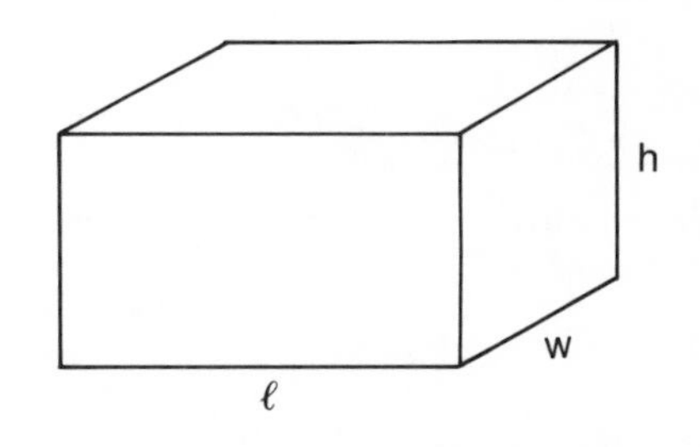

(a) Write the formulas for surface area and volume of a rectangular prism on a spreadsheet.

(b) Set up a spreadsheet and find the surface area and volume of a rectangular prism having dimensions 6.8 cm, 10.4 cm, and 8.4 cm.

9. The formula for surface area of a square-base pyramid is

$$SA = 4(0.5bs) + b^2$$

where b is the length of the base, and s is the slant height.
The formula for volume is

$$V = b^2h/3$$

where b is the length of the base, and h is the height.

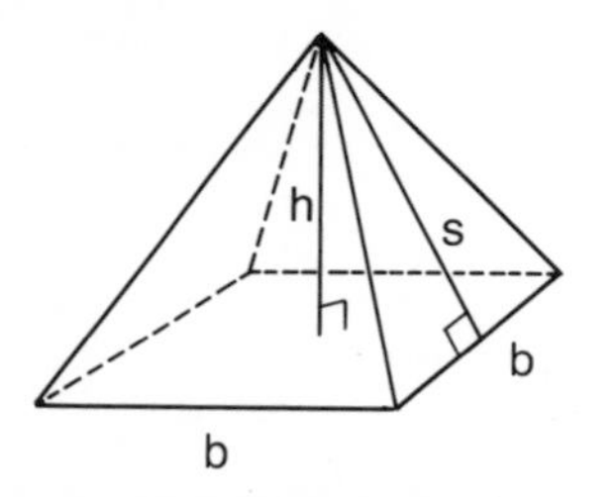

(a) Set up a spreadsheet to calculate surface area and volume if b is located in cell A6 and h is located in cell A7. s is found using another formula.

$$s = \sqrt{h^2 + (0.5b)^2}$$

The formula for s can be written

@SQRT(H^2+(0.5*B)^2)

(Remember to express the values for h and b in terms of cell location when you enter the formula on the spreadsheet.)

(b) Find the surface area and volume of a rectangular pyramid having base 12.5 cm and height 10 cm using the spreadsheet.

10. The formulas for surface area and volume of a cylinder are

$$SA = 2\pi r(h + r)$$
$$V = \pi r^2h$$

The value of r is located in cell C4, and the value for h is in cell C5.

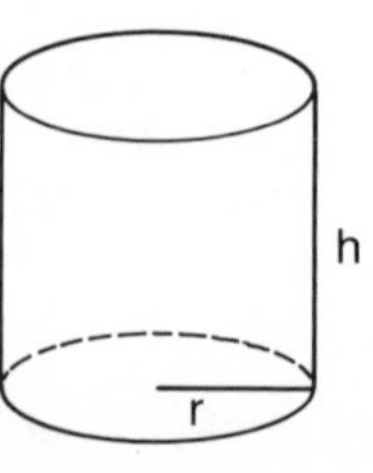

(a) Write spreadsheet formulas for surface area and volume of a cylinder.

(b) Set up a spreadsheet and find the surface area and volume of a cylinder with radius 6.5 and height 15.2 cm.

11. The surface area and volume formulas for a cone are

$$SA = \pi r^2 + \pi rs$$
$$= \pi r(r + s)$$
$$V = \pi r^2h/3$$

The value of r is located in cell B6 and h is in B7. The slant height, s, can be found using the formula $\sqrt{r^2 + h^2}$.

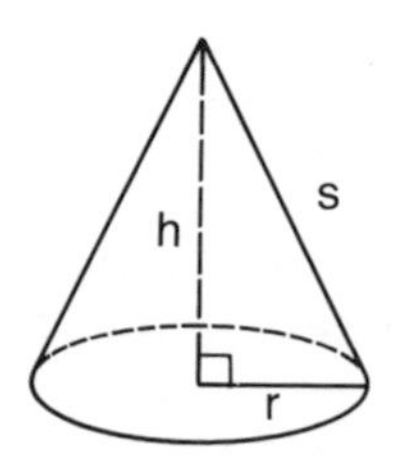

(a) Write the spreadsheet formulas for surface area and volume of a cone.

(b) Set up a spreadsheet and find the surface area and volume of a cone with radius 12.4 cm and height 15 cm.

12. The formula for the volume of the frustum of a cone is

$$V = \frac{\pi}{3}h(a^2 + ab + b^2)$$

where a is the radius of the top of the frustum, b is the radius of the base, and h is the height of the frustum.

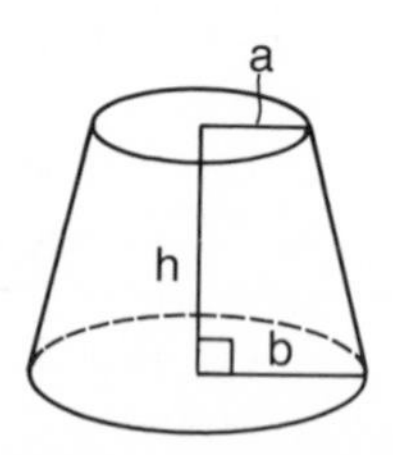

(a) Set up a spreadsheet to find the volume of a frustum of a cone.

(b) Use the spreadsheet to find the volume of a frustum of a cone with small radius 2.4 m, large radius 3.2 m, and height 4.2 m.

15.6 TRIGONOMETRIC FUNCTIONS AND SPREADSHEETS

Many spreadsheets have built in the primary trigonometric functions—sine, cosine, and tangent.

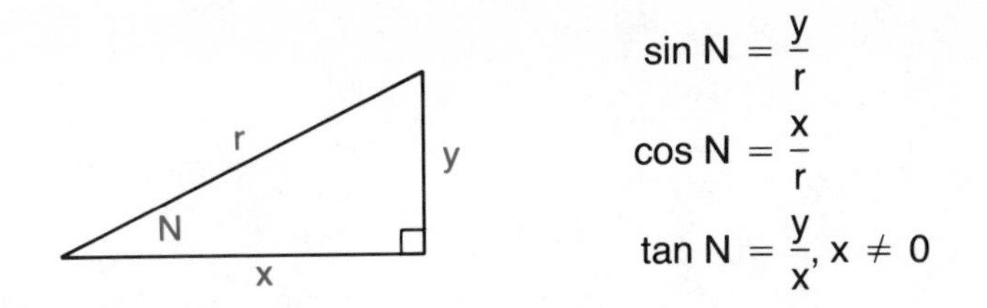

$$\sin N = \frac{y}{r}$$

$$\cos N = \frac{x}{r}$$

$$\tan N = \frac{y}{x}, x \neq 0$$

Most of these spreadsheet functions use radian measure for angles instead of degrees. The diagram shows an angle equal to 1 rad, where r is the length of the radius. This means that

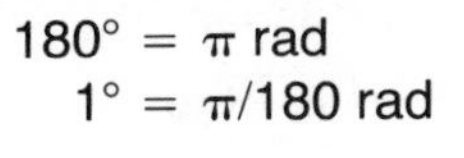

$$180^\circ = \pi \text{ rad}$$
$$1^\circ = \pi/180 \text{ rad}$$

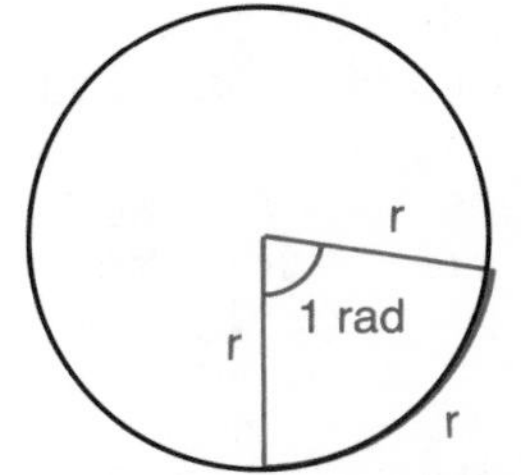

We use the following formula to change radians to degrees in the spreadsheet.

$$N^\circ = N(\pi/180) \text{ rad}$$

The value π can be entered into the spreadsheet using the @ pi function. The trigonometric functions are entered using @SIN, @COS, or @TAN. The symbol @ defines a function for most spreadsheet packages. Using the following functions, it is possible to calculate the trigonometric values for any angle measured in degrees.

@SIN(N*@PI/180)

@COS(N*@PI/180)

@TAN(N*@PI/180)

When entering formulas in spreadsheets, the value for angle N is placed in cell A4 and the formula in B4 is

@SIN(A4*@PI/180)

as in Example 1.

Example 1. Set up a spreadsheet to calculate values of sin N.
Use your spreadsheet to calculate sin 30°.

Solution:
Place headings above the appropriate columns in the spreadsheet. Locate the angle N in column A and the trigonometric function values for sin N in column B.

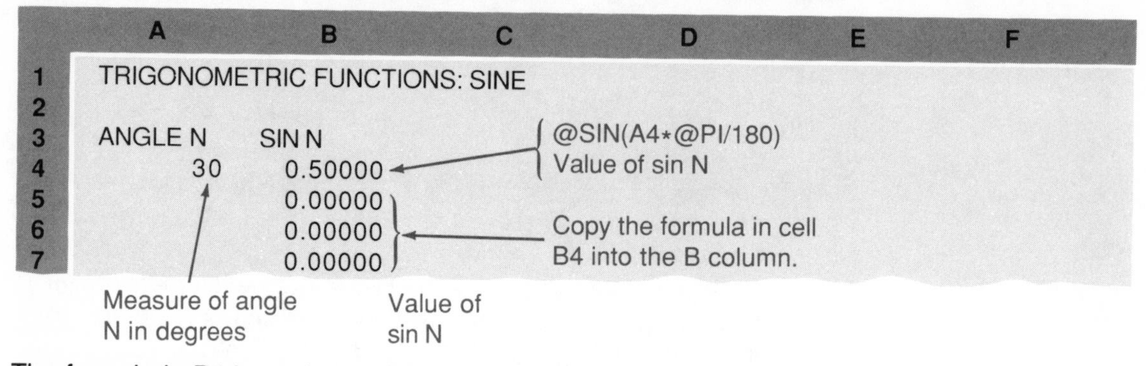

The formula in B4 is copied to the B column of cells using COPY. When additional values for angle N are entered in the A column, the corresponding value for sin N appears in the B column. This process is called replicating the formula.

Example 2. Set up a spreadsheet to calculate the values of the primary trigonometric ratios, sine, cosine, and tangent for the following angle measures:
0°, 1°, 2°, 3°, 4°, 5°, 10°, 15°, 20°, 30°, 40°, 50°, 60°, 70°, 80°, 90°.

Solution:
Extending the results of Example 1, set up columns for the cosine and tangent values. The cosine and tangent formulas are @COS(A4*@PI/180) and @TAN(A4*@PI/180)

	A	B	C	D	E
1	TRIGONOMETRIC FUNCTIONS: SINE, COSINE, TANGENT				
2					
3	ANGLE N	@SIN(A4*@PI/180)	@COS(A4*@PI/180)	@TAN(A4*@PI/180)	
4	0	0.00000	1.00000	0.00000	
5	1	0.01745	0.99985	0.01746	
6	2	0.03490	0.99939	0.03492	
7	3	0.05234	0.99863	0.05241	
8	4	0.06976	0.99756	0.06993	
9	5	0.08716	0.99619	0.08749	
10	10	0.17365	0.98481	0.17633	
11	15	0.25882	0.96593	0.26795	
12	20	0.34202	0.93969	0.36397	
13	30	0.50000	0.86603	0.57735	
14	40	0.64279	0.76604	0.83910	
15	50	0.76604	0.64279	1.19175	Tan 90° is
16	60	0.86603	0.50000	1.73205	undefined
17	70	0.93969	0.34202	2.74748	and is
18	80	0.98481	0.17365	5.67128	represented
19	90	1.00000	0.00000	*********	by *******

EXERCISE 15.6

B

1. Set up a spreadsheet as follows to find the lengths of the sides of right triangles. Write the formulas for x*TAN N, r*SIN N, and x*COS N. Test your formulas using the examples given below.

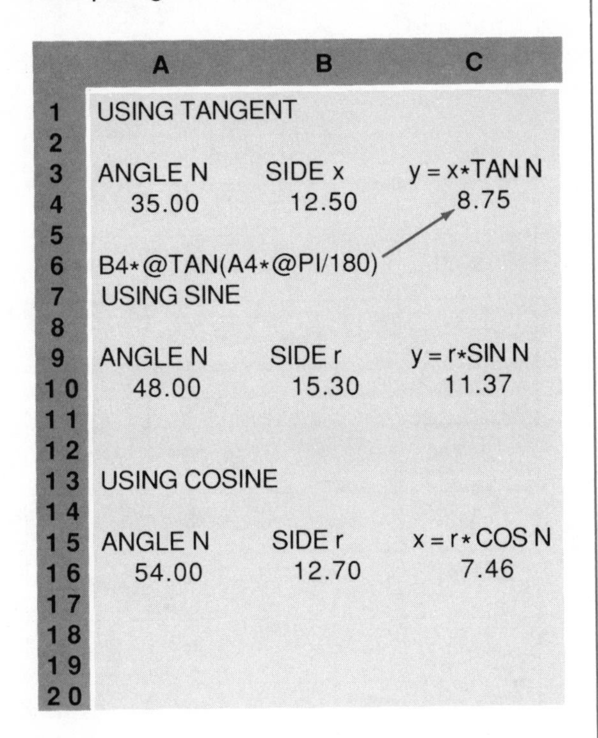

	A	B	C
1	USING TANGENT		
2			
3	ANGLE N	SIDE x	y = x*TAN N
4	35.00	12.50	8.75
5			
6	B4*@TAN(A4*@PI/180)		
7	USING SINE		
8			
9	ANGLE N	SIDE r	y = r*SIN N
10	48.00	15.30	11.37
11			
12			
13	USING COSINE		
14			
15	ANGLE N	SIDE r	x = r*COS N
16	54.00	12.70	7.46
17			
18			
19			
20			

2. Use your spreadsheet to find the length of the indicated side.

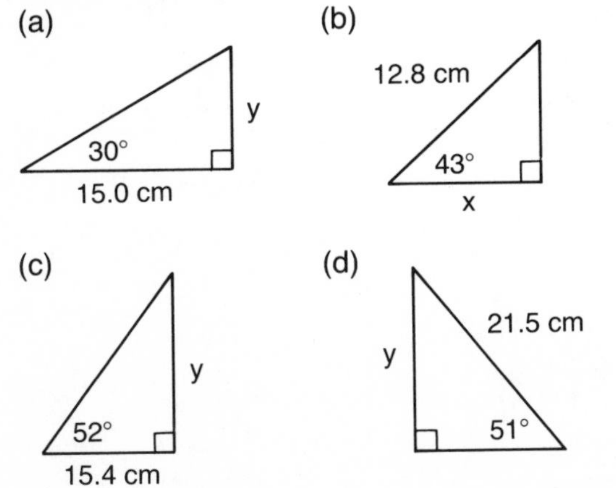

3. (a) Write a spreadsheet formula for
Area = 0.5 ab sin C
to find the area of a triangle.
(b) Set up a spreadsheet and find the area of the given triangles.

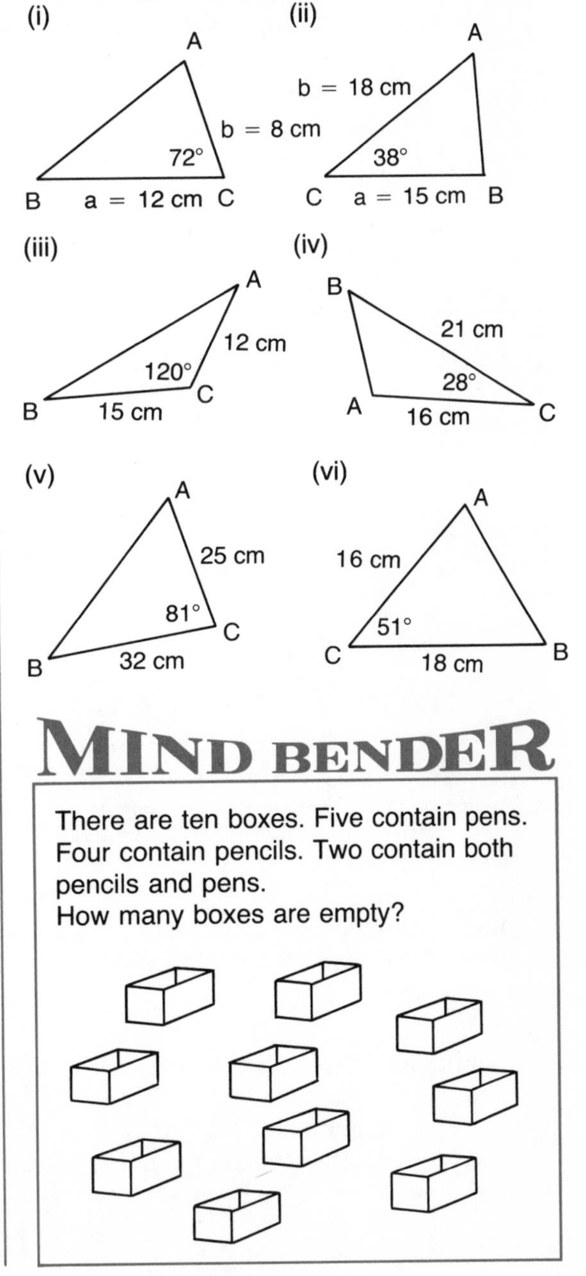

MIND BENDER

There are ten boxes. Five contain pens. Four contain pencils. Two contain both pencils and pens.
How many boxes are empty?

15.7 PORTFOLIOS WITH SPREADSHEETS

The list of investments, such as bonds, investment certificates, or shares on the stock market held by an investor, is called a portfolio. A spreadsheet can be used to calculate the value of a portfolio at any given moment.

Example. The following chart shows an investment portfolio, and the prices of the shares on four consecutive Mondays.

Number of Shares	Name of Company	Price per Share ($)			
		June 2	June 9	June 16	June 23
250	Bank of Montreal	26.50	27.25	25.75	27.00
1000	Canron Inc.	14.50	14.75	13.75	14.25
500	Emco Limited	13.25	13.75	14.50	15.25
200	Federal Industries Inc.	24.50	25.25	26.25	27.50
2000	Haley Industries Ltd.	8.00	8.25	9.25	8.75
3500	IPSCO Inc.	7.75	8.25	8.75	8.25
100	Leon's Furniture Ltd.	24.00	23.75	25.50	25.75
750	Noma Industries Ltd. A	18.25	17.50	17.50	18.00
2500	Omega Hydrocarbons	7.75	8.50	8.75	8.50
150	Torstar Corporation, B	29.50	30.25	31.25	31.75

Use a spreadsheet to calculate the value of the portfolio on each of the consecutive Mondays.

Solution:

Set up the column widths in the spreadsheet with column B at 22 to contain the company names, and columns C, D, E, and F at 10 to contain the portfolio values. Enter the data and formulas to complete the spreadsheet as follows.

	A	B	C	D	E	F
1			STOCK PORTFOLIO			
2	Number of	Name of		Price per share ($)		
3	Shares	Company	June 2	June 9	June 16	June 23
4						
5	250	Bank of Montreal	26.50	27.25	25.75	27.00
6	1000	Canron Inc.	14.50	14.75	13.75	14.25
7	500	Emco Limited	13.25	13.75	14.50	15.25
8	200	Federal Industries Inc.	24.50	25.25	26.25	27.50
9	2000	Haley Industries Ltd.	8.00	8.25	9.25	8.75
10	3500	IPSCO Inc.	7.75	8.25	8.75	8.25
11	100	Leon's Furniture Ltd.	24.00	23.75	25.50	25.75
12	750	Noma Industries Ltd. A	18.25	17.50	17.50	18.00
13	2500	Omega Hydrocarbons	7.75	8.50	8.75	8.50
14	150	Torstar Corporation, B	29.50	30.25	31.25	31.75
15						
16		TOTAL PORTFOLIO VALUE	115662.50	120150.00	124050.00	122587.50
17	The formula in cell E16:					
18	@ SUM (A5*E5, A6*E6, A7*E7, A8*E8, A9*E9. A10*E10, A11*E11, A12*E12, A13*E13, A14*E14)					

The function @SUM(list) is used to find the TOTAL PORTFOLIO VALUE on each of the given days. Check your spreadsheet manual to determine how to use the @SUM function.

EXERCISE 15.7

B 1. (a) Use a spreadsheet to calculate the value of each of the following portfolios.

(b) Update the value of each portfolio using share prices in your daily newspaper.

(i) Portfolio for Jessie Lima

Name of Company	Price per Share ($)	Number of Shares
American Express	58.50	50
AT&T	27.75	100
Colgate Palmolive	51.75	50
Firestone Tire	39.25	150
PepsiCo	37.25	100
Sterling Drugs	43.75	75
F.W. Woolworth	58.25	50
Xerox Corp.	81.25	75

(ii) Portfolio for Timothy Fong

Name of Company	Price per Share ($)	Number of Shares
Bank of Montreal	25.50	200
Cominco Limited	17.75	1000
Great Lakes Forest Ltd.	45.25	100
Magna International Inc.	24.25	500
Parkland Industries Ltd.	9.75	2000
Shepherd Products Ltd.	14.75	500
Fujitsu Limited	32.75	600
Innopac Ltd	10.25	800
CCL Industries Ltd. A	15.25	400
CCL Industries Ltd. B	14.50	1000

(iii) Portfolio for Tiia and Emile Labine

Name of Company	Price per Share ($)	Number of Shares
Alco	11 5/8	500
Bank of British Columbia	22 1/2	600
Bombardier A	23 3/4	400
Bow Valley	18 7/8	1200
Campeau	23	300
Chieftan	14 5/8	200
Comtech	3.90	3000
Denison A	7.50	1000

2. Helen Roberts has the following portfolio. Share prices quoted are correct as of the same base date.

Name of Mutual Fund	Price per Share ($)	Number of Shares
Bolton Tremslay Canadian	16.83	200
Canada Trust Income	9.71	100
First City Growth	5.32	1000
Investors Group Mutual	9.00	400
Montreal Trust Equity	29.72	100
Royfund Equity	22.43	300
Templeton Canadian	6.41	800
Trimark Canadian	11.80	1000

(a) Use a spreadsheet to calculate the value of the portfolio using the share prices given above.
(b) Obtain current share prices from your daily newspaper, and update the value of the portfolio.
(c) What is the change in the value of the portfolio?

3. Some lower priced stocks are quite volatile. Share prices fluctuate rapidly. The following portfolio is taken from the Vancouver Stock Exchange. Unless otherwise stated, prices are quoted in cents.

Name of Company Stock	Price per Share	Number of Shares
Andaurex	75	3000
Arctic Red	45	1000
BC Telephone	$28	100
Emir Oils	66	2000
Fleetwood	64	1000
Inter Globe	67	3000
Iron Horse	22	2000
Night Hawk	210	500
Racer Resources	48	500
Taurus A	105	400
Zuni Energy	175	500

(a) Use a spreadsheet to calculate the value of the portfolio using the share prices given above.
(b) Obtain current share prices from your daily newspaper under Vancouver Stocks and update the value of the portfolio.

Determine the pattern and find the missing number.

8	9	8	7
5	11		15
3	4	8	12
19	25	54	69

15.8 STOCK MARKET INDEXES WITH SPREADSHEETS

In order to know how the stock market is performing, analysts keep track of a small group of the over 15 000 stocks that are available. Such a group of individual stocks is used to calculate an index. Indexes are used to provide a consistent measurement of the stock market's performance. Examples of popular indexes are the Dow Jones Industrial Average, the Standard & Poor's 500 Index, and the Toronto Stock Exchange 300 Index.

PRICE-WEIGHTED INDEX

The Dow Jones Industrial Average measures 30 large industrial companies whose stocks are traded on the New York Stock Exchange. This index is calculated by adding the price per share of all the stocks in the index and dividing by the number of stocks in the index. Originally, this meant that you added the prices for one share of each of the 30 stocks and divided by 30. As stocks began to split (e.g., "two-for-one" means that two new lower priced shares were exchanged for one old higher priced share) the divisor was reduced to keep the index comparable to earlier periods. The shares of companies used by Dow Jones have split so many times that today, the divisor is less than 2, even though over 30 stocks are tracked. This is called a price-weighted index.

$$\text{Price-Weighted Index} = \frac{\text{Sum of share prices}}{\text{Number of stocks}}$$

VALUE-WEIGHTED INDEX

The Standard & Poor's 500 Index tracks a sample of 500 industrial, utility, transportation, and financial stocks. This value-weighted index tracks the entire market value—price per share multiplied by the total number of shares outstanding—of a group of companies instead of the individual price of the shares. The total dollar value of the companies is used to calculate the value of the index.
In order to calculate an index which shows relative change, we take the total market value on any date and divide by the total market value on the base date when the index was first started, and multiply by 100. For example, if the total market value of a group of stocks on the starting base date was $178 425 000 and we wish to calculate an index for a date on which the total market value is $185 372 000, the result is $\frac{185\,372\,000}{178\,425\,000} \times 100 = 103.89351$

$$\text{Total Market value} = \text{Sum of (Price per share} \times \text{Shares outstanding)}$$

$$\text{Value-Weighted Index} = \frac{\text{Total Market Value on Date}}{\text{Total Market Value on Base Date}} \times 100$$

THE TSE 300 COMPOSITE INDEX

"Prices rose sharply on the Toronto Stock Exchange, with the TSE 300 Composite Index up 18.6 at 2768.5."

Radio report

The first stock price index for the Toronto Stock Exchange was compiled in 1934. The current market index was introduced on January 3, 1977 and is called the TSE 300 COMPOSITE INDEX. This index tracks over three-quarters of the dollar value of all Canadian stock trading. In the TSE 300, a total of 300 stocks divided into 14 groups and 41 subgroups are tracked. Each of the stocks, groups, and subgroups are weighted to determine the impact on the total market.

For example, ALCAN contributes 3.29% to the Index, while INCO and NORANDA contribute 1.70% and 0.89%, respectively. These three companies form part of the Metals and Minerals group which contains 25 companies. The Metals and Minerals group contributes more than 9% to the Index.

Following is a list of the 14 groups that make up the TSE 300. The numbers in brackets after each name indicate the number of stocks within that group.

Metals and Minerals (28)
Golds (22)
Oil and Gas (52)
Paper and Forest Products (10)
Consumer Products (20)
Industrial Products (38)
Real Estate and Construction (10)
Transportation (8)
Pipelines (6)
Utilities (16)
Communications and Media (16)
Merchandising (28)
Financial Services (33)
Management Companies (13)

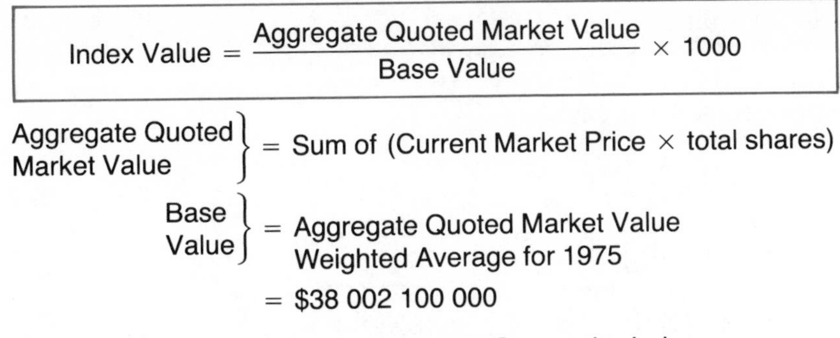

$$\text{Index Value} = \frac{\text{Aggregate Quoted Market Value}}{\text{Base Value}} \times 1000$$

$$\left.\begin{array}{l}\text{Aggregate Quoted}\\ \text{Market Value}\end{array}\right\} = \text{Sum of (Current Market Price} \times \text{total shares)}$$

$$\left.\begin{array}{l}\text{Base}\\ \text{Value}\end{array}\right\} = \begin{array}{l}\text{Aggregate Quoted Market Value}\\ \text{Weighted Average for 1975}\end{array}$$

$$= \$38\ 002\ 100\ 000$$

For example, to calculate the TSE 300 Composite Index on a day in which the Aggregate Quoted Market Value (AQMV) is $125 327 500 000, perform the following calculation:

$$\begin{aligned}\text{Index Value} &= \frac{\text{AQMV}}{\text{Base Value}} \times 1000\\ &= \frac{125\ 327\ 500\ 000}{38\ 002\ 100\ 000} \times 1000\\ &\doteq 3297.9\end{aligned}$$

MAKING YOUR OWN STOCK MARKET INDEX

A simple spreadsheet model can be used to calculate your own stock market index for an industry or segment of the market. Stock market data are readily available in the newspaper, banks, libraries, or stock brokers' offices. Following are some easy steps to developing an index.

Select a group of stocks for your index.
Select stocks with common interests such as banking, retailing, or technology.

Collect the data to make the index.
Collect stock prices, number of outstanding shares, and other data for the base date on which you wish to start the index.

3

Set up the spreadsheet.
Decide on the type of index you want (price-weighted like the Dow Jones, or value-weighted like the Standard & Poor's).
Enter the data for the stocks you have selected to calculate the indexes for that day.

4

Updating the index.
The index can be maintained by entering updated information for a selected date—daily, weekly, monthly.

Example 1. The following list gives the names of five major banks and the value of their stocks on a given date.
Set up a spreadsheet model to calculate a price-weighted index.

Bank of Nova Scotia (BK NS)	\$17 1/4
Bank of Montreal (BK MTL)	\$33 7/8
Royal Bank of Canada (RY BK)	\$32 3/8
Canadian Imperial Bank of Commerce (CIBC)	\$20 1/2
Toronto-Dominion Bank (TD BK)	\$28 1/4

Solution:

	A	B	C	D	E
1	BANKING PRICE-WEIGHTED INDEX				
2	(Sum of share prices)/(Number of stocks)				
3	Symbol	Bank	Price		
4	BK MTL	Bank of Montreal	33.875		
5	BK NS	Bank of Nova Scotia	17.250		
6	CIBC	Canadian Imperial	20.500		
7	RY BK	Royal Bank	32.375		
8	TD BK	Toronto-Dominion	28.250		@SUM(C4..C8)
9					
10		Sum of prices	132.25 ← @SUM(C4..C8)		
11		Number of stocks	5.00		+C10/C11
12					or
13		Price-weighted index	26.45 ← +C10/C11 or (C10/C11)		(C10/C11)
14					

The formulas in column C are transferred to columns D, E, F, .. using the COPY command. The COPY command is used to copy a formula over a range of cells.
To copy the formula @SUM(C4..C8) into the cells D10, E10, F10, .., AG10 we first enter the copy command.

Spreadsheet software	Press
	/C
Enter range	C10 ⟨enter⟩
Enter range to copy	D10..AG10 ⟨enter⟩

To copy the formula +C10/C11 into the cells D13, E13, F13, .., AG13, we continue:

Spreadsheet software	Press
Enter range	C13 ⟨enter⟩
Enter range to copy	D13..AG13 ⟨enter⟩

Example 2. The following list gives the prices of the stocks of nine companies and the outstanding number of shares for each on a given date.

Name of Company	Outstanding Shares	Price per Share ($)
Alberta Energy Co. Ltd.	44 876 570	20 1/2
Bell Canada	246 046 614	25 1/8
Biotech Electronics	5 025 820	3.40
Computrex Centres Ltd.	4 802 600	1.05
Northern Telecom Ltd.	116 562 467	26 5/8
SONY Corporation	231 148 309	31 7/8
McDonalds Corporation	92 179 000	9 1/2
Royal Trustco	46 542 649	17 1/2
Shell Oil	75 215 511	45 7/8

Assume that the total market value on the base date was $7 673 218 542.50.
Set up a spreadsheet model to calculate a value-weighted index.

Solution:

	A	B	C	D	E
1	STUDENT'S VALUE-WEIGHTED INDEX				
2	Sum of (price per share X shares outstanding)				
3			Outstanding	Price per	
4	Symbol	Name of Company	Shares	Share ($)	Value ($)
5		Alberta Energy Co. Ltd.	44876570	20.5	919969685
6		Bell Canada	246046614	25.125	6181921176.8
7		Biotech Electronics	5025820	3.4	17087788
8		Computrex Centres Ltd.	4802600	1.05	5042730
9		Northern Telecom Ltd.	116562467	26.625	3103475683.9
10		SONY Corporation	231148309	31.875	7367852349.4
11		McDonalds Corporation	92179000	9.5	875700500
12		Royal Trustco	46542649	17.5	814496357.5
13		Shell Oil	75215511	45.875	3450511567.1
14					
15	Total Market Value on Base Date:		7643218542.5		
16	Total Market Value on Date:		22736057838		
17	Student's Value-Weighted Index:		297.4671		
18					
19		@SUM(E4..E12)	+C15/C14*100		
20					

C12*D12
Values in column C multiplied by values in column D

The value-weighted index based on these stocks is 297.4671.

EXERCISE 15.8

B

1. (a) Use a spreadsheet to develop a price-weighted index for the following stocks.

Aluminum Company of Canada
ALCAN $26.25
Steel Company of Canada
STELCO $24.125
Dominion Foundries and Steel
DOFASCO $24.375
Algoma Steel Corporation
ALGO $15.875
International Nickel
INCO $20.625
Noranda Mines
NDA $29.125
Bow Valley
BVR $18.50
Lac Minerals
LAC $45.75

(b) Update your index to determine if there has been a change.

2. (a) Use a spreadsheet to develop a value-weighted index for the following stocks.

Name of Company	Price per Share ($)	Outstanding Shares
Fleet Aerospace	11.50	2 534 727
Ford Canada	176.00	8 291 132
Goodyear Canada	56.25	2 572 600
Guaranty Trust	27.75	12 099 399
Hudson's Bay Co.	23.50	28 866 002
ICG Utility Inv.	31.25	4 329 918
Imperial Oil Ltd. B	71.25	1 301 915
Laidlaw Transport	21.50	21 169 880
Manitoba Properties	28.50	15 965 725
Royal Bank	32.50	99 427 000
Seagram Company	103.00	95 145 420

(b) Update the index using current stock prices taken from your daily newspaper. Has the market improved from the index found on the base date in part (a)?

In questions 3 and 4, use your daily newspaper to locate share prices. The number of outstanding shares for any given company can be found in the reference section (FINANCE) of a library.

3. (a) Select a group of eight oil stocks and research the price per share and the number of outstanding shares.
(b) Develop a value-weighted index for the stocks.
(c) Update your index for a five-day period. Note any change.

4. Select a group of stocks consisting of
3 automobile manufacturers,
2 food chains,
3 electronics firms,
3 mining companies.
(a) Develop a price-weighted index.
(b) Update your index for a five-day period. Note any change.
(c) Develop a price-weighted index for the three automobile manufacturers as a subgroup of your index in (a) over the same five-day period.
(d) Develop a price-weighted index for the three mining companies as a subgroup of your index in (a) over the same five-day period.
(e) Draw a graph to show the change in the price-weighted index in (a) and (b) over the five-day period. On the same graph, show the changes in the indexes in parts (c) and (d).

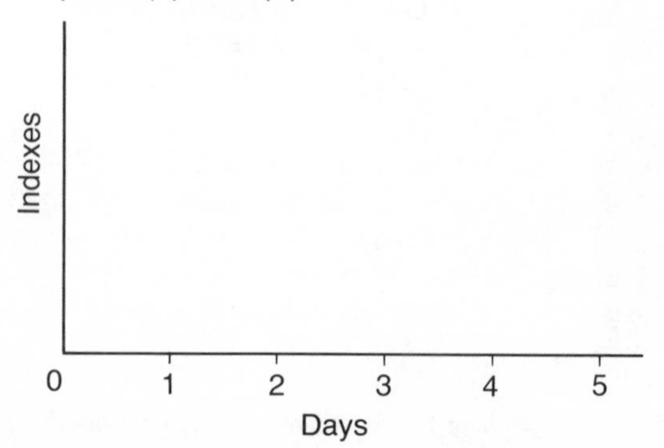

CAREER

CAD/CAM TECHNICIAN

CAD (computer-assisted design) and CAM (computer-assisted manufacturing) technicians use their knowledge of both computer hardware and software.

Jane Artanis, a CAD/CAM technician, helps the user to overcome problems which develop in the system. As a consultant, the technician can also teach the CAD/CAM program to users such as drafters or cartographers.

CAD/CAM technicians require considerable knowledge about computers and printers. Many users of CAD/CAM programs have only basic computer literacy, but know much about their own discipline. They need the services of the technician to get their system to function properly. A good background in mathematics is required to do the calculations in wiring, and to design the software demonstrations.

EXERCISE

1. It is reported that a computer locks up every 24 min when using the CARCAD program. When the computer locks up, the program goes back to the beginning.
How many times will the computer lock up in an 8 h day with continuous use?

2. Each dot on the screen is called a picture element—PIXEL. A character is made up of pixels—5 columns and 7 rows.
Use coordinates (x, y) to make the following figures.

7 □ □ □ □ □ (a) 1
6 □ □ □ □ □ (b) 4
5 □ □ □ □ □ (c) 7
4 □ □ □ □ □ (d) V
3 □ □ □ □ □ (e) t
2 □ □ □ □ □
1 □ □ □ □ □
1 2 3 4 5

15.9 REVIEW EXERCISE

1. Complete the following chart using a spreadsheet to determine which alternatives have the highest score using the PACED decision-making model.

Decision: Entertainment for carnival				
Criteria/Value		Alternatives		
		I Rock Group	II Folk Singer	III Disk Jockey
Cost	7	0	1	2
Popular	5	1	2	0
Draw	10	1	2	0
Breaks	3	0	1	2
Prefer	8	2	1	0

2. Set up a spreadsheet to find the mean of each of the following groups of numbers. Set the format to give answers to two decimal places.
(a) 54, 66, 48, 83, 24, 64, 75, 59, 44
(b) 2.5, 5.6, 1.8, 3.3, 6.8, 9.2, 8.1
(c) 0.25, 0.56, 0.64, 0.37, 0.63, 0.73

3. The following table shows the costs at the Pine Grove Dairy Farm.

Pine Grove Dairy Farm		
Output (litres)	Fixed Costs	Variable Costs
0	250.00	0.00
1000	250.00	500.00
1500	250.00	750.00
2000	250.00	1000.00
2500	250.00	1250.00
3000	250.00	1500.00
3500	250.00	2100.00
4000	250.00	2200.00
4500	250.00	2250.00
5000	250.00	2250.00
5500	250.00	2640.00
6000	250.00	3000.00

(a) Set up a spreadsheet to find the total cost for each type of output given.
(b) Add additional columns to your spreadsheet to find
 (i) average fixed cost,
 (ii) average variable cost,
 (iii) average total cost per litre.
(c) What level of production has the lowest average total cost?

4. A sum of $2000.00 is invested in a Guaranteed Investment Certificate (G.I.C.) at 1% per month for 36 months. Complete the spreadsheet to show the growth of the money over the time period. Use the following columns.

	A	B	C	D
1	Growth of $2000.00 at 1%			
2	Month	Principal	Interest	Amount
3	1	2000.00	20.00	2020.00
4	2	2020.00	↑	↑
5	3	↑		B3 + C3
6	4		0.01 * B3	
7		D3		

5. (a) Use a spreadsheet to calculate the value of the Red Deer Investment Club's portfolio.
(b) Update the value of the portfolio using share prices found in a daily newspaper.
(c) Find the change in value for each stock.

Portfolio for Red Deer Investment Club		
Name of Company	Number of Shares	Price per Share ($)
Algoma Steel	250	17.75
Bell Canada	100	25.75
Campbell Soup	200	20.25
CHUM	150	17.50
Denison A	500	7.75
Dalmy's	150	12.00
Electrohome	50	72.50
ICG Utilities	1000	19.00
Labatt	250	28.25
Noma A	500	16.50

6. Natasha and Anton Marches have a portfolio consisting of the following mutual funds. (Unit prices quoted are of the same base date.)

Name of Mutual Fund	Number of Units	Unit Price ($)
Bolton Tremblay Int'l	200	8.88
AGF HiTech	120	14.38
CGF Group Venture Fund	200	4.62
Eaton Group Viking Cdn	210	17.62
Investors Japan Fund	50	14.39
Scotia Fund Income	60	9.78
Prudential Growth	270	10.63

(a) Use a spreadsheet to calculate the value of the portfolio using the share prices given above.
(b) Obtain current share prices from the daily newspaper and update the value of the portfolio.
(c) What is the change in value of the portfolio?

7. The Homeowners' Co-op Real Estate office made the following house sales during the month of May.

bungalow	\$145 000
duplex	\$167 000
bungalow	\$154 000
bungalow	\$149 500
split-level	\$175 000
duplex	\$225 000
split-level	\$185 000
two-storey	\$245 000
two-storey	\$267 500
bungalow	\$154 000
split-level	\$189 900
split-level	\$183 700
two-storey	\$249 000
duplex	\$164 000
two-storey	\$275 000
two-storey	\$248 500
bungalow	\$152 000

Use a spreadsheet to find
(a) total sales for the office,
(b) average house prices,
(c) average price for each type of house.

8. The formulas for the volumes of a cylinder and of a cone are given below each figure.

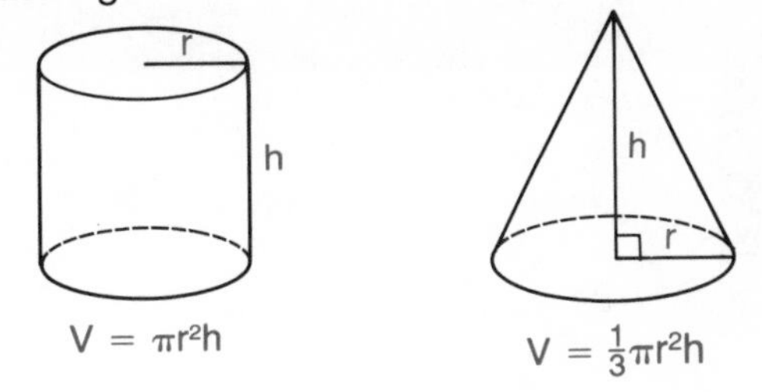

$V = \pi r^2 h$ $\qquad$ $V = \frac{1}{3}\pi r^2 h$

(a) Set up a spreadsheet to find the volume of each figure below.

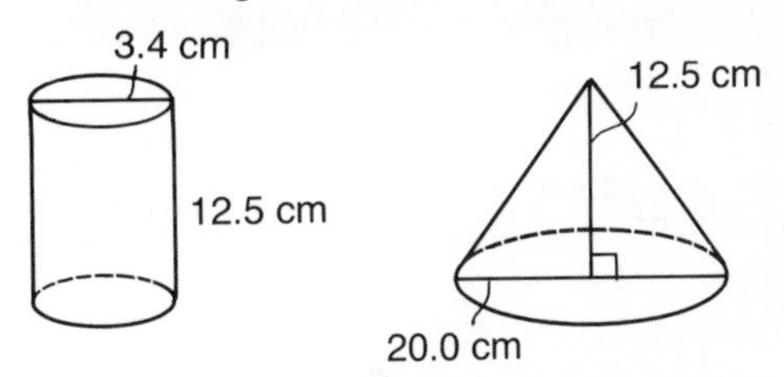

(b) Which figure has the larger volume?

9. Set up a spreadsheet to calculate the values of the primary trigonometric ratios

sine, cosine, tangent

for angles from 0° to 90° at 2° intervals.

10. Set up a spreadsheet to calculate the lengths of the indicated sides of the following triangles.

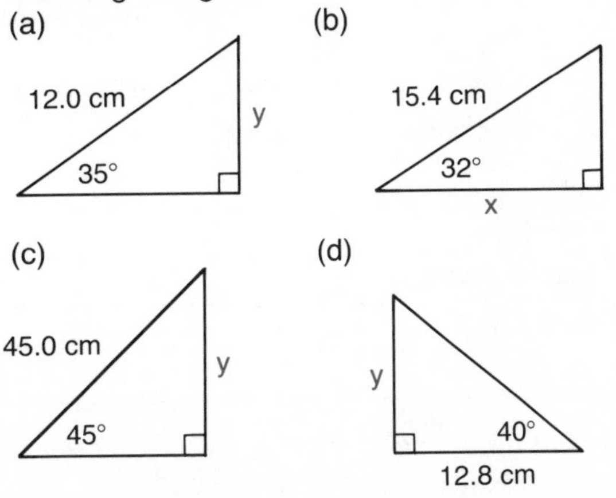

15.10 CHAPTER 15 TEST

1. Write the spreadsheet formula to add the value in cell B4 to the value in cell C6.

2. (a) Write the formulas to calculate perimeter and area of a rectangle in the following spreadsheet.

	A	B	C	D	E	F
1	Rectangle					
2						
3	Length	Width	Perimeter	Area		
4						
5	24.5	18.2				

(b) Write the formulas to calculate circumference and area of a circle in the following spreadsheet.

	A	B	C	D
1	Circle			
2				
3	Radius	Circumference	Area	
4				
5	12.6			

3. If the value for N is located in cell B6, write spreadsheet formulas for each of the following.
(a) sin N (b) cos N (c) tan N

4. Complete the following to determine which alternative has the greatest value. The alternatives for home entertainment are long-playing record, cassette tape, and compact disk.

Decision: Buying an album				
		Alternatives		
Criteria	Value	I Record	II Cassette	III Disk
Quality of sound	8	0	1	2
Cost	10	2	1	0
Portability	5	0	2	1
Loss of popularity	4	2	1	0
Durability	6	0	1	2
Storage	3	0	2	1

5. Set up a spreadsheet to calculate the values of sin N, for N = 10°, 12°, 14°, 16°, ..., 30°

APPENDIX

Table I SQUARE ROOTS

n	$\sqrt{n}$	n	$\sqrt{n}$	n	$\sqrt{n}$	n	$\sqrt{n}$
1	1.000	51	7.141	101	10.050	151	12.288
2	1.414	52	7.211	102	10.010	152	12.329
3	1.732	53	7.280	103	10.149	153	12.369
4	2.000	54	7.349	104	10.198	154	12.410
5	2.236	55	7.416	105	10.247	155	12.450
6	2.450	56	7.483	106	10.296	156	12.490
7	2.646	57	7.550	107	10.344	157	12.530
8	2.828	58	7.616	108	10.392	158	12.570
9	3.000	59	7.681	109	10.440	159	12.610
10	3.162	60	7.746	110	10.488	160	12.649
11	3.317	61	7.810	111	10.536	161	12.689
12	3.464	62	7.874	112	10.583	162	12.728
13	3.606	63	7.937	113	10.630	163	12.767
14	3.742	64	8.000	114	10.677	164	12.806
15	3.873	65	8.062	115	10.724	165	12.845
16	4.000	66	8.124	116	10.770	166	12.884
17	4.123	67	8.185	117	10.817	167	12.923
18	4.243	68	8.246	118	10.863	168	12.961
19	4.359	69	8.307	119	10.909	169	13.000
20	4.472	70	8.367	120	10.954	170	13.038
21	4.583	71	8.426	121	11.000	171	13.077
22	4.690	72	8.485	122	11.045	172	13.115
23	4.796	73	8.544	123	11.091	173	13.153
24	4.899	74	8.602	124	11.136	174	13.191
25	5.000	75	8.660	125	11.180	175	13.229
26	5.099	76	8.718	126	11.225	176	13.266
27	5.196	77	8.775	127	11.269	177	13.304
28	5.292	78	8.832	128	11.314	178	13.342
29	5.385	79	8.888	129	11.358	179	13.379
30	5.477	80	8.944	130	11.402	180	13.416
31	5.568	81	9.000	131	11.446	181	13.454
32	5.657	82	9.055	132	11.489	182	13.491
33	5.745	83	9.110	133	11.533	183	13.528
34	5.831	84	9.165	134	11.576	184	13.565
35	5.916	85	9.220	135	11.619	185	13.601
36	6.000	86	9.274	136	11.662	186	13.638
37	6.083	87	9.327	137	11.705	187	13.675
38	6.164	88	9.381	138	11.747	188	13.711
39	6.245	89	9.434	139	11.790	189	13.748
40	6.325	90	9.487	140	11.832	190	13.784
41	6.403	91	9.539	141	11.874	191	13.820
42	6.481	92	9.592	142	11.916	192	13.856
43	6.557	93	9.644	143	11.958	193	13.892
44	6.633	94	9.695	144	12.000	194	13.928
45	6.708	95	9.747	145	12.042	195	13.964
46	6.782	96	9.798	146	12.083	196	14.000
47	6.856	97	9.849	147	12.124	197	14.036
48	6.928	98	9.900	148	12.166	198	14.071
49	7.000	99	9.950	149	12.207	199	14.107
50	7.071	100	10.000	150	12.247	200	14.142

Table II TRIGONOMETRIC RATIOS

θ°	sin θ	cos θ	tan θ	θ°	sin θ	cos θ	tan θ
0	0.0000	1.0000	0.0000	**46**	0.7193	0.6947	1.0355
1	0.0175	0.9999	0.0175	**47**	0.7314	0.6820	1.0724
2	0.0349	0.9994	0.0349	**48**	0.7431	0.6691	1.1106
3	0.0523	0.9986	0.0524	**49**	0.7547	0.6561	1.1504
4	0.0698	0.9976	0.0699	**50**	0.7660	0.6428	1.1917
5	0.0872	0.9962	0.0875	**51**	0.7772	0.6293	1.2349
6	0.1045	0.9945	0.1051	**52**	0.7880	0.6157	1.2799
7	0.1219	0.9926	0.1228	**53**	0.7986	0.6018	1.3270
8	0.1392	0.9903	0.1405	**54**	0.8090	0.5878	1.3764
9	0.1564	0.9877	0.1584	**55**	0.8192	0.5736	1.4281
10	0.1737	0.9848	0.1763	**56**	0.8290	0.5592	1.4826
11	0.1908	0.9816	0.1944	**57**	0.8387	0.5446	1.5399
12	0.2079	0.9782	0.2126	**58**	0.8481	0.5299	1.6003
13	0.2250	0.9744	0.2309	**59**	0.8572	0.5150	1.6643
14	0.2419	0.9703	0.2493	**60**	0.8660	0.5000	1.7320
15	0.2588	0.9659	0.2680	**61**	0.8746	0.4848	1.8040
16	0.2756	0.9613	0.2867	**62**	0.8830	0.4695	1.8807
17	0.2924	0.9563	0.3057	**63**	0.8910	0.4540	1.9626
18	0.3090	0.9511	0.3249	**64**	0.8988	0.4384	2.0503
19	0.3256	0.9455	0.3443	**65**	0.9063	0.4226	2.1445
20	0.3420	0.9397	0.3640	**66**	0.9136	0.4067	2.2460
21	0.3584	0.9336	0.3839	**67**	0.9205	0.3907	2.3558
22	0.3746	0.9272	0.4040	**68**	0.9272	0.3746	2.4751
23	0.3907	0.9025	0.4245	**69**	0.9336	0.3584	2.6051
24	0.4067	0.9136	0.4452	**70**	0.9397	0.3420	2.7475
25	0.4226	0.9063	0.4663	**71**	0.9455	0.3256	2.9042
26	0.4384	0.8988	0.4877	**72**	0.9511	0.3090	3.0777
27	0.4540	0.8910	0.5095	**73**	0.9563	0.2924	3.2708
28	0.4695	0.8830	0.5317	**74**	0.9613	0.2756	3.4874
29	0.4848	0.8746	0.5543	**75**	0.9659	0.2588	3.7320
30	0.5000	0.8660	0.5774	**76**	0.9703	0.2419	4.0108
31	0.5150	0.8572	0.6009	**77**	0.9744	0.2250	4.3315
32	0.5299	0.8481	0.6249	**78**	0.9782	0.2079	4.7046
33	0.5446	0.8387	0.6494	**79**	0.9816	0.1908	5.1445
34	0.5592	0.8290	0.6745	**80**	0.9848	0.1737	5.6713
35	0.5736	0.8192	0.7002	**81**	0.9877	0.1564	6.3137
36	0.5878	0.8090	0.7265	**82**	0.9903	0.1392	7.1154
37	0.6018	0.7986	0.7536	**83**	0.9926	0.1219	8.1443
38	0.6157	0.7880	0.7813	**84**	0.9945	0.1045	9.5144
39	0.6293	0.7772	0.8098	**85**	0.9962	0.0872	11.430
40	0.6428	0.7660	0.8391	**86**	0.9976	0.0698	14.301
41	0.6561	0.7547	0.8693	**87**	0.9986	9.0523	19.081
42	0.6691	0.7431	0.9004	**88**	0.9994	0.0349	28.636
43	0.6820	0.7314	0.9325	**89**	0.9999	0.0175	57.290
44	0.6947	0.7193	0.9657	**90**	1.0000	0.0000	—
45	0.7071	0.7071	1.0000				

Table III DAYS EXPRESSED IN DECIMAL EQUIVALENTS OF A YEAR—365 d BASIS

For Figuring Interest, Cancellation of Insurance Premiums, Etc.

Day of Month	January Day of Year	January Decimal Equivalent	February Day of Year	February Decimal Equivalent	March Day of Year	March Decimal Equivalent	April Day of Year	April Decimal Equivalent	May Day of Year	May Decimal Equivalent	June Day of Year	June Decimal Equivalent
1	1	0.0027	32	0.0877	60	0.1644	91	0.2493	121	0.3315	152	0.4164
2	2	0.0055	33	0.0904	61	0.1671	92	0.2521	122	0.3342	153	0.4192
3	3	0.0082	34	0.0932	62	0.1699	93	0.2548	123	0.3370	154	0.4219
4	4	0.0110	35	0.0959	63	0.1726	94	0.2575	124	0.3397	155	0.4247
5	5	0.0137	36	0.0986	64	0.1753	95	0.2603	125	0.3425	156	0.4274
6	6	0.0164	37	0.1014	65	0.1781	96	0.2630	126	0.3452	157	0.4301
7	7	0.0192	38	0.1041	66	0.1808	97	0.2658	127	0.3479	158	0.4329
8	8	0.0219	39	0.1068	67	0.1836	98	0.2685	128	0.3507	159	0.4356
9	9	0.0247	40	0.1096	68	0.1863	99	0.2712	129	0.3534	160	0.4384
10	10	0.0274	41	0.1123	69	0.1890	100	0.2740	130	0.3562	161	0.4411
11	11	0.0301	42	0.1151	70	0.1918	101	0.2767	131	0.3589	162	0.4438
12	12	0.0329	43	0.1178	71	0.1945	102	0.2795	132	0.3616	163	0.4466
13	13	0.0356	44	0.1205	72	0.1973	103	0.2822	133	0.3644	164	0.4493
14	14	0.0384	45	0.1233	73	0.2000	104	0.2849	134	0.3671	165	0.4521
15	15	0.0411	46	0.1260	74	0.2027	105	0.2877	135	0.3699	166	0.4548
16	16	0.0438	47	0.1288	75	0.2055	106	0.2904	136	0.3726	167	0.4575
17	17	0.0466	48	0.1315	76	0.2082	107	0.2932	137	0.3753	168	0.4603
18	18	0.0493	49	0.1342	77	0.2110	108	0.2959	138	0.3781	169	0.4630
19	19	0.0521	50	0.1370	78	0.2137	109	0.2986	139	0.3808	170	0.4658
20	20	0.0548	51	0.1397	79	0.2164	110	0.3014	140	0.3836	171	0.4685
21	21	0.0575	52	0.1425	80	0.2192	111	0.3041	141	0.3863	172	0.4712
22	22	0.0603	53	0.1452	81	0.2219	112	0.3068	142	0.3890	173	0.4740
23	23	0.0630	54	0.1479	82	0.2247	113	0.3096	143	0.3918	174	0.4767
24	24	0.0658	55	0.1507	83	0.2274	114	0.3123	144	0.3945	175	0.4795
25	25	0.0685	56	0.1534	84	0.2301	115	0.3151	145	0.3973	176	0.4822
26	26	0.0712	57	0.1562	85	0.2329	116	0.3178	146	0.4000	177	0.4849
27	27	0.0740	58	0.1589	86	0.2356	117	0.3205	147	0.4027	178	0.4877
28	28	0.0767	59	0.1616	87	0.2384	118	0.3233	148	0.4055	179	0.4904
29	29	0.0795			88	0.2411	119	0.3260	149	0.4082	180	0.4932
30	30	0.0822			89	0.2438	120	0.3288	150	0.4110	181	0.4959
31	31	0.0849			90	0.2466			151	0.4137		

Day of Month	July Day of Year	July Decimal Equivalent	August Day of Year	August Decimal Equivalent	September Day of Year	September Decimal Equivalent	October Day of Year	October Decimal Equivalent	November Day of Year	November Decimal Equivalent	December Day of Year	December Decimal Equivalent	Day of Month
1	182	0.4986	213	0.5836	244	0.6685	274	0.7507	305	0.8356	335	0.9178	1
2	183	0.5014	214	0.5863	245	0.6712	275	0.7534	306	0.8384	336	0.9205	2
3	184	0.5041	215	0.5890	246	0.6740	276	0.7562	307	0.8411	337	0.9233	3
4	185	0.5068	216	0.5918	247	0.6767	277	0.7589	308	0.8438	338	0.9260	4
5	186	0.5096	217	0.5945	248	0.6795	278	0.7616	309	0.8466	339	0.9288	5
6	187	0.5123	218	0.5973	249	0.6822	279	0.7644	310	0.8493	340	0.9315	6
7	188	0.5151	219	0.6000	250	0.6849	280	0.7671	311	0.8521	341	0.9342	7
8	189	0.5178	220	0.6027	251	0.6877	281	0.7699	312	0.8548	342	0.9370	8
9	190	0.5205	221	0.6055	252	0.6904	282	0.7726	313	0.8575	343	0.9397	9
10	191	0.5233	222	0.6082	253	0.6932	283	0.7753	314	0.8603	344	0.9425	10
11	192	0.5260	223	0.6110	254	0.6959	284	0.7781	315	0.8630	345	0.9452	11
12	193	0.5288	224	0.6137	255	0.6986	285	0.7808	316	0.8658	346	0.9479	12
13	194	0.5315	225	0.6164	256	0.7014	286	0.7836	317	0.8685	347	0.9507	13
14	195	0.5342	226	0.6192	257	0.7041	287	0.7863	318	0.8712	348	0.9534	14
15	196	0.5370	227	0.6219	258	0.7068	288	0.7890	319	0.8740	349	0.9562	15
16	197	0.5397	228	0.6247	259	0.7096	289	0.7918	320	0.8767	350	0.9589	16
17	198	0.5425	229	0.6274	260	0.7123	290	0.7945	321	0.8795	351	0.9616	17
18	199	0.5452	230	0.6301	261	0.7151	291	0.7973	322	0.8822	352	0.9644	18
19	200	0.5479	231	0.6329	262	0.7178	292	0.8000	323	0.8849	353	0.9671	19
20	201	0.5507	232	0.6356	263	0.7205	293	0.8027	324	0.8877	354	0.9699	20
21	202	0.5534	233	0.6384	264	0.7233	294	0.8055	325	0.8904	355	0.9726	21
22	203	0.5562	234	0.6411	265	0.7260	295	0.8082	326	0.8932	356	0.9753	22
23	204	0.5589	235	0.6438	266	0.7288	296	0.8110	327	0.8959	357	0.9781	23
24	205	0.5616	236	0.6466	267	0.7315	297	0.8137	328	0.8986	358	0.9808	24
25	206	0.5644	237	0.6493	268	0.7342	298	0.8164	329	0.9014	359	0.9836	25
26	207	0.5671	238	0.6521	269	0.7370	299	0.8192	330	0.9041	360	0.9863	26
27	208	0.5699	239	0.6548	270	0.7397	300	0.8219	331	0.9068	361	0.9890	27
28	209	0.5726	240	0.6575	271	0.7425	301	0.8247	332	0.9096	362	0.9918	28
29	210	0.5753	241	0.6603	272	0.7452	302	0.8274	333	0.9123	363	0.9945	29
30	211	0.5781	242	0.6630	273	0.7479	303	0.8301	334	0.9151	364	0.9973	30
31	212	0.5808	243	0.6658			304	0.8329			365	1.0000	31

Table IV AMOUNT OF I $(1 + i)^n$

n \ i	$\frac{1}{2}$%	1%	$1\frac{1}{2}$%	2%	$2\frac{1}{2}$%	3%	$3\frac{1}{2}$%	i / n
1	1.005 00	1.010 00	1.015 00	1.020 00	1.025 00	1.030 00	1.035 00	1
2	1.010 03	1.020 10	1.030 23	1.040 40	1.050 63	1.060 90	1.071 23	2
3	1.015 08	1.030 30	1.045 68	1.061 21	1.076 89	1.092 73	1.108 72	3
4	1.020 15	1.040 60	1.061 36	1.082 43	1.103 81	1.125 51	1.147 52	4
5	1.025 25	1.051 01	1.077 28	1.104 08	1.131 41	1.159 27	1.187 69	5
6	1.030 38	1.061 52	1.093 44	1.126 16	1.159 69	1.194 05	1.229 26	6
7	1.035 53	1.072 14	1.109 84	1.148 69	1.188 69	1.229 87	1.272 28	7
8	1.040 71	1.082 86	1.126 49	1.171 66	1.218 40	1.266 77	1.316 81	8
9	1.045 91	1.093 69	1.143 39	1.195 09	1.248 86	1.304 77	1.362 90	9
10	1.051 14	1.104 62	1.160 54	1.218 99	1.280 08	1.343 92	1.410 60	10
11	1.056 40	1.115 67	1.179 95	1.243 37	1.312 09	1.384 23	1.459 97	11
12	1.061 68	1.126 83	1.195 62	1.268 24	1.344 89	1.425 76	1.511 07	12
13	1.066 99	1.138 09	1.213 55	1.293 61	1.378 51	1.468 53	1.563 96	13
14	1.072 32	1.149 47	1.231 76	1.319 48	1.412 97	1.512 59	1.618 69	14
15	1.077 68	1.160 97	1.250 23	1.345 87	1.448 30	1.557 97	1.675 35	15
16	1.083 07	1.172 58	1.268 99	1.372 79	1.484 51	1.604 71	1.733 99	16
17	1.088 49	1.184 30	1.288 02	1.400 24	1.521 62	1.652 85	1.794 68	17
18	1.093 93	1.196 15	1.307 34	1.428 25	1.559 66	1.702 43	1.857 49	18
19	1.099 40	1.208 11	1.326 95	1.456 81	1.598 65	1.753 51	1.922 50	19
20	1.104 90	1.220 19	1.346 86	1.485 95	1.638 62	1.806 11	1.989 79	20
21	1.110 42	1.232 39	1.367 06	1.515 67	1.679 58	1.860 29	2.059 43	21
22	1.115 97	1.244 72	1.387 56	1.545 98	1.721 57	1.916 10	2.131 51	22
23	1.121 55	1.257 16	1.408 38	1.576 90	1.764 61	1.973 59	2.206 11	23
24	1.127 16	1.269 73	1.429 50	1.608 44	1.808 73	2.032 79	2.283 33	24
25	1.132 80	1.282 43	1.450 95	1.640 61	1.853 94	2.093 78	2.363 24	25
26	1.138 46	1.295 26	1.472 71	1.673 42	1.900 29	2.156 59	2.445 96	26
27	1.144 15	1.308 21	1.494 80	1.706 89	1.947 80	2.221 29	2.531 57	27
28	1.149 87	1.321 29	1.517 22	1.741 02	1.997 50	2.287 93	2.620 17	28
29	1.155 62	1.334 50	1.539 98	1.775 84	2.046 41	2.356 57	2.711 88	29
30	1.161 40	1.347 85	1.563 08	1.811 36	2.097 57	2.427 26	2.806 79	30
31	1.167 21	1.361 33	1.586 53	1.847 59	2.150 01	2.500 08	2.905 03	31
32	1.173 04	1.374 94	1.610 32	1.884 54	2.203 76	2.575 08	3.006 71	32
33	1.178 91	1.388 69	1.634 48	1.922 23	2.258 85	2.652 34	3.111 94	33
34	1.184 80	1.402 58	1.659 00	1.906 68	2.315 32	2.731 91	3.220 86	34
35	1.190 73	1.416 60	1.683 88	1.999 89	2.373 21	2.813 86	3.333 59	35
36	1.196 68	1.430 77	1.709 14	2.039 89	2.432 54	2.898 28	3.450 27	36
37	1.202 66	1.445 08	1.734 78	2.080 69	2.493 35	2.985 23	3.571 03	37
38	1.208 68	1.459 53	1.760 80	2.122 30	2.555 68	3.074 78	3.696 01	38
39	1.214 72	1.474 12	1.787 21	2.164 74	2.619 57	3.167 03	3.825 37	39
40	1.220 79	1.488 86	1.814 02	2.208 04	2.685 06	3.264 04	3.959 26	40

Table IV (Continued)

n \ i	4%	$4\frac{1}{2}$%	5%	$5\frac{1}{2}$%	6%	7%	8%	i / n
1	1.040 00	1.045 00	1.050 00	1.055 00	1.060 00	1.070 00	1.080 00	1
2	1.081 60	1.092 03	1.102 50	1.113 03	1.123 60	1.144 90	1.166 40	2
3	1.124 86	1.141 17	1.157 63	1.174 24	1.191 02	1.225 04	1.259 71	3
4	1.169 86	1.192 52	1.215 51	1.238 82	1.262 48	1.310 80	1.360 49	4
5	1.216 65	1.246 18	1.276 28	1.306 96	1.338 23	1.402 55	1.469 33	5
6	1.265 32	1.302 26	1.340 10	1.378 84	1.418 52	1.500 73	1.586 87	6
7	1.315 93	1.360 86	1.407 10	1.454 68	1.503 63	1.605 78	1.713 82	7
8	1.368 57	1.422 10	1.477 46	1.534 69	1.593 85	1.718 19	1.850 93	8
9	1.423 31	1.486 10	1.551 33	1.619 09	1.689 48	1.838 46	1.999 00	9
10	1.480 24	1.552 97	1.628 89	1.708 14	1.790 85	1.967 15	2.158 93	10
11	1.539 45	1.622 85	1.710 34	1.802 09	1.898 30	2.104 85	2.331 64	11
12	1.601 03	1.695 88	1.795 86	1.901 21	2.012 20	2.252 19	2.518 17	12
13	1.665 07	1.772 20	1.885 65	2.005 77	2.132 93	2.409 85	2.719 62	13
14	1.731 68	1.851 94	1.979 93	2.116 09	2.260 90	2.578 53	2.937 19	14
15	1.800 94	1.935 28	2.078 93	2.232 48	2.396 56	2.759 03	3.172 17	15
16	1.872 98	2.022 37	2.182 87	2.355 26	2.540 35	2.952 16	3.425 94	16
17	1.947 90	2.113 38	2.292 02	2.484 80	2.692 77	3.158 81	3.700 02	17
18	2.025 82	2.208 48	2.406 62	2.621 47	2.854 34	3.379 93	3.996 02	18
19	2.106 85	2.307 86	2.526 95	2.765 65	3.025 60	3.616 53	4.315 70	19
20	2.191 12	2.411 71	2.653 30	2.917 76	3.207 14	3.869 68	4.660 96	20
21	2.278 77	2.520 24	2.785 96	3.078 23	3.399 56	4.140 56	5.033 83	21
22	2.369 92	2.633 65	2.925 26	3.247 54	3.603 54	4.430 40	5.436 54	22
23	2.464 72	2.752 17	3.071 52	3.426 15	3.819 75	4.740 53	5.871 46	23
24	2.563 30	2.876 01	3.225 10	3.614 59	4.048 93	5.072 37	6.341 18	24
25	2.665 84	3.005 43	3.386 35	3.813 39	4.291 87	5.427 43	6.848 48	25
26	2.772 47	3.140 68	3.555 67	4.023 13	4.549 38	5.807 35	7.396 35	26
27	2.883 37	3.282 01	3.733 46	4.244 40	4.822 35	6.213 87	7.988 06	27
28	2.998 70	3.429 70	3.920 13	4.477 84	5.111 69	6.648 84	8.627 11	28
29	3.118 65	3.584 04	4.116 14	4.724 12	5.418 39	7.114 26	9.317 27	29
30	3.243 40	3.745 32	4.321 94	4.983 95	5.743 49	7.612 26	10.062 66	30
31	3.373 13	3.913 86	4.538 04	5.258 07	6.088 10	8.145 11	10.867 67	31
32	3.508 06	4.089 98	4.764 94	5.547 26	6.453 39	8.715 27	11.737 08	32
33	3.648 38	4.274 03	5.003 19	5.852 36	6.840 59	9.325 34	12.676 05	33
34	3.794 32	4.446 36	5.253 35	6.174 24	7.251 03	9.978 11	13.690 13	34
35	3.946 09	4.667 35	5.516 02	6.513 83	7.686 09	10.676 58	14.785 34	35
36	4.130 93	4.877 38	5.791 82	6.872 09	8.147 25	11.423 94	15.968 17	36
37	4.268 09	5.096 86	6.081 41	7.250 05	8.636 09	12.223 62	17.245 63	37
38	4.438 81	5.326 22	6.385 48	7.648 80	9.154 25	13.079 27	18.625 28	38
39	4.616 37	5.565 90	6.704 75	8.069 49	9.703 51	13.994 82	20.115 30	39
40	4.801 02	5.816 36	7.039 99	8.513 31	10.285 72	14.974 46	21.724 52	40

Table V $\frac{1}{(1+i)^n}$

n \ i	$\frac{1}{2}$%	1%	$1\frac{1}{2}$%	2%	$2\frac{1}{2}$%	3%	$3\frac{1}{2}$%	i / n
1	0.995 02	0.990 10	0.985 22	0.980 39	0.975 61	0.970 87	0.966 18	1
2	0.990 07	0.980 30	0.970 66	0.961 17	0.951 81	0.942 60	0.933 51	2
3	0.985 15	0.970 59	0.956 32	0.942 32	0.928 60	0.915 14	0.901 94	3
4	0.980 25	0.960 98	0.942 18	0.923 85	0.905 95	0.888 49	0.871 44	4
5	0.975 37	0.951 47	0.928 26	0.905 73	0.883 85	0.862 61	0.841 97	5
6	0.970 52	0.942 05	0.914 54	0.887 97	0.862 30	0.837 48	0.813 50	6
7	0.965 69	0.932 72	0.901 03	0.870 56	0.841 27	0.813 09	0.785 99	7
8	0.960 89	0.923 48	0.887 71	0.853 49	0.820 75	0.789 41	0.759 41	8
9	0.956 10	0.914 34	0.874 59	0.836 76	0.800 73	0.766 42	0.733 73	9
10	0.951 35	0.905 29	0.861 67	0.820 35	0.781 20	0.744 09	0.708 92	10
11	0.946 61	0.896 32	0.848 93	0.804 26	0.762 14	0.722 42	0.684 95	11
12	0.941 91	0.887 45	0.836 39	0.788 49	0.743 56	0.701 38	0.661 78	12
13	0.937 22	0.878 66	0.824 03	0.773 03	0.725 42	0.680 95	0.639 40	13
14	0.932 56	0.869 96	0.811 85	0.757 88	0.707 73	0.661 12	0.617 78	14
15	0.927 92	0.861 35	0.799 85	0.743 01	0.690 47	0.641 86	0.596 89	15
16	0.923 30	0.852 82	0.788 03	0.728 45	0.673 62	0.623 17	0.576 71	16
17	0.918 71	0.844 38	0.776 39	0.714 16	0.657 20	0.605 02	0.557 20	17
18	0.914 14	0.836 02	0.764 91	0.700 16	0.641 17	0.587 39	0.538 36	18
19	0.909 59	0.827 74	0.753 61	0.686 43	0.625 53	0.570 29	0.520 16	19
20	0.905 06	0.819 54	0.742 47	0.672 97	0.610 27	0.553 68	0.502 57	20
21	0.900 56	0.811 43	0.731 50	0.659 78	0.595 39	0.527 55	0.485 57	21
22	0.896 08	0.803 40	0.720 69	0.646 84	0.580 86	0.521 89	0.469 15	22
23	0.891 62	0.795 44	0.710 04	0.634 16	0.566 70	0.506 69	0.453 29	23
24	0.887 19	0.787 57	0.699 54	0.621 72	0.552 88	0.491 93	0.437 96	24
25	0.882 77	0.779 77	0.689 21	0.609 53	0.539 39	0.477 61	0.423 15	25
26	0.878 38	0.772 05	0.679 02	0.597 58	0.526 23	0.463 69	0.408 84	26
27	0.874 01	0.764 40	0.668 99	0.585 86	0.513 40	0.450 19	0.395 01	27
28	0.869 66	0.756 84	0.659 10	0.574 37	0.500 88	0.437 08	0.381 65	28
29	0.865 33	0.749 34	0.649 36	0.563 11	0.488 66	0.424 35	0.368 75	29
30	0.861 03	0.741 92	0.639 76	0.552 07	0.476 74	0.411 99	0.356 28	30
31	0.856 75	0.734 58	0.630 31	0.541 25	0.465 11	0.399 99	0.344 23	31
32	0.852 48	0.727 30	0.620 99	0.530 63	0.453 77	0.388 34	0.332 59	32
33	0.848 24	0.720 10	0.611 82	0.520 23	0.442 70	0.377 03	0.321 34	33
34	0.844 02	0.712 97	0.602 77	0.510 03	0.431 91	0.366 04	0.310 48	34
35	0.839 82	0.705 91	0.593 87	0.500 03	0.421 37	0.355 38	0.299 98	35
36	0.835 64	0.698 92	0.585 09	0.490 22	0.411 09	0.345 03	0.289 83	36
37	0.831 49	0.692 00	0.576 44	0.480 61	0.401 07	0.334 98	0.280 03	37
38	0.827 35	0.685 15	0.567 92	0.471 19	0.391 28	0.325 23	0.270 56	38
39	0.823 23	0.678 37	0.559 53	0.461 95	0.381 74	0.315 75	0.261 41	39
40	0.819 14	0.671 65	0.551 26	0.452 89	0.372 43	0.306 56	0.252 57	40

Table V (Continued)

n \ i	4%	$4\frac{1}{2}$%	5%	$5\frac{1}{2}$%	6%	7%	8%	i / n
1	0.961 54	0.956 94	0.952 38	0.947 87	0.943 40	0.934 58	0.925 93	1
2	0.924 56	0.915 73	0.907 03	0.898 45	0.890 00	0.873 44	0.857 34	2
3	0.889 00	0.876 30	0.863 84	0.851 61	0.839 62	0.816 30	0.793 83	3
4	0.854 80	0.838 56	0.822 70	0.807 22	0.792 09	0.762 90	0.735 03	4
5	0.821 93	0.802 45	0.783 53	0.765 13	0.747 26	0.712 99	0.680 58	5
6	0.790 31	0.767 90	0.746 22	0.725 25	0.704 96	0.666 34	0.630 17	6
7	0.759 92	0.734 83	0.710 68	0.687 44	0.665 06	0.622 75	0.583 49	7
8	0.730 69	0.703 19	0.676 84	0.651 60	0.627 41	0.582 01	0.540 27	8
9	0.702 59	0.672 90	0.644 61	0.617 63	0.591 90	0.543 93	0.500 25	9
10	0.675 56	0.643 93	0.613 91	0.585 43	0.558 39	0.508 35	0.463 19	10
11	0.649 58	0.616 20	0.584 68	0.554 91	0.526 79	0.475 09	0.428 88	11
12	0.624 60	0.589 66	0.556 84	0.525 98	0.496 97	0.444 01	0.397 11	12
13	0.600 57	0.564 27	0.530 32	0.498 56	0.468 84	0.414 96	0.367 70	13
14	0.577 48	0.539 97	0.505 07	0.472 57	0.442 30	0.387 82	0.340 46	14
15	0.555 26	0.516 72	0.481 02	0.447 93	0.417 27	0.362 45	0.315 24	15
16	0.533 91	0.494 47	0.458 11	0.424 58	0.393 65	0.338 73	0.291 89	16
17	0.513 37	0.473 18	0.436 30	0.402 45	0.371 36	0.316 57	0.270 27	17
18	0.493 63	0.452 80	0.415 52	0.381 47	0.350 34	0.295 86	0.250 25	18
19	0.474 64	0.433 30	0.395 73	0.361 58	0.330 51	0.276 51	0.231 71	19
20	0.456 39	0.414 64	0.376 89	0.342 73	0.311 80	0.258 42	0.214 55	20
21	0.438 83	0.396 79	0.358 94	0.324 86	0.294 16	0.241 51	0.198 66	21
22	0.421 96	0.379 70	0.341 85	0.307 93	0.277 51	0.225 71	0.183 94	22
23	0.405 73	0.363 35	0.325 57	0.291 87	0.261 80	0.210 95	0.170 32	23
24	0.390 12	0.347 70	0.310 07	0.276 66	0.246 98	0.197 15	0.157 70	24
25	0.375 12	0.332 73	0.295 30	0.262 23	0.233 00	0.184 25	0.146 02	25
26	0.360 69	0.318 40	0.281 24	0.248 56	0.219 81	0.172 20	0.135 20	26
27	0.346 82	0.304 69	0.267 85	0.235 60	0.207 37	0.160 93	0.125 19	27
28	0.333 48	0.291 57	0.255 09	0.223 32	0.195 63	0.150 40	0.115 91	28
29	0.320 65	0.279 02	0.242 95	0.211 68	0.184 56	0.140 56	0.107 33	29
30	0.308 32	0.267 00	0.231 38	0.200 64	0.174 11	0.131 37	0.099 38	30
31	0.296 46	0.255 50	0.220 36	0.190 18	0.164 25	0.122 77	0.092 02	31
32	0.285 06	0.244 50	0.209 87	0.180 27	0.154 96	0.114 74	0.085 20	32
33	0.274 09	0.233 97	0.199 87	0.170 87	0.146 19	0.107 23	0.078 89	33
34	0.263 55	0.223 90	0.190 35	0.161 96	0.137 91	0.100 22	0.073 05	34
35	0.253 42	0.214 25	0.181 29	0.153 52	0.130 11	0.093 66	0.067 63	35
36	0.243 67	0.205 03	0.172 66	0.145 52	0.122 74	0.087 54	0.062 62	36
37	0.234 30	0.196 20	0.164 44	0.137 93	0.115 79	0.081 81	0.057 99	37
38	0.225 29	0.187 75	0.156 61	0.130 74	0.109 24	0.076 46	0.053 69	38
39	0.216 62	0.179 67	0.149 15	0.123 92	0.103 06	0.071 46	0.049 71	39
40	0.208 29	0.171 93	0.142 05	0.117 46	0.097 22	0.066 78	0.046 03	40

Table VI MONTHLY PAYMENT TABLE FOR FINANCING $100

Effective Rate	Term in Months	Monthly Payment ($)	Effective Rate	Term in Months	Monthly Payment ($)	Effective Rate	Term in Months	Monthly Payment ($)
10%	6	17.15	**16%**	6	17.44	**22%**	6	17.74
	12	8.78		12	9.06		12	9.33
	18	6.00		18	6.26		18	6.52
	24	4.60		24	4.86		24	5.12
	30	3.76		30	4.02		30	4.28
	36	3.21		36	3.46		36	3.72
11%	6	17.20	**17%**	6	17.49	**23%**	6	17.78
	12	8.83		12	9.10		12	9.37
	18	6.04		18	6.30		18	6.57
	24	4.64		24	4.90		24	5.16
	30	3.81		30	4.07		30	4.32
	36	3.25		36	3.51		36	3.76
12%	6	17.25	**18%**	6	17.54	**24%**	6	17.83
	12	8.88		12	9.15		12	9.42
	18	6.08		18	6.35		18	6.61
	24	4.69		24	4.95		24	5.21
	30	3.85		30	4.11		30	4.37
	36	3.29		36	3.55		36	3.81
13%	6	17.30	**19%**	6	17.59	**25%**	6	17.88
	12	8.92		12	9.19		12	9.46
	18	6.13		18	6.39		18	6.66
	24	4.73		24	4.99		24	5.25
	30	3.89		30	4.15		30	4.41
	36	3.33		36	3.59		36	3.85
14%	6	17.35	**20%**	6	17.64	**26%**	6	17.93
	12	8.97		12	9.24		12	9.51
	18	6.17		18	6.44		18	6.70
	24	4.77		24	5.03		24	5.30
	30	3.94		30	4.19		30	4.45
	36	3.38		36	3.63		36	3.89
15%	6	17.40	**21%**	6	17.69	**27%**	6	17.98
	12	9.01		12	9.28		12	9.55
	18	6.22		18	6.48		18	6.74
	24	4.82		24	5.08		24	5.34
	30	3.98		30	4.24		30	4.50
	36	3.42		36	3.68		36	3.93

Table VII CANADA PENSION PLAN CONTRIBUTIONS

WEEKLY PAY PERIOD

199.39 — 350.96

Remuneration *Rémunération* From-*de*	To-*à*	C.P.P. *R.P.C.*	Remuneration *Rémunération* From-*de*	To-*à*	C.P.P. *R.P.C.*	Remuneration *Rémunération* From-*de*	To-*à*	C.P.P. *R.P.C.*	Remuneration *Rémunération* From-*de*	To-*à*	C.P.P. *R.P.C.*
199.39 -	199.91	2.88	237.29 -	237.80	3.60	275.18 -	275.70	4.32	313.07 -	313.59	5.04
199.92 -	200.43	2.89	237.81 -	238.33	3.61	275.71 -	276.22	4.33	313.60 -	314.12	5.05
200.44 -	200.96	2.90	238.34 -	238.85	3.62	276.23 -	276.75	4.34	314.13 -	314.64	5.06
200.97 -	201.49	2.91	238.86 -	239.38	3.63	276.76 -	277.28	4.35	314.65 -	315.17	5.07
201.50 -	202.01	2.92	239.39 -	239.91	3.64	277.29 -	277.80	4.36	315.18 -	315.70	5.08
202.02 -	202.54	2.93	239.92 -	240.43	3.65	277.81 -	278.33	4.37	315.71 -	316.22	5.09
202.55 -	203.06	2.94	240.44 -	240.96	3.66	278.34 -	278.85	4.38	316.23 -	316.75	5.10
203.07 -	203.59	2.95	240.97 -	241.49	3.67	278.86 -	279.38	4.39	316.76 -	317.28	5.11
203.60 -	204.12	2.96	241.50 -	242.01	3.68	279.39 -	279.91	4.40	317.29 -	317.80	5.12
204.13 -	204.64	2.97	242.02 -	242.54	3.69	279.92 -	280.43	4.41	317.81 -	318.33	5.13
204.65 -	205.17	2.98	242.55 -	243.06	3.70	280.44 -	280.96	4.42	318.34 -	318.85	5.14
205.18 -	205.70	2.99	243.07 -	243.59	3.71	280.97 -	281.49	4.43	318.86 -	319.38	5.15
205.71 -	206.22	3.00	243.60 -	244.12	3.72	281.50 -	282.01	4.44	319.39 -	319.91	5.16
206.23 -	206.75	3.01	244.13 -	244.64	3.73	282.02 -	282.54	4.45	319.92 -	320.43	5.17
206.76 -	207.28	3.02	244.65 -	245.17	3.74	282.55 -	283.06	4.46	320.44 -	320.96	5.18
207.29 -	207.80	3.03	245.18 -	245.70	3.75	283.07 -	283.59	4.47	320.97 -	321.49	5.19
207.81 -	208.33	3.04	245.71 -	246.22	3.76	283.60 -	284.12	4.48	321.50 -	322.01	5.20
208.34 -	208.85	3.05	246.23 -	246.75	3.77	284.13 -	284.64	4.49	322.02 -	322.54	5.21
208.86 -	209.38	3.06	246.76 -	247.28	3.78	284.65 -	285.17	4.50	322.55 -	323.06	5.22
209.39 -	209.91	3.07	247.29 -	247.80	3.79	285.18 -	285.70	4.51	323.07 -	323.59	5.23
209.92 -	210.43	3.08	247.81 -	248.33	3.80	285.71 -	286.22	4.52	323.60 -	324.12	5.24
210.44 -	210.96	3.09	248.34 -	248.85	3.81	286.23 -	286.75	4.53	324.13 -	324.64	5.25
210.97 -	211.49	3.10	248.86 -	249.38	3.82	286.76 -	287.28	4.54	324.65 -	325.17	5.26
211.50 -	212.01	3.11	249.39 -	249.91	3.83	287.29 -	287.80	4.55	325.18 -	325.70	5.27
212.02 -	212.54	3.12	249.92 -	250.43	3.84	287.81 -	288.33	4.56	325.71 -	326.22	5.28
212.55 -	213.06	3.13	250.44 -	250.96	3.85	288.34 -	288.85	4.57	326.23 -	326.75	5.29
213.07 -	213.59	3.14	250.97 -	251.49	3.86	288.86 -	289.38	4.58	326.76 -	327.28	5.30
213.60 -	214.12	3.15	251.50 -	252.01	3.87	289.39 -	289.91	4.59	327.29 -	327.80	5.31
214.13 -	214.64	3.16	252.02 -	252.54	3.88	289.92 -	290.43	4.60	327.81 -	328.33	5.32
214.65 -	215.17	3.17	252.55 -	253.06	3.89	290.44 -	290.96	4.61	328.34 -	328.85	5.33
215.18 -	215.70	3.18	253.07 -	253.59	3.90	290.97 -	291.49	4.62	328.86 -	329.38	5.34
215.71 -	216.22	3.19	253.60 -	254.12	3.91	291.50 -	292.01	4.63	329.39 -	329.91	5.35
216.23 -	216.75	3.20	254.13 -	254.64	3.92	292.02 -	292.54	4.64	329.92 -	330.43	5.36
216.76 -	217.28	3.21	254.65 -	255.17	3.93	292.55 -	293.06	4.65	330.44 -	330.96	5.37
217.29 -	217.80	3.22	255.18 -	255.70	3.94	293.07 -	293.59	4.66	330.97 -	331.49	5.38
217.81 -	218.33	3.23	255.71 -	256.22	3.95	293.60 -	294.12	4.67	331.50 -	332.01	5.39
218.34 -	218.85	3.24	256.23 -	256.75	3.96	294.13 -	294.64	4.68	332.02 -	332.54	5.40
218.86 -	219.38	3.25	256.76 -	257.28	3.97	294.65 -	295.17	4.69	332.55 -	333.06	5.41
219.39 -	219.91	3.26	257.29 -	257.80	3.98	295.18 -	295.70	4.70	333.07 -	333.59	5.42
219.92 -	220.43	3.27	257.81 -	258.33	3.99	295.71 -	296.22	4.71	333.60 -	334.12	5.43
220.44 -	220.96	3.28	258.34 -	258.85	4.00	296.23 -	296.75	4.72	334.13 -	334.64	5.44
220.97 -	221.49	3.29	258.86 -	259.38	4.01	296.76 -	297.28	4.73	334.65 -	335.17	5.45
221.50 -	222.01	3.30	259.39 -	259.91	4.02	297.29 -	297.80	4.74	335.18 -	335.70	5.46
222.02 -	222.54	3.31	259.92 -	260.43	4.03	297.81 -	298.33	4.75	335.71 -	336.22	5.47
222.55 -	223.06	3.32	260.44 -	260.96	4.04	298.34 -	298.85	4.76	336.23 -	336.75	5.48
223.07 -	223.59	3.33	260.97 -	261.49	4.05	298.86 -	299.38	4.77	336.76 -	337.28	5.49
223.60 -	224.12	3.34	261.50 -	262.01	4.06	299.39 -	299.91	4.78	337.29 -	337.80	5.50
224.13 -	224.64	3.35	262.02 -	262.54	4.07	299.92 -	300.43	4.79	337.81 -	338.33	5.51
224.65 -	225.17	3.36	262.55 -	263.06	4.08	300.44 -	300.96	4.80	338.34 -	338.85	5.52
225.18 -	225.70	3.37	263.07 -	263.59	4.09	300.97 -	301.49	4.81	338.86 -	339.38	5.53
225.71 -	226.22	3.38	263.60 -	264.12	4.10	301.50 -	302.01	4.82	339.39 -	339.91	5.54
226.23 -	226.75	3.39	264.13 -	264.64	4.11	302.02 -	302.54	4.83	339.92 -	340.43	5.55
226.76 -	227.28	3.40	264.65 -	265.17	4.12	302.55 -	303.06	4.84	340.44 -	340.96	5.56
227.29 -	227.80	3.41	265.18 -	265.70	4.13	303.07 -	303.59	4.85	340.97 -	341.49	5.57
227.81 -	228.33	3.42	265.71 -	266.22	4.14	303.60 -	304.12	4.86	341.50 -	342.01	5.58
228.34 -	228.85	3.43	266.23 -	266.75	4.15	304.13 -	304.64	4.87	342.02 -	342.54	5.59
228.86 -	229.38	3.44	266.76 -	267.28	4.16	304.65 -	305.17	4.88	342.55 -	343.06	5.60
229.39 -	229.91	3.45	267.29 -	267.80	4.17	305.18 -	305.70	4.89	343.07 -	343.59	5.61
229.92 -	230.43	3.46	267.81 -	268.33	4.18	305.71 -	306.22	4.90	343.60 -	344.12	5.62
230.44 -	230.96	3.47	268.34 -	268.85	4.19	306.23 -	306.75	4.91	344.13 -	344.64	5.63
230.97 -	231.49	3.48	268.86 -	269.38	4.20	306.76 -	307.28	4.92	344.65 -	345.17	5.64
231.50 -	232.01	3.49	269.39 -	269.91	4.21	307.29 -	307.80	4.93	345.18 -	345.70	5.65
232.02 -	232.54	3.50	269.92 -	270.43	4.22	307.81 -	308.33	4.94	345.71 -	346.22	5.66
232.55 -	233.06	3.51	270.44 -	270.96	4.23	308.34 -	308.85	4.95	346.23 -	346.75	5.67
233.07 -	233.59	3.52	270.97 -	271.49	4.24	308.86 -	309.38	4.96	346.76 -	347.28	5.68
233.60 -	234.12	3.53	271.50 -	272.01	4.25	309.39 -	309.91	4.97	347.29 -	347.80	5.69
234.13 -	234.64	3.54	272.02 -	272.54	4.26	309.92 -	310.43	4.98	347.81 -	348.33	5.70
234.65 -	235.17	3.55	272.55 -	273.06	4.27	310.44 -	310.96	4.99	348.34 -	348.85	5.71
235.18 -	235.70	3.56	273.07 -	273.59	4.28	310.97 -	311.49	5.00	348.86 -	349.38	5.72
235.71 -	236.22	3.57	273.60 -	274.12	4.29	311.50 -	312.01	5.01	349.39 -	349.91	5.73
236.23 -	236.75	3.58	274.13 -	274.64	4.30	312.02 -	312.54	5.02	349.92 -	350.43	5.74
236.76 -	237.28	3.59	274.65 -	275.17	4.31	312.55 -	313.06	5.03	350.44 -	350.96	5.75

Table VIII UNEMPLOYMENT INSURANCE PREMIUMS

For minimum and maximum insurable earnings amounts for various pay periods see Schedule II. For the maximum premium deduction for various pay periods see bottom of this page.

Les montants minimum et maximum des gains assurables pour diverses périodes de paie figurent en annexe II. La déduction maximale de primes pour diverses périodes de paie figure au bas de la présente page.

Remuneration *Rémunération* From-*de*	To-*à*	U.I. Premium *Prime d'a.-c.*	Remuneration *Rémunération* From-*de*	To-*à*	U.I. Premium *Prime d'a.-c.*	Remuneration *Rémunération* From-*de*	To-*à*	U.I. Premium *Prime d'a.-c.*	Remuneration *Rémunération* From-*de*	To-*à*	U.I. Premium *Prime d'a.-c.*
245.32 -	245.74	5.77	275.96 -	276.38	6.49	306.60 -	307.02	7.21	337.24 -	337.65	7.93
245.75 -	246.17	5.78	276.39 -	276.80	6.50	307.03 -	307.44	7.22	337.66 -	338.08	7.94
246.18 -	246.59	5.79	276.81 -	277.23	6.51	307.45 -	307.87	7.23	338.09 -	338.51	7.95
246.60 -	247.02	5.80	277.24 -	277.65	6.52	307.88 -	308.29	7.24	338.52 -	338.93	7.96
247.03 -	247.44	5.81	277.66 -	278.08	6.53	308.30 -	308.72	7.25	338.94 -	339.36	7.97
247.45 -	247.87	5.82	278.09 -	278.51	6.54	308.73 -	309.14	7.26	339.37 -	339.78	7.98
247.88 -	248.29	5.83	278.52 -	278.93	6.55	309.15 -	309.57	7.27	339.79 -	340.21	7.99
248.30 -	248.72	5.84	278.94 -	279.36	6.56	309.58 -	309.99	7.28	340.22 -	340.63	8.00
248.73 -	249.14	5.85	279.37 -	279.78	6.57	310.00 -	310.42	7.29	340.64 -	341.06	8.01
249.15 -	249.57	5.86	279.79 -	280.21	6.58	310.43 -	310.85	7.30	341.07 -	341.48	8.02
249.58 -	249.99	5.87	280.22 -	280.63	6.59	310.86 -	311.27	7.31	341.49 -	341.91	8.03
250.00 -	250.42	5.88	280.64 -	281.06	6.60	311.28 -	311.70	7.32	341.92 -	342.34	8.04
250.43 -	250.85	5.89	281.07 -	281.48	6.61	311.71 -	312.12	7.33	342.35 -	342.76	8.05
250.86 -	251.27	5.90	281.49 -	281.91	6.62	312.13 -	312.55	7.34	342.77 -	343.19	8.06
251.28 -	251.70	5.91	281.92 -	282.34	6.63	312.56 -	312.97	7.35	343.20 -	343.61	8.07
251.71 -	252.12	5.92	282.35 -	282.76	6.64	312.98 -	313.40	7.36	343.62 -	344.04	8.08
252.13 -	252.55	5.93	282.77 -	283.19	6.65	313.41 -	313.82	7.37	344.05 -	344.46	8.09
252.56 -	252.97	5.94	283.20 -	283.61	6.66	313.83 -	314.25	7.38	344.47 -	344.89	8.10
252.98 -	253.40	5.95	283.62 -	284.04	6.67	314.26 -	314.68	7.39	344.90 -	345.31	8.11
253.41 -	253.82	5.96	284.05 -	284.46	6.68	314.69 -	315.10	7.40	345.32 -	345.74	8.12
253.83 -	254.25	5.97	284.47 -	284.89	6.69	315.11 -	315.53	7.41	345.75 -	346.17	8.13
254.26 -	254.68	5.98	284.90 -	285.31	6.70	315.54 -	315.95	7.42	346.18 -	346.59	8.14
254.69 -	255.10	5.99	285.32 -	285.74	6.71	315.96 -	316.38	7.43	346.60 -	347.02	8.15
255.11 -	255.53	6.00	285.75 -	286.17	6.72	316.39 -	316.80	7.44	347.03 -	347.44	8.16
255.54 -	255.95	6.01	286.18 -	286.59	6.73	316.81 -	317.23	7.45	347.45 -	347.87	8.17
255.96 -	256.38	6.02	286.60 -	287.02	6.74	317.24 -	317.65	7.46	347.88 -	348.29	8.18
256.39 -	256.80	6.03	287.03 -	287.44	6.75	317.66 -	318.08	7.47	348.30 -	348.72	8.19
256.81 -	257.23	6.04	287.45 -	287.87	6.76	318.09 -	318.51	7.48	348.73 -	349.14	8.20
257.24 -	257.65	6.05	287.88 -	288.29	6.77	318.52 -	318.93	7.49	349.15 -	349.57	8.21
257.66 -	258.08	6.06	288.30 -	288.72	6.78	318.94 -	319.36	7.50	349.58 -	349.99	8.22
258.09 -	258.51	6.07	288.73 -	289.14	6.79	319.37 -	319.78	7.51	350.00 -	350.42	8.23
258.52 -	258.93	6.08	289.15 -	289.57	6.80	319.79 -	320.21	7.52	350.43 -	350.85	8.24
258.94 -	259.36	6.09	289.58 -	289.99	6.81	320.22 -	320.63	7.53	350.86 -	351.27	8.25
259.37 -	259.78	6.10	290.00 -	290.42	6.82	320.64 -	321.06	7.54	351.28 -	351.70	8.26
259.79 -	260.21	6.11	290.43 -	290.85	6.83	321.07 -	321.48	7.55	351.71 -	352.12	8.27
260.22 -	260.63	6.12	290.86 -	291.27	6.84	321.49 -	321.91	7.56	352.13 -	352.55	8.28
260.64 -	261.06	6.13	291.28 -	291.70	6.85	321.92 -	322.34	7.57	352.56 -	352.97	8.29
261.07 -	261.48	6.14	291.71 -	292.12	6.86	322.35 -	322.76	7.58	352.98 -	353.40	8.30
261.49 -	261.91	6.15	292.13 -	292.55	6.87	322.77 -	323.19	7.59	353.41 -	353.82	8.31
261.92 -	262.34	6.16	292.56 -	292.97	6.88	323.20 -	323.61	7.60	353.83 -	354.25	8.32
262.35 -	262.76	6.17	292.98 -	293.40	6.89	323.62 -	324.04	7.61	354.26 -	354.68	8.33
262.77 -	263.19	6.18	293.41 -	293.82	6.90	324.05 -	324.46	7.62	354.69 -	355.10	8.34
263.20 -	263.61	6.19	293.83 -	294.25	6.91	324.47 -	324.89	7.63	355.11 -	355.53	8.35
263.62 -	264.04	6.20	294.26 -	294.68	6.92	324.90 -	325.31	7.64	355.54 -	355.95	8.36
264.05 -	264.46	6.21	294.69 -	295.10	6.93	325.32 -	325.74	7.65	355.96 -	356.38	8.37
264.47 -	264.89	6.22	295.11 -	295.53	6.94	325.75 -	326.17	7.66	356.39 -	356.80	8.38
264.90 -	265.31	6.23	295.54 -	295.95	6.95	326.18 -	326.59	7.67	356.81 -	357.23	8.39
265.32 -	265.74	6.24	295.96 -	296.38	6.96	326.60 -	327.02	7.68	357.24 -	357.65	8.40
265.75 -	266.17	6.25	296.39 -	296.80	6.97	327.03 -	327.44	7.69	357.66 -	358.08	8.41
266.18 -	266.59	6.26	296.81 -	297.23	6.98	327.45 -	327.87	7.70	358.09 -	358.51	8.42
266.60 -	267.02	6.27	297.24 -	297.65	6.99	327.88 -	328.29	7.71	358.52 -	358.93	8.43
267.03 -	267.44	6.28	297.66 -	298.08	7.00	328.30 -	328.72	7.72	358.94 -	359.36	8.44
267.45 -	267.87	6.29	298.09 -	298.51	7.01	328.73 -	329.14	7.73	359.37 -	359.78	8.45
267.88 -	268.29	6.30	298.52 -	298.93	7.02	329.15 -	329.57	7.74	359.79 -	360.21	8.46
268.30 -	268.72	6.31	298.94 -	299.36	7.03	329.58 -	329.99	7.75	360.22 -	360.63	8.47
268.73 -	269.14	6.32	299.37 -	299.78	7.04	330.00 -	330.42	7.76	360.64 -	361.06	8.48
269.15 -	269.57	6.33	299.79 -	300.21	7.05	330.43 -	330.85	7.77	361.07 -	361.48	8.49
269.58 -	269.99	6.34	300.22 -	300.63	7.06	330.86 -	331.27	7.78	361.49 -	361.91	8.50
270.00 -	270.42	6.35	300.64 -	301.06	7.07	331.28 -	331.70	7.79	361.92 -	362.34	8.51
270.43 -	270.85	6.36	301.07 -	301.48	7.08	331.71 -	332.12	7.80	362.35 -	362.76	8.52
270.86 -	271.27	6.37	301.49 -	301.91	7.09	332.13 -	332.55	7.81	362.77 -	363.19	8.53
271.28 -	271.70	6.38	301.92 -	302.34	7.10	332.56 -	332.97	7.82	363.20 -	363.61	8.54
271.71 -	272.12	6.39	302.35 -	302.76	7.11	332.98 -	333.40	7.83	363.62 -	364.04	8.55
272.13 -	272.55	6.40	302.77 -	303.19	7.12	333.41 -	333.82	7.84	364.05 -	364.46	8.56
272.56 -	272.97	6.41	303.20 -	303.61	7.13	333.83 -	334.25	7.85	364.47 -	364.89	8.57
272.98 -	273.40	6.42	303.62 -	304.04	7.14	334.26 -	334.68	7.86	364.90 -	365.31	8.58
273.41 -	273.82	6.43	304.05 -	304.46	7.15	334.69 -	335.10	7.87	365.32 -	365.74	8.59
273.83 -	274.25	6.44	304.47 -	304.89	7.16	335.11 -	335.53	7.88	365.75 -	366.17	8.60
274.26 -	274.68	6.45	304.90 -	305.31	7.17	335.54 -	335.95	7.89	366.18 -	366.59	8.61
274.69 -	275.10	6.46	305.32 -	305.74	7.18	335.96 -	336.38	7.90	366.60 -	367.02	8.62
275.11 -	275.53	6.47	305.75 -	306.17	7.19	336.39 -	336.80	7.91	367.03 -	367.44	8.63
275.54 -	275.95	6.48	306.18 -	306.59	7.20	336.81 -	337.23	7.92	367.45 -	367.87	8.64

Maximum Premium Deduction for a Pay Period of the stated frequency. Déduction maximale de prime pour une période de paie d'une durée donnée.				
	Weekly - Hebdomadaire	12.46	10 pp per year - 10 pp par année	64.77
	Bi-Weekly - Deux semaines	24.91	13 pp per year - 13 pp par année	49.82
	Semi-Monthly - Bi-mensuel	26.99	22 pp per year - 22 pp par année	29.44
	Monthly - Mensuellement	53.97		

Table IX INCOME TAX DEDUCTIONS AT SOURCE

WEEKLY TAX DEDUCTIONS
Basis — 52 Pay Periods per Year

WEEKLY PAY Use appropriate bracket — PAIE PAR SEMAINE Utilisez le palier approprié	IF THE EMPLOYEE'S "NET CLAIM CODE" ON FORM TD1 IS — SI LE «CODE DE DEMANDE NETTE» DE L'EMPLOYÉ SELON LA FORMULE TD1 EST DE													See note on page 36 Voir remarque p. 36
	1	2	3	4	5	6	7	8	9	10	11	12	13	Column A Colonne A
	DEDUCT FROM EACH PAY — *RETENEZ SUR CHAQUE PAIE*													
171.00 - 172.99	15.95	14.00	10.50	7.20	4.60	1.20	.75	.10						
173.00 - 174.99	16.45	14.55	11.05	7.70	6.10	1.35	.90	.20						
175.00 - 176.99	17.00	15.05	11.55	8.20	7.05	1.45	1.00	.35						
177.00 - 178.99	17.50	15.60	12.10	8.65	7.55	1.60	1.15	.45						
179.00 - 180.99	18.05	16.10	12.60	9.20	8.05	1.95	1.25	.60						
181.00 - 182.99	18.55	16.60	13.10	9.70	8.50	2.25	1.40	.70						
183.00 - 184.99	19.05	17.15	13.65	10.20	9.05	2.60	1.50	.80						
185.00 - 186.99	19.60	17.65	14.15	10.75	9.55	2.90	1.75	.95						
187.00 - 188.99	20.10	18.20	14.70	11.25	10.10	3.25	2.05	1.05	.15					
189.00 - 190.99	20.65	18.70	15.20	11.80	10.60	3.60	2.40	1.20	.25					
191.00 - 192.99	21.15	19.25	15.70	12.30	11.10	3.90	2.70	1.30	.40					
193.00 - 194.99	21.65	19.75	16.25	12.80	11.65	5.20	3.05	1.45	.50					
195.00 - 196.99	22.25	20.25	16.75	13.35	12.15	6.70	3.40	1.55	.65					
197.00 - 158.99	22.80	20.80	17.30	13.85	12.70	7.30	3.70	1.90	.75					
199.00 - 200.99	23.35	21.30	17.80	14.40	13.20	7.75	4.30	2.20	.85					
201.00 - 202.99	23.90	21.85	18.35	14.90	13.70	8.25	5.80	2.55	1.00					
203.00 - 204.99	24.45	22.40	18.85	15.40	14.25	8.75	7.00	2.90	1.10	.10				
205.00 - 206.99	25.00	22.95	19.35	15.95	14.75	9.25	7.45	3.20	1.25	.25				
207.00 - 208.99	25.55	23.50	19.90	16.45	15.30	9.80	7.95	3.55	1.35	.35				
209.00 - 210.99	26.10	24.05	20.40	17.00	15.80	10.30	8.45	3.85	1.50	.50				
211.00 - 212.99	26.65	24.60	20.95	17.50	16.30	10.80	8.95	5.00	1.70	.60				
213.00 - 214.99	27.20	25.15	21.45	18.00	16.85	11.35	9.45	6.50	2.00	.75				
215.00 - 216.99	27.75	25.70	22.00	18.55	17.35	11.85	10.00	7.20	2.35	.85				
217.00 - 218.99	28.30	26.25	22.55	19.05	17.90	12.40	10.50	7.70	2.70	1.00				
219.00 - 220.99	28.85	26.80	23.10	19.60	18.40	12.90	11.05	8.20	3.00	1.10	.05			
221.00 - 225.99	29.80	27.80	24.05	20.50	19.30	13.80	11.95	9.05	3.60	1.30	.25			
226.00 - 230.99	31.20	29.15	25.45	21.80	20.60	15.10	13.25	10.35	6.00	1.70	.60			
231.00 - 235.99	32.55	30.55	26.80	23.20	21.95	16.40	14.55	11.65	7.80	2.55	.90			
236.00 - 240.99	33.95	31.90	28.20	24.55	23.35	17.70	15.85	12.95	9.00	3.35	1.20	.20		
241.00 - 245.99	35.30	33.30	29.60	25.95	24.70	19.00	17.15	14.25	10.30	5.00	1.50	.50		
246.00 - 250.99	36.75	34.65	30.95	27.35	26.10	20.30	18.45	15.55	11.60	7.45	2.20	.80	.25	.25
251.00 - 255.99	38.20	36.05	32.35	28.70	27.45	21.60	19.75	16.85	12.90	8.65	3.05	1.10	.55	.55
256.00 - 260.99	39.65	37.50	33.70	30.10	28.85	23.00	21.05	18.15	14.20	9.95	3.85	1.40	.85	.85
261.00 - 265.99	41.10	38.95	35.10	31.45	30.20	24.40	22.40	19.45	15.50	11.25	7.00	2.00	1.15	1.15
266.00 - 270.99	42.55	40.40	36.50	32.85	31.60	25.75	23.80	20.75	16.80	12.55	8.20	2.85		
271.00 - 275.99	44.05	41.90	37.95	34.20	32.95	27.15	25.15	22.10	18.10	13.85	9.45	3.65	1.45	1.45
276.00 - 280.99	45.50	43.35	39.40	35.60	34.35	28.50	26.55	23.50	19.40	15.15	10.75	6.30	2.15	2.15
281.00 - 285.99	46.95	44.80	40.85	37.05	35.70	29.90	27.90	24.85	20.70	16.45	12.05	7.85	2.95	2.95
286.00 - 290.99	48.40	46.25	42.30	38.50	37.20	31.25	29.30	26.25	22.05	17.75	13.35	9.10	3.80	3.80
291.00 - 255.99	49.85	47.70	43.80	39.95	38.65	32.65	30.65	27.60	23.45	19.05	14.65	10.40	6.85	3.80

Table IX *(Continued)*

WEEKLY TAX DEDUCTIONS
Basis — 52 Pay Periods per Year

WEEKLY PAY Use appropriate bracket — PAIE PAR SEMAINE Utilisez le palier approprié	IF THE EMPLOYEE'S "NET CLAIM CODE" ON FORM TD1 IS — SI LE «CODE DE DEMANDE NETTE» DE L'EMPLOYÉ SELON LA FORMULE TD1 EST DE													See note on page 36 Voir remarque p. 36
	1	2	3	4	5	6	7	8	9	10	11	12	13	
	DEDUCT FROM EACH PAY — *RETENEZ SUR CHAQUE PAIE*													Column A Colonne A
296.00 - 300.99	51.30	49.15	45.25	41.40	40.10	34.05	32.05	29.00	24.80	20.35	15.95	11.70	8.05	3.80
301.00 - 305.99	52.75	50.60	46.70	42.85	41.55	35.40	33.40	30.35	26.20	21.65	17.25	13.00	9.30	3.80
306.00 - 310.99	54.20	52.05	48.15	44.30	43.00	36.85	34.80	31.75	27.55	23.05	18.55	14.30	10.60	3.80
311.00 - 315.99	55.65	53.50	49.60	45.75	44.45	38.30	36.20	33.15	28.95	24.45	19.85	15.60	11.90	3.80
316.00 - 320.99	57.10	54.95	51.05	47.20	45.90	39.75	37.65	34.50	30.30	25.80	21.15	16.90	13.20	3.80
321.00 - 325.99	58.55	56.40	52.50	48.65	47.35	41.20	39.10	35.90	31.70	27.20	22.55	18.20	14.50	3.80
326.00 - 330.99	60.00	57.85	53.95	50.10	48.80	42.65	40.55	37.35	33.05	28.55	23.90	19.50	15.80	3.80
331.00 - 335.99	61.45	59.30	55.40	51.60	50.25	44.10	42.00	38.80	34.45	29.95	25.30	20.80	17.10	3.80
336.00 - 340.99	62.90	60.75	56.85	53.05	51.70	45.55	43.45	40.25	35.85	31.35	26.65	22.15	18.40	3.80
341.00 - 345.99	64.40	62.20	58.30	54.50	53.15	47.00	44.90	41.70	37.30	32.70	28.05	23.55	19.70	3.85
346.00 - 350.99	65.85	63.70	59.75	55.95	54.60	48.45	46.40	43.15	38.75	34.10	29.40	24.90	21.00	3.90
351.00 - 355.99	67.40	65.15	61.20	57.40	56.10	49.95	47.85	44.60	40.20	35.45	30.80	26.30	22.40	3.90
356.00 - 360.99	68.90	66.65	62.65	58.85	57.55	51.40	49.30	46.05	41.65	36.90	32.15	27.65	23.75	3.90
361.00 - 365.99	70.45	68.20	64.15	60.30	59.00	52.85	50.75	47.50	43.10	38.35	33.55	29.05	25.15	3.90
366.00 - 370.99	72.00	69.70	65.60	61.75	60.45	54.30	52.20	49.00	44.55	39.80	34.95	30.45	26.50	3.95
371.00 - 375.99	73.50	71.25	67.15	63.20	61.90	55.75	53.65	50.45	46.00	41.25	36.35	31.80	27.90	3.95
376.00 - 380.99	75.05	72.80	68.65	64.65	63.35	57.20	55.10	51.90	47.45	42.70	37.80	33.20	29.25	3.95
381.00 - 385.99	76.55	74.30	70.20	66.15	64.80	58.65	56.55	53.35	48.90	44.15	39.25	34.55	30.65	3.95
386.00 - 390.99	78.10	75.85	71.70	67.70	66.30	60.10	58.00	54.80	50.35	45.60	40.70	35.95	32.00	3.95
391.00 - 395.99	79.65	77.35	73.25	69.20	67.85	61.55	59.45	56.25	51.85	47.05	42.15	37.40	33.40	4.00
396.00 - 400.99	81.15	78.90	74.80	70.75	69.35	63.00	60.90	57.70	53.30	48.55	43.60	38.85	34.75	4.10
401.00 - 405.99	82.70	80.45	76.30	72.25	70.90	64.45	62.35	59.15	54.75	50.00	45.05	40.30	36.15	4.15
406.00 - 410.99	84.20	81.95	77.85	73.80	72.40	65.95	63.80	60.60	56.20	51.45	46.50	41.75	37.65	4.15
411.00 - 415.99	85.75	83.50	79.35	75.35	73.95	67.50	65.25	62.05	57.65	52.90	47.95	43.20	39.10	4.15
416.00 - 420.99	87.30	85.00	80.90	76.85	75.50	69.00	66.80	63.50	59.10	54.35	49.40	44.65	40.55	4.15
421.00 - 425.99	88.80	86.55	82.45	78.40	77.00	70.55	68.35	64.95	60.55	55.80	50.90	46.10	42.00	4.15
426.00 - 430.99	90.35	88.10	83.95	79.90	78.55	72.05	69.85	66.50	62.00	57.25	52.35	47.60	43.45	4.15
431.00 - 435.99	91.85	89.60	85.50	81.45	80.05	73.60	71.40	68.00	63.45	58.70	53.80	49.05	44.90	4.15
436.00 - 440.99	93.40	91.15	87.00	83.00	81.60	75.15	72.90	69.55	64.90	60.15	55.25	50.50	46.35	4.15
441.00 - 445.99	94.95	92.65	88.55	84.50	83.15	76.65	74.45	71.05	66.40	61.60	56.70	51.95	47.80	4.15
446.00 - 450.99	96.50	94.20	90.10	86.05	84.65	78.20	76.00	72.60	67.95	63.05	58.15	53.40	49.25	4.15
451.00 - 455.99	98.25	95.75	91.60	87.55	86.20	79.70	77.50	74.15	69.50	64.50	59.60	54.85	50.70	4.15
456.00 - 460.99	100.00	97.40	93.15	89.10	87.70	81.25	79.05	75.65	71.00	66.00	61.05	56.30	52.15	4.15
461.00 - 465.99	101.75	99.15	94.65	90.65	89.25	82.80	80.55	77.20	72.55	67.55	62.50	57.75	53.60	4.15
466.00 - 470.99	103.55	100.90	96.20	92.15	90.80	84.30	82.10	78.70	74.05	69.05	63.95	59.20	55.05	4.15
471.00 - 480.99	106.15	103.55	98.85	94.45	93.10	86.60	84.40	81.00	76.35	71.35	66.20	61.40	57.25	4.15
481.00 - 490.99	109.70	107.10	102.35	97.70	96.15	89.65	87.45	84.05	79.40	74.40	69.25	64.30	60.15	4.15
491.00 - 500.99	113.20	110.60	105.85	101.25	99.65	92.70	90.50	87.15	82.50	77.50	72.30	67.30	63.05	4.25
501.00 - 510.99	116.75	114.10	109.40	104.75	103.15	95.80	93.60	90.20	85.55	80.55	75.35	70.35	66.00	4.35
511.00 - 520.99	120.25	117.65	112.90	108.25	106.70	99.25	96.70	93.25	88.60	83.60	78.40	73.40	69.05	4.35

ANSWERS

REVIEW AND PREVIEW TO CHAPTER 1

MENTAL MATH

1. (a) 18 (b) 19 (c) −5 (d) 30 (e) 18
 (f) 35 (g) −18 (h) 10 (i) 5 (j) 40
2. (a) 0.6 (b) 0.6 (c) 0.0063 (d) 1.23 (e) 1.2 (f) 3200
 (g) 0.321 (h) 20 (i) 3.5 (j) 56 (k) 1230 (l) 0.2
3. (a) 40 (b) 7 (c) 3.5 (d) 12 (e) 69 (f) 77
 (g) 9300 (h) 7 (i) 8 (j) 108 (k) 12 (l) 76
 (m) 5 (n) 152 (o) 0.045 (p) 7000

PERCENT

1. (a) 5 (b) 75 (c) 1 (d) 84 (e) 1.3 (f) 1.65
 (g) 8.75 (h) 0.875 (i) 1.35 (j) 1.65 (k) 71 (l) 240
2. (a) 50% (b) 25% (c) 25% (d) 10% (e) 20% (f) $1\frac{2}{3}$%
3. (a) 62.5% (b) 75% (c) 250% (d) 125%
 (e) 20% (f) 35% (g) 110% (h) 5%
4. (a) $12.49 (b) $37.46
5. $7.96
6. 46% (nearest percent)
7. $3900.

ROUNDING RULES

1. (a) 60 (b) 540 (c) 9390 (d) 130
2. (a) 13.3 (b) 853.4 (c) 928.5 (d) 0.8
3. (a) 37.43 (b) 6.12 (c) 7.29 (d) 256.20
4. (a) 24.8 (b) 95.6 (c) 81.6 (d) 96.7
 (e) 6.6 (f) 5.2 (g) 7.4
5. (a) 73.341 (b) 442.2675 (c) 242.494 56 (d) 22.3675
 (e) 20.625 (f) 11.729 536 (g) 1.096 610 17 (h) 75.8065
 (i) 20.982 394 7 (j) 0.009 173 469

PRECISION AND ACCURACY IN MEASUREMENT

1. (a) 3 (b) 3 (c) 4 (d) 2 (e) 2 (f) 4
 (g) 3 (h) 5 (i) 4 (j) 3
2. (a) 66.8 (b) 5470 (c) 565
 (d) 3.09 (e) 5.82 (f) 9.00×10^2
3. (a) 42 (b) 100 (c) 600 (d) 60 (e) 1000
 (f) 100 (g) 8 (h) 5 (i) 5 (j) 8
4. (a) 13.354 (b) 568.86 (c) 90.000 (d) 910.1
 (e) 51 (f) 35 (g) 22 (h) 49.0
 (i) 0.17 (j) 5.0×10^2 (k) 7.61×10^5 (l) 0.0856
5. (a) 17.6 cm (b) 26.0 cm (c) 11.2 cm (d) 9.6 cm
6. (a) 47 cm^2 (b) 19 m^2 (c) 24 cm^2 (d) 10.2 cm^2

EXERCISE 1.1

1. (a) 23 (b) 80 (c) 100 (d) 400 (e) 400 (f) 27
 (g) 3 (h) 27
2. (a) 17 (b) 20 (c) 43 (d) 21 (e) 4 (f) 9
 (g) 0 (h) 2461 (i) 36 (j) 49 (k) 5.5 (l) 5
 (m) 11 (n) 7
3. (a) 30 (b) 4 (c) 12 (d) 1 (e) 2 (f) 0.8
 (g) 67 (h) 6
4. (a) $3 \times (2 + 5) - 8 = 13$ (b) $(5 + 3) \times 2 - 4 = 12$
 (c) $3 + 2 \times (5 + 3) - 7 = 12$ (d) $4 \times (5 - 2) + 7 = 19$
 (e) $5 \times (4 + 3) \times 2 - 10 = 60$ (f) $(7 + 5) \times (3 + 4) + 11 = 95$
 (g) $16 - (5 + 4) + 7 = 14$

5. (a) 10.8 (b) 30.62 (c) 12 (d) 11.34
(e) 26.75 (f) 4.89 (g) 3.41 (h) 5.2
6. (a) 66.6 (b) 8.3 (c) 13.6 (d) 59.6
(e) 52.4 (f) 47.6 (g) 640.8
7. (a) 4.12 (b) 12.57 (c) 24.0
8. (a) 7.6 (b) 0.192 (c) 8 (d) 5.4
(e) 1.8 (f) 0.538 (g) 3.9
9. (a) 174 (b) 260 (c) 28 (d) 56
10. (a) 57.25 (b) 19.11 (c) 27.9375 (d) 29
11. (a) 8.45 (b) 54.6875 (c) 30.16 (d) 0.152 375
12. (a) 200.96 (b) 63.585 (c) 124.6266
(d) 17.340 65 (e) 86.052 406 5 (f) 113.983 962 5
13. (a) 66 (b) 10.35 (c) 10.5 (d) 18.0625 (e) 27.225 (f) 28.2

EXERCISE 1.2

1. 6000 L 2. No 3. $27.16 4. 435 5. $138.94 6. 2.723 kg
7. $30.23 8. (a) $23.62 (b) 64.5¢/L 9. $9.03 10. $455.96 11. $4512
12. $5480 per month

EXERCISE 1.3

1. (a) 13 (b) −11 (c) −4 (d) −1 (e) −24 (f) 27
(g) −45 (h) −48 (i) 6 (j) −3 (k) −8 (l) 5
2. (a) 8 (b) −12 (c) −6 (d) −14 (e) 14 (f) −14
(g) 9 (h) 7 (i) −12 (j) −18 (k) −14 (l) 6
3. (a) 35 (b) −24 (c) −48 (d) 36 (e) 36
(f) −48 (g) −22 (h) −12 (i) 6 (j) −12
4. (a) −5 (b) −3 (c) −11 (d) 4 (e) −2 (f) −13
(g) 4 (h) −5 (i) −4 (j) 11 (k) 11 (l) −3
5. (a) −10 (b) 60 (c) 2 (d) 6 (e) 17
(f) 4 (g) −14 (h) −18 (i) 11 (j) −35
6. (a) −8 (b) −8 (c) 16 (d) −16 (e) −27
(f) −27 (g) 25 (h) −25 (i) −1
7. (a) −19 (b) 3 (c) 7 (d) −2 (e) −5 (f) 2
8. (a) 11 (b) −10 (c) 0
9. (a) −20 (b) 11 (c) −13 (d) −1 (e) 6 (f) 14
(g) 12 (h) −16

EXERCISE 1.4

1. (a) $\frac{1}{3}$ (b) $\frac{1}{2}$ (c) $\frac{1}{2}$ (d) $\frac{3}{8}$ (e) $1\frac{1}{2}$ (f) $\frac{1}{24}$
(g) $\frac{2}{15}$ (h) $1\frac{1}{6}$
2. (a) $10\frac{1}{2}$ (b) $12\frac{1}{2}$ (c) $15\frac{1}{9}$ (d) $17\frac{5}{8}$ (e) $1\frac{1}{5}$ (f) $7\frac{8}{9}$
(g) $7\frac{1}{6}$ (h) $\frac{9}{20}$
3. (a) $\frac{2}{15}$ (b) $\frac{1}{3}$ (c) $\frac{3}{8}$ (d) $\frac{9}{10}$ (e) $-44\frac{1}{3}$ (f) $22\frac{1}{2}$
(g) $2\frac{2}{3}$ (h) $28\frac{1}{6}$
4. (a) $\frac{2}{3}$ (b) $1\frac{4}{5}$ (c) $-2\frac{1}{2}$ (d) $\frac{2}{15}$ (e) $\frac{9}{16}$ (f) $\frac{35}{144}$
(g) $3\frac{1}{32}$ (h) $6\frac{3}{8}$
5. (a) $\frac{27}{16}$ (b) $2\frac{15}{16}$ (c) $\frac{3}{4}$ (d) $\frac{19}{20}$

6. (a) $\frac{5}{12}$ (b) 1 (c) $\frac{5}{12}$ (d) $2\frac{4}{9}$ (e) $1\frac{2}{25}$ (f) $\frac{1}{12}$

7. (a) $9\frac{5}{12}$ h (b) $47.08

8. (a) $$14\frac{3}{8}$ (b) $$12\frac{3}{4}$ (c) $$4\frac{3}{8}$ (d) $2100

EXERCISE 1.5

1. (a) 4 : 5 (b) 1 : 3 (c) $\frac{3}{4}$ (d) $\frac{4}{5}$ (e) $\frac{3}{4}$ (f) $\frac{3}{4}$
   (g) 4 : 5 (h) 1 : 5
2. (a) $7\frac{1}{2}$ (b) 3 (c) 3 (d) 1 (e) 18 (f) 32
   (g) 28 (h) 24
3. (a) 3.2 (b) 11.2 (c) 6.5 (d) 25.2 (e) 8.6 (f) 5.1
   (g) 7.1 (h) 8.8 (i) 147.6 (j) 40.2 (k) 17.1 (l) 9.9
4. 900
5. Georgette: $3000, Royale: $1800
6. 12 000
7. 304 g
8. 28.75 g
9. 56
10. 45
11. (a) 49 : 36 (b) 7 : 6

EXERCISE 1.6

1. (a) equivalent (b) not equivalent (c) not equivalent
   (d) equivalent (e) not equivalent (f) not equivalent
2. (a) $\frac{1}{3}$ (b) 4 (c) $\frac{1}{4}$ (d) $\frac{1}{3}$ (e) 5 (f) k
   (g) $\frac{1}{m}$ (h) 2a
3. (a) k = 6, n = 2 (b) m = 5, n = 21 (c) k = 6, m = 33
   (d) k = 5, n = 13 (e) m = 30.6, n = 13.8 (f) m = 7.7, n = 40.3
4. (a) m = 2.6, n = 3.4 (b) k = 3.5, m = 3.4 (c) m = 2.7, p = 7.5
   (d) m = 6.1, n = 2.8 (e) m = 11.1, n = 9.3 (f) k = 23.1, p = 15.4
5. (a) 10 red cars, 40 grey cars (b) 120
6. Sam: 63, Carol: 105, Pat: 147
7. Sue: $13 421.05, Elaine: $17 894.74, Jennifer: $11 184.21

EXERCISE 1.7

1. $10
2. 12.5 m
3. $454.25
4. 592 km
5. approximately 148 L
6. the first store
7. (a) 9.2 L/100 km (b) 8 L/100 km (c) approximately 9.4 L/100 km
8. (a) 57.4 L (b) 77.9 L (c) 98.4 L
9. approximately 1 h 43 min

EXERCISE 1.8

1. (a) 17 (b) 25 (c) 37.5 (d) 20 (e) 54 (f) 324
   (g) 44
2. (a) 7 + 8 * (5 + 6) (b) 42 − 4 * 2 * (7 − 5) (c) 6 * 5 − 8
   (d) 2 * (ℓ + w) (e) 3.14 * r (f) (x + y) / 2
3. (a) −22 (b) −12 (c) 10 (d) 0.375
4. (a) HELLO PROFESSOR (b) 12.5, 38.16

EXERCISE 1.9

1. 6
2. $951.62
3. 38
4. $17.47
5. (a) 37, 43 (b) 50, 61 (c) 11, 5.5
6. 8

7. (a) 132 m (b) \$2810.68 (c) 66 (d) \$812.13 (e) \$4852.81
8. Answers will vary. 10. 4 11. \$183.65
12. (a) 1200 m (b) 8400 m 13. 19
15. (a) consecutive odd numbers (b) They are equal. (d) Evaluate 125^2.

EXERCISE 1.10

1. $5\frac{7}{8}$ 2. $-\frac{39}{44}$ 3. $11\frac{11}{56}$ 4. $2\frac{29}{168}$
5. $26\frac{1}{4}$ 6. $4\frac{19}{30}$ 7. $18\frac{45}{56}$ 8. $\frac{10}{33}$

1.11 REVIEW EXERCISE

1. (a) 4.12 (b) 36 700 (c) 15.2 (d) 6000 (e) 8000 (f) 0.051
2. 17.0 cm (to 3 significant digits)
3. (a) 4 (b) 3 (c) 4 (d) 2
4. 13.4 mm 5. (a) 12 (b) 3 (c) 40 (d) 800
6. (a) 1 (b) 58 (c) 2 (d) 36
7. (a) 28 (b) −4 (c) −10 (d) −5 (e) −4 (f) −11
(g) −11 (h) 3 (i) −5 (j) −27 (k) −27 (l) 5
8. (a) −4 (b) −4 (c) −34 (d) −6 (e) 19 (f) 0
(g) −2 (h) 3
9. (a) $1\frac{1}{4}$ (b) $\frac{17}{24}$ (c) $2\frac{1}{2}$ (d) $\frac{3}{5}$ (e) $\frac{19}{20}$ (f) $\frac{9}{20}$
(g) $5\frac{5}{6}$ (h) $2\frac{3}{10}$ (i) $6\frac{1}{3}$ (j) $2\frac{14}{15}$ (k) $19\frac{3}{8}$ (l) $1\frac{1}{6}$
(m) $\frac{1}{36}$ (n) $-\frac{1}{2}$ (o) $-\frac{3}{4}$ (p) $\frac{8}{27}$
10. (a) 15 (b) 5.76 (c) 60 (d) 8.145
11. A = 2.2, B = 1.5 cm, C = 5.5 cm, D = 1.3 cm
12. $\frac{13}{10}, \frac{13}{11}, \frac{11}{18}, \frac{5}{9}, -\frac{2}{3}, -\frac{5}{6}, -\frac{17}{20}$
13. (a) 8 (b) 32 (c) 6 (d) 15
14. (a) $\frac{1}{2}, \frac{1}{3}$ and $\frac{1}{6}$ (b) $\frac{1}{2}, \frac{2}{7}$ and $\frac{3}{14}$
15. Good News: 50%, Bad News: 12.5%, All The News: 37.5%
16. (a) 600 (b) $\frac{3}{8}$ (c) \$750 (d) $14\frac{3}{8}$ (e) 10
17. (a) \$117.50 (b) \$26.00 (c) (i) 17 (ii) 14 (iii) \$12.00
18. 795 revolutions per minute 19. 7.5 h
20. (a) 3 (b) 15 (c) 64 (d) 256
21. (a) 5 ^ 2 * 3 / 4 (b) h / 2 * (a + b) (c) x ^ y ÷ y ^ x
(d) a ^ (b * c) (e) (x + y) / (x − 2 * y) (f) (a/b) ^ c

1.12 CHAPTER 1 TEST

1. (a) 36 500 (b) 0.07 (c) 13.3 (d) 37.2
2. (a) 4 (b) 2 (c) 2 (d) 3
3. 16 cm^2 (nearest one)
4. (a) 428 (b) 2.0 (c) 6.46×10^3
5. (a) 3 (b) 0 (c) 6 (d) −2
6. (a) x = 1.4 (b) y = 6, z = 15
7. 28.6 mL (nearest tenth) 8. 285 kg
9. (a) 3.14 * r ^ 2 (b) 2 * 3.14 * r * (r + h) 10. 7 h 7 min 48 s

REVIEW AND PREVIEW TO CHAPTER 2

EXERCISE 1

1. (a) $\frac{3}{8}$ (b) $\frac{35}{48}$ (c) $23\frac{2}{5}$ (d) $3\frac{3}{32}$ (e) $6\frac{1}{4}$
   (f) $18\frac{2}{3}$ (g) $\frac{3}{14}$ (h) $1\frac{1}{8}$ (i) $14\frac{14}{15}$ (j) $7\frac{3}{20}$
2. (a) $4\frac{1}{2}$ (b) $1\frac{3}{17}$ (c) $1\frac{2}{3}$ (d) $1\frac{9}{13}$ (e) $2\frac{16}{19}$
   (f) $1\frac{11}{115}$ (g) $1\frac{7}{9}$ (h) $1\frac{9}{16}$ (i) $1\frac{5}{19}$ (j) $\frac{23}{30}$
3. (a) $1\frac{5}{12}$ (b) $4\frac{1}{10}$ (c) $7\frac{11}{12}$ (d) $6\frac{1}{24}$ (e) $12\frac{13}{24}$
   (f) $14\frac{1}{8}$ (g) $10\frac{3}{4}$ (h) $18\frac{7}{12}$ (i) $33\frac{1}{2}$
4. (a) $1\frac{5}{8}$ (b) $3\frac{5}{8}$ (c) $5\frac{3}{4}$ (d) $\frac{7}{8}$ (e) $12\frac{13}{40}$
   (f) $1\frac{11}{20}$ (g) $4\frac{3}{4}$ (h) $7\frac{1}{8}$ (i) $3\frac{9}{20}$ (j) $7\frac{4}{7}$
5. (a) $3\frac{1}{2}$ (b) $\frac{13}{48}$ (c) $\frac{23}{24}$ (d) $4\frac{1}{6}$ (e) $\frac{5}{6}$
   (f) $4\frac{20}{23}$ (g) $1\frac{3}{20}$ (h) $\frac{5}{48}$ (i) $1\frac{2}{7}$

EXERCISE 2

1. (a) 98 (b) 859 (c) 0.2 (d) 1600
   (e) 56 (f) 20 (g) 1300 (h) 0.037
2. (a) 1500 (b) 230 (c) 2 (d) 13 000
   (e) 31 (f) 370 (g) 1700 (h) 1.96
3. (a) 2.1 (b) 3.9 (c) 0.13 (d) 0.330
   (e) 47 (f) 0.25 (g) 1.32 (h) 0.055
4. (a) 72.1 (b) 0.60 (c) 8.7 (d) 11
   (e) 0.24 (f) 350 (g) 30.8 (h) 3.83

EXERCISE 3

1. (a) 4 (b) 9 (c) 25 (d) 64 (e) 1 (f) 16
   (g) 49 (h) 81 (i) 121 (j) 144 (k) 36 (l) 100
2. (a) 25 (b) 4 (c) 8 (d) −8 (e) 64 (f) 16
   (g) 36 (h) 121 (i) 27 (j) −27 (k) 81 (l) 125

EXERCISE 4

1. 40.63 2. 0.5439 3. 43 990 000 4. 0.000 543 5. 154.3
6. 0.1889 7. −58.95 8. 5.67 9. 80 500 000 10. 2.120

EXERCISE 5

1. 5 2. 7 3. 8 4. 10 5. 1 6. 2
7. 13 8. 15 9. 4 10. 9 11. 11 12. 12
13. 6 14. 3 15. 14 16. 100 17. 1.1 18. 1.2
19. 1.5 20. 0.5 21. 0.6 22. 0.9

EXERCISE 2.1

1. (a) 16 (b) 9 (c) 32 (d) 81 (e) 125 (f) 81
   (g) 49 (h) 1000
2. (a) a^7 (b) a^9 (c) a^8 (d) b^{11} (e) $3x^4$ (f) $6x^5$
   (g) $35x^7$ (h) $8a^5$
3. (a) $2a^3$ (b) $3a^3$ (c) $3x^2$ (d) $3m$ (e) $4a$ (f) t^2
4. (a) $\frac{1}{25}$ (b) 1 (c) 1 (d) $\frac{1}{9}$ (e) 1 (f) $\frac{1}{1000}$
5. (a) $\frac{1}{a^2}$ (b) a^6 (c) a^9 (d) x^4 (e) a^4 (f) $\frac{1}{a^4}$
6. (a) 64 (b) 81 (c) m^{15} (d) $16p^{12}$ (e) $625a^4$ (f) $27x^9$
   (g) −1 (h) −1 (i) −1 (j) $5n^{14}$ (k) $8x^6$ (l) −1

7. (a) a^3b^2 (b) $2a^3b$ (c) $3a^2b$ (d) b (e) $2a^4b^4$ (f) $2mn^2$
8. (a) 2^{a+b+c} (b) 4^a8^b (c) 3^c (d) 3^c (e) 2^b (f) a^{2b-1}

EXERCISE 2.2

1. (a) 187.4 (b) 1306.9 (c) 17.9
2. (a) 0.01 (b) 116.90 (c) 1 099 668 524.08
3. (a) 665.25 (b) 2668.20 (c) 400.19 (d) 7.66
4. 14.1 cm^2 (nearest tenth)
5. (a) \$3967.19 (b) \$8447.39 (c) \$4000.00
6. \$1653
7. (a) 20.49 (b) 9360.56
8. (a) \$2205.09 (b) \$3306.73 (c) \$2773.54

EXERCISE 2.3

1. (a) 3 (b) 5 (c) 2 (d) 4 (e) 5 (f) 9 (g) 3 (h) 25 (i) 5
2. (a) $\frac{1}{3}$ (b) $\frac{1}{25}$ (c) $\frac{1}{4}$ (d) $\frac{1}{2}$ (e) $\frac{1}{2}$ (f) $\frac{1}{6}$ (g) 9 (h) 4 (i) 27 (j) 8 (k) 125 (l) $\frac{1}{4}$
3. (a) 3 (b) $\frac{1}{32}$ (c) 8 (d) $\frac{1}{8}$ (e) 16 (f) 625 (g) 8 (h) 2 (i) $\frac{1}{16}$ (j) 4 (i) $\frac{1}{81}$ (j) 3
4. (a) 2 (b) $10^{0.75}$ (c) $10^{0.25}$ (d) $10^{\frac{2}{3}}$ (e) 5 (f) 2
5. (a) a^4 (b) $3ab^2$ (c) $25a^2$ (d) $4a^2$ (e) $27a^3$ (f) $2ab^2$
6. (a) 1.54 (b) 0.7 (c) 0.65 (d) 0.07 (e) 0.280 04 (f) 0.3636 (g) 8.4
7. (a) 27 (b) 64 (c) 48 (d) −810 (e) 3456 (f) 12 800 (g) 2688 (h) 124 416
8. 33 km
9. (a) 12 V (b) 120 V (c) 2 A, $\frac{5}{6}$ A
10. (a) 0.62 m (b) 1.24 m (c) 1.00 cm
11. (a) 4.4 s (b) 4.9 s (c) 5.5 s
12. (a) 2.01 s (b) 1.00 s

EXERCISE 2.4

1. (a) 6.5 (b) 11.3 (c) 5.4 (d) 11.8 (e) 18.6 (f) 7.8 (g) 0.2 (h) 0.2 (i) 0.8
2. (a) 2.6 (b) 1.4 (c) 2.4 (d) 47.4 (e) 44.7 (f) 2 (g) 3.6 (h) 6.7 (i) 4.5 (j) 4.4 (k) 1.3
3. (a) 6.7 (b) 12.1 (c) 16.1
4. 5.7 m
5. 9.0 m
6. 5.3 cm
7. 46.6 cm
8. 9.9 cm
9. 8.6 cm
10. 4.2 cm
11. 6.2 cm
12. 5.2 cm
13. 28.4 m
14. 12.2 km
15. 5.8 km
16. 31.9 km
17. 6.9 cm
18. 9.5 cm
19. (a) 71.2 km/h (b) 65.6 km/h (c) 50.7 km/h
20. 15.5 km
21. 3.6 cm
22. (a) 9 s (b) 3 s
23. (a) 2 s (b) 5 s (c) 3 s
24. (a) 36.0 m^2 (b) 1179.9 m^2 (c) 358.4 m^2
25. 15.6 cm

EXERCISE 2.5

1. (a) 4 (b) 7 (c) 9 (d) 10 (e) 11 (f) $\frac{3}{4}$ (g) $\frac{5}{6}$ (h) $\frac{9}{10}$ (i) $\frac{8}{9}$ (j) $\frac{1}{5}$ (k) 15 (l) 17 (m) 21 (n) 0.1 (o) 0.05
2. (a) $\sqrt{6}$ (b) $\sqrt{55}$ (c) $\sqrt{14}$ (d) $\sqrt{70}$ (e) $\sqrt{35}$ (f) $\sqrt{33}$

(g) $\sqrt{30}$ (h) $\sqrt{10}$ (i) $\sqrt{42}$ (j) $\sqrt{65}$ (k) $\sqrt{143}$ (l) 7

3. (a) $6\sqrt{15}$ (b) $3\sqrt{14}$ (c) $8\sqrt{15}$ (d) $2\sqrt{21}$ (e) $3\sqrt{22}$ (f) $6\sqrt{15}$
(g) $6\sqrt{6}$ (h) $8\sqrt{35}$ (i) $12\sqrt{66}$ (j) $35\sqrt{6}$ (k) $12\sqrt{30}$ (l) 30

4. (a) $2\sqrt{3}$ (b) $3\sqrt{2}$ (c) $5\sqrt{3}$ (d) $3\sqrt{5}$ (e) $7\sqrt{2}$ (f) $4\sqrt{2}$
(g) $2\sqrt{17}$ (h) $2\sqrt{5}$ (i) $10\sqrt{2}$ (j) $2\sqrt{7}$ (k) 21 (l) 32
(m) $6\sqrt{2}$ (n) $5\sqrt{2}$ (o) $2\sqrt{2}$

5. (a) $\sqrt{20}$ (b) $\sqrt{63}$ (c) $\sqrt{18}$ (d) $\sqrt{50}$ (e) $\sqrt{99}$ (f) $\sqrt{500}$
(g) $\sqrt{300}$ (h) $\sqrt{98}$ (i) $\sqrt{200}$ (j) $\sqrt{56}$ (k) $\sqrt{294}$ (l) $\sqrt{396}$
(m) $\sqrt{1200}$ (n) $\sqrt{1250}$ (o) $\sqrt{160}$

6. (a) $7\sqrt{2}$ (b) $2\sqrt{15}$ (c) $7\sqrt{15}$ (d) 7 (e) $3\sqrt{2}$ (f) $5\sqrt{3}$
(g) $25\sqrt{6}$ (h) $5\sqrt{10}$ (i) $6\sqrt{3}$ (j) $70\sqrt{2}$ (k) $30\sqrt{2}$ (l) $30\sqrt{5}$
(m) 6 (n) 30 (o) $90\sqrt{3}$ (p) $5\sqrt{6}$ (q) 36 (r) 144

EXERCISE 2.6

1. (a) 1.12×10^{1} (b) 3.75×10^{0} (c) 2.575×10^{-1} (d) 3.25×10^{-2}
(e) 1.25×10^{-3} (f) 5.78×10^{-4} (g) 5.63×10^{-3} (h) 4.25×10^{-1}
(i) 9.3×10^{7} (j) 1.86×10^{5} (k) 3.5127×10^{4} (l) 4.25×10^{5}
(m) 3.25×10^{1} (n) 3.125×10^{0}

2. (a) 35 000 (b) 265 (c) 78 400 000
(d) 0.046 (e) 0.0057 (f) 0.000 000 000 035 6

3. (a) 4.5×10^{-7} mm (b) 1.49×10^{8} km (c) 9.363×10^{6} km^2
(d) 9.976×10^{6} km^2 (e) 2.725×10^{8} (f) 1×10^{-6} km

4. (a) 1.2 (b) 9×10^{8}, 10.5×10^{8} (c) 3×10^{-2}, 3.7×10^{-2}
(d) 2.7×10^{14}, 3.0×10^{14}

5. (a) -1 (b) 6 (c) -5 (d) 0

6. (a) 4.902×10^{8} (b) 2.885×10^{1} (c) 6.43×10^{-2} (d) 2.55×10^{-1}
(e) 5.67×10^{3} (f) 6.6×10^{0} (g) 1.6×10^{-5} (h) 8×10^{-2}
(i) 1.2×10^{2} (j) 1.2×10^{1} (k) 1.4×10^{0} (l) 2.5×10^{2}

7. 8.58×10^{7} km

EXERCISE 2.7

1. (a) rational (b) irrational (c) rational (d) irrational (e) irrational (f) rational

2. (a) 0.75 (b) 0.625 (c) 0.5625 (d) 1.75 (e) 0.156 25 (f) 0.82
(g) $0.\overline{27}$ (h) $1.\overline{36}$

3. (a) 0.875 (b) $0.\overline{3}$ (c) 0.5 (d) $-0.\overline{428\,571}$
(e) $0.\overline{18}$ (f) $0.8\overline{3}$ (g) 1.25 (h) 1.5
(i) $-0.1\overline{6}$ (j) $4.\overline{3}$ (k) 71.5 (l) $-22.\overline{6}$

4. (a) rational (b) rational (c) rational (d) rational (e) irrational (f) irrational
(g) irrational (h) irrational (i) irrational

EXERCISE 2.8

1. 71
2. {11, 12, 13, ... 51, 52, 53}
3. 101
4. 1000
5. $5.00
6. 40
7. (a) 21 (b) 15 + 45 (c) 3 + 6 + 66
8. 200 m by 100 m
9. 27
10. $4.80 loss
11. 8
12. (a) 18 (b) 25 (c) 6 (d) 4 or 130

EXERCISE 2.9

3. (a) +B5 + B6 (b) +B5 − B6 (c) +B5 × B6 (d) +B5 ÷ B6

4. (a) 7997 (b) 2510 (c) 0.2151
(d) 7.71 (nearest hundredth)

5. (a) 67.63 (b) 0.80 (c) 6922.80 (d) 6.17

6. (a) 74.6 (b) 9555.0 (c) 8.9 (d) −3495.2
7. \$53 316.54
8. (a) \$40 480 (b) \$36 340 (c) \$34 500 (d) \$31 740
10. (i) (a) 191.13 cm^2 (b) 16.62 cm^2 (c) 248.85 cm^2 (d) 46 606.28 cm^2
(ii) (a) 1987.80 cm^3 (b) 50.97 cm^3 (c) 2952.97 cm^3 (d) 7 568 860.03 cm^3
11. (i) \$167 736 (ii) \$147 000 (ii) \$20 736

2.10 REVIEW EXERCISE

1. (a) 16 (b) 16 (c) $\frac{1}{16}$ (d) $\frac{1}{16}$ (e) 4 (f) $\frac{4}{3}$
(g) 1 (h) −27 (i) $\frac{1}{2}$ (j) 2 (k) $\frac{1}{3}$ (l) $-\frac{1}{3}$
2. (a) a^{11} (b) a^3 (c) a^{11} (d) a^{11} (e) $6a^9$ (f) $12x^4$
(g) $\frac{10}{ts}$ (h) $\frac{20x^4}{y^4}$
3. (a) 2^{a+b} (b) 9^b (c) 4m (d) $6t^5$ (e) $4a^4b^2$ (f) $2a^3b^3$
(g) ab^2 (h) xy^2
4. (a) 32 (b) $\frac{1}{9}$ (c) 49 (d) 4 (e) 8 (f) 2
5. (a) 0.197 (b) 32.429 (c) 15 158.674
6. (a) 6.6 (b) 12.2 (c) 3.1 (d) 5.5
7. (a) $\sqrt{90}$ (b) $\sqrt{300}$ (c) $\sqrt{243}$ (d) $\sqrt{240}$ (e) $\sqrt{98}$ (f) $\sqrt{180}$
8. (a) $3\sqrt{7}$ (b) $5\sqrt{5}$ (c) $3\sqrt{3}$ (d) $3\sqrt{6}$ (e) $5\sqrt{15}$ (f) $10\sqrt{5}$
9. (a) 9 (b) $24\sqrt{3}$ (c) $30\sqrt{2}$ (d) $70\sqrt{7}$
10. (a) 1.72×10^5 (b) 3×10^{-4} (c) 8.7×10^7 (d) 1.732×10^5
(e) 7.2×10^{-8} (f) 6.43×10^6 (g) 4.1×10^{-5} (h) 1.02×10^{-2}
11. (a) 3 010 000 (b) 0.000 215 (c) 480 000
(d) 0.000 000 009 8 (e) 0.200 (f) 500
12. (a) 0.23 (b) 1.875 (c) $1.\overline{4}$ (d) $0.\overline{692\ 307}$
(e) 1 (f) 0.4 (g) $0.\overline{2}$ (h) $0.\overline{571\ 428}$
13. (a) irrational (b) rational (c) rational (d) irrational
(e) rational (f) rational (g) rational (h) rational
14. (a) (i) 1.0 m^3 (ii) 4.0 m^3 (iii) 102.1 m^3
(b) (i) 3.1 m^2 (ii) 1.0 m^2 (iii) 4.0 m^2
15. (a) 1.00 m^3 (b) 0.09 m^3 (c) 2.13 m^3
16. (a) 1.00 m^2 (b) 9.99 m^2 (c) 50.00 m^2
17. (a) 12.56 cm^2 (b) 4.84 cm^2 18. 314 19. 40.21 m
20. (a) 4 (b) 9

2.11 CHAPTER 2 TEST

1. (a) −x (b) 3z (c) $\frac{a^4b^4}{2}$ 2. (a) 27 (b) 16 (c) 64
3. (a) $\sqrt{175}$ (b) $5\sqrt{10}$ (c) $24\sqrt{10}$ 4. (a) 20 (b) 6 000 000
5. (a) 59 200 (b) 0.000 030 6. (a) $0.\overline{5}$ (b) −1.4 (c) $0.\overline{45}$
7. (a) irrational (b) rational (c) rational 8. (a) 7.1 cm (b) 6.3 cm

REVIEW AND PREVIEW TO CHAPTER 3

EXERCISE 1

1. (a) 2a + 8 (b) 3a − 6 (c) 4x − 12 (d) 2a − 2b
(e) 7x + 7y (f) 16x + 8 (g) 2a + 4b + 2c (h) 6x − 12y + 42
(i) −2x + 8 (j) −6a + 12b (k) −15a + 10b − 5c (l) −x − 5
(m) 10 − 30x + 20y (n) 14 + 21x − 28y
2. (a) 5x (b) 12m + a (c) 8a − 7b (d) 13ab + m

(e) $13s - 2t$ (f) $10ab + 13bc$ (g) $3ef - 9e + 11$ (h) $5a$
(i) $10x + 2y$ (j) $-x - y$ (k) $17 - 4a + 7b$ (l) $-xy - 7a$
(m) $2d - 13$ (n) $-5x^2 + 5x - 6$ (o) $2a^2 + 6ab$

EXERCISE 2

1. a^{11} 2. b^{15} 3. $8m^{10}$ 4. $6x^3y^2$
5. $-24m^3n^2$ 6. $-18x^4y^5$ 7. $16a^2b^5$ 8. a^2
9. x^2 10. $2m$ 11. $4a$ 12. $-4ab^2$
13. 5 14. $2ab^2$

EXERCISE 3

1. 28 2. 36 3. 24 4. 13 5. 19 6. −21
7. 96 8. −102 9. −2 10. 288 11. 20 12. −49
13. 19 14. 22 15. −1749 16. −13 17. −571

EXERCISE 4

1. (a) 15 m^2 (b) 7.6 m^2 (c) 36 m^2
(d) 25.1 m^2 (nearest tenth) (e) 76.6 m^2 (nearest tenth)
2. (a) 24.6 m, 31.3 m^2 (b) 30.7 m, 39.7 m^2 (c) 30.4 m, 57.8 m^2
(d) 44.0 m, 153.9 m^2 (e) 18.3 m, 22.3 m^2

EXERCISE 3.1

1. (a) $6x + 2$ (b) $8a - 12$ (c) $-2x + 14$ (d) $-3x + 3y$
(e) $-21y - 14$ (f) $2x^2 + 4x$ (g) $-2x + 4$ (h) $-2x^2 + 2xy$
2. (a) $3x - 3y - 3t$ (b) $-2p + 3q + 6$ (c) $2x^3 - 6x^2 - 6x$
(d) $-8a + 12b + 4c$ (e) $2ax - 2ay - 2at$ (f) $a^3b - ab^2 - ab$
3. (a) $5a$ (b) $2x + 16$ (c) $2y + 2$ (d) $14b - 1$
(e) $a - 15$ (f) $5x - 2$ (g) $-2x^2 - x - 11$ (h) $a - 2b + 6c$
(i) $-3a^2 - 8a + 10$ (j) $6x^2 + x + 11$
4. (a) $-7x$ (b) $-6b^2 + 10b - 4$ (c) $x^2 + 11xy - 4x$ (d) $x^2 - 2x + 2$
(e) $-6a + 2b - 1$ (f) $7a^2 - 7ab$ (g) $-3m^2 + mn + 2n^2$ (h) $8a^2 - 3a + 7$
5. (a) (i) $8x - 12$ (ii) $18x - 42$ (iii) $2x^2 + 3x$ (iv) $15x^2 - 12x$
(b) (i) 12 m^2 (ii) 12 m^2 (iii) 27 m^2 (iv) 99 m^2
6. (a) (i) $4k + 12$ (ii) $12k^2 - 16k$ (b) (i) 22m^2 (ii) 35m^2
7. (a) $13m + 58$ (b) $-5x - 13$ (c) $-17a + 8$
(d) $-36b + 19$ (e) $24b^2 - 2b + 10$
8. (a) $-2x^2y - xy^2 - 3x$ (b) $-2a^3b$ (c) $-2m^2n - 14mn^2$
(d) $-x - 5y$ (e) $20y - 2b$ (f) $x - \frac{11}{4}y$
(g) $-x^2 + \frac{5}{6}x$

EXERCISE 3.2

1. (a) $x^2 + 5x + 6$ (b) $a^2 + 4a - 21$ (c) $y^2 - 5y + 6$
(d) $m^2 - 1$ (e) $c^2 - 8c + 12$ (f) $x^2 - 9x + 20$
(g) $2x^2 + 5x - 3$ (h) $6b^2 + b - 2$ (i) $b^2 - 9b + 14$
(j) $m^2 + 13m + 42$ (k) $t^2 + 5t + 6$ (l) $25a^2 - 1$
2. (a) $x^2 + 14x + 49$ (b) $m^2 - 4m + 4$ (c) $4x^2 + 4x + 1$
(d) $16y^2 - 24y + 9$ (e) $4m^2 + 20m + 25$ (f) $1 - 10x + 25x^2$
(g) $a^2 + 6a + 9$ (h) $1 + 6x + 9x^2$
3. (a) $8a^2 - 2ax - 3x^2$ (b) $2a^2 + ab - b^2$ (c) $x^2 - 4xy + 4y^2$
(d) $14d^2 - 14dg - 9g^2$ (e) $36a^2 - 84ab + 49b^2$ (f) $-6x^2 - 13x + 5$
(g) $x^2 + xy - 6y^2$ (h) $9m^2 - 4b^2$ (i) $4a^2 + 4ab + b^2$
(j) $4x^2 - y^2$ (k) $2m^2 + 7m - 4$ (l) $20 - 43x + 21x^2$
4. (a) (i) $x^2 + 6x - 7$ (ii) $4x^2 + 17x + 15$ (iii) $5x^2 + x - 4$
(b) (i) 40.2 cm^2 (nearest tenth) (ii) 172.5 cm^2 (iii) 101.8 cm^2 (nearest tenth)

EXERCISE 3.3

1. (a) $x^2 + 7x - 2$ (b) $m^2 + m - 12$ (c) $6x^2 + 6x$ (d) $17a^2 + 5a + 5$
2. (a) $3x^2 - 2x - 26$ (b) $3a^2 - 13a + 30$ (c) $2m^2 + 8m - 8$
   (d) $10x^2 + 17x$ (e) $2x^2 + 2x + 13$ (f) $a^2 - 14a + 17$
3. (a) $-a^2 - 30a - 80$ (b) $-t^2 + 19t - 18$ (c) $10m^2 + 24m - 17$
   (d) $-2a^2 + 19a + 30$ (e) $x^2 - x - 4$ (f) $-11m^2 + 10m - 2$
4. (a) $-6m^2 - 6m + 2, -46.96$ (b) $-12x^2 + 7x + 59, -432.78$
   (c) $-23x^2 + 30x - 58, -354.27$ (d) $-8t^2 - 2t + 6, -49$
   (e) $-m^2 + 13m + 5, 35.69$

EXERCISE 3.4

1. (a) $5b, a \neq 0$ (b) $4b, c \neq 0$ (c) $-5y, x \neq 0$
   (d) $3c, a \neq 0, b \neq 0$ (e) $-5, c \neq 0, d \neq 0$ (f) $2a, a \neq 0$
2. (a) $x + m$ (b) $3a - b$ (c) $a^2 - 1$
   (d) $-4ab + b$ (e) $3mt - m$ (f) $ab - 2a + 3$
3. (a) $4b - 2c, a \neq 0$ (b) $5c - 1, a \neq 0$ (c) $2x - 1, x \neq 0$
   (d) $2n + 1 + 3t, m \neq 0$
4. (a) $-10a + 5b, a \neq 0, b \neq 0$ (b) $-6x^2 - 4x + 1, x \neq 0$
   (c) $-1 + 2a - 3a^2, a \neq 0$

EXERCISE 3.5

1. (a) 2 (b) 7 (c) 6 (d) x (e) a (f) 5x
   (g) 4ab (h) xy
2. (a) 2 (b) 3 (c) 4 (d) 6 (e) 2b (f) 4
3. (a) $a + b$ (b) $x - y$ (c) $x + 2$ (d) $a - 3$ (e) $a + 2b + 3c$
   (f) $x - 2$ (g) $3x^2 + 2x + 1$
4. (a) 3 (b) 2 (c) x (d) a (e) x (f) x^2
   (g) a
5. (a) $4(a + b)$ (b) $2(x - y)$ (c) $3(x + 2)$ (d) $5(b - 2)$
   (e) $4(2y - 1)$ (f) $2(a + 3b - 4c)$ (g) $2(2x^2 + y)$ (h) $7(x^2 - 2x + 3)$
   (i) $5(4a + b - 3)$ (j) $6(t^2 - t + 2)$
6. (a) $x(x + 3)$ (b) $a(a - 2)$ (c) $a(5x + 6y)$ (d) $x(4y - 7a)$
   (e) $2a(x + y)$ (f) $3m(x - 2y)$ (g) $5t(2x - y)$ (h) $3x(x + 4)$
   (i) $5a(a - 3)$ (j) $4x^2(2x - 1)$
7. (a) $3xy(2x - y)$ (b) $2ab(2a + 3 - 4b)$ (c) $7xy(2xy - y + 1)$
   (d) $2ab(3c - x + 5y)$ (e) $7a(a^2 + 2a - 1)$

EXERCISE 3.6

1. (a) 3 * x + 4 (b) 3.14 * r ^ 2
   (c) x * x + 3 * x + 2 (d) 2 * x ^ 3 + 3 * x ^ 2 − x + 17
   (e) 4 * x ^ 2 − 2 * x ^ 4
2. (a) NEW

```
10 PRINT"PRINTING A TABLE OF VALUES"
20 FOR X = 1 TO 5
30 Y = X * X +5
40 PRINT X,Y
50 NEXT X
60 END
```

RUN

(b) NEW

```
10 PRINT"PRINTING A TABLE OF VALUES"
20 FOR X = 1 TO 6
30 Y = X ^ 3 - 27
40 PRINT X,Y
50 NEXT X
60 END
```

RUN

(c) NEW

```
10 PRINT"PRINTING A TABLE OF VALUES"
20 FOR X = 1 TO 10
30 Y = 2 * X ^ 3 - 5 * X ^ 2 - 6 * X + 10
40 PRINT X,Y
50 NEXT X
60 END
```

RUN

(d) NEW

```
10 PRINT"PRINTING A TABLE OF VALUES"
20 FOR X = 1 TO 2 STEP 0.1
30 Y = X * X -2
40 PRINT X,Y
50 NEXT X
60 END
```

RUN

(e) NEW

```
10 PRINT"PRINTING A TABLE OF VALUES"
20 FOR X = 1 TO 5 STEP 0.5
30 Y = 3.14 * R ^ 2
40 PRINT X,Y
50 NEXT X
60 END
```

RUN

(f) NEW

```
10 PRINT"PRINTING A TABLE OF VALUES"
20 FOR X = 0 TO 16 STEP 2
30 Y = X ^ 3 - 4096
40 PRINT X,Y
50 NEXT X
60 END
```

RUN

3. NEW

```
10 PRINT"PRINTING AN INTEREST TABLE"
20 FOR N = 1 TO 10
30 I = 5000 * (1.0595 ^ N - 1)
40 PRINT N ",  "; "$";A
50 NEXT N
60 END
```

RUN

4. NEW

```
10 PRINT"PRINTING AN INTEREST TABLE"
20 FOR R = 5 TO 10 STEP 0.5
30 I = 10000 * ((1 + R/100) ^ 5 - 1)
40 PRINT R "%,  "; "$";I
50 NEXT R
60 END
```

RUN

EXERCISE 3.7

1. (a) 44 (b) 40 (c) 5 (d) −38 (e) 120 (f) −77
2. (a) 1 (b) −44 (c) 26 (d) −51 (e) −4 (f) −36
3. (a) 5]x − 7]x + 3 (b) 3]x + 4]x − 5]x + 2 (c) 3]x + 0]x − 2]x + 5
   (d) 4]x + 3]x + 0]x − 7 (e) 3]x − 7]x + 5]x − 3 (f) −2]x + 0]x + 7]x − 11
4. (a) 2]x + 0]x − 5]x + 7, 13 (b) 3]x + 7]x − 5]x + 3, 17
   (c) 2]x − 5]x + 0]x + 6, −1 (d) 6]x − 3]x + 0]x + 5, −55
   (e) −2]x + 5]x − 2]x + 3, −12 (f) 3]x + 0]x − 2]x + 3]x − 1, 233
5. (a) −4.9]t + 24.4]t + 1.4
   (b) 20.9 m, 30.6 m, 30.5 m, 20.6 m, 0.9 m
   (c) approximately 31.8 m (after approximately 2.5 s)

EXERCISE 3.8

1. (a) 2, 3 (b) 2, 4 (c) 1, 2 (d) −1, −3 (e) −1, −1
   (f) −3, −4 (g) −2, −5 (h) −4, 3 (i) −2, 4
2. (a) x + 2 (b) m + 1 (c) t + 3 (d) y − 3 (e) a − 3 (f) z − 8
   (g) x + 5 (h) t − 6 (i) r − 2 (j) n − 5 (k) x + 1 (l) y + 6
3. (a) (x + 1)(x + 5) (b) (t + 2)(t + 7) (c) (m + 4)(m + 5) (d) (n + 2)(n + 2)
   (e) (y − 1)(y − 2) (f) (k − 2)(k − 3) (g) (a − 3)(a − 4) (h) (b − 2)(b − 6)
   (i) (x − 6)(x + 4) (j) (m − 3)(m + 4) (k) (x − 7)(x + 5) (l) (n − 3)(n + 8)
   (m) (y − 7)(y + 3) (n) (a − 3)(a − 3) (o) (x − 1)(x − 1) (p) 9(x + 1)(x + 2)
   (q) 5(x − 3)(x + 6) (r) 7(x − 1)(x + 3) (s) 30(y + 1)(y + 1)

EXERCISE 3.9

1. (a) yes (b) no (c) yes (d) yes (e) yes (f) no
   (g) no (h) no
2. (a) 4 (b) 2 (c) 3, 3 (d) x (e) a, a
3. (a) x + 3 (b) a − 10 (c) m + 5 (d) r − 6 (e) 3x + 2 (f) 5m − 1
4. (a) (x − 4)(x + 4) (b) (n − 3)(n + 3) (c) (t − 1)(t + 1) (d) (r − 11)(r + 11)
   (e) (y − 7)(y + 7) (f) (s − 9)(s + 9) (g) (x − 8)(x + 8) (h) (b − 12)(b + 12)
5. (a) (2x − 5)(2x + 5) (b) (3m − 1)(3m + 1) (c) (4t − 7)(4t + 7)
   (d) (5n − 11)(5n + 11) (e) (8x − 3)(8x + 3) (f) (10a − 1)(10a + 1)
   (g) (2s − 9)(2s + 9)
6. (a) (4 − x)(4 + x) (b) (6 − y)(6 + y) (c) (9 − m)(9 + m)
   (d) (10 − t)(10 + t) (e) (3 − 2x)(3 + 2x) (f) (11 − 4m)(11 + 4m)
   (g) (9 − 5t)(9 + 5t) (h) (8 − 3x)(8 + 3x) (i) $(\frac{1}{2}x - 4)(\frac{1}{2}x + 4)$
7. (a) $(x + 2)^2$ (b) $(x - 3)^2$ (c) $(t - 1)^2$ (d) $(r + 5)^2$ (e) $(m - 7)^2$ (f) $(w + 8)^2$
8. (a) $(3x - 5)^2$ (b) $(2x + 1)^2$ (c) $(2t + 3)^2$ (d) $(3s - 4)^2$ (e) $(4t + 5)^2$
   (f) $(3x - 1)^2$ (g) $(5y - 4)^2$ (h) $(2y + 5)^2$ (i) $(6x + 1)^2$ (j) $(2s - 7)^2$
9. (a) 9975 (b) 9951 (c) 10 816 (d) 9025
   (e) 999 999 (f) 998 001 (g) 9775 (h) 999 975

EXERCISE 3.10

1. (a) $86.80 (b) $39.33
2. (a) Fox (b) Seven Seven and A1
3. (a) $537 500.00 (c) 9.7% (d) $545 000.00 (e) $537 500.00

3.11 REVIEW EXERCISE

1. (a) $-x + 19$ (b) $x^2 + 3x - 11$ (c) $3x^2 - 6x + 5$ (d) $5x^2 + 2x + 10$
   (e) $-10x^2 - 8x + 3$ (f) $x^2 + x - 16$ (g) $-6x^2 + 25x - 15$
2. (a) (i) $30x$ (ii) $4x + 8$ (iii) $\frac{3}{2}x + 6$ (iv) $\frac{1}{2}x^2 + x$ (v) $x^2 - 2x + 1$

(vi) $x^2 - 2x + 1$ (vii) $5x^2 - 2x$ (viii) $8x^2 + 24x$ (ix) $3x^2 - 5x + 1$
(x) $3x^2 + 15x + 20$ (xi) $9x^2 + 13x - 18$ (xii) $12x^2 + 17x + 19$
(xiii) $\frac{7}{2}x^2 - 25x + 33$ (xiv) $\frac{9}{2}x^2 + 9x + 3$

(b) (i) 45 cm^2 (ii) 20 cm^2 (iii) 6 cm^2 (iv) 2.6 cm^2 (nearest tenth) (v) 16 cm^2
(vi) 16 cm^2 (vii) 26.2 cm^2 (nearest tenth) (viii) 14 cm^2 (ix) 13 m^2
(x) 38 m^2 (xi) 80.8 m^2 (nearest tenth) (xii) 178 m^2 (xiii) 29.5 m^2
(xiv) 39 m^2

3. (a) $4xy, x \neq 0$ (b) $-5x^2, x \neq 0, y \neq 0$ (c) $6ab, a \neq 0, b \neq 0, y \neq 0$
(d) $3y - 4, x \neq 0$ (e) $4x - 7, x \neq 0$ (f) $2x^2 - 3x - 4$

4. (a) $2(x + 7)$ (b) $(x - 3)(x - 4)$ (c) $(x - 4)(x + 9)$ (d) $(x - 8)(x + 8)$
(e) $(x + 1)(x - 2)$ (f) $3xy(2x + 3)$ (g) $-7ab$ (h) $(y + 2)(y + 5)$
(i) $(5x - 1)(5x + 1)$ (j) $(3x - 5)^2$ (k) $(x + 4)^2$ (l) $5xy(x - 2y)$

5. (a) 3]x − 2]x − 6]x + 5, 141 (b) 2]x − 3]x + 0]x + 10, 37
(c) 1]x + 5]x − 4]x − 6, 14 (d) 1]x + 1]x − 1]x + 0]x + 1, 305

3.12 CHAPTER 3 TEST

1. (a) $-x + 14$ (b) $x^2 - 4x + 4$ (c) $14x - 12$
(d) $2x^2 + 10x + 8$ (e) $12x - 4$ (f) $-12x^2 - 12x - 3$
(g) $6x^2 - 33x - 12$ (h) $-2x^2 + 27x - 5$ (i) $-5x^2 + 3x + 9$

2. (a) $2x - 3, x \neq 0$ (b) $4y^2z, x \neq 0, y \neq 0$

3. (a) $3(x + 4)$ (b) $(x - 9)(x + 9)$ (c) $(5x - 4)(5x + 4)$ (d) $(x - 3)(x - 5)$
(e) $5xy(2 - y)$ (f) $(x - 4)^2$ (g) $(x + 5)(x + 6)$ (h) $3x(x - 2)$

4. 4]x − 1]x + 2]x − 5, 100

REVIEW AND PREVIEW TO CHAPTER 4

EXERCISE 1

1. 1 2. 16 3. 6 4. 35 5. 6 6. 9
7. 12 8. 4 9. 4 10. 10, 64 11. 21, 56 12. 4, 7
13. 3, 24 14. 8, 25 15. 7, 35 16. 1, 5 17. 7, 28 18. 36, 25

EXERCISE 2

1. $3x - 6$ 2. $-3x - 15$ 3. $-2x + 10$ 4. $3 + x$
5. $7x^2 + 7x$ 6. $-2x + 2x^2$ 7. $x^2 - x$ 8. $5x^2 - 10x$
9. $2x^2 + 2x - 4$ 10. $-x^2 + x + 20$ 11. $x^2 + 4x + 4$ 12. $x^2 + 5x + 6$
13. $4x^2 - 11x + 6$ 14. $-15x^2 + 7x + 4$ 15. $-4x^2 + 12x - 9$ 16. $-x^2 + 2x - 1$
17. $-x^2 + 2x - 1$ 18. $2x^2 - 8x - 26$ 19. $2x^2 + 8x - 29$
20. $-2x^2 - 17xy + 32y^2$ 21. $-x^2 - 44x - 51$ 22. $x^4 - y^4$
23. $x^4 - 16$ 24. $4x^2 - 15x + 15$

EXERCISE 3

1. 12 cm^2 3. 6 cm^2 3. 30 cm^2 4. 300 cm^2 5. 30 m^2
6. 60 m^2 7. not possible 8. 18 cm^2 9. 60 cm^2

EXERCISE 4

1. (a) 40 (b) 200 (c) 180 (d) 1050 (e) 180 (f) 140
2. (a) $12x^2y^2$ (b) $60n^4$ (c) $150x^3y^2$ (d) $6m^2n^2$ (e) 18abc
3. (a) $x^2 - 5x + 4$ (b) $x^3 - 7x - 6$ (c) $x^3 + 12x^2 + 47x + 60$
(d) $x^4 - 1$ (e) $6x - 18$

EXERCISE 4.1

1. (a) $x = 17$ (b) $a = 10$ (c) $m = 16$ (d) $a = -6$ (e) $b = -12$ (f) $x = -8$
(g) $x = 5$ (h) $x = 20$ (i) $a = -4$ (j) $a = 3$ (k) $m = -4$ (l) $b = 0$
2. (a) $x = 3$ (b) $b = 3$ (c) $a = 1$ (d) $m = 4$ (e) $x = 3$ (f) $x = 3$
(g) $r = 1$ (h) $m = 0$

3. (a) yes (b) no (c) yes (d) yes (e) no (f) no
(g) yes (h) no (i) no
4. (a) $x = 5$ (b) $y = 2$ (c) $x = -1$ (d) $a = 4$ (e) $y = 1$ (f) $a = 2$
(g) $x = 3$ (h) $x = 6$ (i) $c = 4$ (j) $b = 2$
5. (a) $a = 6$ (b) $k = 9$ (c) $x = 3$ (d) $y = 3$ (e) $x = 2$ (f) $x = \frac{1}{2}$
(g) $x = 0$ (h) $m = 2$ (i) $x = 2$ (j) $x = 5$
6. (a) $x = 2$ (b) $a = -8$ (c) $x = -11$ (d) $m = 5$ (e) $m = -1$ (f) $x = 2$
(g) $a = -2$ (h) $x = 1$
7. (a) $x = 1.20$ (b) $a = -1.76$ (c) $x = 1.11$ (d) $b = 4.19$
(e) $a = -3.14$ (f) $m = -4.73$
8. (a) $7 - b$ (b) $t + m$ (c) $\frac{m}{a}$ (d) $\frac{-a}{2}$
(e) $\frac{m - t}{b}$ (f) $\frac{t + m}{a}$ (g) $d - t$ (h) $\frac{a + 3}{2b}$
9. (a) $x = 30$ (b) $m = 8$ (c) $x = -30$ (d) $x = 2\frac{2}{3}$ (e) $b = 9$ (f) $m = 14$
10. (a) $x = 12$ (b) $x = 2\frac{1}{4}$ (c) $x = -\frac{4}{5}$ (d) $x = -2\frac{6}{7}$
(e) $b = 36$ (f) $a = 7\frac{1}{2}$ (g) $y = -1\frac{7}{9}$ (h) $m = \frac{7}{19}$
11. (a) $x = -7$ (b) $x = 6$ (c) $x = 8\frac{1}{2}$ (d) $a = 2$ (e) $m = -\frac{1}{3}$
12. (a) $x = 38$ (b) $m = -31$ (c) $x = -3$ (d) $x = 3$ (e) $x = 2$

EXERCISE 4.2

1. (a) $k = 2$ (b) $x = 1\frac{1}{3}$ (c) $m = -8$ (d) $a = 1$ (e) $y = -1$
(f) $x = -1\frac{1}{17}$ (g) $x = 6$ (h) $x = -1$ (i) $x = -16$
2. (a) $x = -3$ (b) $x = 1$ (c) $a = 1$ (d) $x = 3\frac{1}{2}$ (e) $x = -5$ (f) $m = -24$
3. (a) $c = 3$ (b) $x = -5$ (c) $s = 3$

EXERCISE 4.3

1. (a) 60 m^3 (b) 10 m
2. (a) 29.8 m^2 (nearest tenth) (b) 13.5 m
3. (a) 130 m (b) 67.5 m
4. (a) 18 cm^2 (b) 55 cm
5. (a) 70 600 m^2 (nearest hundred) (b) 300 m
6. (a) 188 cm (nearest one) (b) 35 cm (nearest one)
7. (a) 0.42 m^3 (nearest hundredth) (b) 42 cm (nearest one)
8. (a) 65.4 cm^3 (nearest tenth) (b) 12 cm
9. (a) 165 m^2 (b) 69.1 m (nearest tenth)
10. (a) \$960 (b) 8.5%
11. (a) \$5000, \$15 000, \$45 000, \$285 000
(b) 87% (c) no
12. (a) $t = \frac{p}{4}$ (b) $v = \frac{d}{t}$ (c) $R = \frac{pv}{t}$ (d) $a = \frac{2s}{n} - \ell$ (e) $r = \frac{A - p}{pt}$
(f) $w = \frac{V}{\ell h}$ (g) $I = \frac{V}{R}$ (h) $\ell = \frac{p}{2} - w$ (i) $a = \frac{2(s - ut)}{t^2}$

EXERCISE 4.4

1. (a) 0, 5 (b) 0, -7 (c) 0, -4 (d) 0, 6
2. (a) -6, 1 (b) 2, 7 (c) -5, 4 (d) 7, -9 (e) 11, 8
(f) -3, 6 (g) $\frac{1}{3}$, $-\frac{5}{3}$ (h) $\frac{3}{4}$, 5 (i) $-\frac{5}{2}$, $-\frac{1}{3}$ (j) $-\frac{11}{9}$, $-\frac{14}{3}$
3. (a) 0, 7 (b) 0, -3 (c) -2, 2 (d) -5, 5 (e) -3, 4

(f) $-6, -3$ (g) $-4, 5$ (h) -4 (i) $-7, 11$ (j) -1
(k) $-8, 5$ (l) 4 (m) $-13, 5$
4. (a) $-2, 6$ (b) $-9, 2$ (c) 2, 6 (d) 4 (e) $-8, 7$
(f) $-6, 1$ (g) 3, 7
5. (a) 1, 6 (b) $-8, 3$ (c) $-4, 7$ (d) 5, 6
6. 11 m by 8 m
7. $-8, -7$ or 7, 8
8. 8 by 6

EXERCISE 4.5

1. 32
2. 60 L
3. 20
4. 10
5. 44
6. 1.5 mm
7. 25 cm
8. 32 cm
9. 24 elephants, 32 ostriches
10. 26, 28, and 30
11. approximately 7 cm
12. 3.7×10^{-7} mm
13. not enough information
14. (a) 52 (b) Home team wins 1 – 0

EXERCISE 4.6

1. no (12.29)
2. (a) 12.87
4. approximately 45 km

4.7 REVIEW EXERCISE

1. (a) -11 (b) 8 (c) 2 (d) -9 (e) -4 (f) -1
(g) 22 (h) 6 (i) 2
2. (a) $2\frac{1}{4}$ (b) -6 (c) 9 (d) -1 (e) 5 (f) 8
(g) -8 (h) 5 (i) 7 (j) 7 (k) 20 (l) -5
(m) 2
3. (a) -1 (b) -2 (c) -2 (d) -3 (e) 2 (f) -1
(g) 3 (h) $7\frac{3}{5}$
4. (a) 15 (b) 10 (c) 10 (d) 5 (e) 10 (f) 200
5. 1.5×10^2 cm^3
6. \$981.75
7. 2301.0 cm^3
8. (a) 0, 8 (b) 0, $\frac{7}{3}$ (c) 0, 5 (d) $-1, -2$
(e) $-1, -4$ (f) $-2, -3$ (g) $-13, 7$ (h) $-8, 8$
9. (a) $-6, -8$ (b) $-9, 7$ (c) 1 (d) $-4, 3$ (e) $-30, 3$
10. 20, 21
11. 12 m by 12 m by 12 m, 10 m by 10 m by 10 m

4.8 CHAPTER 4 TEST

1. (a) 2 (b) $\frac{11}{4}$ (c) $-\frac{9}{38}$ (d) 71 (e) $\frac{1}{4}$ (f) -5
2. 30
3. 20.84 cm
4. $\ell = \dfrac{V}{wh}$
5. $u = \dfrac{s}{t} = \frac{1}{2}at$
6. (a) $0, -19$ (b) $-5, 3$ (c) $-15, 1$ (d) $-8, 3$ (e) 2, 17
7. 9 cm, 14 cm

REVIEW AND PREVIEW TO CHAPTER 5

EXERCISE 1

1. 4.1 cm
2. 2.5 cm
3. 22.8 cm
4. 62.4 m
5. 37.2 m
6. 3.5 m
7. 74.1 m

EXERCISE 2

1. 5 cm
2. 13 cm
3. 7.2 cm (nearest tenth)
4. 9.5 cm (nearest tenth)
5. 9.7 cm (nearest tenth)
6. 12 cm

EXERCISE 4

Answers will vary.

EXERCISE 5.1

1. (a) $I = kt$ (b) 50 (c) 175
2. (a) 80 (b) 0.5 (c) 112.5
3. (a) $V = 1.5l$ (b) 12 V
4. $96 000.00

EXERCISE 5.2

1. (a) T = $18 + $12 h
   (b) (i) $30.00 (ii) $34.00 (iii) $39.00 (iv) $44.00
2. $98.60
3. $1407.00
4. $569.18
5. (a) Publisher B, $175.00 (b) 100 posters

EXERCISE 5.3

1. (b) $\frac{\Delta y}{\Delta x}$ is constant (c) They are equal.
2. (a) (i) $\frac{3}{2}$ (ii) $\frac{3}{2}$ (iii) $\frac{3}{2}$ (b) R, S, and T lie on the same line.
3. (a) $\frac{3}{5}$ (b) positive
4. (a) $-\frac{5}{6}$ (b) negative
5. (a) 0 (b) 0 (c) yes
6. (a) undefined (division by zero) (b) undefined (c) yes
7. (a) $-\frac{3}{4}$ (b) $\frac{5}{3}$ (c) 0 (d) $-\frac{1}{5}$ (e) $-\frac{1}{2}$ (f) undefined
   (g) $\frac{6}{5}$ (h) $-\frac{7}{8}$ (i) $-\frac{3}{7}$ (j) -1 (k) $-\frac{4}{9}$ (l) $-\frac{7}{4}$
8. (a) $-\frac{4}{9}$ (b) $-\frac{4}{9}$ (c) same
9. (a) no (b) yes
10. (a) 2.08 (b) -0.4647 (c) 1.348 (d) -2.62 (e) -0.244
    (f) 0.1561 (g) 4.21 (h) 0.409 (i) 1.385 (j) -0.9712
11. (a) down to left (b) to left (c) down to right
    (d) down to right (e) up to right (f) below
12. 0
13. 5
14. (0, -3)
15. 4
16. 50 m

EXERCISE 5.4

1. (a) 3, 2 (b) 3,4 (c) 3, 9 (d) 8, 2 (e) 2, -5 (f) 3, -7
   (g) -5, 4 (h) -5, 3 (i) 2, 7 (j) -3, 8 (k) 2, -8 (l) 4, 12
3. (b) (i) 3 (ii) -2 (iii) -1 (iv) $\frac{1}{2}$ (v) $\frac{1}{3}$
   (c) (i) -6 (ii) 4 (iii) -3 (iv) 2 (v) 1

EXERCISE 5.5

1. (b) (i) 2, 3 (ii) 2, 0 (iii) 2, -3 (iv) 2, 5
   (c) They are parallel.
   (d) The slope is 2 in each case.
   (e) They are equal.
   (g) m
2. (a) (i) 3 (ii) 4 (iii) -2 (iv) $\frac{1}{2}$ (v) 0 (vi) $-\frac{1}{5}$
   (b) (i) rising upward to the right
   (ii) rising upward to the right
   (iii) rising upward to the left
   (iv) rising upward to the right
   (v) parallel to the x-axis
   (vi) rising upward to the left
   (c) The larger the magnitude of the slope, the steeper the line.
3. (a) (i) 3 (ii) 0 (iii) -3 (iv) 5
   (b) (i) a family of parallel lines with slope 3

(ii) a family of parallel lines with slope $-\frac{1}{2}$

4. (b) (i) 1, 5 (ii) $\frac{2}{3}$, 5 (iii) −3, 5 (iv) 0, 5
   (c) They each have the same y-intercept.
   (d) The y-intercept of each line is 5.
   (e) b
5. (a) (i) 1 (ii) $\frac{2}{3}$ (iii) −3 (iv) 0
   (b) The y-intercept is 5.
   (c) (i) a family of lines with y-intercept 4
   (ii) a family of lines with y-intercept $-\frac{1}{3}$
6. (a) $y = \frac{1}{5}x + b$ (b) $y = mx + 17$ (c) $y = b$ (d) $y = mx$

EXERCISE 5.6

1. (a) (i) −2, 5 (ii) $-\frac{2}{3}, \frac{4}{3}$ (iii) $-\frac{3}{2}$, −3 (iv) $\frac{2}{5}$, −2
2. (a) (5, 0), (0, 2) (b) (4, 0), (0, 3) (c) $(\frac{9}{2}, 0)$, $(0, \frac{9}{4})$
   (d) (2, 0), (0, −3) (e) (1, 0), (0, 1) (f) (−5, 0), (0, −3)
3. (a) $\frac{3}{2}$, −2, 3 (b) $\frac{2}{3}$, −1, $\frac{2}{3}$
   (c) 0, no x-intercept, 3 (d) $-\frac{5}{3}$, 2, $\frac{10}{3}$
   (e) not defined, 4, no y-intercept (f) $-\frac{2}{3}$, $-\frac{7}{2}$, $-\frac{7}{3}$
4. (a) $y = x$ (b) $y = -5x$ (c) $y = mx$
5. (a) $y = 3x + 8$ (b) $y = \frac{3}{4}x - \frac{2}{3}$ (c) $y = -\frac{4}{5}x - \frac{7}{3}$ (d) $y = 5$
6. (a) $y = 3x + 2$ (b) $y = 4x + 2$ (c) $y = x$ (d) $y = -7x + 4$

EXERCISE 5.7

1. (a) $4x + 2y - 6 = 0$; 4, 2, −6
   (b) $2x - y + 4 = 0$; 2, −1, 4
   (c) $3x + 4y - 2 = 0$; 3, 4, −2
   (d) $4x - 5y = 0$; 4, −5, 0
   (e) $2x + 4y - 1 = 0$; 2, 4, −1
   (f) $-5y + 4 = 0$; 0, −5, 4
2. (a) $5x - y - 17 = 0$
   (b) $3x - y - 10 = 0$
   (c) $4x + y + 21 = 0$
   (d) $2x + y + 12 = 0$
   (e) $2x - y + 9 = 0$
   (f) $7x + y + 38 = 0$
   (g) $x - 2y + 9 = 0$
   (h) $x + 3y - 10 = 0$
   (i) $2x + 4y + 11 = 0$
   (j) $100x - 60y - 37 = 0$
   (k) $10x - 100y + 47 = 0$
   (l) $130x + 100y + 19 = 0$
   (m) $61x - 10y - 237 = 0$
3. (a) $3x - y - 1 = 0$; (0, −1), $(\frac{1}{3}, 0)$
   (b) $3x + y + 5 = 0$; (0, −5), $(\frac{1}{3}, -6)$
   (c) $5x - y + 2 = 0$; (0, 2), $(\frac{1}{5}, 3)$
   (d) $2x + y - 1 = 0$; (0, 1), $(\frac{1}{2}, 0)$
   (e) $4x + y + 21 = 0$; (0, −21), $(\frac{1}{4}, -22)$
   (f) $2x - y + 1 = 0$; (1, 3), $(\frac{1}{2}, 2)$
   (g) $x - 5y - 5 = 0$; (0, −1), $(6, \frac{1}{5})$
   (h) $x + 2y + 4 = 0$; (0, −2), (−4, 0)
   (i) $x + 2y + 4 = 0$; (2, −3), (6, −5)
   (j) $5x + 50y - 13 = 0$; (0, 0.26), (2.6, 0)

(k) $35x + 25y + 16 = 0$; $(0, -0.64)$, $(-1, 0.76)$
(l) $2x - y = 0$; $(0, 0)$, $(1, 2)$

EXERCISE 5.8

1. (a) $\frac{5}{2}$ (b) $-\frac{1}{6}$ (c) $\frac{3}{4}$ (d) -1 (e) $-\frac{4}{7}$ (f) $-\frac{5}{7}$
2. (a) $y - 4 = \frac{5}{2}(x - 5)$ (b) $y - 3 = -\frac{1}{6}(x - 1)$
(c) $y - (-3) = \frac{3}{4}(x - 0)$ (d) $y - (-2) = -1(x - 2)$
(e) $y - 3 = -\frac{4}{7}(x - (-4))$ (f) $y - (-6) = -\frac{5}{7}(x - 2)$
3. (a) $x + y - 3 = 0$ (b) $4x - y - 7 = 0$
(c) $8x - 3y - 11 = 0$ (d) $9x + y - 38 = 0$
(e) $13x - 4y + 1 = 0$ (f) $2x - 6y + 1 = 0$
(g) $3x + 2y - 1 = 0$
4. (a) $y = y_1$ (b) $y = 0$
5. (a) $x = x_1$ (b) $x = 0$
6. (a) $x - 2y + 5 = 0$ (b) $3x - 4y + 7 = 0$ (c) $4x - 3y = 0$
(d) $y = 4$ (e) $x = 3$
7. $(a - b)x + (a + b)y - (a^2 + b^2) = 0$

EXERCISE 5.9

1. (a) (i) 2 (ii) $-\frac{1}{2}$ (b) (i) 4 (ii) $-\frac{1}{4}$
(c) (i) -3 (ii) $\frac{1}{3}$ (d) (i) -1 (ii) 1
(e) (i) $\frac{1}{3}$ (ii) -3 (f) (i) $\frac{4}{3}$ (ii) $-\frac{3}{4}$
(g) (i) -6 (ii) $\frac{1}{6}$ (h) (i) 5 (ii) $-\frac{1}{5}$
(i) (i) $-\frac{3}{2}$ (ii) $\frac{2}{3}$ (j) (i) $-\frac{1}{2}$ (ii) 2
(k) (i) $\frac{3}{2}$ (ii) $-\frac{2}{3}$ (l) (i) $\frac{1}{3}$ (ii) -3
2. $4x - y - 14 = 0$
3. $3x + 4y - 65 = 0$
4. $2x + 3y - 12 = 0$
5. $3x + 5y + 21 = 0$
6. (a) $y = -7$ (b) $x = 2$
7. $4x - 3y = 0$
8. $y = -5x + 3$
9. $5x - 4y - 20 = 0$
10. (b) $3x + 4y + 6 = 0$ (c) $x - y - 5 = 0$
11. AB: $4x + 5y - 22 = 0$ BC: $5x - 4y + 34 = 0$
CD: $4x + 5y - 63 = 0$ DA: $5x - 4y - 7 = 0$
13. (b) rectangle

EXERCISE 5.10

1. (a) $d = 50t$ (c) (i) 125 km (ii) 10 h
2. (a) $C = 15 + 1n$ (c) $43.00
3. (b) 80 (c) $920.00 (d) less than 80 (e) more than 80
4. (a) $14.00 (b) $\frac{1}{2}a$
5. 70 m
6. 687.5 cm³
7. approximately 24 m
8. $1300.00
9. (c) $6\frac{2}{3}$ h
10. (a) $V = \frac{3}{4}I$ (b) $\frac{3}{4}$
(d) $V = 6, I = 8$; $V = 3, I = 4$; $V = \frac{3}{2}, I = 2$; $V = 4.5, I = 6$
11. 262.5 kPa
12. (a) $RI = 10$ (b) $I = 10, 5, \frac{5}{2}, 2, \frac{5}{3}, \frac{5}{4}, 1$, respectively
(f) a straight line

EXERCISE 5.11

1. (a) 2 (b) 6 (c) 4 (d) 5 (e) 4 (f) 10
   (g) 4 (h) 6 (i) 8 (j) 8 (k) 5 (l) $\sqrt{106}$
2. (a) $\sqrt{5}$ (b) $\sqrt{29}$ (c) $\sqrt{2}$ (d) $\sqrt{53}$ (e) 6 (f) 7
   (g) $2\sqrt{13}$ (h) $\sqrt{17}$ (i) 5 (j) $\sqrt{13}$ (k) $\sqrt{41}$ (l) $10\sqrt{2}$
3. $5\sqrt{2}$, $2\sqrt{17}$, $\sqrt{106}$
4. $22 + 2\sqrt{85} \doteq 40.4$
5. $2\sqrt{10}$
6. (a) isosceles (b) scalene (c) scalene (d) equilateral
7. 13, 17
8. (a) 32.73 (b) 21.16 (c) 9.977 (d) 3.76
   (e) 0.212 (f) 29.81 (g) 0.0116 (h) 158.7
   (i) 17.2 (nearest tenth) (j) 172.0
10. $(-2, 0)$
11. $(0, -5)$

EXERCISE 5.12

1. (a) (4, 2) (b) $(-2, -3)$ (c) no solutions (d) no solutions
2. (a) They are parallel. (b) They are equal.
3. (a) (i) and (iii) have no solution.
4. (a) $(-3, 2)$ (b) (4, 2) (c) $(\frac{3}{2}, \frac{5}{2})$ (d) $(-\frac{12}{7}, \frac{22}{7})$
5. (a) $0 \leqslant n < 6$ (b) 6 (c) $n > 6$

EXERCISE 5.13

1. (a) $y = -2x + 7$ (b) $y = 2x + 4$ (c) $y = -\frac{2}{3}x + 2$ (d) $y = 2x - \frac{7}{2}$
   (e) $y = \frac{5}{3}x - \frac{4}{3}$ (f) $y = -\frac{2}{3}x - \frac{4}{3}$ (g) $y = -3x - 7$ (h) $y = -\frac{3}{2}x - \frac{7}{2}$
   (i) $y = -\frac{1}{3}x + \frac{7}{3}$ (j) $y = -\frac{1}{6}x - \frac{1}{3}$
2. (a) (3, 8) (b) (4, 11) (c) (2, 5) (d) $(-1, 5)$
3. (a) $(5, -17)$ (b) $(-2, -5)$ (c) $(\frac{3}{4}, \frac{9}{2})$ (d) $(\frac{1}{2}, \frac{7}{2})$ (e) $(-1, 3)$ (f) (3, 0)
4. (a) (2, 4) (b) (12, 4) (c) (7, 3) (d) $(-1, -1)$ (e) $(1, -\frac{1}{2})$ (f) (16, 11)
5. (3, 4), $(1, -2)$, $(-1, 2)$

EXERCISE 5.14

1. (a) (i) $13 - y$ (ii) $3 - \frac{1}{2}y$ (iii) $\frac{1}{3}y + \frac{4}{3}$ (iv) $2y - 9$
   (v) $\frac{3}{2}y + 1$ (vi) $3 - \frac{3}{2}y$ (vii) $\frac{7}{2} - \frac{3}{2}y$ (viii) $\frac{4}{5}y + \frac{8}{5}$
   (ix) $2y + \frac{2}{3}$ (x) $-3y$ (xi) $2y + \frac{5}{2}$ (xii) $\frac{3}{4}y + \frac{1}{4}$
   (b) (i) $13 - x$ (ii) $6 - 2x$ (iii) $3x - 4$ (iv) $\frac{1}{2}x + \frac{9}{2}$
   (v) $\frac{2}{3}x - \frac{2}{3}$ (vi) $-\frac{2}{3}x + 2$ (vii) $-\frac{2}{3}x + \frac{7}{3}$ (viii) $\frac{5}{4}x - 2$
   (ix) $\frac{1}{2}x - \frac{1}{3}$ (x) $-\frac{1}{3}x$ (xi) $\frac{1}{2}x - \frac{5}{4}$ (xii) $\frac{4}{3}x - \frac{1}{3}$
2. (a) (2, 7) (b) $(\frac{8}{5}, \frac{1}{5})$ (c) $(5, -11)$ (d) (2, 0)
3. (a) (8, 2) (b) (3, 8) (c) $(-4, 5)$ (d) $(\frac{3}{4}, \frac{2}{3})$
4. (a) $(\frac{1}{2}, \frac{3}{2})$ (b) $(\frac{1}{3}, \frac{3}{4})$ (c) $(\frac{29}{35}, \frac{3}{5})$ (d) $(\frac{1}{6}, \frac{1}{4})$ (e) (3, 1)

EXERCISE 5.15

1. (a) (3, 2) (b) (3, 2) (c) (2, 2) (d) (4, 5)
2. (a) (3, 0) (b) (2, 1) (c) (5, −1) (d) (3, 2)
3. (a) (3, 2) (b) $(\frac{3}{2}, 3)$ (c) (3, 5) (d) (1, 4)
4. (a) $(-\frac{6}{7}, \frac{30}{7})$ (b) $(\frac{3}{4}, \frac{2}{3})$ (c) (−3, −3)
5. (a) (8, 3) (b) (9, 4) (c) (20, 12)
6. (3, −1)

EXERCISE 5.16

1. (a) $x + 5$ (b) $x + 4$ (c) $y - 3$ (d) $6y$
   (e) $3b$ (f) $4 + m$ (g) $x + 2$ (h) $q - 5$
   (i) $r - 7$ or $7 - r$ (j) $\frac{b}{4}$ (k) $8x$ (l) $2d$
   (m) $x + 3x$ (n) $\frac{2x}{y}$ (o) $4b + 6$ (p) $5\ell + 3$
   (q) $4w - 10$ (r) $a + 2$ (s) $a - 3$ (t) $2s - 40$
   (u) $6p - 4$ (v) $\frac{1}{2}r + 2$ (w) $a + 2a$ (x) $2(a + 2)$
   (y) $\frac{5}{100}C$ (z) $9(s - 10)$
2. (a) $2\ell = 36$ (b) $3a = 27$ (c) $n - 2 = 8$
   (d) $n + 3 = 12$ (e) $\frac{w}{5} = 20$ (f) $2w + 2 = 12$
   (g) $5h - 4 = 16$ (h) $a - 3 = 7$ (i) $2w + 4 = 84$
3. (a) $x + y = 21$ (b) $x + y = 40$ (c) $x - y = 1$
   (d) $2x + 3y = 70$ (e) $\frac{1}{2}x + 3 = 4y$ (f) $2x - \frac{2}{3}y = 5$
   (g) $x - \frac{1}{2}y = 12$ (h) $x + y = 15$
4. (a) $2(x + y) = 46$ (b) $x + y + 9 = 33$ (c) $10x = y$
5. 3, 5 6. 7, 4 7. 5, 8 8. 2, 7 9. 2, 7 10. 9, 4
11. 7 12. 41, 15 13. 15 14. 15, 13 15. 45, 55 16. 24, 14
17. 80 kg, 20 kg 18. \$1600, \$400 19. \$1700, \$1800
20. \$3000, \$2000 21. \$150, \$50 22. \$1500, \$2000
23. (a) 8 d (nearest day) (b) $99\frac{2}{9}$ (c) 21 km/h (nearest one)
    (d) 695 km (nearest one) (e) 12 h (nearest hour)
24. (a) $x + y$ (b) $\frac{x}{85} + \frac{y}{75}$ (c) $\frac{x}{85} - \frac{y}{75}$ or $\frac{y}{75} - \frac{x}{85}$
25. (a) 100 km/h, 90 km/h (b) $\frac{x}{100} - \frac{y}{90}$ or $\frac{y}{90} - \frac{x}{100}$ (c) $x + y$
26. (a) $\frac{x}{100} + \frac{y}{90} = 6$ (b) $x + y = 300$
27. 240 km at 80 km/h; 360 km at 90 km/h
28. 270 km at 90 km/h; 175 km at 70 km/h
29. 2 h, 70 km 30. 6.5 km/h, 2.5 km/h
31. (a) 975 km/h (b) 75 km/h

EXERCISE 5.17

1. $7x - 4y + 3 = 0$ 2. $5x - 2y - 22 = 0$ 3. $7x + 4y - 1 = 0$
4. $16x - 2y - 29 = 0$

5.18 REVIEW EXERCISE

1. (a) $-\frac{4}{3}$ (b) $\frac{1}{2}$ (c) $-\frac{7}{3}$ (d) 3 (e) $\frac{9}{2}$ (f) $\frac{1}{2}$
2. (a) $\sqrt{17}$ (b) $\sqrt{53}$ (c) $2\sqrt{13}$ (d) 4 (e) $\sqrt{85}$ (f) $4\sqrt{2}$ (g) $3\sqrt{2}$ (h) 6
4. (a) $x - 2y - 7 = 0$ (b) $3x + 5y - 32 = 0$ (c) $6x + y + 4 = 0$ (d) $12x - 3y + 2 = 0$ (e) $x + 2y - 9 = 0$ (f) $7x - y - 37 = 0$ (g) $6x - 3y - 5 = 0$ (h) $2x - 3y + 18 = 0$ (i) $2x + y - 6 = 0$ (j) $y = 4$
5. (a) (1, 1) (b) (1, −2) (c) (−2, −2) (d) (2, −1) (e) (1, 0) (f) (2, −3) (g) (10, 6) (h) (14, 15) (i) (−1, 2)
6. (a) 5 (b) 0
7. (b) NO (c) $3x - 4y - 6 = 0$
8. (a) $x - 2y + 10 = 0$ (b) $2x + y - 5 = 0$ (d) $2x + 3y + 11 = 0$ (e) $2x - 5y - 29 = 0$
9. $y = -x + 4$
10. $x + 3y - 9 = 0$
11. $x + 4y - 9 = 0$
12. $5x + 3y + 19 = 0$
13. $2x + 3y - 21 = 0$
14. $3x - 5y - 15 = 0$
15. $-\frac{3}{2}, \frac{7}{2}$
16. (a) $\frac{4}{3}$ (b) −3
17. 1
18. $6x - 7y - 23 = 0$
19. $5x - 3y + 8 = 0$
20. 10.20
21. 31 square units
22. 7, 11
23. 9, 7
24. 13
25. \$1000, \$3000
26. \$600, \$500
27. 3 h at 95 km/h, 4 h at 85 km/h
28. (0, 2)
29. $7x - 3y + 24 = 0$
30. $2x - 3y + 12 = 0$
31. $(\frac{7}{3}, 0)$
32. $9x + 2y + 8 = 0$
33. −4
34. $x + y - 9 = 0$, $4x - 7y + 30 = 0$, $x - 10y + 24 = 0$
35. $6x + y - 32 = 0$

5.19 CHAPTER 5 TEST

1. (a) $\frac{4}{9}$ (b) $\frac{4}{3}$
2. (a) $\sqrt{73}$ (b) 12
3. (a) $2x - y - 8 = 0$ (b) $3x + 5y + 19 = 0$ (c) $2x + 3y - 4 = 0$ (d) $y = 3$
4. (a) −2 (b) $\frac{3}{4}$
5. (a) $\frac{5}{4}$, 5 (b) $-\frac{5}{3}, \frac{5}{4}$
6. (a) $4x - 5y - 20 = 0$ (b) $9x + 5y - 7 = 0$
7. (a) $(2, \frac{1}{2})$ (b) $(\frac{4}{3}, \frac{4}{3})$
8. (a) $C = 25 + 8n$

REVIEW AND PREVIEW TO CHAPTER 6

EXERCISE 1

(a) 230 (b) 23 (c) 2.3 (d) 31 (e) 5.1 (f) 0.2 (g) 0.7 (h) 14.0 (i) 90.8

EXERCISE 2

(a) 2300 (b) 230 (c) 23 (d) 520 (e) 610 (f) 61 (g) 606.1 (h) 0.1 (i) 0.04

EXERCISE 3

(a) 23 000 (b) 2300 (c) 230 (d) 7400 (e) 9010 (f) 10 010 (g) 20 (h) 102 (i) 0.6

EXERCISE 4

(a) 2.3 (b) 0.23 (c) 0.023 (d) 5.2 (e) 6.7 (f) 0.74 (g) 0.001 (h) 0.061 (i) 1.402

EXERCISE 5

(a) 0.23 (b) 0.023 (c) 0.0023 (d) 0.62 (e) 7.85 (f) 90.01
(g) 0.0001 (h) 856.04 (i) 0.000 020 1

EXERCISE 6

(a) 0.023 (b) 0.0023 (c) 0.000 23 (d) 0.0051 (e) 0.104
(f) 11.709 (g) 0.11 (h) 10.17 (i) 0.000 002 3

EXERCISE 7

(a) 51 mm (b) 62 mm (c) 1 mm (d) 0.1 mm (e) 102 mm
(f) 642.0 mm (g) 9010 mm (h) 1002 mm (i) 106.1 mm

EXERCISE 8

(a) 500 cm (b) 510 cm (c) 90 cm (d) 2 cm (e) 640 cm (f) 0.5 cm
(g) 1902 cm (h) 10.5 cm (i) 65 000 cm

EXERCISE 9

(a) 1000 L (b) 1100 L (c) 500 L (d) 1040 L (e) 15 050 L (f) 19 404 L
(g) 2.01 L (h) 20 L (i) 1019 L (j) 6000 L (k) 17 201 L (l) 505 L

EXERCISE 10

(a) 0.5 cm (b) 1.5 cm (c) 0.310 cm (d) 5 cm (e) 50 cm (f) 2.6 cm

EXERCISE 11

(a) 0.5 m (b) 0.1 m (c) 0.15 m (d) 0.015 m (e) 1.05 m (f) 12.15 m
(g) 0.0001 m (h) 1.945 m (i) 0.3264 m

EXERCISE 12

(a) 2 L (b) 2.001 L (c) 0.2 L (d) 0.005 L (e) 35 L (f) 6.402 L
(g) 1.901 L (h) 0.01 L (i) 4.2 L (j) 0.363 L

THREE-DIMENSIONAL FIGURES

EXERCISE

1. (a) 6 units (b) 6 units (c) 6 units (d) 8 units (e) 8 units (f) 16 units

EXERCISE 6.1

1. (a) 96 cm (b) 78 m (c) 20.2 cm (d) 11 km
2. (a) 122 m (b) 74 mm
3. (a) 18.8 cm (b) 75.6 m (c) 20.2 mm
(d) 26.4 km (nearest tenth) (e) 51.2 cm (nearest tenth) (f) 125.8 mm
4. (a) 45 cm (b) 116.8 m
5. (a) 69 m (b) 44 cm (c) 69 m (d) 93.4 cm
6. (a) 12.2 m (b) 12.18 m
7. (a) 60.7 cm (nearest tenth) (b) 29.8 mm (nearest tenth)
(c) 6.4 cm (nearest tenth) (d) 222.8 m (nearest tenth)
(e) 92.1 m (nearest tenth) (f) 227 cm (nearest one)
8. (a) 24 cm (b) 5.6 m (c) 1.8 cm
(d) 7.6 m (e) 7.2 mm (f) $x = 1.6$ cm, $y = 3.1$ cm
9. 122.8 cm (nearest tenth)
10. $1054.90
11. $44.10
12. (a) 440 m (nearest metre) (b) 45.5 turns (nearest tenth)
13. $2677.54
14. 2.9 km
15. 39 900 km (nearest hundred)

EXERCISE 6.2

1. (a) 24 mm^2 (b) 144 m^2 (c) 56 cm^2
(d) 201 cm^2 (nearest one) (e) 136.8 m^2 (nearest tenth) (f) 31.2 cm^2 (nearest tenth)
(g) 0.12 m^2 (h) 2800 m^2 (nearest hundred)
2. (a) 35 m^2 (b) 60 cm^2 (c) 48 cm^2 (d) 36 cm^2

3. (a) 12.2 cm^2 (nearest tenth) (b) 25.6 m^2 (nearest tenth) (c) 32.0 cm^2 (nearest tenth)
(d) 567.4 m^2 (nearest tenth) (e) 1560 cm^2 (nearest ten) (f) 103 cm^2
4. (a) 18.5 cm (b) 8 cm
5. (a) 48 cm^2 (b) 68 cm^2 (c) 82 cm^2 (nearest one)
(d) 104 cm^2 (e) 157 cm^2 (nearest one)
6. (a) 305 m^2 (b) \$2668.75
7. \$1442.38 8. 12 rolls 9. 680 cm^2 (nearest one)
10. (a) 2418 m^2 (b) \$846.30
11. (a) 357 m^2 (nearest one) (b) 81.4 m (nearest tenth) (c) \$116.40
12. 128 m^2 (nearest one)
13. (a) 283 m (nearest one) (b) 330 m (nearest one) (c) 2300 m^2 (nearest ten)

EXERCISE 6.3

2. (a) 400 m^2 (b) 600 m^2 (c) 625 m^2 (d) 483 m^2
(e) 745 m^2 (f) 444 m^2 (g) 696 m^2 (h) 600 m^2
(i) 420 m^2 (j) 643 m^2 (k) 600 m^2 (l) 668 m^2
(m) 380 m^2 (n) 500 m^2 (o) 794 m^2
4. (o)

EXERCISE 6.4

1. (a) 1536 cm^2 (b) 43 cm^2
2. (a) 346 cm^2 (b) 322 cm^2
3. (a) 288 cm^2 (b) 17.0 m^2 (nearest tenth)
(c) 166.8 mm^2 (nearest tenth) (d) 39.7 m^2
4. (a) 280 m^2 (b) \$1008.00
5. 32 m^2
6. (a) 25 200 cm^2 (b) \$504.00

EXERCISE 6.5

1. (a) 409 cm^2 (nearest one) (b) 570 cm^2 (nearest one)
2. (a) 19.8 m^2 (nearest tenth) (b) 143 mm^2 (nearest one)
3. (a) 3630 cm^2 (nearest ten) (b) 688 mm^2 (nearest one)
4. (a) 1570 m^2 (nearest one) (b) \$1884.00
5. 44.0 m^2 (nearest tenth)
6. 1340 cm^2 (nearest ten)
7. 5280 cm^2 (nearest ten)
8. (a) 5.06×10^8 km^2 (b) 6.15×10^{12} km^2 (c) 12 150 (nearest ten)

EXERCISE 6.6

1. (a) 12.6 cm^3 (nearest tenth) (b) 355.0 m^3 (nearest tenth)
(c) 47 200 mm^3 (nearest hundred) (d) 18.1 mm^3 (nearest tenth)
(e) 1.7 m^3 (nearest tenth) (f) 2208 cm^3
(g) 29.9 m^3 (nearest tenth) (h) 325 cm^3
2. (a) 2.5 cm (b) 16 mm
3. (a) 1948 cm^3 (nearest one) (b) 256 cm^3
4. 62 800 L (nearest hundred)
5. 52.5 m^3
6. 675 000 L
8. (a) 11.8 m^3 (nearest tenth) (b) 106 000 kg (nearest thousand)

EXERCISE 6.7

1. (a) 28.8 m^3 (nearest tenth) (b) 444 cm^3 (nearest one)
(c) 697 m^3 (nearest one) (d) 10 300 cm^3 (nearest hundred)
(e) 23.0 cm^3 (nearest tenth) (f) 3.5 m^3 (nearest tenth)
2. (a) 12.0 cm (nearest tenth) (b) approximately 11.34 cm by 11.34 cm
3. (a) 13.0 m^3 (nearest tenth) (b) 163 cm^3 (nearest one)

(c) 9630 m^3 (nearest ten)
(d) 4750 mm^3 (nearest ten)
4. 480 m^3 (nearest ten)
5. 336 m^3 (nearest one)
6. 1000 m^3
7. 2 574 467 m^3 (nearest one)

EXERCISE 6.8

1. (a) 1830 cm^3 (nearest ten)
(b) 12 300 cm^3 (nearest hundred)
(c) 10 200 cm^3 (nearest hundred)
(d) 16.7 m^3 (nearest tenth)
2. 10 L
3. 80.4 cm^3 (nearest tenth)
4. a cylinder

EXERCISE 6.9

1. (a) 2.02×10^8 km^2
(b) 2.63×10^8 km^2
(c) 4.18×10^7 km^2
2. (a) 40%
(b) 52%
(c) 8%
3. 2 : 13 : 10

EXERCISE 6.10

1. 23 421 314 or 41 312 432
2. 1437
3. 7500 cm^3
4. 11:25
5. 100, 144, 169, 225, 324, 400, 441, 484, 529, 900
6. No
7. 24
8. 11 (Answers will vary, depending on the style of type used.)
9. The volume of the balls is greater (by a factor of 2).
10. 22
11. 5 and 8
12. 40 cm^2
13. 8
14. 10 h 17 min 10 s (nearest second)
15. 94
16. 15
17. 276 m^2
18. A, B, C, F, and G
19. 12, 19, and 23

6.11 REVIEW EXERCISE

1. (a) 10 m, 6.25 m^2
(b) 8.0 m^2
2. (a) (i) 9.4 m (ii) 12.6 m
(b) (i) 7.1 m^2 (ii) 12.6 m^2
(c) (i) 7.1 m^3 (ii) 16.7 m^3
(d) (i) 7100 L (ii) 16 700 L
3. (a) 126.5 m
(b) 112.1 m
(c) 1000.0 m^2
4. 2.5 L (nearest tenth)
5. 8.5 L
6. 900 m^3
7. 42 mL
8. 1.75 m^3
9. 147 mL
10. (a) 31.6 m^2
(b) \$42.80
11. (a) 236 bulbs
(b) \$79.93
(c) 11.8 m by 11.8 m
12. (a) $\frac{s}{4}$
(b) 4
13. (a) $\frac{r}{2}$
(b) 2
14. (a) $\frac{s}{6}$
(b) 6
15. (a) $\frac{r}{3}$
(b) 3
16. (a) 1662 cm^3
(b) approximately 23%
17. 3110 cm^2

6.12 CHAPTER 6 TEST

1. (a) 28.0 cm
(b) 11.2 cm
(c) 67.1 cm
2. (a) 4.8 m^2
(b) 89.2 m^2
(c) 60 m^2
3. (a) 134.1 m^2
(b) 2093.3 cm^2
(c) 803.8 m^2
4. (a) 20.5 m^3
(b) 385.3 cm^3
(c) 267.9 m^3
5. (a) 258 cm^2
(b) 21.5%

REVIEW AND PREVIEW TO CHAPTER 7

1. (a) A, B, C
(b) $\overleftrightarrow{AB}$, $\overleftrightarrow{AC}$, $\overleftrightarrow{BC}$
(c) AB, AC, BC
(d) $\overrightarrow{AB}$, $\overrightarrow{BA}$, $\overrightarrow{AC}$, $\overrightarrow{CA}$, $\overrightarrow{BC}$, $\overrightarrow{CB}$
(e) $\angle ABC$, $\angle BAC$, $\angle ACB$

2. (a) $\overline{QR}$, $\overline{RS}$, $\overline{ST}$, $\overline{TQ}$ (b) QR, RS, ST, TQ
(c) $\overrightarrow{QR}$, $\overrightarrow{RQ}$, $\overrightarrow{RS}$, $\overrightarrow{SR}$, $\overrightarrow{ST}$, $\overrightarrow{TS}$, $\overrightarrow{TQ}$, $\overrightarrow{QT}$ (d) $\angle Q$, $\angle R$, $\angle S$, $\angle T$

3. Complementary angles: $\angle x$ and $\angle y$, $\angle a$ and $\angle b$
Supplementary angles: $\angle q$ and $\angle r$, $\angle r$ and $\angle t$, $\angle t$ and $\angle s$, $\angle s$ and $\angle q$

4. (a) $\triangle ABE$, $\triangle ACE$, $\triangle BED$ (b) $\triangle BCD$ (c) $\triangle ABC$, $\triangle ABD$, $\triangle CED$

5. (a) $\triangle EGF$, $\triangle BGC$ (b) $\triangle AGF$, $\triangle CGD$ (c) $\triangle AGB$, $\triangle DGE$

EXERCISE 7.1

1. (a) $\angle a = 87^\circ$, $\angle b = 93^\circ$, $\angle c = 87^\circ$ (b) $\angle a = 121^\circ$, $\angle b = 59^\circ$, $\angle c = 121^\circ$
(c) $\angle a = 67^\circ$ (d) $\angle a = 20^\circ$

2. (a) 45° (b) 60° (c) 50° (d) 76° 3. (a) 84° (b) 73°

4. (a) $\angle a = 41^\circ$, $\angle b = 74^\circ$, $\angle c = 41^\circ$, $\angle d = 65^\circ$
(b) $\angle a = 45^\circ$, $\angle b = 90^\circ$, $\angle c = 45^\circ$, $\angle d = 45^\circ$, $\angle e = 90^\circ$
(c) $\angle a = 74^\circ$, $\angle b = 41^\circ$, $\angle c = 139^\circ$
(d) $\angle a = 23^\circ$, $\angle b = 31^\circ$, $\angle c = 90^\circ$, $\angle d = 90^\circ$
(e) $\angle a = 46^\circ$, $\angle b = 44^\circ$, $\angle c = 46^\circ$
(f) $\angle a = 80^\circ$, $\angle b = 99^\circ$, $\angle c = 95^\circ$, $\angle d = 86^\circ$

5. (a) $a = 65^\circ$ (b) $a = 15^\circ$, $b = 60^\circ$

6. (a) 54° (b) 60° 7. 540°

EXERCISE 7.2

1. (i) (a) $\angle c$ and $\angle f$, $\angle d$ and $\angle e$
(b) $\angle a$ and $\angle e$, $\angle b$ and $\angle f$, $\angle c$ and $\angle g$, $\angle d$ and $\angle h$
(c) $\angle c$ and $\angle e$, $\angle d$ and $\angle f$
(ii) (a) $\angle n$ and $\angle s$, $\angle p$ and $\angle q$
(b) $\angle n$ and $\angle r$, $\angle p$ and $\angle t$, $\angle m$ and $\angle q$, $\angle o$ and $\angle s$
(c) $\angle n$ and $\angle q$, $\angle p$ and $\angle s$

2. (a) $\angle a = 65^\circ$, $\angle b = 65^\circ$, $\angle c = 115^\circ$ (b) $\angle a = 55^\circ$, $\angle b = 125^\circ$, $\angle c = 125^\circ$

3. (a) $\angle a = 110^\circ$, $\angle b = 70^\circ$, $\angle c = 70^\circ$, $\angle d = 110^\circ$, $\angle e = 70^\circ$, $\angle f = 70^\circ$, $\angle g = 110^\circ$
(b) $\angle p = 145^\circ$, $\angle q = 35^\circ$, $\angle r = 145^\circ$, $\angle s = 145^\circ$, $\angle t = 35^\circ$, $\angle u = 35^\circ$, $\angle v = 145^\circ$

4. (a) $\angle a = 67^\circ$, $\angle b = 35^\circ$, $\angle c = 67^\circ$, $\angle d = 102^\circ$
(b) $\angle a = 55^\circ$, $\angle b = 55^\circ$, $\angle c = 70^\circ$, $\angle d = 55^\circ$
(c) $\angle g = 58^\circ$, $\angle h = 38^\circ$, $\angle i = 84^\circ$
(d) $\angle a = 111^\circ$, $\angle b = 69^\circ$, $\angle c = 69^\circ$
(e) $\angle a = 80^\circ$, $\angle b = 100^\circ$, $\angle c = 80^\circ$, $\angle d = 55^\circ$, $\angle e = 125^\circ$
(f) $\angle a = 55^\circ$, $\angle b = 125^\circ$, $\angle c = 90^\circ$, $\angle d = 35^\circ$
(g) $\angle a = 30^\circ$, $\angle b = 60^\circ$, $\angle c = 120^\circ$
(h) $\angle p = 40^\circ$, $\angle q = 50^\circ$, $\angle r = 50^\circ$

5. $\angle DAE = 40^\circ$, $\angle CAD = 140^\circ$, $\angle BAE = 140^\circ$ 6. 102°

7. Alternate angles are equal.

8. (a) 30° (b) 60° 9. 45°

EXERCISE 7.3

1. 60° 2. 30° 3. 30° 4. 90°
5. $x = 70^\circ$, $y = 110^\circ$ 6. $a = 60^\circ$, $b = 70^\circ$, $c = 110^\circ$
7. $a = 45^\circ$, $b = 45^\circ$ 8. $a = 60^\circ$, $b = 40^\circ$, $c = 80^\circ$, $d = 100^\circ$
9. $a = 70^\circ$, $b = 55^\circ$, $c = 55^\circ$ 10. $x = 60^\circ$, $y = 50^\circ$
11. 60° 12. $x = 40^\circ$, $y = 40^\circ$ 13. $x = 100^\circ$, $y = 80^\circ$
14. $x = 30^\circ$, $y = 15^\circ$ 15. $x = 80^\circ$, $y = 20^\circ$
16. $x = 135^\circ$, $y = 135^\circ$ 17. $x = 40^\circ$, $y = 60^\circ$
18. $x = 58^\circ$, $y = 58^\circ$ 19. $x = 40^\circ$, $y = 80^\circ$
20. $x = 45^\circ$, $y = 95^\circ$ 21. $x = 35^\circ$, $y = 145^\circ$
22. $x = 40^\circ$, $y = 40^\circ$ 23. $x = 44^\circ$, $y = 46^\circ$
24. $x = 40^\circ$, $y = 88^\circ$ 25. $x = 132^\circ$, $y = 64^\circ$

26. $x = 42°$, $y = 48°$
27. $x = 75°$, $y = 75°$
28. $x = 82°$, $y = 98°$

EXERCISE 7.4

1. (a) $\angle A = \angle R$, $\angle B = \angle S$, $\angle C = \angle T$
   (b) $AB = RS$, $AC = RT$, $BC = ST$
2. (a) $\angle D = \angle X$, $\angle E = \angle Y$, $\angle F = \angle Z$, $DE = XY$, $DF = XZ$, $EF = YZ$
   (b) $\angle A = \angle R$, $\angle B = \angle S$, $\angle C = \angle T$, $AB = RS$, $AC = RT$, $BC = ST$
3. (a) $\angle A = \angle D$, $\angle B = \angle E$, $\angle C = \angle C$, $AB = DE$, $AC = DC$, $BC = EC$
   (b) $\angle R = \angle T$, $\angle RQS = \angle TQS$, $\angle RSQ = \angle TSQ$, $RQ = TQ$, $RS = TS$, $QS = QS$
   (c) $\angle W = \angle Y$, $\angle WXZ = \angle YXZ$, $\angle WZX = \angle YZX$, $XW = XY$, $XZ = XZ$, $WZ = YZ$
   (d) $\angle A = \angle E$, $\angle B = \angle D$, $\angle ACB = \angle ECD$, $AB = ED$, $AC = EC$, $BC = DC$

EXERCISE 7.5

1. (a) $\triangle ABC \cong \triangle QPR$ (SAS), $\triangle DEF \cong \triangle WXV$ (SSS), $\triangle GHI \cong \triangle CED$ (ASA), $\triangle SUT \cong \triangle GFH$ (SAS)
   (b) In $\triangle ABC$ and $\triangle QPR$: $\angle A = \angle Q$, $\angle B = \angle P$, $\angle C = \angle R$, $AB = QP$, $BC = PR$, $CA = RQ$
   In $\triangle DEF$ and $\triangle WXV$: $\angle D = \angle W$, $\angle E = \angle X$, $\angle F = \angle V$, $DE = WX$, $EF = XV$, $FD = VW$
   In $\triangle GHI$ and $\triangle CED$: $\angle G = \angle C$, $\angle H = \angle E$, $\angle I = \angle D$, $GH = CE$, $HI = ED$, $IG = DC$
2. (i) (a) $\triangle ABC \cong \triangle DFE$
   (b) SSS
   (c) $\angle A = \angle D$, $\angle B = \angle F$, $\angle C = \angle E$, $AB = DF$, $BC = FE$, $CA = ED$
   (ii) (a) $\triangle RTS \cong \triangle NTM$
   (b) SAS
   (c) $\angle R = \angle N$, $\angle RTS = \angle NTM$, $\angle S = \angle M$, $RT = NT$, $TS = TM$, $SR = MN$
   (iii) (a) $\triangle RST \cong \triangle RQP$
   (b) SSS
   (c) $\angle SRT = \angle QRP$, $\angle S = \angle Q$, $\angle T = \angle P$, $RS = RQ$, $ST = QP$, $TR = PR$
   (iv) (a) $\triangle ABC \cong \triangle ADC$
   (b) ASA
   (c) $\angle BAC = \angle DAC$, $\angle B = \angle D$, $\angle BCA = \angle DCA$, $BA = DA$, $BC = DC$, $AC = AC$
   (v) (a) $\triangle VXW \cong \triangle ZXY$
   (b) ASA
   (c) $\angle V = \angle Z$, $\angle VXW = \angle ZXY$, $\angle W = \angle Y$, $VX = ZX$, $XW = XY$, $WV = YZ$

EXERCISE 7.6

1. (a) $x = 67°$, $y = 56°$
   (b) $x = 8.2$ m, $y = 49°$, $z = 72°$
   (c) $x = 41°$, $y = 82°$
   (d) $x = 70°$, $y = 15$ m
   (e) $x = 8.8$ m, $y = 10.5$ m
   (f) $x = 8$ m
   (g) $x = 40°$, $y = 5$ cm
   (h) $x = 70°$, $y = 45°$
   (i) $x = 110°$
   (j) $x = 60°$
2. Since $\triangle ABC \cong \triangle EDC$ (SAS), $AB = ED = 3.1$ km.
3. (a) 5.3 km
   (b) ASA
4. 56 cm

EXERCISE 7.8

1. (a) 45 cm
   (b) 9 m
   (c) 4 cm
   (d) 3.3 m
2. (a) 18 cm
   (b) 10.5 m
   (c) 4.4 cm (nearest tenth)
   (d) 19.5 cm
   (e) 3.9 m (nearest tenth)
   (f) 11.5 m (nearest tenth)
3. 37.5 m
4. 10.8 m (nearest tenth)
5. 78 m (nearest one)
6. 61.6 m
7. 7.5 m (nearest tenth)
8. 4.6 cm (nearest tenth)

EXERCISE 7.9

1. (a) 20 cm (b) 125 cm (c) 25.7 m (d) 9.4 cm
   (e) 9.2 cm (f) 9.4 m (g) 16.2 cm (h) 7.5 m
2. 721 km (nearest one)
3. 6.9 m (nearest tenth)
4. $x = 5$ m, $y = 6.7$ m
5. $x = 103$ m, $y = 133$ m (nearest one)
6. 41.0 cm (nearest tenth)
7. 217.9 cm (nearest tenth)
8. 27.0 m
9. 27.2 cm (nearest tenth)
10. 1.3 m
11. 4.8 m (nearest tenth)
12. 3.8 m (nearest tenth)

EXERCISE 7.10

2. (i) path (d) (ii) path (c) (iii) path (a) (iv) path (b)
3. path (c) (12 m), path (d) (12.08 m), path (b) (12.17 m), path (a) (12.81 m) (nearest hundredth)

EXERCISE 7.11

1. (a) A square of side 100 units
   (b) `REPEAT 4 [FD 100 RT 90]`
2. (a) `REPEAT 90 [FD 1 RT 4]`
   (b) `REPEAT 180 [FD 1 RT 2]`
   (c) `REPEAT 360 [FD 1 RT 1]`
3. (a) `REPEAT 4 [FD 50 RT 90]`
   (b) `RT 30`
   (c) `REPEAT 12 [REPEAT 4 [FD 50 RT 90] RT 30]`

EXERCISE 7.12

1. 3
2. 12
3. $1.69
5. Answers will vary.
6. $10.00
7. (a) 542×63 (b) 356×24
8. The lawn mower must be pushed 400 m, whichever method is used.
9. 29
10. 9
11. 39, 40, 41, 42
12. 52
13. 4.5 h
14. 120 cm
15. 126 cm

7.13 REVIEW EXERCISE

1. (a) $\angle x = 130°$, $\angle y = 25°$, $\angle z = 25°$
   (b) $\angle x = 92°$, $\angle y = 88°$, $\angle z = 96°$
   (c) $\angle m = 120°$, $\angle n = 30°$, $\angle r = 30°$, $\angle s = 120°$, $\angle t = 30°$, $\angle x = 60°$, $\angle y = 60°$, $\angle z = 60°$
2. (a) $a = 30°$, $b = 90°$ (b) $20°$
3. (a) $\angle a = 116°$, $\angle b = 116°$, $\angle c = 64°$, $\angle d = 64°$, $\angle r = 64°$, $\angle s = 116°$, $\angle t = 64°$
   (b) $\angle a = 65°$, $\angle b = 65°$, $\angle c = 65°$, $\angle d = 25°$
4. (a) $x = 25°$, $y = 115°$ (b) $x = 71°$, $y = 66°$
5. (i) (a) $\triangle ABD \cong \triangle ACD$
   (b) SAS
   (c) $AB = AC$, $BD = CD$, $DA = DA$, $\angle BAD = \angle CAD$, $\angle ADB = \angle ADC$, $\angle B = \angle C$
   (ii) (a) $\triangle PQS \cong \triangle PRS$
   (b) SSS
   (c) $PQ = PR$, $QS = RS$, $SP = SP$, $\angle QPS = \angle RPS$, $\angle QSP = \angle RSP$, $\angle Q = \angle R$
   (iii) (a) $\triangle EGH \cong \triangle HFE$
   (b) ASA
   (c) $EG = HF$, $GH = FE$, $HE = EH$, $\angle GEH = \angle FHE$, $\angle GHE = \angle FEH$, $\angle G = \angle F$
   (iv) (a) $\triangle LNP \cong \triangle MOP$
   (b) SAS
   (c) $LN = MO$, $NP = OP$, $PL = PM$, $\angle L = \angle M$, $\angle N = \angle O$, $\angle NPL = \angle OPM$
6. (a) 15 m (b) 2.25 cm (c) 25 cm
7. (a) 9 cm (b) 14.7 m
8. 68°
9. 125°
10. 155°

11. $\angle P = 60°$, QR = 5 m
12. ASA
13. 3.9 km
14. 17 m
15. 1.8 m (nearest tenth)
16. 13 m
17. 72.4 cm by 72.4 cm (nearest tenth)

7.14 CHAPTER 7 TEST

1. (a) $\angle x = 85°$, $\angle y = 30°$, $\angle z = 150°$ (b) $\angle x = 42°$, $\angle y = 84°$, $\angle z = 71°$
2. (a) $\angle a = 80°$, $\angle b = 60°$, $\angle c = 40°$, $\angle d = 140°$
   (b) $\angle a = 85°$, $\angle b = 95°$, $\angle cx = 85°$, $\angle d = 95°$
3. $\triangle ABE \cong DCE$ (ASA), $\triangle PQR \cong \triangle LMN$ (SAS)
4. 614 cm
5. 39 m

REVIEW AND PREVIEW TO CHAPTER 8

1. (a) 0.385 (b) 0.292 (c) 0.688 (d) 9.45 (e) 34.0
   (f) 2.44 (g) 0.280 (h) 6.22 (i) 31.3 (j) 14.4
2. (a) 3.74 (b) 7.63 (c) 187 (d) 34.9 (e) 14.3
   (f) 20.5 (g) 2.25 (h) 5.21 (i) 234 (j) 2.19
3. (a) 63° (b) 30° (c) 45° (d) 26°
4. (a) 7 (b) 24 (c) 22.5 (d) 24 (e) 4 (f) 2
5. (a) 50 cm (b) 4.0 cm (c) 1.4 m (d) 13 m (e) 2.5 m (f) 5.2 cm
6. (a) 3.5 m (b) 9 m (c) 1.0 cm (d) 1.5 cm (e) 3.6 m (f) 6 cm

EXERCISE 8.1

1. (a) $\frac{8}{12} = \frac{20}{30}$ (b) $\frac{a}{5} = \frac{b}{7}$ (c) $\frac{a}{5} = \frac{b}{10}$ (d) $\frac{2}{3} = \frac{6}{9}$
2. (a) 25 cm (b) 9 cm (c) 16 cm
3. f = 7.5 m, i = 7 cm
4. a = 10 m, b = $13\frac{1}{3}$ m
5. 9 m
6. (a) $26\frac{2}{3}$ cm (b) 8.5 cm, 28.5 cm (nearest tenth)

EXERCISE 8.2

1. (a) a — opposite, b — adjacent, c — hypotenuse
   (b) d — hypotenuse, e — opposite, f — adjacent
   (c) j — adjacent, k — opposite, l — hypotenuse
   (d) p — hypotenuse, q — adjacent, r — opposite
2. (a) $\frac{3}{5}$ (b) $\frac{5}{4}$ (c) $\frac{2}{3}$ (d) $\frac{7}{4}$ (e) $\frac{4}{7}$ (f) $\frac{3}{8}$
3. (a) 70.0 m (b) 13.7 m (c) 167.8 m (d) 59.6 cm
4. (a) 128.0 m (b) 14.0 m (c) 3 m (d) 46.6 m
   (e) 83.9 m (f) 249.9 m (g) 8.7 m (h) 14.0 m
5. (a) 37° (b) 53° (c) 45° (d) 60°
6. 23°
7. 17.5 m (nearest tenth)
8. 209.6 m (nearest tenth)

EXERCISE 8.3

1. (a) (i) $\frac{8}{17}$ (ii) $\frac{15}{17}$ (iii) $\frac{8}{15}$ (b) (i) $\frac{4}{5}$ (ii) $\frac{3}{5}$ (iii) $\frac{4}{3}$
   (c) (i) $\frac{1}{2}$ (ii) $\frac{1.7}{2}$ (iii) $\frac{1}{1.7}$ (d) (i) $\frac{x}{10}$ (ii) $\frac{y}{10}$ (iii) $\frac{x}{y}$
   (e) (i) $\frac{y}{r}$ (ii) $\frac{x}{r}$ (iii) $\frac{y}{x}$ (f) (i) $\frac{b}{c}$ (ii) $\frac{a}{c}$ (iii) $\frac{b}{a}$
2. (a) (i) $\frac{3}{5}$ (ii) $\frac{4}{5}$ (iii) $\frac{3}{4}$ (b) (i) $\frac{15}{17}$ (ii) $\frac{8}{17}$ (iii) $\frac{15}{8}$

(c) (i) $\frac{1}{1.4}$ (ii) $\frac{1}{1.4}$ (iii) 1 (d) (i) $\frac{12}{13}$ (ii) $\frac{5}{13}$ (iii) $\frac{12}{5}$

(e) (i) $\frac{24}{25}$ (ii) $\frac{7}{25}$ (iii) $\frac{24}{7}$ (f) (i) $\frac{y}{r}$ (ii) $\frac{x}{r}$ (iii) $\frac{y}{x}$

3. (a) 57.4 m (b) 17.7 cm (c) $x = 26.8$ m, $y = 22.5$ m
   (d) 163.8 m (e) $a = 109.6$ m, $b = 42.3$ m
4. (a) $\frac{1}{\sqrt{2}}$ (b) $\frac{1}{\sqrt{2}}$ (c) 1
5. (a) $\frac{1}{2}$ (b) $\frac{\sqrt{3}}{2}$ (c) $\frac{1}{\sqrt{3}}$
6. (a) $\frac{\sqrt{3}}{2}$ (b) $\frac{1}{2}$ (c) $\sqrt{3}$
7. (a) 35.6 m (b) 18.2 m

EXERCISE 8.4

1. (a) 0.4226 (b) 0.8090 (c) 1.4281 (d) 0.4067 (e) 1.9626 (f) 0.8192
2. (a) 75.3° (b) 38.7° (c) 48.0° (d) 40.7° (e) 49.3° (f) 60.3°

EXERCISE 8.5

1. (a) 2 (b) 3 (c) 3 (d) 3 (e) 4 (f) 2
   (g) 3 (h) 2 (i) 2
2. 4
3. no

EXERCISE 8.6

1. (a) 0.4226 (b) 5.6713 (c) 0.7071 (d) 0.7071 (e) 0.7880 (f) 0.3420
   (g) 1.0000 (h) 0.8660 (i) 0.5317 (j) 0.8480 (k) 0.5000 (l) 0.7660
   (m) 0.5000 (n) 0.2126 (o) 0.9063 (p) 19.081
2. (a) 31° (b) 82° (c) 14° (d) 44° (e) 45° (f) 36°
   (g) 14° (h) 45° (i) 72° (j) 85° (k) 75° (l) 30°
   (m) 39° (n) 90° (o) 58° (p) 12°
3. (a) 13.2 m (b) 101.8 m
4. (a) 24.6 cm (b) 44.1 cm
5. (a) 16.6 m (b) 21.0 cm
6. (a) 7.7 cm (b) 17.7 m (c) 3.7 cm (d) 11.3 m
7. (a) 39° (b) 47°
8. (a) $\angle A = 51°$, $a = 3.3$ cm, $c = 2.6$ cm (b) $f = 60$ m, $\angle E = 53°$, $\angle F = 37°$
9. $a = 7.6$ m, $\angle C = 23°$, $\angle B = 67°$
10. $\angle F = 55°$, $d = 11.5$ m, $f = 16.4$ m
11. 22.5 m (nearest tenth)

EXERCISE 8.7

1. (a) 1.3902 (b) 0.0175 (c) 0.5774 (d) 1.4142 (e) 0.8192 (f) 1.0000
   (g) 1.0038 (h) 0.3249 (i) 1.0515 (j) 0.0000 (k) 5.7588 (l) 7.1154
2. (a) 67° (b) 49° (c) 1° (d) 22° (e) 54° (f) 85°
   (g) 28° (h) 13°
3. (a) 25.6 m (b) 2.0 cm (c) 8.1 mm (d) 1.3 m (e) 212.1 mm (f) 1.6 m
4. 151.0 m
5. 9.3 m
6. 150.0 m
7. 8.7 m

EXERCISE 8.8

1. 147.2 m (nearest tenth)
2. (a) 81.0 m (nearest tenth) (b) 9.1 m (nearest tenth)
3. (a) 303.2 m (nearest tenth) (b) 194.9 m (nearest tenth)
4. 6.18 cm (nearest hundredth)
5. (a) 2753 m (nearest one) (b) 3403 m (nearest one)
6. $a = 2.453$ cm, $b = 2.132$ cm
7. 17° (nearest one)
8. $\angle A = 6°$, $\angle B = 11°$
9. (a) 3.2° (nearest tenth) (b) 9.01 cm (nearest hundredth)
10. 2.8 cm (nearest tenth)
11. $x = 3.85$ cm, $y = 4.93$ cm (nearest hundredth)
12. 8.2 cm (nearest tenth)
13. 11.7 cm (nearest tenth)

EXERCISE 8.9

1. (a) 53°30′ (b) 24°36′ (c) 67°48′ (d) 25°24′ (e) 48°6′ (f) 63°54′
2. (a) 35.4° (b) 55.7° (c) 15.6° (d) 65.9° (e) 23.5° (f) 45.6°
3. (a) 35°15′ (b) 16°45′ (c) 24°16′12″ (d) 72°48′36″ (e) 46°52′12″ (f) 52°17′24″
4. (a) 37.2375° (b) 73.4189° (c) 26.7097° (d) 27.8711° (e) 53.1264° (f) 43.915°
5. (a) 0.419 (b) 0.805 (c) 0.342 (d) 0.598 (e) 0.679 (f) 0.454
6. (a) 0.8249 (b) 1.3476 (c) 0.4455 (d) 0.7177 (d) 0.4574 (f) 0.8969
7. (a) 40°31′ (b) 28°17′ (c) 58°30′ (d) 58°40′ (e) 25°17′ (f) 48°20′ (g) 62°48′ (h) 7°54′
8. (a) 46°29′38″ (b) 64°45′38″ (c) 61°36′30″ (d) 40°22′4″ (e) 50°49′1″ (f) 51°16′47″
9. 28.57 km from C; 31.69 km from B

EXERCISE 8.10

1. B: 12 996 cm², C: 7056 cm², D: 900 cm², E: 4900 cm², F: 10 816 cm², G: 1156 cm², H: 256 cm², I: 4624 cm², J: 2704 cm², L: 14 400 cm²
2. 9 and 9, 3 and 24
3. 7 twenty-dollar bills, 2 ten-dollar bills, and 2 two-dollar bills
4. \$6.50
5. 72 and 73
6. C
7. 14, 15, and 16; 7, 8, 9, 10, and 11; 5, 6, 7, 8, 9, and 10; 1, 2, 3, 4, 5, 6, 7, 8, and 9
8. white
10. 3 packages of 8; 4 packages of 6
12. (a) $1111 \times 11 = 12\,221$, $2222 \times 22 = 48\,884$ (b) 1111×11

8.11 REVIEW EXERCISE

1. (a) 24 cm (b) 5.25 m (c) 1.2 m (d) 36 m
2. (a) $\sin\theta = \frac{1}{2}$, $\cos\theta = \frac{17.3}{20}$, $\tan\theta = \frac{10.0}{17.3}$, $\csc\theta = 2$, $\sec\theta = \frac{20}{17.3}$, $\cot\theta = \frac{17.3}{10.0}$
   (b) $\sin\theta = \frac{17}{27}$, $\cos\theta = \frac{21}{27}$, $\tan\theta = \frac{17}{21}$, $\csc\theta = \frac{27}{17}$, $\sec\theta = \frac{27}{21}$, $\cot\theta = \frac{21}{17}$
   (c) $\sin\theta = \frac{17}{22}$, $\cos\theta = \frac{7}{11}$, $\tan\theta = \frac{17}{14}$, $\csc\theta = \frac{22}{17}$, $\sec\theta = \frac{11}{7}$, $\cot\theta = \frac{14}{17}$
   (d) $\sin\theta = \frac{15.0}{21.2}$, $\cos\theta = \frac{15.0}{21.2}$, $\tan\theta = 1.0$, $\csc\theta = \frac{21.2}{15.0}$, $\sec\theta = \frac{21.2}{15.0}$, $\cot\theta = 1.0$
   (e) $\sin 60° = \frac{\sqrt{3}}{2}$, $\cos 60° = \frac{1}{2}$, $\tan 60° = \sqrt{3}$, $\csc 60° = \frac{2}{\sqrt{3}}$, $\sec 60° = 2$, $\cot 60° = \frac{1}{\sqrt{3}}$
   (f) $\sin 45° = \frac{1}{\sqrt{2}}$, $\cos 45° = \frac{1}{\sqrt{2}}$, $\tan 45° = 1$, $\csc 45° = \sqrt{2}$, $\sec 45° = \sqrt{2}$, $\cot 45° = 1$
3. (a) 1.2 cm (b) 0.94 cm (c) 4.2 m (d) 14 cm (e) 9.6 cm (f) 1.46 cm
4. (a) 49° (b) 67° (c) 34° (d) 62° (e) 45° (f) 47°
5. 2.6 cm (nearest tenth)
6. 743 m (nearest one)
7. 30 m (nearest one)
8. 23.4 m (nearest tenth)
9. 8.2 cm (nearest tenth)
10. 22.6° (nearest tenth)
11. 76.0° (nearest tenth)
12. 63.4° (nearest tenth)

8.12 CHAPTER 8 TEST

1. (a) $\sin\theta = \frac{p}{q}$ (b) $\cos\theta = \frac{r}{q}$ (c) $\tan\theta = \frac{p}{r}$
2. (a) $\frac{12}{13}$ (b) $\frac{5}{12}$
3. (a) 20.5 cm (nearest tenth) (b) 51°
4. $\angle A = 55°$, $b = 8.8$ cm, $c = 15.3$ cm
5. 38.4 m (nearest tenth)
6. 62 m (nearest one)

REVIEW AND PREVIEW TO CHAPTER 9

BASIC OPERATIONS

1. (a) 9, 11, 15, 17, 20, 21, 22, 28, 46, 75, 85
   (b) 9, 24, 24, 29, 31, 33, 33, 47, 56, 83, 85, 85
   (c) $\frac{5}{32}, \frac{3}{16}, \frac{1}{4}, \frac{7}{16}, \frac{1}{2}, \frac{5}{8}, \frac{3}{4}$
2. (a) 50.761 (b) 753.217 (c) 569.574 (d) 969.135
3. (a) 146.52 (b) 1.563 (c) 25.78 (d) 0.024 93
4. (a) 268.65 (b) 0.682 95 (c) 154.3875 (d) 0.023 125
5. (a) 1.30×10^2 (b) 136 (c) 0.0597 (d) 0.0394
6. (a) 5131 (b) 121 236 (c) 110 (d) 409 (e) 1651 (f) 1
7. (a) $\frac{5}{6}$ (b) $1\frac{3}{8}$ (c) $4\frac{7}{10}$ (d) $8\frac{1}{8}$ (e) $5\frac{1}{6}$ (f) $3\frac{3}{8}$
8. (a) $\frac{1}{4}$ (b) $\frac{3}{4}$ (c) $2\frac{1}{4}$ (d) $\frac{5}{6}$ (e) $2\frac{11}{12}$ (f) $2\frac{1}{4}$
9. (a) $\frac{1}{2}$ (b) $\frac{5}{16}$ (c) 2 (d) $3\frac{3}{8}$ (e) $4\frac{17}{32}$ (f) 10
10. (a) 2 (b) $1\frac{1}{5}$ (c) $\frac{3}{5}$ (d) $\frac{1}{4}$ (e) $2\frac{9}{10}$ (f) 2
11. (a) $1\frac{1}{16}$ (b) $2\frac{1}{3}$ (c) $4\frac{7}{8}$ (d) $6\frac{3}{8}$

SUMMATION NOTATION

1. (a) 1 + 2 + 3 + 4 + 5 + 6 + 7 + 8 (b) 2 + 4 + 6 + 8
   (c) 7 + 10 + 13 + 16 + 19 + 22 + 25 (d) 9 + 13 + 17 + 21
   (e) 1 + 4 + 9 + 16 + 25 (f) 12 + 27 + 48 + 75 + 108
2. (a) 15 (b) −10 (c) 31 (d) −1 (e) 30 (f) 150
3. (a) $\sum_{n=1}^{6} 2n$ (b) $\sum_{n=1}^{5} 2^n$ (c) $\sum_{n=1}^{6} (1 - n)$ (d) $\sum_{n=2}^{5} \frac{1}{n}$ (e) $\sum_{n=4}^{9} n^2$ (f) $\sum_{n=2}^{6} \frac{1}{n^2}$

EXERCISE 9.1

1. telephone survey, observational survey, questionnaires
2. checking the quality of a certain product by testing until failure results in a non-saleable product
   (i) letting a sample of light bulbs burn until expiration to determine an average life span
   (ii) determining upper or lower temperature or pressure limits of a product (e.g., aerosol cans)
   (iii) testing the unbreakability of "unbreakable" glass
3. (i) calculating an average examination mark for a class
   (ii) checking all cars in a parking lot for a valid parking permit
   (iii) checking all livestock on a certain farm for disease
4. (a) Year 2 (b) January, February, and December
   (c) (i) June (ii) July (d) June
5. (a) This is not a random sample — interviewer bias.
   (b) The sample would not necessarily contain enough people from the population of interest. Many of these people may be from out of the country and those there who are from the population of interest would generally be more affluent members of the population. This is not a random sample.
   (c) This is not a random sample.
6. (a) 15 (b) 25 (c) 36

EXERCISE 9.2

1. 300

2.

Candidate	Number of Votes
Burns	81 600
Lewchuck	117 867
O'Callaghan	92 933
Ramsay	47 600

EXERCISE 9.3

1. (a) 7 (b) (i) 10 (ii) 13 (iii) 2 (c) 10
2. (a) 26 kg
3. (a) 79 s (d) 101

EXERCISE 9.4

1. (a) Cheetah, Lion, Jack-rabbit, Greyhound, Giraffe, Human
   (b) Cheetah, Lion, Jack-rabbit, Greyhound
   (c) 2 (d) no
2. (a) June
   (b) January and November, March and April, July and August
   (c) 4 (d) December (e) 68
3. (a) Asia (b) Asia and Africa
   (c) Africa and Antarctica (or North and South America)
   (d) Antarctica, Europe, and Oceana
5. (a) (i) approximately 0.125 kg (ii) 0.75 kg (iii) approximately 2.2 kg (iv) 3 kg (v) 4 kg
   (b) approximately 80 000 kJ

EXERCISE 9.5

1. (a) continuous (b) 1400-1500 h
   (c) 1000 h–1100 h and 1800 h–1900 h, 1100 h–1200 h and 1600 h–1700 h
   (d) 29 (e) 11
   (f) (i) 100% (ii) 96% (iii) 35% (iv) 2%
2. (a) discrete
3. (a) continuous (b) 32 kg
4. (a) discrete

EXERCISE 9.6

1. (a) 27 (b) 76 (c) 67 (d) 6
3. (b) 46 (c) 32 (d) 17

EXERCISE 9.7

1.

	mean	median	range	mode
(a)	16.4	16	12	no mode
(b)	5.9	6	6	4
(c)	8.3	8	5	8 and 10
(d)	58.25	61	29	no mode
(e)	200.5	197.5	121	no mode
(f)	58.0	58.0	0.7	no mode
(g)	0.0685	0.070	0.055	0.070
(h)	5.57	5.8	4.6	5.9

2. (a) median: 18, mean: 18, range: 15 (b) median: 17, mean: 17.5, range: 11

EXERCISE 9.8

1. 1433 h
2. weighted mean for girls: 20.0 cm
   weighted mean for boys: 20.7 cm
   mean of all handspans: 20.4 cm
3. girls: median, 20 cm; mode, 20 cm
   boys: median, 21 cm; mode, 20 cm and 21 cm
   girls and boys: median, 20 cm; mode, 20 cm
4. 16.8
6. 5.2 a
7. $59 800

EXERCISE 9.9

1. cumulative means: 75, 84, 94, 108.8, 126.4, 143.7, 162.4, 181, 206.7, 230, 253.8, 276, 296.5, 314.6, 330.5, 345.1, 357.7, 369.4, 380.1, 389.8, 398.5, 406.5, 414.0, 420.9
   moving means: 94, 120, 154.7, 193.3, 234, 272, 332.7, 387.7, 448, 484, 518, 537.3, 548.3, 555.7, 559, 564.3, 567, 571.7, 572.7, 573.7, 575.7, 577.7
2. 50 a cumulative means: 555 000 000, 577 500 000, 626 666 667, 695 000 000, 796 000 000, 913 333 333, 1 268 571 429, 1 797 500 000
   100 a moving means: 577 500 000, 662 500 000, 812 500 000, 1 050 000 000, 1 350 000 000, 2 450 000 000, 4 450 000 000
3. (a) 63, 137, 200.3, 271.2, 343.8, 392.2, 459.4, 522.8, 576

EXERCISE 9.10

2. (a) 1090 (b) 1110 (c) 1040 3. (b) 16 000 (c) 50

EXERCISE 9.11

1. 36 3. 864 cm³ 4. 60 5. 94 6. D
7. $6974.50 8. 79.4 km/h (nearest tenth)
11. $155.00 down and $58 per month is less expensive by $16

9.12 REVIEW EXERCISE

2.

	mean	median	mode
(a)	81.2	86	86
(b)	5.5	5.5	no mode
(c)	0	0	0
(d)	3.27	3.4	2.3
(e)	1.1	1	1
(f)	$4600	$4000	$8000

3. (a) $10.80
4. (b) midpoints: −11, −8, −5, −2, 1, 4, 7, 10, 13
   (c) 2.2 (d) 2.5 (e) 0
7. (a) 41¢/kg (b) 35¢/kg (c) weighted mean

9.13 CHAPTER 9 TEST

1.

	mean	median	mode	range
(a)	6	5	5	7
(b)	5.5	9.75	2.5	11.7
(c)	0	0	0	2

2. 17.1 (nearest tenth)
3. cumulative means: 23, 19.5, 18.3, 17.5, 16.4, 15.5, 14.4, 13.9, 13.9, 13.3, 13.5, 14
   moving means: 17.5, 14.8, 13.5, 11.5, 10.2, 10.8, 10, 12, 14.2

REVIEW AND PREVIEW TO CHAPTER 10

PERCENTAGES

1. (a) $0.30 (b) $5.07 (c) $385.60 (d) $2.74 (e) $2.15 (f) $67.97
   (g) $42.88 (h) $57.06 (i) $103.68 (j) $59.35 (k) $40.25 (l) $247.50
   (m) $16.02 (n) $3.20 (o) $45.18 (p) $22.89 (q) $67.68 (r) $49.38
2. (a) 0.06 (b) 0.08 (c) 0.1 (d) 0.11 (e) 0.055 (f) 0.0675
   (g) 0.125 (h) 0.0775 (i) 0.0925 (j) 0.101 25 (k) 0.116 25 (l) 0.1775

FRACTIONS OF A YEAR

1. 0.0904 2. 0.1726 3. 0.2548 4. 0.4110 5. 0.1644

6. 0.5753 7. 0.2301 8. 0.4986 9. 0.1644 10. 0.2466
11. 0.3288 12. 0.0630 13. 0.1014 14. 0.0822 15. 0.1534
16. 0.1233 17. 0.8219 18. 0.0055 19. 2.4658 20. 0.0082

DAYS AND DATES

1. (a) 0.1890 a (b) 0.2877 a (c) 0.3863 a (d) 0.5425 a (e) 0.5288 a (f) 0.3260 a
   (g) 0.4329 a (h) 0.1233 a (i) 0.3315 a (j) 0.3699 a (k) 0.3753 a (l) 0.1863 a
2. (a) March 8 (b) May 6 (c) May 23 (d) August 18
   (e) October 6 (f) October 7 (g) January 21 (h) May 14

EXERCISE 10.1

1. (b) $I = Prt$, $A = P + I$, $A = P + Prt$ 2. $r = \frac{I}{Pt}$, $t = \frac{I}{Pr}$
3. (a) \$140, \$4140 (b) \$10.40, \$530.40 (c) \$333.31, \$5613.31
   (d) \$45, \$795 (e) \$2.27, \$431.92 (f) \$145.83, \$2645.83
4. (a) \$6 (b) \$66 (c) \$5200 (d) \$750 (e) 8% (f) 12%
   (g) 5 months (h) 1 a
5. (a) \$377.47 (b) \$546.09 (c) \$7597.15 (d) \$127.32
6. \$10 000 7. \$4857.29 8. 5.5% 9. \$1687.50 10. \$557.32
11. \$512.49 12. \$1536.31, July 25 13. (a) \$5.42 (b) 8%

EXERCISE 10.2

1. (a) 5% (b) 12% (c) 4% (d) 3.5% (e) 3% (f) 4.5%
   (g) 2% (h) 3.75% (i) 1% (j) 1.5%
2. (a) $1000(1 + 0.09)^{10}$ (b) $325(1 + 0.01)^{36}$ (c) $117(1 + 0.05)^{3}$ (d) $200(1 + 0.056\ 25)^{7}$
   (e) $5000(1 + 0.02)^{22}$ (f) $4500(1 + 0.045)^{19}$ (g) $600(1 + 0.015)^{27}$ (h) $2500(1 + 0.02)^{27}$
3. (a) \$200 (b) \$240 (c) \$375 (d) \$5 (e) \$360
4. \$131.24, \$631.24 5. \$115.93 6. (a) \$6700.48 (b) \$6500
7. \$3555.25 8. \$337.46

EXERCISE 10.3

1. \$155.82 2. (a) 12 a (b) 9 a

EXERCISE 10.4

1. (a) $i = 0.06$, $n = 12$ (b) $i = 0.045$, $n = 32$ (c) $i = 0.08$, $n = 10$ (d) $i = 0.035$, $n = 10$
   (e) $i = 0.01$, $n = 36$ (f) $i = 0.055$, $n = 18$ (g) $i = 0.025$, $n = 18$ (h) $i = 0.015$, $n = 33$
2. (a) 1.061 36 (b) 1.601 03 (c) 4.660 96 (d) 1.857 49 (e) 5.516 02 (f) 4.048 93
   (g) 1.384 23 (h) 5.852 36 (i) 2.952 16 (j) 2.432 54 (k) 1.132 80 (l) 1.851 94
   (m) 3.869 68 (n) 1.384 23
3. (a) \$141.30 (b) \$34.21 (c) \$1126.10 (d) \$837.68 (e) \$217.25 (f) \$1429.50
   (g) \$1013.49 (h) \$10 272.72 (i) \$3488.77 (j) \$1011.19
4. (a) \$816.48 (b) \$143.11 (c) \$855.46 (d) \$11 260.95
   (e) \$4453.53 (f) \$59 807.40 (g) \$145 409.00
5. (a) 9 a (b) 9 a (c) 8.75 a 6. 7%
7. (a) \$638.55 (b) \$704.00 (c) \$65.45

EXERCISE 10.5

1. (a) \$6.50, 20.2% (b) \$87.05, 24.2% (c) \$37.50, 5.3%
   (d) \$1742.10, 12.5% (e) \$16.80, 30.8% (f) \$78.10, 9.8%
2. (a) \$60.50 (b) 15.4% 3. 12.4% 4. (a) \$7.00 (b) 9.2%
5. \$35 6. \$8.77

7. (a) \$5.48, 10% (b) \$40, 10% (c) \$128, $12\frac{1}{2}$%

(d) \$486.24, $10\frac{1}{2}$% (e) \$500, $3\frac{1}{2}$% (f) \$10 000, 10%

8. 14.8% (both) 9. 10.1% 10. (a) \$69.67 (b) 10.8%

11. 10.7%

12. (a) \$88 400; total interest charged: \$79 891.50
(b) \$339.06; \$94.64

EXERCISE 10.6

1. (a) Total Credits: \$60.00, Interest Charges: \$7.80, Total Debits: \$63.80, New Balance: \$523.80, Minimum Payment: \$53.00
(b) Total Credits: \$120.00, Interest Charges: \$6.49, Total Debits: \$160.24, New Balance: \$472.80, Minimum Payment: \$48.00

EXERCISE 10.7

1. (a) 16 (b) 48 (c) 8 2. 500 3. 59

4. 1 → (e), 2 → (g), 3 → (f), 4 → (b), 5 → (c), 6 → (h), 7 → (a), 8 → (d)

5. 144 m^2 or 256 m^2 or 336 m^2 or 384 m^2 (4 possibilities)

6. Ball no. 8 will swing away from the others.

7. 4 and 50, 5 and 40, 8 and 25, 10 and 20

8. (a) 180 (b) 181 (c) 187 9. (a) 52 (b) Monday

10. $3 + 8 - 1 = 10$
$6 \div 2 + 7 = 10$
$9 - 4 + 5 = 10$

11. $144 - 36\pi \doteq 31$ cm^2 (nearest one)

12. No. Ten coins consisting of quarters, nickels, and pennies will not total 67¢.

13. 20

10.8 REVIEW EXERCISE

1. (a) \$4.28 (b) \$158.27 (c) \$109.31 (d) \$80.44 (e) \$209.63
(f) \$1068.79 (g) \$573.91 (h) \$7428.75 (i) \$230.09 (j) \$206.25

2. (a) \$5 (b) \$9 (c) \$12 (d) \$8 (e) \$10.50 (f) \$7.25
(g) \$16.75 (h) \$12.50 (i) \$4 (j) \$2.50 (k) \$9 (l) \$27

3. (a) \$106 (b) \$108 (c) \$109 (d) \$107 (e) \$112 (f) \$103
(g) \$102 (h) \$102.33 (i) \$103.50 (j) \$101

4. (a) \$267.09 (b) \$1604.48 (c) \$772.19

5. 1014% 6. \$3650 7. 3 months

8. (a) 1.75% (b) 21% 9. \$7548.17

10. (a) 7 (b) 42 (c) 10 (d) 23 (e) 51 (f) 100

11. (a) \$4302.41 (b) \$110.46 (c) \$1389.16
(d) \$2950.22 (e) \$12 942.05 (f) \$1406.77

12. (a) \$594.35 (b) \$114.34 (c) \$2040.74
(d) \$521.53 (e) \$807.52 (f) \$894.39

14. (a) \$57.41 (b) 10.2%

15. (a) 10.4% versus 10.5% (b) \$324.24 versus \$486.24

16. 7.7% 17. (a) \$512 (b) \$28 18. \$534.75 19. \$72.00

10.9 CHAPTER 10 TEST

1. (a) \$2875 (b) \$1480.56 2. \$2000

3. (a) \$3582.15 (b) \$3586.86 (c) \$3590.04

4. \$298.95 5. \$1650, \$150, 9.7%

REVIEW AND PREVIEW TO CHAPTER 11

SIMPLE INTEREST

1. (a) 0.17 (b) 0.09 (c) 0.165 (d) 0.0675 (e) 0.0025 (f) 0.004
2. (a) $12 (b) $18 (c) $26 (d) $14 (e) $21 (f) $14.50
   (g) $33.50 (h) $25 (i) $8 (j) $5 (k) $16.50 (l) $51
3. (a) $212 (b) $210 (c) $218 (d) $214 (e) $228 (f) $206
   (g) $204.50 (h) $204.67 (i) $207 (j) $202.67
4. $21.00

CHEQUES

1. (a) One hundred one — $\frac{40}{100}$ (b) Five — $\frac{67}{100}$
   (c) Fourteen — $\frac{99}{100}$ (d) One thousand twenty-six — $\frac{42}{100}$
   (e) Thirty-four — $\frac{75}{100}$ (f) Seventy-five — $\frac{20}{100}$
2. (a) $743.11, $597.25 (b) $788.97, $626.11
   (c) $791.88, $419.58 (d) $2095.86, $1342.99

COMPOUND INTEREST

1. (a) 5 (b) 46 (c) 15 (d) 14 (e) 45 (f) 125
2. (a) $136.05 (b) $1772.20 (c) $180.61 (d) $17 908.50
   (e) $131.21 (f) $851.33 (g) $114 117 (h) $1 030 000

EXERCISE 11.1

3. (a) $516.13 (b) bank pays interest (c) $3.07
   (d) debits: 2, total amount debit: $900.00, credits: 2, total amount credit: $300.00
4. (a) $416.13 (b) You pay a service charge.
   (c) $2.00 (d) same as 3(d).
5. (a) $5.25 (b) $505.43

EXERCISE 11.2

1. (a) $0.26 (b) $4.90 (c) $0.01 (d) $9.06
2. (a) $8.22, $1008.22 (b) $241.92, $3697.92
   (c) $0.18, $100.18 (d) $139.94, $7706.94
   (e) $95 000, $1 095 000 (f) $37.50, $537.50
3. (a) December 28 balance: $790.00
   (b) $2.08 (c) $4.12 (d) $4.30
4. (a) $653.15 (b) $720.96 (c) $67.81

EXERCISE 11.3

1. (a) $4354.92 (b) $134.53 (c) $3226.57 (d) $134.46
2. (a) $1242.60 (b) $1548.74 (c) $134.42 (d) $270.11
3. $1188.57 4. $517.73 5. $403.02

EXERCISE 11.4

1. (a) $587.73 (b) $631.14 (c) $89.71 (d) $1377.02 (e) $112.68
2. $2458.52 3. $43 292.00 4. $77 648.50, $65 113.00
5. (a) $5310.60 (b) $5791.80 6. $7588.64 7. $12 484.63
8. $1403.83 9. $898.19 10. $15 11. $2011.81

EXERCISE 11.5

2. (a) 3 a (b) $3604.89
3. (b) (i) $3374.62 (ii) $10 860.00 (iii) $4579.55 (iv) $132 068.00
4. $1250.99
5. $4546.70

EXERCISE 11.6

1. (a) $5984.56 (b) $5984.56 versus $5814.38
2. (a) $2235.88 (b) $1252.97
3. $7253.93
4. (a) $4618.30 (b) 4606.12

EXERCISE 11.7

1. (a) 68.06 (b) 41.46 (c) 837.59
2. (a) $712.99 (b) $2498.40 (c) $142.09 (d) $141.76 (e) $2264.45
3. (a) $1025.15 (b) $6219.60 (c) $10 671.79
4. the first by $24.29
5. (a) the second (b) by $322.73
6. $3863.58
7. (a) $7842.59 (b) (i) $9532.75 (ii) $12 774.72
8. (a) $7679.00 (b) $22 084.80
9. $990.38
10. $4781.55

EXERCISE 11.8

1. $3121.58
2. $3695.18

EXERCISE 11.9

1. 990 m^3
2. 24 nickels, 21 quarters
3. 98 and 99
4. 192, 384, and 576; 327, 654, and 981; 273, 546, and 819
5. 1600
6. 6 trees
7. 3
8. $\frac{1}{3}$
9. 10 min
10. no
11. 9
12. 69, 71, 73, and 75
13. 6.14 m (nearest hundredth)
14. $159.25
15. 28.57%

11.10 REVIEW EXERCISE

1. no service charge
2. Register balance: $725.00
3. (a) $771.79 (b) $848.56 (c) $1953.39
4. $7683.01
5. $1030.40
6. $5504.17
7. (a) $11 876.85 (b) $6715.89 (c) $2174.74
8. (a) $813.50 (b) $2717.85 (c) $1024.19 (d) $393.79
9. the first by $3.98
10. $3210.51
11. $426.47
12. $4889.78
13. $1987.96
14. $451.98
15. (a) $307.60 (b) $18.92

11.11 CHAPTER 11 TEST

1. (a) $9.22 (b) $539.95 (c) $3.55
2. $2841.10
3. $4768.83
4. the second by $59.32

REVIEW AND PREVIEW TO CHAPTER 12

ORDER OF OPERATIONS

EXERCISE 2

1. 17.0482
2. 2357.1634
3. 0.3614

4. 0.999
5. 88.974 (nearest thousandth)
6. 72.567
7. −562.794
8. 51.7658
9. 88.89
10. 0.004

PERCENT

EXERCISE 3

1. 4.45
2. 5.805
3. 14.88
4. 419.56
5. 0.014
6. 63.5
7. 241.02
8. 96.04
9. 0.0207
10. 0.2507
11. 42.9% (nearest tenth)
12. 1000%
13. 10%
14. 36.8% (nearest tenth)
15. 11.1% (nearest tenth)
16. 100%
17. 2400%
18. 99.6% (nearest tenth)
19. 9.8% (nearest tenth)
20. 1018.4% (nearest tenth)

ESTIMATION

EXERCISE 4

1. 1028.75
2. 1171.9
3. 131 835
4. 1752.92
5. 32 085
6. 102 875
7. 374 514
8. 46 468
9. 1251.25
10. 3382.4
11. 371.26
12. 370.57
13. 240.76
14. 20.54
15. 1415.24
16. 958.9
17. 69.88
18. 311.21
19. 218.22
20. 459.23
21. (b) $24 983.22

EXERCISE 12.1

1. Answers will vary.
2. Answers will vary.
3. May 1–May 9: 6.5 L/100 km, May 9–May 20: 8.3 L/100 km, May 20–May 31: 7.6 L/100 km, month of May: 7.4 L/100 km
4. (a) $73.80 (b) $347.95 (c) $224.45 (d) $568.85

EXERCISE 12.2

2. (a) $2178.90 (b) $3922.02 (c) $326.84 (d) $10.75
3. (a) $19 744.87 (b) $337.01 (c) $11.08
   (d) $16 176.52 (e) $297.36 (f) $9.78
   (g) $3948.97 (h) $329.08 (i) $10.82
4. $0.90
5. No. The current value, according to age alone, is $6712.86.
6. (a) $5950 (b) 40% (c) $11 050
7. (a) $22 968.81 (b) $4240.40 (c) $353.37 (d) $11.62

EXERCISE 12.3

7. $1329.59
8. (a) $1482.29 (b) $1684.94 (c) $776.51 (d) $875.94
9. Female: $767.09 or $729.41 (good student)
   Male: $1467.02 or $1405.94 (good student)

EXERCISE 12.4

1. $13 545
2. $13 729.66
3. $28 970, (standard options: all options labelled N/C), $4218.60
4. $8760 and $7290
5. Newyorker: $15 014.50, Chev Malibu Classic: $2861, Volvo: $4060, MGB: $6349
6. $35 336.63 (based on the sticker price)

EXERCISE 12.5

3. (a) (i) $26 954.21 (ii) $24 554.21 (iii) 17.5%
   (b) (i) $40 306.02 (ii) $36 306.02 (iii) 16.2%
   (c) (i) $23 053.58 (ii) $22 253.58 (iii) 16.5%

(d) (i) $53 563.24 (ii) $47 563.24 (iii) 13.7%
(e) (i) $21 766.10 (ii) $21 566.10 (iii) 22.0%

5. (a) 21.4% (nearest tenth) (b) 13.6% (nearest tenth)
(c) 15.9% (nearest tenth) (d) 17.5% (nearest tenth)
(e) 15.9% (nearest tenth)
6. (a) $19 217.35, $15 530.76, $5239.45, $20 544.80, $1996.89, respectively
(b) $3304.95, $2062.76, $3239.45, $4754.80, $1796.89, respectively (all below depreciated value)
7. (a) $4763.37 (b) $1587.79 (c) $132.32 (d) $4.35 (e) 10.2%

EXERCISE 12.6

1. $8118.86/a, $676.57/month, $22.24/d, $0.44/km
2. Female (good student amounts in brackets): $18 193.61/a ($18 155.93/a), $1516.13/month ($1512.99/month), $49.85/d ($49.74/d), $0.85/km ($0.85/km)
Male (good student amounts in brackets): $18 893.54/a ($18 832.46/a), $1574.46/month ($1569.37/month), $51.76/d ($51.60/d), $0.88/km ($0.88/km)

EXERCISE 12.7

1. (a) $216 (b) $430 (c) $429 (d) $359
2. the train, by $13.86
3. $0.13/km
4. $0.23/km
5. $45 versus $78.66
6. (a) 23.9% (nearest tenth)
(b) last year: $719 098 875
this year: $891 231 000

EXERCISE 12.8

1. 180°
2. 1 and 2
3. 42 cm
4. 30
5. −40°
6. 13, 37, and 79
7. Answers will vary.
8. $10^2 - 6^2$, $15^2 - 10^2$, $21^2 - 15^2$
9. 220 cubes
10. (a) 25% (b) $1 loss
11. May 3: $541.21, May 4: $665.19, May 10: $698.94, May 11: $376.27, May 17: $367.37, May 20: $410.80, May 22: $344.00, May 24: $445.00
12. 88, 90, 92, and 94

12.9 REVIEW EXERCISE

1. $25 004.58
2. (a) approximately $21 860 (b) approximately $16 830
(c) $1257.50 (d) $10.48
3. $764.86
4. $2512.30
5. 6.7% (nearest tenth)
6. Town Trust at 11.52%
7. (a) $22 955.70/a, $1912.98/month, $62.89/d, $1.53/km
(b) $11 130.40/a, $927.53/month, $30.49/d, $0.74/km
8. $28.42
9. Answers will vary.

12.10 CHAPTER 12 TEST

1. 8.1 L/100 km
2. (a) $12 215.79 (b) 53%
3. 17.0% (nearest tenth)
4. $1435.88/month, $0.82/km

REVIEW AND PREVIEW TO CHAPTER 13

EXERCISE 1

1. (a) 540, 3.75, $0.2\overline{6}$, 5.4, 5.4
   (b) 7, 15, $0.0\overline{6}$, 7.35, 7.35
   (c) 9.1, 12.74, $0.\overline{153\,846}$, 0.1274, 0.1274
   (d) 0.9, 0.09, $0.\overline{1}$, 0.0009, 0.0009
   (e) 200, 1200, $33.\overline{3}$, 0.03, 12
   (f) 300, 1500, $0.01\overline{6}$, 60, 15

EXERCISE 2

1. (a) $41.25 (b) $20.29 (c) $22.99 (d) $24.00 (e) $37.50 (f) $15.30

CALCULATING SKILLS

EXERCISE 3

1. (a) $603.01 (b) $1448.63 (c) $2184.50 (d) $4873.51 (e) $1930.86
   (f) $1387.90 (g) $2014.96 (h) $1227.41 (i) $10 546.28 (j) $2273.79
2. (a) $503.21 (b) $222.32 (c) $221.21 (d) $862.91 (e) $180.84
   (f) $61.69 (g) $388.12 (h) $207.73 (i) $186.29 (j) $728.08
3. (a) $39.85 (b) $3.73 (c) $27.10 (d) $12.61 (e) $90.19
   (f) $80.63 (g) $216.61 (h) $514.62 (i) $576.15 (j) $220.53
4. (a) $61.04 (b) $32.30 (c) $181.33 (d) $628.67 (e) $61.37 (f) $85.86
   (g) 8.6% (h) 13.1% (i) 8.6% (j) 1.3% (k) 3.8% (l) 98.5%
5. (a) $2.90 (b) $3.25 (c) $8.17 (d) $10.02 (e) $85.64 (f) $74.16
   (g) $64.44 (h) $63.64 (i) $623.06 (j) $442.80 (k) $189.48 (l) $476.27

EXERCISE 13.1

1. (a) $62.50, $82.50, +$20.00
   (b) $5.50, $8.75, +$48.75
   (c) $0.12, $12.96, +$4.32
   (d) $295.99, $795.90, $887.97
   (e) $28.00, $648.00, −$88.00
2. (a) $11 937.50 (b) $3858.20
3. $7750
4. $58 880
5. $1148.10
6. (a) $31 015 (b) $132 812 (c) $11 025 (d) $9056
7. (a) $1064 (b) $1393 (c) $15 250 (d) $3220
8. $24 486
9. $265 200
10. (a) $144 565 (b) $108 435 (c) $51 235
11. (a) $19 120 (b) 21.3% (nearest tenth)
12. (a) $12 520, $3660 (b) 18.5% (nearest tenth)

EXERCISE 13.2

1. (a) $23.58 (b) $32.70 (c) $2.20 (d) $41.00 (e) $142.00 (f) $21.20
2. (a) $36.25 (b) $50.10 (c) $31.10 (d) $52.05 (e) $27.00 (f) $55.70
3. (a) $4.40 (b) $30.00 (c) $19.50 (d) $175.00 (e) $100.00 (f) $168.00
4. (a) $5.60 (b) $9.00 (c) $30.00 (d) $70.00 (e) $42.00 (f) $81.00
5. (a) 45%, $52.78 (b) $3.68, $12.88 (c) $3.50, 71.4% (d) $753.06, 42%
6. (a) $18.72, 32.0% (b) $3.99, $1.71 (c) $18.85, $32.50 (d) $1601.10, 27%
7. $3.10, 50%
8. (a) $171 400 (b) 63.4% (c) 38.8%
9. $12.49
10. $675
11. (a) 0 (b) 9.1 (c) 16.7 (d) 23.1 (e) 33.3 (f) 66.7
    (g) 81.8 (h) 92.3 (i) 100
12. (a) 31.6% (b) 47.1% (c) 32.4% (d) 39.4%
13. $96.90
14. $1.61, $5.11
15. $11.00, 36.4%
16. (a) 37.0% (b) $105.22 (c) $40 500
17. (a) $180 000 (b) $1 000 000
18. (a) $27 750 (b) $44 000

EXERCISE 13.3

1. (a) $19.95 (b) $11.97 (c) $7.98 (d) 40%
2. yes

EXERCISE 13.4

1. (a) $69.37 (b) $176.90 (c) $471.01 (d) $1629.52 (e) $4475.29
2. $334.65
3. $31 987.20 versus $29 786.40
4. (a) the first at $9.37 (b) the first at $292.60
5. (a) $23.29 (b) $22.43 (c) total rate of discount
6. (a) $19.80 (b) $17.62
7. (a) $58.45 (b) $58.45 (c) no
8. (a) 32% (b) 37% (c) 23.6% (nearest tenth) (d) 42.7% (nearest tenth) (e) 50.6% (f) 35.5% (nearest tenth)
9. (a) $430.26 (b) $48.94 (c) $10.17 (d) $647.19 (e) $2.92 (f) $16.16
10. 36.6% versus 36.8% (nearest tenth)
11. (a) 22.3% versus 23.3% (nearest tenth) (b) 38.3% versus 36.6% (nearest tenth)
12. (a) (i) @ sum (B4 .. B13) (ii) @ sum (C4 .. C13)
    (b) (i) 0.2 * B14 (ii) 0.15 * C14
    (c) (i) 0.04 * (B14 − B15) (ii) 0.08 * (C14 − C15)
    (d) (i) + B14 − B15 − B16 (ii) + C14 − C15 − C16
    (e) $1105.90 versus $1107.55

EXERCISE 13.5

1. (a) 22% (b) 15% (c) 18% (d) 16% (e) 4.5%
2. 6.8%
3. 5.0%
4. 19.6%
5. (a) $180 (b) 9%
6. 8.0%
7. (a) 10%, 5.0% (b) 10%, 3.0% (c) 15%, 5.0% (d) 9.0%, 8.0%
8. 4.77%
9. (a) $436.16 (b) $7001.77 (c) $4826.34 (d) $19.29 (e) $107.23
10. $2478.22
11. $4139.52
12. (a) $508.60 (b) $518.98 (c) $527.94
13. (a) $4375 (b) $821.92
14. $751.78

EXERCISE 13.6

1. (a) $535.96 (b) $8257.20 (c) $5617.92 (d) $1002.40 (e) $8391.04 (f) $729.34
2. (a) $86.88 (b) $582.42 (c) $219.31 (d) $2.88 (e) $19.77 (f) $7.74
3. $5.17
4. (a) $12 685.75 (b) $1014.86
5. (a) $68.54 (b) $126.13 (c) $3248.35 (d) $23.18 (e) $311.44 (f) $84.52 (g) $207.39 (h) $21.29
6. (a) $7.54 (b) no provincial sales tax (c) $4.80 (d) $6.85 (e) $6.85 (f) $4.80 (g) $6.17 (h) $3.43 (i) $8.22 (j) $4.11

EXERCISE 13.7

1. (a) $170.72 (b) $620.00 (c) $1021.70
2. (a) $59.90 (b) $97.35 (c) $109.75
3. (a) $300.98, $11.98 (b) $532.80, $33.80 (c) $3246, $448
4. (a) $427.99 (b) $481.98 (c) $53.99 (d) 12.6% (nearest tenth)
5. (a) $1926 (b) $2180, $254 (c) $2100, $174
6. (a) 18 months (b) 9.4% (nearest tenth)

EXERCISE 13.8

Answers are given to the nearest tenth.

1. (a) 15.6% (b) 20.1% (c) 33.2% (d) 24.9% (e) 19.2%
2. 20.1%
3. 15.6%
4. store A at 15.4%

EXERCISE 13.9

1. D3: 5.03, D4: 31.75, D5: 44.10, D6: 47.54, D7: 247.37, D8: 136.22, C9: 25, C10: 22, B11: 30, A12: 3500.00
2. (a) $53 820 (b) $104 780 (c) $50 960
3. B4: 3.21, C4: 115.56, D4: 15.56, E4: 15.6 B5: 3.29, C5: 118.44, D5: 18.44, E5: 18.4
   B6: 3.38, C6: 121.68, D6: 21.68, E6: 21.7 B7: 3.46, C7: 124.56, D7: 24.56, E7: 24.6
   B8: 3.55, C8: 127.80, D8: 27.80, E8: 27.8 B9: 3.63, C9: 130.68, D9: 30.68, E9: 30.7
   B10: 3.72, C10: 133.92, D10: 33.92, E10: 33.9 B11: 3.81, C11: 137.16, D11: 37.16, E11: 37.2
   B12: 3.89, C12: 140.04, D12: 40.04, E12: 40.0

EXERCISE 13.10

1. 22.2% (nearest tenth) 2. 6.3% (nearest tenth)

EXERCISE 13.11

1. (a) 29786
   850
   850
   31486

   (b) 3915
   15
   4820
   8750

2. Take goose across; return and take corn across; return with goose and take fox across; return for goose.
3. 2 km
6. 13 8. 6750 9. 187 10. 2D 12. 8

13.12 REVIEW EXERCISE

1. (a) $2550 (b) $7800 2. $9100 3. $57.30 4. $5.11
5. $6.63 6. (a) 31.6% (b) 29.6%
7. (a) 25%, 20%, 10% (b) 25%, 20%, 10% (c) $66\frac{2}{3}$%, 40%, 8%
   (d) 75%, 42.9%, 15% (e) 50%, $33\frac{1}{3}$%, 15%
8. $51.01 9. 38.8% 10. 10% 11. $26.21
12. $170.93 13. $478.18 14. $3.52 15. $362.89
16. (a) $649.94, $74.95 (b) $389.49, $34.61
17. (a) $971.98 (b) $1145.04 (c) $173.06 (d) 17.8%
18. (a) $35 925 (b) $13 112.76 (c) 12% 19. the first at 15.0%
20. (a) $44.10 (b) $61.61 (c) $184.80
21. $2302.50, $1800.00, $802.50

13.13 CHAPTER 13 TEST

1. (a) $18.20 (b) $17.85 (c) $19.04 2. $67.28 3. 34.9%
4. (a) $286.18 (b) $299.60 (c) $13.42 (d) 19.5% (nearest tenth) 5. $88.70

REVIEW AND PREVIEW TO CHAPTER 14

TIME PERIODS

EXERCISE 2

1. 8 h 41 min 2. 7 h 54 min 3. 9 h 35 min 4. 8 h 12 min 5. 12 h 30 min
6. 13 h 55 min 7. 11 h 38 min 8. 14 h 34 min 9. 12 h 30 min 10. 9 h 9 min

CALCULATIONS WITH MONEY

EXERCISE 3

1. $231.73 2. $3762.47 3. $264.06 4. $422.67 5. $996.40
6. $300.06 7. $403.65 8. $95.94 9. 25.5% (nearest tenth)
10. 10% 11. $538.74 12. $0.79 13. $122.22 14. $122.71
15. $452.33 16. $559.14 17. $1454.76 18. $13 583.79

SLOPE

EXERCISE 4

1. 1 2. $\frac{1}{3}$ 3. -1 4. $-\frac{3}{2}$ 5. -1 6. $\frac{3}{5}$

EXERCISE 14.1

1. (a) \$2149.60 (b) \$55 889.60 (c) \$2255.20 (d) 4.9% (nearest tenth)
2. \$21.75
3. \$48 276.48
4. (a) \$25 675 (b) \$493.75 (c) \$98.75 (d) \$12.34
5. (a) \$926.91 (b) \$32 132.88 (c) \$21.47
6. (a) \$146.25, \$214.48, \$65,00 (b) \$425.73
   (c) \$731.25, \$1072.40, \$325.00 (d) \$2128.65
   (e) \$38 025.00, \$55 764.80, \$16 900.00 (f) \$332 069.40
7. (a) \$707.26 (b) \$736.00 (c) \$766.33 (d) \$905.24

EXERCISE 14.2

1. (a) \$174.96 (b) \$2473.56 (c) \$305.96 (d) \$681.47
2. \$1911.48
3. (a) salary plus commission (b) \$1935
4. \$98
5. \$373.87
6. \$28 359.40, \$2363.28
7. \$2214.66

EXERCISE 14.3

1. (a) \$15 (b) 15 (c) \$97.50
2. (a) 7.5% (b) 0.075 (c) \$600.00
3. (a) \$200.00 (b) 5% (c) 0.05 (d) \$500.00
4. (a) 5%, 15%, 22.5% (b) 0.05, 0.15, 0.225 (c) \$675.00
8. (a) \$150.00, 2% (b) 2.5%, 3.75%, 5% (c) \$10 000
   (d) graduated commission (e) (i) \$130 (ii) \$60 (iii) \$60

EXERCISE 14.4

1. C.P.P.: \$4.76, U.I.: \$7.01, INCOME TAX: \$48.40, NET PAY: \$238.33
2. (a) \$61.60 (b) \$94.95 (c) \$84.50
3. (a) \$4.95 (b) \$257.40 (c) 1.6% (nearest tenth)
   (d) \$7.25 (e) \$377.00 (f) 2.4% (nearest tenth)
4. (a) \$46.95 (b) \$33.95 (c) \$52.75 (d) \$60.00
5. (a) 2.6% (nearest tenth) (b) 4.5% (nearest tenth) (c) 4.2% (nearest tenth)
6. (a) \$180.00 (b) \$248.50 (c) \$358.50 (d) \$506.00
7. \$203.43

EXERCISE 14.6

1. 6
3. 6 cm
4. 343
5. 4
6. 4
7. $\frac{1}{2}$
8. (a) 24, 30 (b) 80, 47 (c) 27, 38
9. 23.6 m (nearest tenth)
10. 676
11. 8
14. 12
15. C, D, and E

EXERCISE 14.7

1. \$886.88
2. (a) \$2760.25 (b) \$15.92
3. (a) 283.50 (b) 220.82 (c) 97.25 (d) 1815.16
4. (a) 259.44 (b) 5000 (c) 8.5 (d) 2.25 (e) 2225.25
5. (a) \$200.00 (b) \$295.00 (c) \$645.00 (d) \$240.11 (e) \$570.02 (f) \$792.35
7. (a) \$200.00, 10% (b) 20% (c) \$2000
   (d) salary plus commission, \$80.00 (e) straight commission, \$60.00
8. (a) \$273.86 (b) \$263.59
9. (a) (i) \$260.28 (ii) \$259.78 (b) \$329
11. (a) (i) \$582.80 (ii) \$606.80 (iii) \$629.60 (iv) \$657.20

14.8 CHAPTER 14 TEST

1. (a) \$1459.50 (b) \$37 947.00 (c) \$39 546.00
2. (a) salary plus commission, by \$20.41 (b) \$2670.00
3. (a) \$112.53 (b) \$132.00 (c) \$511.45
4. \$271.67

REVIEW AND PREVIEW TO CHAPTER 15

BASIC COMPUTER LANGUAGE

1. (a) 40 (b) −7 (c) 36 (d) 64
   (e) 9 (f) 5 (g) 7
2. (a) −15/3 (b) 7^3 (c) SQR(2.25) (d) 5.8*2.4
   (e) 6.25+5.8 (f) (−5)^2 (g) (2.4+3.8)/(5.2*1.7)
3. (a) 0 (b) 12.5 (c) 4 (d) 1200
   (e) 69 (f) 18 (g) 6
4. (a) x^2+y^2 (b) x^2/y (c) 5*X+2*Y (d) 2*(L+W)
   (e) 3.14159*R (f) (A+B)*(A−B) (g) 2*3.14159*R (h) L*W
   (i) 0.5*(A+B)*H (j) X^2−2*X−6

SPREADSHEET SOFTWARE

2. \$5369.30
3. taxes: \$26 030, accommodations: \$14 385, transportation: \$4110, food: \$6165, entertainment: \$4110, insurance: \$2055, savings: \$11 645
4. (b) total amount: \$12 992.20

EXERCISE 15.1

1. (c) 200 L (at \$2.85/L)
2. (b) 1600 kg (at \$4.82/kg)

EXERCISE 15.2

1. (a) Wagon (34) (b) Alice (58) (c) Banff (47)
2. Road (52)

EXERCISE 15.4

1. (a) 0.4, −1 (b) 3, 2 (c) 0.5, 0.5
   (d) 1, −1.2 (e) −1.23014, 1.89681 (f) 1.25, −1
   (g) 0.85078, −2.35078 (h) 2, 3 (i) −1.23699, 0.80842
   (j) 1, 0.75 (k) 0.56672, −3.48672 (l) 2.47337, −0.42419
   (m) 1.27778, 1
2. (c) 2.2 m
3. (c) 88.7 km/h (d) 98.7 km/h
4. 32.5 cm

EXERCISE 15.5

1. (a) +B6+B7+B8 (b) 11.000 cm
2. (a) 0.5*B6*B7 (b) 31.320 cm^2
3. (a) 4*A3, +A3^2 (b) 50.000 cm, 156.250 cm^2
4. (a) 2*(A7+B7), +A7+B7 (b) 27.800 cm, 48.000 cm^2
5. (a) +C5*D5 (b) 107.010 cm^2
6. (a) 0.5*(B6+B7)*B8 (b) 140.300 cm^2
7. (a) 6*B3^2, +B3^3 (b) 194.940 cm^2, 185.193 cm^3
8. (a) 2*(B5*B6+B5*B7+B6*B7), +B5*B6*B7 (b) 430.400 cm^2, 594.048 cm^3
9. (a) 4*(0.5*A6*@SQRT(A7^2+(0.5*A6)^2))+A6^2, +A6^2*A7/3
   (b) 451.062 cm^2, 520.833 cm^3
10. (a) 2*@PI*C4*(C5+C4), @PI*C4^2*C5 (b) 886.243 cm^2, 2017.530 cm^3
11. (a) @PI*B6*(B6+@SQRT(B6^2+B7^2)), @PI*B6^2*B7/3
    (b) 1241.198 cm^2, 2415.256 cm^3
12. (b) 104.150 m^3

EXERCISE 15.6

2. (a) 8.66 cm (b) 9.36 cm (c) 19.71 cm (d) 16.71 cm
3. (a) A=0.5*A*B*@SIN(C*@PI/180)
   (b) (i) 45.65 cm^2 (ii) 83.11 cm^2 (iii) 77.94 cm^2 (iv) 78.87 cm^2 (v) 395.08 cm^2 (vi) 111.91 cm^2

EXERCISE 15.7

1. (a) (i) $30 187.50 (ii) $114 825 (iii) $80 487.50 2. (a) $39 886 3. (a) $12 495

15.9 REVIEW EXERCISE

1. Folk Singer (48) 2. (a) 57.44 (b) 5.32 (c) 0.53
3. (c) 5000 L (at $0.50/L) 5. (a) $57 300 6. (a) $12 302.20
7. (a) $3 329 100 (b) $195 829.41
   (c) bungalow: $150 900, duplex: $185 333.33, split level: $183 400, two-storey: $257 000
8. (a) cylinder: 692.721 cm^3, cone: 1308.997 cm^3 (b) cone
10. (a) 6.88 cm (b) 13.06 cm (c) 31.82 cm (d) 10.74 cm

15.10 CHAPTER 15 TEST

1. +B4+C6 2. (a) 2*(A5+B5), +A5*B5 (b) 2*@PI*A5, @PI*A5^2
3. (a) @SIN(B6*@PI/180) (b) @COS(B6*@PI/180) (c) @TAN(B6*@PI/180)
4. Cassette (44)

GLOSSARY

absolute value The positive number of any pair of opposite real numbers, denoted by $|a|$.
accountant A professional who keeps business records and advises clients on financial management.
acute angle An angle whose measure is between 0° and 90°.
acute triangle A triangle with all angles acute.
adjacent angles Two angles with a common vertex, a common side, and no interior points in common.
alternate angles Two angles between two lines on opposite sides of a transversal.
altitude of a triangle A line from a vertex, perpendicular to the opposite side.
amortization schedule A schedule that shows the repayment of a loan in a series of equal payments, with the breakdown of principal and interest.
angle A figure formed by two rays with a common endpoint called the vertex.
angle bisector A ray that divides an angle into two angles having the same measure.
angle of elevation (depression) The angle between a horizontal line through an observer and the line of sight from the observer through the object above (below) the observer.
annual A period of 12 months or 1 a.
annuity A series of payments made at regular intervals.
area The number of unit squares contained in a region.
assessed value The value at which a property is taxed.
average The average of n numbers is the sum of the numbers divided by n.
axiom A statement that is assumed to be true. Also called a postulate.
axis A number line used for reference in locating points on a coordinate plane.
axis of symmetry A line that is invariant under a reflection.

bank statement A form prepared by the bank, listing all cheques cashed and deposits made over a specific period of time.
bar graph A graph using bars to represent data.
base of a trapezoid One of the parallel sides of the trapezoid.
BASIC Beginners All-purpose Symbolic Instruction Code is a computer language.
binomial A polynomial consisting of two terms.
bond A certificate, issued by a government or a corporation, promising to pay the holder a fixed sum of money on a given date with interest.
broken line graph A graph using line segments to represent data.
broker An agent who buys and sells investments for others.
brokerage fee The amount charged by a broker for buying and selling investments.
budget A financial plan for disposing of one's income.

carrying charge The interest that is added to the balance by a lender.
cash discount The reduction allowed on an invoice price if paid within a specified time.
central angle of a circle An angle subtended by an arc of a circle with the vertex at the centre.
centroid The point of intersection of the three medians of a triangle.
chartered bank A financial institution that provides savings, loan, and chequing services as well as payment of bills and rental of safety deposit boxes.
chord of a circle A line segment having its endpoints on the circumference.
circle The set of all points in the plane that are equidistant from a fixed point called the centre.
circle graph A graph using sectors of a circle to represent data.
circumcentre The centre of the circle that passes through the three vertices of a triangle.
circumference The perimeter of a circle.
circumscribed circle A circle is circumscribed about a polygon if all the vertices of the polygon lie on the circle.
collinear points Points that lie in the same straight line.
commission A percentage of sales that a salesperson receives as pay or incentive.
comparison shopping The attempts of a buyer of goods and services to determine the best buy or value of goods.

complementary angles Two angles whose sum is 90°.
compound interest The interest paid on the principal plus any previous interest not paid.
concentric circles Circles having the same centre.
congruent angles Angles with the same measure.
congruent figures Two figures that are equal in all respects — that is, there exists an isometry that maps one figure onto the other.
conic section The intersection of a double cone and a plane — circle, ellipse, parabola, or hyperbola.
consecutive even (odd) numbers Numbers obtained by counting by twos from any even (odd) number.
consecutive numbers Numbers obtained by counting by ones from any given number.
consistent equations Equations in a system that has at least one solution.
construction The process of drawing a geometric figure using only a ruler and a compass.
coordinate A real number paired with a point on a number line.
coordinate plane A one-to-one pairing of all ordered pairs of real numbers with all points of a plane. Also called the Cartesian coordinate plane.
corollary A theorem that follows directly from the proof of another theorem.
cosecant ratio In a right triangle, the ratio of the length of the hypotenuse to the length of the opposite side.
cosine ratio In a right triangle, the ratio of the length of the adjacent side to the length of the hypotenuse.
cotangent ratio In a right triangle, the ratio of the length of the adjacent side to the length of the opposite side.
coterminal angles Angles that have the same initial and terminal rays (arms).
credit card A card issued by banks, large stores, and companies that enables the holder to make purchases and delay payment for about 30 d, or to pay by instalments with interest.
cubic polynomial A polynomial of the form $ax^3 + bx^2 + cx + d$, where $a \neq 0$.

deductions Funds withheld by an employer from an employee's paycheque. Also refers to the amounts a taxpayer deducts from gross income to arrive at taxable income.
degree A unit of angle measure equal to $\frac{1}{360}$ of a rotation.
degree of a monomial The sum of the exponents of the variables.
degree of a polynomial The greatest of the degrees of its terms after it has been simplified.
dependent equations Equations in a system that has infinitely many solutions.
depreciation The decrease in the value of a property or article due to age or wear and tear.
diagonal A line segment with endpoints on two non-adjacent vertices of a polygon.
diameter of a circle A chord that contains the centre of the circle. The largest chord.
direct variation A function defined by a function of the form $y = kx$.
discount A deduction from the original price of an article.
discriminant The discriminant of the quadratic equation $ax^2 + bx + c = 0$ is $b^2 - 4ac$.
distance from a point to a line The length of the perpendicular segment drawn from the point to the line.
dividend The return or yield on an investment.
domain of a function The set of numbers for which the function is defined. The set of all first coordinates of the ordered pairs in the function.
domain of a variable The set of numbers that can serve as replacements for a variable.
down payment The amount of money paid at the time that a purchase is made.

END statement The last statement in a computer program.
estimate To estimate is to arrive at an approximate calculation by rounding all numbers to the highest place value and calculating mentally.
equation An open sentence formed by two expressions separated by an equal sign.
equidistant At the same distance.
equilateral triangle A triangle with all sides equal.
equivalent equations Equations that have the same solution over a given domain.
exponent The number of times the base occurs in a power.
expressing in simplest form Dividing the numerator and denominator of a fraction by the highest common factor.

exterior angle of a polygon An angle formed by extending one side of a triangle and the other side at the same vertex.

factor Number that is multiplied by another number to give a product.
factorial notation Notation used to indicate the product of consecutive integers beginning with 1.

$$n! = 1 \times 2 \times 3 \times ... \times (n - 1) \times n$$

factoring Finding the factors of a number or expression over a given set.
fixed costs Regular expenses, such as rent, over which there is no control.
FOR – NEXT statement Used to loop through the same set of statements several times on a computer.
formula An equation stating the relationship among quantities that can be represented by variables.
function A rule that assigns to each element in the domain a single element in the range.

greatest common factor The greatest integer that is a factor of two or more integers.
greatest monomial factor The factor of two or more monomials that has the greatest coefficient and the greatest degree.
gross profit The difference between net sales and the cost of goods sold.

histogram A bar graph used to summarize and display a large set of data.
hypotenuse The side opposite the right angle in a right triangle.

identity An equation whose sides are equivalent expressions. The equation is true for every value of the variables.
identity elements The identity element for addition is 0, since $a + 0 = a$. The identity element for multiplication is 1, since $a \times 1 = a$.
imaginary unit i The number i that is a solution to the equation $i^2 = -1$.
included angle The angle whose rays contain the sides of a triangle.
inconsistent equations The equations in a system that has no solutions.
inequality Two expressions separated by an inequality symbol.
inflation During a period of inflation, available currency and credit increase beyond the available goods, resulting in price increases.
inscribed angle An angle subtended by an arc of a circle with its vertex on the cirumference.
inscribed polygon A polygon with its vertices on the circle.
integer A member of the set $\{..., -3, -2, -1, 0, 1, 2, 3, ...\}$.
interest The amount of money paid as rent or earned for the use of another's money.
intersection The elements that two sets have in common.
inventory A listing of items that are on hand, and their value.
inverse variation A function defined by an equation of the form $xy = k, (k \neq 0)$.
invest To invest means to put money into a bank account, stocks, bonds, mutual funds, or real estate to obtain a gain or income.
irrational number A real number that cannot be expressed in the form $\frac{a}{b}$, a, b, $\in$ I, and $b \neq 0$.
isosceles triangle A triangle with two sides equal.

lateral area The sum of the areas of the faces of a polyhedron other than the base.
least common multiple The monomial with the smallest positive coefficient and smallest degree that is a multiple of several monomials.
LET statement Assigns a value or an expression to a variable.
linear equation An equation in which each term is either a constant or has degree 1.
linear function A function of the form $f(x) = mx + b$.
line segment Two points on a line and the points between them.
line symmetry A figure has line symmetry if there is a line such that the figure coincides with its reflection image over the line.
list price The price that the manufacturer advises the retailer to put on the tag.
locus A set of points that satisfy a given condition.

market price The current price of a stock, bond, or mutual fund on the stock exchange.

mass The amount of matter in an object. The base unit for measuring mass is the kilogram.
maturity value The total amount due on the date of payment of a note.
mean The sum of the values divided by the number of values.
median The middle number when a set of numbers is arranged in order from smallest to largest or largest to smallest.
midpoint The point that divides a line segment into two equal parts.
mixed number A number that is part whole number and part fraction, such as $5\frac{3}{4}$.
mode The number that occurs most often in a set of numbers.
monomial A number, a variable, or a product of numbers and variables.
mortgage A legal claim to certain real property of the borrower in respect of payments that have to be made for a loan.
mutual fund A financial institution that invests the money of numerous individuals in securities of various types and gives the individual a prorated share.

natural numbers The set of numbers {1, 2, 3, 4, 5, 6, ...}.
net A pattern for constructing a polyhedron.
net loss Results when the cost of goods sold and the operating expenses are greater than the gross income.
net profit (net income) Results when the gross income is greater than the cost of the goods sold and the operating expenses.
NEW The first statement in a computer program.
nonagon A polygon with nine sides.
number line A pictorial representation of a set of numbers.
numeral A symbol that represents a number.

obtuse angle An angle greater than 90° but less than 180°.
obtuse triangle A triangle with one obtuse angle.
octagon A polygon with eight sides.
octahedron A polyhedron with eight faces.
ordered pair A pair of numbers used to name a point on a graph.
order of operations The rules to be followed when simplifying expressions. These rules are sometimes referred to as BODMAS or BEDMAS.
origin The intersection of the horizontal and vertical axes on a graph. It is described by the ordered pair (0,0).
orthocentre The point where the altitudes of a triangle intersect.

PACED plan A process of decision making in which one identifies the problem, states some alternative solutions to the problem, lists criteria for making the decision, evaluates each alternative based on the criteria, and makes the decision.
palindrome A number such as 232 that reads the same forwards as backwards.
parallel lines Two lines in the same plane that never meet.
parallelogram A quadrilateral with opposite sides parallel.
parameter An arbitrary constant.
partial variation A relation between two variables that involves a fixed amount plus a variable amount such as $C = nd + 15$.
pentagon A polygon with five sides.
percent A fraction (or ratio) in which the denominator is 100.
perimeter The distance around a polygon.
periodic Occurring at regular time intervals.
perpendicular bisector The line that cuts a line segment into two equal parts at right angles.
perpendicular lines Lines that intersect at right angles.
pi (π) The quotient that results when the circumference of a circle is divided by the diameter.
pictograph A graph using pictures to represent data.
polygon A closed figure formed by line segments.
polyhedron A three-dimensional object having polygons as faces.
polynomial A monomial or the sum of monomials.
population The entire set of items from which data is taken.
portfolio The list of investments, such as bonds, stocks, or certificates, held by an investor.
postulate A statement that is accepted without proof.

power A product obtained by using a base as a factor one or more times.
present value The principal amount that must be invested now to produce a given amount at a later date.
prime number A number with exactly two factors — itself and 1.
principal The amount of money that is borrowed.
principal square root The positive square root.
prism A polyhedron with two parallel and congruent bases in the shape of polygons.
proportion An equation stating that two ratios are equal.
pyramid A polyhedron with three or more triangular faces and the base in the shape of a polygon.
Pythagorean theorem The area of the square drawn on the hypotenuse of a right-angled triangle is equal to the sum of the areas of the squares drawn on the other two sides.

quadrant One of the four regions formed by the intersection of the x-axis and y-axis.
quadratic equation A polynomial equation of degree 2.
quadratic formula The formula

$$x = \frac{-b \pm \sqrt{b^2 - 4ac}}{2a}$$

for the roots of a quadratic equation.
quadrilateral A polygon with four sides.
quotient The result of a division.

radian If an angle that is the central angle of a circle cuts off an arc whose length is equal to the length of the radius of the circle, then the measure of the central angle is 1 radian.
radical sign The symbol $\sqrt{}$.
radius The length of the line segment that joins the centre and a point on the circumference of a circle.
random sample A sample in which each member of the population has the same chance of being selected.
range The set of all values of a function. The set of all second coordinates of the ordered pairs of a relation.
rate A ratio of two measurements having different units.
rate of return An indicator, expressed as a percent, of whether an investment is profitable.
ratio A comparison of two numbers.
rational number A number that can be expressed as the ratio of two integers.
ray Part of a line extending in one direction without end.

real numbers The set of all the rational and irrational numbers.
reciprocals Two numbers that have a product of 1.
rectangle A parallelogram with four right angles.
reflex angle An angle whose measure is greater than 180° and less than 360°.
regular polygon A polygon in which all sides and angles are equal.
relation A set of ordered pairs.
repeating decimal A decimal in which one or more digits repeat without end.
retail price The price at which goods are sold to consumers.
rhombus A parallelogram in which all sides are equal.
right angle An angle whose measure is 90°.
right cone A cone in which the axis is perpendicular to the base.
right cylinder A cylinder in which the sides are perpendicular to the bases.
right prism A prism in which the lateral edges are perpendicular to the bases.
right triangle A triangle with one right angle.
root of an equation A solution of the equation.
rounding The process of replacing a number by an approximate number.

scale drawing A drawing in which distances are reductions or enlargements of actual distances.
scalene triangle A triangle with no two sides equal.
scientific notation Numbers written with one digit (not zero) to the left of the decimal place and a power of ten.

$$2700 = 2.7 \times 10^3$$

secant ratio In a right triangle, the ratio of the length of the hypotenuse to the length of the adjacent side.
sector angle An angle with vertex at the centre of a circle and subtended by an arc of the circle.

sector of a circle A region bounded by two radii and an arc.
securities The written statements of the ownership of an investment in stocks or bonds.
segment of a circle A region bounded by a chord and an arc.
semi-annual Twice a year, or every 6 months.
sequence A set of numbers written in a definite order.
set A collection of objects.
share (of stock) A part ownership in a corporation.
shell A three-dimensional object whose interior is empty.
similar figures Figures having corresponding angles equal and corresponding sides proportional.
sine ratio In a right triangle, the ratio of the length of the opposite side to the length of the hypotenuse.
skeleton A representation of the edges of a polyhedron.
slope of a line For a non-vertical line containing two distinct points, (x_1, y_1) and (x_2, y_2), the number

$$m = \frac{y_2 - y_1}{x_2 - x_1}.$$

solid A three-dimensional object whose interior is completely filled.
solution set A replacement for a variable that results in a true sentence.
sphere The set of all points in space that are a given distance from a given point.
spreadsheet The electronic spreadsheet is a computer application that allows the storing of information in cells and the performing of a variety of computations using formulas.
square A quadrilateral with four congruent sides and four right angles.
square root The square root of a number is the number that multiplies itself to give the number.
standard form of a linear equation A linear equation written in the form $ax + by + c = 0$.
statistics The science of collecting and analysing numerical information.
stem and leaf plot A graph using digits of numbers to display data.
stock exchange A place where shares and bonds are sold.
straight angle An angle whose measure is 180°.
supplementary angles Two angles whose sum is 180°.
surface area The sum of all the areas of all faces of a polyhedron.

tangent ratio In a right triangle, the ratio of the length of the opposite side to the length of the adjacent side.
tangent to a circle A line in the plane of a circle that intersects the circle in exactly one point.
tax refund The amount of overpayment that has been made and is returned to the taxpayer.
term of a polynomial The product of one or more numerical factors and variable factors.
terminating decimal A decimal whose digits terminate.
tetrahedron A polyhedron with four triangular faces.
theorem A mathematical statement that can be proved.
trade discount The reduction in the list price given by a manufacturer to retailers.
transversal A line that intersects two lines in the same plane in two distinct points.
trapezoid A quadrilateral with one pair of parallel sides.
triangle A polygon with three sides.
trinomial A polynomial with three terms.

union of sets The set of all elements that belong to at least one of the sets.
unit price The price of an item stated as the price for a single unit of the item.

variable A letter or symbol used to represent a number.
variable costs Costs, such as labour and materials, that are flexible and change from time to time.
vertex of an angle The common endpoint of two rays.
vertex of a polygon The point where two adjacent sides meet in a polygon.
volume The number of cubic units contained in a solid.

whole numbers Numbers in the set {0, 1, 2, 3, 4, 5, ...}.

x-axis The horizontal line used as a scale for the independent variable in the Cartesian coordinate system.
x-intercept The x-coordinate of the point where a curve crosses the x-axis.

y-axis The vertical line used as a scale for the dependent variable in the Cartesian coordinate system.
y-intercept The y-coordinate of the point where a curve crosses the y-axis.

zero-product property If $ab = 0$, then $a = 0$ or $b = 0$.

INDEX

NOTES AND PHOTOGRAPH CREDITS

p. 12: Courtesy Agriculture Canada. p. 13: The Metropolitan Toronto and Region Conservation Authority. p. 19: Compliments of Bloor Cycle. p. 22: Ontario Ministry of Natural Resources. p. 24: Courtesy of Apple Canada Ltd. p. 28: Molson Breweries of Canada Limited. p. 33: Courtesy of Toronto Stock Exchange. p. 64: Xerox Canada Inc. p. 75: Courtesy of Geological Survey of Canada. p. 88: OWL Rafting Inc., on the Ottawa River. p. 112: Promotion Australia. p. 124: (upper) Nova Scotia Tourism. p. 170: Photography by Graig Abel. p. 184: Photograph by Harold M. Lambert. p. 189: (middle) Courtesy of Caledon Balloon Adventures, Caledon, Ont.; (lower) Courtesy of Jamieson Crozier. p. 201: Photography courtesy of the Montreal Baseball Club Ltd. (Montreal Expos). p. 203: Photo courtesy Canadian National. p. 206: H. Armstrong Roberts/Miller Comstock Inc. p. 215: Air Canada. p. 228: Photo by Don Ford. p. 229: 3-piece suit designed by Linda Lundstrom. p. 246: With permission of Sharp Electronics of Canada Ltd. p. 252: Zeiss Jena GDR. p. 258: H. Armstrong Roberts/Miller Comstock Inc. p. 266: (left) Courtesy of Metropolitan Toronto Police Museum; (right) Courtesy of D'Arcy Masius Benton & Bowles Canada Inc. p. 268: H. Armstrong Roberts/Miller Comstock Inc. p. 270: H. Armstrong Roberts/Miller Comstock Inc. p. 272: Photograph by Harold M. Lambert. p. 285: Eric Hayes/Miller Comstock Inc. p. 292: Photo by Don Ford. p. 293: (left) Photo courtesy of Nissan Canada. p. 300: Photo by Don Ford. p. 303: (upper and lower) University of Toronto. p. 305: Conklin Shows at the Canadian National Exhibition (CNE) Toronto. p. 325: Courtesy of Homelite Textron. p. 326: Photo courtesy of Guaranty Trust Company of Canada. p. 328: Photo courtesy of Guaranty Trust Company of Canada. p. 331: Compliments of the Canadian Ladies' Golf Association. Photo shot at: 17th Canadian Ladies' Junior Championship, North Battleford, Saskatchewan. p. 338: Photo courtesy of Guaranty Trust Company of Canada. p. 368: (upper) H. Armstrong Roberts/Miller Comstock Inc. p. 369: Photograph by Harold M. Lambert. p. 374: SNOOPY: © 1958 United Feature Syndicate, Inc. p. 375: Courtesy of Metropolitan Toronto Police Museum. p. 384: Photo courtesy of Nissan Canada. p. 389: (upper left) Courtesy of VIA Rail Public Affairs; (lower left) Air Canada; (bottom left) Photo by Don Ford; (upper right) Photo by Don Ford. p. 402: Courtesy of Nova Scotia Information Service. p. 409: Photograph courtesy of Hal Stoyles — author of *Marketing Today: A Retail Focus*. p. 417. Photo by Don Ford. p. 419: Courtesy of Yamaha Motor Canada Ltd. p. 423: McClure/Miller Comstock Inc. p. 426: Courtesy of Camco Inc. p. 428: Courtesy of IBM Corporation. p. 429: Courtesy Ryerson Polytechnical Institute. p. 436: Photo by Don Ford. p. 437: Photo courtesy of Cincinnati Time, Toronto. p. 455: Government of Canada Building, Taxation Data Centre, Sudbury, Ontario. p. 471: Photography courtesy of the Montreal Baseball Club Ltd. (Montreal Expos). p, 488: With permission of The Toronto Stock Exchange. p. 493: Photo courtesy of Hewlett-Packard (Canada) Ltd.

Portions of text for some of the Careers appearing on pp. 115, 229, 259, 331, 391, 429, 459, 493: Career Selector, written and produced by the Ontario Women's Directorate, is a series of seven booklets which list job descriptions, training, and qualifications required for over 200 different occupations.

Tables used on pp. 450, 451, 452, 454, 507, 508, 509, 510: Courtesy of Revenue Canada Taxation. Reproduced with permission of the Minister of Supply and Services Canada.